Kirk-Othmer

ENCYCLOPEDIA
OF CHEMICAL
TECHNOLOGY

Second Edition

VOLUME 18

Shale Oil
to
Steroids

Interscience Publishers
a division of John Wiley & Sons, Inc.
New York · London · Sydney · Toronto

Kirk-Othmer

ENCYCLOPEDIA

OF CHEMICAL

TECHNOLOGY

Second completely revised edition

VOLUME 18

Shale Oil
to
Steroids

CONTENTS

EDITORIAL STAFF FOR VOLUME 18

Associate Editor: EVA PAROLLA DUKES

Estelle P. Henson   Nancy Hutto   Anna Klingsberg   Jane Maxwell

CONTRIBUTORS TO VOLUME 18

A. R. Anderson, *Anderson Development Company,* Silicon compounds (Silicon ethers and esters; Silicon halides)

F. N. Anderson, *Mallinckrodt Chemical Works,* Sodium compounds (Sodium iodides)

A. A. Ballman, *Bell Telephone Laboratories, Inc.,* Silica (Synthetic quartz crystals)

F. L. Bosqui, *Consultant,* Size separation

C. H. Chatfield, *Handy & Harman,* Solders and brazing alloys

C. M. Cooper, *Michigan State University,* Solvent recovery

John C. Cowan, *United States Department of Agriculture, Agricultural Research Service,* Soybeans

C. D. Coxe, *Handy & Harman,* Silver and silver alloys

Thomas D. Coyle, *National Bureau of Standards,* Silica (Introduction)

Mark F. Dante, *Shell Chemical Company,* Solvents, industrial

John E. Doyle, *Castle Co.,* Sterilization

William H. Dumbaugh, *Corning Glass Works,* Silica (Vitreous silica)

Richard B. Engdahl, *Battelle Memorial Institute,* Smokes, fumes, and smog

Howard W. Fiedelman, *Morton International, Inc.,* Sodium compounds (Sodium chloride)

Robert A. Gregg, *Uniroyal, Inc.,* Spandex

R. E. Gustafson, *Cameron and Jones, Inc.,* Shale oil

A. C. Hayes, *School of Textiles, North Carolina State University,* Silk

C. S. Helling, *U.S. Department of Agriculture,* Soil chemistry of pesticides

Joseph J. Jacobs, *Jacobs Engineering Co.,* Sodium compounds (Sodium sulfates)

P. C. Kearney, *U.S. Department of Agriculture,* Soil chemistry of pesticides

Eugene J. Kuhajek, *Morton International, Inc.,* Sodium compounds (Sodium chloride)

R. A. Laudise, *Bell Telephone Laboratories, Inc.,* Silica (Synthetic quartz crystals)

Charles H. Lemke, *E. I. du Pont de Nemours & Co., Inc.,* Sodium

Harold McGannon, *U.S. Steel Corporation,* Steel

P. K. Maher, *Davison Chemical Division, W. R. Grace & Co.,* Silica (Amorphous silica)

James W. Martin, *William Zinsser & Co.,* Shellac

Robert Meals, *General Electric Co.,* Silicon compounds (Silicones)

S. W. Moline, *Union Carbide Corporation,* Sorbic acid

Clyde Orr, Jr., *Georgia Institute of Technology, School of Chemical Engineering,* Size reduction

L. C. Pan, *Chemical Construction Corporation,* Sodium compounds (Sodium nitrate; Sodium nitrite)

S. M. Parmerter, *Corn Refining Company,* Starch

William H. Peacock, *American Cyanamid Company,* Stains, industrial

J. R. Plimmer, *U.S. Department of Agriculture,* Soil chemistry of pesticides

Edwin P. Plueddemann, *Dow Corning Corporation,* Silicon compounds (Silylating agents)

Eric Rau, *FMC Corporation,* Sodium compounds (Sodium carbonates)

J. K. Rice, *Cyrus Wm. Rice & Co.,* Steam

Walter R. Runyan, *Texas Instruments, Inc.,* Silicon and silicides (Pure silicon)

F. V. Ryer, *Lever Brothers Co., Inc.,* Soap

William F. Schroeder, *Archer Daniels Midland Company,* Shortenings and other food fats

Peter C. Schultz, *Corning Glass Works,* Silica (Vitreous silica)

J. S. Sconce, *Hooker Chemical Corporation,* Sodium compounds (Sodium sulfides)

E. G. Simms, *Ohio Ferro-Alloys Corp.,* Silicon and silicides (Metallurgical silicon and silicides)

V. A. Stenger, *The Dow Chemical Company,* Sodium compounds (Sodium bromides)

R. W. Tate, *Delavan Manufacturing Company,* Sprays

David Taub, *Merck & Co., Inc.,* Steroids

Thomas N. Tischer, *Eastman Kodak Company,* Silver compounds

Charles H. Van Dyke, *Carnegie-Mellon University,* Silicon compounds (Introduction; Silanes)

John H. Wills, *Philadelphia Quartz Company,* Silicon compounds (Synthetic inorganic silicates)

Thomas B. Windholz, *Merck & Co., Inc.,* Steroids

John W. Wyart, *Celanese Chemical Company,* Solvents, industrial

ABBREVIATIONS AND SYMBOLS

A	ampere(s)	APHA	American Public Health Association
A	anion (eg, H*A*)	API	American Petroleum Institute
Å	Angstrom unit(s)	app	apparatus
AATCC	American Association of Textile Chemists and Colorists	approx	approximate(ly)
abs	absolute	aq	aqueous
ac	alternating current	Ar	aryl
ac-	alicyclic (eg, *ac*-derivatives of tetrahydronaphthalene)	*as-*	asymmetric(al) (eg, *as*-trichlorobenzene)
accel(d)	accelerated(d)	ASA	American Standards Association. Later (1966) called USASI
acceln	acceleration		
ACS	American Chemical Society	ASHRAE	American Society of Heating, Refrigerating and Air-Conditioning Engineers
addn	addition		
AEC	Atomic Energy Commission		
AGA	American Gas Association		
Ah	ampere-hour(s)	ASM	American Society for Metals
AIChE	American Institute of Chemical Engineers	ASME	American Society of Mechanical Engineers
AIME	American Institute of Mining and Metallurgical Engineers	ASTM	American Society for Testing and Materials
AIP	American Institute of Physics	atm	atmosphere(s), atmospheric
AISI	American Iron and Steel Institute	at. no.	atomic number
		at. wt	atomic weight
alc	alcohol(ic)	av	average
alk	alkaline (not alkali)	b	barn(s)
Alk	alkyl	b (as in b_{11})	boiling (at 11 mm Hg)
AMA	American Medical Association		
A-min	ampere-minute(s)	bbl	barrel(s)
amt	amount (noun)	bcc	body-centered cubic
anhyd	anhydrous	Bé	Baumé
AOAC	Association of Official Analytical (formerly Agricultural) Chemists	Bhn	Brinell hardness number
		bp	boiling point
		BP	*British Pharmacopoeia* (General Medical Council in London)
AOCS	American Oil Chemists' Society		
		Btu	British thermal unit(s)

bu	bushel(s)	crystd	crystallized
C	Celsius (centigrade); coulomb(s)	crystn	crystallization
		cSt	centistokes
C-	denoting attachment to carbon (eg, *C*-acetyl-indoline)	cu	cubic
		d	density (conveniently, specific gravity)
ca	circa, approximately	*d*	differential operator
CA	Chemical Abstracts	*d*-	*dextro*-, dextrorotatory
cal	calorie(s)	D	Debye unit(s)
calcd	calculated	D-	denoting configurational relationship (as to *dextro*-glyceraldehyde)
cfm, ft³/min	cubic foot (feet) per minute	db	dry-bulb
cg	centigram(s)	dB	decibel(s)
cgs	centimeter-gram-second	dc	direct current
Ci	curie(s)	dec, decomp	decompose(s)
CI	Colour Index (number); the CI numbers given in *ECT*, 2nd ed., are from the new *Colour Index* (1956) and Suppl. (1963), *Soc. Dyers Colourists*, Bradford, England, and *AATCC*, U.S.A.	decompd	decomposed
		decompn	decomposition
		den	denier(s)
		den/fil	denier(s) per filament
		deriv	derivative
		detd	determined
		detn	determination
		diam	diameter
CIE	Commission Internationale de l'Eclairage (see also ICI)	dielec	dielectric (adj.)
		dil	dilute
		DIN	Deutsche Industrienormen
cif	cost, insurance, freight	distd	distilled
cl	carload lots	distn	distillation
cm	centimeter(s)	dl	deciliter(s)
coeff	coefficient	*dl*-, DL	racemic
compd, cpd	compound (noun)	dm	decimeter(s)
		DOT	Department of Transportation
compn	composition		
concd	concentrated	dp	dewpoint
concn	concentration	dyn	dyne(s)
cond	conductivity	*e*	electron; base of natural logarithms
const	constant		
cont	continued	ed.	edited, edition, editor
cor	corrected	elec	electric(al)
cp	chemically pure	emf	electromotive force
cP	centipoise(s)	emu	electromagnetic unit(s)
cpd, compd	compound (noun)	eng	engineering
		equil	equilibrium(s)
cps	cycles per second	equiv	equivalent
crit	critical	esp	especially
cryst	crystalline	ESR	electron spin resonance

est(d)	estimate(d)	Hz	hertz(es)
estn	estimation	i, insol	insoluble
esu	electrostatic unit(s)	^{i} (eg, Pr^i)	iso (eg, isopropyl)
eu	entropy unit(s)	i-	inactive (eg, i-methionine)
eV	electron volt(s)	IACS	International Annealed
expt(l)	experiment(al)		Copper Standard
ext(d)	extract(ed)	ibp	initial boiling point
extn	extraction	ICC	Interstate Commerce
F	Fahrenheit; farad(s)		Commission
F	faraday constant	ICI	International Commission
FAO	Food and Agriculture		on Illumination (see also
	Organization of the		CIE); Imperial Chemical
	United Nations		Industries, Ltd.
fcc	face-centered cubic	ICT	International Critical
Fed, fedl	federal (eg, Fed Spec)		Tables
fl oz	fluid ounce(s)	ID	inner diameter
fob	free on board	IEEE	Institute of Electrical and
fp	freezing point		Electronics Engineers
frz	freezing	in.	inch(es)
ft	foot (feet)	insol, i	insoluble
ft-lb	foot-pound(s)	IPT	Institute of Petroleum
ft^3/min,			Technologists
cfm	cubic foot (feet) per minute	ir	infrared
g	gram(s)	ISO	International Organization
g	gravitational acceleration		for Standardization
G	gauss(es)	IU	International Unit(s)
G	Gibbs free energy	IUPAC	International Union of
gal	gallon(s)		Pure and Applied
gal/min,			Chemistry
gpm	gallon(s) per minute	J	joule(s)
g/den	gram(s) per denier	K	Kelvin
gem-	geminal (attached to the	K	dissociation coustant
	same atom)	kbar	kilobar(s)
g-mol	gram-molecular (as in	kc	kilocycle(s)
	g-mol wt)	kcal	kilogram-calorie(s)
g-mole	gram-mole(s)	keV	kilo electron volt(s)
G-Oe	gauss-oersted(s)	kg	kilogram(s)
gpm,		kG	kilogauss(es)
gal/min	gallon(s) per minute	kgf	kilogram force(s)
gr	grain(s)	kJ	kilojoule(s)
h, hr	hour(s)	kp	kilopond(s) (equals kilo-
hl	hectoliter(s)		gram force(s)
hmw	high-molecular-weight	kV	kilovolt(s)
	(adj.)	kVa	kilovolt-ampere(s)
hp	horsepower(s)	kW	kilowatt(s)
hr, h	hour(s)	kWh	kilowatt-hour(s)
hyd	hydrated, hydrous	l	liter(s)
hyg	hygroscopic	l-	$levo$-, levorotatory

L-	denoting configurational relationship (as to *levo*-glyceraldehyde)
lb	pound(s)
LC_{50}	concentration lethal to 50% of the animals tested
lcl	less than carload lots
LD_{50}	dose lethal to 50% of the animals tested
liq	liquid
lm	lumen
lmw	low-molecular-weight (adj.)
ln	logarithm (natural)
log	logarithm (common)
m	meter(s)
m	molal
m-	meta (eg, *m*-xylene)
M	metal
M	molar (as applied to concentration; not molal)
mA	milliampere(s)
mAh	milliampere-hour(s)
manuf	manufacture
manufd, mfd	manufactured
manufg, mfg	manufacturing
max	maximum
Mc	megacycle(s)
MCA	Manufacturing Chemists' Association
mcal	millicalorie(s)
mech	mechanical
meq	milliequivalent(s)
MeV	million electron volt(s)
mfd, manufd	manufactured
mfg, manufg	manufacturing
mg	milligram(s)
min	minimum; minute(s)
misc	miscellaneous
mixt	mixture
ml	milliliter(s)
MLD	minimum lethal dose
mm	millimeter(s)
mM	millimole(s)

m*M*	millimolar
mo(s)	month(s)
mol	molecule, molecular
mol wt	molecular weight
mp	melting point
mph	miles per hour
MR	molar refraction
mV	millivolt(s)
mμ	millimicron(s) (10^{-9} m)
^{n} (eg, Bu^{n}), *n*-	normal (eg, normal butyl)
n (as, n_{D}^{20})	index of refraction (for 20°C and sodium light)
n-, ^{n}	normal (eg, *n*-butyl, Bu^{n})
N	normal (as applied to concentration)
N-	denoting attachment to nitrogen (eg, *N*-methylaniline)
NASA	National Aeronautics and Space Administration
ND	*New Drugs* (NND changed to ND in 1965)
NF	*National Formulary* (American Pharmaceutical Association)
nm	nuclear magneton; nanometer(s) (10^{-9} m)
NMR	nuclear magnetic resonance
NND	*New and Nonofficial Drugs* (AMA) (1958–1965). Later called ND
NNR	*New and Nonofficial Remedies* (1907–1958). Later called NND
no.	number
NOIBN	not otherwise indexed by name (DOT specification for shipping containers)
o-	ortho (eg, *o*-xylene)
O-	denoting attachment to oxygen (eg, *O*-acetylhydroxylamine)
Ω	ohm(s)
Ω-cm	ohm-centimeter(s)
OD	outer diameter
Oe	oersted(s)

o/w	oil-in-water (eg, o/w emulsion)
owf	on weight of fiber
oz	ounce(s)
p-	para (eg, *p*-xylene)
P	poise(s)
pdr	powder
PhI	*Pharmacopoeia Internationalis*, 2 vols. and Suppl., World Health Organization, Geneva, 1951, 1955, and 1959
phr	parts per hundred of rubber or resin
pos	positive (adj.)
powd	powdered
ppb	parts per billion (parts per 10^9)
ppm	parts per million
ppt(d)	precipitate(d)
pptn	precipitation
Pr. (no.)	Foreign prototype (number); dyestuff designation used in *AATCC Year Books* for dyes not listed in the old *Colour Index* (1924 ed.; 1928 Suppl.); obsolete since new *Colour Index* was published (1956 ed.; 1963 Suppl.)
prepd	prepared
prepn	preparation
psi	pound(s) per square inch
psia	pound(s) per square inch absolute
psig	pound(s) per square inch gage
pt	point
pts	parts
qual	qualitative
quant	quantitative
qv	which see (quod vide)
R	Rankine; roentgen; univalent hydrocarbon radical (or hydrogen)
rad	radian

Rep	roentgen(s) equivalent physical
resp	respectively
rh	relative humidity
Rhe	unit of fluidity (1/P)
RI	Ring Index (number); from *The Ring Index*, Reinhold Publishing Corp., N.Y., 1940
rms	root mean square
rpm	revolutions per minute
rps	revolutions per second
RRI	Revised Ring Index (number); from *The Ring Index*, 2nd ed., American Chemical Society, Washington, D.C., 1960
RT	room temperature
s, sol	soluble
^{s} (eg, Bu^s), *sec*-	secondary (eg, *sec*-butyl)
s-, *sym*-	symmetrical (eg, *s*-dichloroethylene)
S-	denoting attachment to sulfur (eg, *S*-methyl-cysteine)
SAE	Society of Automotive Engineers
satd	saturated
satn	saturation
scf, SCF	standard cubic foot (feet) (760 mm Hg, 63°F)
scfm	standard cubic feet per minute
Sch	Schultz number (designation for dyes from *Farbstofftabellen*, 4 vols., Akademie Verlag, Leipzig, 1931–1939)
sec	second(s)
sec-, ^{s}	secondary (eg, *sec*-butyl; Bu^s)
SFs	Saybolt Furol second(s)
sl s, sl sol	slightly soluble
sol, s	soluble
soln	solution
soly	solubility
sp	specific

sp, spp	species (sing. and pl.)		(ASA changed to USASI
Spec	specification		in 1966)
sp gr	specific gravity	USP	(*The*) *United States*
SPI	Society of the Plastics		*Pharmacopeia* (Mack
	Industry		Publishing Co., Easton,
sq	square		Pa.)
St	stokes	uv	ultraviolet
STP	standard temperature and	V	volt(s)
	pressure (760 mm Hg,	*v-, vic-*	vicinal (attached to
	0°C)		adjacent atoms)
subl	sublime(s), subliming	var	variety
SUs	Saybolt Universal	*vic-, v-*	vicinal (attached to
	second(s)		adjacent atoms)
sym, s-	symmetrical (eg, *sym-*	vol	volume(s) (not volatile)
	dichloroethylene)	v s, v sol	very soluble
ᵗ (eg, Buᵗ),		vs	versus
t-, tert-	tertiary (eg, tertiary butyl)	v/v	volume per volume
t-, tert-, ᵗ	tertiary (eg, *t*-butyl)	W	watt(s)
TAPPI	Technical Association of	Wh	watt-hour(s)
	the Pulp and Paper	w/o	water-in-oil (eg, w/o
	Industry		emulsion)
tech	technical	wt	weight
temp	temperature	w/v	weight per volume
tert-, t-, ᵗ	tertiary (eg, *tert*-butyl)	w/w	weight per weight
theoret	theoretical	xu (ca	
Twad	Twaddell	10^{-11}	
USASI	United States of America	cm)	x unit(s)
	Standards Institute	yd	yard(s)
		yr	year(s)

Quantities

Some standard abbreviations (prefixes) for very small and very large quantities are as follows:

deci (10^{-1})	d	deka (10^{1})	dk
centi (10^{-2})	c	hecto (10^{2})	h
milli (10^{-3})	m	kilo (10^{3})	k
micro (10^{-6})	μ	mega (10^{6})	M
nono (10^{-9})	n	giga (10^{9})	G (or B)
pico (10^{-12})	p	tera (10^{12})	T
femto (10^{-15})	f		
atto (10^{-18})	a		

S continued

SHALE OIL

Shale oil is a dark viscous organic liquid obtained by pyrolyzing oil shale. It is similar to petroleum in that the refining steps and end-use products are generally the same. Oil shale is a somewhat vague term but generally refers to a wide variety of laminated sedimentary rocks containing organic matter that can be released only by destructive distillation. Some removal of organic matter by solvents is possible (1), but the amount removed is very small and this permits a distinction to be made from lignite, torbanites, and cannel coal, as well as tar sands, which are rock or sand formations actually impregnated with oil. Oil shales generally contain over one-third mineral matter and are thus distinguished from coal which commonly contains only minor amounts of minerals. The organic portion, being a mixture of complex chemical compounds, has had the term "kerogen" applied to it (Greek derivation meaning "producer of wax"). Kerogen is not a definite material, however, and kerogens from different shales are dissimilar.

Oil shales were formed in ancient shallow lakes by the slow deposition of aquatic organisms, spores, pollen grains, and vegetable matter such as shreads of wood, bark, and leaves, along with inorganic matter intimately mingled. The inorganic material consists mainly of clay with fine sand, calcite, dolomite, and iron compounds. As the lakes dried out, the deposits became compacted and over geologic time were transformed into impermeable rocks.

Oil shale is considered one of the primary sources of liquid fuels to supplement and augment those now commonly obtained from petroleum. Petroleum resources represent less than 4% of the known fuel reserves of the United States, so other sources eventually must be utilized to meet the country's continually expanding demand for liquid fuels. Although coal is the most abundant fuel resource, oil shale appears to be more economically attractive as an alternative source of liquid fuels if distance to market is not a factor (2).

Oil shale is also considered as a possible supplement for natural gas (3) as well as a feedstock for such petrochemical products as ethylene, sulfur, and ammonia.

Properties and Composition

Oil Shale. Physical and chemical data for many of the world's best-known oil shales are summarized in Table 1. As can be seen, deposits vary greatly in richness and ironically the deposits being commercially exploited are not necessarily the richest.

Table 1. Characteristics of Selected Oil Shales and Shale Oils (4)

	Australia, Glen Davis[a]	Brazil, Irati (5)	Brazil, Paraiba[a]	Canada, Nova Scotia[b]	Estonia, Kukersite[a] (45)	France, Autun[b] (45)	Israel, Um Barek[b]	Lebanon[b]	Manchuria, Fushun[b]	New Zealand, Orepuki[b]	Scotland, Westwood mine[a]	South Africa, Ermelo[a]	Spain, Puerto-llano[b]	Sweden, Kvarntorp[a]	Thailand, Mae-sod[b]	United States, Colorado (6)	Yugoslavia, Aleksinac (7)
modified Fischer assay																	
oil, gal/ton	82.9	19.0	31.3	51.4	54.1	25.8	15.6	61.5	7.6	66.2	22.2	45.6	46.9	13.9	71.4	27.7	27.0
oil, %	30.9	7.4	11.5	18.8	22.0	9.7	6.4	24.8	3.0	24.8	8.2	17.6	17.6	5.7	26.1	10.6	10.0
water, %	0.7	1.7	6.2	0.8	1.9	3.2	2.2	11.0	4.9	8.3	2.2	3.0	1.8	2.0	3.8	0.7	5.8
spent shale, %	64.1	87.7	78.4	77.7	70.5	84.0	88.4	56.5	90.3	57.6	86.6	75.6	78.4	87.2	66.3	86.6	79.9
gas and loss, %	4.3	3.2	3.9	2.7	5.6	3.1	3.0	7.7	1.8	9.3	3.0	3.8	2.2	5.1	3.8	2.1	4.3
conversion of organic material to oil,[c] %	66		59	60[d]	66.0	44	48		33	45	56[d]	34	57[d]	26	71	70	48
rock characteristics																	
sp gr, at 60°F	1.60	1.18	1.14			2.03			2.29	1.46	2.22	1.58	1.80	2.09	1.61	2.16	
heating value, Btu/lb	8,100	2,700	3,520	5,420	5,780	3,810			1,460	9,150	2,540	8,230	5,380	3,870	6,630	2,590	3,680
ash, %	51.6		71.4	62.4		70.8	60.0	18.8	82.7	32.7	77.8	42.5	62.8	72.1	56.4	65.7	67.0
organic carbon, %	39.7	76.5	16.5	26.3	47.0	18.8	10.6		7.9	45.7	12.3	43.8	26.0	18.8	30.8	12.4	20.7
oil assay																	
gravity, API (see Vol. 14, p. 835)	27.4	18.9	29.2	29.2	13.5	25.6	14.3	15.7	22.2	25.6	29.2	20.6	25.6	12.8	29.2	23.0	25.6
carbon, %	85.4	84.8	84.3		83.0	84.9	79.6	83.2	85.7	83.4		84.8		85.0	84.4	84.6	84.4
hydrogen, %	12.0	11.4	12.0		9.5	11.4	9.8	10.3	10.7	11.8		11.1		9.0	12.4	11.5	11.1
nitrogen, %	0.5		1.1		0.1	0.8	1.4	0.6		0.6			0.9	0.7	1.1	2.0	
sulfur, %	0.4	1.7	0.2		1.1	0.3	6.2	1.5		0.6		0.6	0.3	1.7	0.4	0.6	
ash analysis, %																	
SiO₂	81.5	66.0	55.8	61.1	31.0	55.1	26.0[e]		62.3	44.2	55.7	61.3	56.6	62.4	60.8	42.7	41.0
Al₂O₃	10.1	17.4	26.7	30.1	7.8	27.6			26.7	28.1	25.1	30.5	27.6	17.6	19.9	13.2	12.9
Fe₂O₃	3.0	10.8	8.5	5.0	5.8	9.3			6.1	20.5	9.9	2.9	9.1	10.7	4.8	4.6	11.2
CaO	0.8	1.9	2.8	1.1	39.0	1.7	45.0[e]		0.1	4.6	2.6	1.6	2.6	1.2	3.3	23.3	22.6
MgO	0.8	1.5	3.7	1.6	4.5	1.9			1.8	1.4	3.1	1.7	2.2	1.7	3.8	10.0	3.6
other oxides	3.8	0.9	2.5	1.1	3.2	4.4			3.0	1.2	3.6	2.1	1.9	6.4	7.4	7.2	1.6

[a] Average sample.
[b] Selected sample.
[c] Based on recovery of carbon in oil from organic carbon in shale.
[d] Carbon content of oil estimated as 84%.
[e] Approximate.

Colorado shale varies from light gray to mahogany brown. Others may be black (Scotland, Canada, Australia), black-brown with satin luster (Scotland), gray (Scotland), pale yellow (Brazil), pale brick red, red brown, olive green, or dark red (Estonia). In general, rich specimens have comparatively little lamination and are commonly of massive structure. Lean specimens are frequently finely laminated, such as the Paraiba "paper shale" of Brazil which is easily fractured along the lamination planes. On the other hand, Green River shales of Colorado are particularly consolidated and impervious.

Considerable work has been done by the U.S. Bureau of Mines on Green River formation shale. Results (8) indicate a highly consolidated organic–inorganic system with no significant micropore structure or internal surface. The inorganic part consists of essentially nonspherical particles, smaller than 44 μ, which have considerable surface area. The distribution of the organic matter within the inorganic matrix is essentially inter- rather than intraparticle; that is to say, the organic matter is between the particles. An estimate made from surface-area data suggests that only a small amount of the organic is either directly or chemically bonded to the mineral constituents.

Studies of the kerogen portion have been attempted by painstaking removal of the inorganic material by successive treatment with hydrochloric acid (to remove carbonates and soluble materials), hydrofluoric acid (to remove silica or silicates), and nitric acid or zinc–hydrochloric acid (to remove pyrite). Jones and Dickert (9) cite evidence that some primary valence bonding exists between the organic and the carbonates through carboxylic acid groups. In addition, porphyrins in the kerogen may be chelated with some of the minerals. Beneficiation of this inorganic–organic mixture by the usual ore-dressing techniques (sink-float) has not resulted in appreciable enrichment in organic matter. The typical kerogen molecule is a polymer with a molecular weight well above 3000. Its structure is highly naphthenic (alicyclic) with closely associated aromatic and nitrogen and sulfur heterocyclic ring systems randomly distributed (10).

Generalized kerogen compositions (in percent) are as follows: carbon, 66–88; hydrogen, 7.1–12.8; nitrogen, 0.1–3.0; sulfur, 0.1–8.8; and oxygen, 0.75–27.4. Some kerogens broadly resemble coal in constitution in that there is definite evidence of a benzenoid structure, which, however, is less pronounced than that in coal. In other kerogens, notably Estonian kukersite, this is not the case, however.

Shale Oils. Destructive pyrolysis of the crushed shale at atmospheric pressure and temperatures of ca 900°F yields shale oil. Under these conditions a disproportionation of carbon and hydrogen structures, equivalent to "internal hydrogenation," occurs. Ideally, a large percentage of the organic converts to a liquid, some converts to light gases, and the remainder stays as a carbon-rich residue on the inorganic matrix. Typical oil compositions are shown in Table 1. Grades are generally measured by the modified Fischer assay method.

Shale oil in some respects may be considered as intermediate in composition between petroleum and coal tar. This may be illustrated by the range of values for C/H ratio: 7–9 for shale oil, 6–7 for petroleum, and 10–16 for coal carbonization products. A representative Colorado oil consists of 39% hydrocarbons (many being unsaturated) and 61% organic compounds containing oxygen, nitrogen, and sulfur. The nitrogen compounds include homologs of pyridine, quinoline, pyrrole, and benzonitrile. Sulfur exists in thiophene structures, along with some disulfides. Oxygen compounds are primarily phenol homologs. The oil is deficient in low-boiling constituents,

Table 2. Colorado Shale-Oil Composition (10)

Composition	Fraction distilled, %, at temperature range, °C, indicated							
	10 190–270	20 270–310	30 310–350	40 350–380	50 380–410	60 410–440	70 440–470	80 470–485
polycyclic aromatics, %	9	9	9	10	7.5	2	2	2
monocyclic aromatics, %	6	8.5	6	6.5	4.5	2	2	2
branched olefins and cycloolefins, %	15	24.5	19	14	12.5	6	6	6
straight-chain olefins, %	26	9	11	10.5	8.5	2.5	2.5	2.5
branched paraffins and naphthenes, %	7	6	4	3	3	4.5	4.5	4.5
straight-chain paraffins, %	8	8	8.5	8.5	12	3.5	3.5	3.5
oxygen compounds, %	12	17	17.5	17	14	21.5	21.5	21.5
sulfur compounds, %	5	4	4.5	5	5.5	7	7	7
nitrogen compounds, %	12	14	20.5	25.5	32.5	51	51	51

Table 3. Properties of Oils Produced from Colorado Oil Shale by Various Retorting Methods

Retorting method	Gravity, API°	Sulfur, %	Nitrogen, %	Analysis of distillate boiling to 300°C		
				Saturates, %	Olefins, %	Aromatics, %
Union Oil (11)	18.2	0.71	1.89	21	55	24
Tosco (Aspeco) (12)	20.6	0.75	1.8			
gas combustion (6)	19.7	0.64	2.12	27	45	28
1000°F hi-temp (13)		0.85	2.25	18	57	25
1200°F hi-temp		1.05	3.00	7.5	39.5	53
1400°F hi-temp		1.20	3.30	0	2.5	97.5
1600°F hi-temp		1.25	1.55	0	0	100

the gasoline-boiling-range fractions amounting to less than 3%. Also, only 53% can be distilled below 572°F (300°C) at a pressure of 40 mm Hg. The pour point is 80–90°F and the viscosity is 280 SUs at 100°F. The distribution of components in each boiling-point fraction is shown in Table 2.

The retorting method may affect the properties of oils produced from a given shale as shown in Table 3. The oils from the first three methods are somewhat similar, which is to be expected since oil is formed and removed from these retorts rapidly as the shale is heated into normal retorting-temperature range (about 700–900°F). The high-temperature data are from an entrained-solids apparatus which heats the shale rapidly to the desired temperature. Increased aromatic content is one noteworthy result of such treatment.

Occurrence and Reserves

World. Oil-shale deposits occur in many countries of the world and in sedimentary rocks of virtually all ages. Table 4 lists a number of deposits by country and gives some of their characteristics. Thickness and grade are given only as an index to relative size and richness and must be regarded as approximate. Torbanite is a substance intermediate in characteristics between oil shale and coal. Other names, such as tasmanite, tripolite, kukersite, and ichthyol, are local synonyms for torbanite or oil shale. In addition to these, oil shales are reported to occur in Arabia, Argentina, Austria, Chile, Czechoslovakia, India, Ireland, Lebanon, Nicaragua, Norway, Panama, Peru, Poland, Syria, Turkey, Uruguay, Wales, and Yemen.

Table 5 lists shale-oil reserves by country. As with all mineral-reserve estimates, differing degrees of certainty attach to the various numbers. These figures therefore represent a mix of proved and probable reserves, but do not include potential or suspected shale-oil resources.

United States. Oil shales of the Green River formation in Colorado, Utah, and Wyoming are the most commercially significant of the many deposits in this country. These lacustrine beds are Eocene in age and occur in the Piceance Creek, Uinta, and Green River basins as well as several smaller basins.

The Piceance Creek basin of Colorado covers about 1500 square miles, and the Green River and lesser basins in Wyoming cover about 9600 square miles. The thickest and richest beds are in the center of the Piceance Creek basin where they probably reach 2000 ft of 25 gal/ton average material which lies under approx 1000 ft of barren overburden (20,24).

Table 4. Oil Shale Deposits

Country	Deposits	Geologic age	Type of material	Thick-ness, ft	Assay, U.S. gal/ short ton	References	Remarks
Australia	New South Wales	Permo-Carboniferous	torbanite	to 7	86		
	Queensland	Paleozoic	torbanite	2–3	100		
	Queensland	Cenozoic	oil shale	to 88	15		
	Tasmania	Permo-Carboniferous	tasmanite	3–6	25–35	(14)	
Brazil	Paraiba	Pliocene	oil shale	60	15–18	(5,14)	
	Irati	Permian	oil shale	100–328	13–20	(5,14)	approx 1000-mile outcrop and large part of deposit unexplored
Bulgaria	Breznik	Jurassic	oil shale	160	30	(14,15)	
Burma	see Thailand						
Canada	Sask./Manitoba	Cretaceous	oil shale				
	New Brunswick	Mississippian	oil shale	200	25	(14)	
China	Fushun, Manchuria	Tertiary	oil shale	450	15	(15,16)	forms overburden for coal deposit. Mined since 1923
Democratic Republic of Congo	Stanleyville Basin	Triassic	oil shale	30	25	(14)	
France	Autun	Permian	oil shale	3–11	10–18	(14)	
	St. Hilaire	Permian	oil shale	12	18		
	Séverac-le-Chateau	Jurassic	oil shale	30–50	10	(14)	
	Vagnas	Cenozoic	oil shale	23	27		
Germany	Württemberg	Jurassic	oil shale	16	12		
	Braunschweig	Jurassic	oil shale	16	12		
Great Britain	Lothians, Scotland	Mississippian	oil shale	4–12	16–40	(14)	mined extensively until 1963

	Location	Age					Remarks
	Norfolk	Jurassic	oil shale	4–7	17–35	(15)	similar to diatomite
	Kimmeridge, Dorset	Jurassic	oil shale	2	10–45	(15)	
Italy	Sicily	Tertiary	tripolite	16	25	(14,15)	overlies coal seams
Israel	Um-Barek	Cretaceous	oil shale	to 140	12	(15,17)	
New Zealand	Orepuki	Tertiary	oil shale	5	50	(14,15)	produced liquid fuel through 1960
Republic of South Africa	Ermelo, Transvaal	Paleozoic and Mesozoic	torbanite	3	48	(15,18)	
Spain	Puertollano, Ciudad Real	Carboniferous	oil shale	14	30–35	(15,19)	associated with coals
Sweden	Kvarntorp, Narke	Cambrian-Ordovician	oil shale	50	15	(14,15)	liquid fuels with by-products ammonia, sulfur, lime, and ceramic materials up to 1962
Switzerland	Meride, Ticino	Triassic	ichthyol	to 30	55	(15)	
Thailand and Burma	Mae Sod	Pliocene	oil shale	20	25–70	(14,15)	
United States	Piceance basin, Colorado	Eocene	oil shale	1940	10–65	(15,20)	largest-known deposit in the world
	Uinta basin, Utah	Eocene	oil shale	700	10–65	(21)	
	Green River basin, Wyoming	Eocene	oil shale	15–80	10–65	(15)	
	Indiana, Kentucky	Devonian	oil shale	to 400	10	(15)	
	Brooks Range, Alaska	Mesozoic	tasmanite	4	130	(22)	deposit examined only locally
U.S.S.R.	Estonia	Ordovician	kukersite	10	50	(14,15)	liquid and gaseous fuel synthesized
Yugoslavia	Alexinac, Morava valley	Oligocene	oil shale	250–400	25–40	(14)	
	Valjevo, Kolubara valley	Miocene	oil shale	175		(14)	

Table 5. Major Shale-Oil Reserves (23)

Country or area	Oil in place, million bbl[a]
Argentina	400
Australia (including Tasmania)	270
Brazil	800,000
Balkans and other Central Europe[b]	340
Burma	2,000
Canada	50,000
Chile	20
China	
Fushun, Manchuria	2,100
other deposits	26,000
England	1,000
France	425
Germany (West)	2,000
Israel	20
Jordan	45
Sicily	35,000
Luxembourg	700
New Zealand	560
Republic of the Congo	100,000
Republic of South Africa	130
Scotland	580
Spain	280
Sweden	2,500
Thailand	800
United States	2,200,000
U.S.S.R.	
Estonia and adjacent Leningrad Area	22,000
other European U.S.S.R.	13,000
Siberia	80,000
total	3,340,170[c]

[a] Conversion to barrels of 42 U.S. gallons each is based on shale oil having an assumed specific gravity of 0.92 at 60°F (27.8°C); for an oil of this gravity, one barrel weighs 322 lb.

[b] Includes Bulgaria, Yugoslavia, Albania, Greece, Czechoslovakia, Austria, and Switzerland.

[c] This compares with 12,500 million barrels of world reserves of petroleum (See Petroleum (Resources)).

A unit of these shales, some 110 ft thick near the center of the basin and assaying 25–30 gal of oil per ton, is called the "mahogany zone" in subsurface or "mahogany ledge" on outcrop, where it is commonly a cliff former. Near the top of this zone a remarkably persistent, 1-ft-thick band of barren tuff, the mahogany marker, is used as a stratigraphic reference (25).

Table 6. Oil Shale Reserves of United States (oil in place, billion bbl) (14)

Location	Quality, gal/ton	
	10–25	25–65
Wyoming	370	30
Utah	230	90
Colorado	800	400
central and eastern U.S.	200	

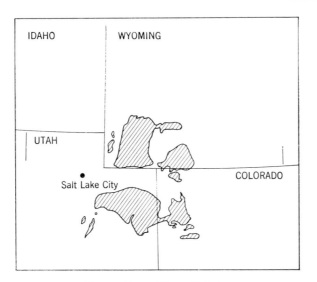

Fig. 1. Green River oil shale.

Trona, $Na_2CO_3 \cdot NaHCO_3 \cdot 2H_2O$, occurs interbedded with the oil shale of Wyoming's Green River basin and is being mined for soda ash there. Nahcolite, $NaHCO_3$, and dawsonite, $NaAlCO_3(OH)_2$, occur in considerable quantity in the Piceance Creek basin. These two saline minerals are regarded as potential sources of soda ash and aluminum, respectively.

Oil shale occurs in at least twenty-eight states, including Idaho, Illinois, Indiana, Kansas, Michigan, Arkansas, Nevada, New York, New Mexico, Ohio, Oklahoma, Pennsylvania, Tennessee, and Texas (14). However, these deposits seldom exceed 15 gal/ton over thicknesses of 15 ft or more and are of less economic significance than those of the Green River formation (Fig. 1).

Marine shales of Devonian age underlying about 250,000 square miles from as far west as Oklahoma to as far east as Pennsylvania contain minor amounts of kerogen. These shales generally assay less than 10 gal of oil per ton, although in their richest zones in Indiana and Kentucky they are generally included in resource appraisals (14).

Total U.S. reserves as given in Table 5 are further subdivided as to locality in Table 6.

Production

Foreign Industry. The first recorded reference to processing oil shale is in a patent issued in England in 1694 to distill "oyle from a kind of stone." Sellique devised the process that started the French shale-oil industry in 1838, and James Young and his associates commercialized a process for making oil from boghead coal at Bathgate, Scotland, in 1850. Robert Bell started production of oil from shales west of Edinburgh, Scotland in 1862. Both "coal oil" and shale oil were produced in the U.S. and Canada before Colonel Drake drilled the first oil well near Titusville, Pa., in 1859. The first Australian shale was retorted in December 1865 at America Creek, Woolongong District, New South Wales. Later small-scale shale industries started in Brazil in 1881, New Zealand in 1900, Switzerland in 1915, Sweden and Estonia in 1921, Spain in 1922, Manchuria in 1929, and South Africa in 1935.

Although the French industry was the first to process oil shale commercially, it has operated only intermittently, the various shutdowns being at the St. Hilaire plant in 1948, the Séverac-le-Chateau plant in 1951, and the Autun plant in 1957. The Australian operations also were intermittent. The latest venture at Glen Davis, New South Wales, started operations in 1940 but was closed down in May 1952, and the plant was dismantled. Estonian industry has been continuous and was expanded by the Russians after World War II (27). A thermal power plant at Narva uses oil shale as fuel and has a capacity of 1625 MW. The two largest processing complexes are located at Kohtla Jarve and Kivioeli. A gas-only installation is at Slantsky. Combined production is now over 100 million ft^3/day and is piped to Leningrad, Tallin, and Narva. All phases of the industry (gas, tar, oil) have had to be subsidized throughout most of the postwar period. More diversification to chemicals and specialty products in recent years, however, has moved operations into the black.

The Spanish operations had been on a small scale until a major expansion to 1 million tons per year at Puertollano was completed in 1955. Even so, the process was outdated and uneconomical (28) and the mine was closed in 1966. The South African plant at Ermelo experienced various expansions from its opening but it ceased operations in the early 1960s because of depletion of the deposit (28). Small intermittent operations have been underway in Brazil for many years, and present plans envision a large-scale commercial operation in the near future (see Fig. 2). Postwar research in Germany has resulted in a process for utilizing oil shale to produce cement and electric power. An industrial plant was put in operation at Dotternhausen in 1961.

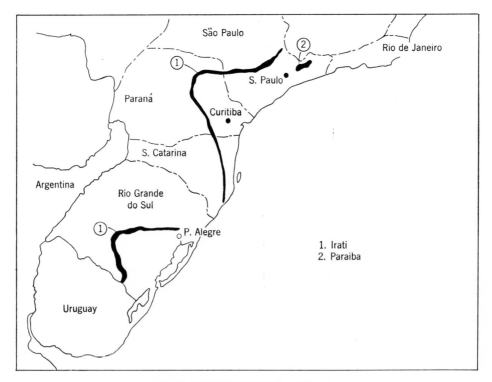

Fig. 2. Oil shales in southern Brazil.

During World War II, the oil-shale plants at Fushun, Manchuria, controlled by the Japanese, reached an annual throughput of 4,700,000 tons of shale and produced 1,317,300 bbl of crude shale oil. During the Korean conflict operations were augmented greatly by the communist Chinese. Production has continued to expand since and may be 40,000 bbl/day presently. Combining of coal with oil shale and relatively efficient processing methods make shale oil economical. Scottish Oils Ltd., once the largest shale operation (producing 780,000 bbl in 1952), and a source of fuels, waxes, and fertilizer for more than 100 years, was curtailed in 1963. High-grade reserves were depleted and facilities were shut down or converted to other uses. The large operation at Kvarntorp, Sweden, has declined also, availability of petroleum being the cause along with the limited size of Swedish reserves. The refinery and chemical plants have converted to imported petroleum and oil shale is considered a standby source (29).

Domestic Industry. Many small experimental plants have been operated for short periods in the U.S. From 1944 to 1955 the Bureau of Mines carried on intensive research work, developing and operating an experimental mine and several pilot-plant retorting and refining units. The Union Oil Company also opened a mine and constructed and operated a semicommercial-sized retort (1000 tons/day) from 1957 to 1959. The Oil Shale Corporation has been active in research from about 1956 with work on both pilot-plant and semicommercial scale (1000-tons/day retort).

Mining. Since oil-shale deposits vary widely as to size, grade, depth of burial, and strength of the shale and overlying rock, a very wide variety of mining methods has been applied to them. Where the deposits are at or near the surface and the cost of removing overburden is low, open-pit methods have been used. Where underground mining is required, the room-and-pillar method has been used. This approach is in use for extraction of Estonian oil shales. The longwall method has been applied to some deposits (14).

Although no major commercial shale-oil operation has as yet been conducted in the United States, the U.S. Bureau of Mines did operate an experimental plant near Rifle, Colorado, from 1944 to 1956. At their "demonstration mine" the Bureau developed a two-level room-and-pillar method which is particularly suitable to the low-cost, high-tonnage requirements of economic oil-shale production in this country. Cost of delivering crushed shale to a retort stockpile based on the application of this method was projected to be $0.56/ton including depreciation, taxes, administration, and overhead but not including any charges for the plant or for oil-shale land (24).

With increasing interest in the very thick deposits of the center part of the Piceance Creek basin, other systems including block caving and combinations of mining and in situ recovery methods have been advocated (30), as well as the use of nuclear explosives (31).

Oil-Shale Retorting. Application of heat is the only means that has been found for producing shale oil, and numerous mechanical devices, known as retorts, have been developed to this end. More than 3000 foreign and domestic patents on retorting processes and equipment have been issued (32). Detailed descriptions of the better-known processes are available in the literature (33).

Retorting involves the crushing and heating of large quantities of raw shale and the cooling and discharging of almost equally large quantities of spent shale. In addition, oil-shale retorting plants must have facilities for collecting the retort products and for separating the oil from the water and dust carried out with it.

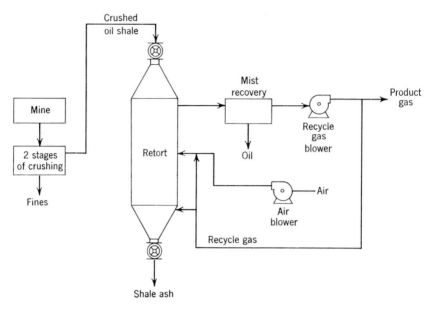

Fig. 3. Flow diagram of the gas-combustion retorting process.

Above-Ground Retorting. Research and development work carried on in the United States, the Soviet Union, and Brazil has been toward perfecting large-capacity retorts to serve large-capacity plants. The sum total of government and industry efforts in the U.S. in the last few decades indicates that any of three retorting processes are likely to be used for commercial operations on Colorado shales.

One of these is the gas-combustion process (Fig. 3) which was invented and developed by engineers of the U.S. Bureau of Mines (6). Several pilot plants were built in the late 1940s and early 1950s, the largest having a nominal rating of 150 tons/day. The name comes from the fact that part of the off-gas is recycled for combustion within the retort. Current designs call for a vertical cylindrical vessel containing a bed of broken shale. Shale enters at the top, passes successively through preheating, retorting, combustion, and cooling zones, and leaves at the bottom. The recycle gas entering the bottom of the retort absorbs heat from the spent shale. A little below the middle of the retort vessel, air is injected, providing oxygen necessary to burn the gas and some of the residual carbon in the shale that has passed through the retorting zone. The resulting hot combustion gases heat the raw shale, and the oil vapors and gaseous products evolved are swept upward with the combustion gases. The oil-laden gas stream is cooled by the incoming cold shale, the oil condenses in the form of a mist, and is carried from the retort by the gas. An oil-recovery system separates the oil from the gas stream. Part of the gas then is recycled and the remainder leaves the system. In an industrial plant, the gas could be burned at the plant site to generate electric power or to supply heat for refining processes. It has a heating value of about 100 Btu/ft³.

Attractive features of the process are high thermal efficiency, high oil yields, and high retorting rate, and no water requirement for condensing the oil product. This last feature is of great importance in the semiarid region where the Green River deposit is located.

The Union Oil Company of California developed a countercurrent internal-combustion type of retorting process (34) in which shale is forced upward through a slightly

conical-shaped vessel (Fig. 4).   Shale is fed into the lower small end by a hydraulic pis-
ton and spent shale is discharged by overflowing the upper lip of the cone at the top.   The
shale charge is first ignited on the upper surface, and air is drawn downward through
the shale causing the combustion zone to progress downward.   Shale rate is adjusted
so that the zone stays about 2 ft below the surface of the bed and the incoming air helps

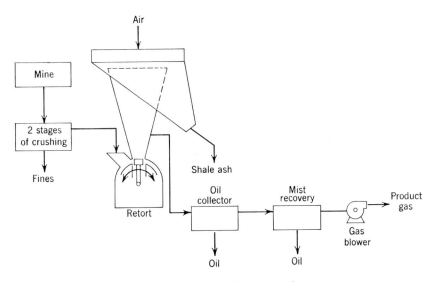

Fig. 4.   Flow diagram of the Union retorting process.

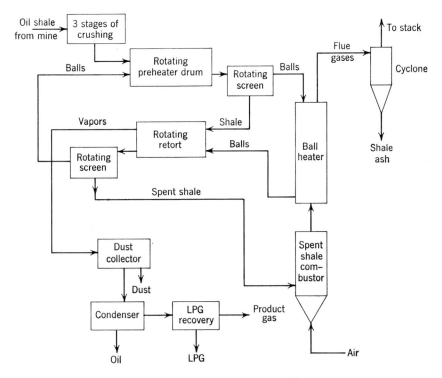

Fig. 5.   Tosco retorting process flow diagram.

to partially cool the spent shale before it overflows. Educted oils and gases pass downward through cool incoming shale and partially condense. A pool of oil occupies the bottom of the retort during operation to form an air seal and to provide lubrication of the moving parts. The oil–gas stream is extracted from near the bottom of the retort, and the constituents are separated mechanically. The Union retort also requires no water for cooling, is thermally efficient, and can handle a wide range of sizes.

The Oil Shale Corporation (Tosco) has adapted the Aspeco retorting method for use on Colorado oil shale (12). This process consists of the cocurrent flow of hot ceramic balls and cold oil shale in a rotating drum (Fig. 5). The shale takes up heat from the balls and the oil vapors produced are drawn off to a collection system. The spent shale is transferred to a furnace where residue carbon is burned to reheat the balls. Oil produced does not differ greatly from that produced by the gas-combustion or Union retorts with the exception of a 15–20°F lower pour point. Main advantages are high throughput rate in proportion to size of equipment and the production of a high-BTU off-gas, since there is no dilution by combustion products.

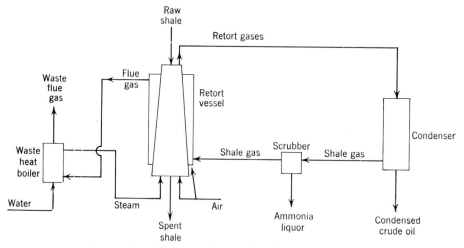

Fig. 6. Flow diagram of the modified Pumpherston process.

Of interest also is a retort known as the N-T-U, which is based on the same principle as the Union process but is designed for batchwise rather than continuous operation. A large unit was built by the Bureau of Mines in the late 1940s, primarily as a quick method of obtaining large quantities of shale oil for experimental studies. In the N-T-U process, air enters at the top of the retort, combustion begins at the top of the stationary shale bed, and gradually moves down to the bottom of the retort. Pilot-plant studies have been made by the Bureau of Mines on various other retorting schemes (34a).

Petrobras, the Brazilian National Oil Company, has been working on the "Petrosix" process in which externally heated recycle gases are passed into the middle of a downward-moving bed of broken shale in a cylindrical vessel. Cool recycle gas is admitted at the bottom to cool the retorted shale. The combined cooling and pyrolyzing gases carry off the oil in the form of a mist which is separated in cyclones and electrostatic precipitators. The off-gas is of high heating value and some is burned to indirectly heat the pyrolysis gas. The remainder can be pipelined or utilized for petrochemical manufacture.

In the U.S.S.R. considerable progress has been made in developing a retort with a "refractory heat carrier" (35). Crushed oil shale is fed to the retort together with spent shale ash (the heat carrier) which has been heated to 850°C. The shale is then semi-coked at temperatures of 350–520°C. Efforts resulted in the construction of an industrial plant with a retorting capacity of 500 tons/day. Tests indicate that 1000-ton/day retorts and larger can be made a major tool of the oil-shale industry.

Conventional equipment in Estonia has consisted of tunnel ovens and Pintsch retorts (36). In 1961–1963 the older Pintsch-type compartment retorts were modified from vertical gas flow to horizontal-transverse flow to give better heat distribution in the shale bed.

Retorts used in Scotland since about 1860 were primarily of the Pumpherston type (Fig. 6). Heat from the combustion of gases is circulated through a system of flues up and around an elliptical or cylindrical retort vessel, heating the downward-flowing bed of shale. The oil-laden retort gas is withdrawn from the top of the vessel, the oil is condensed, and the gas is burned to produce the heat for retorting. Steam usually is injected in the bottom of the shale bed to "sweep" the oil from the retort. Modifications of this process include the Rockesholm or HG retort (Hultman and Gustafsson) used in Sweden, the Henderson retorts used in Spain, and the Fell retorts formerly used in Australia. A more recent modification, the Westwood retort, was used in Scotland and employs not only external heating but also internal combustion of retort gas, some of the gas being recycled and injected into the bottom of the shale bed with the steam and air.

In France Pumpherston retorts were used at Autun; the plants at St. Hilaire and Séverac-le-Chateau used modified Grand Paroisse (or Lantz) and modified Cantieny and Marecaux retorts. The modified Grand Paroisse process is characterized by a crossflow of hot gas through a shale bed that is retained on two sides by louvers. The shale flows by gravity down through preheating, retorting, and spent-shale cooling sections.

The Bergh retort, originally the preferred process in Sweden, was modified to permit increased throughput and is now called the Kvarntorp retort after the location of the Swedish shale-oil plant. Residual carbon and sulfur remaining in the retorted shale are burned as the shale emerges from the bottom of 8–10-in. diam tubes. The resulting hot combustion gases pass upward around the tubes, thus heating them to retorting temperatures.

Also operated in Sweden were IM (Industry Method) tunnel ovens in which the oil shale was heated indirectly in cars that were pulled slowly through 200-ft long ovens.

Other retorting processes have been used in various other countries, including Germany, Manchuria, and South Africa. In many foreign retorts steam is introduced to act as a carrier or sweep gas to remove the retort products, to react with the nitrogen in the shale to form ammonia, to enrich the gas by a water–gas reaction, or for any combination of these.

Fines are usually screened from the feed for retorts that use direct contact of the shale with hot gas as the method of heating. A dust problem is common to processes that use finely ground feed material or where attrition of the shale is caused by revolving of the retort vessel or movement of internal parts. If carryover of the dust cannot be prevented, the dust must be subsequently separated from the oil. Internal-combustion retorts must be provided with close temperature control, as too high a temperature can cause coking or clinkering when processing some shales, such as the richer beds of the Green River formation.

One unique development in the utilization of oil shale is the hydrogasification process developed by the Institute of Gas Technology (37). In this process the organic matter of the shale is converted to a high-Btu fuel gas by reaction with hydrogen at 1200–2000 psi and 1000–1500°F. The gas is comparable to natural gas with high methane content. The economics are such that considerably higher natural gas prices are necessary before it can be commercially competitive. The process can be modified slightly to give ethane as the predominant product, thus suggesting utilization of oil shale as a raw material for ethylene manufacture.

In-Situ Retorting. In view of the materials handling involved in above-ground retorting, it is not surprising that retorting of the raw shale in place may be an attractive alternative. Experiments using the novel Ljungstrom system have been made in Sweden. This method utilized electrical-resistance heating to retort the shale underground (38). A series of holes was drilled vertically into the shale formation and electric heaters inserted. The oil vapors and gases thus produced were drawn off through special exhaust holes and collected. Yield was about 1 liter of oil and 1 m³ of gas for each 6.4 kWh expended.

In the United States, the techniques that have been tried are similar to those applied in fire floods of petroleum reservoirs. Among the problems found are the essentially zero permeability of the formation, the low porosity, and the possible disintegration of the burned shale, thus plugging combustion passageways. Sinclair Oil Company conducted some in-situ retorting through drill holes on its properties in Colorado (39). Communication was established between closely spaced holes, the shales were successfully ignited, and educt was obtained. Other work has been done using superheated steam. Equity Oil Company also made tests in Colorado using hot methane gas and successfully produced a 42° API oil. The wells were in a highly faulted and fractured area, however.

An imminent variation of the above is the use of nuclear explosives in deeply buried oil shale formations (31). Other underground explosions have shown that a chimney-shaped cavity is formed which fills with broken rock. It is hoped that this will occur in oil shale and that the jumbled mass can be retorted with methods similar to those used in above-ground retorts. Since the cavity would have dimensions in the hundreds of feet, one explosion could provide oil production for a year.

Shale-Oil Refining. Early shale-oil refining operations were quite crude and were principally for the production of paraffin waxes and burning oils for lamps. Later, with the development of internal-combustion engines, the light distillates were used to produce gasoline, the intermediate distillates for diesel oils, and the heavy distillates for lubricants. Burning oils and waxes still retained their importance, and many new or special products (such as naphthas, distillate and residual fuels, tar acids and bases, asphalts, resins, coke solvents, and chemicals) were produced to meet specific market demands in the different countries.

Shale-oil refining research and process development conducted by the Bureau of Mines and industrial laboratories in the United States has been devoted to the adaptation of petroleum-refining techniques and to the development of new processes more suitable to shale oil. The characteristics of shale oil previously discussed indicate differences from petroleum that affect the refining methods that may be applied. For example, catalytic cracking, a common beneficiation process practiced by the petroleum industry, is not directly applicable to shale oil, as the activity of the common cracking catalysts is inhibited by the nitrogen compounds. Also, some catalytic desulfurization and reforming processes are not as successful on shale oil as on petroleum. On the other hand, hydrogenation, even at low pressures (400–1500 psi), reduces the sulfur and nitrogen content of shale-oil fractions and stabilizes the more reactive unsaturated components to reduce their gum- and color-forming tendencies (40). The nitrogen and sulfur are removed as ammonia and hydrogen sulfide, both of which may be valuable by-products.

The various types of thermal processing common to the petroleum industry have been applied experimentally to Colorado shale oil under a wide variety of conditions. Viscosity breaking has produced a crude oil suitable for pipeline transportation. Further upgrading is advantageous, however, because large amounts of by-product retort gas are available at no cost. One possibility might involve fractionation of the raw shale oil with coking of the bottoms and catalytic hydrogenation and hydrocracking of the overhead and coker distillate. Yield of "synthetic crude" might approximate 98% of the crude shale oil, with hydrogen requirements of less than 2000 scf per barrel. Hydrogen could be supplied by steam-reforming of natural gas or perhaps of the refining gases produced on-site. The high-quality (43°API, no sulfur, 500 ppm N) synthetic crude would be pipelined to existing refineries and processed to final end-use products on a parallel with petroleum refining.

Through about 100 years of experience, the Scottish industry developed a refining procedure well suited to its crude oil and the market demand for products. Operations involved atmospheric distillation of the crude oil into a naphtha, a waxfree cut, a heavy oil and paraffin, and a residue. The heavy oil and paraffin were chilled and filtered to separate the paraffin, which was further refined into several grades of wax. The residue from the distillation of the waxfree and dewaxed oils was thermally cracked to produce additional crude spirit, which was treated for use as motor fuel, additional diesel fuel, and coke. Also, detergents were made as by-products.

The shale-oil refining operation at Autun, France, consisted essentially of atmospheric distillation to produce gasoline and residual oil and thermal cracking of the residual oil to produce additional gasoline and coke. The coke compared favorably with petroleum coke and found a ready market in France. The ammonia from the retort gases was used to produce ammonium sulfate.

Swedish refining operations at Kvarntorp (29) consisted of atmospheric distillation to produce gas, light oil, and fuel oil. Only the light oil was given additional treatment; it was washed with caustic soda, treated in three stages with cold sulfuric acid, then with methyl alcohol and caustic soda, and finally, with sodium plumbite solution. The treated oil was distilled into light naphtha to 212°F (100°C), heavy naphtha to 392°F (200°C), and kerosine to 518°F (270°C).

Operations at Puertollano, Spain, produced gasoline, gas oil, diesel and light fuel oil, paraffin wax, and lubricants. The Calvo Sotelo plant produced largely lubricants and wax.

In Estonia (35,36) thermal cracking is used on crude shale oil to produce gasoline, diesel fuel, kerosine, fuel oil, impregnating oil for railroad ties, and a low-quality asphalt. The gasoline and diesel oil are treated with caustic soda and sulfuric acid and then distilled. Minor products from refining include some thirty different chemicals.

The shale oil refineries at Glen Davis, Australia, Boksburg North, Transvaal, Republic of South Africa, and Fushun, Manchuria, each had, as its principal refining units, combination crude-distillation and thermal-cracking units in which crude oil and cracked products were fractionated in a main fractionating tower and light and heavy oil streams were cracked separately. In Australia, only gasoline was marketed, the gas, coke, or residual fuel being used in the plant. The South African operations differed in that a portion of the intermediate distillate was refined to kerosine and the residual oil was vacuum-distilled to produce asphalt and lighter oils that were used as cracking stock and asphalt cutback stocks. The gasoline fraction, which amounts to about 40% of the crude oil, was treated with acid and caustic, then blended with alcohol and benzene to produce a 70-octane fuel. The asphaltic products amounted to 38% of the crude oil. Manchurian operations during World War II were principally for the production of gasoline, diesel, and heavier fuels for the Japanese navy, and lubricants and wax for domestic use.

Uses

As enumerated under Shale-oil refining, the end uses of shale oil are myriad. The largest potential in the U.S. is for gasoline and jet fuels. Probable by-products at shale-oil plants include ammonia, sulfur, and coke. Organic chemicals of various types also are possibilities. At refineries such products as asphalt, waxes, and detergents are possible.

A large portion of Estonian oil shale is used for power production and for town-gas manufacture. Coproducts of the gas operation are benzene, sulfur, tar oil, and shale coke. Where shale oil is the main product, most is used as fuel. Refined products are gasoline, diesel fuel, impregnating oil, and asphalt. Polyphenols are recovered from the condensation water of various retorts and consist mainly of homologs of resorcinol. These are used for making adhesives, tanning agents, and phenolic molding compounds. Lower-boiling phenols (below 300°C) are used for varnishes, resins, synthetic fibers, detergents, and adhesives. There are reports also of a carbamide-resin plant and a formaldehyde plant. Other products are toluene, xylene, butyl alcohol, acetone, pesticides and herbicides, drying oils for the printing industry, aniline dyes, foam plastics, synthetic rubber, and ion-exchange resins. The huge quantities of shale ash remaining after retorting or burning are being utilized to some extent. A plant at Punane Kunda (Estonia) uses ash to make portland cement, and other plants manufacture cellular building blocks, rock wool, and mortar.

Economic Aspects

Commercial oil-shale industries have dwindled to the extent that they exist only in Estonia and Manchuria now, with slight activity in West Germany. Other areas have ceased production because of economics. Estonia, being a state-socialist venture, presents a different picture and officials have admitted to unprofitable operations (35) throughout most of the postwar period. But because of apparent lack of petroleum and gas reserves, the Russians continued to pour capital into oil-shale development. With the subsequent discovery of large oil and gas reserves, there has been more concern about the lack of profitability of shale. Shale gas produced at $2.96 per million Btu is no match for Russian natural gas valued at $1.07 per million Btu. And shale oil at $11 per barrel does not compete with petroleum at $3. Shifting emphasis to petrochemicals reportedly has changed the outlook, and profitable operations are now claimed.

Time schedules for commercial development in the United States have for some time indicated that shale oil was just around the corner. Each year the schedule is pushed back, however. There is no doubt that interest is very high among large oil companies as evidenced by the oil-shale reserves held and being acquired and the efforts applied to research. Commercialization might have already come about except for two main factors: the enormous investment required to initiate even the minimum-sized operation (from an economic standpoint), and policies of the Federal Government that have not encouraged development. Cost estimates (41–44) indicate that shale oil can be competitive with petroleum, but a plant producing at least 25,000 bbl/day is necessary to take advantage of the inherent efficiencies of large mining equipment (since mining is the largest single cost in shale-oil production). Investments of about $2000 per daily barrel of production are estimated, with production costs of $1.60–2.20 per barrel exclusive of pipelining and refining.

Most of the oil-shale land is held by the Federal Government and since 1930 public lands have been closed to leasing.

Bibliography

"Shale Oil" in *ECT* 1st ed., Vol. 12, pp. 207–221, by Boyd Guthrie and H. M. Thorne, Bureau of Mines, U.S. Department of the Interior.

1. W. E. Robinson and K. E. Stanfield, *U.S. Bur. Mines Inform. Circ. 7968* (1960).
2. R. J. Cameron, "A Comparative Study of Oil Shale, Tar Sands and Coal as Sources of Oil," *Papers Meeting Society of Petroleum Engineers (SPE) of AIME, Dallas, Texas, March 4, 1968.*
3. *Chem. Eng. Progr.* **62** (8), 49 (Aug. 1966).
4. H. M. Thorne et al., *U.S. Bur. Mines Inform. Circ. 8216* (1964).
5. Carlos A. S. Ribeiro et al., *Xisto Energia em Potencial, Assessoria Geral de Relações Publicas da Petrobras,* Rio de Janeiro, 1964 (plus private communication from Petrobras SIX).
6. Arthur Matzick et al., *U.S. Bur. Mines Bull. 635* (1966).
7. Matic Dimitrije and Ivan Mijatovic, "Retorting of Yugoslav Oil Shales by Gas Combustion Retort," *Papers Meeting AIChE, Denver, Colo., Aug. 1962.*
8. *J. Chem. Engr. Data* **5** (4), 558 (Oct. 1960).
9. D. G. Jones and J. J. Dickert, Jr., "Composition and Reactions of Oil Shale of the Green River Formation," *Papers Meeting AIChE, Denver, Colo., Aug. 1962.*
10. *Ind. Eng. Chem.* **56** (9), 32 (Sept. 1964).
11. R. F. Stevens, G. U. Dinneen, and J. S. Ball, *U.S. Bur. Mines Rept. Invest. 4898* (Aug. 1952).
12. T. D. Nevens, W. J. Culbertson, Jr., and J. R. Hobaugh, "Retorting Colorado Oil Shale by the Aspeco Process," *Paper 1018-G, Meeting SPE of AIME, March 1958.*
13. G. U. Dinneen, "Effect of Retorting Temperature on the Composition of Shale Oil," *Papers Meeting AIChE, Denver, Colo., Aug. 1962.*
14. Donald C. Duncan and Vernon E. Swanson, "Organic-Rich Shale of the United States and World Land Areas," *U.S. Geol. Surv. Circ. 523* (1965).
15. F. C. Jaffee, "Oil Shale Nomenclature, Uses, Reserves, and Production," *Colorado School of Mines, Mineral Ind. Bull.* **5** (2), 6–7 (1962).
16. K. P. Wang, "Mining and Metallurgy," *Sciences in Communist China, Am. Assoc. Advan. Sci., Publ. No. 68* (1960).
17. E. Gil-Av, S. Heller, and F. Steckel, "The Um Barek Oil Shale," *Israel Res. Council Bull., Section B,* **4** (2) (1954).
18. H. M. Thorne and A. J. Kraemer, "Oil Shale Operations in the Union of South Africa," *U.S. Bur. Mines Rept. Invest. 5019* (1954).
19. O. Reitz and H. U. Kohrt, "Hydrierung von Spanischem Schieferöl im Werk Puertollano der Empresa Nacional Calvo Sotelo," *Erdöl Kohle* **11,** 18–22 (1958).
20. K. E. Stanfield, J. W. Smith, H. N. Smith, and W. A. Robb, "Oil Yields of Green River Oil Shale in Colorado, 1954–57," *U.S. Bur. Mines Rept. Invest. 5614* (1960).
21. W. B. Cashion, "Geology and Fuel Resources of the Green River Formation, Southeastern Uinta Basin, Utah and Colorado," *U.S. Geol. Surv. Profess. Papers 548* (1967).

22. John R. Donnell, Irvin L. Talleur, and Harry A. Tourtelot, "Alaskan Oil Shale," *Quart. Colorado School Mines* **62** (3), 39 (July 1967).

23. L. W. Schramm and J. D. Lankford, "Oil Shale" in "Mineral Facts and Problems," *U.S. Bur. Mines Bull. 630* (1965).

24. J. H. East and E. D. Gardner, "Oil Shale Mining, Rifle, Colorado 1944–56," *U.S. Bur. Mines Bull. 611* (1964).

25. John R. Donnell, "Tertiary Geology and Oil Shale Resources of the Piceance Creek Basin between the Colorado and White Rivers, Northwestern Colorado," *U.S. Geol. Surv. Bull. 1082L* (1961).

26. Donald C. Duncan, "Oil Shale in the United States," Independent Petroleum Assoc. of America, Tulsa, Okla., 1958.

27. *Oil Gas J.* **63** (42), 92 (Oct. 18, 1965).

28. R. J. Cameron, "Foreign Oil Shale Industries and Their Influence on U.S. Oil Shale Development," *Papers Oil Shale Symposium, Colorado School of Mines, Denver, April 1964.*

29. Claes Gejrot, "The Development of the Swedish Oil Industry," *Papers Meeting AIChE, Denver, Colo., Aug. 1962.*

30. U.S. Pat. 3,316,020 (April 25, 1967), Eric V. Bergstrom (to Mobil Oil Corp.).

31. M. A. Lekas et al., "The Bronco Oil Shale Study," *Publ. PNE-1400*, Clearinghouse for Fed. Sci. and Tech. Inf., Springfield, Va., 1967.

32. S. Klosky, *U.S. Bur. Mines Bull. 467* (1948); *468* (1949); and *574* (1958).

33. D. R. Williamson, *Colo. School Mines, Mineral Ind. Bull.* **8** (2), 9–16 (March 1965).

34. F. L. Hartley and C. S. Brinegar, "Oil Shale-Energy for the Future," *Proc. 5th World Petrol. Congr., New York, 1959*, Sect. II, Paper 4.

34a. "Annual Report, Sec. of Interior, 1948; 1949; 1952," *U.S. Bur. Mines Rept. Invest. 4457* (1949); *4652* (1950); *4943* (1953). Inst. of Petroleum, *Oil Shale and Cannel Coal*, Mason House, London, 1951, Vol. II. H. M. Thorne et al., *Ind. Eng. Chem.* **43**, 20–27 (1951). W. E. Wells and J. R. Ruark, *U.S. Bur. Mines Rept. Invest. 4874* (1952).

35. Wladyslaw J. Cieslewicz, "Present Trends in Estonian-Russian Work on Oil Shale," *Papers 4th Ann. Oil Shale Symposium, Colorado School of Mines, Denver, April 1967.*

36. *Ind. Eng. Chem.* **54** (1), 42 (Jan. 1962).

37. *Chem. Eng. Progr.* **62** (8), 49 (Aug. 1966).

38. U.S. Pat. 2,634,961 (April 14, 1953), F. Ljungstrom (to Svenska Skifferolje Aktiebolaget).

39. *Oil Gas J.* **62** (29), 84 (July 20, 1964).

40. *Chem. Eng. Progr.* **62** (8), 61, 71 (Aug. 1966).

41. *The Western Economic J.* **2** (1), 60 (1963).

42. *Tosco Presentation to Oil Shale Advisory Board*, U.S. Dept. of Interior, Nov. 1964.

43. *J. Petrol. Technol.* **10** (8), 25 (Aug. 1958).

44. Anon., "A Cost Analysis of an Oil Shale Installation in Colorado (Circa 1966)," Exhibit G-667, BLM Hearing Colo. 359 & 360, 1967. (Reproduced in *Oil Shale Related Fuels* **4** (4) (Dec. 1967), quarterly report of Cameron and Jones, Inc., Denver, Colo.)

45. I. M. Ozerov and V. I. Polozov, "Principles of Oil Shale Commercial Classification," *Papers U.N. Symposium Development Utilization Oil Shale Resources, Tallin, U.S.S.R., Aug. 1968.*

R. E. Gustafson
Cameron and Jones, Inc.

SHAMPOOS. See Vol. 6, p. 353; Vol. 10, p. 769.

SHAVING LOTIONS. See Vol. 6, p. 354; Vol. 14, p. 741

SHELLAC

Shellac is the purified product of the hardened resinous secretion (lac) of an insect which is parasitic on selected trees and bushes of India, Burma, and Thailand. This tiny scale insect, *Kerria lacca* (formerly *Laccifer lacca* (Kerr)), is of the super-family Coccoidea and secretes the lac as a protective covering for its larva. Lac is the only known commercial resin of animal origin. Its outstanding properties and versatility as a resin are attested to by its continued widespread use in industry.

Shellac is a hard, tough, amorphous resin which is nontoxic and produces films of good water resistance and exceptional gloss. Its chemical formula has eluded chemists even after many years of analysis, but is generally believed to be a physical mixture of two resins secreted simultaneously by the lac insect. These resins are composed of a number of aliphatic polyhydroxy acids present in the form of lactones, lactides, and inter-esters. Associated with the secreted resin are a water-soluble dye, laccaic acid, a water-insoluble dye, erythrolaccin, and a wax, also produced by the insect.

The value of shellac as a protective and decorative coating probably evolved from the use of the blood-red dye laccaic acid extracted from the resin. Lac is believed to have been used in India for two or three thousand years. Records of the great Mogul ruler of India, Akbar, tell of mixing lac and pigments to decorate public buildings in 1590. Jan Huyghen van Linschooten, sent to India by the King of Portugal, wrote in 1596 of the use of lac as a protective and decorative coating. Krishnaswami (1) and Dave (2) both give interesting accounts of early writings which refer to lac. A somewhat critical analysis of the first use of lac (3) and its early history, suggests that its name may have originated in South China. (See also Vol. 7, p. 627.)

Physical Properties

In considering the physical, mechanical, and other properties of shellac, it must be remembered that it is a natural product of animal origin and will differ somewhat from one source to another. Moreover, some of the earlier studies on the properties of shellac were conducted before it was known that temperature and humidity had an influence on results. Hence, the value of the results recorded is questionable.

Table 1. General Physical Properties

Property	Value
specific gravity at 15.5°C	1.110–1.217
molecular weight	964–1,100
energy of activation of	
viscous flow E_0 of molten lac, kcal	28.74–38.13
temperature coefficient of	
refractive indexes at 40–50°C	$1.12–2.1 \times 10^{-4}$

There are a number of commercially available grades of shellac produced from different sources of raw lac, which vary in the amount of coloring matter, wax, and impurities (present in small percentages). Analytical values vary to some degree because of test methods and origin of samples. Tables 1–5 list the average values recorded in the literature. Commercial samples should fall within the range given in the tables.

Table 2. Mechanical Properties

Property	Value
hardness on copper	
Shore	60–61
Brinell	18.1–19.1
Vickers	16.2–17.0
scratch (1-mm ball)	4.5–5.5
abrasion resistance, sand (ASTM	
D968), l/mil	90–110
ultimate tensile strength at 20°C,	
kg/cm^2	132
modulus of elasticity, kg/cm^2	
by sound transmission at 20°C	11.15×10^3
by beam method at 15–20°C	13.5×10^3
adhesion, psi, to	
glass	1,100
brass	2,500–3,300
copper	3,300
steel	3,200
an optically plane surface	6,400

Table 3. Thermal Properties

Property	Value
melting point, °C	77–90
softening range, $t_f - t_g$, °C	30.5–56.5
heat of fusion, cal/g	12.6
specific heat at 10–40°C, cal/(g)(°C)	0.36–0.38
thermal conductivity, mW/(cm^2)(°C/cm), at 35°C	2.42
at 63°C	2.09
thermal expansion (cubical), $\Delta V/V(46°) = \alpha(\Delta t) + \beta(\Delta t)^2$	
at −80–46°C, α, per °C	2.73×10^{-4}
β, per (°C)^2	0.39×10^{-6}
at 46–200°C, α, per °C	13.10×10^{-4}
β, per (°C)^2	0.62×10^{-6}
fluidity, Rhe, at 57°C	1×10^{-8}
at 70°C	200×10^{-8}
polymerization time (ASTM D411-52) at 150°C, min	10–120
flow (ASTM D411-52)	
method A at 125°C, sec	55–700
method B at 100°C, mm	10–100

The most important electrical property of shellac is its nonconductivity after it has been subject to an electric arc. This "nontracking" property is found in shellac varnish film, in moldings made from shellac, and in synthetic-resin moldings containing shellac.

The most important optical property of shellac is its stability to ultraviolet radiation. It also retains its electrical insulating properties under the influence of ultraviolet radiation.

Solubility. Gardner and Whitmore (4) studied the solubility of shellac in a large number of organic solvents and showed shellac to be soluble in solvents containing

Table 4. Electrical Properties

Property	Value
dielectric constant (K) at 20°C, cgs	3.23–4.61
volume resistivity, Ω-cm, at 20°C	1.8×10^{16}
at 30°C	1.2×10^{16}
surface resistivity, Ω, at 20% rh	2.2×10^{14}
at 40% rh	1.1×10^{14}
dielectric strength at 20°C, V/cm	$200–480 \times 10^{3}$
surface flashover strength at 60% rh, V/cm	6.2×10^{3}
power factor, $\tan \theta$, at 20°C	$4.4–7.2 \times 10^{-3}$
loss factor, $K \tan \theta$, at 20°C	$1.52–2.8 \times 10^{-2}$
permittivity	2.3–3.8
magnetic susceptibility, cgs	0.30×10^{-6}
sound transmission at 20°C, m/sec	970

Table 5. Optical Properties

Property	Value
refractive index at 20°C	1.515–1.524
optical activity $[\alpha]_D^{25}$	+60.71
double refraction (no tension)	isotropic
under tension	negative

alcoholic hydroxyl groups. The best solvents are the lower alcohols, methyl and ethyl, but it is also soluble in amyl alcohols and in glycols and glycol ethers. It will dissolve in acetone if a small amount of a polar solvent, such as water or alcohol, is present.

Shellac is insoluble in esters, ether (other than glycol ethers), hydrocarbons, chlorinated solvents, and water. But, although shellac is insoluble in water, water solutions can readily be made by the addition of an alkali. Borax, ammonia, morpholine, triethanolamine, and soda ash are the alkalis most commonly used to prepare aqueous alkali solutions of shellac.

Chemistry of Shellac

Shellac contains approximately 67.9% carbon, 9.1% hydrogen, and 23.0% oxygen. This gives an empirical formula of C_4H_6O. A number of investigators (5,6) have studied the molecular weight of shellac and conclude it to be about 1000. With this molecular weight, the average shellac molecule has a formula of $C_{60}H_{90}O_{15}$ and contains one free acid group, three ester linkages, five hydroxyl groups, and a possibly free or potential aldehyde group, as indicated by its chemical constants of acid value, hydroxyl value, saponification value, and carbonyl value. It is an acidic resin with an ionization constant (K) of 1.8×10^{-5} (7).

One interesting feature of shellac is that it contains none of the essential constituents found in other natural resins, such as the oxidized polyterpenic acids, aromatic acids, resinals, resinotannols, phenolic compounds, resenes, or essential oils, but is composed of hydroxy fatty acid derivatives which are totally absent in other natural resins. This is not surprising since lac is of animal origin and the others are of plant origin.

Table 6. Chemical Constants of Shellac

Property	Orange	Bleached	Hard resin	Soft resin
acid value, mg KOH/g	65–75	73–95	55–60	103–110
saponification value, mg KOH/g	220–232	185–260	218–225	207–229
ester value, mg KOH/g	155–167	103–155	163–165	104–119
hydroxyl value, mg KOH/g	250–280	230–260	116–117	235–240
iodine value, cg I/g				
Wijs (1 hr)	13–16	7–10	11–13	50–55
carbonyl value				
sodium sulfite method	7.8–27.5		17.6	17.3
molecular weight	1,006	949	1,900–2,000	513–556

Shellac consists of a number of aliphatic polyhydroxy acids present in the form of lactones, lactides, and inter-esters. Harries and Nagel (8) separated shellac into two fractions using ether as the solvent, obtaining 30% of a *soft resin*, soluble in the solvent, and 70% of a *hard resin*, insoluble in ether. Shellac is believed to be a physical combination of two resins secreted by the lac insect, and Venugopalan (9) states that the hard and soft resins are secreted at different rates. The pure hard resin is secreted at a regular rate; the soft resin, at a very irregular rate. There does not seem to be any likelihood of a chemical bond between the two components.

Table 6 lists some chemical constants of orange and bleached shellac as well as the constants for the hard- and soft-resin components separated by means of solvent extraction.

Of the compounds separated from shellac none has been more fully explored than *aleuritic acid*. It was first separated by Tschirch and Farner (10) and later identified by Nagel (11) as 9,10,16-trihydroxypalmitic acid, $HOCH_2(CH_2)_5CH(OH)CH(OH)$- $(CH_2)_7COOH$, mp 101.5°C. It was found to be optically inactive. In addition (12), there are several isomers of aleuritic acid having the same or lower melting points, such as 89–90°C and 97–97.5°C. Aleuritic acid is readily obtained by saponifying dewaxed shellac with a 20% sodium hydroxide solution, allowing the saponified product to stand at room temperature for about six days, and then filtering off the sodium aleuritate. Yields as high as 43% have been reported (13).

The position of its hydroxyl and acid groups make aleuritic acid an ideal starting material for macrocyclic ketones such as civetone and dihydrocivetone (14). Small quantities of aleuritic acid are produced, to be made into ambrettolite, which is the natural constituent of ambrette seed (see Perfumes). The preparation of α-dicarboxylic acids and ω-hydroxy acids in synthesizing perfume compounds from aleuritic acid has been reported (15).

Glucose monoaleuritate, a water-soluble nontoxic, nonhemolytic compound (16), shows promise as an isocaloric substitute to maintain nitrogen balance and weight during postoperative recovery.

Harries and Nagel (8) also isolated another acid from saponified shellac, which they named *shellolic acid*, $C_{15}H_{20}O_6$, melting at 199.5–201°C, and decomposing at 202–203°C. This is a dihydroxy dibasic acid which reacts readily with active hydrogen to give a dihydroshelloic acid (mp 157–158°C).

Since a number of investigators have had considerable difficulty in obtaining shellolic acid, the question has arisen whether it is present in shellac as such, or whether the hydrogen chloride used as a catalyst in preparing the crystalline dimethyl ester, may not cause some structural or isomeric change during its isolation.

In studies by acid degradation and synthesis, Yates and Field (17) have identified shellolic acid as a sesquiterpene of the form given in structure (**1**), with the rare cedrene skeleton, where R is COOH. Carruthers et al. (18) have confirmed the sesquiterpene structure of shellolic acid proposed by Yates and Field.

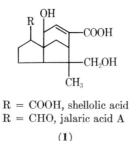

R = COOH, shellolic acid
R = CHO, jalaric acid A

(**1**)

Kamath and Mainkar (19) found that even under mild conditions of saponification the alkali-labile groups of shellac undergo some change, so the acids separated may not be the primary products of hydrolysis. The changes may be due to reactions such as aldol condensation, Cannizzaro reaction, hydrogen disproportionation, and dehydrogenation.

Wadis, Mhaskar, and Sukh Dev (20) obtained a pure aldehydic acid, $C_{15}H_{20}O_5$, mp 178–180°C, first isolated by Kamath and Potnis (21), which they called jalaric acid A. Its infrared spectrum shows the presence of hydroxy-α,β-unsaturated carboxyl and aldehyde groups, and a conjugated trisubstituted ethylenic linkage. When oxidized at room temperature with alkaline silver oxide, the acid yields two dicarboxylic acids. One has been identified as shellolic acid and the other as an isomer of shellolic acid. This behavior of jalaric acid has been attributed to epimerization under the alkaline conditions of silver oxide oxidation. Wadia and co-workers gave the name jalaric acid B to this epimer of jalaric acid A. They further concluded that the isomer of shellolic acid is an epi-shellolic acid. They also deduced that jalaric acid A is the actual compound in shellac and that shellolic acid is produced from it. From these studies and proton-magnetic resonance, they concluded that the configuration of jalaric acid A has the form given in structure (**1**), where R is CHO. Khurana et al. (22) isolated two more acids, laksholic acid (mp 183°C) and its epimer, epi-laksholic acid (mp 203°C). These are trihydroxy monobasic acids having the same structure given in structure (**1**), where R is CH₂OH.

Shaeffer, Weinberger, and Gardner (23) divided shellac into two fractions using chloroform as the solvent. Each fraction was separately extracted with other solvents—ether, ethyl acetate, acetone, and ligroin—in an attempt to obtain homogeneous components from the shellac. Weinberger and Gardner (24) found that the two largest fractions, A (30%) and B (13.5%), approximated molecular formulas $C_{32}H_{54}O_9$ and $C_{48}H_{84}O_{14}$, respectively. On saponification, A gave equivalent quantities of aleuritic acid and another acidic component which for all practical purposes behaved like a monohydroxy lactone.

$$OC\text{——}C_{14}H_{22}(OH)COOH$$
$$\llcorner_O\lrcorner$$

the resin.   The insect also secretes a wax filament to prevent the pores from becoming blocked.   As the insect grows, it continues to secrete the lac resin.

In India the two main strains of the lac insect are the *Kusmi* and *Rangeeni*, each having two life cycles a year.   With the two strains and the two life cycles there are four lac crops, as described in Table 7.

Manufacturing

When the life cycle of the insect has been completed and the lac is ready for harvest, the raiyat cuts the coated twigs, and scrapes off the encrustation or chops up the twigs into small pieces, called *sticklac*, which he takes to the nearest market.   It is collected by buyers at these village markets and transferred to refining centers.

The sticklac is scraped to remove the lac or crushed to separate the lac resin from the sticks.   At this stage the crushed lac contains a mixture of resin, insect remains, dye, twigs, and other impurities.   The material is screened to remove the large sticks and is then known as *bueli*.   The bueli is washed with water to remove the water-soluble dye and float off the small pieces of sticks and insect bodies.   After a few washings, the ground lac is dried and is known as *seedlac*.

The shellacs of commerce are made from the seedlac and are grouped under three processes (handmade, machine-made, and bleached) which reflect their method of manufacture.

Handmade Shellac.   This indigenous process involves a primitive method used by small native factories and has changed little since its inception.   The process involves squeezing molten seedlac through a long, thin canvas bag, leaving the impurities such as twigs and sand in the bag.   The molten lac is stretched into thin sheets by a native worker using his hands, feet, and teeth.   The sheets are then cooled and broken up into flakes.

Button lac is another form of heat-purified lac.   Here the melted lac is cast into button-shaped cakes instead of being drawn into sheets.

Grades produced by this process are T.N., Superfine, Lemon No. 1 and No. 2, button lac, etc.

Machine-made Shellac.   These shellacs are produced by either a heat process or a solvent process.   In the *heat process*, seedlac is melted on steam-heated grids; then the molten lac is forced through a filter cloth or fine wire screen with the aid of hydraulic pressure.   The filtered material is dropped on rollers, where it is squeezed out and removed in thin sheets.

The *solvent process* produces three types of shellac—wax-containing, dewaxed, and dewaxed-decolorized shellacs.   For the wax-containing grades, the raw seedlac and solvent (usually ethyl alcohol) are heated in a tank under reflux for one or two hours and then filtered to remove the undissolved impurities.   The filtrate is then fed into a series of evaporators to concentrate the material to a viscous melt.   This is dropped onto rollers, where it is squeezed and removed in flake form.

Dewaxed shellacs are made by dissolving seedlac in either cooled alcohol of high proof or weaker alcohol at slightly elevated temperatures.   The solutions are passed through filter presses to remove the wax and then concentrated into a viscous melt and removed in flake form.

Dewaxed-decolorized shellacs are produced by the same process that is used for dewaxed grades except that after dewaxing, the solutions are treated with activated carbon to remove the darker coloring materials in the shellac.   By using light-colored seedlac and varying the amount of carbon and contact time, grades of shellac varying in color from very light yellow to a dark orange can be produced.

Bleached Shellacs. These are manufactured in two grades—*regular bleached shellac*, containing the natural shellac wax; and *refined waxfree bleached shellac*. Seedlac is dissolved in an aqueous sodium carbonate solution at high temperature. The solution is then either centrifuged or passed through a fine screen to remove insoluble lac along with sand, wood, or other insoluble materials. If regular bleached shellac is to be made, the centrifuged solution is bleached with a dilute solution of sodium hypochlorite. After bleaching, the solution is acidified with sulfuric acid to precipitate the resin from solution. The precipitated shellac is filtered off, washed free of acid, and dried to form small granules. To make refined waxfree bleached shellac, the centrifuged solution is dewaxed by high-speed separation or filter press. The effluent is bleached and precipitated by the same method as that used to make the regular shellac.

Economic Aspects

India has held a monopoly on the raw lac trade ever since it became an industrial commodity in Western countries. Before World War II, practically all the lac collected outside India—in the region from Burma to Vietnam—was exported as sticklac to India, where it was refined and exported along with Indian lac. Since the war, Thailand has progressively increased her production and now exports substantial amounts of lac, in the form of seedlac, to the U.S. and other countries besides India. It had reached the point where, in 1961, Thailand's export of seedlac exceeded that of India.

Very little lac is consumed in the producing countries of India and Thailand, and about 95% is exported to the highly developed industrial countries in America and Europe. The U.S. has been, and still is, the largest importer and consuming country of lac. Great Britain also consumes large quantities of processed lac. In recent years the U.S.S.R. and China also have become prominent shellac-importing countries.

The U.S. is the largest importer of all forms of lac in total and consumes large quantities of seedlac from both India and Thailand in manufacturing bleached shellac. Great Britain imports mostly handmade and machine-made shellac; the U.S.S.R. and China import only handmade shellac. West Germany is almost the sole importer of the by-products of the handmade shellac industry, *Kiree* (refuse lac), for manufacturing shellac by solvent processes.

Total exports of lac from India and Thailand reached a peak in 1956, when about 100 million lb were exported, but since then they have leveled off at around 60–70 million lb.

Until 1958, shellac was always subject to rapid and wide fluctuations in price and this was possibly the main reason for its displacement in a number of industries by synthetic resins which have long-term price stability. During World War II, shellac prices were controlled by the Indian Government, but control was lifted in 1946. Decontrol resulted in a very sharp increase in prices which, in the free market, found their own levels. About 1950, due to the Korean War and government stockpiling there was another sudden increase in price. From 1956 to 1958, variations in prices were influenced by speculation and a shrinkage in the demand for shellac by consuming countries. This caused a fall in prices. In 1958, the continued fall in prices of shellac caused grave concern to the Government of India because of the reduced foreign

6. S. Basu, *J. Indian Chem. Soc.* **25,** 103 (1948).

7. N. R. Kamath and S. P. Potnis, *J. Sci. Ind. Res. (India)* **15B,** 437 (1955).

8. C. D. Harries and W. Nagel, *Ber.* **55B,** 3833 (1922).

9. M. Venugopalan, *Indian Lac Res. Inst. Bull.* **3** (1929).

10. A. Tschirch and A. Farner, *Arch. Pharm.* **35** (1899); A. Farner, Ph.D. Dissertation, Bern University, Bern, 1899.

11. W. Nagel, *Ber.* **60B,** 605 (1927).

12. P. K. Bose, Y. Sankaranarayanan, and C. S. Sen Gupta, *Chemistry of Lac,* Indian Lac Research Institute, 1963, Chap. IV.

13. B. S. Gidvani, *J. Chem. Soc.* **1944,** 306.

14. H. Hunsdiecker, *Ber.* **76B,** 142 (1943).

15. Indian Pat. 65543 (1958), H. H. Mathur and S. O. Bhattacharya.

16. H. H. LeVeen, *Am. J. Clin. Nutr.* **5,** 251 (1957); *Chem. Abstr.* **51,** 13090 (1957).

17. B. Yates and G. F. Field, *J. Am. Chem. Soc.* **82,** 5764 (1960).

18. W. Carruthers, J. W. Cook, N. A. Glen, and F. D. Gunstone, *J. Chem. Soc.* **1961,** 5251.

19. N. R. Kamath and V. B. Mainkar, *J. Sci. Ind. Res.* **14B,** 555 (1955).

20. M. S. Wadis, V. V. Mhaskar, and Sukh Dev, *Tetrahedron Letters* **1963** (8), 513.

21. N. R. Kamath and S. P. Potnis, *Intern. Congr. Pure Appl. Chem., XIV, Congr. Handbook,* 1955, p. 186.

22. R. G. Khurana, M. S. Wadis, V. V. Mhaskar, and Sukh Dev, *Tetrahedron Letters* **1964,** 1537.

23. B. B. Schaeffer, H. Weinberger, and W. H. Gardner, *Ind. Eng. Chem.* **30,** 451 (1938).

24. H. Weinberger and W. H. Gardner, *Ind. Eng. Chem.* **30,** 454 (1938).

25. P. M. Kirk, P. E. Spoerri, and W. H. Gardner, *J. Am. Chem. Soc.* **63,** 1243 (1941).

26. S. C. Sen Gupta and P. K. Bose, *J. Sci. Ind. Res.* **11B,** 458 (1952).

27. W. W. Christie, F. D. Gunstone, and H. G. Prentice, *J. Chem. Soc.* **1963,** 5768.

28. W. W. Christie, F. D. Gunstone, H. G. Prentice, and S. C. Sen Gupta, *J. Chem. Soc. Suppl.* **1964,** 5833.

29. R. Burwood, G. Read, K. Schofield, and D. E. Wright, *J. Chem. Soc.* **1965,** 6067.

30. E. D. Pandhare, A. V. Rama Rao, R. Srinivasan, and K. Venkataraman, *Tetrahedron Suppl.* **8,** Part 1, 229 (1966).

31. H. Singh, T. R. Seshadri, and G. B. V. Subramanian, *Tetrahedron Letters* **1966** (10), 1101.

32. P. Yates, A. C. Mackay, L. M. Punde, and M. Amin, *Chem. Ind. (London)* **1964,** 1991.

33. A. H. Warth, *The Chemistry and Technology of Waxes,* 2nd ed., Reinhold Publishing Corp., New York, 1956, pp. 112–113.

34. E. Faurot-Bouchet and G. Michel, *J. Am. Oil Chem. Soc.* **41,** 418 (1964).

35. M. Rangaswami and R. W. Aldis, *Indian Lac Res. Inst. Bull.* **14** (1933).

36. Brit. Pat. 963,608 (Nov. 4, 1964), D. Lovering (to William Zinsser & Co.).

37. U.S. Pat. 2,961,420 (Nov. 22, 1960), R. J. Frey, Jr. and M. Roth (to Monsanto Co.).

38. *Shellacs for Flexographic Inks,* PD#53-2-1, William Zinsser & Co., New York, 1963.

JAMES W. MARTIN
William Zinsser & Co.

SHELLFISH. See Fish and shellfish.

SHERARDIZING. See Vol. 13, p. 264.

SHERBET. See Vol. 13, p. 546.

SHORTENINGS AND OTHER FOOD FATS

Shortenings are edible fats which are used to shorten or tenderize foods. See Fats and fatty oils. In the U.S. the term is usually applied to an edible fat which is plastic and workable at room temperatures; however, the term is also commonly used to denote virtually any edible fat that is capable of providing tenderness, richness, or palatability to the food in which it is used. Lard (see Vol. 13, pp. 179, 182) and butter (see Milk and milk products) are shortening agents, but in general usage the word "shortening" designates a fat that has undergone special processing to provide, among other things, light color and bland flavor. This is done largely by removing the distinctive and often unpalatable factors present in the raw fats or oils.

The use of pourable shortenings is increasing. These are fats which are relatively fluid at room temperatures; they may be either limpid, or opaque due to the addition of suspended high-melting fats and/or emulsifying agents. The term "liquid" also is used (or misused) frequently in referring to normally plastic fats which are handled melted at elevated temperatures.

Shortenings tenderize foods, particularly baked foods (see Bakery processes), by interposing films or clumps of fat throughout the food in such manner that the protein and carbohydrate components do not cook to a continuous hardened mass. In cakes and icings, plastic shortening makes possible the incorporation of tiny air bubbles that greatly assist in the attainment of a fine delicate structure. Pourable shortenings containing emulsifying agents, or limpid oils when used with properly selected emulsifiers, can be used to produce most types of cakes by appropriately altering the cake formulations. Similarly, pourable shortenings can also be used in bread and related types of foods wherein the incorporation of finely dispersed air is unnecessary.

Shortenings are used in frying, serving primarily as heat-transfer media and secondarily as antisticking agents. Some of the shortening is invariably absorbed by the food and may then serve as a tenderizer. However used, shortenings provide richness of flavor and the highest calorific value of any food.

Before about 1900, the principal plastic shortenings throughout the world were lard and butter. However, successful commercial processes were developed for refining, hydrogenation, and deodorization, making possible the use of vegetable oils not previously considered edible. In the U.S. it was natural to utilize as a source of oils the tremendous tonnage of cast-off cottonseed (qv), and later the steadily increasing supply of soybeans (qv) planted primarily as an oil crop. Within a few years hydrogenated vegetable shortening (originally made from cottonseed oil) became the quality standard for home and industrial use. During the same period, 1902–1950, the U.S. vegetable-margarine industry (see Margarine), made possible by the same technical progress, was almost stifled by restrictive federal and state legislation. Meanwhile, European countries utilized the same technical advances to further the manufacture of margarine, which the people used like butter without substantial alteration of their food preferences. Hence vegetable shortening other than margarine is primarily a U.S. product. Two technical developments, interesterification (rearrangement) (2–10,15), and the development of harmless but effective chemical antioxidants, have made possible the production of excellent animal-fat shortenings. Antioxidants also benefit vegetable-fat products, but to a much lesser degree. Interesterification is the basis for many specialized animal or vegetable fats, or blends of these, designed to satisfy various specific needs.

Properties and Test Methods

PHYSICAL PROPERTIES

The functional characteristics of plastic shortenings are largely measured by physical means (1). The consistency of a shortening, or its variation in consistency over a range of temperatures (the *plastic range*), is often extremely important. Many attempts have been made to associate consistency with some other physical property of the shortening such as *melting point, congeal point* (obtained in a practical plant test by cooling in a bath of water instead of in air, as for the solidification point), and *slipping point* (the temperature at which a plug of shortening will slip out of a hollow cylinder that is open at both ends), but these are of limited value because they almost invariably measure a characteristic at a temperature greatly apart from normal room temperature and, more importantly, the methods are highly empirical. Performance tests on the finished shortening, under conditions of actual or anticipated use, are the final criteria. Valuable information concerning the consistency is furnished, however, by simple tests made on the finished product after storage at various temperatures with an instrument such as the ASTM grease penetrometer, which measures the firmness of plastic shortening prior to disturbance of its crystal structure. A more complex instrument, called the "shortening rheometer" (23), provides data regarding changes in firmness while the shortening is repeatedly extruded through small holes in a metal plate; the rate of softening as well as the firmness can be important for certain applications. The "shear press" is another instrument which has been used to measure firmness and plastic properties that are slightly different from either penetrometer or rheometer measurements. These tests are empirical and there are no officially accepted testing procedures for the use of these instruments.

Shortenings, like other plastic fats, consist of an intimate mixture of microscopic solid crystals and liquid fat. The hardness of the shortening generally can be correlated with the *Solid Fat Index* (1), which is estimated dilatometrically over a range of temperatures, but accurate determination of the true solid fat percentage at any temperature is an extremely complex problem, involving the following factors:

1. Solid fats are soluble in liquid fats at temperatures well below their melting points. Figure 1 illustrates this by showing the gradual solution of extremely high-melting completely hydrogenated soybean oil in liquid soybean oil at temperatures below its melting point of 73°C.

2. The melting dilation of different triglycerides varies widely, eg approximately 0.08 ml/g for triolein and 0.12–0.16 for two different crystal forms of tristearin.

3. Crystalline fats can exist in two or more distinct crystalline forms; usually the lower-melting forms will change to a higher-melting form as the temperature is increased to approach the melting point of the lower form. The expansion coefficient of different common liquid triglycerides varies slightly, but it can be measured without difficulty. The expansion coefficient for solid fats is only about one-half as great as that for a liquid fat; its measurement, and the application of a correction factor, is rather involved. Consequently, the difference between these coefficients is usually ignored.

A relatively simple procedure has been agreed upon (1) which is almost universally used in the U.S.; the values obtained, being approximate percentages only, are referred to as Solid Fat Index (SFI) values as mentioned above. These values are not infallible guides, however. For example, the fat shown in Figure 1 can be either a

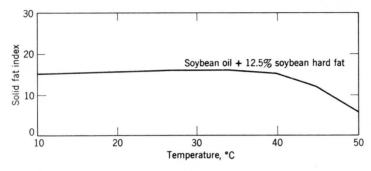

Fig. 1. Dilatometric demonstration of mutual solubility of fats.

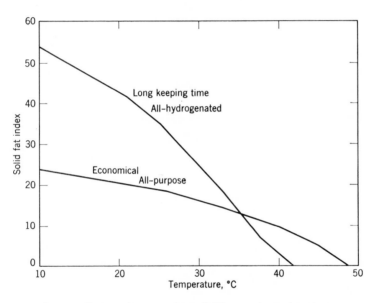

Fig. 2. Dilatometric comparison of different shortening types.

pourable suspension or a soft plastic material, depending on the method of chilling. Numerous investigators have patented discoveries related to this phenomenon, so only a partial listing is given (3,11–14).

Figure 2 compares a soft all-purpose shortening (see p. 43) of wide plastic range possessing high congeal, high melting-point, and high iodine values, with a very hard selectively hydrogenated shortening that contains no added hard stocks and possesses low congeal, low melting-point, and low iodine values. The all-hydrogenated shortening was made under conditions which promote the formation, from more highly unsaturated fats, of isomers of oleic and linoleic acids, with the double bonds in various positions, or in the trans configuration. The glycerides of these isomers have melting points of approx 40°C, whereas normal configurations are liquid at 10°C. The sharply falling curve in Figure 2 is due to these glycerides. This shortening is quite firm at 20°C and extremely soft at 35°C.

Figure 3 illustrates the type of difference that is noted when a plastic all-hydrogenated baker's shortening is varied in overall hardness, as might be done to compensate for summer and winter weather conditions. The shortenings have been hydrogenated under the same conditions; the difference is due primarily to the addition of more high-melting fats in the firmer shortening.

Finished shortenings usually contain 8–14% by volume of finely dispersed air or nitrogen, and appear smooth and creamy white. The melted fat will have a light yellow color with varying shades of reddish tint. The color is commonly evaluated numerically by comparison with the Lovibond red and yellow color standards (1). See also Vol. 5, p. 808. The fat may be faintly greenish from the presence of traces of chlorophyll or related pigments.

The important factors of *flavor* and *odor* have not yet been evaluated by any chemical or physical test, organoleptic evaluation being the only known method. Each raw fat or oil has a strong characteristic odor and flavor which, though almost completely removed by processing, can still be identified by discriminating experts.

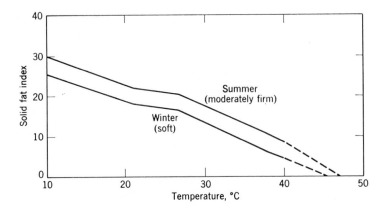

Fig. 3. Dilatometric comparison of similar all-hydrogenated plastic shortenings.

Some of these flavors and odors may reappear on intense heating or exposure to light, and again may become objectionable. This phenomenon, commonly called *flavor reversion*, is most pronounced in shortenings made from oils such as soybean oil that contain linolenic acid, $C_{17}H_{29}COOH$ (three double bonds), or other highly unsaturated fatty acids. Flavor reversion may become so objectionable to some people that certain oils cannot be used alone in shortenings for deep-fat frying. Great progress has been made in overcoming this difficulty in soybean oil, and since 1950 this has constituted the chief raw material for vegetable shortening. Coconut oil is susceptible to the development of a soapy flavor, especially in foods containing moisture and inorganic salts, because hydrolysis of the oil tends to occur.

A low *interfacial tension* against water is an indication of the presence of monoglycerides or other emulsifying agent(s) in the shortening, and may be used to qualitatively detect the presence of these materials.

The *smoke point* (see Vol. 8, p. 792) is directly related to the free fatty acids content and is usually above about 450°F, except in shortenings containing emulsifiers. It is a less important characteristic of frying shortenings than is often assumed, since all shortenings undergo sufficient hydrolysis and/or contamination with nonfat materials after continued use, to lower the original smoke point materially. Other physical characteristics, such as viscosity, refractive index, flash point, and fire point, are not of general usefulness for evaluating shortenings. See Fats and fatty oils.

Table 1. Typical Fatty Acid Compositions of Fats and Oils by Gas–Liquid Chromatography[a]

Fatty acid composition of fat or oil, %

Fat or oil / No. carbon atoms in fatty acid	4	6	8	10	12	14	14	15	16	16	17	18	18	18	18	20	20	22	22	24	24
No. double bonds in fatty acid	0	0	0	0	0	0	1	0	0	1	0	0	1	2	3	0	1	0	1	0	1
butter fat	1.2	2.2	1.2	3.1	3.5	11.4	1.5	1.3	27.8	2.2	0.9	12.7	27.8	2.2	0.6						
coconut		0.6	9.1	6.6	47.9	17.8			8.2			2.9	5.4	1.5							
cocoa butter									28.7			35.0	32.0	3.3							
palm kernel		0.2	3.8		49.7	16.4			8.1			2.4	13.2	2.1							
palm						1.1			48.0			4.1	37.5	9.4							
olive									12.4	0.8		2.5	72.6	10.6	0.6	0.5					
cottonseed						0.7			22.9	0.5		2.2	16.7	57.1							
soybean									11.0			4.1	22.9	54.4	7.5						
peanut									11.6	0.1		3.5	44.1	33.2	0.3	1.6	0.9	3.3		1.4	
rice bran						0.3			15.9	0.2		1.8	44.8	35.3	1.2	0.5					
safflower						0.1			7.0			2.6	13.0	76.7	0.4	0.1					
safflower[b]									6.0			2.3	70.3	21.0		0.5					
sesame									10.7			7.7	39.0	41.7	0.3	0.5					
sunflower									6.7			4.2	18.1	71.1				0.1			
corn									12.0	0.1		2.0	26.3	58.4	1.1	0.2					
rapeseed									2.2	0.2		1.0	17.9	14.3	7.2	0.6	11.4	0.5	43.7	0.4	0.4
lard						1.4			25.3	2.7	0.4	14.5	43.8	10.3	1.2	0.2					
beef fat						3.5	1.2		25.0	3.8	1.8	22.1	39.3	2.2	0.4						

[a] Data reported by Humko Products Div., National Dairy Products Corp., as representative of recent samples. Values are subject to variations due to crop varieties, feeding of animals, climatic conditions, etc.

[b] New variety high in oleic acid now designated as UC-1; slightly different from other reports (22).

CHEMICAL PROPERTIES

Nearly all chemical characteristics of processed shortenings may vary widely between products, because any fat is a complex mixture of different triglycerides, and shortenings are generally blends of several quite different fats. The technique of *gas–liquid chromatography* (GLC) (see Chromatography) has considerable value for accurately determining the percentage composition of the fatty acids in a fat. Typical compositions can be seen in Table 1. The method has not been standardized because of the many variations which are used to obtain specificity for certain fatty acids, and because of the many different instrumentation variables. The basic technique also has been applied to the determination of the triglyceride molecular structure (16) and to the quantitative analysis for surface-active materials (emulsifiers).

Thin-layer chromatography (TLC), also an unstandardized method, has achieved wide acceptance as a useful tool in determining the triglyceride composition of fats, but is perhaps more useful in detecting and determining minor components of fats, such as emulsifiers, antioxidants, et cetera. The literature regarding TLC is voluminous, readily located, and rapidly expanding; consequently, no specific references have been given. The *iodine value* measures the unsaturated carbon–carbon bonds in the fatty acid and may range from 50 for beef fat or highly hydrogenated oils, to 90 or more for a blend of liquid and hydrogenated vegetable oils, expressed as milligrams of iodine per kilogram of fat. It is so dependent upon the oils used that close comparisons are significant primarily to the manufacturer. The amount of *free fatty acids* is quite low, less than 0.1% except for some emulsifying shortenings, where it may be slightly higher. High values are generally associated with insufficient care in processing, although an apparently high value may be due to small amounts of mineral or organic acids added as synergistic antioxidants. *Unsaponifiable matter* content is low (below 1.0%), and is a measure of the fat-soluble nonfat material, such as lecithin, gums, and hydrocarbons. Careful refining is capable of reducing this value to 0.5% or less. *Moisture* is present in all crude fats but is practically absent in finished shortenings, having been removed by deodorization. The *saponification value* may vary slightly for various fats but not enough for identification of raw materials, except that the values for coconut and palm kernel oils are sufficiently high for their presence to be detected. The *monoglyceride content* (1) is of considerable use in evaluating emulsifying shortenings; values range below about 3% from widely used shortenings. Accelerated stability measurements according to the *active oxygen method* (1) or the *Schaal oven test* (17–18) are generally accepted tests to evaluate quickly the resistance to oxidation (development of rancidity). The *oxygen bomb stability test* has been proposed as a tentative test (1) for this same purpose. Oxidation products (as indicated by *peroxide value*) are a sign of oxidative deterioration. The peroxide value of freshly deodorized shortenings is usually zero and is rarely more than a few tenths of one milliequivalent when the shortening is several weeks old. *Inorganic matter* is practically nonexistent and generally consists of soaps or small amounts of mineral acids.

Manufacture

RAW MATERIALS

The principal shortening crude materials and the amounts used are shown in Table 2; the per capita consumption of the various types of food fats is shown in

Table 2. Factory Consumption of Oils and Fats in Shortenings, million lb

	1935–39 av	1949	1959	1963	1967[a]
cottonseed	1,014	532	320	330	273
soybean	119	713	1,143	1,228	1,741
peanut	68	12	1	3	24
corn	1	1	5	3	12
safflower				3	7
coconut	28	20	20	19	40
palm				14	61
lard	4	118	493	594	576
beef	117	31	257	413	506
other	195	67	5	4	4
total	1,546	1,494	2,244	2,611	3,243

[a] Preliminary figures.

Table 3. Per Capita Civilian Use of Food Fats, lb

	1935–39 av	1949	1959	1963	1967[a]
butter	17.0	10.5	7.9	6.9	5.5
lard (as such)	11.0	11.8	8.8	6.4	5.4
margarine	2.9	5.8	9.2	9.6	10.5
shortening	11.8	9.7	12.6	13.5	15.9
liquid oils	6.5	7.9	11.2	13.1	14.3
all food products[b]	45.4	42.6	46.2	46.3	48.7

[a] Preliminary figures.

[b] Butter and margarine adjusted to actual fat content of about 80.5%.

Table 3. Data are compiled and condensed from the *U.S. Department of Agriculture, Fats and Oils Situation, April 1968.*

Cottonseed, peanut, soybean, and coconut oils are refined, hydrogenated, and deodorized before use as shortenings (see Vol. 8, pp. 798–807). Lard and beef fat may be used without treatment, but can be greatly improved for most purposes by processing them in the same manner as any other crude fat.

Raw *cottonseed oil* is dark brown in color with a strong odor and flavor, and contains a considerable percentage of free fatty acids, gums, and nonlipid materials that are removed by refining. It has long been a preferred material for shortening manufacture.

Soybean oil is usually considerably lighter in color, with a characteristic flavor which after refining is often described as "grassy" or "hay-like." The raw oil, obtained by solvent extraction, contains a significant percentage of phospholipids which are usually removed by water-washing, thus producing degummed oil with crude soybean lecithin as a by-product. Tremendously increased production, coupled with a considerably lower market price, has made this the primary vegetable oil in spite of its peculiar, persistent flavor.

Peanut oil is an excellent raw material with good stability and flavor, but the production is small and quite variable, and the price is usually several cents a pound above that of cottonseed oil.

Coconut oil is imported and subject to wide price fluctuation. It is unsuitable as a major ingredient for shortening, but may be used advantageously in small proportions and enjoys considerable favor as a specialty fat for foods in which its abrupt melting behavior is desirable.

Safflower oil has come into significance since about 1962 (see Table 2), initially because of its high linoleic acid content. When it is economically justifiable, safflower oil can be hydrogenated for use in shortenings and similar products. A new variety of the plant (UC-1), which provides oil with a low linoleic and a high oleic acid content (see Table 1), is said to show promise as a liquid shortening with excellent resistance to oxidation and polymerization (22); however, it is not yet commercially available.

Sesame oil, sunflowerseed oil, and *palm oil* are suitable for shortening manufacture but the supply is limited and variable on the U.S. market.

Lard, the rendered fat from hogs, is the principal fat of animal origin. It is quite variable in physical and chemical characteristics. Although considered to be edible, with large amounts used "as produced" by the meat packers, it is usually strong-flavored and contains a sizable quantity of nonlipid material.

Beef fat or *tallow,* the rendered fat from cattle, has been produced in increasing quantity during recent years. It is firmer than lard, is generally less variable in physical and chemical characteristics, but has a pronounced characteristic flavor and generally contains a considerable amount of nonlipid material.

PROCESSING

After refining and hydrogenation, and just before deodorization, two or more different hydrogenated stocks are usually blended in order to provide a more uniform product with wider plastic range or other special characteristics. Wider plastic range generally can be provided by blending stocks of widely differing hardness. Emulsifying shortenings usually contain emulsifiers which would be damaged by prolonged deodorization, so they are generally added and blended after or near the end of deodorization.

Antioxidants (qv). Vegetable oils contain enough natural antioxidants to protect them from oxidative rancidity, and these carry through in sufficient quantity to provide adequate protection in vegetable shortenings for most purposes. Animal fats contain practically no natural antioxidants, and benefit greatly from their addition. These may be concentrated from natural sources, as are gum guaiac and tocopherols, but the ones now most used, *n*-propyl gallate, butylated hydroxyanisole (BHA), butylated hydroxytoluene (BHT), and trihydroxybutyrophenone (THBP), are produced synthetically. Antioxidants usually function synergistically with each other or with synergists such as citric acid, and small amounts of two or more are used. Maximum amounts of the various permissible agents are specified by the U.S. Department of Agriculture, Bureau of Animal Industry, for animal fat shortenings, and by the U.S. Food and Drug Administration for other products. Most of these materials are to some degree heat labile and are added after deodorization at temperatures of 60°C or lower.

Rearrangement or Interesterification. This method was first widely used for improving the characteristics of lard, which possesses a peculiar natural arrangement of fatty acid radicals (2–10,15). The fatty acids are distributed among the triglycerides in such a way that there is a more than random percentage of molecules which melt between about 20° and 30°C. This natural configuration leads to several undesirable physical properties, that is, a grainy appearance and poor creaming properties due to the presence of large needle-like crystals. The fatty acid radicals may be randomly rearranged by use of a suitable catalyst; for example, sodium methoxide, CH_3ONa, at moderate temperatures, very effectively alters the basic crystalline habit of the fat (see Fig. 4). After the addition of considerable amounts of highly hydrogenated fat(s) and strong deodorization, the product becomes a very bland and highly acceptable

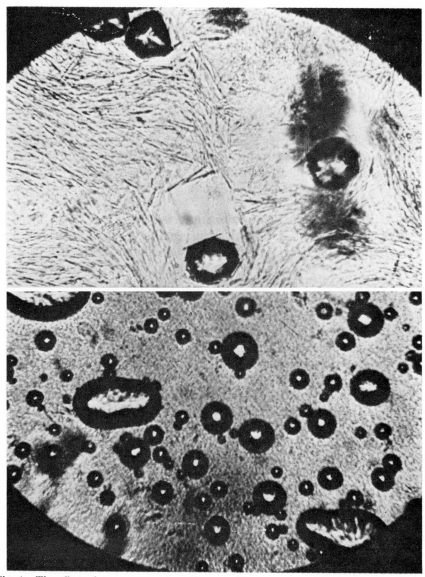

Fig. 4. The effect of rearrangement on the crystalline structure of lard ($\times 180$). (The characteristic needle-like crystals of hydrogenated lard at the top are almost completely eliminated when the product is rearranged.)

shortening with exceptional resistance to melting at higher than normal room temperatures.

Rearrangement is also useful in combining fats to provide special properties. For example, a mixture consisting predominantly of beef fat, with a minor amount of coconut oil, can be rearranged to yield a shortening with certain advantages. Directed rearrangement (3) is accomplished by conducting the reaction at a temperature below the crystallization temperature of fully saturated triglycerides, so that they are effectively precipitated from the reaction mixture as they are formed. When equilibrium is reached the liquid portion of fat consists predominantly of triunsaturated glycerides, which can be separated readily by centrifuging or filtration; this technique can be used to produce excellent salad oil from vegetable oils. Alternatively, the fat can be melted (after neutralizing the catalyst) and the triglyceride mixture will be suitable for the manufacture of both plastic and pourable opaque shortenings.

Emulsification. See Emulsions. An impressive variety of emulsifiers are available for use in both plastic and fluid shortenings. More than one is often needed to provide the optimum aerating power, emulsifying characteristics, fluidity (in fluid fats), plasticity, resistance to oxidation, inhibition of staling in bakery products, and flavor stability. Virtually all suitable emulsifiers are esters of fatty acids having fourteen or more carbon atoms combined with an alcohol containing three or more carbon atoms, which may have been further modified to increase the hydrophilic nature of the molecule. The selection of the proper emulsifier(s) for a certain product remains largely an art.

Fractional Crystallization. When fats are cooled slowly (see below under Plasticizing and tempering) the higher-melting triglycerides precipitate first and may be separated by filtering, pressing, or centrifuging the mixture. This has been done for many years to produce "winterized" cottonseed salad oil, lard oil, and oleo oil (from beef fat). More recently, lightly hydrogenated (approx 105–115 iodine value) soybean oil has been similarly treated to produce a salad oil which is more satisfactory than normal soybean oil, because of its bland flavor and better resistance to oxidation. Crystallization in an appropriate solvent can provide processing economies to the manufacturer, and is being used increasingly.

This process may be employed also in various ways to produce specialty shortenings, originally intended for use in confectionery, that are now finding wider application in a variety of food products. For example, palm kernel oil may be cooled slightly and then filtered to provide a fat that is quite firm at room temperatures, yet melts completely at well below body temperature. Another recent development employs fractional crystallization from solvent at successively lower temperatures to yield three or more fats with special properties. This process has the advantage of utilizing economical domestic fats to produce special shortenings that can command a premium selling price; the intermediate fraction is quite firm at room temperatures yet has a low melting point, and the final fraction can be a liquid fat with acceptable properties for use in deep-fat frying (19–21).

Disproportionation. This term is applied to a process which serves the dual functions of partial rearrangement and the removal of short-chain fatty acids. It is applicable to coconut and similar oils containing fatty acids with less than about ten carbon atoms. The fat and the desired quantity and kind of long-chain fatty acids (usually fourteen carbon atoms or more), with or without a catalyst, are reacted together at elevated temperatures under a partial vacuum. The short-chain fatty acids are distilled off as they are liberated in the course of the replacement esterification reaction. The conditions are varied to achieve the desired replacement. This process is used to only a limited extent in the U.S.; it is more widely used in Europe, to produce special shortenings for use primarily in confectionery products.

Plasticizing and Tempering. These operations are extremely important in the manufacture of shortening with the optimum appearance and working properties. A slowly cooled fat crystallizes in large granular clusters from which liquid oil readily separates. When the fat is chilled rapidly, with violent agitation to assure efficient heat transfer and with the inclusion of approximately 10% air by volume, the result is a supercooled fat that is semiliquid and may be readily handled in pipelines. This plasticizing process is normally carried out in a Votator chilling machine, from which the shortening is moved without delay to volumetric filling machines which deliver it to the final package. There the product continues to crystallize for many hours. Since the final form of the crystals is to a large extent dependent upon the storage temperature during the first day or so, warehouse conditions are closely controlled so as to provide optimum shortening quality. This is known as the initial tempering period.

Subsequent tempering stages are not normally a part of the manufacture, but may be practiced by some. Since temperature changes usually take place during later shipment and storage of shortenings, it is often necessary to retemper the material in order to regain the proper plasticity. If shortening is warmed to a temperature near its melting point, the crystalline characteristics will be permanently altered, and it becomes impossible to restore the shortening to its optimum quality simply by re-tempering. In such cases the shortening must be replasticized.

Shortening Types

All-Purpose Shortening. The simplest vegetable shortening consists of approximately 15–20% fully hydrogenated fat blended with liquid vegetable oil. The liquid portion may be lightly hydrogenated to provide better resistance to rancidity. A somewhat similar product may be made from lard by adding about 5% fully hydrogenated fat. Both mixtures result in a plastic product at room temperatures, and combinations of the two are common. Such products, originally called compounds, today form the basis for moderately priced all-purpose shortenings sold for household and industrial use. The Bureau of Animal Industry, U.S. Department of Agriculture, inspects the production of all shortenings containing animal fats, and requires labeling to indicate that both animal and vegetable fats are present, but they need not be named in order of predominance. The U.S. Food and Drug Administration requires only the statement "made from vegetable oils" for all vegetable products, but the economically priced all-purpose vegetable shortenings usually state "made from hardened vegetable oils." This type of product does not possess outstanding creaming qualities, seldom contains any added emulsifiers to assist in making cakes and icings, and is only moderately resistant to oxidation, so it is best suited for general use such as pan frying and the less critical baking operations.

All-Hydrogenated Shortenings. With further development of hydrogenation techniques, it became possible to hydrogenate fats and oils partially to a predetermined hardness, and to reduce considerably the proportion of highly hydrogenated fat. Thus there evolved a class of shortenings that possess excellent creaming and aerating qualities and much greater resistance to oxidation, known as all-hydrogenated shortenings, because all of the fat has been hydrogenated. The plastic range of these shortenings is somewhat narrower than that of all-purpose shortenings, and they are usually recommended for use only within a relatively few degrees of room temperature (72°F).

All-hydrogenated shortenings may be blended from several partially hydrogenated stocks, and the resulting shortenings have somewhat wider plastic range characteristics. The stocks used in the blending process may have widely varying stability toward oxidation, depending upon the degree and manner of hydrogenation. The shortening resulting from a blend of these stocks may have a somewhat shorter stability toward oxidation than an all-hydrogenated shortening made without blending. The possible variations in blending of the base oils and hydrogenated stocks are almost infinite, thus making possible the manufacture of a wide variety of all-hydrogenated shortenings designed for specific uses. Vegetable shortenings of this type are usually labeled "made from hydrogenated vegetable oils."

Emulsifying-Type Shortening. This class of shortening was introduced in the early 1930s and in a few years became recognized as outstanding for the production of cakes, fat-bearing icings, and similar products containing high percentages of sugar and moisture. Originally these shortenings were made by adding approximately 2–4% of monoglycerides to the all-hydrogenated shortening, and the method still predominates. The emulsifier is generally made by esterifying a fat with an excess of glycerol so that a mixture of mono-, di-, and triglycerides is formed containing approx 40% of the monoester. This monoester may be concentrated until it is more than 90% pure, and such a product is said to be effective in amounts of 2% or less. Other emulsifiers are used to a limited extent for special effects (see under Emulsification, p. 42). This type of shortening, with monoglyceride content near 2%, constitutes the major portion of the better quality household shortening ordinarily sold in one- and three-pound cans. It is well suited to domestic baking, is relatively stable and plastic, and has a smoke point not too low for household frying duty. (In recent years many household shortenings have been formulated so as to contain about 25% minimum polyunsaturated fatty acids for nutritional reasons.) With increased monoglyceride content, such shortenings have greater emulsifying power and are widely used in industrial baking, but are not suitable for frying operations. Carefully processed mono- and diglycerides do not significantly lower the oxidative stability for such shortenings. Shortening containing emulsifier sells for a slightly higher price than the unemulsified product, and must be appropriately labeled.

Long-Stability Shortening. With the further development of hydrogenation, it was found that the reaction could be performed so as to produce shortenings with much greater resistance to oxidation, although the plastic range was extremely narrow, through virtual elimination of polyunsaturated fatty acid radicals. Such shortenings are used where extreme resistance to the onset of rancidity is desirable, as in the deep-fat frying of potato chips and the like, in the baking of cookies, crackers, and similar products, in concentrated rations for the Armed Forces, and in packaged, prepared, dry-baking mixes. A small amount (10 ppm max) of certain specific dimethylpolysiloxanes (see Silicones under Silicon compounds) is permitted in shortenings as an antifoaming agent.

Fluid Shortenings. There has been a great and continuing increase in the per capita use of liquid oils (see Table 3), for several reasons. The increased use of convenience foods has encouraged consumers to use a shortening which can be poured. Moreover, prepared mixes and other packaged products have reduced the need for plastic shortening in the home kitchen. In recent years there has been much emphasis on the purported nutritional advantages of liquid shortenings that contain relatively high percentages of polyunsaturated accompanied by low percentages of saturated fatty acids, primarily in preventing or alleviating diseases associated with the blood circulatory system. Thus, salad oils are widely used as shortenings for general kitchen purposes.

For the same reasons of convenience, efficiency, and nutrition, liquid shortenings have been developed for the food processing industry. Several frying fats are available; some, containing a small amount of finely dispersed, highly hydrogenated fat, are opaque at room temperatures (see under Rearrangement, p. 40). A number of patents have been issued covering products of this type (2–15).   Other liquid frying fats may be produced by fractional crystallization (see p. 42), and the UC-1 variety of safflower oil shows promise (Table 1) (22).

Emulsifiers are added to suspended opaque fluid shortenings specifically for use in yeast-raised bakery products, and in cakes.   Several clear liquid shortenings have been marketed specifically for use in cake making, which contain highly specific emulsifier systems.

Specialty Fats.   *Cocoa butter*, obtained by extraction from cocoa beans, is expensive and often too low in melting point.   Fats high in lauric acid, mostly *coconut* and *palm kernel oils*, provide suitable adjuncts or substitutes for cocoa butter, when blended, rearranged, fractionally crystallized, and/or disproportionated.   A few cocoa butter-like fats, made from nonlauric raw materials, are available and in some ways they are superior to the lauric-type fats.   Substantial and apparently increasing quantities of special-purpose shortening fats have been developed.   Nearly all such products, comprising predominantly one triglyceride structure, are quite subject to polymorphic transformation so that they must be handled with special precautions to develop and retain the optimum gloss and other physical properties.   These *confectionery* or *coating fats*, as well as hydrogenated coconut and palm kernel oils, also find considerable use in dairy-type products such as whippable toppings, imitation coffee cream (coffee whiteners), vegetable-fat ice cream (Mellorene), and filled and imitation milk.   Lecithin is frequently added to these fats when they are to be used in low-moisture formulations in order to reduce the surface tension and control the viscosity of the product when melted.

Bibliography

"Shortenings" in *ECT* 1st ed., Vol. 12, pp. 260–268, by W. F. Schroeder, The HumKo Company.

1. American Oil Chemists' Society, *Official and Tentative Methods*, Chicago, Ill.
2. D. Swern, ed., *Bailey's Industrial Oil and Fat Products*, 3rd ed., Interscience Publishers, a division of John Wiley & Sons, Inc., New York, 1964, pp. 958–970.
3. U.S. Pat. 2,442,531 (June 1, 1948), E. W. Eckey (to Proctor & Gamble Co.).
4. U.S. Pat. 2,571,315 (Oct. 16, 1951), R. J. VanderWal and L. A. VanAkkern (to Armour & Co.).
5. U.S. Pats. 2,625,478–2,625,482 (Jan. 13, 1953), K. F. Mattil and F. Norris (to Swift & Co.).
6. U.S. Pat. 2,625,483 (Jan. 13, 1953), K. F. Mattil and DeWitt Nelson (to Swift & Co.).
7. U.S. Pat. 2,625,484 (Jan. 13, 1953), W. E. Dominick, DeWitt Nelson, and K. F. Mattil (to Swift & Co.).
8. U.S. Pat. 2,625,485 (Jan. 13, 1953), W. E. Dominick and DeWitt Nelson (to Swift & Co.).
9. U.S. Pats. 2,625,486–2,625,487 (Jan. 13, 1953), DeWitt Nelson and K. F. Mattil (to Swift & Co.).
10. U.S. Pat. 2,872,463 (Feb. 3, 1959), L. A. VanAkkern (to Swift & Co.).
11. U.S. Pat. 2,521,219 (Sept. 5, 1950), G. W. Holman and O. Quimby (to Proctor & Gamble Co.).
12. U.S. Pat. 2,521,242 (Sept. 5, 1950), P. J. Mitchell (to Proctor & Gamble Co.).
13. U.S. Pat. 2,815,285 (Dec. 3, 1957), G. W. Holman and J. H. Sanders (to Proctor & Gamble Co.).
14. U.S. Pat. 3,369,909 (Feb. 20, 1968), W. F. Schroeder and J. R. Wynne (to National Dairy Products Corp.).
15. L. H. Going, *J. Am. Oil Chemists' Soc.* **44**, 414A (1967).
16. C. Litchfield, R. D. Harlow, and R. Heiser, *J. Am. Oil Chemists' Soc.* **42**, 849 (1965).
17. R. M. Bohn and R. S. Olson, *Oil Soap* **11**, 210 (1934).
18. R. T. Joyner and J. E. McIntyre, *Oil Soap* **15**, 184 (1938).
19. W. Landmann, N. V. Lovegren, and R. O. Feuge, *J. Am. Oil Chemists' Soc.* **38**, 466 (1961).
20. J. Spadaro, N. V. Lovegren, R. O. Feuge, and E. L. Patton, *J. Am. Oil Chemists' Soc.* **38**, 461 (1961).

21. K. M. Decossas, S. P. Koltun, J. J. Stadaro, R. O. Feuge, E. F. Pollard, and E. L. Patton, *J. Am. Oil Chemists' Soc.* **39** (1962).
22. G. Fuller, M. J. Diamond, and J. H. Applewhite, *J. Am. Oil Chemists' Soc.* **44,** 264 (1967).
23. S. J. Loska, Jr., and E. Jaska, *J. Am. Oil Chemists' Soc.* **34,** 495 (1957).

General References

E. W. Eckey, *Vegetable Fats and Oils*, Reinhold Publishing Corp., New York, 1954.
Institute of Shortening and Edible Oils, *Food, Fats and Oils*, Bulletin, Washington, D.C., 1963.
V. C. Mehlenbacher, *The Analysis of Fats and Oils*, The Garrard Press, Champaign, Ill., 1960.

WILLIAM F. SCHROEDER
Archer Daniels Midland Company

SHRIMP MEAL. See Vol. 8, p. 867.

SIDERITE, $FeCO_3$. See Vol. 15, p. 517.

SIENNA, BURNT. See Vol. 15, p. 518.

SIEVES. See Size measurement; Size separation.

SIGNALLING SMOKES. See Vol. 4, p. 903.

SILANES; SILANOLS. See Silicon compounds.

SILICA

INTRODUCTION†

Silica or silicon dioxide, SiO_2, is the most common binary compound of silicon and oxygen, the two elements of greatest terrestrial abundance. It makes up some 60% by weight of the earth's crust, occurring either alone or in combination with other oxides in the silicates. It is thus among the most frequently encountered chemical substances, with a rich chemistry which makes it of major importance both geologically and because of the technological significance of the properties of its various forms. Silica itself is used in large quantities as a constituent of building materials in concrete, bricks, and building stones, and in its various amorphous forms as a desiccant, adsorbent, reinforcing agent, and catalyst component. It finds numerous specialized applications in forms such as piezoelectric crystals and vitreous-silica optical elements and glassware. Silica is a basic material of the glass and ceramics industries and an important raw material for the production of soluble silicates, silicon and its alloys, silicon carbide, silicon-based chemicals, and the silicones.

Structure and Bonding

Silicon shares with the other elements of the fourth main group of the periodic system the property of forming an oxide of formula MO_2. All of these compounds show

† Contribution of the National Bureau of Standards; not subject to copyright.

acidic properties, most distinctly in the case of CO_2 and SiO_2, with amphoteric character becoming more pronounced for the heavier members of the group. Like the dioxides of germanium, tin, and lead, silica is a solid of high melting point, although it differs from these in having, in its common forms, a three-dimensional lattice based on four-coordinate silicon whereas the heavier analogs possess more ionic structures of the rutile type (except for a high-temperature form of GeO_2 which has the quartz structure). Carbon dioxide is markedly different, and is a gas which condenses at $-78.5°C$ under one atmosphere to a molecular solid with a linear OCO structure. The principal source of the structural difference between CO_2 and SiO_2 can be found in the ability of carbon, along with other elements of the second period, to form strong π bonds using valence-shell p orbitals. For elements of the third and later periods, p_π-p_π overlap is considerably less favorable than for these lighter elements. The π bonding is accordingly diminished, and the possibility of association through formation of additional σ bonds is correspondingly enhanced. Consequently, there are numerous examples of formally similar compounds of the second and third periods in which the lighter compounds are monomeric molecular species, while the heavier analogs of the same stoichiometry have oligomeric or polymeric structures. Among these are the analogous compounds BCl_3-Al_2Cl_6 (g), CS_2-$(SiS_2)_x$, N_2-P_4, HNO_3-$(HPO_3)_x$, and N_2O_3-P_4O_8.

The basic structural unit of most of the forms of silica and of the silicate minerals is a tetrahedral arrangement of four oxygen atoms surrounding a central silicon atom. Structural systematics of these materials may be considered in terms of the set of empirical rules dealing with the stability of ionic crystals formulated by Pauling (1). Tetrahedral geometry can be anticipated from the ratio of the radii of the Si^{4+} cation (0.41 Å in sixfold coordination) and the O^{2-} anion (1.40 Å). The SiO_2 stoichiometry requires that on the average each oxygen must be shared by silicons in two tetrahedra, while in accordance with the electrostatic valency rule a single oxygen cannot be shared between more than two tetrahedra. Sharing of corners is the common mode of linkage of the coordination polyhedra; sharing of edges is rarely, and sharing of faces never, encountered because of the decrease in stability that would result from the close approach of the silicon cations.

Structurally, silica represents a limiting case in which an infinite three-dimensional network is formed by the sharing of all oxygen atoms of a given tetrahedron with neighboring groupings. The possibility of linking tetrahedra with some corners remaining unshared gives rise to a wide range of structural possibilities, some of which are encountered in the silicates. In structures for which all corners of the tetrahedra are not shared, each unshared oxygen atom contributes to the anionic groups thus formed a valency of -1, which is satisfied by the presence of other cations in the silicate structure. The various ways in which the SiO_4 tetrahedra may be linked form a basis for a classification (2) of the silicates on structural grounds which is summarized here in Figure 1 because of the close relation to the structural chemistry of silica itself. The scheme used here is essentially that of Wells (3) the nomenclature of the similar scheme of Fleischer (4) is also indicated:

(*1*) Structures containing discrete SiO_4^{4-} tetrahedra are classified as *nesosilicates*. (*2*) Structures containing discrete $Si_2O_7^{6-}$ polyhedra sharing a single oxygen atom are classified as *sorosilicates*. (*3*) These are structures of general formula $(SiO_3)_n^{2n-}$ composed of tetrahedra sharing two oxygen atoms. This mode of linkage may give rise to discrete cyclic anions such as $Si_3O_9^{6-}$, $Si_4O_{12}^{8-}$, $Si_6O_{18}^{12-}$ (*cyclosilicates*), or to single-chain structures as in the pyroxenes (*inosilicates*). Different spatial configura-

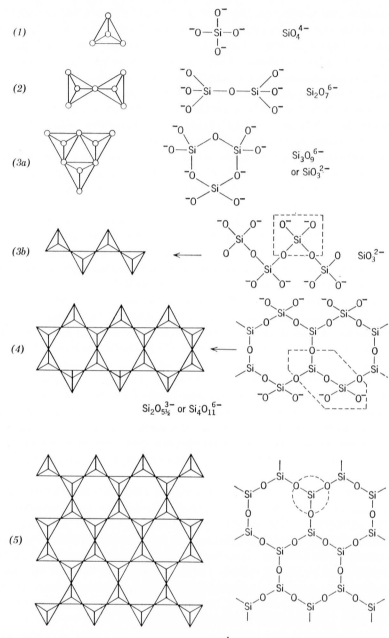

Fig. 1. Schematic representation of modes of linkage of SiO$_4$ tetrahedra in basic silicate structures (2). The Si atoms in (4) and (5) which appear to be joined to only three O atoms, are joined to a fourth also, which is above the plane of the diagram.

tions of the single chains are possible, resulting in structures with different numbers of tetrahedra in the spatially repeating unit. (4) These are double-chain structures in which the SiO$_4$ tetrahedra are topologically inequivalent in the sense that some silicon atoms share two, and some share three oxygen atoms. They may be considered as arising from the lateral linking of single chains as in the amphiboles, in which the repeating unit is $Si_4O_{11}^{6-}$. The composition of such double chains depends on the spatial configuration of the corresponding single chains. These structures are frequently classified as *inosilicates* along with the single-chain structures. (*5*) These are sheet structures (*phyllosilicates*) in which three oxygen atoms of each SiO_4 tetrahedron are shared. A sheet structure consisting of linked rings formed by six tetrahedra is characteristic of the micas. An alternative structure containing alternate four- and eight-membered rings is found in the mineral apophyllite.

(*6*) The structures in which SiO_4 tetrahedra share all four oxygen atoms lead to the principal forms of silica. Replacement of some silicon atoms by aluminum leads to a negatively charged framework of composition $Al_xSi_y.O_{2(x+y)}$ in which positive ions are accommodated in holes in the structure. Examples of these "framework" silicates (*tectosilicates*) include the *feldspars, zeolites,* and *ultramarines*.

Although the view of silica and the silicates in terms of Pauling's rules suggests an ionic model, it should be emphasized that the silicon–oxygen bond possesses appreciable covalency. Pauling (*5,6*) has estimated an Si—O bond distance of 1.63 Å (observed value 1.62 Å) from the sum of the covalent radii modified by the Schomaker-Stevenson correction for the electronegativity difference between Si and O and a shortening correction for double bonding between oxygen and silicon. On the basis of this model, the residual charge on the silicon atom in SiO_4^{4-} arising from partial ionic character is reduced by π bonding to a value in accord with the electroneutrality principle. Pauling's estimate for this residual charge is approximately $+1$ electronic units (*5*). From the viewpoint of the covalent bonding model, the silicon atom forms bonds to oxygen utilizing four equivalent sp^3 hybrid orbitals with possible participation of p_π-d_π bonding, and the resulting tetrahedral geometry is that found universally in the uncomplexed molecular compounds of silicon. Since the bonding in the silicates is not dissimilar to that in other silicon compounds, it is not surprising that the various silicate structures have parallels in molecular silicon–oxygen chemistry, where oxygen bridging between silicon atoms is commonly encountered. Thus, the silicon–oxygen ring system of the cyclosilicates is found in the organocyclosiloxanes, while the single-chain silicates are formally similar to linear silicone polymers, in which the unshared oxygen atoms are replaced by univalent organic groups. The organosiloxanes include, however, some structural types not encountered as silicate analogs, such as discrete, three-dimensional polyhedra based on sharing of three oxygens per silicon atom (*7*). The relationship between the organopolysiloxanes and the silicates may be invoked to relate some structural and chemical properties of various silicates to those of their organic analogs (*8*).

Forms of Silica

Silica exists in a variety of polymorphic crystalline forms (*9*) as well as in amorphous modifications and as a liquid. At atmospheric pressure, the stable crystalline phases are quartz (below 867°C), tridymite (from 867 to 1470°C), and cristobalite (from 1470°C to the melting point at 1723°C). Each of these in turn has polymorphic forms existing in different temperature ranges. In addition, three high-pressure phases—coesite, stishovite, and keatite—and a structurally unique fibrous form, silica W, are known. The transformations of one polymorphic form to another are of two types. The transition from the low-temperature form of quartz to the high-temperature form, or the similar inversions encountered in tridymite and cristobalite, are typical of high-low transformations. These changes involve relatively minor structural rearrangements and small energy differences. They occur rapidly and reversibly at the transition temperatures, although often demonstrating temperature hysteresis. Changes such as the conversion of quartz to tridymite or of the latter to cristobalite are of a different type, the so-called reconstructive conversions. These are characterized by more extensive structural changes and occur much less readily than the high-low transitions, often requiring the presence of mineralizers.

The stable phases by definition show no changes in properties with time at constant temperature and pressure. Metastable or unstable phases may persist essentially indefinitely at temperatures and pressures outside their range of stability. Thus tridymite and cristobalite may be investigated at temperatures lying within the stability range of quartz and may undergo transitions of the high-low type at these temperatures. Such thermodynamically unstable but kinetically stable phases are said to be thermally "stranded." Under particular conditions, a metastable or unstable phase may convert either to the phase that is stable under those conditions or into some other phase which is lower in free energy than the first but also unstable or metastable. Pure quartz, for example, when heated to temperatures between 867 and 1470°C, is usually found to convert to a disordered cristobalite rather than to tridymite. Such appearance of phases of intermediate stability is in accord with the "Ostwald step rule."

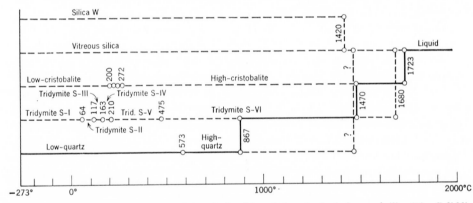

Fig. 2. Graphic representation of the relationships of the principal phases of silica (9). Solid lines indicate temperature range of stable phases; dashed lines indicate ranges of metastable or unstable phases. Courtesy Rutgers University Press.

A schematic representation of some of the forms of silica is shown in Figure 2, which indicates the high-low thermal inversions and the temperature ranges of the stable forms. The stability relations of the silica minerals are shown by Figure 3. This diagram, which is essentially that developed in the classical studies of Fenner (11), gives schematically the relation of vapor pressure to temperature on the basis that vapor pressure will increase with temperature, and that the lowest vapor pressure corresponds to the most stable form. The actual values of the vapor pressures are largely unknown, so that the ordinate must be considered to be only an indication of relative stabilities. The various forms of tridymite now recognized by some workers are not all indicated on this diagram. A temperature-pressure diagram taken to

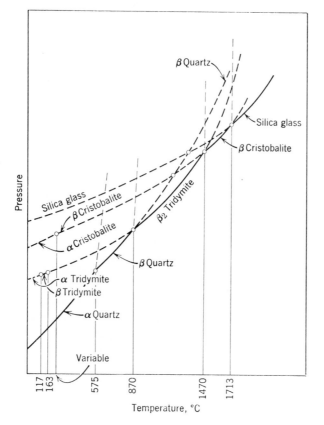

Fig. 3. Stability relations of the silica minerals.

higher pressures would show the high-pressure phase, coesite. It would also show that the quartz-tridymite transition temperature increases with pressure, and that at sufficiently high pressures neither tridymite nor cristobalite is a stable phase (12,13).

Quartz. The atomic arrangement in high quartz (β quartz) consists of linked tetrahedra forming helices which, in a given crystal, are either right- or left-handed (Fig. 4a) (14). The hexagonal unit cell contains three SiO_2 units with $a_0 = 5.01$ Å, and $c_0 = 5.47$ Å at about 600°C (15). The Si—O distance is 1.62 Å. The structure of low quartz (α quartz) is closely similar, but somewhat less regular (Fig. 5). The unit cell has dimensions $a_0 = 4.913$ Å, and $c_0 = 5.405$ Å, with three formula units in the hexagonal unit cell and an Si—O distance of 1.61 Å in the almost regular tetrahedra. The sixfold symmetry of the high-temperature form is reduced to threefold in low quartz. The high-low inversion involves only a slight relative displacement of the atoms in the structure. Quartz is optically active, individual crystals being either dextro- or levorotatory with $\alpha = 21.71°$/mm for the sodium D line. The sense of rotation is unchanged on passing from the low to the high form.

The most common form of silica is low quartz, which by virtue of its piezoelectric and other properties is of considerable commercial importance. Some of the properties of low quartz are summarized under Synthetic quartz crystals, p. 106.

The high-low thermal inversion of quartz is accompanied by discontinuities in

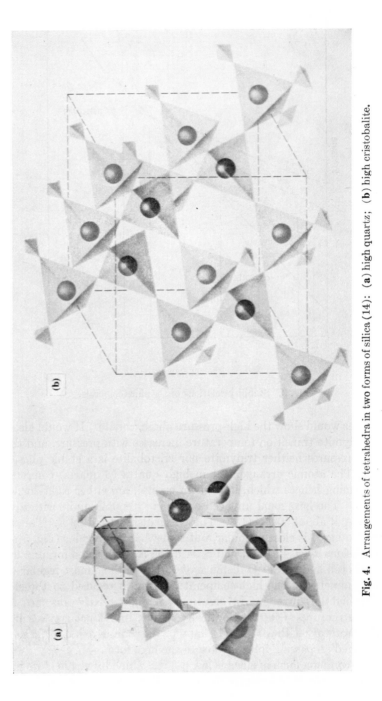

Fig. 4. Arrangements of tetrahedra in two forms of silica (14): (**a**) high quartz; (**b**) high cristobalite.

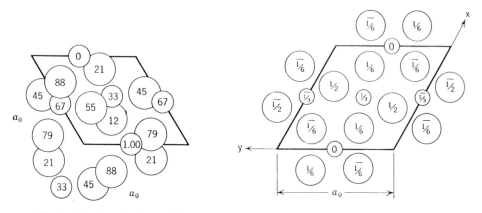

Fig. 5. Basal projections of the structures of (**a**) low quartz, and (**b**) high quartz (15).

many physical properties, including density, indices of refraction and birefringence, optical rotatory power, dielectric constant, and thermal expansion coefficients. It is not established, however, that all these changes are precisely coincident with the "inversion point," which is the temperature at which a crystal undergoes an abrupt, reversible change in dimensions and structure. The most commonly used method of observing the transition is probably differential thermal analysis, by which the absorption or evolution of heat accompanying the change can be readily detected. The accepted value of the inversion temperature is 573°C under atmospheric pressure, measured with rising temperature. The inversion temperature of natural quartz samples may vary over some 40°C, and a variation of as much at 160°C has been found for synthetic samples (16). This variation is believed to be associated with formation of solid solutions. Substitution of small amounts of germanium for silicon raises the inversion temperature, while introduction of interstitial lithium (with substitution of aluminum preserving charge balance) diminishes it.

The pressure dependence of the high-low inversion was investigated by Gibson (17) up to 2.6 kbar, and by Yoder (18) up to 10 kbar. The change in the inversion temperature was found in the latter study to obey the equation:

$$\Delta T = 1.6 + 2.871 \times 10^{-2}p - 4.284 \times 10^{-7}p^2$$

where p is the pressure expressed in bars. Using the value of dT/dP near zero pressure and a value of 3.25 cm³/kg for the increase in volume at the inversion point, application of the Clapeyron equation gives 9.6 J/g (2.3 cal/g) as the heat of inversion, which may be compared with calorimetrically determined values ranging from 17.6 to 20.1 J/g (4.2–4.8 cal/g) (19,20).

Tridymite. Tridymite is the stable form of silica from 867 to 1470°C at atmospheric pressure. Owing to the sluggishness of the reconstructive tridymite-quartz conversion, which requires mineralizers such as sodium tungstate or the action of water under pressure, tridymite may persist as a metastable phase below 867°C. It has been found naturally in volcanic rocks and in stony meteorites.

Fenner (11) observed two high-low inversions in tridymite, at 117 and 163°C. The three forms were designated α, β_1, and β_2 in order of increasing temperature. Sosman (21) named these forms low-tridymite, lower-high tridymite, and upper-high tridymite. Further work has revealed a considerably more complex situation, which is

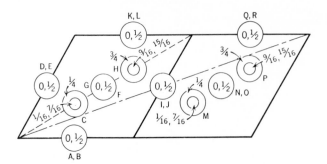

Fig. 6. A projection on its base of the atomic contents of two of the hexagonal units of high, or β, tridymite (15).

discussed in detail by Sosman in his work on the phases of silica (9). Hill and Roy suggest that there are several varieties of tridymite, a monotropic tridymite M, which is transformed to stable tridymite S by a transition of the reconstructive type, and possibly a highly disordered tridymite U (22). Sosman recognizes six modifications of tridymite S, denoted S-I to S-VI in order of rising temperatures, with high-low inversions at 64, 117, 163, 210, and 475°C, and three modifications of tridymite M, with inversions at 117 and 163°C.

The structure of tridymite is more open than that of quartz and is similar to that of cristobalite (Fig. 6). The high-temperature form, probably S-IV, has a hexagonal unit cell containing four SiO_2 units with $a_0 = 5.03$ Å, and $c_0 = 8.22$ Å above 200°C. The Si—O distance is 1.52 Å.

The existence of tridymite as a distinct phase of pure crystalline silica has been questioned by some workers (23–27). According to this view, the only true crystalline phases of pure silica at atmospheric pressure are quartz and a highly-ordered three-layer cristobalite, with a transition temperature in the neighborhood of 1060°C. Tridymites are considered to be defect structures with two-layer sequences predominating, and the stability of tridymite as found in natural samples and in fired silica bricks is attributed to the presence of foreign ions. This view is, however, disputed by others who cite evidence of the formation of tridymite from very pure silicon and water, and of the conversion of tridymite M, but not tridymite S, to cristobalite below 1470°C (22).

Cristobalite. Cristobalite is the high-temperature form of silica, stable from 1470 to 1723°C. It is capable of metastable existence, and is often obtained, below 1470°C. It occurs naturally in some volcanic rocks. Pure, well-crystallized cristobalite has a high-low inversion at about 270°C, but the inversion temperature is markedly variable and may occur as low as 170°C (28). The inversion temperature and the sharpness of the transition are dependent on the history of the sample and may be associated with the presence of foreign substances and with crystal perfection (28). The structure of high-cristobalite is cubic, with $a_0 = 7.16$ Å at 290°C in the eight-molecule unit cell (Fig. 7). The oxygen atoms of the SiO_4 tetrahedra of tridymite and cristobalite have the relationship of hexagonal close packing to cubic close packing, the difference between the structures being like the difference in the wurtzite and zincblende structures. The idealized tridymite structure thus involves two-layer sequences of SiO_4 tetrahedra, and the idealized cristobalite structures, three-layer sequences (23).

Keatite. Keatite has been prepared (29) by the crystallization of amorphous precipitated silica in a hydrothermal bomb, using dilute alkali hydroxide or carbonate

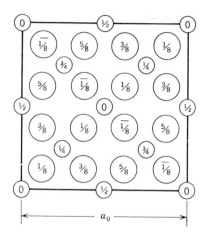

Fig. 7. A projection on a cube face of the positions given the atoms in the unit of high, β, cristobalite, according to the original assignment of structure (15).

solutions at temperatures of 380–585°C and pressures of 350–1200 bar. The structure (30) is tetragonal with twelve SiO_2 units in the unit cell; $a_0 = 7.45$ Å, and $c_0 = 8.604$ Å. Keatite has a negative volumetric expansion coefficient from 20 to 550°C. It is unchanged by heating at 1100°C, but is transformed completely to cristobalite in three hours at 1620°C.

Coesite. Coesite, the second most dense phase of silica (3.01 g/cm³), was first prepared in the laboratory by heating a mixture of sodium metasilicate and diammonium hydrogen phosphate at 500–800°C at pressures of 15–35 kbar. Mineralizers other than the phosphate can be used, and the material has also been prepared by oxidation of silicon with silver carbonate under pressure (31). The structure is monoclinic, with $a_0 = b_0 = 7.17$ Å, $c_0 = 12.38$ Å, $\gamma = 120°$, and sixteen SiO_2 molecules per unit cell. Coesite persists as a "barically stranded" phase at atmospheric pressure, and is a stable phase at high pressure. The existence of a true equilibrium between coesite and quartz has been demonstrated. The data of Boyd and England (32) in the range 20–40 kbar and 700–1700°C are represented by the equation

$$p = 19.5 + 0.0112t$$

where p is the pressure in kilobars and t the temperature in °C. Coesite has been found in nature in the Meteor Crater in Arizona.

Stishovite. Stishovite was first prepared (33) in the laboratory in 1961 at 1200–1400°C and pressures above 160 kbar and was subsequently discovered, along with natural coesite, in the Arizona meteor crater. It is the densest known phase of silica (4.35 g/cm³). The structure is like that of rutile, TiO_2, the silicon atom being octahedrally coordinated by six oxygens (34).

Silica W. This phase, the lightest of the phases of silica (1.97 g/cm³), was prepared by Weiss and Weiss by the disproportionation of silicon monoxide (35). It takes the form of microcrystalline fibers and differs radically from all other phases of silica in that the SiO_4 tetrahedra share edges rather than corners. The structure consists of parallel chains and is analogous to that of SiS_2 and $SiSe_2$. Silica W reacts rapidly with traces of water vapor, transforming to amorphous silica with the silica tetrahedra sharing corners rather than edges.

Amorphous Forms. High cristobalite melts slowly at 1723°C (International Temperature Scale of 1948) to the liquid form, the latent heat of the transformation being 7.70 kJ/mole (1.84 kcal/mole) (36). Because of the slowness of the tridymite-cristobalite conversion, it is possible to observe the melting point of the metastable form at 1680°C. Similarly, quartz melts at a temperature lower than that of either cristobalite or tridymite, probably about 1470°C, but the rate of fusion is comparable to the rate at which cristobalite is formed (37).

On cooling the liquid, vitreous silica is obtained. The chemical inertness and low thermal expansion of this material make it an exceedingly useful material (see p. 99). At pressures of 31–33 kbar, vitreous silica undergoes a pressure inversion which results in a sharp and reversible break in compressibility (38). The name "suprapiezovitreous silica" has been proposed for silica glass above this inversion point. At higher pressures, above 100 kbar, vitreous silica becomes permanently compressed to a density of 2.61 g/cm³, an increase of about 18% (39). This condensed form has been called compacted vitreous silica.

Irradiation of quartz, cristobalite, tridymite, and silica glass with fast neutrons produces an amorphous material with a density of 2.26, representing an increase of 2.6% for vitreous silica and a decrease of 14.7% for quartz (40,41).

Silica vaporizes principally by dissociation to gaseous SiO and O_2, and these are the predominant vapor species, with some contribution from atomic oxygen and gaseous SiO_2 (42,43). The total vapor pressure over the liquid at the melting point is in the range 10^{-4} to 10^{-5} atm. The thermochemistry of the vaporization of silica has been reviewed by Schick (44), who estimates the boiling point as 3070 ± 75°K (2797 ± 75°C). Experimental values ranging from 2230 to 3500°C have been reported. The heat of vaporization of SiO_2 at the melting point is given as 134 kcal/mole, while the heat of the reaction

$$SiO_2 \text{ (l)} \rightarrow SiO \pm \tfrac{1}{2} O_2$$

is 179 kcal/mole.

Chemical Properties

Silica is chemically resistant at ordinary temperatures to many common reagents. It is, however, unjustified to conclude that the substance is unreactive, since it undergoes a wide variety of chemical transformations under appropriate conditions, particularly at high temperatures or when volatile products can escape from the reaction. Reactivity is strongly dependent upon the form, pretreatment, and state of subdivision of the particular sample investigated. Finely divided amorphous silica is in many circumstances considerably more reactive than crystalline silica in bulk. The reactivity of high-surface-area amorphous silica is conditioned by the presence of surface hydroxyl (silanol) groups, half of which may be retained even after heating to temperatures as high as 400°C (45). A large body of information on the reactivity of these surface groups has been developed in the course of surface-chemistry investigations (46), but since these are not properly characteristic of the substance SiO_2, they will not be considered here. However, it must be borne in mind that silanol groups can be expected to be present on the surface of any silica sample and to exert an influence as reactive sites.

There exist two useful surveys of the chemical properties of silica (47), both of which include numerous references to the primary literature.

Common aqueous acids are virtually without effect on silica, except for hydrofluoric acid by which it is attacked with the formation of fluosilicic acid, H_2SiF_6. The rate at which the various forms of silica are dissolved by aqueous HF decreases with increasing density, ρ, in the sequence: vitreous silica ($\rho = 2.2$ g/cm³) > tridymite ($\rho = 2.26$ g/cm³) $\sim$ cristobalite ($\rho = 2.33$ g/cm³) > quartz ($\rho = 2.65$ g/cm³). Coesite ($\rho = 3.01$ g/cm³) is practically insoluble in aqueous HF. Stishovite ($\rho = 4.35$ g/cm³) is even less soluble, perhaps owing to the presence in the latter of a filled octahedral coordination shell about the silicon atom. Low quartz is attacked on the plane perpendicular to the optic axis at a rate about a hundred times greater than that on the prism faces, possibly reflecting the different surface structures on different crystal planes (49). Phosphoric acid attacks silica glass at elevated temperatures, forming a crystalline silicophosphate. The solubility of silica in aqueous phosphoric acid is greater in dilute than in more concentrated solutions (50). Quartz and vitreous silica are affected only slightly by aqueous alkali at room temperature. At higher temperatures, the rate of attack is greater, precipitated amorphous silica being more reactive than silica glass, which in turn is more reactive than quartz.

Silica is reduced to silicon at elevated temperatures by hydrogen, carbon, and a variety of metallic elements. Reduction by hydrogen occurs at 1300–1400°C; the formation of gaseous silicon monoxide is also important at these temperatures. At pressures of 400 atm or more, in the presence of aluminum and aluminum halides, silica can be converted to silane in high yields by reaction with hydrogen (51). Silicon itself is not hydrogenated under these conditions. The formation of silicon by reduction with carbon is important in the technical preparation of the element and its alloys and in the preparation of silicon carbide in the electric furnace. Reduction with lithium and sodium occurs at 200–250°C, with the formation of metal oxide and silicate. At 800–900°C, silica is reduced by calcium, magnesium, and aluminum. Other metals reported to reduce silica to the element include manganese, iron, niobium, uranium, lanthanum, cerium, and neodymium (52).

Of the halogens, only fluorine attacks silica readily, forming SiF_4 and O_2. A number of halogen compounds of the nonmetals and metalloids react more or less readily, with the formation of volatile silicon–halogen compounds. Thus, for example, hydrogen fluoride reacts to form SiF_4; nitrosyl fluoride reacts slowly at 150°C, forming SiF_4 and N_2O_3 (53); selenium oxyfluoride, $SeOF_2$, decomposes silica almost quantitatively to SiF_4, forming SeO_2 (54); and BrF_3 reacts quantitatively to yield SiF_4, O_2, and Br_2 (55). Reaction with boron trifluoride, thermally (56) or in a microwave discharge (57), produces boron oxyfluorides among other products, and hexafluoroethane reacts with silica glass at 800°C, giving CF_4, CO, and CO_2 (58). A number of chlorides including BCl_3, S_2Cl_2, and PCl_3 will also react with silica at elevated temperatures to produce $SiCl_4$. The formation of $SiCl_4$ by direct chlorination of mixtures of silica and carbon is of some technical importance.

The acidic character of silica is shown by reaction with a large number of basic oxides with the formation of silicates. The phase relations of numerous oxide systems involving silica are summarized in the publication *Phase Diagrams for Ceramists* (10). Reactions of silica at elevated temperatures with alkali and alkaline earth carbonates result in the displacement of the more volatile acid, CO_2, and the formation of the corresponding silicates. Similar reactions occur with a number of nitrates and sulfates. Treatment of silica at high temperature with sulfides leads to the formation of thiosilicates or of silicon disulfide, SiS_2.

Several reports have appeared of reaction of silica with organic and organometallic compounds leading to the formation of compounds containing Si—C and Si—O—C bonds. Treatment of silica with alkyl or aryl Grignard reagents, followed by hydrolysis, gives organocyclosiloxanes in high yields (59), and small amounts of low-molecular-weight silicon compounds can be obtained by reaction of methanol or sodium methoxide with silica over a period of days or weeks (60). Other studies indicate that fracture of silica as in grinding produces active sites capable of reacting with alcohols to form surface esters and with olefins to yield oligomerized species bonded to the surface through nonhydrolyzable (Si—C) bonds (61).

An important aspect of the chemistry of silica is the properties of the silica–water system. The interaction of the various forms of silica with water is significant geologically, in areas such as steam power engineering where the volatilization of silica and its deposition on turbine blades may occur, in the production of synthetic quartz crystals by hydrothermal processes, and in the preparation of commercially important soluble silicates, colloidal silica, and silica gel. Investigations of the SiO_2–H_2O system have in general fallen into two areas: a large number of studies of the solubility of silica and the nature of the resulting solutions, and a smaller number of investigations of the effect of water on the melting behavior of the crystalline phases of silica.

The solubility of amorphous silica in water is approximately 0.01–0.015 wt % ($1.67 - 2.5 \times 10^{-3}$ molar) at 25°C and 0.04 wt % at 100°C (62). The solubility of several forms of amorphous silica such as finely divided powder produced by combustion of silane, sols of colloidal silica, and silica gel have been found to be essentially identical. The crystalline modifications of silica are considerably less soluble, owing to the free-energy differences between the amorphous and crystalline forms. Reported values for the solubility of quartz range from 0.0006 to 0.003%. Results obtained at high temperatures indicate that the solubility of the crystalline modifications of silica is in the order tridymite > cristobalite > quartz, an order which parallels to some extent the chemical reactivity of these forms.

The solution in equilibrium with amorphous silica at ordinary temperatures contains monomeric monosilicic acid, $Si(OH)_4$. The acid is dibasic, dissociating in two steps (63):

$$Si(OH)_4 + H_2O \rightleftharpoons SiO(OH)_3^- + H_3O^+ \qquad pK_1 = 9.8 \ (20°\,C)$$

$$SiO(OH)_3^- + H_2O \rightleftharpoons SiO_2(OH)_2^{2-} + H_3O^+ \qquad pK_2 = 11.8 \ (20°\,C)$$

The possibility of six-coordinate silicon species in aqueous solution has been suggested by several workers; Raman studies have indicated, however, that monosilicic acid as it exists in solution involves a tetracoordinate silicon species (64). The solubility of silica in water is roughly independent of pH up to about pH 8, but increases greatly in more alkaline solutions, being 0.112% at pH 10.6 (62).

Solutions of monosilicic acid may also be obtained by careful hydrolysis of tetrahalo-, tetraalkoxy, and tetraacyloxysilanes, by electrolysis or acidification of alkali silicate solutions, or by ion exchange. By operating under carefully controlled conditions, at low temperature and pH, solutions may be obtained that will remain supersaturated with respect to amorphous silica for hours at temperatures near 0°C. Eventually, however, polymerization reactions involving the formation of siloxane linkages occur, leading ultimately to the formation of colloidal particles and further aggregation or gel formation. The rate of polymerization is dependent on pH, being minimal at about pH 3, reaching a maximum around pH 6, and declining in more alkaline media (65–67). In alkaline solutions, it is suggested that the polymerization proceeds by the reaction of silicate ions and unionized mono- and polysilicic acids:

$$-\overset{|}{\underset{|}{Si}}-O^- + HO-\overset{|}{\underset{|}{Si}}- \rightarrow -\overset{|}{\underset{|}{Si}}-O-\overset{|}{\underset{|}{Si}}- + OH^-$$

The decrease in rate at high pH is attributed to mutual repulsions of silicate anions. The reaction is also slow at low pH where the concentration of unionized monosilicic acid is high. Several mechanisms may be involved since the reaction is reported to be third order below pH 3.2 and second order from pH 3.2–6 (65). Catalysis by acid or fluoride may be significant in highly acid solutions.

Considerable information is available on the dissolution of silica in water at high temperatures and pressures. For amorphous silica up to 200°C, the solubility in liquid water is given by the equation (68)

$$C = 0.382(13.6 + t) \times 10^{-3}$$

where C is the concentration of dissolved silica in wt % and t is the temperature in °C. The solubility of quartz in liquid H_2O goes through a maximum at about 330°C, at which temperature the saturated solution contains 0.07% silica, and declines rapidly as the temperature approaches the critical point, which for the silica–water system is close to that of pure water (69). Cristobalite is somewhat more soluble than quartz, ca 0.17% at 250°C. Above the critical point, at sufficiently high pressures, silica has a significant solubility in gaseous H_2O, solubility increasing with pressure at constant temperature. The volatile species carried by steam at pressures above a few hundred atmospheres is primarily $Si(OH)_4$, with some higher-molecular-weight species, possibly $Si_2O(OH)_6$, present at lower pressure (70). At constant pressures below 600 bar, the solubility reaches a maximum and declines at higher temperatures; at higher pressures it increases smoothly with temperature. The occurrence of the solubility maximum is due to the pressure-volume-temperature relationships of the solvent near the critical point, and at constant vapor density the solubility increases regularly with temperature. Thus, the important factor in determining solubility is the density of the solvent phase (69,71). The solubility of quartz from 6 to 2000 bar and from 30 to 600°C can be expressed as:

$$x = 3334d^2 \, e^{(Q/RT + h)}$$

where x is the solubility in g/kg of water, d is the density of liquid phase in g/ml, T is the absolute temperature in °K, Q is the heat of solution of quartz in water in cal/mole, and h is a constant. Mean values are $Q = -9470$ cal/mole and $h = 0.362$ (72). The solubility in water above the critical point is greatly enhanced by the presence of dilute alkali or carbonate, being some thirteen times greater in 0.05N K_2CO_3 than in H_2O. Chlorides are without effect on solubility, while KF solutions enhance it (73).

The presence of water vapor at a pressure of 2 kbar reduces the melting point of crystalline silica from 1723 to approximately 1120°C. A quadruple point cristobalite–tridymite–melt–vapor exists at about 1470°C and 400 bar, and a second quadruple point, tridymite–quartz–melt–vapor at 1500 bar and 1160°C. The critical end point of the univariant P-T equilibrium curve occurs at 1080°C and 9700 bar, at which point the composition is approximately 75 wt % SiO_2 to 25 wt % H_2O. The data indicate considerable solubility of SiO_2 in water at relatively modest pressures, which has important geological implications (74).

Bibliography

"Silica and the Silicate Minerals" treated in *ECT* 1st ed. under "Silica and Inorganic Silicates," Vol. 12, pp. 268–303, by George W. Morey, Geophysical Laboratory, Carnegie Institution of Washington.

1. L. Pauling, *The Nature of the Chemical Bond*, 3rd ed., Cornell University Press, Ithaca, N.Y., 1960.
2. W. E. Addision, *Structural Principles in Inorganic Compounds*, John Wiley & Sons, Inc., New York, 1963, p. 141.
3. A. F. Wells, *Crystal Chemistry*, 3rd ed., Oxford University Press, London, 1962, Chap. 21.
4. M. Fleischer, *Proc. ASTM* **47**, 1090 (1947).
5. Reference 3, p. 792.
6. L. Pauling, *J. Phys. Chem.* **56**, 361 (1952).
7. A. J. Barry, W. H. Daudt, J. J. Domicone, and J. Gilkey, *J. Am. Chem. Soc.* **77**, 4248 (1955).
8. W. Noll, *Angew. Chem. Intern. Ed. Engl.* **2**, 73 (1963).
9. R. B. Sosman, *The Phases of Silica*, Rutgers University Press, New Brunswick, N.J., 1965.
10. E. M. Levin, C. R. Robbins, and H. F. McMurdie, *Phase Diagrams for Ceramists*, American Ceramic Society, Columbus, Ohio, 1964.
11. C. N. Fenner, *Am. J. Sci.* **36**, 331 (1913).
12. O. F. Tuttle and J. L. England, *Bull. Geol. Soc. Am.* **66**, 109 (1955).
13. M. A. Mosesman and K. S. Pitzer, *J. Am. Chem. Soc.* **63**, 2348 (1941).
14. W. G. Moffatt, G. W. Pearsall, and J. Wulff, *The Structure and Properties of Materials*, Vol. 1, John Wiley & Sons, Inc., New York, 1964.
15. R. W. G. Wyckoff, *Crystal Structures*, Vol. 1, 2nd ed., Interscience Publishers, a division of John Wiley & Sons, Inc., New York, 1963.
16. M. L. Keith and O. F. Tuttle, *Am. J. Sci.* **250A**, 203 (1952).
17. R. E. Gibson, *J. Phys. Chem.* **32**, 1197 (1928).
18. H. S. Yoder, *Trans. Am. Geophys. Union* **31**, 827 (1950).
19. W. M. Cohn, *J. Am. Ceram. Soc.* **7**, 475 (1924).
20. K. K. Kelley, *U.S. Bur. Mines Bull.* **476**, 153 (1949).
21. R. B. Sosman, *The Properties of Silica*, American Chemical Society Monograph 37, Reinhold Publishing Corp., New York, 1927.
22. V. G. Hill and R. Roy, *Trans. Brit. Ceram. Soc.* **57**, 496 (1958).
23. O. W. Flörke, *Ber. Deut. Keram. Ges.* **32**, 369 (1955).
24. O. W. Flörke, *Silikattechn.* **12**, 304 (1961).
25. A. S. Berezhnoi, *Silicon and Its Binary Systems*, Consultants Bureau, New York, 1960, p. 117.
26. Y. E. Budnikov and Yu E. Pivinskii, *Russ. Chem. Rev. English Transl.* **1967**, 210.
27. W. F. Ford, *The Effect of Heat on Ceramics*, MacLaren & Sons, London, 1967, pp. 82–83.
28. O. W. Flörke, *Ber. Deut. Keram. Ges.* **33**, 319 (1956).
29. P. P. Keat, *Science* **120**, 328 (1954).
30. J. Shropshire, P. P. Keat, and P. A. Vaughan, *Z. Kryst.* **112**, 409 (1959).
31. L. Coes, *Science* **118**, 131 (1953).
32. F. R. Boyd and J. L. England, *J. Geophys. Res.* **65**, 749 (1960).
33. S. M. Stishov and S. V. Popova, *Geokhimiya* **1961**, 837.
34. S. M. Stishov and N. V. Belov, *Dokl. Akad. Nauk* **143**, 951 (1962).
35. A. Weiss and W. Weiss, *Z. Anorg. Allgem. Chem.* **276**, 95 (1954).
36. F. D. Rossini, D. D. Wagman, W. H. Evans, S. Levine, and I. Jaffe, "Selected Values of Chemical Thermodynamic Properties," *Natl. Bur. Std. U.S. Circ.* **500** (1952).
37. See Reference 9, Chap. 7, for a discussion of the melting points of silica.
38. P. W. Bridgman, *Am. J. Sci.* **237**, 7 (1939).
39. P. W. Bridgman and I. Simon, *J. Appl. Phys.* **24**, 405 (1953).
40. M. Wittels and F. A. Sherrill, *Phys. Rev.* **93**, 1117 (1954).
41. W. Primak, L. H. Fuchs, and P. Day, *J. Am. Ceram. Soc.* **38**, 135 (1955).
42. R. F. Porter, W. A. Chupka, and M. C. Inghram, *J. Chem. Phys.* **23**, 216 (1955).
43. L. Brewer and D. F. Mastick, *J. Chem. Phys.* **19**, 834 (1951).
44. H. L. Schick, *Chem. Rev.* **60**, 331 (1960).
45. G. J. Young, *J. Colloid Sci.* **13**, 67 (1958).

46. H. P. Boehm, *Advan. Catalysis* **16,** 179 (1966).
47. R. Calas, P. Pascal, and J. Wyart, *Nouveau Traité de Chimie Minérale*, Vol. 8, Part 2 (Silicium), Masson et Cie, Paris, 1965; *Gmelins Handbuch der anorganischen Chemie*, Vol. 15, Part B (Silicium), Verlag Chemie GmbH, Weinheim, 1959.
48. R. Schwarz, *Z. Anorg. Chem.* **76,** 122 (1912).
49. F. M. Ernsberger, *J. Phys. Chem. Solids* **13,** 347 (1960).
50. V. N. Sveshnikova and E. P. Damlova, *Zh. Neorg. Khim.* **2,** 928 (1957).
51. H. L. Jackson, F. D. Marsh, and E. L. Muetterties, *Inorg. Chem.* **2,** 43 (1963).
52. F. Trombe and M. Foëx, *Compt. Rend.* **216,** 268 (1943).
53. O. Ruff, W. Menzel, and W. Neumann, *Z. Anorg. Chem.* **208,** 293 (1932).
54. E. B. R. Prideaux and C. B. Cox, *J. Chem. Soc.* **1928,** 739.
55. H. J. Emeleus and A. A. Woolf, *J. Chem. Soc.* **1950,** 164.
56. P. Baumgarten and W. Bruns, *Chem. Ber.* **74B,** 1232 (1941).
57. F. E. Brinckman and G. Gordon, *Proc. Intern. Symp. Decomposition of Organometallic Compounds to Refractory Ceramics, Metals, and Metal Alloys, Dayton, Ohio, Nov. 1967.*
58. L. White and O. K. Rice, *J. Am. Chem. Soc.* **69,** 267 (1947).
59. Ger. Pat. 1,028,784 (April 1958), H. Kautsky; *Chem. Abstr.* **54,** 15246f (1960).
60. E. Daubach, *Z. Naturforsch.* **8B,** 58 (1953).
61. R. E. Benson and J. E. Castle, *J. Phys. Chem.* **62,** 840 (1958).
62. G. B. Alexander, W. M. Heston, and H. K. Iler, *J. Phys. Chem.* **58,** 453 (1954).
63. S. A. Greenberg, *J. Chem. Ed.* **36,** 218 (1959).
64. D. Fortnum and J. O. Edwards, *J. Inorg. Nucl. Chem.* **2,** 264 (1956).
65. G. B. Alexander, *J. Am. Chem. Soc.* **76,** 2094 (1954).
66. S. A. Greenberg and D. Sinclair, *J. Phys. Chem.* **59,** 435 (1955).
67. R. K. Iler, *The Colloid Chemistry of Silica and the Silicates*, Cornell University Press, N.Y. 1955.
68. Reference 25, p. 137.
69. G. C. Kennedy, *Econ. Geol.* **45,** 639 (1950).
70. E. L. Brady, *J. Phys. Chem.* **57,** 706 (1953).
71. G. W. Morey and J. M. Hesselgesser, *Trans. ASME* **73,** 865 (1951).
72. R. Mosebach, *J. Geol.* **65,** 347 (1957).
73. J. Wyart and G. Sabatier, *Compt. Rend.* **240,** 1905 (1955).
74. G. C. Kennedy, G. J. Wasserburg, H. C. Heard, and R. C. Newton, *Am. J. Sci.* **260,** 501 (1962).

THOMAS D. COYLE
National Bureau of Standards

AMORPHOUS SILICA

Amorphous silica is substantially dehydrated, polymerized silica which may be considered as a condensation polymer of silicic acid. Amorphous silicas are usually further categorized as silica gel, colloidal silica, precipitated silica, or fumed silica. These subclassifications are related to the method of preparation in each case. Silica gel is generally prepared by the destabilization of an aqueous silicate solution to form a "hydrogel." A "hydrogel" can be formed by simple ion-exchange removal of alkali from a sufficiently concentrated sodium silicate solution. Usually, however, the destabilization is caused by acid neutralization. A dehydrated hydrogel is called a xerogel.

Silica Gel. When the soluble silicate solution is acidified, a hydrosol results which later forms either a continuous silica hydrogel or a gelatinous precipitate, depending on concentration, degree of neutralization, and the method of mixing. In most procedures, the final gel is obtained by washing the hydrogel to free it of electrolytes, and drying to such an extent that the resulting gel is essentially free of water.

Colloidal Silica. Colloidal silica or silica sol is a colloidal suspension of silica particles in water. The silica particles are generally 7–40 mμ spheres at a silica concentration between 20 and 50%. Commercial silica sols contain a trace of sodium or other alkali metal ions to stabilize the colloid. Colloidal silicas are prepared either by peptization of silica hydrogel or by gradual destabilization of alkali silicates.

Precipitated Silica. Precipitated silicas are also formed by the destabilization of soluble silicates, usually by acid neutralization. The destabilization is carried out in a solution which also contains polymerization inhibitors, such as inorganic salts, which cause an extremely fine precipitate of hydrated silica to be formed. This precipitate is then filtered, washed essentially free of occluded salts, and dried to the desired degree.

Fumed Silica. The final form of amorphous silica, which we have designated as fumed silica, can be formed by several processes. Some depend on volatilizing and recondensing silica, others on reacting silicon tetrachloride with hydrogen and oxygen.

The precipitated silicas sell for as low as 8¢/lb and as high as about 60–70¢/lb. The hydrophobic silicas go to about $1.00 or perhaps a little higher. The xerogels range from about 20–45¢/lb, depending in part on volume. The fumed silicas are sold for about 60–70¢/lb, and the silica sols are sold on a basis of about 45–55¢/lb of silica.

History

Silica gel was first known in the hydrogel form. Its discovery is often ascribed to Sir Thomas Graham, who prepared it in 1861 by dialyzing dilute silica sols obtained by mixing aqueous solutions of sodium silicate and hydrochloric acid. However, the material was known to earlier chemists including Van Helmont who in 1640 reported that amorphous silica in contact with an excess of alkali became "liquid" and that addition of acid quantitatively precipitates the silica from solution. Graham's contribution seems to have been primarily the development of methods of making silica sols and quite incidentally the discovery that the hydrogel may be formed when a hydrosol is destabilized by dialyzing out the electrolytes. This tedious method of preparation seems to have been the only known procedure for making silica gel for more than half a century after Graham's experiments and the material remained an item of purely academic interest until after the beginning of World War I, when silica gel became of interest as an adsorbent in gas masks.

A method involving acid gelation of an alkali silicate was perfected in 1919. Shortly before this a small pilot plant manufacturing silica gel was put into operation at the Technical Development Division, Chemical Warfare Service, Astoria, New York. Semicommercial production of silica gel began in 1920 at the Curtis Bay, Maryland, plant of Davison Chemical Co. In 1928, when the demand for silica gel had increased, a large commercial plant was built; this has been added to from time to time, particularly in World War II when there was extensive use of silica gel as a desiccant for protective packaging. Several other companies have manufactured silica gel at various times. Currently there are three others. Eagle Chemical Company, Joliet, Illinois, makes granular silica gel, Monsanto Chemical Company makes a small-particle, low-density, silica aerogel by replacing the hydrogel water prior to the drying step (1), and Socony-Mobil Oil Company makes a silica gel bead slightly modified by the incorporation of about 3% alumina.

Colloidal silicas were commercialized about 1940 by National Aluminate Company and are now produced by E. I. du Pont de Nemours & Co., Inc., Monsanto Chemical Company, and Nalco Chemical Company.

Precipitated silicas were pioneered by Mallinckrodt Chemical Company and Pittsburgh Plate Glass Company in the 1940s. Other forms are now offered by Philadelphia Quartz Company and J. M. Huber Company.

The ultrafine fumed silicas were also commercialized in the years immediately following World War II by Degussa in Germany and the Cabot Corporation in the United States. They are also manufactured in other industrial countries.

Manufacture

Silica Gel. There are two commercial methods for the manufacture of silica gel, the bulk set method and the slurry method. The *bulk set process* consists of the following steps:

1. A silica hydrosol is prepared by mixing sodium silicate with a strong mineral acid.

2. The hydrosol is allowed to set to a rigid all-embracing gel and the resulting mass of hydrogel is broken up mechanically. The silica concentration, temperature, and pH of neutralization can have a marked effect on the gelling time and on final gel properties such as density, surface area, and pore volume.

3. The hydrogel particles are then washed free of electrolytes. Again the temperature, pH, and time of washing can drastically alter the properties of the final silica product.

4. The washed hydrogel is finally dried and/or "activated" by thermal means. The final gel properties can again be altered by the rate of drying. The silica gel from this process is a glassy, granular product.

For bead modification, a silica hydrosol with short set time is formed by adjusting the pH of the sodium silicate–acid mix. The hydrosol is then dispersed by running it down a rotating, fluted cone into a suitable oil bath. The droplets complete gelation to hydrogel beads, which are then washed and dried by conventional methods.

The *slurry process* consists of mixing sodium silicate with an acid at a pH and silica concentration such that a gelatinous precipitate is formed; mixing may be by batch or semicontinuous process. The silica hydrogel can then be washed either before or after drying. The drying is usually achieved by rapid spray drying. These silica gels are often used as a catalyst base (see Catalysis).

Colloidal Silica. Colloidal silicas are prepared either by peptizing silica hydrogel or by gradual growth of silica micelles (3). Hydrogel peptization is achieved by hydrothermal treatment at elevated pH, temperature, and pressure; small silica micelles solubilize and gradually repolymerize to larger particles to form the final 20 mμ colloidal silica. Alternatively, dilute active silica (or silicic acid) species of about 300 mol wt are formed by ion-exchange removal of sodium ions from sodium silicate. This active silica is gradually fed to a tank of silica micelles in water at 80–100°C. The fresh active silica reacts with the heel particles, causing gradual growth until the desired 20–50 mμ size is achieved. The sol is then concentrated by evaporation to the desired level and small amounts of sodium hydroxide are added to achieve maximum stability.

Precipitated Silica. Precipitated silicas are prepared by mixing sodium silicate and mineral acid in a solution containing a calcium salt to limit silica polymerization and cause precipitation of very fine silica particles which are washed free of electrolyte and dried.

Fumed Silica. Fumed silicas are prepared by three methods: (*1*) In high-temperature arc processes silica is used as part of the electrodes. The silica is vaporized and recondensed as a fine silica dust; (2) Crystalline silica such as sand is fed directly to the high-temperature plasma jet; and (3) In the flame-hydrolysis process silicon tetrachloride is reacted with hydrogen and oxygen in a flame to form a very fine silica plus hydrochloric acid. This is the preferred commercial method.

Properties

Silica Gel. It is generally agreed that the gelation of silica hydrosol is an outward manifestation of polymerization of the silica units. When the gelation is carried out at an acid pH the silica micelles are extremely small. The three-dimensional crosslink-

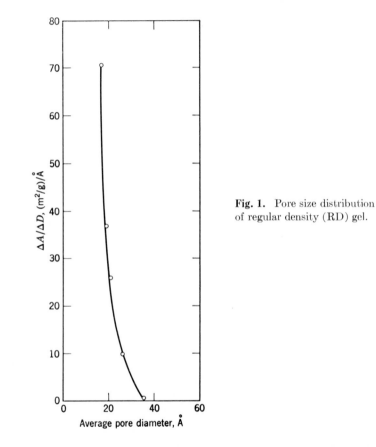

Fig. 1. Pore size distribution of regular density (RD) gel.

Table 1. Representative Properties of the Three Main Types of Silica Gel

Properties	Regular density	Intermediate density	Low density
density, g/ml			
apparent (bulk)	0.67–0.75	0.35–0.40	0.12–0.17
particle	1.1–1.2	0.65–0.75	
true	2.20	2.20	2.20
surface area, m²/g	750–800	300–350	100–200
pore volume, ml/g	0.37–0.40	0.9–1.1	1.4–2.0
av pore diameter, Å	22–26	120–160	180–220

ing of these fine micelles by condensation polymerization (which continues during the washing and drying steps) leads to a "haystack" structure of extremely fine "pores."

$$Si–OH + HO–Si \rightarrow Si–O–Si + H_2O$$

The small size of the silica micelles leads to a product with a surface area of more than 800 m²/g. When the silica hydrogel is washed or aged at a high pH and temperature, silica transport occurs, leading to growth of the silica micelles. As a result the average pore diameter is larger, pore volume increases, and surface area decreases.

By modification of the preparation technique a wide variety of gel types can be prepared. It is convenient to reduce these to three main types: (a) regular density (RD) silica gel, with a large internal surface area; (b) intermediate density (ID) silica gel, with a lower surface area and a pore volume more than twice as large as the regular density type; and (c) low density (LD) silica gel (aerogel) with a somewhat lower surface area and an even larger pore volume. The general properties of these three types of gel are given in Table 1. The differences in density and surface properties should be particularly noted. The pore size distributions, determined from the incremental nitrogen desorption isotherms (see Adsorption), are shown in Figures 1 and 2.

Regular density silica gel is distinguished by its extremely fine pores which account for its high capacity to adsorb water and other polar molecules. Under static test this adsorbent-type silica is able to adsorb approx 7% water at 10% rh and 25°C. The adsorption capacity rises to nearly 40% at 80% rh. Under practical dynamic adsorption conditions useful water adsorption capacities as high as 25% are achieved. (An adsorption of 25% means 25 g of water adsorbed/100 g of activated sorbent.)

One property of RD silica gel which is important arises from the fact that the product is not completely dehydrated silica. It contains "bound water," which is present as hydroxyl groups attached to the silica matrix. These groups are important in determining the structure and sorptive characteristics. Experience has shown that for regular density silica gel this water content should be about 6% by wt in order to

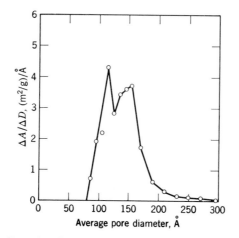

Fig. 2. Pore size distribution of intermediate density (ID) gel.

maintain the maximum adsorptive capacity of the gel. Overactivation (too low a bound water content as the result of overheating) is as detrimental as failure to activate the gel completely.

The general adsorptive mechanism of regular silica gel is similar to that characteristic of other porous solids. Its unique properties include a high selectivity for polar molecules, high surface area, and a large percentage of small pores.

Intermediate density silica gel is characterized by a much larger average pore diameter and pore volume. Most of the fine pores are not created in its preparation. The silica micelle (the fundamental polymeric monomer) is much larger, resulting in fewer point-to-point polymerization crosslinks so that the silica gel particle is soft and friable as compared to the hard, glassy RD product. Due to the lack of fine pores ID silica gel has little sorptive capacity at low relative humidities. However, due to its high pore volume it has a sorption capacity of 90–100% at a relative humidity near saturation.

The soft friable ID silica gel can be ground readily to yield a silica powder with a particle size from 1 to 20 μ.

Low density silical gel is characterized by an even larger average pore diameter and pore volume than the ID type. It is usually prepared as a fine powder with a size between 1 and 5 μ and an extremely low density.

Colloidal Silica. Colloidal silica is an aqueous, colloidal suspension of 20–50% silica in water. The silica particles are dense, nearly unifom spheres. Analysis shows a dehydrated silica particle with OH groups on the outside of the particle. The sols are generally stabilized by a small amount of NaOH. Some properties of commercial silica sols are listed in Table 2.

Precipitated Silica. Precipitated silica is a very finely divided silica in which the degree of polymerization is limited by the preparation technique. The ultimate silica particle has a size of about 20–50 mμ and forms an agglomerated particle of 1–5 μ. Precipitated silicas have a surface area of 100–200 m²/g and are often contaminated with calcium or other cations from the precipitating salt. Some typical properties of a commercial precipitated silica are listed in Table 3.

Table 2. Commercial Silica Sols

Silica sol	SiO$_2$, %	Particle diameter	pH
Syton[a]	30	up to 500 mμ; majority 80–140 mμ	9.8
Ludox[b]	15–30	10–30 mμ; av 17 mμ	8.5–10.5
Nalcoag[c]	30–50	13–50 mμ	8.5–10.0

[a] Monsanto Inorganic Chemicals Div.
[b] E. I. du Pont de Nemours & Co., Inc.
[c] Nalco Chemical Co.

Table 3. Properties of Typical Precipitated Silicas

SiO$_2$, %	85	87.5
CaO, %	0.1	0.75
R$_2$O$_3$, %	0.14	0.95
NaCl, %	0.04	1.6
Na$_2$O, %	0–1.5	1.0
loss (105°C), %	5–6	6.3
loss (1200°C), %	11.0	10.0
ultimate particle size, μ	0.012	0.022
sintering temperature, °C	500–700	500–600
surface area, m²/g	200–400	140–160
pH	4–8.5	6.5–7.3
bulk density, lb/ft³	4–10	15
refractive index	1.45	1.46

Precipitated silicas are prepared differently by each manufacturer using patented processes. Those with high calcium content are prepared by first precipitating a fine calcium silicate and then replacing the calcium by treatment with an acid. Fine silica may also be prepared from treatment of kaolin clay, and by direct precipitation from silica sols or sodium silicate solutions neutralized in the presence of salts or miscible hydrogen-bonding solvents under carefully prescribed conditions. Details of washing and drying are also controlled in order to minimize aggregation of the ultimate particles which separate under the initial conditions (4).

Fumed Silica (pyrogenic silica) (5). The fumed silicas are generally very pure. The high-temperature arc and plasma-jet types are highly dehydroxylated and at this time have not found widespread use. The fumed silica prepared from silicon tetrachloride by high-temperature hydrolysis is about 99.8% SiO_2. It consists of clusters of particles, 10–40 mμ in size, with a surface area of from 50 to 380 m^2/g, and has a refractive index of 1.45. Like all fine silicas the particles have a negative charge. The surface area of this product is the outside surface of the spheres, and the surface itself consists of both silanol groups (**1**) and siloxane groups (**2**).

It has been determined that there is one silanol group for every 30 sq Å of surface. Typical properties of a commercial pyrogenic silica are listed in Table 4.

Table 4. Typical Properties of a Flame-Hydrolyzed Fumed Silica

silica content (dry basis), %	99.7–99.9
particle size, μ	0.007–0.05
surface area, m^2/g	50–400
bulk density, lb/ft^3	2.3–7
loss on ignition (1000°C), moisturefree basis	0.5–2.5

Hydrophobic Silica. This is a special form, made from silica gel, precipitated silica, or fumed silica by standard treatments with silanes or polysiloxanes. Esterified coatings from high-boiling alcohols may also be applied.

Applications

Silica Gel. *Adsorption* is the primary use for the RD silica gel and depends on its selective surface properties. *Desiccation* or drying is a primary adsorbent use. Silica gel is used to dry air and other gases in systems that are either static or dynamic with respect to gas movement, and it is also used to dry organic compounds in the liquid phase. See also Drying; Drying agents.

Static dehumidification refers to the drying of a gas in an enclosed space, in which there is no deliberate circulation of air through the desiccant. The most notable specific use in this field was developed early in World War II as part of a method widely used by the Armed Forces for protecting material against corrosion and mildew. The method is known as "protective packaging" and is based upon the combined use of a

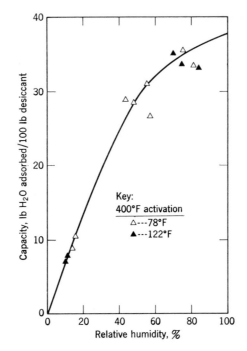

Fig. 3. Dynamic capacity of silica gel 03.

desiccant and moisture vapor barriers around the packaged item.   The barriers are designed to control or eliminate moisture vapor access to the packaged article.   In this application no rigorous procedure can be given for calculating the quantity of desiccant required to maintain a certain maximum relative humidity for a given length of time; however, formulas have been devised for calculating roughly the quantity of silica gel required to do a given job.   The widespread use of protective packaging was continued in the mothballing of U.S. Navy ships after World War II.

More recently a modification of this use has arisen in the dual-pane window industry, where a small amount of silica gel is included between the two panes to lower the water vapor pressure and keep it low throughout the life of the window and thus prevent fogging during cold weather.   In addition, most garden clubs now use silica gel to dry flowers and preserve them for months.

Dynamic dehumidification refers to the drying of a moving gas stream to produce an effluent suitable for some specific use or to produce an atmosphere of controlled humidity.   This process is subject to much more rigorous design methods than static dehumidification, and it is normally carried out in dual-column equipment of specific design.   Recently, accurate design equations have been developed and a computer program utilized to solve the equations and optimize the process design for a particular application.   The use of silica gel in such applications depends in a general way upon two properties: (a) the ability to adsorb comparatively large quantities of water at any given relative humidity level; (b) the ability to dry a gas to very low dewpoints, for example -40 to $-100°$F, depending on conditions.

Figure 3 shows the relation between dynamic water vapor adsorption capacity and relative humidity for silica gel 03 (6).

When a silica gel bed is approaching exhaustion in an adsorption cycle, the inlet end is approximately at moisture equilibrium with entering air and the exit end is approaching equilibrium with air at the moisture level of the desired maximum for the particular operation. For drying to low dewpoints of less than $-60°F$ a bed length of at least 3 ft is desirable since the mass transfer zone (MTZ) will often exceed 2 ft.

Silica gel can be used, under favorable conditions, to dry a gas to a dew point of $-100°F$. It is entirely practical to design for a level of about $-90°F$ with a large throughput of gas on the adsorption cycle. The exact performance in a given case is related to a number of factors such as inlet temperature, pressure, and superficial linear velocity. Like all adsorbents, silica gel is more efficient at higher total pressures, because the increased density of gas is accompanied by an increased heat capacity, which causes the heat of adsorption to be dissipated more rapidly. This leads to a shortening of the MTZ as it moves through the bed, thereby increasing the useful capacity for a given column.

When silica gel is used for an extended period (thousands of cycles), there is a loss of adsorption capacity; allowance is made for this decrease by assuming that about 15% more gel will be required in a given case than is calculated from the data.

Regeneration conditions for silica gel are subject to appreciable variation, according to the quantity to be treated, the equipment available, and the degree of completeness of regeneration required. Small quantities are usually completely regenerated in a forced-draft oven at 400°F in 3 hr, if in a 1–2 in. layer. Additional time at this temperature is not harmful; that is, it will not "overactivate" the gel. In large installations, the gel may be regenerated for some purposes at a temperature as low as 250°F, although 300–350°F is more desirable, especially if the gel is used to dry a gas to low dewpoints ($-40°$ and lower). Hot gas is blown through the gel by either direct- or indirect-fired heating. The heat requirement is variable, since it is affected by the heat capacity of the unit and by radiation losses, as well as by the adsorbed water content of the spent gel. For most adsorbers operating at atmospheric pressure, about 2500 Btu/lb of adsorbed water is required from the activating gas.

Humidity-indicating silica gel is a gel which contains a colored pigment such as cobalt nitrate or cobalt ammonium chloride which will give several reproducible color changes at specific relative humidities.

Liquid drying is effective for liquids in which water is sparingly soluble. Studies have shown that organic compounds which dissolve water to the extent of 1000 ppm or less can be dried to 0–10 ppm. Data relating residual water in the liquid with adsorbed water content of the gel at equilibrium are shown in Table 5 for drying dichlorodifluoromethane (refrigerant-12).

Selective adsorption uses of silica gel are quite numerous. One of the most important is the recovery of liquid hydrocarbons during the dehydration of natural gas, an

Table 5. Moisture Equilibrium Between PA-400 Silica Gel and Refrigerant-12 (Freon) at 77°F

Adsorbed water content, % of activated wt	Residual water in refrigerant-12, ppm
1	2.5
2	4
4	7
6	10.5
8	14.5

application which has changed an expensive operational necessity into a profitable operation. Gasoline can frequently be profitably adsorbed from streams considered too lean for other methods. Silica gel is very effective for this purpose because of its large pore volume. Hydrocarbon recovery units with silica gel, operating on cycles of 30–120 min, can recover up to 3 gal of butanes, pentanes, and hexanes/100 lb of silica gel and can obtain recovery efficiencies as high as 95% at 100°F. For practical purposes, recovery of 2.5 gal of liquid/100 lb of silica gel is considered more normal. The adsorptive capacity varies inversely with the efficiency of recovery. In general, lower inlet gas temperatures and a 500°F minimum reactivation-bed temperature favor high recovery efficiency. The ability of silica gel to resist fouling by adsorbed hydrocarbons is a valuable asset in this application.

Since silica gel has a greater affinity for water than for hydrocarbons, the water adsorbed from the gas will gradually displace all hydrocarbons. Consequently, optimum hydrocarbon recovery is obtained by reactivating the bed when it reaches the desired hydrocarbon breakpoint, rather than the moisture breakpoint.

Another highly critical separation is that of acetylene and other hydrocarbons from the oxygen-rich stream in liquid oxygen plants. It is imperative, because of the explosion hazard, that the adsorbent used be of extreme purity, high capacity, and selective for acetylene and such hydrocarbons as ethane and ethylene. In addition, over the past few years, gas and liquid-phase chromatographic applications have mushroomed not only in industry where precision control of inlet and outlet streams necessitate its use, but also in hospitals, universities, and commercial research laboratories. Therefore, because of its selective sorption properties silica gel is widely used in many chromatographic applications.

Other Uses. The ID silica gel finds its chief application as a fine-particle silica powder. One important use of these silicas is as a flatting agent. In this case the silica is incorporated into surface coatings, synthetic fabrics, and plastics to make the surface appear more attractive. A matte finish of any desired sheen is thus possible in either lacquer, vinyl, or varnish film without the hand rubbing formerly required. This use finds broad commercial value in the production of furniture, since most wood furnitures have a lacquer finish and a flatting agent is used to achieve an acceptable flat coating. Artificial leather, whether produced with a smooth or embossed surface, possesses a high-gloss finish. To produce a dull or flat surface, a thin top coat of vinyl lacquer containing a silica flatting agent is used on the plastic sheeting surface.

Fine silicas, prepared from ID silica gel with carefully controlled particle size and porosity, have been found satisfactory for preventing blocking or ink transfer in paper and plastic sheetings.

Silicas are used as thickeners for forming pharmaceutical ointments, recreating thixotropic inks, and forming thixotropic cements and adhesives. For these applications it is essential that the silica have the proper particle size, shape, and porosity. The fine-particle ID silicas have several advantages when used in adhesive formulations and when incorporated in insulation for low-temperature installations. Recently a large new application has arisen in the food industry, where the fine-particle silicas are used for anticaking to facilitate the free flow of food or spice powders.

Colloidal Silica. There are a number of practical uses for commercial silica sols. In the paper industry colloidal silica has been used in blueprint and other photosensitive papers. The paper is prepared for receiving a sensitized solution by applying a coating of colloidal silica to the surface, in order to intensify the color of the finished blueprint.

A somewhat similar use is the addition of a colloidal dispersion of silica to the diazo-type sensitizing solution. The colloidal silica fills the interstices of the absorbent carrier, such as paper, and helps to retain the color-forming components of the diazo-type composition at or near the surface. Colloidal silica yields prints of much greater density, brightness, sharpness, clarity, and definition, and requires a much shorter exposure period. Colloidal silicas are also employed in the impregnation of paper used in plastic laminates and in the treatment of adhesive tapes prior to the application of the pressure-sensitive adhesive film.

An important use for colloidal silica involves its incorporation into floor wax to impart increased skid resistance, without detracting from the other properties of the protective finish. The aqueous sol is mixed with an aqueous wax dispersion to give hard glossy waxed finishes which are much less slippery because the silica particles in the surface increase the coefficient of friction, yet are too fine to detract from the clarity and brilliance of the finish.

In the textile industry the application of colloidal silica reduces the slippage of rayon and the snagging of sheer hosiery, and lowers the surface luster of filament yarns. The use of the silica, along with resins and wetting agents, provides a continuous film on the fiber.

Colloidal silica has also been applied to cellophane film in such a way that the film has a charge opposite to that of the silica particles and holds the particles to the film.

Colloidal silica, especially of particle size smaller than 30-mμ diam, is employed for modifying the characteristics of organic polymers, particularly elastomers and resin adhesives. Similarly, aqueous emulsions of polyvinyl acetate, phenolic resins, or water-based paints can be improved by the addition of colloidal silica.

Colloidal silica is employed as a binder of many different materials. An important use of this type is as a binder for sand molds and for glass fibers.

Precipitated Silica. Precipitated silicas are widely used in the rubber industry as fillers and reinforcing pigments, and in the paper industry both as a filler and in coating formulations. Other applications include use as a carrier and diluent for high-concentration insecticides and agricultural chemicals, anticaking substances, absorbing liquids and sticky solids, as well as for viscosity control purposes in plastics, inks, textiles, coating, and pharmaceuticals. These reactive forms of silica are also used in manufacturing molecular sieve catalysts.

Fumed Silica. The fumed silicas of the flame-hydrolyzed type find wide application in the plastics and rubber industries as reinforcing and thickening or thixotropic agents. Products such as automobile bodies, boats, bathtubs, chairs, and parts for airplanes and household appliances have been improved in quality by the use of these ultrafine silicas.

One of the most important uses of these silicas as a thixotropic agent in the plastics industry is in the field of polyester–glass reinforced plastics. Polyester resins themselves are not thixotropic. When used in molding and coating operations where sections of the mold are slanting or sloping, they drain away from the glass substrate, with the result that the product when cured is not uniform in composition or thickness. The resin itself has a very small original viscosity, approx 4 P, which remains constant at all shear rates. With the addition of only a small amount of the ultrafine silica, however, a tremendous change in viscosity with shear is obtained. The net result is that while the silica-thickened resin can be easily applied by spraying or brushing, it will quickly build up to a heavy, thick consistency as soon as the spraying or brushing action has ceased and will not drain away from the reinforcing glass substrate before curing takes place.

The ultrafine fumed silica is also used with epoxy resins to give the same thickening and thixotropic effects observed with polyesters. In general, 2–5% silica is found to be sufficient to prevent the drainage of epoxy resins.

Fumed silicas are used as a means of increasing the thixotropic consistency of plastisols and organosols. (See Vol. 5, p. 682.) These vinyl dispersions are then particularly adaptable to the deposition of heavy layers of the durable coating by the "dip-coating" process. Generally, the thixotropic plastisols and organosols are employed for dip application where the rapid deposition of heavy coatings is required. The exact amount of silica to be added depends, of course, on the final consistency desired, but for most applications quantities of about 2 parts of silica/100 parts of resin are sufficient.

Ultrafine fumed silica can be used as an effective thickening and gelling agent for plastigels. The preparation of plastigels from vinyl dispersions involves the addition of a thickening and gelling agent to a plastisol formulation in a high-shear mixer. The compatibility of fumed silica with the system has been observed and plastigel formulations have been stored for nearly two years with little migration of the plasticizer to the surface.

Hydrophobic Silica. The primary uses are as dispersions in mineral-oil compositions for defoaming aqueous systems and as carriers to promote aerosol formation with lacrimators and the like.

Bibliography

"Silica and Silicates (Silica Gel)" in *ECT* 1st. ed., Vol. 12, pp. 345–360, by S. S. Hubbard, The Davison Chemical Corporation.

1. U.S. Pat. 2,249,767 (1941), S. S. Kistler; *J. Phys. Chem.* **35,** 52 (1932).
2. U.S. Pats. 2,385,217 (1945), 2,384,945 (1945), 2,463,467 (1949), M. M. Marisic (to Socony-Mobil Oil Co.)
3. R. K. Iler, *The Colloid Chemistry of Silica and Silicates*, Cornell University Press, Ithaca, N.Y., 1955.
4. U.S. Pats. 2,805,955 (1957), E. M. Allen; 3,208,823 (1965), J. F. Austin and C. L. Baker; 2,348,072 (1944), E. R. Kanhofer.
5. Kenneth A. Loftman, "Physical Characteristics and Surface Properties of Pyrogenic Oxides of Silicon and Aluminum," in W. Kuhn, H. Lamprey, and C. Scheer, eds., *Ultrafine Particles*, John Wiley & Sons, Inc., New York, 1963, pp. 196–205.
6. H. Lee and W. P. Cummings, *Chem. Eng. Prog.* **63,** 42–49 (1967).

General Reference

J. G. Vail, *Soluble Silicates*, ACS Monograph No. 116, Vol. 1, Chap. 5; Vol. 2, Chap. 9, Reinhold Publishing Corp., New York, 1952.

P. K. Maher
Davison Chemical Division
W. R. Grace & Co.

VITREOUS SILICA

Vitreous silica is a glass composed essentially of SiO_2. It has been the subject of considerable study for two reasons. Primarily, it is a material with many unique and useful properties, such as low thermal expansion, high thermal shock resistance, high ultraviolet transparency, good refractory qualities, and chemical inertness. A second reason is the simplicity of its chemical constitution. However, when one begins to study vitreous silica, it soon becomes apparent that it is actually a very complicated material whose properties can vary, depending on raw material, method of manufacture, and thermal history.

The question arises as to why, if vitreous silica has such outstanding properties, it is not used even more extensively than in its present wide range of applications. The answer is the high cost of manufacture as compared to most glasses, caused by very high viscosity, small temperature coefficient of viscosity, and volatility at forming temperatures. This means that even at 2000°C the melt is very stiff and difficult to shape, particularly by mass production methods.

There are two general forms of vitreous silica, transparent and nontransparent. The nontransparent fused material contains a large number of microscopic bubbles which create a milky appearance caused by the scattering of light. This material, sometimes called translucent fused silica, is more economical to produce than the transparent type and is often used where optical properties are not important. Another nontransparent type is opaque and is formed by sintering powdered vitreous silica.

The following companies are the principal manufacturers and suppliers of vitreous silica in the United States: Amersil, Inc., Hillside, N.J. (associated with Heraeus-Schott Quarzschmelze G.m.b.H.); Corning Glass Works, Corning, N.Y.; Dynasil Corporation of America, Berlin, N.J.; General Electric Company, Lamp Glass Dept., Willoughby, Ohio; Glasrock Products Inc., Atlanta, Ga. (slip-cast vitreous silica); Thermal American Fused Quartz Company, Montville, N.J. (associated with Thermal Syndicate Ltd.); Westinghouse Lamp Division, Bloomfield, N.J. (principally lamp envelopes).

The principal manufacturers overseas are the following: Berliner Quarzschmelze, Heindersdorf, East Berlin, D.D.R.; Heraeus-Schott Quarzschmelze G.m.b.H., Hanau, West Germany; Osram G.m.b.H., West Berlin, West Germany (principally lamp envelopes); Thermal Quarzschmelze G.m.b.H., Wiesbaden-Biebrick, West Germany; Westdeutsche Quarzschmelze G.m.b.H., Geesthacht/Elbe, West Germany; N. V. Philips' Gloeilampenfabrieken, Eindhoven, Netherlands (principally lamp envelopes); Quartz et Silice, Paris, France; Toshiba Denko Company, Ltd., Tokyo, Japan.

History. Probably the earliest record of vitreous silica was in a communication from Marcet (1), a physician, to a Dr. Thomson, dated July, 1813. By directing a current of oxygen horizontally through the flame of an alcohol lamp, Marcet was able to produce a flame of intense heat with which he melted wires of platinum and iron. He simply noted that "... small needles of quartz are readily melted and vitrified by the same means." In 1821, Clarke (2) verified these findings when he melted white opaque quartz in an oxy–hydrogen flame and found that the resultant material was as limpid and transparent as rock crystal.

Gaudin (3), in 1839, was the first investigator to describe some of the properties of vitreous silica and probably the first to work it successfully. Using a gas–oxygen flame, he formed threads, hooks, and droplets of the glass and exhibited them to the Academy of Sciences at Paris. This material was very volatile at temperatures just above its fusion point. The resultant glass had remarkable strength, an elasticity which resembled that of iron, and was not broken up when rapidly cooled from the molten state. As a result of these excellent properties, Gaudin felt that the glass could be put to many uses, including small springs, torsion threads, and high-temperature forceps. He also observed that the sandstone near Paris could be made into a glass which, instead of being transparent, formed silky white threads and pearllike droplets. In fact, he noted that these droplets served as very good imitation pearls due to their high strength and luster.

Due primarily to a lack of sufficient power and facilities to melt and form vitreous silica, the further development of this material was almost dormant until the end of the nineteenth century. During this interim, H. Deville (4), in 1856, melted 30 g of quartz sand in a coke furnace and obtained a glass resembling Gaudin's and A. Gautier, in 1869, succeeded in forming very narrow tubes of vitreous silica, as reported by Shenstone and Lacell (6). Then, with advances in the commercial development of electrical and oxy–hydrogen power came the revival of vitreous silica investigations (5). According to Shenstone and Lacell (6), vitreous silica was independently rediscovered and applied by Prof. C. V. Boys in 1887 in Great Britain and his observations formed the basis for the redevelopment of this material.

Shenstone and Lacell (6), in 1900, made the important discovery of how to eliminate splintering during the fusion of quartz crystals. Splintering during the melting process creates air lines in the final product (see below under Methods of manufacture, p. 76). They found that if the crystals were heated to a red heat and quenched in water to obtain fracture into tiny crystals, these crystals could be successfully fused without splintering. This method has been a key principle on which the clear fused-quartz industry was founded. Shenstone and Lacell also described techniques for the hand formation of rods, tubes, and bulbs of various sizes from these treated crystals and Shenstone, in other articles (7,8), described his production of vitreous silica thermometers.

The first patents were issued to the Deutsche Gold- und Silberscheideanstalt (9) in 1899 and to Bottomley, Hutton, and Paget in Great Britain in 1904 (10,11). They cover the manufacture of translucent vitreous silica by fusion of sand surrounding a graphite rod through which a current is passed and subsequent manipulation of the hot plastic material. A similar patent was obtained by Thomson (12) in the United States, also in 1904. In 1910, Kent and Lacell (13) patented a method of feeding powdered quartz crystal into an arc which allowed vitreous silica to be built up in the absence of any contaminating refractory.

According to Stephenson (5), the first sales of fused silica were made in 1906 and consisted principally of pipes and muffles. The same year saw the incorporation of the Thermal Syndicate Ltd. This industry has since developed to an annual business of approx $30 million in 1967 in the United States alone (14).

Nomenclature (15–17). The nomenclature of this material has been confusing, ambiguous, and often incorrect. The following is a list of most of the terms:

Vitreous Silica is the most unambiguous general term which covers the entire field of noncrystalline silica.

Silica Glass, while technically correct, can be misinterpreted as covering any glass composition containing silica.

Fused Silica should apply to any form of vitreous silica manufactured by fusion. However, it has been used by some to denote all vitreous silica not produced by quartz fusion and by others for only the translucent vitreous silica.

Synthetic Fused Silica is a term used to describe the material formed by vapor-phase hydrolysis.

Fused Quartz is the material formed by direct melting of quartz crystals. This term is used by some to denote all forms of vitreous silica and by others to specify all transparent vitreous silica.

Quartz Glass is the same as fused quartz but is ambiguous since quartz is crystalline and glass is vitreous.

Quartz is a crystalline form of silica. This much-abused term for designation of vitreous silica is absolutely incorrect.

The words transparent, nontransparent, or translucent sometimes precede the above terms to further describe the material.

Occurrence in Nature. There are a number of cases where vitreous silica occurs as the result of natural phenomena (18). A bolt of lightning can fuse quartz sand at a temperature high enough to give glass tubes called fulgurites. The best-known deposit of this type of vitreous silica, the mineral lechatelierite, is in the Libyan desert.

Deposits of natural fused quartz have also been found near Canyon Diablo, Arizona, and in small meteorite craters in Australia and Arabia. There is an uncertainty about their origin, but the most accepted theory is that pressure, created at the moment of meteorite impact, caused adiabatic instantaneous heating of sandstone to well above the quartz melting point.

As an interesting modification of this theory, Skinner and Fahey (19) propose that impact pressure creates stishovite, a crystalline form of SiO_2 with Si in sixfold coordination, which transforms to a glass with sixfold-coordinated Si. This dense glass then converts to the observed fourfold-coordinated silica glass. The process can take place in a matter of 14 min at 400°C and in 1–2 min at 800°C.

Manufacture

Nontransparent Vitreous Silica is produced by fusion of high-purity quartz sand crystals. One method is to place a charge of sand around a strong, conducting graphite rod through which a current is passed. The fusion product thus formed is plastic and can be blown into molds, drawn into tubing, or shaped by rolling or pressing. Separation from the graphite rod is facilitated by gaseous products formed by interfacial reaction. Since the outside surface is sandy, the product is known as sand-surface ware. A mat finish may be obtained by mechanical buffing, and a glazed surface can be produced by use of an electric carbon arc or flame to quickly fuse the outside surface, producing a product called glazed ware. Drawn tubing with the glazed surface is called satin tubing due to the appearance caused by the striated bubbles (10).

The Rotosil (Amersil, Inc.) process employed by Heraeus and Amersil is used for the production of tubular or cylindrical shapes and permits greater uniformity and dimensional control than the older process. The quartz sand is washed in hydrofluoric acid and distilled water. Silica is soluble in hydrofluoric acid (see under Chemical properties, p. 82) so that washing in hydrofluoric acid strips away the surface layer along with any attached impurities. Purity is extremely important, not only because impurities can degrade performance of the final product, but also because they can accelerate the crystallization rate during manufacture. The sand is then placed in a horizontal steel tube which is rotated to hold the sand around the circumference by centrifugal force. A carbon arc is passed slowly down the center of the drum to fuse the sand. A modification, using open rotating molds on a vertical axis, allows formation of crucibles, beakers, and bowls (20).

Clear Fused Quartz. On heating, quartz undergoes an inversion from low to high at 573°C in which volume and elastic constants undergo a very rapid change. If heating is rapid and nonuniform, large differences in temperature can occur between portions of a large crystal. Both of these conditions can cause fracture of the crystal. If this phenomenon occurs during the melting process, gaseous inclusions in the form of air lines are present in the final product. One method of overcoming this problem is to pretreat the quartz crystals by washing in hydrofluoric acid and distilled water, drying, then heating to about 800°C and plunging into distilled water to facilitate subsequent crushing. This not only overcomes splintering problems, but small particles with a larger surface area are especially advantageous for vacuum melting, since they melt faster and expel gaseous impurities to a greater extent than the raw quartz crystals.

The melting point of quartz is below 1450°C and probably above 1400°C. It is difficult to determine, since from the melting point of quartz to the melting point of cristobalite at 1723°C, both glass and cristobalite are formed when quartz is heated in air for longer than 15 min. Quartz microcrystals are present even after heating at 1860°C for 30 min; however, crystallinity disappears at 1900°C on heating for 1 hr (21). Fusion is generally carried out in an oxy–hydrogen flame or in molybdenum or carbon crucibles in an inert or reducing atmosphere. There are electric melting procedures in which a vacuum is used to minimize the gas content in the pore space prior to fusion. Sometimes this is followed by applied pressure to contract the remaining bubbles.

While almost all fused-quartz production is carried out above the melting point of cristobalite, Skaupy and Weissenberg (22) developed a technique for producing vitreous silica from quartz below 1723°C. One example of their method involves pressing powdered quartz into a given shape in a mold, sintering at 1500°C for 8 min, then raising the temperature to 1650°C for 2 min. Due to the rapid heating, no cristobalite is present and the product is vitreous. In all cases, the sintering process takes no more than 15 min in the 1400–1710°C zone.

The Heraeus process involves the feeding of quartz crystals through an oxy–hydrogen flame onto a fused quartz tube which is rotated and withdrawn slowly from the burner as clear fused quartz is built up (23). In order to obtain a high-purity material, particularly for lamp envelopes, chlorine or a chlorine compound is introduced into the system above 1600°C and preferably between 1800 and 2200°C. Any impurities in the quartz which form volatile chlorides, such as sodium, magnesium, calcium, barium, aluminum, copper, zinc, titanium, or iron, are removed (24).

In the Osram (Osram G.m.b.H.) process, quartz is fed into the top of a resistance-heated tubular furnace and is melted in a molybdenum crucible protected by an inert or reducing gas. Tubing is drawn from the bottom (25).

Vapor Phase Hydrolysis. This process is capable of producing very high-purity (with the exception of hydroxyl groups), good optical-quality vitreous silica. Oxygen is passed through a volatile silicon compound, such as silicon tetrachloride, and the resulting mixture is fed along with natural gas into a burner. Hydrogen is often used rather than natural gas, especially by European manufacturers. Hydrolysis takes place in the resulting flame, producing vitreous silica. (See also Silica, amorphous.) The product can be formed by deposition on a substrate of preheated sand and consolidation to clear glass using the heat from the burners (26). The resulting vitreous silica is high in water content.

Hydroxyl-free vitreous silica may also be produced by vapor-phase hydrolysis. The vitreous silica particles (about 0.1 μ diam) formed by the hydrolysis reaction are not consolidated in the burner flame, but deposited on an air-cooled aluminum mandrel. As the mandrel rotates and moves laterally through the flame, layers of these particles are built up, since the particles adhere tightly to each other. The deposited shape is then removed from the aluminum and placed over a graphite mandrel which is about one-third the size of the aluminum. The particles consolidate in about 30 min to a clear glass at 1450–1500°C in an electrically heated furnace containing hydrogen or a hydrogen–nitrogen mixture. The glass assumes the shape of the graphite mandrel.

Another vapor-phase method for producing hydroxyl-free vitreous silica was developed by Winterburn (27) using an oxygen plasma. A volatile, hydrogen-free silicon compound, such as silicon tetrachloride, is introduced into a hydrogen-free stream of oxygen which is passed through an induction-coupled plasma torch. The resulting silica is deposited on a refractory substrate and fired to a clear transparent glass in the flame.

Sintering Processes. Since fabrication of large shapes is very difficult, sintering techniques have been developed to obtain large pieces with good dimensional control.

In a typical hot-pressing technique, vitreous silica is crushed, washed, and screened to about 5-μ size. The powder is pressed into shapes at pressures of 1000–2500 psi and at 1100–1200°C for up to 90 min (28).

A slip-casting method uses a water slip of powdered vitreous silica which is poured into a plaster mold. After removal from the mold, the body is dried slowly and then fired at about 1100–1200°C for 1 to 4 hr (29).

Fibers. Fused quartz fibers can be prepared in various sizes depending on the fabrication method used. The shortest fibers are prepared by heating a rod of fused quartz in an oxy–gas or oxy–hydrogen flame, pulling the softened rod apart, then moving the pieces back and forth in the horizontal flame. The force of the flame blows the fibers horizontally and they are caught on a cloth or board a few feet from the flame. The fibers are deposited at random in a tangled mass (30).

A long fine fiber can be formed when a piece of stock is held vertically in a long flame. The stock of 25 μ diam (originally drawn down in a flame from larger stock) gives fibers of 1–10 μ diam. Fibers up to 60 ft in length have been obtained by heating a 25-μ fiber anchored at one end and the other end fastened to an arrow angled at about 45° from the horizontal in a crossbow. When proper viscosity is reached the crossbow is fired giving a long uniform fiber about 5–10 μ in diam (31).

One method of forming a continuous fiber is to heat the tip of a fused quartz rod placed in a rotating chuck with a gas–oxygen flame. When the fused quartz is sufficiently softened, it is touched with another piece of fused quartz and pulled over a drum which rotates at a predetermined rate. The flame is moved slowly to maintain its position on the tip of the gradually shortening rod. The rod diameter is 2–6 mm, giving fiber diameters from 25–200 μ. Fiber diameter is dependent on size of original stock, temperature, and drum speed (32).

RAW MATERIALS

Quartz (33–35). The primary source of raw material for the fused quartz industry is Brazil, which supplied 96% of United States imports in 1965. That year, 858,223 lb of quartz at a value of $170,258 were imported for fusing.

The remainder of the quartz imports comes from the Malagasy Republic, although the quartz may actually be routed from there and from Brazil through other countries, such as Argentina, Japan, Canada, and the United Kingdom. There are also a number of deposits in the Soviet Union.

The highest grades of quartz are optical and electronic grades. Optical grade is the highest quality and must be colorless and free of defects. It is used for wedges, prisms, lenses, and other components, and also for gem stones. Electronic grade is not necessarily colorless but must be free of certain defects and is used in, among other things, production of crystal-controlled oscillator units for accurate frequency control. The price of these higher quality crystals was about $2.82/lb in 1965. Brazilian quartz for fusing is called lasca. It has the following specifications: water white, no internal feathers and inclusions, clean surfaces, and a median weight of 10–25 g. In packing, the quartz must be dry and free of oil, sawdust, and trash. The average cost of this quartz was $0.20/lb in 1965.

The Brazilian deposits are found in a primitive area twice the size of Texas. The important mining centers are in central Minas Gerais, southeastern Goiaz, north central Goiaz between the Araguaia and Tocantins rivers and in northwestern Bahia along the São Franscisco River. Other sources may be found in the state of Para and near Cristalina, Goiaz, where deposits were discovered in early 1965. Quartz may be found in veins, pegmatites, eluvial deposits, alluvial deposits, and in variations of veins and pegmatites that may grade into each other. The principal Brazilian sources are in veins and eluvial deposits which are enhanced by deep tropical weathering. The eluvial deposits are the richest and most easily worked sources. Because of their tendency to fracture and their unpredictable distribution, quartz crystals are mined by tedious hand labor. A mine is generally worked by a group of people in an open cut that may be terraced, and the quartz is often transported by basket or wheelbarrow. The ratio of eye-clear crystal to excavated material ranges from 1:1000 to 1:100,000.

In the United States, minor sources of quartz crystal have been found in the Calaveras and Tulare Counties of California, and in Arkansas, southwestern Virginia, and North Carolina.

Sand (36). Sand can also be melted to form fused quartz. This fused quartz has a higher impurity level than that made from Brazilian quartz. Sand is mostly used for the nontransparent variety; however, if vacuum techniques are used, reasonably clear material can be made. There are at least 5000 sources of sand in the United States alone, so the choice of raw material is dictated by the purity desired, grain size, and location.

Silicon Tetrachloride (37). The most common raw material for the production of synthetic vitreous silica is silicon tetrachloride (see under Silicon compounds).

Structure

One of the first important theories of the structure of vitreous silica was presented by Randall, Rooksby, and Cooper in 1930 (38). Because of the coincidence of the maxima of the x-ray diffraction peaks for vitreous silica and cristobalite, they concluded that vitreous silica consists of units of "crystallites" of cristobalite. These crystallites were about 15–20 Å in size. The Russian school of glass science has championed the crystallite theory, as seen by the work of Porai-Koshits and others (39–42).

New theories of the structure of vitreous silica are continually being proposed, indicating the lack of certainty of the actual structure. However, almost all new structural proposals refer to the original random network theory of Zachariasen (43). In 1932, he set forth the following description of vitreous silica:

1. It is built up of tetrahedra with oxygen atoms at the corners surrounding a silicon atom in the center.

2. The tetrahedra share only corners in such a way that an oxygen atom is linked to two silicon atoms.

3. The oxygen–silicon–oxygen bond angle varies throughout the network, in contrast to the crystalline forms.

4. The extended three-dimensional network lacks symmetry and periodicity.

The work of Warren (44,45) involving x-ray diffraction, with subsequent Fourier analysis, further establishes the random network theory with the following findings:

1. The x-ray diffraction pattern is a typical amorphous pattern showing broad diffuse rings.

2. Well-defined peaks correspond to an Si—O distance of 1.62 Å, an Si—Si distance of 3.15 Å, and an O—O distance of 2.65 Å.

3. The ratio of the O—O distance to the Si—O distance equals $\sqrt{8:3}$ and 3.85 oxygens (ie, approximately 4) surround each silicon. Thus, the structural units are almost perfect tetrahedra.

4. The Si—O—Si angle is 153°, but can vary by as much as 15–20° on either side.

5. The peaks become more diffuse beyond 3.15 Å, indicating the absence of structural order much beyond one tetrahedron.

The Warren results are in general agreement with the neutron diffraction studies of Milligan, Levy, and Peterson, who found well-resolved peaks at about 1.58, 2.56, 3.02, 4.0, and 5.1 Å (46).

Newer structural concepts have been postulated to explain certain property anomalies which could not be explained by other theories, but they have been less widely accepted. In 1957, in an attempt to reconcile the random network and crystallite concepts, Tilton (47) proposed that vitreous silica is a stressed assemblage of pentagonal dodecahedral cages, called "vitrons." Robinson (48) modified the pentagonal dodecahedra theory by permitting distortion or puckering of the structure. One disadvantage of these concepts is that calculated density is about 10% less than actual density.

With the advent of computers, theoretical structures have been generated from a prescribed set of geometrical rules, and actual construction, using wire tetrapod units, provided a means of checking structural accuracy. Ordway (49) constructed a 300-unit structure and observed that in the early stages of construction the structure resembles that proposed by Tilton. Growth beyond a thirteen-unit vitron, however, was truly random. Evans and King (50) modified the Ordway approach and generated a completely random structure of 651 tetrapods. Pictures of the model are shown in Figure 1. The entire model is shown in the large photograph, while the insert shows a close-up view of the construction. The silicon positions are represented by each juncture of four wires and the oxygens are visualized as being midway along the wires

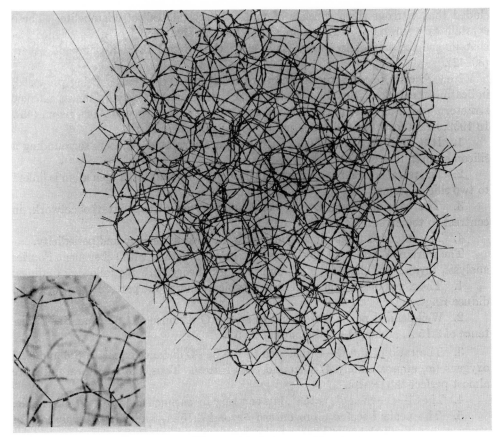

Fig. 1. Evans-King model of vitreous silica structure.

joining each juncture. Though no attempt was made to incorporate atom diameters into the model, the bond angles and lengths, as represented by the wire tetrapods, are to scale. The small flags attached between tetrapods were used for counting purposes and the thin wires were used for suspension of the model. The radial distribution of atoms corresponds to Warren's x-ray scattering data. The density is 2.08 g/cm³, which is appreciably greater than that of Tilton and Robinson, although slightly less than the 2.20 g/cm³ actual measured value. Chiariello (51) made a similar study using models containing up to 500 tetrapods and found an average density of 2.05 g/cm³, again slightly lower than the measured value. The actual true density has never been determined, since absolutely pure stoichiometric vitreous silica has never been made.

Smyth (52,53) has succeeded in relating some of the physical properties of vitreous silica to its structure. Theoretical calculations based on the random network theory offer partial explanations for such properties as thermal capacity, thermal expansion, compressibility, elasticity, viscous flow, and stress-optical effects. His findings are in reasonably good agreement with experimental evidence.

Chemical Properties

Chemical Constitution. Stoichiometric vitreous silica contains two oxygens for every one silicon, but it is extremely doubtful if such a material, in fact, exists. There

Table 1. Maximum Recorded Impurity Levels in the Various Types of Vitreous Silica[a]

Impurity, ppm	Translucent vitreous silica	Transparent vitreous silica[c]		
		type 1	type 2	type 3[d]
aluminum	500	74	68	<0.25
antimony	nd[b]	0.3	0.1	0.1
arsenic	nd	nd	nd	<0.02
boron	9	4	3	0.1
calcium	200	16	0.4	<0.1
chromium	nd	0.1	nd	0.03
cobalt	nd	nd	nd	0.0001
copper	nd	1	1	<1
gallium	nd	nd	nd	<0.02
gold	nd	nd	nd	<0.1
hydroxyl	nd	60	450	1200
iron	77	7	1.5	<0.2
lithium	3	7	1	nd
magnesium	150	4	nd	nd
manganese	nd	1	0.2	<0.02
mercury	nd	nd	nd	<0.1
phosphorus	nd	0.01	0.005	<0.001
potassium	37	6	<1	0.1
sodium	60	9	5	<0.1
titanium	120	3	2	nd
uranium	nd	nd	0.0006	nd
zinc	nd	nd	nd	<0.1
zirconium	15	3	nd	nd

[a] Data taken from the literature, private communications, and various manufacturers' publications. Courtesy Thermal Syndicate Ltd.

[b] No data available = nd.

[c] The types referred to are those described in the text. The type of raw material is not specified.

[d] The metallic impurities in type 4 vitreous silica are similar to those in type 3 material.

are generally small amounts of impurities present from the starting materials, and water is incorporated in the structure as $-$OH.

Hetherington (54) has classified transparent vitreous silicas in the following manner:

Type 1—electrically fused quartz crystal;

Type 2—flame-fused quartz crystal;

Type 3—flame-fused synthetic vitreous silica;

Type 4—low-hydroxyl-content synthetic vitreous silica.

The maximum impurity levels of the different types of vitreous silicas are shown in Table 1. Type 4 has metallic impurity levels similar to those of type 3; however, the hydroxyl content of type 4 is negligible. The impurity levels of the different fused quartz types depend to a large extent on purity and treatment of the quartz crystals. Manufacturers' literature should be consulted for material designation and the corresponding correct combination of metal and hydroxyl impurity levels (55–58).

In the presence of water vapor at high temperatures the following reaction can take place:

$$-Si-O-Si- + H_2O \rightarrow -Si-OH + HO-Si-$$

A certain amount of reduction of SiO_2 also takes place, depending on the method of manufacture. In the presence of carbon the following reaction may possibly occur:

$$SiO_2 + C \rightarrow SiO + CO$$

This reduction can take place at temperatures as low as 1200°C with pure carbon (58). A similar reduction with tungsten, tantalum, or molybdenum can occur at 1300–1400°C in vacuum (59). This type of reaction is very important in quartz fusion, since SiO_2 is not volatile, even over 1800°C, but SiO and Si have appreciable vapor pressures.

Chemical Reactivity. The resistance of nontransparent vitreous silica to chemical attack is slightly less than the resistance of transparent vitreous silica. This is primarily due to the higher surface area of the nontransparent variety caused by the presence of a large number of bubbles. Most data are on the transparent material.

Metals do not generally react below 1000°C or their melting point, whichever is lower. There are exceptions, such as magnesium, alkali metals, and aluminum, which readily reduces silica at 700–800°C. Alkali metal vapor attack takes place at temperatures as low as 200°C. The mechanism of sodium-vapor attack involves a diffusion of sodium into the glass, followed by a reduction of the silica by the following reaction:

$$4\,Na + 5\,SiO_2 \rightarrow 2\,Na_2Si_2O_5 + Si$$

This is evidenced by a blackening of the vitreous silica and a flaking of the surface. As evidence for the diffusion step, the sodium absorption by the much denser quartz is 12 mg/(1000 hr)(cm²) at 350°C, whereas vitreous silica absorbs 23 mg/(1000 hr)(cm²) at 286°C (60). Molten sodium is much less reactive.

Fused basic salts and basic oxides react at elevated temperatures. Reaction with alkaline-earth oxides takes place at about 900°C. Halides may tend to dissolve vitreous silica at high temperatures, fluorides being the most reactive. Fused borates react appreciably (58).

Dry halogen gases do not react below 300°C. Reaction with hydrogen is very slight at 1000°C, but much higher temperatures may bring reduction (58).

Hydrofluoric acid attacks vitreous silica readily, as shown by the following reaction:

$$SiO_2 + 4\,HF \rightarrow 2\,H_2O + SiF_4 \uparrow$$

In the presence of an excess of hydrofluoric acid, the volatile reaction product may also be H_2SiF_6. Table 2 shows the effects of two different hydrofluoric acid solutions on various silica phases, including vitreous silica (61). In all cases, the samples were of a uniform particle size of approx 0.04 mm diam. Phosphoric acid causes some attack at about 150°C (57). Other acids do not react. In 5% HCl at 95°C, there is a surface erosion of less than 2.5×10^{-6} cm in 24 hr (56). Similar results are obtained with H_2SO_4.

Table 2. Dissolving Rates of Phases of Silica (61)

Silica phases	Proportion dissolved, %	
	HF, 5%, ½ hr	HF, 1%, 1 hr
quartz	30.1	5.2
tridymite	76.3	20.3
cristobalite	74.3	25.8
vitreous silica	96.6	52.9

Reaction with dilute basic solutions is very slight at room temperature. In 5% NaOH at 95°C, the vitreous silica surface erodes about 1×10^{-3} cm in 24 hr; however, crazing of the surface may occur (56).

There is no reaction with water and steam at moderate temperatures and pressures. At temperatures of about 200–400°C and pressures of about 145–4350 psi, the solubility, L, of vitreous silica in g SiO_2/kg H_2O can be expressed as follows:

$$\log L = 2 \log D - \frac{2679}{T} + 4.972$$

where D = density of the vapor phase, and T = absolute temperature.

The solution occurs as a biomolecular, heterogeneous gas reaction (62):

$$SiO_2 + 2\,H(OH) = [Si(OH)_4]$$

At 400°C and 2000 psi, the solubilities in g/million g of H_2O of translucent vitreous silica, clear vitreous silica, and quartz are 36, 31, and 5.2, respectively. At 500°C, clear vitreous silica has a solubility of 346 g/million g of H_2O at 5000 psi, and 4179 g/million g of H_2O at 15,000 psi (63).

Devitrification of vitreous silica can occur as cristobalite formation at all temperatures from 1000°C to the 1723°C cristobalite liquidus with a maximum growth rate at approx 1600°C, provided it is under normal atmospheric pressure. Crystals form and grow from nuclei found predominantly at the glass surface, but internal crystallization, though rarely seen, can also occur (64). In all observations to date, the crystallization process has been the result of heterogeneous nucleation, regardless of whether it began internally or externally.

The general effect of temperature on devitrification rate for crystals growing inward from the glass surface is shown in Figure 2. The measurements were made by Ainslie, Morelock, and Turnbull (65) on General Electric 204A fused silica, heat-treated in air. Wagstaff (64) determined the growth rate–temperature relation for

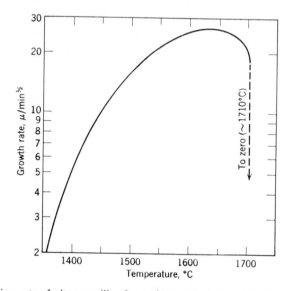

Fig. 2. Devitrification rate of vitreous silica for surface nucleated cristobalite as a function of temperature (65). The rate of growth is proportional to the square root of the time.

internally nucleated cristobalite crystals in a low-hydroxyl-content fused quartz. At all temperatures studied (ie, 1350–1620°C), the observed growth rates were linear with time and were the lowest measured for vitreous silica. For example, the growth rate at 1350°C was 6.5×10^{-4} μ/min and increased to 9.0×10^{-2} μ/min at 1620°C. Because the growth was internal and free from surface contamination, the rates seem to be very near the intrinsic rates for the material.

The devitrification rate is extremely sensitive to both surface and bulk impurities, especially alkali. Fingerprints can be "developed" by heating a piece of vitreous silica which has been touched, causing an accelerated crystal growth rate in the area of finger contact. As little as 0.32 wt % soda, added as a bulk impurity, increases the maximum devitrification rate twenty or thirty times and lowers the temperature of the maximum to about 1400°C (66). The addition of small amounts of alumina to fused silica also increases the devitrification rate, reaching a maximum when the $Al^{3+}:Si^{4+}$ ratio is approx 0.225×10^{-2} (66).

The water content and stoichiometry of the glass also affect the devitrification rate. A high hydroxyl content in the glass, and water vapor and oxygen in the atmosphere, all tend to enhance devitrification, while oxygen deficiency of the glass and neutral or reducing atmospheres tend to inhibit devitrification (65,68–71). The oxygen affects the rate by diffusing through the cristobalite layer to the glass–crystal interface and oxidizing the glass, thereby bringing it closer to stoichiometry (68–70). The water vapor and hydroxyl show a similar effect, probably by dissociating at the elevated temperatures to give free oxygen and also by weakening the glass structure through the formation of silicon–hydroxyl bonds (68–70). The effect of stoichiometry on the devitrification rate is the basis for the development of a vitreous silica resistant to crystallization formed by the addition of silicon to silica (71).

The effect of pressure on devitrification was investigated by Uhlmann et al. (72). Using Spectrosil (Thermal Syndicate Ltd.) and G.E. Type 204 (General Electric Co.) fused silicas, they found that at pressures above 25 kbar devitrification occurred at temperatures as low as 500°C, and at 40 kbar at temperatures as low as 450°C. Heat treatments at these temperatures lasted for 70 hr. Though the temperatures and pressures were in the stability field of coesite, both coesite and quartz were observed. Both the devitrification rate and the formation of the stable phase (coesite) was enhanced by the presence of water. This is due in part to the increased solubility of water in the amorphous phase caused by the high pressures (ie, resulting in increased molecular mobility). Standard kinetic theory cannot explain the low-temperature crystallization at high pressures.

Yalmann and Corwin (73) have found that the formation of cristobalite from vitreous silica occurs at temperatures as low as 400°C when the pressure is equal to 0.35 kbar and the glass is immersed in weak NaOH solutions. In stronger NaOH solutions, quartz is formed. The formation of the crystalline phases is due to the hydrolysis of the anions present. No crystallization occurred with HF, H_2SO_4, and H_3PO_4 in $KHSO_4$ solutions or in pure water.

Physical Properties

Vitreous silica has many outstanding properties making it a very useful material, and a number of these properties are abnormal when compared to other glasses and even other solids (74). The following anomalous properties are, more or less, inter-dependent:

1. The expansion coefficient is negative below about −80 to −100°C, and is positive and very small above these temperatures.

2. The elastic moduli increase with increasing temperatures above about −190°C.

3. Young's modulus increases linearly with applied longitudinal stress at −196°C, whereas that of soda glass decreases (75).

4. The compressibility increases as the pressure increases in the low to moderate (0 to about 35,000 kg/cm²) pressure range.

5. The equilibrium density decreases with increasing temperature from within the transformation range to about 1500°C. The density also decreases with heat treatment in the transformation range in contrast to that of most glasses.

6. The bulk modulus shows a negative pressure dependence.

7. There is a divergence from diffusion-controlled permeation of hydrogen at elevated temperatures.

8. The temperature coefficient of sound velocity is positive over the range 0–800°C (76).

Physical properties are quite dependent on thermal history, as illustrated with some of the properties listed below.

Thermal Expansion. Most manufacturers' literature (56–58) quotes a linear expansion coefficient within the 0–300°C range of about 5.4 to 5.6 × 10^{-7}/°C. The effect of thermal history on low-temperature expansion of Homosil (Heraeus-Schott Quarzschmelze G.m.b.H.) and Osram's vitreous silicas, as determined by Brückner (77) can be seen in Figure 3. The 1000, 1300, and 1720°C curves are for samples held at these temperatures until equilibrium density was achieved, then quenched in water. The effect of temperature on linear expansion of vitreous silica is compared with that of typical soda-lime and borosilicate glasses in Figure 4.

Viscosity. The viscosity of vitreous silica in the transformation range is dependent primarily on thermal history and impurity (especially hydroxyl) content.

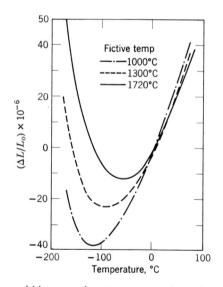

Fig. 3. Effect of thermal history on low-temperature thermal expansion of vitreous silica (77).

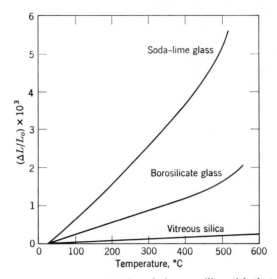

Fig. 4. Comparison of thermal expansion of vitreous silica with that of other glasses.

Hetherington, Jack, and Kennedy (78) have shown that I. R. Vitreosil (Thermal American Fused Quartz Co.) with a fictive temperature of 1400°C has a 10^{13}-P viscosity at about 1070°C, whereas a 1000°C fictive material has a 10^{13}-P viscosity at about 1320°C (for fictive temperature, see Vol. 10, p. 534). Hydroxyl-containing (>0.1 wt %) vitreous silicas, such as Corning Code 7940, Heraeus Suprasil, Thermal Syndicate Spectrosil, and G. E. Type 151, have annealing points of 1017 ± 50°C (46–49,55). Hydroxylfree (<0.001 wt %) high-purity fused quartz glasses, such as I. R. Vitreosil, some of the General Electric types, and various Amersil grades, have softening points up to about 100°C higher than the hydroxyl-containing types; the annealing and strain points are also about 100°C higher.

A complete viscosity–temperature curve is shown in Figure 5 for Amersil commercial-grade fused quartz. Low-temperature data are by Fontana and Plummer (79) and high-temperature data are by Brückner (80). Intermediate-temperature data are difficult to obtain because of devitrification.

Mechanical Properties. The Young's modulus at room temperature is 730 kbar; the shear modulus is 311 kbar; and the Poisson's ratio is 0.17. There may be small differences of about ±10 kbar, depending on the type of vitreous silica. The relationship of elastic moduli with temperature is approximately parabolic, increasing from room temperature to a maximum at about 1050–1200°C. The Young's modulus at the maximum is 11% higher than the room temperature value and the shear modulus increases by about 9% (81).

Strength. The theoretical ultimate strength has been calculated by Kelly (82) to be 2.3 × 10^6 psi; Hillig (83) and Náray-Szabó and Ladik (84), on the other hand, derived higher values of 3.4 × 10^6 psi. Strength values close to theoretical have been obtained experimentally using carefully prepared flame-drawn rods with diameters as large as 1 mm and testing them under both bend and elongation conditions. For example, tests by Morley, Andrews, and Whitney (85) and Hillig (86), gave values in excess of 1.9 × 10^6 psi at −196°C. Thus, it is the strongest known bulk material attaining nearly 60% of the estimated theoretical strength of 3.4 × 10^6 psi. The

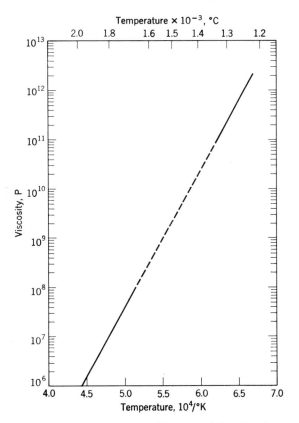

Fig. 5. Viscosity–temperature curve for Amersil commercial-grade vitreous silica (79,80).

inability to actually attain the theoretical value may be due to intrinsic surface flaws (82,85,87,88). However, the strength of this material is also impaired by temperature, atmosphere, and mechanical abrasion. Morley (88) has shown the effect of temperature on flame-drawn fiber strength (see Figure 6). Hammond and Ravity (89) considered the influence of environment on the strength of fused silica rods and found that the strength decreased in the presence of saturated vapors of a variety of alcohols, benzene, acetone, and water. The most drastic decrease was caused by water vapor (ie, almost a 50% decrease from a strength of 13,200 psi).

Mechanical abrasion is a primary cause of decreased strength and as a result, the values for manufactured materials are considerably lower than the theoretical values. For example, transparent vitreous silica has an impact strength of 12,100 psi, whereas nontransparent impact strength is 11,750 psi (58). The modulus of rupture of a transparent rod abraded by sand blasting with a −65- to +100-grit sand for 5 sec is 7160 psi at 25°C (56). This value increases to approx 9400 psi at 550°C and 10,800 psi at 900°C. The effect of mechanical damage is vividly demonstrated by the work of Hillig (90) in which the ambient temperature strength of a flame-drawn fiber was decreased from approx 680,000 psi to 50,000 psi by merely placing a finger upon it.

The Knoop indentation hardness of vitreous silica is in the 545–575 kg/mm² range. The diamond pyramidal (Vickers) hardness is in the 710–720 kg/mm² range. Westbrook (91) found that the Vickers hardness for fused quartz decreases with in-

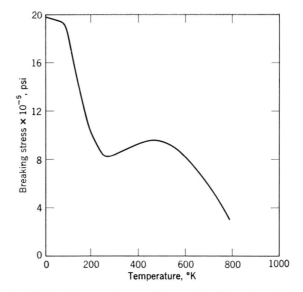

Fig. 6. Effect of temperature on vitreous silica fiber strength (88).

creasing temperature but with two significant irregularities. There is a rather sudden decrease at about 70°C and a small positive discontinuity at about 570°C which, he postulates, may be due to a memory of quartz structure. Mackenzie (92) also found a maximum at 570°C which he attributed to the presence of small amounts of quartz microcrystals.

Density. The density is quite dependent on thermal history and type of vitreous silica. The density of transparent Vitreosil is 2.21 g/cm³, of translucent Vitreosil 2.07–2.15 g/cm³, and of Corning 7940 2.202 g/cm³ (56,58).

The material can be densified under pressure and the amount of densification is dependent on time, temperature, and pressure. In general, the density increases with an increase in these variables, but the results obtained by various investigators on transparent glass are widely divergent. For example, Bridgman and Simon (93) found that the density did not increase at all under a pressure of 100 kbar at 25°C, while Roy and Cohen (94) found an increase of 11% under the same conditions, and Christiansen, Kistler, and Gogarty (95) found an increase of 4%. At 25°C and approx 200 kbar pressure, Bridgman and Simon (93) found an increase in density of 7.5% and Christiansen et al. an increase of 13%. The reason for the large scatter in results, under presumably similar conditions, remains unclear. Possibly it reflects differences in the amount of shear stress applied by the various investigators, for Mackenzie (96) has postulated that the densification is primarily the result of structural rearrangement under shear. He also investigated the effects of time and temperature on densification and found that a density increase of almost 19% was obtained when the glass was subjected to a pressure of 80 kbar at 575°C for 2 min. In all these cases, the resulting samples remained completely amorphous, though the densities and refractive indices were similar to those of cristobalite and in some cases approached those of α-quartz (94,96). Other investigators have found that crystallization does take place when the glass is subjected to similar pressures (80 kbar) for a very long time at temperatures as low as 450°C (see above under Devitrification, p. 84). Densification of vitreous silica

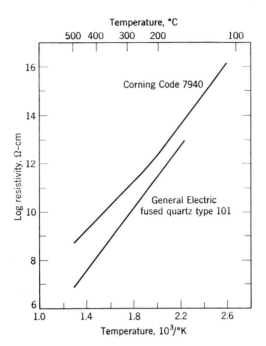

Fig. 7. Relationship of dc resistivity to temperature of vitreous silicas. Corning Code 7940 has a high-hydroxy-low-alkali content; G.E. Type 101 has a low-hydroxyl-high-alkali content.

by as much as 3% has also been attained by fast neutron irradiation (97) (see below under Radiation effects, p. 95).

Electrical Properties. The dc conductivity of vitreous silica is due primarily to impurities and, particularly, alkali ions. Therefore, the high resistivities are the result of a low concentration of conducting species. Actually, the vitreous silica network is relatively open, and small differences in sodium content on the order of a few parts per million can significantly affect resistivity (98). The log resistivity–reciprocal temperature curves for a high-hydroxyl–low-alkali and a low-hydroxyl–higher-alkali vitreous silica are shown in Figure 7 (99). One interesting point to note is the small but significant change in slope of the hydroxyl-containing Corning Code 7940 curve at about 225°C. There are a number of theories for this anomaly but none have been confirmed.

The dielectric properties for two types of vitreous silica are listed in Table 3 (99).

Ultrasonic Properties. Vitreous silica of high purity, such as the synthetic type, has an unusually low loss for high-frequency ultrasonic waves. The loss A is a linear function of frequency f up to the 30–40 MHz region and can be expressed as

$$A = Bf$$

where $B = 0.08$ dB/(ft/MHz) for shear waves and 0.05 dB/(ft/MHz) for compressional waves (100).

Anderson and Bömmel (101) postulate that the ultrasonic relaxation loss is due to a thermally activated structural relaxation associated with a shifting of bridging oxygen atoms between two equilibrium positions.

Table 3. Dielectric Properties of Vitreous Silica (99)

Property	Corning Code 7940[a]	G.E. Type 101[b]
dielectric constant		
at 25°C, 1 kHz	3.95	3.95
1 MHz	3.95	3.93
8600 MHz	3.78	
at 300°C, 1 kHz	3.98	4.00
1 MHz	3.96	3.96
8600 MHz	3.78	
loss tangent		
at 25°C, 1 kHz	0.00006	0.0003
1 MHz	0.00002	0.0002
8600 MHz	0.00018	
at 300°C, 1 kHz	0.0058	0.089
1 MHz	0.0002	0.0008
8600 MHz	0.00018	

[a] Corning Glass Works: sodium content <0.001 wt %; water content >0.1 wt %.
[b] General Electric Company: sodium content >0.001; water content <0.005.

The velocity, v, of ultrasonic waves in an infinite medium is given by

$$v = \sqrt{M/d}$$

where M = appropriate elastic modulus and d = 2.20 g/cm³ (density).

With a shear modulus of 3.11×10^{11} (g)(cm)/(sec)(cm²) vitreous silica has a plane shearwave velocity of 3.76×10^5 cm/sec.

Gaseous Diffusion. According to Norton (102) and Lee et al. (103–106), the permeability P, diffusivity D, and solubility S, of a gas in a solid for a given temperature can be determined using the following equations:

$$P = P_o \exp\ (-E_p/RT)$$

$$D = D_o \exp\ (-E_d/RT)$$

$$S = S_o \exp\ (-E_s/RT)$$

where P_o, D_o, and S_o = constants

E_p, E_d, and E_s = activation energies for various processes

R = gas constant

T = absolute temperature

When the gas pressure outside of the specimen is 1 atm and any two of the above values (P, D, or S) are known for a given temperature, then the third may be obtained using the following simple relation:

$$P = DS$$

The important gas diffusion parameters for vitreous silica, as determined experimentally by various investigators, are summarized in Table 4. In addition to the gases shown, Norton (102) determined the permeabilities for argon and nitrogen at 700°C. In both cases, he found the values to be less than 10^{-15} ml/(sec)(cm²)(mm Hg/cm). His results for helium, hydrogen, deuterium, and neon are in good agreement with the results obtained by Lee et al. (103–106) and are incorporated in Table 4.

Table 4. Gaseous Diffusion through Vitreous Silica

Gas	Sample type[a]	P_o, mole/(cm)(sec)	E_p, kcal/mole	D_o, cm²/sec	E_d, kcal/mole	S_o, mole/cm³	E_s, kcal/mole	Temp, °C
helium	fused quartz[b]			3.04×10^{-4}	5.58 ± 0.06	1.99×10^{17}	-0.068 ± 0.06	24–300
helium	fused quartz[b]			7.40×10^{-4}	6.61 ± 0.04	1.28×10^{17}	-1.17 ± 0.12	300–1034
helium	G.E. fused quartz[b]		4.9					−80–600
neon 20	G.E. 204 fused quartz	$1.25 \pm 0.17 \times 10^{13}$	9.42 ± 0.14	$2.21 \pm 0.12 \times 10^{-4}$	11.37 ± 0.08	$5.59 \pm 0.84 \times 10^{16}$	-1.95 ± 0.15	440–985
neon 22	not identified	$1.20 \pm 0.17 \times 10^{13}$	9.39 ± 0.15	$2.08 \pm 0.17 \times 10^{-4}$	11.34 ± 0.13	$5.75 \pm 0.92 \times 10^{16}$	-1.95 ± 0.17	440–985
hydrogen	G.E. 204 fused quartz and Suprasil	5.30×10^{13}	9.02	5.65×10^{-4}	10.4	9.4×10^{18}	−1.38	300–1000
hydrogen	O. G. Vitreosil			9.5×10^{-4}	15.8			800–1050
deuterium	G.E. 204 fused quartz and Suprasil	5.12×10^{13}	9.36	5.10×10^{-4}	10.5	1.0×10^{17}	−1.1	300–1000
deuterium	Corning 7943	1.9×10^{10}		1.5×10^{-7}		1.2×10^{17}		985
oxygen	Amersil[b]			2×10^{-9}	29			850–1250
oxygen	I.R. Vitreosil			2.7×10^{-4}	27			800–1050
oxygen	not identified		22		27			950–1080
oxygen	not identified			1.51×10^{-2}	71.2 ± 5.3			925–1225
oxygen	fused quartz[b]				56			900–1200

[a] Type of vitreous silica used in measurements; see Table 6.   [b] Only identification given.

References: Helium–fused quartz (103); helium–G. E. fused quartz (102); neon 20 and neon 22 (104), hydrogen–G. E. fused quartz and deuterium–G. E. fused quartz (105,112); hydrogen–O. G. Vitreosil and oxygen–I. R. Vitreosil (108); deuterium–Corning (106); oxygen–Amersil (107); oxygen–not identified (109,110); oxygen–fused quartz (111).

Hetherington and Jack (107) note that there are two different mechanisms involved in the oxidation of vitreous silica, depending on whether the material contains hydroxyls or not. For hydroxyl-containing material, the rapid oxidation probably occurs by the diffusion and removal of hydrogen, according to the following reaction:

$$-\underset{|}{\overset{|}{Si}}{}^{3+} \; HO-\underset{|}{\overset{|}{Si}}{}^{4+}- \;\rightarrow\; -\underset{|}{\overset{|}{Si}}{}^{4+}-O-\underset{|}{\overset{|}{Si}}{}^{4+}- \; + \; \tfrac{1}{2}\,H_2$$

On the other hand, in hydroxyl-free vitreous silica the oxidation is much slower and is controlled by the diffusion of oxygen through the solid according to the following reaction:

$$-\underset{|}{\overset{|}{Si}}{}^{3+} \, \underset{|}{\overset{|}{Si}}{}^{3+}- \; + \; \tfrac{1}{2}\,O_2 \;\rightarrow\; -\underset{|}{\overset{|}{Si}}{}^{4+}-O-\underset{|}{\overset{|}{Si}}{}^{4+}-$$

The discrepancies in experimental values obtained for oxygen diffusion have not been resolved. Williams (108) suggests, however, that the values obtained by Sucov (110) and Haul and Dümbgen (111), for D_o and E_d for oxygen, may not be meaningful, due to their use of short exchange times and absolute surface area measurements.

The diffusion parameters for the diffusion of ^{22}Na in Infrasil (Amersil, Inc.) fused quartz have also been determined (112). Between 1000 and 573°C, they are $D_o = 3.44 \times 10^{-2}$ cm²/sec and $E_d = 21.1$ kcal/mole; $D_o = 0.398$ and $E_d = 25.8$ between 573 and 250°C; and $D_o = 2.13$ and $E_d = 28.3$ between 250 and 170°C.

Thermal Properties. The mean heat capacity (0–900°C) can be calculated from $(167 + 0.189t - 0.000125t^2) \times 10^{-3}$ cal/g(°C), where t is temperature in °C. This gives a value of 0.17 cal/(g)(°C) at 25°C (58).

Carwile and Hage (113) have collected thermal conductivity data on clear transparent vitreous silica from a number of different literature references and the best values are shown in Table 5. The difference in thermal conductivity from one type to another, including low and high hydroxyl content, is small. The thermal conductivity of the translucent form may be as much as 1% lower than that of the clear type when the heat flow is parallel to the striations.

Table 5. Thermal Conductivity of Vitreous Silica (113)

Temperature, °K	Thermal conductivity, cal/(cm²)(sec)(°C/cm)	Temperature, °K	Thermal conductivity, cal/(cm²)(sec)(°C/cm)
100	0.00161	400	0.00361
200	0.00269	500	0.00388
300	0.00328	600	0.00415

Thermal diffusivity at 25°C is 0.009 cm²/sec, and at 400°C it should be 8–10% lower; at still higher temperatures it increases rapidly (114).

Optical Properties. Optical transmission can be a good method for distinguishing the type of vitreous silica, since it reflects the raw material and the method of manufacture. The ultraviolet cutoff for ultrapure material of 1 cm thickness is slightly lower than 160 nm. Various impurities, such as ferric ion, which is very absorbing, or network defects, caused by reducing conditions, move this cutoff to longer wavelengths.

An absorption band at 242 nm is characteristic of many reduced vitreous silicas, such as I. R. Vitreosil, General Electric fused-quartz types, and Amersil grades Homosil and Optosil. Garino-Canina (115) attributed this band to germanium impurity present in a partially reduced state. Reduced silicon Si^{2+} has also been postulated by H. Mohn (116) as causing the absorption. Hetherington, Jack, and Ramsay (117) show that the band could also be the result of a reduced center Si^{3+} associated with a network substitutent like Al^{3+}. Turner and Lee (118) suggest absorption by a trapped electron or hole in the vicinity of an impurity or associated vacancy, which could be insensitive to the specific impurity. All explanations have some merit but are not completely satisfactory.

Examination of Heraeus fused quartz by Kats and Stevels (119) revealed that fluorescence could be observed at 280 and 390 nm with 253.7 nm excitation. Corning Code 7940 vitreous silica, which is very low in impurities, such as alumina, does not have the 242 nm absorption band, which is required to initiate the fluorescence.

Water incorporated in vitreous silica as —OH has a strong fundamental absorption band at 2.73 μ with an overtone at 1.38 μ. The Si—O vibration has two strong fundamental absorption bands which affect the transmission of vitreous silica. The fundamental vibration at 8.83 μ has a strong overtone at 4.45 μ which is the practical infrared cutoff for vitreous silica of usable thickness. Another strong Si—O absorption at 12.41 μ combined with the strong —OH absorption at 2.73 μ to produce a peak at 2.22 μ. This peak only occurs in high-hydroxyl-content glass (120).

Vitreous silicas have transmission curves of one of the types shown in Figure 8. The curves represent only the general shapes and should not be used for exact transmittance values. The types of vitreous silica and their corresponding curve designations are listed in Table 6. The glasses corresponding to curve A were prepared by vapor-phase hydrolysis and those corresponding to curve C were melted in a dry atmosphere, probably vacuum. Curve B only approximately represents the designated glasses in Table 6. Glasses melted electrically with a relatively high-hydroxyl-content raw material

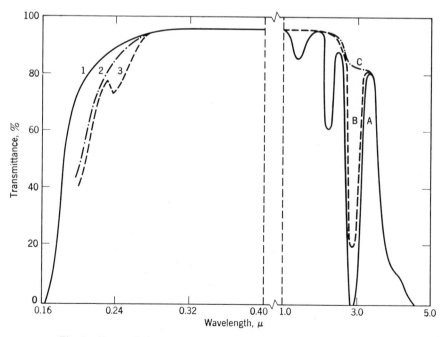

Fig. 8. Transmission curves for vitreous silicas, thickness 1 cm.

Table 6. Correlation of Type of Vitreous Silica with Spectra in Figure 8

Manufacturer	Type	uv curve	ir curve
Amersil, Inc. (Heraeus)	Optosil (Herasil)	3	B
	Homosil	3	B
	Ultrasil	2	B
	Infrasil	2	C
	Suprasil	1	A
Corning Glass Works	Code 7940	1	A
	Code 7943	3	C
Dynasil Corp. of America	Dynasil	1	A
General Electric Company	Types 102, 104	3	B
	Types 105, 106, 204	3	C
	Type 125	2	C
	Type 151	1	A
Quartz et Silice	Pursil 453	3	C
	Pursil Ultra	2	C
	Tetrasil	1	A
Thermal American Fused Quartz Co.;	I. R. Vitreosil	3	C
Thermal Syndicate Ltd.	Vitreosil 055, 066, 077	3	B
	Spectrosil	1	A
	Spectrosil WF	1	C
Westdeutsche Quarzschmelze G.m.b.H.	Synsil	1	A

may have a minimum at 2.73 μ of up to 20% higher than that shown. Glasses melted in a gas–oxygen atmosphere may have a minimum of up to 20% lower than that shown. The peak at 2.22 μ becomes apparent as the 2.73 minimum drops below 20%.

The spectral normal emissivity of Corning Code 7940 vitreous silica, as computed by Parker (121) from room temperature measurements of transmittance and reflectance, is shown in Figure 9. The total normal emissivity of Code 7940 vitreous silica, as reported by Clayton (122), is shown in Figure 10.

Malitson measured the refractive indices of three synthetic vitreous silicas (Corning Code 7940, Dynasil high-purity synthetic fused silica, and G. E. Type 151) for 60 wavelengths from 0.21 to 3.71 μ at 20°C (123). Brixner compared the Malitson data to computed indices using the following four-term Sellmeier dispersion equation (124):

$$n^2 - 1 = \sum_i (\lambda^2 \times a_{2i-1}) (\lambda^2 - a_{2i}^2)$$

where n = refractive index
λ = corresponding wavelength
a = a parameter
i = index number of the equation term

With systematic errors removed from computed data, agreements with an average deviation of 4.3×10^{-6} were obtained. The refractive index at room temperature is 1.53429 at 0.21386 μ; 1.46313 at 0.48613 μ; 1.45841 at 0.58926 μ; 1.45637 at 0.65627 μ; and 1.39936 at 3.7067 μ. Reciprocal relative dispersion is 67.8. Refractive index changes with temperature about $+1.00 \times 10^{-5}$/°C from 0 to 100°C (121).

The birefringence constant is 3.40 nm/(cm)(kg/cm²).

Radiation Effects. Radiation damage in vitreous silica can be divided into two major categories, depending upon the type of radiation used. Major structural changes are generally due to high-energy particle radiation, such as a neutron stream, while electronic changes are usually the result of ionizing radiation, such as a beam of

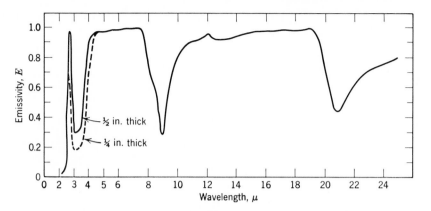

Fig. 9. Spectral normal emissivity of vitreous silica (121).

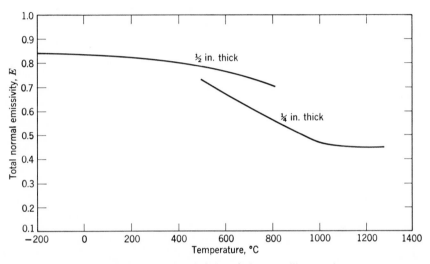

Fig. 10. Total normal emissivity of vitreous silica (122).

electrons, x rays, γ rays, or protons. Damage by ionizing radiation manifests itself in the formation of optical absorption centers (also called color centers) in the irradiated material. Though the predominant effect of neutron radiation is structural, electronic changes can also occur and, in the same vein, if the ionizing radiation is of very high intensity, then some structural defects may be produced.

Irradiation by fast neutrons causes a densification of vitreous silica which reaches a saturation value of 2.26 g/cm³ (ie, an increase of roughly 3%) after a dose of approx 1×10^{20} neutrons/cm² Doses of up to 2×10^{20} neutrons/cm² do not further affect this density value (125). Wittels and Sherrill (126) have shown that quartz, tridymite, and cristobalite also saturate with the same density after heavy neutron irradiation. This means a density decrease of 14.7% for quartz and 0.26% for cristobalite. The resulting glasslike material is the same in each case, showing no x-ray diffraction pattern, identical density, thermal expansion (127), and elastic properties (128). Other properties are also affected, ie, the heat capacity is lower than that of vitreous silica (129), the thermal conductivity increases by a factor of 2 (130), and the refractive index, n_D, increases to 1.4690 (131). Sosman (132) named this new phase amorphous "silica M" after metamict, a word used in earlier research to designate minerals disordered by radiation in the geological past.

A number of mechanisms have been proposed by which this common irradiated state is obtained, the most widely accepted being the "thermal spike" theory. It considers the heat generated in the wake of a fast particle passing through a solid as being sufficient to cause severe structural disturbances which are then frozen in by rapid cooling. Many property changes can be accounted for with this theory (131).

The actual structure of the new phase so produced is still in doubt. There is general agreement that it is basically amorphous, though it exhibits a higher degree of order than vitreous silica. Weissman and Nakajima (133) have found that an electron diffraction pattern resembling that of α-quartz can be obtained from very heavily irradiated vitreous silica. No crystallinity was observed in samples given doses below 8.6×10^{19} nvt (integrated flux: n = number of neutrons, v = velocity, t = time of exposure). They note that this induced crystallinity contains a large number of lattice defects and thus escapes detection by x-ray diffraction methods. This α-quartz model is further supported by the fact that amorphous silica M changes to polycrystalline quartz when heated at 940°C for 16 hr (132). Confirmation of these results is required before this theory can be fully accepted.

Irradiation by both x rays and γ rays produces absorption centers in vitreous silica, while major structural damage is negligible. These absorption centers show up primarily in the visible and ultraviolet regions of the electromagnetic spectrum. Little change is seen in the infrared region. The types and number of absorption centers produced are very dependent upon the purity of the vitreous silica and the total radiation dosage received. The rate of coloration of high-purity vitreous silica (ie, very low concentration of metallic impurities, such as type 3, Table 1) is very slow and doses of 10^7 rad and more are required to obtain appreciable absorption. For comparable absorption intensities in less pure material (ie, types 1 and 2, Table 1) approximately two orders of magnitude less radiation is required (134). Extensive research has been conducted in the field of radiation-induced absorption centers in vitreous silica but only the major centers and their probable causes are discussed here. An excellent review of past work, including a thorough compilation of all absorption centers studied, is found in reference 135.

Figure 11 shows a typical absorption curve for vitreous silica containing metallic impurities after irradiation by x rays (136). The sample was a Heraeus fused quartz (the major impurity was aluminum), and the radiation dose was 10^6 rad. The primary absorption centers are at 550, 300, and between 220 and 215 nm. The 550 nm band is due to a center consisting of an interstitial alkali cation associated with a network substituent of lower valency than silicon (eg, aluminum) (135). Only alkalis contribute to the coloration at 550 nm, lithium being more effective than sodium, and sodium more effective than potassium. Pure silica doped with aluminum alone shows virtually no coloration after irradiation (137). The intensity of the band is determined by that component which is present in the lower concentration. The presence of hydrogen does not appear to contribute to the 550-nm color center production (137).

The absorption band at 300 nm may also be associated with alkali ions. It is possibly the result of a trapped electron stabilized by an alkali ion. The band shifts to longer wavelengths with heavier alkali ions and growth rates for the band show a definite dependence on the type of alkali (135,137).

The 215 nm band is postulated by Cohen (138) to be intrinsic to silica, since it can be produced in Corning Code 7940 glass by long-term x-ray irradiation. Hetherington,

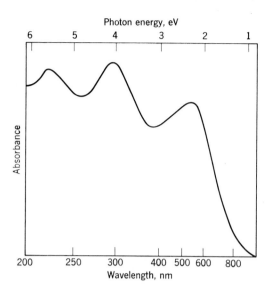

Fig. 11. Absorption spectrum of irradiated impure vitreous silica (136).

Jack, and Ramsay (139) propose that after irradiation this band may be due to centers (v = vacancy),

$$Si^{3+}—[v]—Si^{3+} \text{ or } Si^{4+}—O\ldots Si^{3+}$$

since the band is more pronounced in hydroxyl-free than in hydroxyl-containing synthetic vitreous silica. These sites would readily react with water. This band in impure vitreous silica may also be associated with aluminum (135).

Figure 12 shows the typical absorption curve obtained for a metal-free vitreous silica after a large dose of γ rays (2.6×10^8 rad). The measurements were made by Levy (140) on Corning Code 7940 glass. The resolved bands shown in Figure 12 were also determined by Levy. The major band is at approximately 215 nm, with three smaller bands at 230, 260, and 280 nm. The 215 nm band was discussed in the last paragraph. The 230 nm band is probably due to an electron trapped at a silicon atom of which one oxygen bond is incomplete (135). The causes of the other two bands (ie, 260 and 280 nm) remain unclear.

Flameworking and Sealing. Vitreous silica is a difficult glass to flamework because of its extremely high viscosity and volatilization problems. However, this difficulty is somewhat compensated for by excellent resistance to thermal shock.

A gas–oxygen flame is satisfactory for most manipulations and an oxy–hydrogen flame with a ratio of the oxygen-to-hydrogen volume of about 1 to 2 has also been used to provide a little more energy. An oxy–acetylene flame gives even more heat, but excessive volatilization occurs.

When silica volatilizes, vapors condense on the cooler portion of the piece, forming a white bloom. If this bloom becomes too heavy, it can be removed by heating or by dissolving in dilute hydrofluoric acid. It must be remembered that dilute hydrofluoric acid also attacks the substrate, therefore a mild careful treatment is prescribed. To

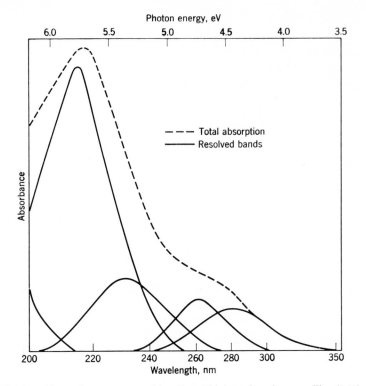

Fig. 12. Absorption spectrum of irradiated high-purity vitreous silica (140).

minimize volatilization, it is best to work the vitreous silica at as low a temperature as possible.

Annealing of flameworked pieces is generally not necessary, because of the low thermal expansion. However, if the pieces are very massive they should be annealed at a temperature corresponding approximately to the annealing point of the specific type and for a time determined by the size of the piece. Once the piece is uniformly heated throughout, stress is relieved in a matter of minutes.

There are occasions when vitreous silica must be connected to other glasses, such as Corning Code 7740 borosilicate glass. This can be done by a graded seal, sealing first to Code 7230 glass (expansion coefficient $\alpha = 14 \times 10^{-7}$ cm/(cm)(°C), 0–300°C), which, in turn, is sealed to Code 7240 glass ($\alpha = 21 \times 10^{-7}$ cm/(cm)(°C)), which then can be sealed to Code 7740 glass ($\alpha = 32.5 \times 10^{-7}$ cm/(cm)(°C)).

Sealing to metals can be a serious problem since the thermal expansion of metals is so much higher than that of vitreous silica. Nevertheless, such sealing is necessary, particularly in the case of mercury-vapor lamps where vacuum tight lead connections are necessary. This is done with a molybdenum foil seal, which uses the principle that a very thin foil is able to contract during cooling without inducing stress in the glass. The molybdenum foil is connected to tungsten electrodes and placed in the tube which is flushed with a neutral gas. The tube is heated on the outside very strongly with a gas–oxygen flame. It collapses around the foil and is mechanically pinched to make firm contact with the foil. This seal is a particular case of the more general seal invented by Houskeeper (141).

Applications

Chemical. Because of excellent chemical durability, high purity, thermal shock resistance, and high-temperature capability, vitreous silica has a wide range of applications in chemical analysis and material preparation. Tubing, rods, crucibles, dishes, boats, and other containers and special apparatus of both transparent and nontransparent varieties are available(55,57,58). A few examples of the many applications are as follows: distillation of acids; sintering metals and carbides; ashing and ignitions; preparation of high-purity materials; calcining fluorescent powders for lamps, television tubes, and luminous paints; and chlorination of minerals and hydrocarbons.

Thermal. The protection of precious metal thermocouples in high-temperature pyrometry is an important application of vitreous silica. Although satin tubing is usually employed for this, transparent tubes are much superior for protecting couples when used in a reducing atmosphere (142).

The electrical resistivity, impermeability, and low expansion of vitreous silica naturally qualify it for use in the construction of gas-heated or electrically heated devices using a silica tube, muffle, or other shape. In its simplest form an electric resistance furnace consists of a vitreous silica tube or pipe on which the resistance element is wound. Because of its indifference to temperature gradients, a tubular furnace of vitreous silica may be made to operate at different temperatures at various portions of the tube, either by arrangement of the heating elements or by cooling sections of the tube with water. Vitreous silica pipes may be employed in vacuum-induction and gas-fired furnaces (143).

Radiant heaters employing resistance wire encased in vitreous silica tubes have the property of modifying the emitted radiation, furnishing a higher proportion of shorter wavelengths $(1-2\,\mu)$ which constitute the desirable radiations (143). Immersion heaters for use with acid solutions are of similar construction. An overhead heating unit consisting of a resistance wire sealed inside a vitreous silica container permits acid liquids to be concentrated or evaporated without ebullition or spattering. Some radiators have been developed for power requirements of up to 3 kW and approx 25 in. long for a large variety of applications which require high radiation efficiencies. They are used as sources of energy in heat exchangers, high-duty enamel drying equipment, and copying devices (143).

Electronic. In electronic systems, such as radar and computers, it is sometimes necessary to delay electrical signals. This is done with a transducer which converts electrical signals to ultrasonic elastic waves; these pass through a connecting medium to another transducer which reconverts the elastic waves to electrical signals. Vitreous silica makes an ideal connecting medium since it has excellent physical stability, low ultrasonic transmission losses, and transmits an ultrasonic signal almost 100,000 times slower than an electric signal in a wire. The vitreous silica delay line is in the form of a flat plate in the shape of a polyhedron. The facets of the edges of this plate are ground to a predetermined angle with one another with great precision. The transducer is fastened to one of these facets. The plates may be designed for path lengths of 1.5 in. to nearly 40 ft long giving delay times for shear waves of 10 to 3000 μ sec (144).

Thin films of vitreous silica have been used extensively in silicon transistor technology. These dielectric films serve as insulating layers between conductor stripes and a semiconductor surface in integrated circuits, and as a surface passivation material in devices such as planar diodes, transistors, and injection lasers. They are also used for diffusion masking, as etchant surfaces, and for encapsulation and protection of completed electronic devices. They also serve an important function in multilayer conductor-insulation technology where a variety of conducting paths are deposited in overlay patterns and insulating layers are required for separation (145). For example, the manufacture of highly complex multilayer devices for use as diodes, transistors, and capacitors, in which vitreous silica films play an essential role, is described in a patent (146).

Another important aspect of dielectric film technology is the ability to generate accurately complicated patterns in the film. This is done by using high-resolution photolithography, a process for which SiO_2 films are extremely useful. The process involves the following steps: First, a layer of SiO_2 is deposited on a suitable substrate, such as a silicon wafer; second, this layer is coated with a photo-resistant film which is generally sensitive to radiation below 5000 Å; third, the piece is exposed to ultraviolet radiation through a mask with the required pattern; fourth, the piece is developed and, if positive photo-resist was used, the areas of the film which were exposed to radiation are developed off (negative photo-resistant film allows the regions left unexposed to be developed off); fifth, the piece is placed in a suitable etch solution (ie, a mixture of ammonium fluoride, concentrated hydrofluoric acid, and water) and the exposed SiO_2 regions are etched away, leaving behind those SiO_2 regions which are still coated with photo-resist. The resultant piece consists of a suitable substrate coated with a thin layer of SiO_2 of the required pattern. This patterned SiO_2 layer can then be used as a mask for any subsequent metal-diffusion operations in later steps in the manufacture of the device.

Vitreous silica thin films are usually deposited by either vapor deposition or radio-frequency sputtering. (See Vol. 9, p. 200.) Vapor deposition is generally accomplished by the pyrolytic decomposition of tetraethoxy silane or one of the other alkoxysilanes. SiO_2 has been the material most extensively used in radio-frequency sputtering of dielectric films and the results indicate that these films are of very high quality (145).

Semiconductor materials must be exceptionally pure, so any material used in their preparation must be ultrapure. Certain types of transparent vitreous silica are used for growing single crystals of silicon, for floating-zone methods, and for the preparation of gallium and indium arsenides.

Lighting. One of the most important applications of clear fused quartz is envelope material for mercury-vapor lamps (147). In addition to resistance to deformation at temperatures and pressures of the lamp operation, fused quartz has the ultraviolet transmission to permit color correction. This color correction is accomplished by coating the inside of the outer envelope of the mercury-vapor lamp with phosphor. Ultraviolet light from the arc passes through the fused quartz envelope and excites the phosphor, producing a color more toward the red end of the spectrum (148). A newer development to obtain better color is the addition of metal halides to the lamp which also employs a fused quartz envelope (149,150).

An important innovation in lighting has been the incandescent tungsten–iodine cycle lamp which first became available in 1959 for general lighting use. The basic principle of the lamp is that tungsten, evaporating from the filament, deposits on the envelope wall where it reacts with iodine vapor to form volatile tungsten iodide. The tungsten iodide then diffuses back to the filament where it dissociates to iodine vapor and tungsten. This enables a higher temperature operation, therefore a higher efficiency and a longer life than the conventional incandescent lamp has. In order for this series of reactions to occur, the wall temperature must be at least 250°C and is even better in the vicinity of 600°C. Fused quartz has been an essential part of this lamp development since it is one of the few readily available transparent materials which has the temperature capability to be used as the lamp envelope material. These lamps are used for applications such as the illumination of airfields, floodlighting of sports arenas and buildings, slide and film projectors, automobile lighting, and specialized optical instruments (151,152).

Mechanical. The volume of vitreous silica used in fiber application is very small compared to the total vitreous silica volume. However, there have been some interesting and significant applications in the laboratory, particularly in the area of measurements.

Some of the more important applications date from the sorption balance of McBain and Bakr (153) which employed small vitreous silica springs enclosed in glass tubes. They used fiber of 0.02 cm diam in 15 coils of 1.25 cm diam and 5.986 cm long. A platinum bucket, which weighed 0.2019 g, contained up to 0.5 g charcoal and the balance could be read to 0.0002 g. The sorption of gases was determined over a wide range of temperatures and pressures. Other uses for this type of balance have been for density determinations, measurements of heat loss and evaporation, study of chemical reactions between gas and solid phases, and weighing wet tissues of plant and animal origin (32,153). The advantages of using vitreous silica for this balance are its resistance to corrosion, ease of cleaning and sterilization in an enclosed tube, and very little damping from internal friction.

Because of its low and regular thermal expansion vitreous silica is employed for the construction of apparatus used in measuring the thermal expansion of solids. The National Bureau of Standards has published a detailed account of the different methods used for this purpose (154). The most common form of dilatometer, improved by the Bureau over a similar type used abroad, utilizes a vitreous silica tube closed at the bottom and containing the sample under test. A movable rod of vitreous silica, resting on the sample, actuates a dial indicator resting on the top of the rod. The assembly containing the sample is placed in a furnace, bath, or cooling chamber to attain the desired temperature.

An adaptation of this device, containing a calibrated sample, may be used for controlling or indicating temperatures. The linear motion can be converted into angular movement which may be magnified mechanically.

Optical. The excellent ultraviolet transmission, resistance to radiation darkening, and physical and chemical stability make vitreous silica unique in the field of refractive optic materials. It is used for prisms, lenses, cells, windows, and other optical components where ultraviolet transmission is important. It is used for solar cell covers which must resist radiation darkening.

One of the more recent applications is in windows of spacecraft. The Apollo 7 has five windows through which the astronauts can make visual observations, take photographs, and shoot live television pictures. The windows are made of three panes of glass separated by an evacuated space to retard heat transfer. The outer pane, which is exposed to the rigors of space flight and reentry, is made of high-optical-quality vitreous silica, and the inner two panels are of strengthened aluminosilicate glass.

The ability of vitreous silica to withstand dimensional change with changing temperature has made it ideally suited for mirror blanks of telescopes (155–157).

102   SILICA (VITREOUS)

As technology has improved to produce massive pieces, this application has grown to one of the largest in the industry, with respect to both quantity and dollars. Three of the larger mirror blanks are the 150-in. diam and 20-in. thick blank for the European Southern Observatory in Chile, the 157-in. diam blank for the Queen Elizabeth II telescope in Canada's Mount Kobau National Observatory, and a fused quartz blank for the 150-in. reflector at Kitt Peak National Observatory. Since these massive pieces are too heavy for such uses as incorporation in spaceborne systems, structures were developed with about one third the weight of the solid blank of comparable diameter and thickness. The solid surface plate is supported rigidly by an array of slotted struts or some other cellular structure of vitreous silica. Lightweight mirror blanks up to 80-in. diam have been fabricated.

Bibliography

"Silica and Silicates (Vitreous Silica)" in *ECT* 1st ed., Vol. 12, pp. 335–344, by W. Winship, The Thermal Syndicate Ltd.

1. A. Marcet, *Ann. Phil.* **2**, 99–100 (1813).
2. E. D. Clarke, *Ann. Phil. Ser. 2* **1**, 419–426 (1821).
3. Gaudin, *Compt. Rend. Acad. Sci. Paris* **8**, 678–679, 711–713 (1839).
4. H. Sainte-Claire Deville, *Ann. Chim. Phys.* **46**, 182–203 (1856).
5. G. E. Stephenson, *J. Soc. Glass Technol.* **39**, 37T–47T (1955).
6. W. A. Shenstone and H. G. Lacell, *Nature* **62** (1592), 20–22 (1900).
7. W. A. Shenstone, *Nature* **61** (1588), 540 (1900).
8. *Ibid.*, **64** (1649), 126 (1901).
9. Ger. Pat. 113,817 (1899) (to Deutsche Gold- u. Silber-Scheideanstalt).
10. Brit. Pat. 10,670 (1904), J. F. Bottomley, R. S. Hutton, and R. A. S. Paget.
11. Brit. Pat. 18,437 (1904), J. F. Bottomley and R. A. S. Paget.
12. U.S. Pat. 778,286 (1904), E. Thomson.
13. Brit. Pat. 10,930 (1910), H. A. Kent and H. G. Lacell.
14. U.S. Tariff Commission, unofficial communication, 1968.
15. R. B. Sosman, *The Phases of Silica*, Rutgers University Press, New Brunswick, N.J., 1965, pp. 148–150.
16. J. S. Laufer, *J. Opt. Soc. Am.* **55**, 458–460 (1965).
17. G. Hetherington, *J. Brit. Ceram. Soc.* **3** (4), 595–598 (1966).
18. Reference 15, pp. 164, 165.
19. B. J. Skinner and J. J. Fahey, *J. Geophys. Res.* **68** (19), 5595–5604 (1963).
20. J. Fortey, *BIOS Final Report 1202* (1947).
21. J. D. Mackenzie, *J. Am. Ceram. Soc.* **43**, 615–620 (1920).
22. U.S. Pat. 2,270,718 (Jan. 20, 1942), F. Skaupy and G. Weissenberg.
23. U.S. Pat. 2,904,713 (Sept. 15, 1959), W. H. Heraeus and H. Mohn (to Heraeus Quarzschmelze G.m.b.H.).
24. U.S. Pat. 3,128,166 (April 7, 1964), H. Mohn (to Heraeus Quarzschmelze G.m.b.H.).
25. U.S. Pat. 2,155,131 (April 18, 1939), W. Hanlein (to Patent-Treuhand-Gesellschaft für Elektrische Glühlampen G.m.b.H.).
26. U.S. Pat. 2,272,342 (Feb. 10, 1942), J. F. Hyde (to Corning Glass Works).
27. U.S. Pat. 3,275,408 (Sept. 27, 1966), J. A. Winterburn (to The Thermal Syndicate Ltd.).
28. T. Vasilos, *J. Am. Ceram. Soc.* **43**, 517–519 (1960).
29. J. D. Fleming, *Am. Ceram. Soc. Bull.* **40**, 748–750 (1961).
30. N. J. Tighe, *Natl. Bur. Std. (U.S.) Circ. 569*, (Jan. 25, 1956).
31. P. L. Kirk and R. Craig, *Rev. Sci. Instr.* **19**, 779–780 (1948).
32. P. L. Kirk and F. L. Scheffer, *Rev. Sci. Instr.* **19**, 785–790 (1948).
33. *Minerals Yearbook U.S. Bur. Mines, 1965*, Vol. I, 1076–1077 (1967).
34. *Industrial Minerals and Rocks*, 3rd ed., The American Institute of Mining, Metallurgical, and Petroleum Engineers, New York, 1960, pp. 687–698.

35. "Mineral Facts and Problems," *U.S. Bur. Mines, Bull.* **630**, 739–744 (1965).

36. *Ibid.*, 779–788 (1965).

37. S. J. Johnstone, *Minerals for the Chemical and Allied Industries*, John Wiley & Sons, Inc., New York, 1954, p. 440.

38. J. T. Randall, H. P. Rooksby, and B. S. Cooper, *J. Soc. Glass Technol.* **14**, 219–229 (1930).

39. N. N. Valenkov and E. A. Porai-Koshits, *Nature* **137**, 273 (1936); *Z. Krist.* **95**, 195 (1936).

40. K. S. Evstropyev, in *The Structure of Glass*, U.S.S.R. Academy of Science Press, Moscow, 1953, *Proc. of a Conf. on the Structure of Glass, Leningrad, 1953;* translation: Consultants Bureau, New York, 1958, pp. 9–15.

41. E. A. Porai-Koshits, in *The Structure of Glass*, U.S.S.R. Academy of Science Press, Moscow, 1953, *Proc. of a Conf. on the Structure of Glass; Leningrad, 1953;* translation: Consultants Bureau, New York, 1958, pp. 25–35.

42. A. A. Lebedev, *Bull. Acad. Sci. U.S.S.R. Phys. Ser. (English Transl.)* **4** (4), 585 (1940); *Chem. Abstr.* **35**, 3779⁹ (1941).

43. W. H. Zachariasen, *J. Am. Chem. Soc.* **54**, 3841–3851 (1932).

44. B. E. Warren, *J. Appl. Phys.* **8**, 645–654 (1937).

45. B. E. Warren, *Oral communication, 69th Annual American Ceramic Society Meeting, New York, 1967.*

46. W. O. Milligan, H. A. Levy, and S. W. Peterson, *Phys. Rev.* **83**, 226–227 (1951).

47. L. W. Tilton, *J. Res. Natl. Bur. Std. A* **59**, 139–154 (1957).

48. H. A. Robinson, *J. Phys. Chem. Solids* **26**, 209–222 (1965).

49. F. Ordway, *Science* **143**, 800–801 (1964).

50. D. L. Evans and S. V. King, *Nature* **212**, 1353–1354 (1966).

51. J. M. Chiariello, M.S. Thesis, Rutgers University, New Brunswick, N.J., 1967.

52. H. T. Smyth, *Theory of Glass Structure*, Rutgers University, School of Ceramics, New Brunswick, N.J., 1961.

53. H. T. Smyth, *Theoretical and Experimental Properties of Simple Glasses*, Rutgers University, School of Ceramics, New Brunswick, N.J., 1966; *Chem. Abstr.* **49**, 10659i (1955) and **47**, 10695e, 11935 (1953).

54. G. Hetherington, *J. Brit. Ceram. Soc.* **3**, 595–598 (1966).

55. *Amersil Fused Silica and Quartz*, Amersil, Inc., Hillside, N.J., 1967.

56. *Corning Fused Silica No. 7940*, Corning Glass Works, Corning, N.Y., 1965.

57. *Fused Quartz Catalog*, Lamp Glass Department, General Electric Company, Willoughby, Ohio, 1967.

58. *Vitreosil*, Thermal American Fused Quartz Company, Montville, N.J., 1966.

59. A. deRudney, *Vacuum* **1**, 204–205 (1951).

60. C. A. Elyard and H. Rawson, *Advances in Glass Technology, Proc. Intern. Congr. Glass 6th, Washington, D.C., 1962*, Plenum Press, New York, pp. 270–286.

61. Reference 15, p. 146.

62. R. Moseback, *J. Geol.* **65**, 347–363 (1957).

63. G. W. Morey and J. M. Hesselgasser, *Am. Soc. Mech. Engrs. Trans.* **73**, 865–875 (1951).

64. F. E. Wagstaff, *J. Am. Ceram. Soc.* **51** (8), 449–452 (1968).

65. N. G. Ainslie, C. R. Morelock, and D. Turnbull, *Symposium on Nucleation and Crystallization in Glasses and Melts, Toronto, 1961, American Ceramic Society, 1962*, pp. 97–107.

66. H. Rawson, *Inorganic Glass-Forming Systems*, Academic Press, Inc., New York, 1967, pp. 48–61.

67. S. D. Brown and S. S. Kistler, *J. Am. Ceram. Soc.* **42** (6), 263–270 (1959).

68. F. E. Wagstaff, S. D. Brown, and I. B. Cutler, *Phys. Chem. Glasses* **5** (3), 76–81 (1964).

69. A. G. Boganov, V. S. Rudenko, and G. L. Bashina, *Izv. Akad. Nauk SSSR, Neorgan. Materialy* **2** (2), 363–375 (1966).

70. F. E. Wagstaff and K. J. Richards, *J. Am. Ceram. Soc.* **48** (7), 382–383 (1965).

71. U.S. Pat. 3,370,921 (Feb. 27, 1968), F. E. Wagstaff; *Chem. Abstr.* **68**, 98316j (1968).

72. D. R. Uhlmann, J. F. Hays, and D. Turnbull, *Phys. Chem. Glasses* **7** (5), 159–168 (1966).

73. R. G. Yalman and J. F. Corwin, *J. Phys. Chem.* **61**, 1432–1437 (1957).

74. O. L. Anderson and G. J. Dienes, in V. D. Frechette, ed., *Non-Crystalline Solids*, John Wiley & Sons, Inc., New York, 1960, pp. 449–486.

75. F. P. Mallinder and B. A. Procter, *Phys. Chem. Glasses* **5**, 91 (1964).

76. G. W. Morey, *The Properties of Glass*, Reinhold Publishing Corp., New York, 1954, pp. 319–320.
77. R. Brückner, *Glastech. Ber.* **37** (10), 459–475 (1964).
78. G. Hetherington, K. H. Jack, and J. C. Kennedy, *Phys. Chem. Glasses* **5**, 130–136 (1964).
79. E. H. Fontana and W. A. Plummer, *Phys. Chem. Glasses* **7**, 139–146 (1966).
80. R. Brückner, *Glastech. Ber.* **37** (9), 413–425 (1964).
81. S. Spinner, *J. Am. Ceram. Soc.* **45**, 394–397 (1962).
82. A. Kelly, *Strong Solids*, Clarendon Press, Oxford, 1966, p. 5.
83. W. B. Hillig, in J. D. Mackenzie, ed., *Modern Aspects of Vitreous State*, Vol. 2, Butterworth & Co., Washington, D.C., 1962, p. 190.
84. I. Náray-Szabó and J. Ladik, *Nature* **188**, 226–227 (1960).
85. J. G. Morley, P. A. Andrews, and I. Whitney, *Phys. Chem. Glasses* **5**, 1 (1964).
86. W. B. Hillig, *Symposium on the Strength of Glasses and the Means to Improve It*, Union Scientifique Continentale du Verre, Charleroix, Belgium, 1962, p. 206.
87. F. M. Ernsberger, in J. E. Burke, ed., *Progress in Ceramic Science*, Vol. 3, Pergamon Press, Inc., New York, 1963, pp. 59–75.
88. J. G. Morley, *Proc. Roy. Soc. (London)*, *Ser. A* **282**, 43 (1964).
89. M. L. Hammond and S. F. Ravity, *J. Am. Ceram. Soc.* **46** (7), 329–332 (1963).
90. W. B. Hillig, *J. Appl. Phys.* **32**, 741 (1961).
91. J. H. Westbrook, *Phys. Chem. Glasses* **1**, 32–36 (1960).
92. J. D. Mackenzie, *J. Am. Ceram. Soc.* **43**, 615–620 (1960).
93. P. W. Bridgman and I. Simon, *J. Appl. Phys.* **24** (4), 405–413 (1953).
94. R. Roy and H. M. Cohen, *Nature* **190**, 798–799 (1961).
95. E. B. Christiansen, S. S. Kistler, and W. B. Gogarty, *J. Am. Ceram. Soc.* **45** (4), 172–177 (1962).
96. J. D. Mackenzie, *J. Am. Ceram. Soc.* **46** (10), 461–470 (1963).
97. W. Primak, L. H. Fuchs, and D. Day, *J. Am. Ceram. Soc.* **38**, 135–139 (1955).
98. A. E. Owen and R. W. Douglas, *J. Soc. Glass Technol.* **43**, 159T–178T (1959).
99. M. T. Splann and W. H. Barney, private communication, Corning Glass Works, 1968.
100. M. D. Fagan, *Proc. Natl. Electron Conf.* **7**, 380–389 (1951).
101. O. L. Anderson and H. E. Bömmel, *J. Am. Ceram. Soc.* **38**, 125 (1955).
102. F. J. Norton, *J. Am. Ceram. Soc.* **36** (3), 90–96 (1953).
103. D. E. Swets, R. W. Lee, and R. C. Frank, *J. Chem. Phys.* **34** (1), 17–22 (1961).
104. R. C. Frank, D. E. Swets, and R. W. Lee, *J. Chem. Phys.* **35** (4), 1451–1459 (1961).
105. R. W. Lee, *J. Chem. Phys.* **38** (2), 448–455 (1963).
106. R. W. Lee and D. L. Fry, *Phys. Chem. Glasses* **7** (1), 19–28 (1966).
107. G. Hetherington and K. H. Jack, *Phys. Chem. Glasses* **5** (5), 147–149 (1964).
108. E. L. Williams, *J. Am. Ceram. Soc.* **48** (4), 190–194 (1965).
109. F. J. Norton, *Nature* **191**, 701 (1961).
110. E. W. Sucov, *J. Am. Ceram. Soc.* **46** (1), 14–20 (1963).
111. R. Haul and G. Dümbgen, *Z. Elektrochem.* **66** (8–9), 636–641 (1962).
112. G. H. Frischat, *J. Am. Ceram. Soc.* **51** (9), 528–530 (1968).
113. L. C. K. Carwile and H. J. Hage, *U.S. Army Technical Report 67-7-PR* (July 1966).
114. E. B. Shand, *Glass Engineering Handbook*, McGraw-Hill Book Co., New York, 1958, p. 30.
115. V. Garino-Canina, *Verres Refractaires* **6**, 313–323 (1958).
116. H. Mohn, *60 Jahre Quarzglas—25 Jahre Hochvakuumtechnik*, W. C. Heraeus G.m.b.H., Hanau, Germany, 1961, p. 114.
117. G. Hetherington, K. H. Jack, and M. W. Ramsay, *Phys. Chem. Glasses* **6** (1), 6–15 (1965).
118. W. H. Turner and H. A. Lee, *J. Chem. Phys.* **43**, 1428–1429 (1965).
119. A. Kats and J. M. Stevels, *Philips Res. Rept.* **11**, 115–156 (1956).
120. R. V. Adams and R. W. Douglas, *J. Soc. Glass Technol.* **43**, 147T–158T (1959).
121. C. J. Parker, private communication, Corning Glass Works, 1968.
122. W. A. Clayton, *Space/Aeronautics*, 129–132 (June 1963).
123. I. H. Malitson, *J. Opt. Soc. Am.* **55**, 1205–1209 (1965).
124. B. Brixner, *J. Opt. Soc. Am.* **57**, 674–676 (1967).
125. E. Lell, N. J. Kreidl, and J. R. Hensler, in J. Burke, ed., *Progress in Ceramic Science*, Vol. 4, Pergamon Press, Inc., New York, 1966.

126. M. C. Wittels and F. A. Sherrill, *Phys. Rev.* **93**, 1117–1118 (1954).

127. I. Simon, *J. Am. Ceram. Soc.* **41**, 116 (1958).

128. G. Mayer and M. Lecomte, *J. Phys. Radium* **21**, 846–852 (1960); *Chem. Abstr.* **51**, 15285a (1957) and **53**, 10136b (1959).

129. A. E. Clark and R. E. Strakna, *Phys. Chem. Glasses* **3**, 121–126 (1962).

130. A. F. Cohen, *J. Appl. Phys.* **29**, 591–593 (1958).

131. W. Primak, *Phys. Rev.* **110**, 1240–1254 (1958).

132. Reference 15, pp. 150, 173–175.

133. S. Weissman and K. Nakajima, *J. Appl. Phys.* **34**, 3152–3153 (1963).

134. G. W. Arnold, Jr., *J. Phys. Chem. Solids* **13**, 306–320 (1960).

135. Reference 125, pp. 3–93.

136. J. M. Stevels, in V. D. Frechette, ed., *Non-Crystalline Solids*, John Wiley & Sons, Inc., New York, 1960, pp. 412–441.

137. E. Lell, *Phys. Chem. Glasses* **3**, 84–94 (1962).

138. A. J. Cohen, *J. Chem. Phys.* **23**, 765–766 (1955).

139. G. Hetherington, K. H. Jack, and M. W. Ramsay, *Phys. Chem. Glasses* **6**, 6–15 (1965).

140. P. W. Levy, *Phys. Chem. Solids* **13**, 287–295 (1960).

141. W. G. Houskeeper, *J. Am. Inst. Elec. Engr.* **42**, 954 (1923).

142. R. A. Ragatz and O. A. Hougen, *Chem. Met. Engr.* **33**, 415 (1926).

143. Reference 116, pp. 174–177.

144. E. B. Shand, *Glass Engineering Handbook*, McGraw-Hill Book Co., New York, 1958, pp. 354, 355.

145. L. V. Gregor and R. E. Jones, *Solid State Technol.* **11** (5), 40–46 (1968).

146. U.S. Pat. 3,373,063 (March 5, 1968), M. Suzuki and S. Tauchi (to Hitachi, Ltd.).

147. E. W. Beggs, *Illum. Engr.* **42**, 435–465 (1947).

148. H. D. Frazer and W. S. Till, *Illum. Engr.* **47**, 207–212 (1952).

149. D. A. Larson, H. D. Fraser, W. V. Cushing, and M. C. Unglert, *Illum. Engr.* **58**, 434–438 (1963).

150. E. C. Martt, L. J. Smialek, and A. C. Green, *Illum. Engr.* **59**, 34–38 (1964).

151. J. A. Moore and C. M. Jolly, *Gen. Elec. Corp. J.* **29**, 99–106 (1962).

152. T. M. Lemons and E. R. Meyer, *Illum. Engr.* **59**, 723, 728 (1964).

153. J. W. McBain and A. M. Bakr, *J. Am. Ceram. Soc.* **48**, 690–695 (1926).

154. P. Hidnert and W. Sauder, *Natl. Bur. Std. (U.S.) Circ. 486* (1950).

155. C. J. Parker, *Appl. Opt.* **7**, 740–741 (1968).

156. C. L. Rathmann, C. H. Mann, and M. E. Nordberg, *Appl. Opt.* **7**, 819–823 (1968).

157. Reference 116, pp. 143–149.

WILLIAM H. DUMBAUGH
AND PETER C. SCHULTZ
Corning Glass Works

SYNTHETIC QUARTZ CRYSTALS

Silicon dioxide, SiO_2, exists in both crystalline and glassy forms. In the former the most common polymorph is α-quartz (low quartz), which exhibits the hexagonal lattice type. For the relationship between some of the crystalline forms, see p. 51. As can be seen, α-quartz is stable only below about 573°C at atmospheric pressure. Some of the properties of α-quartz are listed in Table 1.

Use and Sources of Supply

The major use of α-quartz depends upon the fact that it is piezoelectric. Thus, quartz finds its main use in electrical systems for frequency control, modulation, and demodulation, where crystals are used in electrical oscillators and filters. Quartz also has been used as an electro-mechanical transducer in ultrasonic generators and various pickups. Finally a small, but important, use is as the prism material in spectrographs

Table 1. Properties of α-Quartz[a]

Property	Value
structural	
crystal class	32^b
lattice const, Å	
a	4.913
b	5.405^c
optical	
indices of refraction (Na D line)	
n_O	1.5442
n_E	1.5533^d
optically active (Na D line)	
α, degree/mm	27.71
transmission, good from	$\sim$1500 Å–3 μ
electrical	
resistivity, Ω-cm	10^{15}
dielectric const	
ϵ_1^T	4.58
ϵ_3	4.70
piezoelectric coupling coefficient, $\%$	10
piezoelectric const, stat coulomb/dyn	
d_{11}	-6.93×10^{-8}
d_{14}	2.18×10^{-8}
mechanical	
hardness, Mohs	7
thermal conductivity, cal/(sec)(cm²)(°C/cm)	0.029–0.016
acoustic Q	0.1×10^6–3×10^6

[a] Many properties are directionally dependent; therefore, the values listed are indicative only.
[b] Trigonal trapezohedral class of the rhombohedral subsystem.
[c] Variable, depending on purity.
[d] Birefringent; $n_E - n_O = 0.0091$.

and spectrophotometers. The piezoelectric properties, design of filters and oscillators, etc, are discussed by Mason (1) and Heising (2).

Quartz also finds modest uses for optical applications, primarily as prisms where its dispersion makes it useful in monochromators for spectrophotometers in the region from 0.16 to 3.5 μ. Ordinary synthetic quartz is usually not of good enough quality for such uses mainly because of scattering and absorption at 2.6 μ associated with (OH) in the lattice.

Quartz crystals for electronic uses must be free of electrical and optical twinning, voids, inclusions of foreign minerals and liquids (veils), and must be large enough for convenient processing. The principal source of electronic-grade natural quartz is Brazil, but most modern quartz producers use synthesized quartz for electronic devices. The price for electronic-grade natural quartz is about $40/lb. Smaller, less perfect crystals (lascas) are imported for melting to make vitreous silica and to be used as a starting material for synthetic quartz growth. A typical recent price for lascas was about $0.50/lb.

The principal regions where natural quartz of size and perfection suitable for electronic applications is found are in the states of Minas Gerais, Goiaz, and Bahia in Brazil. The quartz occurs in veins, pipes, and pockets in Precambrian sedimentary rocks. About 33 million lb of quartz were exported from Brazil between 1910 and 1945.

The expense of natural quartz is due to the facts that deposits are scattered, mining is often done on a desultory basis by individuals, and only a small yield of crystals large and perfect enough to be usable is obtained at a given site.

At present, synthetic quartz is produced by about half a dozen foreign suppliers and six U.S. concerns: American Hydrothermal, Inc., Groton, Mass.; P. R. Hoffman Co., Carlisle, Pa.; Sawyer Research Products, Inc., Eastlake, Ohio; Thermal-Kinetic Corp., Tucson, Ariz.; Transcom Electronics, Inc., Newport, R.I.; and Western Electric Co., Inc., North Andover, Mass., which produces quartz for its own use and that of its affiliated companies only.

The price for electronic-grade synthetic quartz is about \$20/lb. World production of synthetic quartz probably exceeded 75,000 lb in 1967. More than 17×10^6 piezo-electric quartz containing units were produced in the United States in 1965, the last reported year (3). The yield of quartz units is more than three times greater from synthetic quartz than from natural quartz, and substantial additional savings accrue from its use because raw crystal inspection, orientation, sawing, and other production steps are simplified.

Quartz Synthesis

α-Quartz cannot be crystallized from its pure melt because viscous SiO_2 melts almost always form silica glass upon cooling. When crystals are formed, they are high-temperature polymorphs of SiO_2 (cristobalite and tridymite) which do not easily transform to "untwinned" α-quartz. α-Quartz is soluble in a variety of molten salts but the melts are quite viscous and crystallization below the α-β transition temperature is not practical. Silicon dioxide is insoluble in most aqueous solvents at ambient conditions except in HF solutions and α-quartz is not the stable solid phase in equilibrium with such solutions. No successful vapor transport reaction for α-quartz growth has been discovered. However, α-quartz is stable and soluble in water at elevated temperatures and pressures (hydrothermal conditions). The solubility at a convenient temperature (400°C) and pressure (25,000 psi) is only a few tenths of a wt % and is not large enough for crystal growth. However, reactions of the type

$$2\,OH^- + SiO_2 \rightleftharpoons SiO_3{}^{2-} + H_2O$$

take place in basic solutions under hydrothermal conditions with the result that the wt solubility of quartz is increased to several %. α-Quartz is the stable solid phase in equilibrium with such solutions and large crystals can be grown. This is the basis of the processes presently used for commercial quartz growth.

The first known successful attempt to grow quartz crystals hydrothermally was reported by Spezia (4) in 1905. Small crystals were formed in a thermal gradient from a sodium silicate solution. In Germany during World War II, Nacken (5) grew quartz crystals in an isothermal system by using α-quartz seeds and vitreous silica nutrient. After the war, several laboratories began research programs aimed at practical quartz production. This work is described in the publications of Kohman (6), Hale (7), Thomas (8), Laudise (9), and others. It soon became apparent that processes depending upon the supersaturation caused by the presence of silica glass were impractical. Metastable phases have a higher solubility than stable phases, but the supersaturation caused by their presence persists only as long as they are present. In the case of silica glass, its surface rather quickly devitrifies under hydrothermal conditions and growth on α-quartz seeds ceases. All successful quartz growth processes depend upon the supersaturation produced by dissolving small particles of lascas-quartz nutrient in a hot region of the high-pressure system and crystallizing it onto α-quartz seeds in a cooler part of the system.   Thus, it is necessary to employ a solvent in which quartz is the stable solid phase with reasonable solubility, in which the dependence of solubility upon temperature produces an appropriate supersaturation (ΔS) with an appropriate temperature differential (ΔT) between the dissolving and the growth zone.   All commercial processes use either NaOH or Na_2CO_3.   The dissolving mechanism is similar in both solvents since CO_3^{-2} hydrolyzes to produce OH^-.   Sodium salts are required because the mineral acmite, $Na_2O.4SiO_2.Fe_2O_3$, forms on the steel walls of the high-pressure vessels when Na^+ and silicates are present.   Acmite is relatively insoluble under hydrothermal conditions and forms a protective coat on the walls allowing the use of unlined, relatively inexpensive, vessels.   The slope of the solubility vs temperature curve is greater in CO_3^{2-} than in OH^- solutions.   Thus, with a given ΔT, the ΔS and hence the crystal-growth rate are larger in CO_3^{2-} solutions.   However, operation at the optimum high rate of crystallization may be achieved by using larger ΔT's in OH^- solutions.   This has the added advantage that temperature control problems are not as severe, since small changes in ΔT do not produce large changes in ΔS in OH^- solutions and the process is less likely to go out of control by heterogeneous nucleation on the vessel walls.   The OH^- process was developed by Bell Telephone Laboratories (10,11) and is used by the Western Electric Company (12); it will be described here. It is usually operated at higher pressures than the CO_3^{2-} process and quartz is grown at faster rates; less precise temperature control is required.

Equipment.   Figure 1 illustrates a typical commercial quartz-growing autoclave. The material of construction for use at 25,000 psi and 400°C can be a low-carbon steel, such as 4140, or various types of low-alloy steel.   The closure is a so-called modified Bridgman closure of the type developed by Autoclave Engineers, Erie, Pa.   It depends upon P. W. Bridgman's unsupported area principal (13); that is, the pressure in the vessel is transmitted through the plunger to the seal surfaces which initially are nearly line contacts.   Thus, the pressure in the seal surface greatly exceeds the pressure in the vessel, since most of the area of the plunger is unsupported.   Hydrothermal equipment is further discussed by Laudise and Nielsen (14).

The baffle is a perforated metal disc which restricts convective circulation within the vessel and thus creates two isothermal regions, the dissolving and the growth zones. Therefore all seed crystals experience the same ΔT and ΔS and grow uniformly, and no growth takes place on the nutrient.   The autoclave is heated by appropriately placed external resistance heaters; the temperature is measured and controlled from externally placed thermocouples and the pressure is measured by strain and Bourdon gages.

Typical Run.   In a typical run, small-particle-size α-quartz nutrient is added to a large autoclave, a 5% open area baffle is inserted, and also a frame holding many seed plates, whose principal surface is (0001) or an orientation close to that, is placed within the autoclave.   The autoclave is filled to 82% of its free volume with 1.0 molal NaOH and closed.   The vessel is heated so that the nutrient zone is at a temperature of about 400°C and the growth zone at a temperature of about 350°C.   Under these conditions, the pressure is about 24,000 psi.   The vessel is held at these conditions for from 2 to 3 weeks and then cooled.   The grown crystals are removed, rinsed with distilled water, and are ready for processing.   A typical rate of growth under such conditions would be about 80 mil/day (0.080 in./day).

Effect of Conditions on Rate.   It is essential for commercial growth to obtain a high rate with usable perfection at pressure and temperature conditions where the

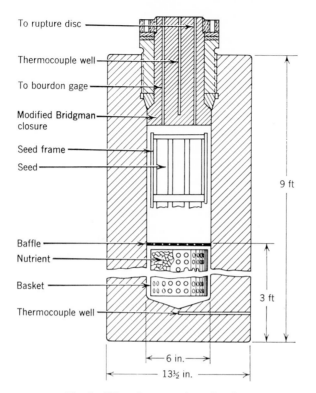

Fig. 1. Pilot plant autoclave flowsheet.

equipment design is economical. Many studies of the dependence of rate on the process parameters have been made (10), the results of which are important for production analysis. They may be summarized as follows:

1. Growth rate depends upon crystallographic direction; (0001) is one of the fastest directions.
2. Growth rate is linear with ΔT (because ΔS is approximately linear with ΔT).
3. Growth rate has an Arrhenius equation dependence upon the temperature in the crystallization zone, as shown in the following equation:

$$R \propto e^{-\Delta E/R'T}$$

where R = rate in a particular crystallographic direction; E = energy of activation; T = absolute temperature; R' = gas constant;
4. Growth rate is increased by an increase in fill, ie, percent of free volume filled with solvent at room temperature.

Piezoelectric useful quartz must be free of twins, bubbles, and particulate inclusions. If the seeds used in quartz synthesis are untwinned and if the growth takes place at an appropriate rate and appropriate pressure-temperature conditions, synthetic quartz will be free of these imperfections. If the rate is too high for the pressure-temperature conditions, then the growth becomes limited by the rapidity with which silica can diffuse across a locally depleted zone close to the growing seed. The result is imperfect or "crevice flawed" growth. Such growth contains many voids and liquid inclusions and is unusable for piezoelectric applications. Its cause is analogous to the cause of dendritic growth in the preparation of metal crystals. The success of commercial processes depends upon careful mapping of the pressure, temperature, and temperature differential conditions so as to find regions where crevice flawing does not occur at commercially useful rates.

An additional requirement for piezoelectrically useful quartz is that the acoustic or mechanical Q be high. The acoustic Q of a piezoelectric material is a figure of merit which is equal to the Q of the resistance-capacitance-conductance circuit, which is electrically equivalent to the piezoelectric resonator circuit. The higher the Q of a piezoelectric material, the more efficiently it converts mechanical to electrical energy. In low-Q materials much energy is lost by thermal pressures in this conversion. The acoustic Q of ordinary materials may be thought of as being higher the longer they ring when struck mechanically. Lead is not used to make bells because it has a low Q. For a discussion of measurement and control of acoustic Q, see references 15–17.

Table 2 lists the acoustic Q of quartz prepared under a variety of conditions. The acoustic Q of natural quartz is $\sim 1 \times 10^6$–2×10^6.

Table 2. Acoustic Q of Synthetic Quartz Prepared under a Variety of Conditions

Synthetic quartz-growth solution	Q
$1M$ NaOH	1×10^5
$1M$ NaOH + LiOH ($\sim 0.2M$)	2×10^5–3×10^5
$1M$ NaOH + LiNO$_2$ ($\sim 0.2M$)	0.5×10^6–1×10^6
$1M$ NaOH + LiNO$_2$ (~ 0.2)^a	2×10^6

^{a} Crystallization in silver-lined tube.

Infrared absorption studies have shown that Q correlates with an absorption at $3\ \mu$ associated with an OH stretching frequency (18). Indeed, infrared absorption provides a useful tool for Q evaluation in rapid production quality control. Infrared and other studies show that Q degradation is caused by proton inclusion in the grown quartz. The distribution constant for proton (or OH) is reduced by the presence of Li$^+$ and greatly reduced in the presence of lithium nitrite with the result that quartz, grown in the presence of LiNO$_2$, has a Q high enough for nearly all commercial devices. A study of the mechanism of proton exclusion has been reported (19). Further improvement in Q takes place when iron is excluded by growth in a silver system (20). Indeed, under these conditions quartz with optical properties as good as optical-quality natural quartz may be grown. We may expect the commercialization of this process in the future.

Bibliography

"Synthetic Quartz Crystals" in *ECT* 1st ed., Vol. 12, pp. 331–335, by G. T. Kohman, Bell Telephone Laboratories.

1. W. P. Mason, *Piezoelectric Crystals and Their Application to Ultrasonics*, D. Van Nostrand Co., Inc., New York, 1950.
2. R. A. Heising, *Quartz Crystals for Electrical Circuits*, D. Van Nostrand, Co., Inc., New York, 1946.
3. *Minerals Yearbook*, Vol. I, U.S. Bureau of Mines, Govt. Printing Office, Washington, D.C., 1966, pp. 1076–1077.
4. G. R. Spezia, *Accad. Sci. Torino*, **44**, 95 (1908).

5. R. Nacken, *U.S. Dept. Comm. Office Tech. Service Report, PB-6498* (1945).

6. A. C. Walker and G. T. Kohman, *Trans. Am. Inst. Elec. Engr.* **67**, 565 (1948).

7. D. R. Hale, *Science* **108**, 393 (1948).

8. C. S. Brown, R. C. Kell, L. A. Thomas, N. Wooster, and W. A. Wooster, *Nature* **167**, 940 (1951).

9. R. A. Laudise, *J. Am. Chem. Soc.* **81**, 562 (1959).

10. R. A. Laudise, "Hydrothermal Synthesis of Single Crystals," in F. A. Cotton, ed., *Progress in Inorganic Chemistry*, Vol. III, John Wiley & Sons, Inc., New York, 1962, pp. 1–47.

11. A. A. Ballman and R. A. Laudise, in J. J. Gilman, ed., *The Art and Science of Growing Crystals*, John Wiley & Sons, Inc., New York, 1963, pp. 231–251.

12. R. A. Laudise and R. A. Sullivan, *Chem. Eng. Progr.* **55**, 55 (1959).

13. P. W. Bridgman, *Proc. Amer. Acad. Arts Sci.* **49**, 625 (1914).

14. R. A. Laudise and J. W. Nielsen, "Hydrothermal Crystalgrowth," in F. Seitz and D. Turnbull, eds., *Solid State Physics*, Academic Press, Inc., New York, 1961, pp. 149–222.

15. J. C. King, A. A. Ballman, and R. A. Laudise, *J. Phys. Chem. Solids* **23**, 1019 (1962).

16. A. A. Ballman, R. A. Laudise, and D. W. Rudd, *Appl. Phys. Letters* **8**, 53 (1966).

17. A. A. Ballman, *Am. Mineralogist* **46**, 439 (1961).

18. D. M. Dodd and D. B. Fraser, *J. Phys. Chem. Solids* **26**, 673 (1965).

19. R. A. Laudise, A. A. Ballman, and J. C. King, *J. Phys. Chem. Solids* **26**, 1305 (1965).

20. A. A. Ballman, D. M. Dodd, N. A. Kuebler, R. A. Laudise, D. L. Wood, and D. W. Rudd, *Appl.* **7**, (7), 1387 (1968).

R. A. LAUDISE AND A. A. BALLMAN
Bell Telephone Laboratories, Inc.

SILICA BRICK.   See Refractories.

SILICATES.   See Silicon compounds.

SILICIDES.   See Silicon and silicides.

SILICON AND SILICIDES

Technologically, this subject is divided into two sharply different branches, pure silicon, used mainly for semiconductors, and metallurgical silicon and silicides.

PURE SILICON

Silicon (from the Latin "silex, silicis" for flint) is the 14th element of the periodic series (at. wt 28.083) and was first reported by Berzelius in 1817. Elemental silicon has never been found in nature, but, occurring in various minerals, such as silica and the silicates, it accounts for approx 25% of the earth's crust. Silicon has a diamond lattice, and a gray metallic luster. There have been various reports of a hexagonal modification, none of which have been substantiated. It is true that hexagonally shaped platelets of silicon sometimes occur, but they arise from special growth conditions and are still cubic in structure. x-Ray diffraction lines reported for the hexagonal form were probably due to silicon carbide on the surface of the silicon or mixed with it.

Silicon has a hardness intermediate between that of germanium and quartz. It is a brittle material with little indication of plastic flow at room temperature. There is a ductile region above 800°C, but even then considerable work hardening occurs and temperatures near 1300°C are required for appreciable deformation. Sawing, lapping, and polishing may be done in a manner quite similar to that used for glass and quartz except that account must be taken of silicon's greater thermal conductivity. The surface takes a fine optical finish and the material has been considered as an item of jewelry, but, probably because it is opaque and lacks scratch resistance, has never been accepted.

Since the latent heat of fusion is exceptionally high, silicon has been suggested as a heat storage medium; but technological problems associated with storing the melt, coupled with a high melting point and a 9% expansion on freezing, has prevented actual use. For infrared wavelengths between 1 and 9 μ, high-purity silicon is quite transparent and in the past has been widely used for infrared windows and for lenses and prisms. The transmissivity diminishes rapidly, however, as the temperature increases; therefore silicon has been largely supplanted by various infrared glasses.

Properties

Tables 1–3 summarize many of the physical properties of silicon (1–4). For most of them numerous values are available in the literature. Wherever possible and appropriate, recent data obtained from high-purity single crystals have been chosen for tabulation.

Vapor pressure, thermal expansion coefficient, and thermal conductivity of silicon are illustrated in Figures 1, 2, and 3, respectively. For the optical properties of high-purity silicon, see Figure 4a (absorption coefficient), 4b (refractive index), and 4c (transmission).

Electrical Properties (3,4). See also Semiconductors. The band structure of silicon is shown in Figure 5. It has a multivalley conduction band and three parabolic valence bands. Because of this structure, electrical properties which are isotropic

Table 1. Physical Properties of Silicon

Property	Value
melting point, °C	1412
boiling point, °C	3145
density, g/cm³	2.3290
crit pressure, atm	1450
crit temperature, °C	4920
heat of fusion, kcal/mole	12.1
heat of vaporization,[a] kcal/mole	71
heat capacity,[b] at 300°K, cal/mole	4.8
surface tension, at freezing point, dyn/cm²	720
elastic constants, dyn/cm²	
C_{11}	1.6740×10^{12}
C_{12}	0.6523×10^{12}
C_{44}	0.7959×10^{12}
breaking strength,[c] psi	
sawed surface	10,000
polished, large samples	30,000–50,000
polished, very small samples	200,000

[a] At boiling point.

[b] From 400–1200°K: $5.79 + 0.56 \times 10^{-3}T - 1.09 \times 10^{-5}T^2$.

[c] Bending.

Table 2. Structure of Silicon

crystal structure	cubic, diamond
lattice spacing, Å	5.43080
atoms per unit cell	8
space group	Fd3M
ionic radius, Å	
Si^{4+}	0.41
Si^{4-}	2
atomic radius, Å	1.17
electronegativity	1.8

Table 3. Isotopes of Silicon

Isotope	Natural abundance, %	Half-life
^{27}Si		4.2 sec
^{28}Si	92.28	
^{29}Si	4.6	
^{30}Si	3.05	
^{31}Si		170 min
^{32}Si		700 yr

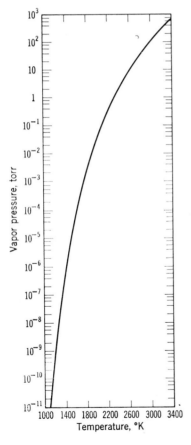

Fig. 1. Vapor pressure of silicon.

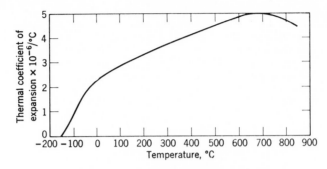

Fig. 2. Thermal expansion coefficient of silicon.

in the bulk (eg, conductivity and mobility) exhibit marked anisotropy in thin sections, such as inversion layers. Ordinarily, transitions are indirect and at room temperature the gap energy E_g, is **1.12** eV. For intrinsic silicon, ie, equal numbers of holes and electrons, the number of thermally generated carriers, n_i, at 300°C, is given as follows:

$$n_i = [1.5 \times 10^{33} T^3 \exp (-1.2/kT)]^{\frac{1}{2}} = 1.4 \times 10^{10}/cm^3$$

where T = temperature, °C; k = Boltzmann's constant.

This corresponds to a room temperature resistivity of approx 230,000 Ω-cm. By doping with various impurities, particularly the group IIIA's for p-type, and the group VA's for n-type, the resistivity can be varied from a few thousandths to a few thousand Ω-cm. Difficulties in purification presently prevent reaching the intrinsic limit, except by compensation.

Table 4 gives the position of levels within the silicon band gap caused by various impurities. Figures 6a and 6b show the variation of carrier mobility with the number

Table 4. Position of Impurity Levels in Silicon

Impurity	Donor or acceptor	Below conduction band, eV	Above valence band, eV
Ag	D		0.31
	A	0.21	
Al	A		0.057
As	D	0.049	
Au	D		0.33
	A	0.54	
B	A		0.045
Cu	A		0.49
	D		0.24
Fe	D	0.55	
	D		0.40
Ga	A		0.065
In	A		0.16
Li	D	0.033	
Mn	D	0.53	
P	D	0.044	
Sb	D	0.039	
S	D	0.18	
	D	0.37	
Zn	A	0.55	
	A		0.30

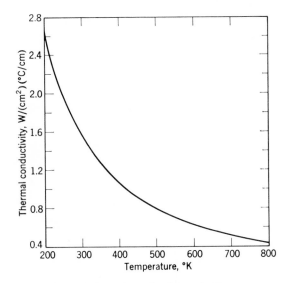

Fig. 3. Thermal conductivity of silicon.

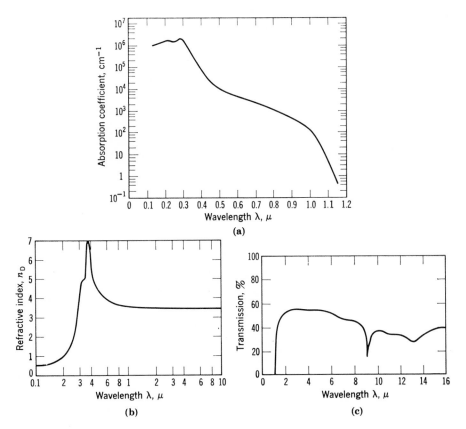

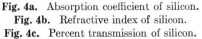

Fig. 4a. Absorption coefficient of silicon.
Fig. 4b. Refractive index of silicon.
Fig. 4c. Percent transmission of silicon.

of impurities for a typical shallow level donor and acceptor.   The carrier lifetime is not as well behaved as the mobility but it also depends on the impurity type and concentration and on crystal perfection and may range in value from 10^{-9} to 10^{-3} sec.

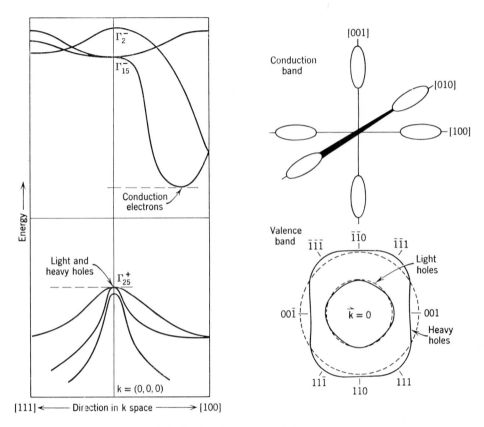

Fig. 5.   Band structure of silicon.

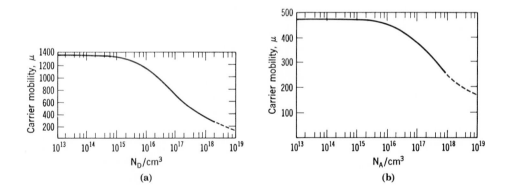

Fig. 6a.   Carrier mobility, μ, in cm²/V-sec, vs the impurity concentration, N_D, in n-type silicon at 300°K.

Fig. 6b.   Carrier mobility, μ, in cm²/V-sec, vs the impurity concentration, N_A, in p-type silicon at 300°K.

Table 5. Detection Limits for Impurities in Silicon, ppm atomic (5)

0.000 ← Emission spectrographic detection limit
0.000 ← Mass spectrographic detection limit
0.000 ← Neutron activation analysis detection limit, based on 1-g sample, 24-hr irradiation at $10^{13} n/(\mathrm{sec})(\mathrm{cm}^2)$, 24-hr decay

IA	IIA	IIIA	IVA	VA	VIA	VIIA	VIII	VIII	VIII	IB	IIB	IIIB	IVB	VB	VIB	VIIB	0
H																	He
— — —																	— — —
Li	Be											B	C	N	O	F	Ne
— 0.003 —	— 0.002 —											— 0.003 —	— 1.0 —	— 0.2 —	— 5.0 —	— 0.005 —	— — —
Na	Mg											Al	Si	P	S	Cl	A
— 0.02 3 × 10^{-5}	0.04 0.03 —											0.05 0.004 —	— — —	— 1.0 0.001	— 0.5 0.2	— 0.04 —	— — —
K	Ca	Sc	Ti	V	Cr	Mn	Fe	Co	Ni	Cu	Zn	Ga	Ge	As	Se	Br	Kr
— 0.01 0.002	— 0.01 0.3	— 0.006 6 × 10^{-5}	0.1 0.006 —	— 0.006 —	— 0.003 0.004	0.01 0.003 0.0008	0.03 0.04 1.0	— 2.0 0.0005	0.2 0.06 0.15	0.02 0.003 5 × 10^{-5}	— 0.004 0.002	— 0.003 2 × 10^{-5}	— 0.006 0.03	— 0.002 0.0001	— 0.004 0.005	— 0.004 2 × 10^{-5}	— — —
Rb	Sr	Y	Zr	Nb	Mo	Tc	Ru	Rh	Pd	Ag	Cd	In	Sn	Sb	Te	I	Xe
— 15 0.003	— 20 0.01	— — 3 × 10^{-5}	— 0.12 0.03	— 0.002 —	— 0.01 0.0003	— — —	— 0.007 0.0002	— 0.002 —	— 0.008 0.0001	0.001 0.004 0.003	— 0.016 0.0003	— 2.0 0.0007	— 0.006 0.1	— 0.004 1 × 10^{-5}	— 0.006 0.001	— 0.002 —	— — —
Cs	Ba	La	Hf	Ta	W	Re	Os	Ir	Pt	Au	Hg	Tl	Pb	Bi	Po	At	Rn
— 0.002 0.0002	— 0.003; 0.04	— 0.002 6 × 10^{-6}	— 0.007 0.0001	— 0.2 0.001	— 0.007 6 × 10^{-6}	— 0.003 8 × 10^{-7}	— 0.005 0.0004	— 0.003 3 × 10^{-6}	— 0.007 0.0006	0.2 6.0 3 × 10^{-7}	— 0.03 4 × 10^{-5}	— 0.003 0.02	1 0.004 8	0.2 0.002 0.002	— — —	— — —	— — —
Fr	Ra	Ac															
— — —	— — —	— — —															
				Ce	Pr	Nd	Pm	Sm	Eu	Gd	Tb	Dy	Ho	Er	Tm	Yb	Lu
				— 0.5 0.0004	— 0.5 6 × 10^{-5}	— 0.03 0.0002	— — —	— 0.008 10^{-6}	— 0.004 9 × 10^{-8}	— 0.008 2 × 10^{-5}	— 0.002 1 × 10^{-5}	— 0.006 0.0003	— 0.002 2 × 10^{-6}	— 0.006 6 × 10^{-6}	— 0.2 2 × 10^{-5}	— 0.02 4 × 10^{-6}	— 0.003 5 × 10^{-}
				Th	Pa	U											
				— 0.002 —	— — —	— 0.002 —											

Analysis

Wet Chemistry. In most methods the available silicon is first converted to silica or silicic acid. For organic materials simple ashing is usually sufficient, but for inorganic materials a fluxing agent, such as Na_2CO_3 or $Na_2B_4O_7$, followed by an acid treatment to precipitate gelatinous silicic acid, is required. A qualitative test may be made by means of the yellow color of the silicomolybdate complex formed by the reaction of silicic acid with ammonium molybdate. Quantitative analysis by colorimetry is also possible at this point, or alternatively, the precipitate may be dried and the amount of SiO_2 determined by dissolving in HF.

Spectrography. Silicon has very strong lines and can be easily detected in the 1–10 ppm range. The two intense lines occur at 2516.123 and 2881.578 Å.

Neutron Activation. Neutron activation may be used for the determination of silicon, eg, the n-p reaction to give aluminum 28 with a 2.3 min half-life.

x-Ray. For nondestructive analysis, both x-ray diffraction and x-ray fluorescence may be used. The latter has a sensitivity of about 30 ppm.

Determination of Impurities. For the analysis of trace impurities in silicon the following methods may be used: optical spectroscopy, solid-mass spectroscopy, neutron activation analysis, x-ray fluorescence, or various indirect methods which require the measurement of some electrical property dependent on the impurity content. These determinations may be difficult because the amounts involved are often parts per billion or less. Table 5 shows the sensitivities currently possible with some of the direct techniques (5).

Indirect measurements provide a more powerful tool for the detection of impurities. For example, if resistivity is used as a measure of impurity concentration, the presence of fractions of parts per trillion (10^{12}) of electrically active impurities is detectable, but the element or elements involved are unidentifiable. The more complicated Hall measurements as a function of temperature can be used to determine activation energies of the impurities present, but because many of them have multiple energy levels, or levels very close to those of other impurities, it is always difficult and sometimes impossible to separate the effects of different impurities.

In the event that information on a one-dimensional spatial distribution of impurities is desired, resistivity measurements, radioactive tracers, or neutron activation analysis, combined with the repeated removal of thin, relatively large area sections, can be used to obtain resolution down to a few hundred Å. For three-dimensional studies, electron microprobe, autoradiography, or resistivity probes, combined with sectioning, may be used, though the resolution is considerably reduced in directions parallel to the surface.

The analytical chemistry of silicon is further discussed in references 6 and 7.

Reactions

Silicon forms a protective oxide rather rapidly and thus is quite stable at room temperature. It does not react with acids, except with a mixture of nitric and hydrofluoric acids. In this case silicon is oxidized by the nitric acid, followed by the removal of the oxide by the hydrofluoric acid. But silicon dissolves readily in hot alkali solutions with the formation of silicates and hydrogen.

$$Si + 2\,OH^- + H_2O \rightarrow SiO_3^{2+} + 2\,H_2$$

Silicon forms alloys and silicides, Me_xSi_y, with most metals; alloys are not formed with Bi, Tl, Pb, and Hg.

At elevated temperatures silicon reacts directly with the halogens or their anhydrous acids to give the various halides.

$$2\,X_2 + Si \rightarrow SiX_4$$

$$4\,HX + Si \rightarrow SiX_4 + 2\,H_2$$

The addition of hydrogen to the system produces, besides silicon halide, various subhalides and halosilanes, though in order to obtain high yields more complicated reactions are usually required.

For further discussion of the reactions of silicon, see references 1, 2, 8, and 9.

Manufacture and Purification

Methods of preparation differ, depending on the purity required (3). The direct reduction of silica is normally used for silicon of 99% purity or less, whereas for the semiconductor trade, additional steps lead to further purification. The maximum amount of impurity that can be tolerated in silicon to be used for semiconductor devices varies with the nature of the impurity and of the end product, but usually it is in the parts-per-billion range.

Quartzite rock may be quite economically reduced by coke and charcoal in an electric furnace to give a low-purity product which can then be used as raw material for further processing. The overall reaction is

$$SiO_2 + 2\,C \rightarrow Si + 2\,CO$$

but the following reaction with excess silicon is used to remove any silicon carbide that may be formed:

$$2\,SiC + SiO_2 \rightarrow 3\,Si + 2\,CO$$

This metallurgical grade is quite inexpensive (less than 20¢/lb in the 1960s) since there is an abundance of raw material. However, because of difficulties in purification, the semiconductor grades command a price of from fifty to several hundred dollars per pound.

Table 6 summarizes U.S. silicon production for the past several years and shows the vast difference in usage between the semiconductor and metallurgical grades. In

Table 6. U.S. Production of Silicon, tons[a]

Silicon, %	1961	1962	1963	1964	1965	1966
100[b]	31	41	38	38		
96–99	42,000	64,000	65,000	69,000	78,000	82,000
90–95	4,300	3,000	2,000	1,400	400	780
81–89	7,000	10,000	14,000	15,000	25,000	22,000
71–80	75,000	59,000	64,000	64,000	73,000	76,000
56–70	32,000	27,000	21,000	41,000	48,000	39,000
21–55	182,000	270,000	276,000	352,000	365,000	358,000
40–50[c]	27,000	43,000	46,000	63,000	75,000	63,000

[a] Data collected from Minerals Yearbook, U.S. Bureau of Mines, U.S. Govt. Printing Office, Washington, D.C., 1961–1966.

[b] Semiconductor grade.

[c] Briquets.

addition, various processes using carbon or aluminum to reduce silicates have been patented, but the reduction of silica by carbon is the most widely used method. Many of the impurities contained in silicon prepared in this manner are contained at the grain boundaries and consist of various silicates and silicides. Accordingly, if the silicon is crushed and subjected to appropriate acid treatments considerable purification can be effected.

Further purification may be obtained metallurgically by melting the silicon and allowing freezing to proceed from one end of the container to the other. Since most impurities are partially rejected at the freezing interface, they will be swept to the end of the ingot. By this method much of the silicon used for early radar microwaves diodes was prepared. Unfortunately, molten silicon reacts with the container and sticks to the wall as it freezes, producing cracked ingots. Furthermore, normal freeze permits only low inherent purification; consequently float zone refining gives better results with silicon.

In this method a small molten zone is repeatedly moved through a silicon rod supported only at each end and thus gradually sweeps the impurities to one end. Actually, float zoning is most often used after silicon of the highest possible purity has been prepared by other means. See also Zone refining.

Silicon (or ferrosilicon) can be chlorinated to give either $SiCl_4$ or $SiHCl_3$, which are liquids at room temperature. These may be purified by distillation or passage through an adsorption column, followed by reduction to silicon. Other halides, such as the iodide or bromide, may be used, or the chloride may be converted to SiH_4, which, after further purification, is then reduced.

The first commercial process for the production of semiconductor-grade silicon used zinc to reduce silicon tetrachloride. Zinc is an acceptable reducing agent since it is available in reasonable purity, does not form a silicide, is relatively noncorrosive, and is not explosive in the presence of air. Since the solubility of zinc in silicon is quite low, contamination by zinc or zinc compounds is minimal, and they can easily be removed by solvents which do not attack silicon. In this process, the zinc and silicon tetrachloride are separately vaporized and metered and are then introduced into the reaction chamber in approx stoichiometric proportions. The chamber temperature is not critical but should be in the 900–1100°C range. The reaction equipment is made of high-purity fused silica in order to minimize contamination. The silicon grows in dendrites, or needles, from the walls of the container. The reaction products and unreacted components are condensed and the zinc and $ZnCl_2$ are reclaimed. The silicon needles can be leached with HCl to remove any zinc which may remain.

The decomposition of silicon tetraiodide to form silicon is a straightforward process, and because of the ease of purification, the iodide has been used to produce extremely high-purity silicon. In order to obtain reasonable deposition rates, low pressure is essential and thus a combination of vacuum pumps and iodine traps is required. Iodine is expensive and has to be recovered. The process has not proved commercially feasible, even though some companies have operated plants on a limited basis.

The silane process is, in principle, very simple and involves only the pyrolytic decomposition of silane. It is not widely used, however, because of the difficulty of producing and handling the silane.

Trichlorosilane decomposes thermally at a slow rate to give silicon. Silicon tetrachloride is apparently stable up to at least 1200°C. Either of them reacts with hydrogen and silicon is produced with reasonable efficiencies and rates. The overall reactions can be written as follows:

$$SiCl_4 + 2 H_2 \rightarrow 4 HCl + Si$$
$$SiHCl_3 + H_2 \rightarrow 3 HCl + Si$$

These are simplified equations. For example, in the first reaction considerable $SiHCl_3$, $SiCl_2$, and long-chain polymers are produced, as well as HCl and silicon. The second reaction probably proceeds in the following manner:

$$2 SiHCl_3 + heat \rightarrow SiCl_4 + H_2 + Si$$
$$SiCl_4 + H_2 \rightarrow Si + HCl + polymers$$

In either the hydrogen-reduction or the thermal-decomposition process, lower temperatures favor the production of very small, brownish particles. For example, $SiCl_4$ reduction at 800°C gives mostly powder. Hydrogen reduction of either $SiCl_4$ or $SiHCl_3$ above 1000°C produces a distinctly crystalline looking deposit which may vary from dendrites to large, well-defined crystals. The reactor may be a heated fused silica tube with deposition occurring on the inner walls, or a heated silicon rod may be used and the flows arranged so that the silicon rod increases in diameter.

Applications

Semiconductor. Radiofrequency silicon detectors were reported as early as 1906 and by the mid-1930s microwave diodes were in use in many laboratories. In 1950 a silicon transistor was reported, followed in 1958 by the silicon integrated circuit. Thus silicon, one of the earliest known semiconductors, is still the most widely used. It is plentiful and relatively inexpensive. Silicon devices can be used over as wide a range of temperatures as most other electronic components. Its surface can be protected by its own relatively inert oxide and its electrical properties are such that it can cover the extremes of signal processing from dc to gigahertz frequencies, and of power control from mW and V to kW and kV.

In some specialized areas, eg, light emission, other materials are superior to silicon, and indeed exhibit useful phenomena not present in silicon. However, the demand for these special properties is still quite small and silicon is expected to be the mainstay of the semiconductor industry for many years. As can be seen from Table 7, the annual use of silicon for semiconductors averaged 30–40 tons for five years, but the number of active devices has increased greatly during the same time.

Table 7. Annual Production, Price, and Devices of 100% Silicon (Semiconductor Grade)

Year	Production, tons[a]	Av price/ lb, $[a]	Total Si devices, millions[b]
1961	31	100	130
1962	41	60	200
1963	38	56	280
1964	38	56	480
1965		50	840
1966		50	1380

[a] Data collected from *Minerals Yearbook*, U.S. Bureau of Mines, U.S. Govt. Printing Office, Washington, D.C., 1962–1967.

[b] Data collected from *Electronic Industries Association Yearbook*, Electronic Industries Association, Washington, D.C., 1967.

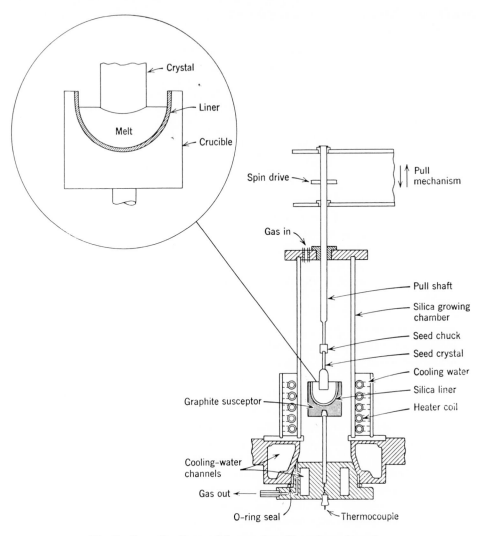

Fig. 7. Crystal puller used for growing silicon from the melt.

Because most devices require single-crystal semiconductors for best performance, the growth of single crystals of silicon has been extensively studied since the 1950s and, depending on the desired properties, a number of processes are available. The most common and least expensive is the Czochralski process, named after J. Czochralski who first described it in 1918. It is also sometimes called the Teal-Little method in honor of G. K. Teal and J. B. Little who first applied the process to semiconductor materials. The general method is sketched in Figure 7 and proceeds by allowing silicon to freeze gradually onto a seed which may be withdrawn from the melt or rotated. The freezing (growth) rate is controlled by a combination of the melt temperature and the radiation and conduction heat loss from the crystal. Crystals as small as $\frac{1}{8}$ in. in diam and as large as 6 in. in diam have been grown by this process. The most common size is between 1 and 2 in. in diam and 12–14 in. long. Growth rates vary with the diam but are usually in the in./hr range. The major disadvantage of this method is the necessity

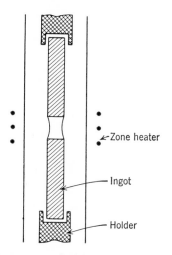

Fig. 8. Float-zone method for the purification of silicon.

to keep the reactive molten silicon free of contaminants for hours at a time. These contaminants arise from the fused silica container—which is slowly dissolved by the silicon—from gaseous impurities in the inert atmosphere, and from vaporization of hot portions of the furnace.

In order to minimize the purification problem, float zoning, as shown in Figure 8 and quite similar to the previously described zone refining, is often used. A polycrystalline rod is held vertically and a molten zone caused to traverse the length. The length of the zone and the diameter of the rod are carefully chosen so that surface tension keeps the molten zone in place. Crystals of the highest purity are produced in this manner but the max diam presently obtained is slightly less than 2 in.

The Teal-Little method produces a crystal characterized by a dislocation density count of 10^3–10^4/cm² and a high oxygen content. The float zone crystal has a much lower oxygen content and a dislocation density of from 10^4–10^5/cm². Various proprietary processes combine the advantages of both the pulled and the float-zone crystals to give one with low oxygen content and zero dislocations.

Most semiconductor applications require thin, flat, single crystal slices with damage-free surfaces for subsequent processing. Both the Teal-Little and the float-zone methods generate long rods from which slices must be sawed, lapped, and polished. In attempts to circumvent all of these steps, two modifications of melt growth have been proposed in order to grow single crystal ribbons directly. One depends on a shaped heat zone and the other on the growth characteristics of twinned crystals. Crystal orientation is chosen in each case so that the two wide sides of the ribbon are bounded by slow growing (111) planes.

Silicon can be grown from various fluxes, usually metals, if a lower temperature process is desired. The major disadvantages are the inclusion of the flux in the crystal and the inability to remove the native oxide from the seed surface so that a crystal of high perfection can be grown.

Vapor-phase growth at temperatures well below the melting point is now widely used for adding thin layers to slices and is usually referred to as "epitaxy." (See Film deposition processes.) The primary advantage of gas-phase growth is that it allows doping impurities to be changed quite rapidly so that rather thin layers of quite differ-

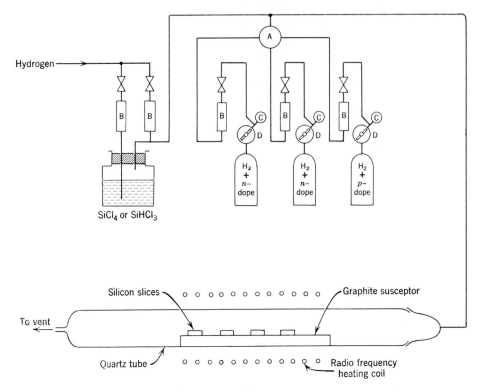

Fig. 9. Hydrogen reduction of SiCl₄ and SiHCl₃. LEGEND: A—selector; B—flow meter; C—pressure gage; D—pressure regulator.

ent resistivity can be grown sequentially. The method of transport may be by direct evaporation or by chemical means. In the latter, any of the reactions used for the manufacturing of semiconductor-grade silicon can, in principle, be used, but present practice is restricted to the thermal decomposition of silane and the hydrogen reduction of SiCl₄ and SiHCl₃. Equipment for the latter is sketched in Figure 9. In addition, a disproportional reaction, such as

$$\underbrace{\overbrace{Si + SiCl_4 \rightleftarrows 2\, SiCl_2 \rightleftarrows Si + SiCl_4}^{T_2}}_{T_1}$$

Table 8. Resistivity and Impurity Concentrations of Silicon Devices

Device	Approx resistivity, Ω-cm	Approx impurity concn, pts/billion (atomic)
particle detector	100–2000	0.1–1.0
high-voltage rectifier	50–200	1–2
power transistor	10–25	5–10
small signal transistor	1–10	10–100
integrated circuits	0.2–1.0	100–1000
low-voltage regulator diodes	0.61–0.1	10–100

may be used to transport silicon from a polycrystalline feed stock held at a temperature T_1 to a growing surface with a temperature T_2. Depending on the transport agent chosen—iodine in this example—the concentration of each species and the actual temperature of each zone, T_1 may be either higher or lower than T_2 (10).

During growth by any of these processes, various doping elements (As, P, Sb, for n-type, Ga, Al, B, for p-type) must be added in carefully controlled amounts. The exact quantities depend on the type of device to be made from the crystals, but Table 8 lists some representative values. For vapor-phase doping, an easily vaporizable compound is used, which is either thermally decomposed or reduced along with the silicon compound. Typical examples are diborane, phosphine, and boron tribromide. Melt growth doping is accomplished by introducing the proper quantity into the melt before or during the growing operation. In this case either elemental dopants (Ga, As, etc) or silicon-dopant alloys are required in order to prevent contamination of the melt.

Bibliography

1. J. W. Mellor, *A Comprehensive Treatise on Inorganic and Theoretical Chemistry*, Vol. IV, Longmans, Green & Co., Inc., New York, 1957.
2. A. S. Berezhnoi, *Silicon and Its Binary Systems* (translated from Russian), Consultants Bureau, New York, 1960.
3. W. R. Runyan, *Silicon Semiconductor Technology*, McGraw-Hill Book Co., Inc., New York, 1965.
4. N. B. Hannay, *Semiconductors*, Reinhold Publishing Corp., New York, 1959.
5. H. M. Klein and G. B. Larrabee, unpublished work, Texas Instruments, Inc.
6. H. R. Shell, "Silicon," in I. M. Kolthoff and P. J. Elving, eds., *Treatise on Analytical Chemistry*, Part II, Vol. II, Interscience Publishers, a div. of John Wiley & Sons, Inc., New York, 1962, pp. 107–206.
7. H. J. Horner, "Organic Analysis: Silicon," in reference 6, Vol. XII, 1963, pp. 224–293.
8. E. A. V. Ebsworth, *Volatile Silicon Compounds*, The Macmillan Company, New York, 1963.
9. M. Sneed, M. Cannon, and R. C. Brasted, eds., *Comprehensive Inorganic Chemistry*, Vol. 7, D. Van Nostrand Company, Inc., New York, 1958.
10. H. Schafer, *Chemical Transport Reactions*, Academic Press, Inc., New York, 1964.

WALTER R. RUNYAN
Texas Instruments, Inc.

METALLURGICAL SILICON AND SILICIDES

The similarity exhibited between carbon and silicon in their compounds also exists between the carbides and the silicides, and many of the methods used for forming the carbides can be used for forming the silicides. The most important and most widely used method is the reduction of the metal oxides, the metal silicates, or both with carbon or silicon in an electric furnace. When carbon reduction is employed, the metal carbides usually form first due to a lower temperature requirement. Then, as silicon is formed, it displaces the carbon, because metal silicides have a higher heat of formation than do metal carbides. The metal silicides form well-defined crystals having a brilliant metallic luster; they are usually hard and possess a high-melting point. The following metals form definite silicides: B, Ba, Be, Ca, Co, Cr, Cu, Fe, Li, Mg, Mn, Mo, Nb, Ni, Pb, Pt, Ru, Sr, Ta, Ti, U, V, W, Zr, and the rare earth elements (2). Most of these elements form several silicides; for example, iron forms Fe_5Si_3, Fe_3Si_2, $FeSi$, $FeSi_2$, Fe_2Si_5, and others. See Figure 1.

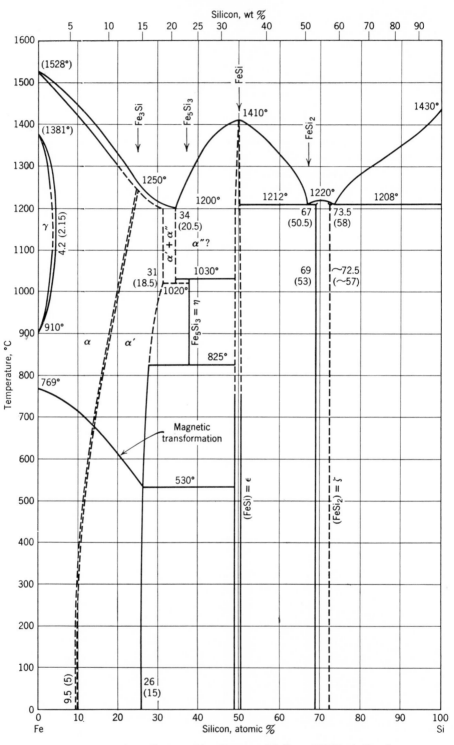

Fig. 1. Fe–Si phase diagram (2).   Courtesy McGraw-Hill Book Co., Inc.

Silicon does not form silicides with the following metals: Ag, Al, As, Au, Bi, Cd, Hg, Na, Ru, Th, Sb, and Zn. It is soluble in aluminum in the solid state, maximum solubility being 1.65 wt % at 577°C (2). It is soluble in silver, gold, and zinc at temperatures above the melting points of these metals. References 2–4 give phase diagrams of systems containing silicides; reference 2 is the most detailed and complete.

Production and Uses of Metallurgical Silicon and Silicides

The commercial production of silicon in the form of binary and ternary ferroalloys started near the beginning of the twentieth century with the development of the electric-arc furnace and the blast furnace, and the subsequent rise in production of iron and steel. Alloys containing 6–95% Si are extensively used by the iron and steel industry, and silicon is present in most commercial grades of steel and cast iron. For these applications, pure silicon is of negligible commercial importance due to its high cost. Therefore, it is normally used in the form of various grades of ferrosilicon.

Table 1. Product Data, 1968 (6)

Name	Composition	Price (fob producing plant) for bulk shipments
standard 50% ferrosilicon	47–51% Si, remainder mainly Fe	13.10¢/lb of Si
standard 65% ferrosilicon	65–70% Si, remainder mainly Fe	14.90¢/lb of Si
standard 75% ferrosilicon	73–78% Si, remainder mainly Fe	14.90¢/lb of Si
standard 85% ferrosilicon	83–88% Si, remainder mainly Fe	15.3¢/lb of Si
silicon metal	97.75% Si min, 0.07% Ca max, 0.51–1.00% Fe max	15.55¢/lb of Si
calcium–silicon	30–33% Ca, 60–65% Si, 1.50–3.00% Fe	19.80¢/lb of alloy
calcium–manganese–silicon	16–20% Ca, 14–18% Mn, 54–59% Si	21.65¢/lb of alloy
ferrochrome silicon	38–42% Cr, 38–42% Si, 0.05% C max	11.90¢/lb of Cr
magnesium ferrosilicon	44–48% Si, 8–10% Mg, 1.00–1.50% Ca, 0.50% Ce	20.80¢/lb of Si
Simanal	approx 20% each of Si, Mn, Al, balance mainly Fe	19.25¢/lb of alloy
silicomanganese	65–68% Mn, 12.5–18.5% Si, 1.50–3.00% C, balance mainly Fe	8.0¢/lb of alloy
SMZ alloy	60–65% Si, 5–7% Zr, 5–7% Mn, 3–4% Ca, balance mainly Fe	19.25¢/lb of Si

Ternary ferroalloys are also available for the simultaneous addition of silicon and a second alloying element; most often the second alloying element is either manganese or chromium (5). They also are widely used in the production of both iron and steel.

In the iron and steel industry, silicon alloys, often referred to as silicides, are used for alloying, deoxidizing, and reducing other alloying agents such as Mn, Cr, W, and Mo. In the nonferrous metal industry, silicon is used primarily as an alloying agent for Cu, Al, Mg, and Ni. In the form of 75% ferrosilicon, it is used as a reducing agent in the production of magnesium by the Pidgeon process. The reaction between ferrosilicon and caustic soda can be used to make hydrogen.

It is estimated that the production of silicon alloys in the U.S. in 1967 was roughly 2 million short tons. This includes all electric furnace production plus blast furnace production of silvery iron.

The most important commercial grades of silicon alloys are those used by the iron and steel industry, namely those of Fe, Mn, Cr, V, Al, Ti, Zr, W, B, Ca, Mg, Ta, and Nb. See Table 1.

Since silicon is an effective and economical deoxidizer, it is used to refine most grades of carbon and alloy steels. In importance, it is second only to manganese in steelmaking. As an alloying element in steels, it is used to increase tensile strength and elastic limit, improve resistance to corrosion and high-temperature oxidation, improve electrical characteristics, and decrease yield point. As a reducing agent, it serves to reduce metal oxides from the slag, thereby permitting the desired element, such as chromium, to sink and be recovered as an alloying agent in the steel. The wide range of properties available in cast iron is controlled primarily by carbon and silicon content (5). Silicon in cast iron reduces the stability of iron carbide and promotes the formation of graphitic carbon. As an effective graphitizer in cast iron, silicon softens the iron, and improves its fluidity and machinability. For wear resistance, silicon ranges from 0.50 to 1.50%. In ductile iron, silicon ranges from 1.50 to 3.00%. Higher percentages of silicon improve the corrosion resistance of both gray and ductile cast irons, and increase their resistance to oxidation at elevated temperatures.

Ferrosilicon ranges in silicon content from 6 to 95%. Most of this alloy with up to 12% Si is made in blast furnaces. All silicon ferroalloys with above 15% Si are produced in submerged-arc electric furnaces. Ferrosilicon is the most extensively used of all the silicides. In blast furnaces, it is made by carbon reduction of silica rock and iron from iron ore in the presence of coke and limestone. In the electric furnaces, the higher silicon grades are made by melting low-alloy steel scrap as a source of iron and reducing high-purity silica rock with carbon.

Silvery iron, containing 6–20% Si, is magnetic, which is an advantage in loading and unloading. It is used primarily as a furnace "block" added in lump form for initial deoxidation (5). The 22–25% Si grade is also magnetic, which makes it easy to handle. It is also used as a furnace block. The low silicon content of both these alloys makes them unsuitable for ladle addition since the large quantity normally required would cause excessive chilling of the steel. The most extensively used silicon alloy is 50% ferrosilicon. It is the cheapest silicon alloy in terms of silicon content (5). It is used as a deoxidizer and alloying agent in the production of killed and semikilled steels. Its melting point of 2200°F is the lowest of the iron–silicon alloys. Iron foundries add this alloy to the cupola and subsequently to the ladle for purpose of inoculation. Inoculation may be defined as a change in the physical properties of iron not explainable by the change in chemistry. In practice, inoculation consists of holding back from the base iron some portion of the desired silicon level and making this addition to the ladle. The effects of this method are (*1*) decreased chilling tendency and reduced iron carbide formation without appreciable effect on pearlitic stability; (*2*) increased randomness of graphite flakes and decrease in flake size; (*3*) decreased section sensitivity; (*4*) increased ratio of tensile strength to hardness; and (*5*) improved machinability at all strength levels.

The low-aluminum grade (0.40% Al max) 50% ferrosilicon is used as a source of silicon for electrical steels containing less than 2.00% Si where the low residual aluminum content is an important factor in obtaining desired electrical properties, such as significant reduction of eddy currents. This alloy is endothermic and for this application is normally limited to heats of over 100 tons or where the heat loss from the addition is of little importance (5). The 65% ferrosilicon grade is thermodynamically balanced with respect to its heat effect on molten steel; the heating effect developed by the silicon going into solution just balances the amount of heat required to raise the ferrosilicon to the temperature of the molten steel. The 65% ferrosilicon grade is normally used as a ladle addition where the endothermic effect of 50% ferrosilicon cannot be tolerated. The 75 and 90% ferrosilicon grades are used mainly for the alloying of high-alloy steels which require large additions of silicon. The 85% grade is used mainly by the cast-iron foundries as an inoculant.

Boron silicides, usually in alloy combination with iron silicides, are made by either the carbon or silicon reduction of the oxides in an electric furnace. It is used to increase the hardness of steel. Only a few thousandths of a percent of boron in steel is needed for this purpose and replaces considerably greater amounts of more expensive alloys such as chromium (7).

Calcium silicide or calcium and *calcium–manganese–silicon* are made in the submerged-arc electric furnace by carbon reduction of lime, silica rock, and various manganese-bearing materials. The commercial analysis of calcium silicide is 30–33% Ca, 60–65% Si, and 3% Fe max. For calcium–manganese–silicon alloys the analysis is 16–20% Ca, 14–18% Mn, and 53–59% Si. These two alloys, in combination, are an efficient and effective deoxidizer and degassifier of steel. They produce silicate inclusions that are least harmful to physical properties and prevent the formation of alumina-type inclusions, a major source of fatigue failure in highly stressed alloy steels. As a sulfide former they promote random distribution of sulfides, thereby minimizing undesirable stringer- or chain-type inclusions. In cast iron, they are used as an inoculant. The manganese assists in obtaining a completely pearlitic matrix which improves strength and machinability of the castings.

Chromium silicides or ferrochrome–silicon alloys are made in the same manner as ferrosilicon alloys in the electric furnace. They range in composition from an alloy containing 1.25% C, 30% Si, and 50% Cr to an alloy containing 0.05% C, 50% Si, and 35% Cr. The higher-carbon grades are used principally in low-alloy steel. The silicon content makes them readily soluble in iron, allowing appreciable addition of chromium to ladle with little increase in chill depth. Up to 1.00% Cr may be added without rendering even thin-section castings unmachinable (5). The 0.05%-C grades were originally developed for economical production of stainless steel and their use is primarily confined to this application. The silicon in the alloy reduces metal oxides, principally chromium, from the slag back into the bath while the chromium in the alloy dissolves in the metal.

Copper silicon, containing up to 30% Cu, the remainder being mainly silicon, made by adding secondary copper to molten silicon "metal" (approx 98% Si), has been used experimentally by the aluminum industry. No combination of these two elements as an alloy has found wide acceptance and presently little, if any, of this alloy is being used. Copper and silicon in varying proportions and sometimes in combination with other elements, such as Mg, Cr, and Ni, improve the castability, weldability, strength, and wear resistance of aluminum, and also reduce the coefficient of thermal expansion.

Magnesium silicides in alloy combination with other silicides, such as Fe, Mn, Cu, Ni, and rare earth elements are now extensively used in the production of *ductile* or *nodular cast iron*. The silicides most widely used are: nickel–iron–silicon–magnesium, iron–silicon–magnesium, iron–silicon–magnesium–rare earths, and combinations of nickel–magnesium with magnesium and with the above silicides. The magnesium content of most of these alloys ranges from 5 to 10%; but

Table 2. Specifications for Nodular Iron

Class	Minimum tensile strength, psi	Minimum yield strength, psi	Minimum elongation, % in 2 in.	Condition
80–60–03	80,000	60,000	3.0	as cast
60–45–10	60,000	45,000	10.0	usually annealed
120–90–02	120,000	90,000	2.0	heat treated
100–70–03	100,000	70,000	3.0	heat treated
60–45–15	60,000	45,000	15.0	ferritized by anneal
60–40–15	60,000	40,000	15.0	ferritized by anneal to 190 BHN max

for special applications, it may be as high as 50%, or even higher. In those alloys containing rare earth elements, the rare earth content usually ranges from 0.1 to 1.5%. Nodular cast iron is made by converting the flakes of graphite in gray iron into tiny balls or spherulites. This is brought about by the addition of one or more elements to the molten metal. Magnesium, cerium, calcium, lithium, sodium, barium, and other elements will produce spherulitic graphite structures (4). Of these elements, magnesium and cerium (rare earths) are commercially important. The addition of nickel to nodular iron, from 1.50 to 1.95%, significantly increases the strength of the pearlitic matrix. Conversion of the graphite flakes into spherulites increases tensile strength and notch hardness of cast iron and subsequent heat treatment produces desirable mechanical properties not obtainable from iron containing graphite in the form of flakes.

The composition of unalloyed nodular iron approximates that of gray iron as follows: 3.20–4.10% total C, 1.80–2.80% Si, up to 0.80% Mn, 0.10% max P, and 0.03% max S. The great majority of nodular iron castings are heat treated before use. Most are given a ferritizing anneal or are normalized; some are quenched and tempered. See Table 2.

The advent of nodular cast iron made possible the first crownless press rolls for paper machinery. One of the better known uses of nodular iron is in the production of automobile crankshafts. It is also widely used to make centrifugal pump casings, coke oven doors, transmission auxiliary equipment, fan hubs, and many other products where uniform castings of good appearance and improved machinability are desired or are necessary.

Roughly 300,000 tons of nodular cast iron were produced in the U.S. in 1967.

Rare earth silicides in the form of a ferroalloy, containing up to 30% total rare earths, have been used experimentally by the iron and steel industry (for nodular iron, to make the graphite spheroidal rather than flaky). In cases where the silicon can be used as a deoxidizer and/or alloying agent, the introduction of rare earth elements as silicides usually represents a more economical way of introducing rare earths rather than adding them as misch metal.

Silicon–aluminum alloys containing up to 80% Al, the balance being mostly silicon, are made by direct carbon reduction of high-purity clay or mixtures of the oxides in the electric furnace. These alloys can also be made by melting together silicon and aluminum. Their main use is for addition of silicon to molten aluminum for alloying purposes. For better control of impurities and for economic reasons, most producers of aluminum now prefer to use a special grade of commercial silicon metal as a source of silicon in place of the silicon–aluminum alloys. Silicon–aluminum alloys containing 10–50% Si, 10–20% Al, the remainder usually being mostly Fe, Mn, Cr, or Zr, or a combination of these, are made by carbon reduction of the oxides in the electric furnace. These alloys are used preferably as a ladle addition in iron and steel for final deoxidation and alloying. The most important alloys of this group are Alsifer (Foote Mineral Co.), containing approx 20% Al, 40% Si, and remainder mainly Fe; ferroaluminum silicon, containing approx 10% Al, 50% Si, and remainder mainly Fe; and Simanal (Ohio-Ferro Alloys Corp.), containing approx 20% Si, 20% Mn, 20% Al, and remainder mainly Fe. As an alloying agent, these alloys are used to control the grain size of steel. They also reduce the harmful effect of nitrogen present in steel; and Simanal, for example, changes the alumina inclusions by forming them into globular and scattered types that are the least harmful in steel.

Manganese silicides, usually containing varying amounts of iron and carbon, are made by carbon reduction of manganese ore and/or manganese slag in the presence of silica in the electric furnace. The lower-silicon grades are referred to as silicomanganese. Their compositions are in the range of 0.60–3.00% C, 12–27% Si, 50–68% Mn, and the remainder is mainly iron. Silicomanganese is particularly suitable for introducing manganese into low-carbon steel in which the added silicon is not objectionable. It is also an excellent and economical deoxidizer for open-hearth and electric-furnace steel, both acid and basic (5). Use of silicomanganese is often preferred to separate additions of manganese and silicon because of its low-carbon content and the consequent improved cleanliness of the steel produced. Ferromanganese silicon, containing approx 65% Mn, 30% Si, 0.06% C, 0.04% P, and with the remainder being mainly iron, is the only other manganese–silicon compound presently of commercial importance. It is the source of manganese lowest in carbon and is extensively used in producing the 200 and 300 series of stainless steel. In the 200 series, ferromanganese silicon is normally used for complete slag reduction and to obtain as much of the required manganese as the silicon residual will allow. Its composition is particularly well suited for the 300 series where the maintenance of a high manganese-to-silicon ratio is desirable during the final stages of slag reduction.

Titanium silicides are sometimes made by adding titanium scrap to molten silicon metal. One grade produced commercially contains 40–50% Ti and 45–50% Si. Similar to chromium silicides and others, the use of titanium silicides represents an economical way of introducing titanium to molten steel in cases where the silicon is needed for slag reduction and the addition of silicon to the steel is not objectionable.

Vanadium silicides can be made by the reduction of vanadium ore and/or vanadium concentrates in the electric furnace. The method of application is essentially the same as that used for titanium silicides; and for the same reason, that is, in some cases, use of the silicides represents the most economical way of introducing vanadium to molten steel.

Silicon–zirconium alloys containing 30–65% Si and 5–40% Zr are made in the electric furnace by carbon reduction of the oxides. These alloys are used by the iron and steel industry as a deoxidizer and a scavenger. Zirconium readily combines with oxygen, nitrogen, and sulfur, forming nonmetallic inclusions that either float out of the molten bath or are rendered least harmful. One particular grade, commonly referred to as SMZ (Union Carbide Corp.), is used in the production of gray iron castings to control the depth of chill at edges and corners and in light sections.

Silicon "metal," having a purity of approx 98% Si, is obtained by carbon reduction of nearly pure silica in the electric furnace. In 1967, probably about 75,000 tons of this material was produced in the U.S. Silicon metal is used extensively by the non-ferrous metal industry, mainly in the production of aluminum and copper alloys. It is used in amounts of from 5 to 22% Si in aluminum alloys. In these alloys, silicon improves castability, reduces shrinkage and hot-cracking tendencies, and increases corrosion resistance, hardness, tensile strength, and wear resistance. In copper, silicon metal is added as an alloying agent in producing the silicon bronzes. In these alloys, silicon improves fluidity and physical properties, and minimizes dross formation (5).

One commercial grade of silicon metal (containing 0.55–0.65% Fe, 0.35–0.45% Al, 0.20–0.30% Ca, where % Fe must be 0.20% higher than % Al) is used by the chemical industry as a basic raw material in the production of silicones. See Silicon compounds.

Silicon cermets, consisting of ceramic particles bonded with silicon metal, exhibit outstanding resistance to oxidation and can be fired in a variety of atmospheres up to 2000°C. Cermets possess greater thermal conductivity and greater resistance to thermal shock than do ceramics. They are used to make high-temperature sleeve bearings and cutting tools. See Tool materials.

Silicon metal has found limited use as a component of refractory materials for acid open-hearth and electric-furnace linings. Its oxidation to silica increases the fusion temperature which increases the refractoriness of the lining.

Bibliography

"Silicon and Silicon Alloys" in *ECT* 1st ed., Vol. 12, pp. 360–365, by J. C. Vignos, Ohio Ferro-Alloys Corporation.

1. H. Moissan, *The Electric Furnace*, transl. by V. Lenher, 2nd ed., Chemical Publishing Co., Easton, Pa., 1920.
2. M. Hansen, *Constitution of Binary Alloys*, 2nd ed., McGraw-Hill Book Co., Inc., New York, 1958.
3. J. W. Mellor, *A Comprehensive Treatise on Inorganic and Theoretical Chemistry*, Vol. VI, 1930, John Wiley & Sons, Inc., New York and Longmans, Green, and Co., Ltd., London.
4. *Metals Handbook*, Vol. 1, 8th ed., American Society for Metals, Metals Park, Novelty, Ohio, 1961, p. 1221.
5. D. N. Matter, *Silicon: Its Alloys and Their Use*, Ohio Ferro-Alloys Corp., Canton, Ohio, 1961.
6. *Steel Magazine* (March 25, 1968).
7. *The Steel Making Process and the Function of Silicon in Steel*, Tech. Bull., Ohio Ferro-Alloys Corp., Canton, Ohio, 1961.

E. G. Simms
Ohio Ferro-Alloys Corporation

SILICON CARBIDE, SiC. See Vol. 4, p. 114.

SILICON COMPOUNDS

INTRODUCTION

One of man's most widely pursued subjects has been how to make new and useful materials from silicon. This is not surprising, since silicon is the second most abundant element in the earth's crust and it forms a wide variety of both inorganic and organic compounds. Although the inorganic compounds have been known since ancient times, the organic compounds have received recognition and application only in recent years. The reason for this lies partly in the fact that organic compounds of silicon are not found in nature and many technological difficulties had to be overcome in their synthesis. Today, the great potential as well as the actual utility of these compounds in the silicone and related industries has stimulated the study of silicon compounds from both the theoretical and the practical point of view.

Silicon is never found as a free element in nature, but rather is normally combined with oxygen in various complex configurations. Its most abundant compound is SiO_2, commonly known as "silica" (qv). The first organic derivative of silicon which contained a Si–C bond was prepared in about 1863 by Friedel and Crafts (1); however the study of organosilicon compounds did not get started in an organized way until the work of Frederick S. Kipping began in 1899 (2). Shortly after this, Stock began his classic research on the simple hydrides of silicon, ie, the silanes (3). Even though the usefulness of various inorganic compounds of silicon had been demonstrated for hundreds of years in such areas as ceramics, the practical utilization of organic derivatives of silicon was not actively pursued until the 1930s when Hyde, Patnode, McGregor, and Rochow in the U.S., and Andrianov and Dolgov in the U.S.S.R. began their classic researches on the preparation and practical applications of organosilicon compounds. Investigations were intensified in this area during World War II, and with the tremendous success achieved, the silicone industry was born.

Although the usefulness of both inorganic and organic silicon compounds has now been clearly demonstrated, the application of the parent silanes to practical problems has not been too successful. One important use of these derivatives has been in the preparation of ultrapure silicon through their thermal decomposition (4,5) (see Silicon). Also, an important method for preparing organohalosilanes, the precursors to silicones, is by the addition of a silane derivative containing at least one Si–H bond to an unsaturated organic compound (6), eg,

$$HSiCl_3 + H_2C{=}CH_2 \rightarrow CH_3CH_2SiCl_3$$

The simple derivatives of the parent silanes continue to be studied at an expanding rate, since they have been the source of extremely significant advances in the understanding of chemical bonding, structure, and certain fundamental properties of silicon compounds in general (7). This area has been a challenge for the modern theories of valency and only recently have many of the derivatives been prepared, their structures and properties studied, and theoretical interpretations of the results been proposed. Many questions still remain to be answered, particularly in the areas of nuclear magnetic resonance spectroscopy, structure, and that panacea of most silicon chemists, the use of silicon's $3d$ orbitals.

Bibliography

"Silicon Compounds" in *ECT* 1st ed., Vol. 12, pp. 365–392, by E. G. Rochow, Harvard University; "Silicones" in *ECT* 1st ed., Vol. 12, pp. 393–413, by R. R. McGregor, Mellon Institute of Industrial Research.

1. C. Friedel and J. M. Crafts, *Compt. Rend.* **56**, 592 (1863).
2. H. W. Post, *Silicones and Other Organic Silicon Compounds*, Reinhold Publishing Corp., New York, 1949, Chap. 3.
3. A. Stock, *Hydrides of Boron and Silicon*, Cornell University Press, Ithaca, 1933.
4. J. M. Wilson, *Research* **12**, 91 (1959).
5. C. H. Lewis, H. C. Kelly, M. B. Giusto, and S. Johnson, *J. Electrochem. Soc.* **108**, 1114 (1961).
6. R. J. H. Voorhoeve, *Organohalosilanes, Precursors to Silicones*, American Elsevier Publishing Co., New York, 1967.
7. E. A. V. Ebsworth, *Volatile Silicon Compounds*, The Macmillan Co., New York, 1963.

CHARLES H. VAN DYKE
Carnegie-Mellon University

SYNTHETIC INORGANIC SILICATES

The synthetic inorganic silicates are, for the most part, the so-called "soluble silicates" formed with the alkali metal and quaternary ammonium bases. Insoluble synthetic inorganic silicates, which are products of reaction with the alkali metal silicates are also considered.

The soluble silicates are generally recognized as viscous aqueous alkaline solutions with a high proportion of silica largely in an ionized form. In the anhydrous state, they are vitreous and crystalline. With varying proportions (or ratios) of silica to alkali metal oxide, the cooled melts form glasses over a broad range of composition. In some portions of this range, the glasses dissolve readily in water, but in other portions the rate of solution is extremely low. In other ranges there may be a rapid formation of definite crystalline compounds not all of which are readily soluble. The simple alkali metal silicates are practically unknown as minerals except for some insoluble lithium silicate crystals and the recently discovered highly siliceous crystalline sodium silicates at Lake Magadi, Kenya (1).

Knowledge of soluble glass may be traced to ancient Phoenician sailors as Vail suggests, and there are alchemical records (2). Goethe experimented with it about 1768 but industrial development clearly stems from the broad range of experiments made by von Fuchs about 1825 and his promotional efforts. Industrial manufacture traces to Walcker who dissolved sand in liquid caustic solutions about 1828 and Dunn and van Baerle who developed dissolvers. Some "waterglass," as von Fuchs called it, was produced in the U.S.A. before Elkinton patented his furnace in 1863, as a major step in replacing the rosin then popular in laundry soaps. Vail was instrumental in the development of adhesives for the manufacture of corrugated boxes and the recognition of the importance of silicate as a promoter of detergency in soap. De Brunn and Patrick developed silica and aluminosilicate gels and C. L. Baker has been largely responsible for the great growth of crystallized alkali silicates and their methods of manufacture. Since their introduction about 1930, production has increased to about 550 million lb/yr.

Sodium silicates are among the basic alkalis of industry; for a few applications potassium and recently lithium or quaternary ammonium silicates are preferred. Cesium and rubidium silicates are not produced in commercial quantities. The first large demand for sodium silicate was as a "builder" for bar soap (see Detergency) and it continues as an important component in powdered soaps as well as synthetic and liquid detergents. The next major use in historical sequence was as an adhesive for corrugated boxes. A third major use is for the preparation of silica gels, either pure or complex, which are formed by the reaction of metal ions and acids with the soluble silicates for use largely as a base for catalysts and as pigments and absorbents. The miscellaneous uses of soluble silicates in cements, coatings, textile bleaching, abrasives, water treatment, soil treatment, etc, make a fourth division nearly equivalent to any of the others in tonnage production.

Terminology. While the recognized chemical nomenclature is now more generally used, the forms "silicate of soda" for sodium silicate and "silicate of potash" for potassium silicate are still encountered in commerce. The more colloquial term "waterglass" is now nearly obsolete, at least in the United States. It is generally taken to refer to a concentrated viscous solution of sodium silicate having a ratio of about $3.3 SiO_2/Na_2O$.

In the patent literature especially, one must be wary of reference to $Na_2O:SiO_2$ or Na_2SiO_3, as these formulas are often used loosely to refer to sodium silicate solutions of higher silica ratios. The term "ratio" itself is used as in ceramic chemistry to relate the composition in terms of the oxides. Reference to "more alkaline ratios" and "more siliceous ratios" indicates higher proportions of the respective oxides in the compounds. There is no intention to suggest relative pH or concentration. At times reference may be made to "neutral" soluble silicates and to "alkaline" soluble silicates. The "neutral" soluble silicate glass or solution usually has a ratio of about $3.3 SiO_2/Na_2O$. An "alkaline" glass or solution is usually thought of as having a ratio of about $2.0 SiO_2/Na_2O$, but the crystalline sodium metasilicates and crystalline products of higher proportion of alkali metal oxide are also sometimes referred to as the "alkaline" silicates.

The soluble silicates may be described by referring them to the hypothetical orthosilicic acid, $Si(OH)_4$ or H_4SiO_4, and the metasilicic acid H_2SiO_3; these are often used both for formulas calculated from analysis and for products having a definite composition. Thus the mixture called sodium orthosilicate has the analytical composition $2NaO \cdot SiO_2 \cdot 2H_2O$ or $Na_4SiO_4 \cdot 2H_2O$, and likewise the *definite compound*, anhydrous sodium metasilicate, may be referred to as Na_2SiO_3 or $Na_2O \cdot SiO_2$, using the molecular oxide formula.

In this review commercial products are designated by the names used in industry. These names include "sodium sesquisilicate" for $3Na_2O.2SiO_2$ and its hydrates. Products of indefinite composition are frequently encountered and it is convenient to specify them in terms of the ratio as, for example, 2.1 SiO_2/Na_2O. These ratios as given are to be understood on a *mole basis* unless the weight ratio is specifically indicated. This is different from the usual industrial practice of specifying the soluble silicates in terms of the *ratio by weight* of SiO_2 to metal oxide (M_2O), or in the case of the alkaline crystalline products the ratio by weight of Na_2O to SiO_2. For the sodium salt, the weight ratio is quite close to that of the mole ratio. Thus a weight ratio, such as 3.22 SiO_2/Na_2O, of a sodium silicate is transformed to the mole ratio (in this case 3.32 SiO_2/Na_2O) by the multiplication factor 1.03; for potassium silicate the weight-percent ratio is multiplied by the factor 1.57 to give the mole ratio. For lithium silicate and tetraethanolamine silicate the factors are respectively 0.50 and 6.65.

Lithium silicate has only recently become commercially available and is usually specified on the basis of the mole ratio. The quaternary ammonium silicates also have become available in commerce and have usually been specified according to the mole ratio of silica to quaternary ammonium ion rather than quaternary ammonium oxide. For this, the multiplication factor to convert from the weight ratio is 3.32.

Commercial Products

Commercial sodium silicates are amorphous vitreous or crystalline hydrated and anhydrous powders and aqueous liquids with viscosities ranging from 0.5 to 600,000 P at 20° (Fig. 1). The potassium silicates are sold either as glass or as aqueous liquid, while the synthetic lithium silicates are sold only as liquids since the glasses and crystalline solids are virtually insoluble. The soluble quaternary ammonium silicates are available both as liquids and easily soluble solids. Typical amorphous commercial silicates, sodium and potassium, are listed in Table 1. The sodium silicates vary from

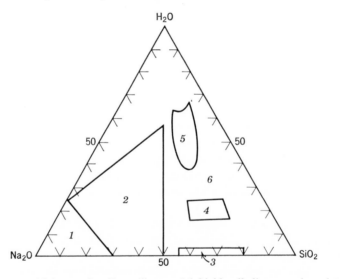

Fig. 1. Commercial forms of sodium silicate: (*1*) highly alkaline granular mixtures including sodium orthosilicate; (*2*) granular crystallized compositions, principally sodium metasilicate and its hydrates; (*3*) glasses; (*4*) dehydrated liquids; (*5*) commercial liquids; (*6*) usually unstable liquids and gels.

Table 1. Typical Amorphous Commercial Silicates, Sodium and Potassium

Commercial silicates	Wt ratio,[a] SiO$_2$/M$_2$O	Mole ratio,[a] SiO$_2$/M$_2$O	M$_2$O,[a] %	SiO$_2$, %	Softening point,[b] °C	Flow point,[c] °C	H$_2$O, %	Baumé, 20°C	Sp gr, d$_{20}^{20}$	Viscosity, 20°C, P	pH
Anhydrous glasses											
sodium silicates	3.22	3.33	23.5	75.7	655	840					
	2.00	2.06	33.0	66.0	590	760					
potassium silicates	2.50	3.92	28.3	70.7	700	905					
Hydrated amorphous powders											
sodium silicates	3.22	3.33	19.2	61.8			18.5				
	2.00	2.06	27.0	54.0			18.5				
Solutions											
sodium silicates	1.60	1.65	19.7	31.5				58.5	1.68	70	12.8
	2.00	2.06	18.0	36.0				59.3	1.69	700	12.2
	2.50	2.58	10.6	26.5				42.0	1.41	0.6	11.7
	2.88	2.97	11.0	31.7				47.0	1.49	9.6	11.5
	3.22	3.32	8.9	28.7				41.0	1.39	1.8	11.3
	3.75	3.86	6.8	25.3				35.0	1.32	2.2	10.8
potassium silicates	2.50	3.93	8.3	20.8				29.8	1.259	0.4	11.30
	2.20	3.45	9.05	19.9				30.0	1.261	0.07	11.55
	2.10	3.30	12.5	26.3				40.0	1.381	10.5	11.70
	1.80	2.83	16.4	29.5				47.7	1.490	13.0	12.15

[a] M represents Na and K respectively.
[b] Viscosity reaches 4 × 10^7 P.
[c] Viscosity reaches 10^5 P.

about 0.5 SiO_2/Na_2O to 4 SiO_2/Na_2O. The glasses are classified as to particle-size range and ratio. The liquids are differentiated on the basis of specific gravity (°Baumé) and ratio, which ranges from about 1.6 SiO_2/Na_2O to 4 SiO_2/Na_2O (see Table 1). The potassium silicates vary from about 1.5 SiO_2/K_2O to 2.5 SiO_2/K_2O on a weight basis which corresponds on a molecular basis to 2.3 SiO_2/K_2O to 3.8 SiO_2/K_2O.

The crystalline products which are commercially available are the anhydrous sodium metasilicate and the hydrated metasilicates, $Na_2SiO_3.5H_2O$ and $Na_2SiO_3.-9H_2O$. The hydrated sodium sesquisilicate, $Na_3HSiO_4.5H_2O$ ($3Na_2O.2SiO_2.11H_2O$) is also available. The anhydrous sodium sesquisilicate and the technically anhydrous orthosilicate are generally conceded to be mixtures of caustic soda and sodium metasilicate, sometimes in integral form. (An "integral" mixture is one in which each particle is an aggregate or agglomerate of the components of the mixture bound together in approximately average proportions without compound formation; a "me-

Table 2. Typical Commercial Lithium Silicate Solutions

Wt ratio, SiO_2/Li_2O	Mole ratio, SiO_2/Li_2O	Li_2O, %	Na_2O, %	SiO_2, %	Density, g/cm³	Viscosity, cP	pH
9.4	4.7	2.2		20.7	1.17		10.6–10.8
9.6	4.8	2.1		20.0		4	11
11.8	5.9	1.6		18.8	1.18		
17.0	8.5	1.2		20.0		2.5	11
$SiO_2/(Li_2O + Na_2O)$	$SiO_2/(Li_2O + Na_2O)$						
6.5	4.1	1.8	1.2	19.6	1.19		10.7

Table 3. Typical Commercial Quaternary Ammonium Silicate Solutions

Mole ratio $SiO_2/\overset{+}{N}R_4$	Mole ratio $SiO_2/(\overset{+}{N}R_4)_2O$	Wt % ratio,[a] $SiO_2/(\overset{+}{N}R_4)_2O$	NR_4, %	SiO_2, %	Sp gr, d_{20}^{20}	Viscosity, 20°C, P	pH
			Solutions				
0.5	1.2	0.37	54.5	10.0	1.24	10.7	>13
4.5	10.8	2.8	21.5	30.0	1.23	0.2	11.5
7.5	18.0	5.5	11.0	30.0	1.26	0.2	11.2
9.5	22.4	7.0	12.9	45.0	1.41	0.6	11.1
12.5	30.0	9.0	10.0	45.0	1.40	0.6	11.1
			Hydrated amorphous powders[a]				
7.5	15.6	4.3	28.4	66.5			
9.5	19.7	5.9	24.0	71.0			

[a] Both solutions contain 5.0% H_2O and the time to complete solution at 25°C (50 g water) is 2 min max.

chanical" mixture is one formed merely by mixing until the separate and distinct particles of the components are distributed evenly but remain subject to unmixing.)

Very little has been published on the properties of lithium silicate solutions. Table 2 gives some of the properties of commercially available lithium silicates (3). Typical properties of the commercial quaternary ammonium silicate solutions are shown in Table 3. Silicates with simple cations, such as the tetraethanol and methyl triethanol ammonium ion, are readily available and more complex cations may be obtained on order.

Manufacture

Typically, sodium and potassium silicates are manufactured in ordinary glass furnaces by melting sand with soda ash at about 1450°C (see Glass) (4). The ratio of the glass, or the aqueous liquid, is determined by the proportion of sand and alkali added to the furnace. The reaction follows the simple equation

$$Na_2CO_3 + n\ SiO_2 \rightarrow Na_2O. nSiO_2 + CO_2 \uparrow$$

Until recently sodium sulfate was the more economical source of alkali in Europe. The complex reaction of the sand, sodium sulfate, and carbon charged to the furnace may be consolidated roughly as

$$2\ Na_2SO_4 + 2\ C + n\ SiO_3 \rightarrow 2\ Na_2O. nSiO_2 + S\uparrow + SO_2\uparrow + 2\ CO_2\uparrow$$

Furnaces of the open-hearth regenerative or recuperative type are used but special care and specification of construction materials are needed because, compared to ordinary insoluble glass, the melting temperature is higher and the melt more corrosive. Where the cost of electric power is sufficiently low, electric glass-melting furnaces are very satisfactory (5). These processes are readily amenable to the improved operating conditions possible with computer controls.

Commercial soda ash (see Alkali and chlorine industries) in the U.S. is quite pure and makes little contribution to the impurities in the final product. Natural ash from Wyoming trona (see Sodium compounds) has even less chloride (usually below 40 ppm) and usually less sulfate than the product of the ammonia–soda process. It does, however, sometimes have over 200 ppm of iron, calcium, and magnesium insolubles compared to less than 100 for Solvay process ash. The product from western-desert salt-lake brines is a little higher in sulfates and chlorides and may have over 1% of borax but less insoluble impurities. This is not always true of the sodium hydroxide or of the sodium sulfate and carbon mixtures, a fact which is sometimes significant in applications where high purity is critical. Since when soda ash is used the amount of impurity in the sand controls the amount of insoluble product in the glass, care is taken to control and maintain a low proportion of impurities in the glass by using a suitable sand (Table 4). The usual sources of No. 1 glass sand are the bank sands of New Jersey and the sandstones of the Allegheny mountains and the Mississippi Valley deposited by ancient seas. This sand, crushed and screened to about 20–100 mesh and washed with water (and acid if necessary), has less than 0.03% Fe_2O_3 and costs from about $2.25 to $4.50 per ton fob the mine depending on the usual economic factors. The freight costs often exceed the material cost.

The glass formed may be dissolved in rotary dissolvers at atmospheric pressure as it is drawn from the furnace or, after cooling and crushing, may be dissolved under pressure with steam. The liquid product is sold at the highest concentration which may be

Table 4. Range of Composition of Typical Sodium Silicate Glasses,
3.3 SiO_2/Na_2O, Manufactured at Different Plants

Assay	Wt %	
	low	high
Na_2O	23.21	23.89
SiO_2	75.36	76.00
K_2O	0.00	0.10
Fe_2O_3	0.005	0.030
TiO_2	0.004	0.052
Al_2O_3	0.15	0.51
CaO	0.032	0.17
MgO	0.004	0.10
CaO	0.00012	0.0022
NiO	0.00008	0.0026
SO_3	0.008	0.19
CO_2	nil	0.23
Cl	0.025	0.12
ignition loss	0.03	0.36
ratio by wt SiO_2/Na_2O	3.154	3.249

readily handled and is usually quite turbid from a suspension of fine undissolved glass and unmelted sand and the reaction products of impurities in the sand and water. Much of this impurity will settle out rather rapidly and quite satisfactory alkali-resistant filter aids are available for filtration.

With the increasing availability of caustic soda (see Alkali and chlorine industries) there is a tendency to substitute sodium hydroxide for the carbonate or the sulfate either in the glass-melting operation or by dissolving sand directly in liquid caustic. By the latter means, a ratio as high as about 2.7 SiO_2/Na_2O may be obtained; even more siliceous ratios can be obtained by dissolving pure amorphous silica, removing the alkali electrolytically, or by treatment with polymeric resin exchange gels.

The anhydrous crystalline products may be made by melting sodium carbonate and sand at the intended ratio. Such glasses crystallize very rapidly, but the higher the proportion of sodium carbonate the greater is the proportion of carbon dioxide retained in the melt and crystals. Therefore, the anhydrous solids which are more alkaline than the metasilicate are often mechanical or integral mixtures of sodium metasilicate and caustic soda. The hydrated crystalline products are usually formed by preparing a solution of the hydrate composition at a temperature above the melting point and cooling and crystallizing the mass. Numerous variations of this process have been suggested, one of the more interesting being the mixture of fine sand and liquid caustic which on warming and stirring liquefies, finally recrystallizes, and eventually breaks up into a free-flowing mass of integral particles of sodium metasilicate and sodium hydroxide.

Noncrystalline hydrated solids dissolve more rapidly than the anhydrous glasses. Where the hydration is slight the water is usually added by steaming the crushed glass. Where more rapid solution is required, stable solids with more water content may be made by drying the siliceous liquids using ordinary spray-drying techniques.

The ASTM has set up standards for sodium metasilicate (both anhydrous and pentahydrate) and sodium sesquisilicate pentahydrate, as shown in Table 5. AWWA (American Water Works Association) Tentative Spec B409-55T covers 3.25 $SiO_2/$

Table 5. ASTM Standards for Sodium Metasilicate (Anhydrous and Pentahydrate) and Sodium Sesquisilicate Pentahydrate

| | ASTM D537-57 | | | | ASTM D594-41 | |
| | Type 1 | | Type 2 | | | |
Composition	% min	% max	% min	% max	% min	% max
$Na_2SiO_3 \cdot 5H_2O$	98.0					
Na_2SiO_3			91.5			
$3Na_2O \cdot 2SiO_2 \cdot 11H_2O$					9.70	
total alkalinity to methyl orange as Na_2O	28.5	30.0	50.0	52.0	35.5	37.5
total silica as SiO_2	27.5	29.0	45.0		22.5	
matter insoluble in water		0.2		0.3		0.2
carbonates as CO_2		1.2		2.0		

Na_2O at 40°Bé liquid. Government agencies also have procurement specifications. These hydrated crystalline powders are furnished in airtight containers, either drums or bags, with a liner and closure sealed against vapor.

The aqueous liquids are shipped in iron containers and must not be stored in aluminum, galvanized iron, or zinc containers. Dilute hot solutions of 2 SiO_2/Na_2O or more alkaline solutions react vigorously with tin, zinc, or aluminum on initial contact. At ordinary temperatures reaction is very slow even with the more alkaline liquids. The reaction rate is also increased by dilution of the commercial liquid silicates. With very viscous alkaline solutions, attack is negligible except where condensation occurs on the walls above the liquid level. The disilicate solution at concentrations below 55% solids will etch tin, and more alkaline solutions may attack solder.

The insolubility of lithium silicate glasses precludes the preparation of lithium silicate solutions by the ordinary methods, but it has been known since about 1920 that silica gel may be dissolved in a lithium hydroxide solution (6). This may be done at either room temperature or higher temperatures and they also may be formed by the reaction of lithium hydroxide with dealkalized sols and dealkalized silicate solutions (7). Information on the actual methods of manufacture of the commercial quaternary ammonium silicates and production statistics have not been published (see Alkanolamines).

Properties of Anhydrous Silicates

The structure and properties of glasses in general and simple binary glasses in particular are described under Glass. The binary and ternary soluble silicate glasses have been widely used in basic study of theoretical problems, and data are available over a wide range of temperatures and compositions. Briefly, these soluble silicates are simple, two-component systems which form glasses approaching ideality as the proportion of silica is reduced. Somewhat more complex tertiary and quaternary systems may be formed by combining two or more alkali metal oxides. The small silicon ion with a complete octet electron shell and a positive charge has a low polarizability and a strong positive force field. With oxygen it shares electrons with about 51% of ionic bonding and the remainder directional or covalent. The interatomic distance

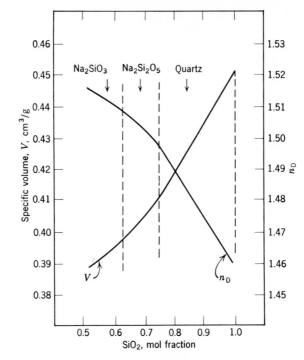

Fig. 2. Refractive index and specific volume of annealed sodium silicate glasses at 20°C (13). Slope changes according to the equilibrium phase range. Courtesy American Ceramic Society.

between silicon and oxygen is generally taken as about 1.62 Å, but may be 1.67 for a bridging link and 1.592 for a nonbridging link in a metasilicate chain (8). For Si—Si, the distance is usually taken as 3.2 Å.

Generalizations on the physicochemical properties of silicate glasses are usually explained by the distribution of the cations in holes in the network of silica and the field strength of the cations in relation to the extent of polarization of the silica. Oxide glasses are very stable and have relatively high softening temperatures because they are a completely crosslinked network with bridging oxygen ions. The crosslinking can be reduced and the softening temperature lowered by introducing metal ions such as sodium or potassium which, having shed an electron, form fairly weak ionic bonds with nonbridging oxygen (Table 6) (9,10). Such ionic bonds lack directionality and there is

Table 6. Coordination and Bond Strength of Oxides in Soluble Silicate Glasses (9,10)

Oxide of	Coordination number	Total dissociation energy M—O, kcal/mole	M—O single bond dissociation energy, kcal/mole	Atom radius, Å	M—O, Å
Si	4	424	106	1.17	1.62
Li	4	144	36	1.50	2.16
Na	6	120	20	1.86	2.30
K	9	115	13	2.27	2.73
Rb	10	115	12	2.43	2.88
Cs	12	114	10	2.62	3.09

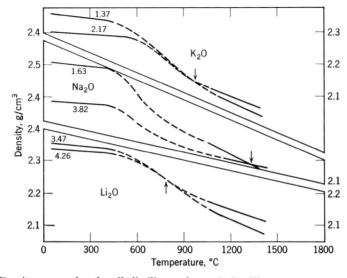

Fig. 3. Density curves for the alkali silicate glasses (15). The curves cross in regions of inversion (arrow) common to each series. The SiO_2/M_2O wt % ratio is shown on each curve. Courtesy Elsevier Publishing Co.

a more or less abrupt change in the properties of the glasses and melts at about 30 mole % metal oxide. The rate of solution, surface tension, and viscosity increase more rapidly with increase in alkali. The coefficient of expansion, the density, and the refractive index increase less rapidly, and the dielectric loss and specific resistance decrease less rapidly. Because of its great field strength, the small lithium ion surrounds itself with single-bonded oxygen ions and forms compact structures. Such a glass has a greater chemical resistance, lower expansion, and higher refractive index than a sodium or potassium glass of analogous composition on a molar basis (11). As the bond between the alkali cation and oxygen is weakened with increasing radius of the alkali ion, the hydration capacity and the rate of solution are increased and the softening temperature is lowered (12).

The refractive index of silicate glasses decreases with increase in concentrations of silica (Fig. 2) (13). As it may be determined simply and precisely it is useful in the control of automated processes. For sodium silicate glasses a simple relationship is

$$N_D = 0.143d + 1.1494$$

where d is the density (14). Somewhat more complicated equations are available for determining the refractive index and dispersion ratio or Abbe number to considerable precision (2). Infrared absorption is dominated by the silica. In the ultraviolet range the 3 SiO_2/M_2O glasses have excellent transmission and may be used to study metallic additives.

The density has been widely studied since it enters into many calculations, sometimes as its reciprocal, specific volume. For sodium silicate the variation of specific volume appears in Figure 2. At 300°C glasses of the same mole ratio are more dense with larger alkali ions than with smaller, but this relationship is reversed by 1400°Cs With the same alkali ion, glasses with the more siliceous ratio change less with tempera. ture increase so that the density-temperature curves for high- and low-ratio glasse-cross (15) (Fig. 3).

The deformation temperature at which viscous flow (10^{11} to 10^{12} P) counteracts thermal expansion becomes approximately constant at about 10 mole % Li_2O, 32 mole % Na_2O, and 45 mole % K_2O.   Glasses under load just below the annealing range of

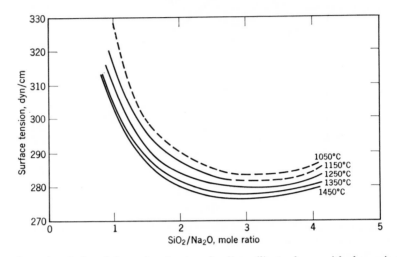

Fig. 4.   Isothermal variation of the surface tension of sodium silicate glasses with change in ratio (2). A minimum is reached at about 3.   Courtesy Reinhold Publishing Corp.

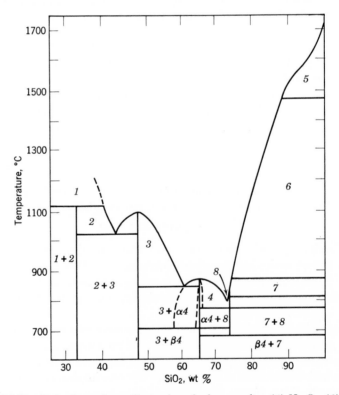

Fig. 5.   Solubility limits for sodium silicates in anhydrous melt: (*1*) Na_2O; (*2*) Na_4SiO_4; (*3*) Na_2SiO_3; (*4*) $Na_2Si_2O_5$; (*5*) cristobalite; (*6*) tridymite; (*7*) quartz; (*8*) $Na_6Si_8O_{19}$ (2).   Courtesy Reinhold Publishing Corp.

about 10^{13} P show an instantaneous elongation and a time-related elongation which are both greater at higher proportions of alkali oxide. Study of the molten glasses is complicated by volatilization of the alkali. The effect is much greater for potassium glasses than lithium glasses and at high concentrations and temperatures. Data by Parmelee for the surface tension of sodium glasses from 1050 to 1450°C appear to be accurate (2) (Fig. 4). In the lithium system the surface tension is higher than in the sodium system and increases much more rapidly with increasing alkali ion; the potassium and larger alkali ions have a lower value and fall off rapidly with increasing alkali.

The interfacial tension between these glasses and the oxide film in most metals decreases as the oxide film becomes more basic. Siliceous sodium silicates (eg 3 $SiO_2/$ Na_2O) will wet gold or platinum with a contact angle of 90° or more, but an oxidized platinum surface has a much smaller contact angle of 40° or lower. Separation into two liquid phases may occur in the siliceous range of glasses below about 20 mole % of sodium oxide, apparently because too few oxygen ions are present to screen the sodium ions satisfactorily. This screening demand increases from cesium to rubidium to potassium to sodium to lithium, so that the fields of glass formation decrease in that order. There is actual phase separation and opalescence in lithium and sodium systems and some hint of it in potassium systems. Crystallization has been studied in most of these binary and some ternary systems, and the diagram for sodium silicates is shown in Figure 5. The metasilicate and more alkaline salts usually crystallize rapidly, but the disilicate and more siliceous salts are often difficult to initiate and grow slowly. The rate of growth of sodium disilicate crystals at 810°C has been found convenient to study and the rate is 55 μ/min at an undercooling of 60°C. The melting entropy is 7.3 cal/mole.

Data on thermodynamic properties are scattered and usually fragmentary (2). Sharp determined an equation for mean specific heat,

$$C_m = A_0T + C_0/(0.00146T + 1)$$

where A_0 and C_0 are the sum of the weight fractions in the glass multiplied by the constants A and C, respectively, for each component (16). These constants are:

Component	A	C
SiO_2	0.000468	0.1657
Na_2O	0.0008299	0.2229
K_2O	0.000445	0.1756

Charles gives activity coefficients and free energy of mixing for binary glasses between 600 and 1700°C (17).

The sodium and potassium silicate glasses begin to soften between about 550 and 670°C and to flow between 730 and 870°C, the potassium silicates having the higher softening and flow points. The anhydrous sodium metasilicate, since it is crystalline, has a definite melting point at 1089°C, and therefore has the highest flow point of all commercially available silicates (Table 7) (3). The general range of viscosity of molten sodium silicates above the softening range is given in Figure 6 (18).

Mixed sodium and potassium silicate glasses reach a viscosity of 10^{10} P at lower temperatures than either of the simple glasses. At 590°C this minimum is at about 18 mole % of total alkali as K_2O, whereas at 508°C the minimum is about 35%. The surface hardness of sodium silicate glasses, measured by the Vickers diamond pyramid test, ranges from about 388 to 505 kg/mm² and ternary mixtures exhibit a maximum

Table 7. High-Temperature Behavior of Anhydrous Sodium and Potassium Silicates (3)

Silicates	Mole ratio, SiO_2/M_2O	SiO_2, %	M_2O, %	Approx softening point,[a] °C	Approx flow point,[b] °C
sodium	3.87	79.0	21.0	665	870
	3.33	76.3	23.7	655	840
	3.00	74.4	25.6	640	825
	2.48	70.6	29.4	615	790
	2.07	66.7	33.3	590	760
	1.65	61.5	38.5	565	730
	1.00	49.2	50.8		1089[c]
potassium	3.92	71.4	28.6	690–740	910
	3.30	67.7	32.3	690–740	890

[a] Viscosity reaches 4×10^7 P.   [b] Viscosity reaches 10^5 P.   [c] True melting point.

hardness at about 12 mole % Na_2O and 8 mole % K_2O. The modulus of compressibility of the binary glasses is on the order of 10^{12} dyn/cm^2.

The mobility of the alkali ions in the silicate glasses is evident from electrolysis and diffusion experiments. The specific resistance has been determined for the binary and some ternary and quaternary systems from room temperature to the maximum at about 1450°C. The general trend is shown in Figure 6. Equivalent conductances are in the order of $Li_2O > Na_2O > K_2O$, but below 22% M_2O the order is $Na_2O > Li_2O > K_2O$

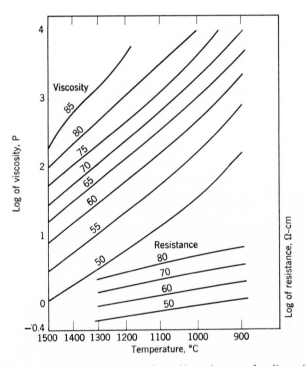

Fig. 6. Smoothed curves of the viscosity and specific resistance of sodium silicate glasses with 50–85% SiO_2 at temperatures of 900–1500°C prepared from published data (18). Courtesy Elsevier Publishing Co.

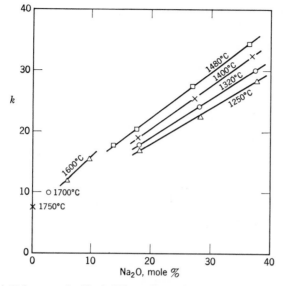

Fig. 7. Solubility of H_2O vapor in Na_2O–SiO_2 melts (19); k is Ostwald's solubility coefficient. Courtesy *Glass Industry*.

The solubility of CO_2 rises steeply with increasing alkali content (from less than 0.005% at 30% Na_2O to 0.06% at 40% Na_2O at 1000°C) and decreasing temperature (from less than 0.005% at 1200°C to 0.06% at 40% Na_2O at 1000°C) at normal pressures. Helium is also quite soluble in molten lithium, sodium, and potassium silicates. Water especially changes the properties of the glass since it ruptures the Si—O—Si bridge to form SiOH. Figure 7 shows the solubility of water vapor in sodium silicate melts at temperatures from about 1250 to 1750°C with up to about 40 mole % of Na_2O, in terms of Ostwald's solubility coefficient, k, the volume of water vapor dissolved in a unit volume of melt (19). The limiting value of the hydration ratio H_2O/SiO_2 theoretically possible for glass compositions in the range of $M_2O \cdot (2–5)SiO_2$ is 1.5, 4.5, 11.0, 13.0, and 15.0 for lithium, sodium, potassium, rubidium, and cesium, respectively. The maximum value of the SiO_2/M_2O ratio of alkali silicate glasses at which they may be dissolved in hot water at normal pressure is less than 2 for lithium silicate, much less than 4 for sodium silicate, in the range 4.5–5.0 for potassium silicate, and about 5.0–5.5 for rubidium and cesium silicates. For most applications the soluble silicates are used as aqueous solutions and therefore the process of dissolving the glasses is of commercial importance. Sodium silicate glasses more alkaline than about a disilicate (2 SiO_2/Na_2O) dissolve fairly readily, and glasses of about the metasilicate ratio and more alkaline usually crystallize and are quite rapidly soluble even in cool water. The glasses more siliceous than the disilicate will dissolve, but very slowly unless they are first hydrated by steam under some pressure. The amount of water should be restricted in order to reduce the initial leaching of alkali which leaves a difficultly soluble siliceous residue. Three parts of water to one part of glass is usually recommended for the more siliceous sodium glasses. During hydration under steam pressure, water penetrates progressively more deeply, but the line of demarcation between the hydrated and virtually anhydrous glass is clear in a cross section of such glass after cooling. As hydration proceeds the outer layer progressively dissolves away, forming a solution with approximately the ratio of the original glass. The rate

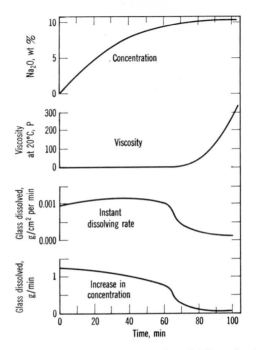

Fig. 8. Effect of SiO_2/Na_2O ratio and temperature on the solubility of sodium silicate glasses (2). Courtesy Reinhold Publishing Corp.

of agitation has been found to affect the clarity of the final solution. The solution rate is largely dependent on the ratio, concentration, temperature, pressure, and particle size (Fig. 8).

Potassium silicate glasses are more hygroscopic and dissolve more rapidly in water than sodium silicates under comparable conditions, whereas lithium silicate glasses are so insoluble or reprecipitate so rapidly that they are not useful for preparing commer-

Table 8. Solution Rates of Amorphous Sodium and Potassium Silicate Powders (3 parts water + 1 part silicate powder) (3)

Silicate (wt % ratio)	Particle (Tyler screen) sizing, mesh	Time needed to dissolve		
		50%	75%	100%
At 25°C (77°F)				
3.22 ratio sodium, anhydrous glass	−65	60 hr		
3.22 ratio sodium, hydrated (18.5% H_2O)	−100	19 min	45 min	
2.00 ratio sodium, anhydrous glass	−65	10 hr	70 hr	
2.00 ratio sodium, hydrated (18.5% H_2O)	−100	27 sec	54 sec	
2.50 ratio potassium, anhydrous glass	−65	60 min	7.5 hr	48 hr
At 50°C (122°F)				
3.22 ratio sodium, anhydrous glass	−65	15% in 30 min		
3.22 ratio sodium, hydrated (18.5% H_2O)	−100	54 sec	76 sec	100 sec
2.00 ratio sodium, anhydrous glass	−65	17 min	1 hr	
2.00 ratio sodium, hydrated (18.5% H_2O)	−100	15 sec	22 sec	29 sec
2.50 ratio potassium, anhydrous glass	−65	12 min	45 min	

cial solutions, and other methods must be employed. An idea of the relative solution rates of hydrated and anhydrous glasses may be obtained from Table 8.

Properties of Hydrous Silicates

The liquid aqueous soluble silicate solutions are clear or opalescent, colloidal Newtonian liquids until they reach the concentration at which the viscosity rises sharply. More pure solutions may be obtained by special techniques using highly purified forms of silica and caustic soda or soda ash. These solutions have well-marked colloidal properties which are responsible for many properties not found in strictly ionic solutions, especially when the ratio rises above about 2 SiO_2/Na_2O. The negatively charged colloidal ions are often spoken of as micelles. The micelles are stabilized by the alkali ions, some of which appear to be trapped within the micelle and others absorbed on the surface, while others are ionized in the solution. The replacement of these ions by hydrogen or by other ions of the substrate or additive usually results in gelation or solidification. Some moisture will remain in a soluble silicate film until it is heated above about 550°C. These films are more resilient than the anhydrous glass itself.

The properties of the liquid silicates vary along smooth curves without sharp breaks. Since the ion, micelle, and colloidal silica components are in dynamic equilibrium, phase diagrams based on three-component systems can be determined. However, the rate of establishing equilibrium is finite and can be accelerated by the usual methods, such as increasing temperature.

While the exact constitution of alkali silicate solutions is not clearly established, it has been convenient to speak of "crystalloidal" and "colloidal" silica since these forms are readily differentiated by determining the greenish-yellow molybdate complex which forms only with ionized and unionized silicic acid. Therefore, the crystalloidal silicate is considered as monomeric, and colloidal silicate as polymeric or aggregated. In the more alkaline solutions the ions are usually assumed to be the dissociation products of orthosilicic acid, H_4SiO_4. The first dissociation constant, pK_1, is reported as 9.85 and the second, pK_2, as 11.8.

The colloidal component has been studied by light scattering, and the polymerization or aggregation increases with increasing ratio, as shown by the weight-average molecular weights of sodium silicate and potassium silicate in Table 9 (3). The aggregation is increased by decreasing pH or by sufficient dilution. In very dilute solutions the effect of decreasing pH may dominate. It is generally agreed that after dilution equilibrium is established rapidly, but may require considerable time after shifting the ratio. There is, however, some conflict in the apparent effect of dilution when turbidity measurements and determinations of crystalloidal silica are compared. The constitution of the colloidal constituent has been further studied by preparing trimethylsilyl derivatives which are subsequently analyzed by gas chromatography (20). For sodium silicate solutions the monomer SiO_4^{4-} was always the most abundant species, followed in turn by the dimer $Si_2O_7^{6-}$ and the trimer $Si_3O_{10}^{8-}$. A cyclic tetramer $(SiO_3)_4^{8-}$ was found, as well as polysilicate structures of higher complexity. These relationships were affected by the nature of the cation.

It is well known that the lithium ion is much smaller and has a much greater charge density than other alkali metal ions. However, it is more hydrated, and therefore is larger in aqueous solution than the other alkali metal ions and stabilizes colloidal

Table 9. Weight-Average Molecular Weights in Alkali Metal Silicate
Solutions of Varying Ratios (3)

Alkali metal silicates	Mole ratio	Wt-av mol wt in soln
sodium silicates, SiO_2/Na_2O	0.48	60
	1.01	90
	1.69	120
	2.09	160
	2.62	265
	3.30	320
potassium silicates, SiO_2/K_2O	1.00	56
	1.75	115
	2.50	295
	2.80	304
	3.31	495
	3.62	628
	3.97	848

silica at much higher SiO_2/Li_2O ratios than the others (Table 10) (21). For instance, it forms stable solutions at ratios above 20 SiO_2/Li_2O. However, below the disilicate ratio an insoluble precipitate will form on heating merely to about 50°C. The solutions at higher ratios resemble silica sols in their properties and colloidal silica predominates over crystalloidal silica above ratios of about 5 SiO_2/Li_2O.

Table 10. Comparison of Ionic Relationship of Alkali Metal Ions with
Coordination No. 6 in Water Solutions (21)

Properties	Li	Na	K	Rb	Cs
crystal radius, Å	0.60	0.95	1.33	1.48	1.69
approx hydrated radius, Å	3.40	2.76	2.32	2.28	2.28
approx hydration number (from transference data)	25.3	16.6	10.5		9.9
hydration energy, kcal/mol	12.3	9.7	7.7	7.0	6.3
ionic mobility at infinite dilution, 18°C	33.5	43.5	64.6	67.5	68

The aqueous liquids can be completely identified by any two properties chosen from a group such as the density, ratio, % alkali, % silica, and viscosity. The viscosity and specific gravity are usually indicated in specifying silicate solutions. When stored properly in tightly closed steel drums or other containers made of nonreactive materials, the solutions are stable for years. They will react slowly with glass and absorb carbon dioxide, or lose water even though corked tightly. All these factors, or the addition of an extraneous salt, may cause a considerable change in viscosity. Even thermodynamically unstable 3.3 SiO_2/Na_2O solutions have been stored for fifteen years in iron bombs without forming crystals or even showing a measurable change in viscosity. However, crystallization may occur if the solution is kept hot or is seeded. The more alkaline sodium silicate liquids, when concentrated to a thick gum, are quite sticky or tacky and may be pulled out like taffy. At the more siliceous end of the range such highly concentrated solutions show little tack but are plastic enough to form into balls which show a surprising elasticity, even somewhat better than that of a tennis ball.

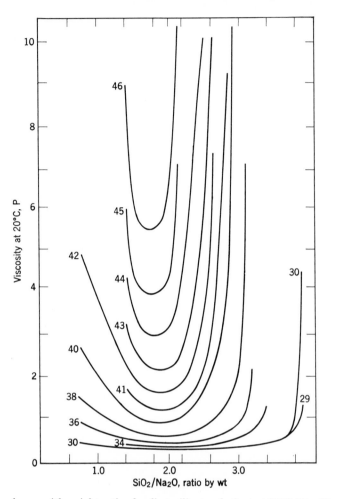

Fig. 9. Viscosity change with weight ratio of sodium silicate solutions at 20°C (2). Numbers on lines are % solids.

Sodium silicate solutions are notable for the very distinct minimum viscosity at about 2.0 SiO_2/Na_2O for solutions of constant solids content (Fig. 9). Potassium silicate solutions of similar mole ratio and concentration are much more viscous than the comparable sodium silicate. Potassium silicate solutions also possess very little tack, showing that the structural characteristics are different from those of similar sodium silicate solutions. Mixtures of sodium and potassium silicate solutions show a definite maximum viscosity at compositions which are controlled by the ratio and concentration of the original solution. The maximum is more pronounced at higher mole ratios and shifts toward higher potassium silicate proportions in the mixture as the mole ratio increases. For similar ratios and similar solids content, lithium silicate solutions have higher viscosities than those of sodium silicate solutions. Lithium silicate solutions above a solids content of about 15% show a maximum viscosity value at a mole ratio of 4.8 SiO_2/Li_2O as shown in Figure 10 (22).

The variety of concentrations and ratios of the quaternary ammonium silicates, which may be made available in stable form, is much greater than that of the alkali

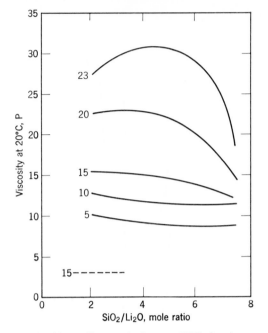

Fig. 10. The viscosity of lithium silicate solutions at 20°C showing a maximum viscosity with increasing concentration and ratio instead of the minimum found in the sodium silicate system (22).

metal silicates (3). Much higher ratios with good solubility can be prepared. These solutions may be readily dehydrated and redissolved in water. The anhydrous products of ratios below $2.5\,SiO_2/NR_4^+$ are viscous oils, anhydrous materials in the ratio range of 3–6.5 are pliable sticky solids, and at higher ratios the anhydrous materials are dry and form free-flowing powders. The solutions also maintain reasonably low viscosities at concentrations of up to 50% silica.

A mixture of sodium and potassium silicate dries somewhat more rapidly than either alone, but the drying of sodium silicate films is more complete than that of potassium silicates of similar composition; the water retention is a direct function of the alkalinity with the higher ratio silicates retaining less water. If the drying is carried out rapidly at about the boiling point, the solutions intumesce and form a solid mass of bubbles having thirty to 100 times the original volume. Films of lithium silicate solution at higher silica ratio dry more quickly than those at lower ratios but show little strength of adhesion to glass or metal. They also tend to retain less water at temperatures of about 100°C or more than do the other alkali metal silicate films. The organic alkali of the quaternary ammonium silicates can be destroyed and volatilized by heating. The effect is a function of the molecular weight of the cation and its ratio as well as the temperature and duration of heating. Between 250 and 300°C most of the organic ion is lost by volatilization.

The boiling point and freezing point are not much affected by concentration in silicate solutions having colloidal silica ions. Ice tends to separate more readily from concentrated solutions of the more siliceous sodium silicates; a solution of $3.9\,SiO_2/Na_2O$ with 6.4% Na_2O was found to form ice crystals at about 0°C, but was readily homogenized after thawing. Potassium, lithium, and organic ammonium silicate solutions are not usually affected by freezing at commercial concentrations.   All that is required is thorough remixing.

The thermodynamic properties have been investigated inadequately.   McCready reported the specific heat in a range of sodium silicate solutions (2).   At 2 moles of

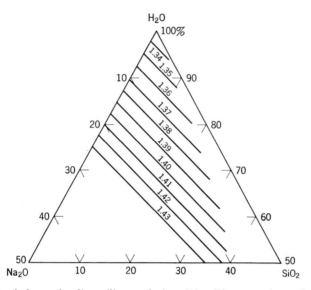

Fig. 11.   Refractive indexes of sodium silicate solutions (2).   These may be used as a partial check on analyses.   Lines show constant refractive index.   Courtesy Reinhold Publishing Corp.

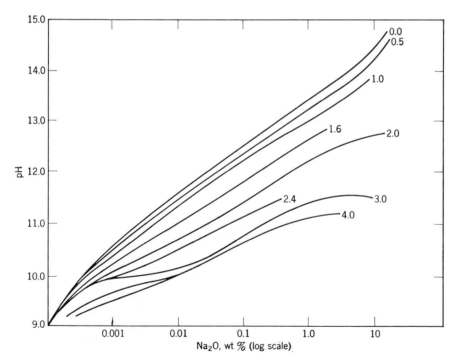

Fig. 12.   pH of sodium silicate solutions at 20°C (2).   Numbers on lines are SiO_2/Na_2O ratio by weight. Courtesy Reinhold Publishing Corp.

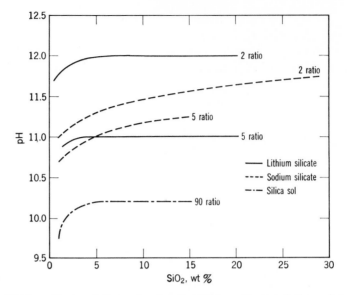

Fig. 13. pH of lithium silicate solutions, showing that lithium silicate solutions of similar composition vary in pH much more widely than the other alkali silicates (22).

Na_2O per 1000 g, the specific heat varies from about 0.87 for Na_2SiO_3 to 0.72 for $3.3\,SiO_2/Na_2O$ solution. The heats of solution of glass in water have been reported as about 250 cal/g for a disilicate and 135 cal/g for $3.3\,SiO_2/Na_2O$.

The electrical conductivity is high in alkaline solutions at low solids concentration where dissociation is nearly complete, but even in the most alkaline solutions conductivity is low at high concentrations. The time after dilution for the silicate to readjust to its equilibrium condition and to reach stable conductivity values increases with decreasing radius of the alkali ion and increasing silica ratio, except in lithium silicates which form an exception. Index of refraction increases with density and decreases with increase in ratio. This is a sensitive method of analysis and, in applying it, it is important to be sure that equilibrium has been established. The lines of constant refractive index over a wide range of sodium silicate compositions at 20°C are shown in Figure 11. Although the silicate ion affects the intensity of alkalinity (pH), the micelle has a greater effect since the pH is lower at high ratios of SiO_2 to Na_2O. For ratios of $3.0\,SiO_2/Na_2O$ and higher, the pH reaches a maximum of 11.5 as the total concentration is increased, and there are indications of such a maximum at about pH 13 when the ratio is 2.0 (Fig. 12). Sodium metasilicate has a pH of nearly 14 at 10% Na_2O. Potassium silicate and quaternary alkanolammonium silicates at similar mole ratio and concentration of alkali are not very different in pH from the sodium silicates. At mole ratios lower than about $3.5\,SiO_2/Li_2O$, lithium silicate solutions have a higher pH than the sodium silicate solutions of a comparable molecular ratio but, above this ratio, the other alkali metal silicate solutions become higher (Fig. 13).

As the solutions are titrated with acids the silica micelles appear to condense and finally form a gelatinous mass which contains all the liquid at concentrations even as low as 200 moles of water for each mole of SiO_2. At even lower concentrations only a sol will result. Purified sols containing 50% of silica are now formed by a complex series of steps including removal of the salts of neutralization, addition of stabilizers,

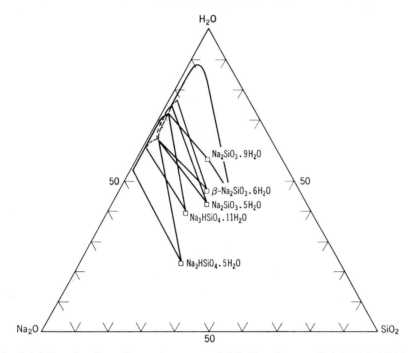

Fig. 14. Solubility of sodium silicates in water at 25°C (2). Courtesy Reinhold Publishing Corp.

and heat treatment to condense the silica particles. Because of the higher stability, lithium and quaternary ammonium silicate solutions can be concentrated to higher solids content before gelation occurs than aqueous sodium and potassium silicate systems.

The sodium and potassium silicate solutions at commercial concentrations are miscible with only small amounts of the usual organic water-miscible solvents. The polyols, such as glycerol, sorbitol, sugar, and glycols, are generally miscible to a much larger degree. Lithium silicate and quaternary alkanolammonium silicate solutions are much more compatible with the ordinary water-miscible organic solvents.

Soluble silicates have often been suggested as a basis for removing unwanted metal ions in the purification of aqueous solutions since they form insoluble precipitates with all metal ions in group II, or higher, of the periodic table. Most of these precipitates, however, have some slight solubility, and other methods of purification have been preferred. The precipitates are almost always amorphous, the composition varying according to the silica-to-alkali ratio of the soluble silicate used, the concentrations of the reactants, the pH of the solution, and the temperature of the reaction. In some cases gels are formed but often a gelatinous coagulated mass of approximately the original silica ratio separates. Crystallinity may be developed by heat treatment. The "silicate garden" is a popular scientific demonstration. Water-soluble salts of heavy metals dropped into a diluted soluble silicate quickly form a gel at the interface but osmotic pressure brings about a tubular growth resembling a fungus. Since many of these precipitates are colored, interesting effects may be achieved.

Crystallization in the system $Na_2O–SiO_2–H_2O$ has been studied much more completely than that in the systems with potassium oxide or the other alkali metal oxides. Approximately eighteen crystalline sodium silicates have been identified in

Table 11. Physical Properties of the More Common Crystalline Alkali Silicates

Name	Formula	Melting point, °C	Density, g/ml	Heat of formation, ΔH, cal/formula wt at 25°C	Refractive indexes		
					α	β	γ
Sodium silicates							
sodium orthosilicate	$Na_4SiO_4(2Na_2O.SiO_2)$	1118[a]	2.5	−497,800	1.524		1.537
sodium sesquisilicate	$Na_6Si_2O_7(3Na_2O.2SiO_2)$	1122[a]	2.96	−856,300	1.524		1.529
sodium sesquisilicate pentahydrate	$Na_6Si_2O_7.11H_2O$ ($Na_3HSiO_4.5H_2O$)	88		−1,648,000	1.502	1.510	1.524
sodium metasilicate	$Na_2SiO_3(Na_2O.SiO_2)$	1089	2.614	−364,700	1.49	1.50	1.51
sodium metasilicate pentahydrate	$Na_2SiO_3.5H_2O$ ($Na_2O.SiO_2.5H_2O$)	72.2	1.749	−722,100	1.447	1.454	1.467
sodium metasilicate hexahydrate	$Na_2SiO_3.6H_2O$ ($Na_2O.SiO_2.6H_2O$)	70[b]	1.807	−792,600	1.488[b]	1.475[c]	1.495[b]
		62.9[c]			1.465[c]		1.485[c]
sodium metasilicate octahydrate	$Na_2SiO_3.8H_2O$ ($Na_2O.SiO_2.8H_2O$)	48.35	1.672	−934,800	1.457	1.463	1.465
sodium metasilicate enneahydrate	$Na_2SiO_3.9H_2O$ ($Na_2O.SiO_2.9H_2O$)	47.85	1.646	−1,005,100	1.451	1.456	1.460
sodium disilicate	$Na_2Si_2O_5(Na_2O.2SiO_2)$	874	2.496	−576,100	1.500	1.510	1.518
sodium trisilicate	$Na_6Si_8O_{19}$ ($3Na_2O.8SiO_2$)	808[a]	2.47				
"sodium tetrasilicate"	$Na_6Si_{13}O_{29}.11H_2O$ ($3Na_2O.13SiO_2.11H_2O$)		1.13[b]		1.471[b]	1.503 (av)	1.485[b]
					1.458[c]		1.487[c]
Potassium silicates							
potassium metasilicate	$K_2SiO_3(K_2O.SiO_2)$	976			1.520		1.528
potassium metasilicate hemihydrate	$K_2SiO_3.0.5H_2O$ ($K_2O.SiO_2.0.5H_2O$)	above 600				1.50 (av)	
potassium metasilicate monohydrate	$K_2SiO_3.H_2O$ ($K_2O.SiO_2.H_2O$)	370[a]				1.50 (av)	
potassium disilicate	$K_2Si_2O_5(K_2O.2SiO_2)$	1045			1.503		1.513
potassium disilicate monohydrate	$K_2Si_2O_5.H_2O$ ($K_2O.2SiO_2.H_2O$)	405[a]				1.50 (estd)	
potassium tetrasilicate	$K_2Si_4O_9(K_2O.4SiO_2)$	770	2.335	−999,200	1.477	1.530	1.482
potassium tetrasilicate monohydrate	$K_2Si_4O_9.H_2O$ ($K_2O.4SiO_2.H_2O$)	515	2.417		1.495		1.535

[a] Transition or inversion.   [b] α Form.   [c] β Form.

this system. Those which have been found in stable or metastable equilibrium with water at 70°C are shown in Figure 14. Some of the highly siliceous ones are quite insoluble; Eugster (1) has recently identified two very complex hydrated sodium silicate crystals as mineral specimens.

Sodium metasilicate pentahydrate melts incongruently at about 72.2°C and is usually prepared by allowing a solution of the 5 hydrate composition to crystallize completely. At ordinary temperatures or below 62°C the hexahydrate crystallizes readily and solutions within the stability range of the 6 or 9 hydrate at a given temperature should not be stored for long periods. In the ratio range of 2–1.5 SiO_2/Na_2O no crystallization has been observed below 100°C, but at ratios more siliceous than the disilicate, either sodium tetrasilicate will form on long standing or the separation can be accelerated by increasing the temperature to about 70°C or somewhat higher.

The system $K_2O–SiO_2–H_2O$ has been studied from 200 to 600°C; it has six silicate solid phases. The vapor pressure in this system never reaches its critical curve as it does in the sodium system and the solubilities of both the metasilicate and the disilicate increase with increasing temperature, so that potassium silicate can be used effectively in boiler waters at higher temperatures than sodium silicate.

The physical properties of most of the soluble crystals are given in Table 11.

Synthetic Insoluble Silicates

Industrially important synthetic insoluble silicates include various forms of hydrated calcium and magnesium silicate, aluminum, lead, and zinc silicate.

Aluminum Silicate. Precipitation of aluminum silicate by the addition of aluminum sulfate to soluble silicate solutions has been widely used in beater sizing of paper (qv) and to form coatings on pigments, as well as to form products valuable for decolorizing mineral oils. Such products have been used for much the same purposes as other precipitated metallic silicates and in the manufacture of ultramarine. An aluminum silicate rubber and paper filler has a pH of about 8, a specific gravity of 2.35, and a particle size of about 106 Å.

Artificial aluminosilicate zeolites are made by the combination of sodium silicate and sodium aluminate to form a hydrous gel which usually has the composition $Na_2O.-Al_2O_3.5SiO_2$ as sold. This product, when carefully prepared, is nearly insoluble and resistant to abrasion, and with care can be used almost indefinitely in cyclic processes for the removal of bases, such as calcium or magnesium, which are present in hard water, sugar juices, maple syrup, etc. See also Ion exchange. It is also used in pharmaceutical antacids.

For many years petroleum-cracking catalysts were amorphous combinations of precipitated alumina and silica in molecular ratios ranging from 50 SiO_2/Al_2O_3 to about 5 SiO_2/Al_2O_3. The higher proportions of alumina became more acceptable and were combined usually with magnesia or rare earth oxides. Since about 1964 the so-called "molecular sieve" catalysts have increased their share of the market for petroleum-cracking catalysts to over 90% of capacity. The molecular sieves are crystalline aluminosilicate zeolites formed by heating compositions of carefully controlled proportions of silica, alumina, and alkalis under conditions found to promote the required crystal structure. The alkali metal ions may be exchanged for hydrogen, ammonium or, preferably for cracking catalysts, rare earth metals. The early sieves were called type A and had effective pore sizes depending on the cation: potassium 3 Å, sodium 4 Å, calcium 5 Å. The newer cracking sieves are similar to the mineral faujasite with 4.6-

SiO_2/Al_2O_3 and Na, Ca, and Mg ions. The synthetic crystal zeolite X has a pore size of about 8 Å with calcium (type 10) and about 9 Å with sodium (type 13X). The X type is about $Na_2O.Al_2O_3.2.5SiO_2$ and the Y type about $Na_2O.Al_2O_34.5SiO_2$ with windows of about 5 Å and 8 Å and rooms or supercages of about 13 Å. These latter are especially active when the alkali ion is exchanged for a rare earth ion. The crystallized active silicates are embedded in a matrix of from 97 to 85% amorphous silica–alumina gel or clay although the trend is to higher proportions of active Y-type sieve. Such composites convert 75 to 80% of the treated crude to gasoline compared to 60% for earlier catalysts.

Calcium Silicate. The chemistry of calcium silicates has been examined extensively, primarily in an attempt to understand the setting of hydraulic cements. Others have been interested in the artificial preparation of minerals and still others in the use or action of calcium silicates in soils, fertilizers, and as pharmaceutical compounds such as absorbents or antacid. See Cement.

Study of the fractional precipitation of silicates from $3.1 SiO_2/Na_2O$ solutions indicates that the calcium silicates are the most soluble of the series copper, zinc, manganese, cadmium, lead, nickel, silver, magnesium, and calcium, in that order. This is similar to the order of precipitation for the hydroxides. With an increasing concentration of sodium silicate, the solubility of calcium carbonate therein decreases, but the solubility of gypsum is little affected. The reaction of certain calcium carbonates with sodium silicate has been used in other countries in forming secondary roads. Mixtures of the soluble silicate with calcium carbonate as aragonite increase in viscosity rapidly as the silicate solution is changed to a more alkaline ratio. Setting time decreases with rising temperature. Whereas a disilicate mixture may set in 6 hr at 30°C, it may set in 2 hr at 40°C. A $3.3 SiO_2/Na_2O$ solution at 41°Bé may take 100 hr to set at 30°C and 20 hr at 40°C. Calcite is much less reactive than aragonite.

By treating a clay with a soluble calcium compound and a soluble silicate a new gelatinous surface is formed on the clay, permitting it to be used as a plasticizing agent in cements, pigments, and fillers for paints, rubber, and plastics. Calcium silicate hydrates have been used as absorbents for decolorizing and purifying sugar solutions, fermented beverages, mineral oil, and for medicinal purposes. A typical rubber filler has the approximate composition $CaO.3.5 SiO_2.1.8 H_2O$, and a particle size of about 30 mμ.

Copper Silicate. Solutions of copper salts precipitate complex substances from sodium silicate solutions. Ammoniacal copper solutions may be used or copper sulfate may be ground with sodium metasilicate in the presence of glycerin. Such products find use as pigments, catalysts, and insecticides.

Lead Silicates. Anhydrous lead silicate pigments are usually made by roasting the lead oxide with silica. Silica gel, litharge, and acetic acid may react wet and the product is then dried. Other lead silicates which may be formed into an impalpable powder are prepared by allowing lead acetate to react with dilute sodium silicate solutions. If necessary, the filtered cake may be frozen to reduce the gelatinous character. These products are easily dispersed in natural and synthetic rubbers. Since they are opaque to ultraviolet radiation, they are used to protect rubber compositions and films against deterioration by sunlight. They may also be used as fillers for flexible films of such polymers as polyvinyl chloride.

Lead metasilicate, $PbO.SiO_2$, melts at 766°C and lead orthosilicate, $2PbO.SiO_2$, at about 746°C. There is also $3PbO.2SiO_2$, which appears to melt at about 715°C.

The index of refraction of the orthosilicate is about 2.07, and for the metasilicate $\alpha = 1.947$, $\beta = 1.961$, and $\gamma = 1.968$.

Magnesium Silicate. The reactions of magnesium hydroxide and various magnesium salts with sodium silicate solutions have been examined for many years. Von Fuchs noted early that the hydroxide reacts rapidly. Calcined magnesium oxide has been reported to react only slowly even at 100°C and can be burned so hard that it will not react with a silicate solution at the boiling point. However, the soluble magnesium sulfate rapidly forms an amorphous mass.

Certain commercial magnesium silicates, which are effective in decolorizing oils and rosin and in the clarification of mineral oil and drycleaning solvents, have been found to have the approximate composition $2MgO.3SiO_2.2H_2O$. Similar products with higher water content or different ratio are sold as antacids for pharmaceutical use and in the control of stomach ulcers. Magnesium silicates can also be used to stabilize emulsions of mineral oil and as antioxidants in preventing the rancidity and discoloration of soaps. Carefully prepared products are effective as catalysts in amination reactions and for cracking and reforming crude oil.

Solutions of peroxide for bleaching paper and other fibers are effectively stabilized with amorphous magnesium silicate (reaction product of magnesium sulfate and a soluble silicate) which precipitates and prevents the catalytic action of heavy metal ions.

The reaction between magnesium compounds and silica has also been used to reduce the solubility of magnesium in hot-process lime-soda softeners and to remove silica from water supplies, such as those destined for boiler water and for ice manufacture. In boiler-water treatment, sufficient silicate must be present to react completely with the magnesium and form a sludge which can be readily blown out. If too little silicate is present, a very sticky scale may result. Precipitation of a magnesium silicate corresponding to serpentine, $3MgO.2SiO_2.2H_2O$, is advocated.

Zinc Silicate. Zinc metasilicate has been formed either by heating zinc oxide and silica or by heat-treating the precipitate from a solution of zinc sulfate and sodium silicate. The monohydrate of the zinc metasilicate has been reported from the aqueous system with a melting point in the range of 1430°C and refractive indexes of 1.623 and 1.616.

Zinc oxide mixed with various liquid silicates is found to react with the production of willemite, Zn_2SiO_4, and a crystalline material having the probable formula $ZnNa_2SiO_4.H_2O$, although the composition depends on the temperature and time of treatment as well as on the ratio of the silicate solution.

The precipitated zinc silicates may be used to form phosphors by heat treatment, although the phosphors are usually formed from the oxides. The dried materials may be used as spray ingredients or to remove traces of copper from gasoline.

Analysis

The precautions to be observed in the most thoroughly tested methods of analysis of soluble silicates are described by Vail (2). Standard methods are given by TAPPI (Tentative Standard T632 ts 63) and AWWA (Tentative Standard B404-55T) for aqueous liquid silicates, and ASTM (ASTM Standard D501-67) for the determination of Na_2O, SiO_2, and H_2O and insoluble matter in the alkaline crystals. Since the solutions contain so little impurity the analytical methods are simple, but carefully standardized procedures must be followed. Silica is ordinarily determined by the usual gravimetric technique but a satisfactory and rapid volumetric method of titration with $2N$ hydrochloric acid takes advantage of the reaction with fluoride ion. A dilute alkaline sample is made strongly acid with a measured amount of $2N$ HCl, excess NaF is added, and titration continued to the endpoint. SiO_2 is calculated, after correction for Na_2O, according to the relation

$$SiO_2 + 6\,F^- + 4\,H^+ \rightarrow SiF_6{}^{2-} + 2\,H_2O$$

Alkali is usually determined by acid titration, but the determination of sodium and potassium by the flame photometer, especially for differentiation of the two, has been highly developed.

Table 12. Standard Indexes for Powder Diffraction Diagrams of Some Sodium Silicates

Crystal	Line	d, Å	I/I_0
Na_2SiO_3	Mo Kα	3.04	1.00
		2.40	0.64
		2.57	0.48
		5.3	0.20
$Na_2SiO_3.5H_2O$	Cu Kα 0.708	3.33	1.00
		3.17	1.00
		2.71	1.00
		6.20	0.90
$Na_2SiO_3.6H_2O$		2.76	1.00
		2.60	(0.75)
		2.51	(0.75)
$Na_2SiO_3.8H_2O$		2.70	1.00
		2.87	(0.25)
		2.57	(0.25)
$Na_2SiO_3.9H_2O$	Mo Kα	2.79	1.00
		3.83	0.30
		2.92	0.20
		8.7	0.10
$Na_2Si_2O_5$		1.82	1.00
		2.96	
		1.155	
$Na_6Si_8O_{19}$	Cu Kα	4.12	medium
		3.33	medium
		2.45	strong
		2.11	medium

NOTE: d is the interplanar spacing, and I/I_0 the ratio of line intensity to strongest line intensity.

More dilute concentrations of silica may be determined using either the yellow silicomolybdate complex or the reduced blue phase which form with crystalloidal silica and provide a sensitive colorimetric determination. The colloidal silica must be broken down to the crystalloidal form with alkali before it will react, and this therefore provides a useful method of differentiating crystalloidal from colloidal silica.

The determination of water by ignition requires patient handling. Carbon dioxide is determined by absorption with sodium hydroxide in weighed absorption tubes. Viscosity is usually tested with a Stormer viscometer, and specific gravity with a hydrometer calibrated in degrees Baumé at either 20 or 25°C. Published indexes used for identifying individual crystalline soluble silicates by powder diffraction methods are listed in Table 12.

Health and Safety Factors

The ordinary liquid soluble silicates are not hazardous as industrial chemicals. There is a record of one man who drank 200 ml of a neutral liquid sodium silicate with a resulting severe internal upset, but no fatal or serious result. The commercial liquids at about 3 SiO_2/Na_2O have an LD_{50} value for rats of about 2.5 mg/kg. About 0.002% of powdered sodium silicate has been added to dairy feed since 1912 on the recommendation of Ohio State University to make up for dietary deficiencies of silica in alfalfa, which affect bone formation and pregnancy, and to avoid the common problem of stiffening of leg joints in older cattle. Liquid silicates have been tested orally as medicine for asthma and tuberculosis, injected intravenously for arteriosclerosis, and given rectally to neutralize intestinal acidity. The U.S. Public Health Service has stated that "the use of small amounts of sodium silicate added to drinking water would, as far as known, produce no ill-effects upon the user of the water" (2). Large-scale surveys have been made in cities which have used silicates in treating water. The U.S. Food and Drug Administration does not object to the use of silicates in coatings and adhesives in contact with foods, and small amounts of liquid silicates are accepted and regularly used to prevent corrosion in canned drinking water. Neither potassium nor lithium silicate solutions are known to be more hazardous, and the organic ammonium silicates have been found to be nontoxic according to experience and the standard test methods. None of these compounds should be allowed in contact with the eyes, and the liquids more alkaline than about the 2.4 SiO_2/Na_2O should be treated with caution. When a film of liquid silicate is allowed to dry it becomes brittle and the conchoidal fracture produces sharp edges which may readily cut the skin and permit infection from outside sources or adhering dirt. The silicate powders are so soluble that there is no danger from silicosis and the silicate dust does not accumulate in the lungs. Spots of silicate on clothing may ordinarily be allowed to dry and then picked off. If larger amounts have wet the cloth it should be rinsed with warm water. Spots on glass may be removed by repeated treatment with a 2 or 3% solution of ammonium bifluoride, NH_4HF_2.

The orthosilicates and anhydrous sesquisilicates are strong alkalis and release about 50% of the heat of solution of caustic soda. The ordinary precautions for handling caustic soda should be followed. The Manufacturing Chemists Association has suggested proper labels for such containers, as well as for the other commercial silicates. Goggles or a face shield should be used in handling these very alkaline products, and the granules should be added slowly to the solution when dissolving. They should be flushed off the skin immediately, and eyes should be flushed for at least fifteen minutes in case of contact with a particle of the alkali. Sodium metasilicate pentahydrate has a negative heat of solution and sodium sesquisilicate pentahydrate releases only about 2% of the heat which is released by flaked caustic, so that the rate of corrosion of the skin is greatly moderated. These products are considered corrosive in contact with the skin but, if handled with caution and not allowed to remain in contact with the wet skin, they are not dangerous. The removal of natural oils from the skin by alkaline solutions can produce dermatitis and should be avoided by the use of protective creams or an acid detergent following exposure. Proper labels to be used where these products are sold for household use (as defined by the Food and Drug Administration) are available from the manufacturers.

Economic Aspects

At one time sodium silicate was popularly recognized as a solution for the storage of eggs for winter use, but now there is no general household contact except minor use for hardening cement and kits for the preparation of the "silicate gardens" mentioned earlier, and the unrecognized presence in many household detergents. They are, however, very widely used in industry, and this demand supports the production of over 600 thousand short tons of anhydrous glass and 275 thousand short tons of anhydrous alkali silicate in the United States annually, perhaps about half of the world production. The U.S. Bureau of Census figures are shown in Table 13. Production roughly parallels the general U.S. production index for all goods. The abundant supply of staple raw materials for their production, their relatively low cost, their broad range of properties varying with the ratio, concentration, and alkali, make the soluble silicates available as replacements for phosphate, starch, and other chemicals which are sometimes in short supply or form undesirable waste or pollutants. They are, therefore, an important factor in any planning for the conservation of natural resources.

Table 13. Production, Shipments, and Value of Soluble Silicates Manufactured in the U.S.A.

Year	Production, short tons	Shipments, short tons	Value of shipments, $1000
Anhydrous glass			
1950	486,203	437,341	19,703
1955	629,168	465,858	26,201
1960	497,348	401,167	26,644
1962	553,337	451,616	28,818
1964	564,579	454,162	29,383
1966	623,317	459,481	29,880
1967	606,029		
Sodium metasilicate and orthosilicate[a]			
1950	128,869	113,897	7,015
1955	194,609	164,889	12,807
1960	230,912	176,500	15,165
1962	255,143	192,196	15,849
1964	269,815	229,452	18,253
1966	274,622	226,547	20,398

[a] Calculated as $Na_2SiO_3 \cdot 5H_2O$ and Na_4SiO_4.

The general price level of the silicates tends to rise slowly with major economic shifts, such as the general inflationary trend which boosts costs for labor and raw materials and overheads faster than the rate of improvement in manufacturing techniques can lower manufacturing costs for such basic chemicals. The present costs on an anhydrous basis are about $3.50/100 lb in bulk fob works for 3.2 ratio glass by the carload and $4.70/100 lb for 2.0 glass on the same basis. Anhydrous sodium metasilicate in bags by the carload fob works sells for about $6.35/100 lb. Since the demand for soluble silicates is highly diversified and the volume of production is closely related to the economic and industrial growth of the U.S. and world commerce in general, it is expected that demand will continue to increase although the amounts required for specific industries will shift with technological developments.

Figures for the production of lithium silicates and quaternary ammonium silicates are not available but are no doubt small since they have been introduced only recently. Liquid lithium silicate with the mole ratio 5.9 SiO_2/LiO_2 at 18.8% SiO_2 is quoted at $2.80 per lb in drum lots, and a liquid quaternary ammonium silicate with 10% cation and 45% SiO_2 costs about $0.50 per lb in bulk.

Uses

There are over fifty well-recognized applications of the soluble silicates requiring quantities of industrial significance. These economical, incombustible, nonflammable, colorless, odorless, and unputrifiable products are used in industry by the millions of pounds but, in most cases, they require special care and effort in application. The proper formulation and controls for most applications have been worked out over many years of practical experience and must be recognized for proper utilization.

Detergents for commercial and household use consume a large proportion of the production of sodium silicate. See Detergency; Laundering. Large quantities are also used alone or in mixture with other alkalis for metal and heavy-duty cleaning, adding up to about 15% of U.S. production. Soluble silicates have held an important place in detergents for 100 years in spite of such major shifts as the introduction of powdered soaps and later the development of synthetic detergents. The leading household detergent preparations consistently have been those with a large percentage of soluble silicate, which contributes significantly to the effectiveness of detergents and cleaners by maintaining a sufficiently high pH in the system through its buffering ability. The soluble silicates perform certain basic functions such as saponification of animal and vegetable oils and fats, emulsification of mineral oils, deflocculation of solid dirt particles, suspension of soil, prevention of redeposition of suspended dirt, and prevention of corrosion of soft metals—particularly tin, aluminum, copper and brass, and their alloys—by other ingredients in the detergent mixture. The optimum performance of detergents or metal cleaners is obtained when silicates are present in excess, or at least equal, concentrations relative to phosphates (3).

The phenomenal growth of the corrugated-box industry in the period beginning about 1910, when corrugated boxes were admitted for use by the railroads, has required a large tonnage of silicate adhesives. These adhesives may be formulated for high-speed operation and meet rigid requirements for rapid setting with high moisture loss. Their strong adhesion when drying on hot metal has caused a time-consuming clean-up problem which cannot yet be overcome without increasing the initial cost of the adhesive. Although boxboard and paper adhesion consumes about 13% of the U.S. production of soluble silicates, they are no longer the major adhesive used in corrugated-board manufacture. Another large-scale outlet is for the production of silica gels. This industry expanded greatly in the forties with the need for desiccant gels and catalysts to crack crude oil for high-octane gasoline. In a variety of industries increasing volumes of water and wastes are clarified with activated silica sols used as coagulants and coagulant aids. Such gel and sol applications take about 35% of U.S. production (see Silica, amorphous under Silica).

The development of cements has been primarily in the hands of specialty cement manufacturers, who are in touch with the steel and other industries requiring refractories and refractory or acid-resistant cements. Roofing granules and weather-resistant shingles are now widely accepted and require the highly insoluble binders formed by reaction with the silicates. These applications take about 9% of U.S. production. In these fields there are special needs for potassium and lithium silicates. The potassium silicates are used as binders in the manufacture of welding rods prepared at high pressure with stiff complex mixtures. They help control the sputtering of the arc. Potassium silicates are also widely used in the bonding of phosphors for oscilloscopes and black-and-white television screens. A very rapidly expanding application is the development of binders for molds for casting metal. The straight sodium silicate binder has been used to a small extent for many years. A more recent development is a process for wetting the sand granules of the refractory and then setting them quickly by gassing with carbon dioxide. A partially gelatinized bond is formed which is brittle and weak enough after firing to break away from the object. Even more recently the use of powdered ferrosilicon (90–99% Si) to set the silicate bond has received wide study and increasing acceptance. In some refractory cement applications the higher softening and flow points of potassium silicate glasses, and especially the fact that they are manufactured at more siliceous mole ratios than sodium silicates, has increased the demand. In gunning and ramming compounds the greater tackiness of the sodium silicates is important and the use of mixtures of sodium–potassium silicates, because they exhibit viscosity maxima in aqueous solutions and viscosity minima in a glassy melt, has been of interest. A great variety of acid-resistant silicate cements are available for setting up bricks and blocks or coating surfaces.

The potassium silicates find extensive use as coatings where blooming (surface crystallization of sodium sulfate or carbonate) is a drawback. Thermal control coatings resistant to ionizing radiation for space vehicles are based on potassium and sodium silicate systems. The resistance of silicates to temperatures above 550°C makes them almost unique among industrial binders as fire-resistant adhesives, as impregnants for asbestos and other insulation, and for paints resistant to high temperature. The quaternary ammonium silicates decompose at temperatures below 300°C and leave an inorganic film.

The "zinc-rich" aqueous or inorganic paints protect ferrous metals from corrosion by establishing a galvanic action between the iron substrate and the metallic zinc powder in the paint. The vehicle is a soluble silicate which sets as the binder and maintains the galvanic contact between the metals. Sodium silicates require a second coat of reactive acids or metal oxides to become insoluble, but high-ratio lithium silicates, and particularly the high-ratio quaternary alkanolammonium silicates, are self-curing in reasonable times and may be used under any conditions which permit evaporation of water from the system. The surface-active properties are made use of to an increasing extent in flotation sequence primarily as slime dispersants and surface conditioners for a variety of ores. See Flotation. The textile industry requires large tonnages for stabilizing bleach baths and for separating and cleaning fibers. The silicates are added to the pulp in the manufacture of paper to improve printability and handling, and grease-resistant films are formed by coating paper with soluble silicates. Bleaching in the paper mill also requires soluble silicate stabilizers. Such chemical reactions and treatments take about 6% of U.S. production. Other well-known applications include the impregnation of wood and porous metals, preparation of abrasive wheels, oil reclamation and refining, manufacture of plywood shooks (sheets of 2 or 3 plies for temporary service), pottery slips and glazes, enamels, treatment of boiler water, water-based paints, concrete hardening, clay refining, zeolites, fireworks, soil solidification, and the fabrication of electrical components where the dielectric properties can be controlled by the composition. Such miscellaneous applications make up the final 10% of U.S. consumption.

Bibliography

"Soluble Silicates and Synthetic Insoluble Silicates" in *ECT* 1st ed., Vol. 12, pp. 303–330, by J. H. Wills, Philadelphia Quartz Company.

1. H. P. Eugster, *Science* **157**, 1177 (1967).
2. J. G. Vail, *Soluble Silicates*, Vol. I, ACS Monograph No. 116, Reinhold Publishing Corp., New York, 1952.
3. H. H. Weldes and K. R. Lange, *Preprint 39D, Am. Soc. Chem. Eng., Mater. Conf., Symp. Glass and Related Materials, Part III, Philadelphia, April 1968*.
4. Jos. Crosfield & Sons, Ltd., *Chem. Ind. London* **1967** (25), 1053–1055 (1967).
5. H. Fontana, *Vetro Silicati* **10** (55/1), 19–20 (1966); E. Borel, *Verres Refractaires* **17** (6), 397–400 (1963).
6. K. A. Vesterberg, *Z. Anorg. Allgem. Chem.* **110**, 48–54 (1920).
7. U.S. Pat. 2,668,149 (1954), R. K. Iler (to E. I. du Pont de Nemours & Co., Inc.)
8. W. S. McDonald and D. W. J. Cruickshank, *Acta Cryst.* **22** (1), 37–43 (1967).
9. K. H. Sun, *J. Am. Ceram. Soc.* **30**, 277–281 (1947).
10. G. Donnay and J. W. Gryder, *Carnegie Inst. Wash. Ann. Rept. Director Geophys. Lab., 1963–1964*, pp. 238–239.
11. S. K. Dubrovo, *Vitreous Lithium Silicates*, transl. from Russian by Consultants Bureau, New York, 1964.
12. M. A. Mateev and A. S. Agarkov, *Inorg. Mater.* **2** (5), 776–781 (1966).
13. C. L. Babcock, *J. Am. Ceram. Soc.* **51** (3), 163–169 (1968).
14. I. Szabo-Naray, *Acta Phys. Acad. Sci. Hung.* (in German) **20** (3), 299–303 (1966); *Chem. Abstr.* **65**, 453h.
15. H. F. Shermer, *J. Res. Natl. Bur. Std.* **57**, 97–101 (1956).
16. D. E. Sharp and L. B. Ginther, *J. Am. Ceram. Soc.* **34**, 260–271 (1951); D. E. Sharp and J. Moore, *J. Am. Ceram. Soc.* **41** (11), 461–463 (1958).
17. R. J. Charles, *J. Am. Ceram. Soc.* **49**, 55–62 (1966); **50**, 631 (1967); *Sci. Am.* **217** (3), 126–128, 130, 132, 134, 136 (1967).
18. J. H. Wills in R. Houwink and G. Salomon, eds., *Adhesion and Adhesives*, Vol. I, Elsevier Publishing Co., New York, 1965, Chap. 8.
19. H. Scholze, *Glass Ind.* **47** (11), 622–628 (1966).
20. C. W. Lentz, *Inorg. Chem.* **3**, 574–579 (1964).
21. E. A. Cotton and G. Wilkinson, *Advanced Inorganic Chemistry*, 2nd ed., Interscience Publishers, a division of John Wiley & Sons, Inc., New York, 1966.
22. H. H. Weldes and J. S. S. Bobb, unpublished work of Philadelphia Quartz Co.

General References

The two-volume ACS Monograph No. 116, *Soluble Silicates*, by J. G. Vail, assisted by J. H. Wills, published by Reinhold Publishing Corp., New York, 1952, covers the properties and uses up to about 1952. This builds on ACS Monograph No. 46, *Soluble Silicates in Industry* also by J. G. Vail, published in 1928 by the Chemical Catalog Co., New York, with a number of tables of data not otherwise available. W. Eitel in *Silicate Science*, Academic Press, Inc., New York, 1964, is an outstanding compilation of reviews of work done on various metal silicates. It is published in five volumes. Volumes 2, 3, and 4 are most likely to review publications on the properties of soluble silicates. R. K. Iler in *The Colloid Chemistry of Silica and Silicates*, Cornell University Press, Ithaca, 1955, takes a more theoretical approach to sols and soluble silicate solutions. A review of the properties of silicates in respect to adhesion with specific reference to the properties of soluble silicate glasses is found in R. Houwink and G. Salomon, eds., *Adhesion and Adhesives*, Vol. I, Elsevier Publishing Co., New York, 1965, Chap. 8.

The more general surveys of silicate glasses treat the binary alkali silicates. G. W. Morey's ACS Monograph No. 77, *The Properties of Glass*, Reinhold Publishing Corp., New York, 1938, is a classic. W. A. Weyl and E. C. Marboe in *The Constitution of Glasses: A Dynamic Interpretation*, Vols. 1 and 2, John Wiley & Sons, Inc., New York, 1963, take a different approach with many references. Chapter 8 by W. A. Weyl in F. R. Eirich, ed., *Rheology*, Academic Press, Inc., New York, 1960, includes a good review of the properties of soluble silicate glasses. See also Glass.

John H. Wills
Philadelphia Quartz Company

SILICON HALIDES

Silicon forms tetrahalides with all the halogens (Table 1). It also forms halohydrides (Table 2), some higher halides, that is, halogenated polysilanes (Table 3), and a number of mixed halides (Table 4). For silicon tetrafluoride, other fluorosilanes, fluorosilic acid, and fluorosilicates, see Vol. 9, pp. 651–661.

The silicon halides are very reactive materials and are used to produce many commercial inorganic and organic silicon compounds. The reactivity increases with the atomic weight of the halogen atom, and in most reactions the silicon–halogen bond is broken. Nearly all of these reactions are probably initiated by nucleophilic attack at the silicon atom.

Tetrafluorosilane reacts with hydrogen only above $2000°C$ (1) whereas tetrachloro- and tetraiodosilane are reduced by hydrogen at temperatures above $1000°C$ (2,3). Silicon halides are stable to oxygen at room temperature, but react at high temperatures (4–6). The silicon halohydrides and the mixed halides, however, have a lesser degree of thermal stability. No reactions occur with nitrogen under normal conditions. The alkali metals react under certain conditions, as would be expected, giving amorphous silicon.

$$SiF_4 + 4\,Na \rightarrow Si + 4\,NaF$$

Magnesium does not form stable Grignard reagents with silicon halides although some of the silicon halohydrides do react forming silanes (7).

$$2\,HSiBr_3 + 3\,Mg \rightarrow 2\,(SiH)_x + 3\,MgBr_2$$

All silicon halides are reduced readily by hydride ions, or by complex hydrides, to silicon hydrides (8–10).

$$4\,R_2AlH + SiCl_4 \rightarrow SiH_4 + 4\,R_2AlCl$$

They also react readily with amines, ie, with ammonia, forming silicon nitrogen polymers, and with alcohols, forming alkoxides (see under Silicon esters); and at high temperatures with hydrogen sulfide, forming compounds with $SiCl_4$ such as Cl_3SiSH and $Cl_3SiSSiCl_3$.

An important reaction is with metal alkyls and metal alkyl halides. The Grignard reaction, for example, was used commercially by Dow Corning to prepare organosilicon compounds prior to the discovery of the direct reaction by Rochow in 1945 (11), and it is still used for the preparation of some intermediates.

$$SiCl_4 + RMgX \rightarrow R_nSiCl_{4-n} + MgXCl$$

With the exception of the fluoride, the silicon tetrahalides boil at a lower temperature than their carbon analogs, probably due to a reduction in intermolecular forces (Table 1).

Table 1. Silicon Tetrahalides

Compound	Melting point, °C	Boiling point, °C	Density	Bond energy, kcal
SiF_4		−95.7	1.66^{-95}	135
$SiCl_4$	68.8	56.8	1.48^{20}	91
$SiBr_4$	5	155.0	2.81^{29}	74
SiI_4	124	290.0		56

Table 2. Silicon Halohydrides

Compound	Melting point, °C	Boiling point, °C	Density
H_3SiF		−99.0	
H_2SiF_2	−122.0	−77.8	
$HSiF_3$	−131.2	−97.5	
H_3SiCl	−118.0	−30.4	1.145^{-113}
H_2SiCl_2	−122.0	8.3	1.42^{-122}
$HSiCl_3$	−128.2	31.8	1.3313^{25}
H_3SiBr	−94.0	1.9	1.531^{20}
H_2SiBr_2	−70.1	66.0	2.17^{0}
$HSiBr_3$	−73.0	111.8	2.7^{17}
H_3SiI	−57.0	45.4	$2.035^{14.8}$
H_2SiI_2	−1.0	149.5	$2.724^{20.5}$
$HSiI_3$	8.0	111.0^{22}	3.314^{20}

The physical properties of the halohydrides are given in Table 2. The fact that these are mobile, reactive materials gives them their usefulness as chemical intermediates. The halohydrides can undergo olefin addition reactions, for example, thus producing important silicone monomers. The following reaction illustrates that aliphatic groups containing two or more carbon atoms may be attached to silicon in this way:

$$HSiCl_3 + RCH{=}CH_2 \rightarrow RCH_2CH_2SiCl_3$$

The higher halosilanes, that is, the halogenated polysilanes, are known and are beginning to receive some commercial interest. The physical properties of some of these compounds are listed in Table 3. The nomenclature is via the silane root, ie,

Table 3. Some Halogenated Polysilanes

Compound	Melting point, °C	Boiling point, °C	Density
Si_2F_6	−18.6	−19.1	
Si_2Cl_6	−1.0	144.5	1.5624^{15}
Si_3Cl_8	−67.0	216.0	1.61^{15}
Si_4Cl_{10}	93.6	100.0	
Si_5Cl_{12}	−80.0	150.0 (15 mm)	
Si_6Cl_{14}	319.0 dec		
Si_2Br_6	95.0	240.0	
Si_3Br_8	133.0		
Si_4Br_{10}	185.0		
Si_2I_6	250.0 dec		

Si_2Cl_6 is hexachlorodisilane, Si_3Cl_8 is octachlorotrisilane, etc; these compounds are also referred to as silicon subhalides.

When two different tetrahalides are heated together they equilibrate, forming mixed silicon halides.

$$SiX_4 + SiY_4 \rightleftharpoons SiXY_3, SiX_2Y_2, SiX_3Y$$

These reactions are sometimes called entropy-driven reactions, since the total silicon bonds from one halide species to another remain constant. Some physical properties of these compounds are listed in Table 4.

Table 4. Mixed Silicon Halides

Compounds	Melting point, °C	Boiling point, °C	Compounds	Melting point, °C	Boiling point, °C
$SiClBr_3$	-208	128	$SiFBr_3$	-82.5	83.8
$SiCl_2Br_2$	-45.5	104.4	$SiFCl_3$	-120.8	12.2
$SiCl_3Br$	-62.0	80	SiF_2Br_2	-66.9	13.7
$SiClI_3$	2.0	234–237	SiF_2Cl_2	-139.7	-32.2
$SiCl_2I_2$	<-60.0	172	SiF_3Cl	-142.0	-70.0
$SiCl_3I$	<-60.0	113–114	SiF_3Br	-70.5	-41.7
$SiBr_3I$	14.0	192	$SiFCl_2Br$	-112.3	35.5
$SiBr_2I_2$	38.0	230–231	$SiFClBr_2$	-99.2	59.5
$SiBrI_3$	53.0	255			

Synthesis

Halogens react more readily with silicon than with carbon. Fluorine and silicon combine even at room temperature to give silicon tetrafluoride. Chlorine reacts with silicon at 500°C giving nearly quantitative yields of silicon tetrachloride (12), and both bromine and iodine react at a red heat.

Hydrogen halides, as well as free halides, react freely with elemental silicon and most other silicon compounds at moderate temperatures (13–16),

$$Si + 4 HF \rightarrow SiF_4 + 2 H_2$$

$$2 Si + 7 HCl \rightarrow HSiCl_3 + SiCl_4 + 3 H_2$$

as do organic halides (11). In the latter case, organosilicon halides are the main products.

$$Si + CH_3Cl \xrightarrow{Cu} (CH_3)_nSiCl_{4-n}$$

Inorganic halides can also be used to halogenate silicon–hydrogen bonds (17).

$$HgCl_2 + (C_2H_5)_2SiH_2 \rightarrow (C_2H_5)_2SiHCl + Hg + HCl$$

Table 5. Boiling Points of Silicon Oxychlorides

Compounds	Boiling point, °C	Compounds	Boiling point, °C
Si_2OCl_6	137	$Si_5O_4Cl_{12}$	130–131 (15 mm)
$Si_3O_2Cl_8$	76 (15 mm)	$Si_6O_5Cl_{14}$	139–141 (15 mm)
$Si_4O_4Cl_8$	91 (15 mm)	$Si_7O_6Cl_{16}$	145–147 (15 mm)
$Si_4O_3Cl_{10}$	109–110 (15 mm)		

Chlorination of silicon in conjunction with oxygen will give chlorosiloxanes (18).

$$Si + Cl_2 + O_2 \rightarrow Si_nO_{n-1}Cl_{2n+2}$$

The boiling points of the chlorosiloxanes series are given in Table 5.

The oxybromides of silicon are also known and fall into a similar homologous series (19).

The following equations will serve to illustrate the major preparative routes:

$$SiO_2 + 2\,C + 2\,Cl_2 \rightarrow SiCl_4 + 2\,CO$$

$$Si + 2\,Cl_2 \rightarrow SiCl_4$$

$$CaSi + Cl_2 \rightarrow SiCl_4 + Si_2Cl_6 + Si_3Cl_8 + \text{higher chloropolysilanes}$$

$$SiH_4 + 4\,Cl_2 \rightarrow SiCl_4 + 4\,HCl$$

$$SiS_2 + 4\,Cl_2 \rightarrow SiCl_4 + 2\,SCl_2$$

$$SiC + 2\,Cl_2 \rightarrow SiCl_4 + C$$

$$2\,Si + 6\,HCl \rightarrow 2\,HSiCl_3 + 2\,H_2$$

$$SiO_2 + 4\,HF \rightarrow SiF_4 + 2\,H_2O$$

$$HSiCl_3 + SbF_3 \rightarrow HSiF_3 + SbCl_3$$

$$SiO_2 + 2\,COCl_2 \rightarrow SiCl_4 + 2\,CO_2$$

$$Si + Cl_2 + O_2 \rightarrow Si_nO_{n-1}Cl_{2n+2}$$

$$4\,BCl_3 + 3\,SiO_2 \rightarrow 3\,SiCl_4 + 2\,B_2O_3$$

Production

Commercial production of silicon halides is confined to silicon tetrachloride, trichlorosilane, and organosilicon halides. The latter are intermediates in silicone production (see under Silicones).

Silicon tetrachloride, $SiCl_4$. Silicon tetrachloride is the most important representative of the halosilanes. Its great importance is due to the ready availability of raw materials for its manufacture, the simplicity of its preparation, its low cost, and its chemical properties. Because of this its industrial production has been widely

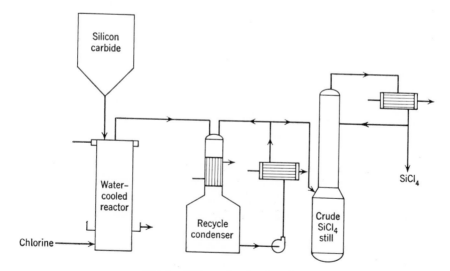

Fig. 1. $SiCl_4$ production flowsheet.

developed in a number of countries. The major large commercial production is by the exothermic reaction of silicon carbide with chlorine (see Fig. 1). The silicon carbide used is usually a by-product material not suitable for abrasive purposes. A new high-temperature process starting with clay has been developed, but no results have been published as yet. Several processes starting with silica have been proposed, but none have met with commercial success.

Silicon tetrachloride is sold both in technical (99.5%) and special high-purity grades. Spectrographically pure, boronfree material is specifically purified for use in making transistor-grade silicon. See Table 6 for physical properties.

Table 6. Physical Properties of Silicon Tetrachloride

Property	Value
character	colorless fuming liquid
refractive index, n_D^{25}	1.4146
specific gravity, 25/25°C	1.4736
viscosity at 25°C, cSt	0.35
vapor pressure, mm	
at −34.4°C	10
at 5.0°C	100
at 38.4°C	400
heat of vaporization, cal/g	40.3
heat of formation, kcal/mole	
liquid	153.0
gas	145.7
coefficient of expansion, per °C	0.0011
specific heat	0.20
solubility	soluble in organic solvents; decomposes in H_2O and alcohol

There are presently only two producers in the U.S., Stauffer Chemical Company and VanDeMark Chemical Company, Inc. Annual production is on the order of 35–40 million lb. Its major application is for the production of fume silica (see under Silica); the rest is used in the synthesis of silicon esters, in special glass for the electronic industries, and for high-purity silicon. The present prices range from $0.12/lb for technical grade to $0.15/lb for pure grade.

Trichlorosilane, $HSiCl_3$. Trichlorosilane has been made commercially only since about 1947. It is produced in a fluid-bed reactor by passing hydrogen chloride through silicon or copper silicon powder at moderate temperatures (280–300°C). The manufacturing equipment used is very similar to that for the production of silicon tetrachloride (see Fig. 1) except that refrigeration must be used for condensing the reaction products.

Present production of trichlorosilane is carried out primarily by the silicon producers in as much as one of its main uses is as a precursor to various silicone monomers. A high-purity grade is also made for silicon transistor production. Prices are approx $0.80/lb for technical grade and $2.00/lb for pure grade. See Table 7 for physical properties.

Others. Pilot quantities of the higher silicon chlorides or subchlorides, hexachlorodisilane, Si_2Cl_6, and octachlorotrisilane, Si_3Cl_8, are also being produced in the U.S. by the Anderson Development Company and are finding new application in the

Table 7. Physical Properties of Trichlorosilane

Property	Value
character	colorless fuming liquid
refractive index, n_D^{25}	1.3983
specific gravity at 25/4°C	1.3313
viscosity at 25°C, cSt	0.23
vapor pressure, mm	
at −54°C	10
at −26°C	60
at −16°C	100
at 14.6°C	400
heat of vaporization, cal/g	46.7
flash point, Cleveland open cup, °F	−18
autoignition temperature, °F	220
specific heat	0.23
coefficient of expansion, per °C	0.0019
solubility	soluble in organic solvents; decomposes in H_2O and alcohol

synthesis of specific silicon suboxide polymers (20). These are produced by the reaction of *t*-butyl alcohol on the subchlorides.

$$Si_2Cl_6 + t\text{-}C_4H_9OH \rightarrow \ \rangle Si\text{—}OH + t\text{-}C_4H_9Cl$$
$$\downarrow \Delta$$
$$Si_2O_3$$

In this manner acyclic, unicyclic, and general R′-cyclic suboxides are produced from the corresponding subchlorides.

$$Si_nCl_{2n+2} \rightarrow Si_nO_{n+1}$$
$$Si_nCl_{2n} \rightarrow (SiO)_n$$
$$Si_nCl_{2(n+1-R)} \rightarrow Si_nO_{n+1-R}$$

Research quantities of other silicon halides, such as the bromides and iodides, are also made available by several research supply houses.

Bibliography

"Silicon Halides" treated under "Silicon Compounds," in *ECT* 1st ed., Vol. 12, pp. 368–370, by E. G. Rochow, Harvard University.

1. N. C. Cook, J. K. Wolfe, and J. D. Cobine, *128th Meeting Am. Chem. Soc., Minneapolis, Minn. 48M (1955)*.
2. R. Schwarz and H. Merckbach, *Z. Anorg. Allgem. Chem.* **232**, 241 (1937).
3. F. B. Litton and H. C. Anderson, *J. Electrochem. Soc.* **101**, 287 (1954).
4. A. D. Gaunt, H. Mackle, and L. E. Sutton, *Trans. Faraday Soc.* **47**, 943 (1951).
5. C. Friedel and A. Ladenburg, *Liebigs Ann. Chem.* **147**, 355 (1868).
6. D. W. S. Chambers and C. J. Wilkins, *J. Chem. Soc.* **1960**, 5088.
7. G. Schott, W. Herrmann, and R. Hirschmann, *Angew. Chem.* **68**, 213 (1956).
8. A. E. Finholt, A. G. Bond, K. E. Wilzbach, and H. I. Schlesinger, *J. Am. Chem. Soc.* **69**, 2692 (1947).
9. J. E. Baines and C. Eaborn, *J. Chem. Soc.* **1956**, 1436.
10. A. R. Anderson, unpublished observations.
11. E. G. Rochow, *J. Am. Chem. Soc.* **67**, 963 (1945).

12. K. A. Andrianov, *Dokl. Akad. Nauk SSSR* **28**, 66 (1940).
13. H. Buff and F. Wohler, *Ann. Chem.* **104**, 94 (1857).
14. S. Friedel and J. Crafts, *Ann. Chem.* **147**, 355 (1863).
15. L. Gatterman, *Chem. Ber.* **22**, 186 (1889).
16. *Inorg. Syn.* **1**, 38 (1939).
17. H. H. Anderson, *J. Am. Chem. Soc.* **81**, 4785 (1959).
18. W. C. Schumb and D. F. Holloway, *J. Am. Chem. Soc.* **63**, 2753 (1941).
19. W. C. Schumb and C. H. Klein, *J. Am. Chem. Soc.* **59**, 261 (1937).
20. L. Spialter and J. S. Smith, III, *Proceedings of the 1967 International Symposium, on the Decomposition of Organometallic Compounds to Refractory Ceramics, Metals and Metal Alloys*, University of Dayton Press, Dayton, Ohio, 1968.

A. R. ANDERSON
Anderson Development Company

SILANES

1. Introduction

The study of compounds derived from second-row elements continues to be one of the most active research areas in inorganic chemistry. The hydrides of silicon and their derivatives merit special attention in this respect because of their number, reasonable thermal stability, and simplicity. No other second-row element forms as many hydride derivatives as does silicon. The compounds are formally analogous to the well-known alkane and alkyl series of carbon compounds and, as a result, an inorganic silicon chemistry analogous to organic carbon chemistry has rapidly developed, but to a limited extent.

The pioneering work in this field was done by Stock and his co-workers in the early 1900s and is summarized in Stock's Baker lectures (1). Since most of the compounds are very sensitive to traces of moisture and oxygen, specialized vacuum techniques were developed for their study and are still in use today. Scrupulously dry high-vacuum systems are recommended for all studies which involve handling the silanes and their derivatives (1,2).

The accessibility of relatively large quantities of the parent silanes and the desire to know more about the role of silicon's $3d$ orbitals in chemical bonding has prompted a resurgence of research in this field in recent years (3–9). This has led to the synthesis of many new and intriguing derivatives of the silanes, with many more expected in the future. Apart from their intrinsic chemical interest, the compounds are invaluable as models for explaining the properties and bonding of more complex systems. As a class, silanes are particularly suitable for study by modern experimental methods such as mass spectrometry and nuclear magnetic resonance (NMR), and by other spectroscopic techniques. Results of these studies have significantly increased the understanding of some of the fundamental concepts associated with the structure, bonding, and constitution of silicon compounds and also other compounds derived from the second-row elements.

2. A General Survey of the Silanes

The parent silicon hydrides, known collectively as the silanes, have the general formula Si_nH_{2n+2}. The first member of the series is called monosilane (or simply silane); higher members are called disilane (Si_2H_6), trisilane (Si_3H_8), etc, according to the number of silicon atoms present. Although the existence of the parent silicon hydrides above mono-, di-, and trisilane has been known for many years, only recently have techniques been available which permit their isolation and study. With the aid of gas chromatography, a number of higher parent silanes, up to Si_8H_{18}, have now been identified and in certain cases isolated (10–17).

Most of the chemistry of the silanes has been limited to studies of SiH_4 and Si_2H_6, where a wide variety of interesting derivatives have been made by replacing one or more of the hydrogen atoms by inorganic or organic groups. Derivatives of the silanes are known which contain elements of groups I, III, IV, V, VI, VII, and certain transition metals. Representative examples are given in Table 2, p. 207. At the present time there are no characterized derivatives in which silicon is multiply bonded to other atoms through the formal type of double or triple bonds commonly found in carbon compounds. Most reports of such unsaturated derivatives have proved to be in error (3). A number of suggestions have been advanced to explain the absence of bonds of this type. For example, it has been suggested that the $(p–p)$ π overlap required in a formal double or triple bond would be weak for second-row elements because of the diffuse character of their $(n > 2)p$ orbitals (18). Further, strong inner-shell electron repulsions may prevent any significant bond contraction generally required for good π overlap in multiple bonds (6,19). Thermodynamic arguments based on strong σ-bonds and weak π-bonds can also be applied to the problem (3). Since the energies of σ-bonds between silicon and electronegative atoms are larger than those of analogous bonds with carbon, silicon has a greater tendency to form two σ-bonds than carbon, rather than one σ- and one π-bond. Thus, monomeric derivatives of the type $R_2Si{=}O$ are not known but exist as polymers of the type $(-Si(R)_2OSi(R)_2O-)_x$. According to this model, the monomer will be the thermodynamically more stable form only if $E(Si{=}O)$ is greater than $2E(Si{-}O)$. The overall problem is undoubtedly more complex than this, since entropy and kinetic factors should also be considered.

Monosubstituted derivatives of SiH_4 and Si_2H_6 are generally referred to as "silyl" and "disilanyl" compounds, respectively; thus, SiH_3I is named silyl iodide, and SiH_3-SiH_2I is named disilanyl iodide. An alternative nomenclature system employs the base word "-silane" (or "-disilane") in naming the derivative and would name SiH_3I as iodosilane. When more than one hydrogen is substituted in the silanes, the compounds are generally named by using the latter terminology. Thus, SiH_2I_2 and $ISiH_2SiH_2I$ are called diiodosilane and 1,2-diiododisilane, respectively. Alternative nomenclature systems for these latter derivatives have been proposed but are not commonly used (7). Complete nomenclature rules for compounds of silicon have been described very well in a number of sources and will not be belabored here (7,20). Examples of the rules will be provided throughout the article.

It is evident from the above discussion that the formulas of the silicon hydrides and many of their derivatives are identical with the formulas of their well-known carbon analogs. However, this is just about the only similarity between the two hydride systems. In situations where bonding, structural aspects, and chemical reactions are of concern, a significant difference generally exists between carbon and silicon compounds. Many of these differences have been ascribed to the presence of unfilled $3d$ orbitals available for bonding in the valence shell of silicon, but not in carbon (3–9). The d orbitals can be used in the formation of additional σ-bonds, with the result that silicon under certain conditions can expand its coordination number to values greater than four. Although four is the most frequently encountered coordination number in silicon compounds, various six-coordinate, eg, the SiF_6^{2-} ion, and five-coordinate, eg,

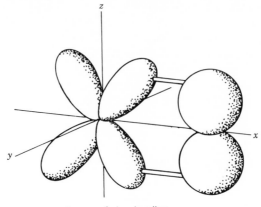

$(p_z \longrightarrow d_{xz})$ π bonding

Fig. 1. Orbital model for a $(p \rightarrow d)$ π bond.

the $SiH_3N(CH_3)_2$ pentamer (see p. 199) complexes are known (21). The corresponding carbon compounds are not known. For valence shell expansion, at least one electron-withdrawing substituent must be bonded to silicon.

In addition to this σ expansion, when an atom or group which contains filled lone-pair orbitals of π symmetry relative to the σ-bond is bound to silicon, an internal type of π-bond with the d orbitals can result (3–7,22) (see Figure 1). The extent of the π-bond is subject to some debate, but the general idea has been used by many workers to explain various unusual properties exhibited by silicon compounds. For example, $(p \rightarrow d)$ π bonding has been used to explain why the silicon–halogen, silicon–oxygen, and silicon–nitrogen bond lengths are normally shorter than the values calculated from the sum of covalent radii, even after the Schomaker-Stevenson correction for ionic character is applied (3–7,22). In addition, the abnormally wide Si–N–Si and Si–O–Si bond angles and the low Lewis basicities of siloxanes and silylamines can be accounted for by $(p \rightarrow d)$ π bonding (3–7,22). Additional unusual features of silicon compounds are pointed out in section 5, p. 181. This type of bonding is thought to be important in silicon linkages which contain elements of groups V, VI, and VII and to become more important as the electronegativity of the donor atom increases. A similar π interaction is possible between silicon's $3d$ orbitals and the filled d orbitals of transition metals and also with the π orbitals of cyanide, olefinic, acetylenic, aromatic, or other α-unsaturated ligands.

For the most part, silicon compounds are more reactive than their carbon analogs, exemplified by the fact that SiH_3Cl is hydrolyzed almost instantaneously by cold water (to form $(SiH_3)_2O$), whereas CH_3Cl does not readily react (3–6). This behavior has not been attributed to thermodynamic effects, since, in general, silicon forms stronger bonds to various common elements than does carbon (23). The greater reactivity of the silicon compounds has been attributed to a kinetic effect, where the larger size of the silicon atom ($r_{Si} = 1.17$ Å, $r_C = 0.77$ Å), the smaller electronegativity of silicon (Si $= 1.8$, C $= 2.5$), and the ability of silicon to expand its coordination number to values greater than four are all important factors in promoting S_N2-type reactions commonly found in silicon chemistry (3–9). The larger size makes silicon more vulnerable to attack than carbon, the smaller electronegativity makes silicon linkages to most nonmetals more polar than analogous carbon linkages, hence more susceptible to attack by polar reagents, and the presence of the vacant $3d$ orbitals about silicon permits the facile formation of intermediate complexes. Detailed kinetic studies of chemical reactions which involve the silicon hydrides are practically nonexistent. However, a considerable amount of kinetic work has been carried out with organosilicon compounds (7,9).

In the following sections, a detailed discussion of the silicon hydrides and their derivatives is presented. For comparative purposes in certain instances, mention will also be made of organosilicon compounds and the derivatives of the germanium hydrides.

3. Preparation and Properties of the Parent Silanes

The oldest method used to prepare the parent silicon hydrides is by the acidic solvolysis of an electropositive metal silicide such as magnesium silicide, Mg_2Si (1,24). Water has been the most common solvent; however, other solvents with appropriate acids have also been successfully employed. These include liquid ammonia (with NH_4Br) and anhydrous hydrazine (with $N_2H_4.HCl$) (25,26). By using Mg_2Si and aqueous HCl, Stock obtained a mixture of silanes, the composition of which was approx 40% SiH_4, 30% Si_2H_6, 15% Si_3H_8, 10% Si_4H_{10}, and 5% of the higher silanes (1).

$$Mg_2Si + H_2O \xrightarrow{H^+} Si_nH_{2n+2} \text{ mixtures up to } Si_8H_{18} \qquad (1)$$

Approximately 23% of the silicon from the Mg_2Si was converted into the silanes. The yield and relative proportions of the hydrides formed are greatly affected by the method of preparation of the Mg_2Si (24,25).

The most convenient method for preparing large amounts of SiH_4 and Si_2H_6 is by the reduction of $SiCl_4$ or Si_2Cl_6 with $LiAlH_4$ (see Vol. 11, p. 217) in an appropriate solvent (27). At the present time, both halides are commercially available. The

$$SiCl_4 + LiAlH_4 \xrightarrow{ether} SiH_4 + LiCl + AlCl_3 \qquad (2)$$

reactions are almost quantitative, although in the Si_2Cl_6 reduction, an appreciable amount of SiH_4 has been observed under certain experimental conditions (28). Large quantities of SiH_4 can also be obtained in the quantitative reduction of $SiCl_4$ with LiH at 400°C in a LiCl–KCl melt (29), and by the direct hydrogenation of silica, silicates, or $SiCl_4$ with hydrogen under superatmospheric pressure in a NaCl–AlCl$_3$ eutectic containing aluminum metal (30). In the absence of any solvent, SiH_4 has been pre-

$$3\,SiO_2 + 4\,Al + 2\,AlX_3 + 6\,H_2 \xrightarrow[900\,atm]{200°C} 6/n\,(AlOX)_n + 3\,SiH_4 \;(76\% \text{ conversion}) \qquad (3)$$

$$3\,SiCl_4 + 4\,Al + 6\,H_2 \xrightarrow[900\,atm]{175°C} 4\,AlCl_3 + 3\,SiH_4 \;(70\text{–}100\% \text{ conversion}) \qquad (4)$$

pared in about 10% yield by heating silica and $LiAlH_4$ to 200°C (31). Disilane can be prepared in yields up to 67% by the reaction of SiH_3I (vapor phase) with sodium amalgam at room temperatures (32), and in a 35% yield by the reaction of $KSiH_3$ with SiH_3Br in 1,2-dimethoxyethane (33). An extension of this latter reaction led to the preparation of Si_3H_8 in an 18% yield by employing $KSiH_3$ and SiH_3SiH_2Br (33). Disilane and other higher hydrides have been conveniently synthesized by subjecting SiH_4 to a silent electrical discharge (10,34,35). In one such experiment, a 63% yield of higher silanes from SiH_4 has been reported, the composition being 66% Si_2H_6, 23%

Table 1. First Members of the Parent Silanes

Compound	Melting point, °C	Boiling point, °C
SiH_4[a]	-185.0	-111.9
Si_2H_6	-132.5	-14.5
Si_3H_8	-117.4	52.9
$n\text{-}Si_4H_{10}$	-89.9	108.1
$iso\text{-}Si_4H_{10}$	-99.1	101.4

[a] Pure SiH_4 from which semiconductor grade silicon can be prepared, available from Matheson Co., Inc., East Rutherford, N.J.

Si_3H_8, and 11% uncharacterized higher silanes (34). Both $n\text{-}Si_4H_{10}$ and $iso\text{-}Si_4H_{10}$ have been separated from the latter mixture by gas chromatography and characterized (10).

The parent silanes for which melting points (1,36), boiling points (1,36), infrared (ir) (10,28,34,37–39), and proton NMR data (10,40–42) have been obtained are listed in Table 1. Characterization of other higher parent systems is much less complete. Identification has been made in most cases by their chromatographic behavior (11–17). No unsaturated or cyclic silicon hydrides have been isolated thus far.

Solid polymeric silanes which have a variable hydrogen content, $(SiH_2)_x$, $(SiH)_x$, and $(SiH_{0.4-1.8})_x$, are well known in silicon hydride chemistry, particularly in decomposition studies. They have been prepared by the thermal and photochemical decomposition of the silanes (43–45) and also by the treatment of H_2SiBr_2 or $HSiBr_3$ with magnesium (46–48), or $HSiCl_3$ with sodium (49), reduction of $(SiBr_2)_x$ with $LiAlH_4$ (50), and the treatment of calcium monosilicide with an HCl–ethanol solution or glacial acetic acid (51). Little information is available about the structures of these compounds, but they are not believed to contain silicon–silicon double or triple bonds. They are all light-brown or yellow amorphous materials having no definite melting points.

The thermal stability of the parent silicon hydrides decreases with increasing numbers of silicon atoms present (1). Silane can be stored at room temperature in glass or metal containers for long periods of time with little or no thermal decomposition, although decomposition will take place at higher temperatures. Chromatographically pure Si_2H_6 decomposes slowly at room temperature or $-78°C$, the decomposition being 2.5 and 1.4%, respectively, after 244 days (52). Impurities present in the higher silanes appear to catalyze the decompositions (24,28,52). Higher silanes decompose almost completely after several months at room temperature, producing mixtures of

$$Si_2H_6 \rightarrow SiH_4 + (SiH)_x + \tfrac{1}{2}H_2 \tag{5}$$

$$Si_5H_{12} \rightarrow 2\ (SiH)_x + Si_2H_6 + SiH_4 \tag{6}$$

the simple hydrides and some form of the solid hydrides (1). The exclusion of light appears to increase the stability of the higher parent hydrides (1).

Trisilane and higher-molecular-weight straight-chain silanes form true clathrate compounds with urea and thiourea (52a). The stability of the clathrate increases as the size of the silane increases and certain of the high-molecular-weight silane–urea clathrates, eg, that of Si_5H_{12}, are stable in air at room temperature.

4. Reactions of the Parent Silanes

Most of the parent hydrides of silicon react explosively with oxygen and appropriate precautions must be taken to exclude air from their storage and reaction systems.

Only under certain critical experimental conditions can SiH_4, Si_2H_6, and Si_3H_8 be mixed with oxygen without spontaneous inflammation (53). Extreme care is urged in all experimental work.

A. REACTIONS WITH WATER AND ALCOHOLS

The parent silanes do not react with pure water or slightly acidified water under normal conditions. A rapid reaction occurs, however, in basic solution, with the quantitative evolution of hydrogen (1). A trace amount of alkali leached from certain glass is sufficient to lead to the hydrolysis of the silanes (1). Complete basic hydrolysis

$$SiH_4 + 2\ KOH + H_2O \rightarrow K_2SiO_3 + 4\ H_2 \tag{7}$$

$$Si_2H_6 + 4\ KOH + 2\ H_2O \rightarrow 2\ K_2SiO_3 + 7\ H_2 \tag{8}$$

followed by the quantitative measurement of hydrogen formed is often used to determine the number of Si–H and Si–Si bonds present in a particular compound. One molecule of H_2 is liberated for each Si–H and Si–Si bond present. The total silicon content can be obtained from analysis of the resulting silicate solution.

Silane reacts with methanol at room temperature to produce methoxymonosilanes of types $Si(OCH_3)_4$, $HSi(OCH_3)_3$, and $H_2Si(OCH_3)_2$, but not H_3SiOCH_3 (54). The reaction is catalyzed by copper metal. Analogous reactions occur with the Si–H bonds of organosilanes (7) and, although studies with the higher hydrides of silicon have not been reported, the results should be similar to the ones obtained for SiH_4. In the presence of alkoxide ions, SiH_4 reacts with various alcohols (except CH_3OH) to produce tetraalkoxysilanes and hydrogen (55).

B. REACTIONS WITH HALOGENS, HYDROGEN HALIDES, AND OTHER COVALENT HALIDES

Most compounds which contain Si–H bonds react very rapidly with the free halogens. An explosive reaction takes place when Cl or Br is allowed to react with SiH_4 at room temperature, presumably forming halogenated silane derivatives (1). At lower temperatures, the reactions are moderated considerably. Halogen deriva-

$$SiH_4 + Br_2 \xrightarrow{-80°C} SiH_3Br\ (+ SiH_2Br_2) + HBr \tag{9}$$

tives are also formed when the silanes are allowed to react with anhydrous hydrogen halides (HCl, HBr, HI) in the presence of an appropriate aluminum halide catalyst (1,56–59). The reactions are generally quite moderate and can be carried out at room

$$SiH_4\ (or\ Si_2H_6) + HX \xrightarrow[X\ =\ Cl,\ Br,\ I]{Al_2X_6} SiH_3X\ (or\ SiH_3SiH_2X) + H_2 \tag{10}$$

temperature or slightly above (80–100°C). Reactions with Si_2H_6 occur at lower temperatures than they do with SiH_4 and HBr reacts more readily than does HCl or HI. Increasing the temperature and/or the duration of the reactions generally leads to the formation of more fully halogenated derivatives.

The higher silanes react with a number of other covalent halides under relatively mild conditions, producing halogenated polysilanes. An explosive reaction is reported to take place between Si_2H_6, Si_3H_8, or Si_4H_{10} and CCl_4, or $CHCl_3$ in the presence of a trace amount of air (1). Trisilane and $CHCl_3$ in the presence of Al_2Cl_6 catalyst react at about 50–70°C to form CH_4, CH_3Cl, CH_2Cl_2, and polychlorotrisilanes of the type $Si_3H_4Cl_4$, etc (1). Tetrasilane is reported to react slowly with CHI_3 at room temperature and rapidly with PI_3 at 100°C without a catalyst to give polyiodotetrasilanes (24). The reaction of Si_4H_{10} with $CHCl_3$ and $CHBr_3$, only takes place in the presence of a catalyst. Boron trichloride is quantitatively reduced to B_2H_6 by Si_2H_6 and Si_3H_8 with the formation of chlorodisilanes and chlorotrisilanes, respectively (see section 5A, p. 181) (60,61). In the above studies, corresponding reactions did not occur when SiH_4 was employed. Disilane does not react with BF_3 under similar conditions; however, both SiH_4 and Si_2H_6 react with BBr_3 to give bromosilanes and bromodisilanes, respectively (60,62).

C. REACTIONS WITH METALS AND METAL DERIVATIVES

Silane reacts with alkali metals (potassium has been most commonly studied) dissolved in various solvents, forming, as the chief product, the silyl derivative of the metal (eg, $KSiH_3$) (63–66). When 1,2-dimethoxyethane (monoglyme) or bis(2-methoxyethyl) ether (diglyme) are used as solvents, two competing reactions occur, ie,

$$SiH_4 + 2\,M \rightarrow SiH_3M + MH \tag{11}$$

$$SiH_4 + M \rightarrow SiH_3M + \tfrac{1}{2}\,H_2 \tag{12}$$

With hexamethylphosphoramide as solvent, only reaction 12 occurs (63). Disilane also reacts with potassium in 1,2-dimethoxyethane to form $KSiH_3$, although SiH_4 and nonvolatile polysilanes are also produced (66,67). Pure crystalline $KSiH_3$ prepared from SiH_4 and potassium in 1,2-dimethoxyethane has been obtained by slow evaporation of the solvent. When liquid ammonia is employed as solvent, only a small fraction of SiH_4 is converted into the metal salt; most of the SiH_4 undergoes an ammonolysis reaction (68). Silane undergoes complete ammonolysis when allowed to react with a

$$SiH_4 + (2 + x)\,NH_3 \rightarrow Si(NH)_2 x NH_3 + 4\,H_2 \tag{13}$$

dilute solution of KNH_2 in liquid ammonia (68).

Disilane undergoes disproportionation in 1,2-dimethoxyethane, forming SiH_4 and a solid material $(-SiH_2-)_x$ when an alkali metal salt such as KH or LiCl is present (33,69). In the alkali metal hydride systems, a slower second reaction occurs, forming

$$x\,Si_2H_6 \xrightarrow{\text{salt}} x\,SiH_4 + 1/x\,(-SiH_2-)_x \tag{14}$$

the alkali metal silyl derivatives. Treatment of Si_2H_6 with $KSiH_3$ yields SiH_4 and a

$$1/x\,(-SiH_2-)_x + MH \xrightarrow{\text{M = K or Li}} MSiH_3 \tag{15}$$

solid material $(-SiH_2-)_x$ which also apparently contains disilanyl and trisilanyl ions as their potassium salts (70). These can be formed by the following sequence of reactions:

$$Si_2H_6 \xrightarrow{\text{KSiH}_3} SiH_4 + 1/x\,(SiH_2)_x \tag{16}$$

$$KSiH_3 + Si_2H_6 \rightarrow SiH_4 + KSi_2H_5 \tag{17}$$

$$KSi_2H_5 + Si_2H_6 \rightarrow SiH_4 + KSi_3H_7 \tag{18}$$

The latter two potassium salts have been proposed, since SiH_4, Si_2H_6, and Si_3H_8 are formed on treatment of the solid material with HCl.

$$KSi_2H_5 + HCl \rightarrow Si_2H_6 + KCl \tag{19}$$

$$KSi_3H_7 + HCl \rightarrow Si_3H_8 + KCl \tag{20}$$

Silane, Si_2H_6, and certain alkylsilanes undergo stepwise halogenation when allowed to pass through solid AgCl or AgBr in a heated tube. This appears to be one of the best preparations of the halogenated silanes (71,72).

$$SiH_4 + 2\ AgCl \xrightarrow{\ 260°C\ } SiH_3Cl + HCl + 2\ Ag \tag{21}$$

Silane and Si_2H_6 react with alkyllithium compounds, forming various alkylsilanes. Complete substitution is generally favored; however, less-substituted products can be isolated by proper choice of a solvent (55). All four methylsilanes, vinylsilane, and divinylsilane have been isolated from the reaction of SiH_4 and the appropriate alkyllithium compound with propyl ether as solvent (73). Methyldisilane and CH_3CH_2-SiH_2SiH_3 have been obtained from Si_2H_6 in a similar type of reaction (73,74). Organic derivatives of SiH_4 and Si_2H_6 which contain Si–H bonds can be further alkylated by using this method (55,73,75).

$$R_ySiH_{4-y} + (4 - y)\ R'Li \rightarrow R_ySiR'_{4-y} + (4 - y)\ LiH \tag{22}$$

$$(y = 0\text{--}3;\ R = \text{alkyl or aryl groups})$$

D. REACTIONS IN ELECTRICAL DISCHARGE, IRRADIATION, AND PYROLYSIS SYSTEMS

Early reports of the decomposition of SiH_4 in an electrical discharge indicated that the main products were hydrogen, solid silicon subhydrides of composition $SiH_{1.2-1.7}$, and small quantities of higher silanes (51). When water vapor was present, no higher silanes were obtained (76). However, more recent studies indicate that under certain conditions reasonably large quantities of higher silanes up to n- and iso-Si_4H_{10} together with smaller amounts of various isomers of higher silanes up to Si_8H_{18} can be produced by using this method (10,34,35). In addition, mixed hydride derivatives can be prepared by subjecting mixtures of SiH_4 and certain other volatile hydrides to such a discharge. Thus, SiH_3GeH_3, SiH_3PH_2, and SiH_3AsH_2 have been prepared from SiH_4-GeH_4, SiH_4-PH_3, and SiH_4-AsH_3 mixtures, respectively (77–79). Although both disilyl-phosphine, $(SiH_3)_2PH$, and disilanylphosphine, $SiH_3SiH_2PH_2$, are obtained in the SiH_4-PH_3 system, they can be obtained free of each other in the discharge of SiH_4-SiH_3PH_2 and Si_2H_6-PH_3 systems, respectively (80). Methyldisilane, $CH_3SiH_2SiH_3$, can be isolated from the products of a SiH_4-CH_3SiH_3 or a SiH_4-$(CH_3)_2O$ discharge system (73,81). The two isomeric dimethyl derivatives of Si_2H_6 can also be prepared in this manner; the 1,2-derivative is made from the discharge of CH_3SiH_3, and the 1,1-derivative from the discharge of a mixture of $(CH_3)_2SiH_2$ and SiH_4 (73).

Photolysis studies of SiH_4 have employed a sensitizer such as mercury vapor, since SiH_4 does not absorb ultraviolet (uv) radiation above 1850 Å (44). The $^3P_1$ mercury-sensitized photolysis of SiH_4 led to the formation of H_2, Si_2H_6, Si_3H_8, and polymeric solid silanes, where the quantum yields of H_2 and Si_2H_6 were estimated to be 1.8 and 0.6, respectively (43,82). It seems that several primary steps occur in the decomposition; these reactions involve SiH_3 and SiH_2 radicals and/or atomic Si, as well as atomic and molecular hydrogen (44). The photolysis of SiH_4 in the presence of GeH_4 or CH_3I produces SiH_3GeH_3 or CH_3SiH_3, respectively (45). This technique has also been used to catalyze the addition of SiH_4 to ethylene, acetylene, and vinylsilane (82). The quenching efficiency of the Si–H bond for $^3P_1$ mercury atoms is known to be much greater than that of the C–H bond. Thus, the photolysis of alkylsilanes leads to the exclusive loss of a hydrogen atom from the Si–H bond when available, with the formation of H_2 and the corresponding disilane (83). The major products of the vacuum

$$CH_3SiH_3 + Hg(^3P_1) \rightarrow H_2 + CH_3SiH_2\text{–}SiH_2CH_3 + Hg(^1S_0) \tag{23}$$

ultraviolet photolysis (1470 Å radiation from a low-pressure xenon resonance lamp) of CH_3SiH_3 are H_2, CH_4, $CH_3SiH_2SiH_2CH_3$, $CH_3SiH_2SiH_3$, and a solid polymer (84). The two silane products are believed to be formed by the insertion of "silene" intermediates (CH_3SiH and SiH_2) into the Si–H bonds of CH_3SiH_3 (84). Similar results are obtained in the xenon-sensitized photolysis of CH_3SiH_3 (84).

$$CH_3SiH + CH_3SiH_3 \rightarrow CH_3SiH_2SiH_2CH_3 \tag{24}$$

$$SiH_2 + CH_3SiH_3 \rightarrow CH_3SiH_2SiH_3 \tag{25}$$

The ultraviolet photolysis of a mixture of SiH_4 and BCl_3 in the presence of azomethane produces B_2H_6 in a 67% yield together with SiH_3Cl and SiH_2Cl_2 (85). No reaction occurs without the azomethane sensitizer (60).

The neutron irradiation of gaseous PH_3 has produced SiH_4 through the well-known nuclear transformation $^{31}P(n,p)^{31}Si$ (86). Irradiation of a PH_3–SiH_4 mixture produces Si_2H_6, which is thought to arise via a SiH_2 precursor (86).

$$^{31}SiH_2 + SiH_4 \rightarrow H_3Si^{31}SiH_3 \tag{26}$$

The SiH_3^- radical produced by the photolysis or γ-ray irradiation of SiH_4 has been trapped and studied in rare-gas matrices at 4.2°K (87,88) (see p. 208). The corresponding CH_3, GeH_3, and SnH_3 radicals have also been prepared by the latter irradiation (88).

All the silanes decompose to silicon and hydrogen at temperatures above about 500°C, but at selected temperatures, under controlled conditions, "cracking" can occur, producing, in certain cases, higher and lower silanes (1). At about 500°C, SiH_4 is partly converted into Si_2H_6, presumably through the initial formation of SiH_3 radicals (89). Higher silanes decompose at somewhat lower temperatures ($\sim$300–350°C) forming SiH_4, hydrogen, silicon, and solid silicon subhydrides in most cases. Small amounts of higher silanes have been detected in the thermal decomposition of Si_2H_6 at 300°C by using a flow system (90); however, in a static system no higher silanes are detected (91). Pyrolysis of a mixture of SiH_4 and PH_3 at 450°C led to the first synthesis of SiH_3PH_2 (92).

In an important commercial process, ultrapure semiconductor-grade silicon is prepared by the thermal decomposition of SiH_4 under various conditions (93). Silicon which is obtained by the normal reduction of sand with coke at high temperatures is not pure enough for use in semiconductor applications. Many problems have been encountered with zone refining of the element; for example, boron cannot be removed since it is distributed almost equally between solid and liquid silicon. The success of chemical methods such as the zinc reduction of $SiCl_4$ or the thermal decomposition of SiI_4 or SiH_4 for preparing pure silicon thus depends on the purity of the starting compounds. The thermal decomposition of SiH_4 is particularly attractive since the hydride is easily prepared and purified (free from boron impurities), and because of the high percentage of silicon in the starting compound.

E. REACTIONS WITH COMPOUNDS CONTAINING MULTIPLE BONDS

One of the most widely studied reactions in silicon chemistry is the addition of silicon hydrides to olefins and acetylenes (7). Most of the investigations have concerned the addition of halosilanes such as $HSiCl_3$, and many industrially important organosilicon compounds, especially those which contain organofunctional groups, are prepared by this process. The reactions are generally done in the presence of a catalyst

$$HSiCl_3 + C_2H_4 \xrightarrow{160–400°C} CH_3CH_2SiCl_3 \qquad (27)$$

(peroxide, tertiary base, metals, or metal salts), although the application of heat is often sufficient to induce addition. Irradiation of the systems with ultraviolet or γ rays also promotes the addition. The large amount of technical literature which exists on this reaction and its mechanism has been comprehensively reviewed (7,8,94).

In a static system at 450°C, SiH_4 adds to ethylene to form $CH_3CH_2SiH_3$, although numerous side reactions also occur, producing mixtures of methylsilanes, ethylsilanes, methylethylsilanes, methylpropylsilanes, and various higher-molecular-weight organopolysilanes (95). When the analogous reaction is carried out in a flow system (450–510°C, normal pressures), the products isolated are $CH_3CH_2SiH_3$, $(CH_3CH_2)_2SiH_2$, and small amounts of Si_2H_6, Si_3H_8, and a compound tentatively identified as $CH_3CH_2SiH_2SiH_3$ (82). Under similar conditions, SiH_4 and acetylene produce mainly ethynaldivinylsilane, $(CH_2{=}CH)_2SiH(C{\equiv}CH)$, although some vinylsilane, $CH_2{=}CHSiH_3$, is also obtained (82). The thermally induced reactions presumably proceed by a free-radical mechanism.

The silicon hydrides also add to the C=O bond. For example, SiH_4 reacts with acetone at 450°C to give $C_3H_7OSiH_3$ and other side products (96). A similar type of reaction occurs with ethylene oxide (96).

$$SiH_4 + \underset{\underset{O}{\diagdown\diagup}}{CH_2{-}CH_2} \xrightarrow{450°C} CH_3CH_2OSiH_3 + \text{other products} \qquad (28)$$

5. Compounds of the Parent Silanes

A. HALOGEN AND PSEUDOHALOGEN DERIVATIVES

Preparations. Monosubstituted halogen derivatives of SiH_4, Si_2H_6, and many of the simple organosubstituted silanes are usually prepared by one of the following reaction schemes (97):

1. The reaction of the parent silane with either anhydrous hydrogen halides (in the presence of the appropriate aluminum halide catalyst) or free halogens (Br_2 or I_2) at low temperatures (see section 4B, p. 177) (1,56–59). Polyhalosilanes of the type SiH_2X_2, $SiHX_3$, and $XSiH_2SiH_2X$ also form in the reactions, and excess parent silane is generally employed to minimize their formation.

2. The reaction of phenylsilane and p-chlorophenylsilane with hydrogen halides (HF, HCl, HBr, HI) in the absence of a solvent or catalyst (97–105). This is a con-

$$ClC_6H_4SiH_3 + HI \rightarrow SiH_3I + ClC_6H_5 \qquad (29)$$

venient procedure for preparing reasonably large quantities of SiH_3– halides, which avoids the use of SiH_4. Deuterated halogen derivatives can also be made by using this method (104). Under certain conditions, the Si–H bonds of the phenylsilane are also

$$C_6H_5SiH_3 + HI \xrightarrow{120°C} C_6H_5SiH_2I + H_2 \qquad (30)$$

halogenated (100). Iodine reacts with phenylsilane according to equation 31 (100).

$$2\, C_6H_5SiH_3 + I_2 \rightarrow C_6H_6 + SiH_3I + C_6H_5SiH_2I \qquad (31)$$

3. The reaction of SiH_4 and Si_2H_6 with silver salts (AgCl or AgBr) at high temperatures (90–280°C) in a flow system (71,72).

4. The reaction of silicon ethers and amines with covalent halides. The covalent halides most frequently used are the boron and aluminum halides (106–111). Both SiH_3F and SiH_3SiH_2F can be conveniently prepared by this method (107,110,111).

$$3 (SiH_3)_2O + 2 BF_3 \xrightarrow{-78°C} 6 SiH_3F + B_2O_3 \tag{32}$$

$$(SiH_3SiH_2)_3N + BF_3 \xrightarrow{-78°C} SiH_3SiH_2F + (SiH_3SiH_2)_2NBF_2 \tag{33}$$

Silyl fluoride and other polyfluoro derivatives of SiH_4 have also been prepared by the reaction of the appropriate chloride derivative with a mild fluorinating agent such as SbF_3 (112–114).

Certain halogen derivatives of the silanes also can be conveniently prepared in rather specific reaction systems. For example, SiH_4 reacts with BBr_3 to form SiH_3Br and SiH_2Br_2, although under similar conditions it does not react with BCl_3 (62). Disilane reacts with either BCl_3 or BBr_3, forming the corresponding monohalogen and certain polyhalogen derivatives (61,62). The monochlorotrisilane isomer $(SiH_3)_2SiHCl$ can be prepared from the reaction of Si_3H_8 with BCl_3 (61).

Polysubstituted halogen derivatives can be prepared through extensions of the above reactions. For example, certain disubstituted halides of SiH_4 (often called "silylene halides" or "silicon halohydrides") can be conveniently prepared by the reaction of hydrogen halides with derivatives of the type $C_6H_5SiH_2X$ or $(C_6H_5)_2SiH_2$ (97–99,101–103).

$$C_6H_5SiH_2I + HI \rightarrow SiH_2I_2 + C_6H_6 \tag{34}$$

$$(C_6H_5)_2SiH_2 + 2 HI \rightarrow SiH_2I_2 + 2 C_6H_6 \tag{35}$$

Mixed halogen derivatives can also be made by using this procedure (101). In the reaction of hydrogen halides with silanes, increasing the temperature, prolonging the reaction, or not having excess parent silane present generally leads to the formation of increased amounts of the polyhalogen derivatives.

$$SiH_4 + n\ HX \xrightarrow{Al_2X_6} SiH_{4-n}X_n + n\ H_2 \tag{36}$$

Although the formation of polyhalogen derivatives of Si_2H_6 has been reported in a number of publications, only a few attempts have been made to characterize them. From the HCl–Si_2H_6 reaction, $Cl_2SiHSiH_3$, $Cl_2SiHSiH_2Cl$, and (presumably) Cl_2SiH-$SiHCl_2$ have been obtained, and from the $AgCl$–Si_2H_6 reaction, $ClSiH_2SiH_2Cl$ has been isolated (72). Analogous polyhalogen derivatives have also been isolated from the reaction of Si_2H_6 with BCl_3 or BBr_3 (61,62).

Trisubstituted halogen derivatives of SiH_4 have been prepared on an industrial scale by treating silicon, ferrosilicon, or a metal silicide with anhydrous hydrogen halides (HCl, HBr, and HI) at elevated temperatures (6). A large-scale synthesis of both $SiHCl_3$ and SiH_2Cl_2 is based on the reaction of a mixture of H_2 and HCl with silicon at high temperatures (6). Dichlorosilane can also be obtained from the acid-catalyzed disproportionation of $SiHCl_3$ (115).

$$2 HSiCl_3 \rightarrow H_2SiCl_2 + SiCl_4 \tag{37}$$

By making use of the so-called "conversion series," pseudohalogens, halogens, and other derivatives of SiH_4 and Si_2H_6 can be prepared by the reaction of specific derivatives with appropriate salts of heavy metals such as silver, mercury, or lead. The conversion series for silver salts and SiH_3- derivatives is given below (4).

$$SiH_3I \rightarrow (SiH_3)_2Se \rightarrow (SiH_3)_2S \rightarrow SiH_3Br \rightarrow SiH_3CN \rightarrow$$
$$SiH_3Cl \rightarrow SiH_3NCS \rightarrow SiH_3NCO \rightarrow (SiH_3)_2O \rightarrow SiH_3F$$

In the application of this method, conversions will only take place if the desired derivative appears later in the series than the starting derivative. For example, SiH_3CN can be prepared in good yields by passing the vapor of SiH_3I (but not SiH_3F) over AgCN at room temperature (116).

$$SiH_3I + AgCN \rightarrow SiH_3CN + AgI \tag{38}$$

The pseudohalogen derivatives, SiH_3NCO, SiH_3NCS, and SiH_3NCSe, can also be prepared in this manner (116–118), but a more recent preparation of the first two compounds involves the reaction of $(SiH_3)_3N$ with the appropriate pseudohalogen hydride (119). This latter method can also be used for the synthesis of SiH_3N_3 (from $(SiH_3)_3N$ or $CH_3CH_2N(SiH_3)_2$) but not SiH_3CN (119,120).

$$(SiH_3)_3N + 4 HN_3 \rightarrow 3 SiH_3N_3 + NH_4N_3 \tag{39}$$

No pure pseudohalides of Si_2H_6 have been isolated, although impure SiH_3SiH_2CN (whether the normal cyanide or isocyanide was not determined) has been prepared by passing the vapors of SiH_3SiH_2I over AgCN (121).

Chemical Properties. The simple halogen derivatives of the silanes are reasonably stable thermally and can be handled routinely without decomposition, provided standard vacuum line techniques are used. However, on heating or allowing the halides to stand at room temperature for prolonged periods, decomposition will occur, mainly via disproportionation if conditions are not too severe. For the SiH_3- halides, the tendency for disproportionation decreases along the series SiH_3F, SiH_3Cl, SiH_3Br, and

$$2 SiH_3Cl \rightleftharpoons SiH_2Cl_2 + SiH_4 \tag{40}$$

$$2 SiH_3SiH_2Cl \rightleftharpoons Si_2H_4Cl_2 + Si_2H_6 \tag{41}$$

SiH_3I, and in certain cases the reactions are reversible (1,4–6). Until recently, SiH_3-SiH_2- halides had not been isolated in a pure state due to the rapid disproportionation reactions they undergo. However, in several cases (Cl and Br), trace amounts of aluminum halides have been found to catalyze the disproportionations greatly (121,122). By using careful purification techniques or procedures which do not involve the use of aluminum halides, all the SiH_3SiH_2- halides have been isolated (57,58,110,121,122).

All compounds which contain silicon–halogen or –pseudohalogen linkages undergo hydrolysis, alcoholysis, and ammonolysis very readily.

$$\overset{\diagdown}{\underset{\diagup}{\rule{0pt}{0pt}}}Si\text{-}OH\left(\overset{\diagdown}{\rule{0pt}{0pt}}Si\text{-}O\text{-}Si\overset{\diagup}{\rule{0pt}{0pt}}\right) + HX \tag{42}$$

H_2O

$$\overset{\diagdown}{\underset{\diagup}{\rule{0pt}{0pt}}}SiX \xrightarrow{ROH} \overset{\diagdown}{\underset{\diagup}{\rule{0pt}{0pt}}}Si\text{-}OR + HX \tag{43}$$

$2 \diagdown NH$

$$\overset{\diagdown}{\underset{\diagup}{\rule{0pt}{0pt}}}Si\text{-}N\overset{\diagup}{\underset{\diagdown}{\rule{0pt}{0pt}}} + \overset{\diagdown}{\underset{\diagup}{\rule{0pt}{0pt}}}NH_2{}^+X^- \tag{44}$$

The final product in the hydrolysis of the SiH_3-, SiH_3SiH_2-, or any of the partially organosubstituted silyl halides is exclusively the corresponding siloxane ($\equiv SiOSi \equiv$) derivative, although secondary decomposition reactions may also occur (4–6). The reaction presumably proceeds through a silanol intermediate, which spontaneously condenses to the siloxane.

$$H_3Si-O \rightarrow SiH_3 \rightarrow (SiH_3)_2O + H_2O \tag{45}$$

The silanol derivatives can be isolated in the hydrolysis of the fully organosubstituted silicon halides (7,8).

In a similar manner, hydrolysis of polyhalogen derivatives of SiH_4 leads to the formation of materials which contain polymeric siloxane linkages rather than compounds of the type $H_2Si(OH)_2$, $HSi(OH)_3$, or $H_2Si{=}O$. Hydrolysis of dihalosilanes

$$x\,H_2SiCl_2 + 2x\,H_2O \rightarrow x\,H_2Si(OH)_2 \rightarrow (-\underset{H}{\overset{H}{Si}}-O-)_x + x\,H_2O \tag{46}$$

(except SiH_2F_2) results in the formation of a mixture of polymers, the simplest of which is the tetramer $(SiH_2O)_4$ (123). Hydrolysis of $HSiCl_3$ yields a solid of composition $(HSiO_{1.5})_x$, the structure and some properties of which have been studied (124).

Direct interaction between organosilicon halides and alcohols has been an important method for the preparation of organosilicon alkoxides (equation 43) (7,8). However, this method is practically useless as a preparative route to alkoxide derivatives of the parent silanes since reactions also occur at the Si–H bonds. For example, a vigorous reaction occurs between SiH_3I and CH_3OH at approx –60°C, producing nonvolatile oils, mixtures of unidentified liquids, H and only a trace of SiH_3OCH_3 (125).

Reactions of SiH_3- halides and partially organosubstituted halides with ammonia and primary and secondary amines parallel their reactions with water and alcohols. For example, the reaction of SiH_3Cl with NH_3 produces $(SiH_3)_3N$, with probable intermediates of the type SiH_3NH_2 and $(SiH_3)_2NH$ spontaneously undergoing condensation or decomposition reactions (1).

$$2\,SiH_3NH_2 \rightarrow (SiH_3)_2NH + NH_3 \tag{47}$$

$$3\,(SiH_3)_2NH \rightarrow 2\,(SiH_3)_3N + NH_3 \tag{48}$$

Reactions of the halides with substituted amines are discussed in section 5C, p. 195 (see also Fig. 2).

Reactions of ammonia with di- and trihalosilanes produce polymeric materials presumably formed through a variety of condensation reactions (4–6).

$$SiH_2Cl_2 + 4\,NH_3 \rightarrow SiH_2(NH_2)_2 + 2\,NH_4Cl \tag{49}$$

$$x\,SiH_2(NH_2)_2 \rightarrow (SiH_2NH)_x + x\,NH_3 \tag{50}$$

Halide and pseudohalide derivatives of the silicon hydrides form solid adducts with various nitrogen bases, such as trialkylamines or pyridine. The parent silanes do not form adducts with these compounds; hence, the presence of at least one halogen or other suitable electronegative ligand is necessary for adduct formation (126). However, increasing the number of halogens on silicon does not necessarily increase the stability of the adducts, but may, in certain cases, decrease their stability, as shown in the stability series given below for the 1:1 trimethylamine–chlorosilane adducts reported (22).

$$SiCl_4 . N(CH_3)_3 < HSiCl_3 . N(CH_3)_3 < H_2SiCl_2 . N(CH_3)_3 = H_3SiCl . N(CH_3)_3$$
$$\textbf{(1)} \qquad\qquad \textbf{(2)} \qquad\qquad \textbf{(3)} \qquad\qquad \textbf{(4)}$$

Four factors are important in discussing the stabilities of the adducts: (a) basicity of the donor ligand, (b) electronegativity and number of the halogen atoms attached, (c) the type of ligand other than the halogen atom attached to silicon, and (d) steric considerations. In the series cited above, (a) and (c) are not applicable; (b) would predict the opposite order of stability, hence steric problems associated with increasing the number of chlorine atoms about silicon have been invoked to explain the

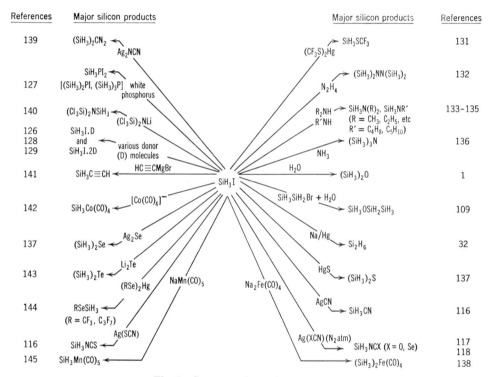

Fig. 2. Some reactions of silyl iodide.

experimental results. As expected from electronegativity considerations, $HSiF_3 . N-(CH_3)_3$ is more stable than $HSiCl_3 . N(CH_3)_3$. Substitution of CH_3- groups for hydrogen atoms decreases the acceptor properties of the parent halides (126). Silyl iodide forms 1:1 adducts with trimethyl- and triethylphosphine at room temperature; however, with trimethylarsine, a poorer donor molecule, the adduct which forms is only stable at low temperatures and is completely dissociated above 120°C (127).

The stoichiometry of the adducts depends on the particular halide used and the type of donor molecule (126–129 and references contained therein). Most of the halides actually form two adducts with trimethylamine, one of which has a 1:1 composition, and the other a 2:1 (base:halide) or approx 2:1 composition. Silyl fluoride, SiH_2F_2, $SiHF_3$, SiH_3CN, SiH_3NCS, and SiH_3NCO form only 1:1 adducts with trimethylamine. Pyridine forms 2:1 adducts with most of the halides, although SiH_2Br_2,

SiH_2I_2, $SiHBr_3$, and $SiHI_3$, form $4:1$ adducts. Tetramethylenediamine forms $1:1$ complexes with most of the halosilanes. Silyl iodide forms a $1:1$ adduct with $(CH_3)_2NSiH_3$ which slowly decomposes at room temperature to give $(CH_3)_2NSiH_2I$ and $((CH_3)_2N)_2$-$SiHI$ (129).

From conductivity measurements and infrared analyses, the nitrogen base adducts of the bromo- and iodosilanes are formulated as being ionic in the solid state and in acetonitrile solution (128). For example, in acetonitrile, $SiH_3I.2py$ (py = pyridine) behaves as a $1:1$ electrolyte (ie, $SiH_3.2py^+$, I^-) and $SiH_2I_2.4py$ behaves as a $1:2$ electrolyte (ie, $SiH_2.4py^{2+}$, $2I^-$). Both $SiH_3I.N(CH_3)_3$ and $SiH_3I.2N(CH_3)_3$ are good conductors in acetonitrile (128). The chlorosilane adducts are also believed to be ionic; however, the fluorosilanes and pseudohalosilanes appear to form nonionic (molecular or macromolecular) adducts (128).

Little information is available about the adducts formed between the silicon halides and compounds which contain group VI donor atoms (O, S, etc). Existing data imply that adducts of this type are weaker than adducts formed with group V donor molecules and are formed only at low temperatures, if at all (130).

The chemistry of SiH_3I has been investigated more fully than that of the other SiH_3- halides. A summary of the important reactions which have been investigated is given in Figure 2. In many, but not all, cases analogous reactions occur with the other halides.

Structural Considerations and Properties Specific to the Pseudohalogen Derivatives. The tetrahedral configuration of ligands in the tetravalent silicon halides and pseudohalides has been confirmed by numerous structural investigations (3–6). The Si–ligand bond lengths in many instances are shorter than the values calculated from the sum of the covalent radii. For example, the observed and calculated Si–F bond lengths in SiH_3F are 1.595 ± 0.01 Å (microwave) and 1.89 Å, respectively (146). Even with the Shomaker-Stevenson correction term which accounts for the ionic character in the bond, the calculated value is 1.69 Å. To account for this shortening, it is thought that in addition to the normal σ-bond in the Si–X linkage, there is appreciable dative π-bonding between the filled p orbitals of the halogen and the vacant d orbitals of silicon, the so-called $(p \rightarrow d)$ π bond (22,147) (see Figure 1). The importance of this type of bonding increases as the electronegativity of the donor atom increases.

The dipole moments of SiH_3F, SiH_3Cl, and SiH_3Br are roughly the same, ie, 1.27, 1.30, and 1.32 D, respectively (5). The values are distinctly lower than the dipole moments of CH_3F (1.79 D), CH_3Cl (1.87 D), and CH_3Br (1.80 D), even though silicon is more electropositive than carbon and the Si–X bond lengths are larger than the C–X bond lengths (5). Although this again has been attributed to $(p \rightarrow d)$ π bonding in the Si–halogen linkage, differences in the magnitude and direction of the bond dipoles of the $\overset{\leftarrow+}{C-H}$ (0.4 D) and $\overset{+\rightarrow}{Si-H}$ (1.0 D) bonds may also be responsible for this observation (148).

Only one complete structure study of a SiH_3SiH_2- derivative has ever been reported, ie, that of SiH_3SiH_2F (149). The Si–F and Si–Si bond distances in this compound, 1.598 ± 0.008 Å and 2.332 ± 0.005 Å, respectively (microwave), are very close to the corresponding values in other silicon–fluorine compounds and Si_2H_6. The dipole moments of CH_3CH_2F, CH_3SiH_2F, and SiH_3SiH_2F are 1.94, 1.71, and 1.26 D, respectively (149,150).

Although the structures and chemical properties of halide and pseudohalide derivatives of the silanes are similar in many respects, the latter also exhibit some unique properties which depend on the nature of the pseudohalogen. For example, the cyanide (CN), cyanate (OCN), thiocyanate (SCN), and selenocyanate (SeCN) derivatives should exist in two isomeric forms, the "normal" and "iso" configurations. The results of numerous spectroscopic studies on the compound prepared from AgCN and SiH_3I indicate that contrary to earlier assumptions, the structure is exclusively of the normal type, ie, SiH_3CN (141,151–153). Germyl cyanide, GeH_3CN, is also known to have this structure (154). Results of infrared studies on the $(CH_3)_3Si-$ derivative have suggested that at room temperature the compound exists in an equilibrium between the normal and iso configurations, the former being prevalent (155,156). The isomers can be distinguished by unique infrared absorptions at 4.76 μ for the isocyanide isomer and 4.58 μ for the cyanide isomer. The fraction of isocyanide isomer increases as the temperature is raised.

In contrast to the normal and predominantly normal cyanide structures observed for SiH_3CN and $(CH_3)_3SiCN$, respectively, the structures of SiH_3NCO, SiH_3NCS, and SiH_3NCSe and the corresponding organosilicon derivatives which are known, all have the iso configuration (117,118,157–159). The heavy-atom skeletons in the compounds have been found to be linear from the following measurements: SiH_3NCO (ir and microwave (117,157)), SiH_3NCS (Raman-infrared and microwave (158,159)), and SiH_3-$NCSe$ (ir (118)). However, the heavy-atom skeletons in the corresponding carbon compounds are nonlinear. For example, the CNC bond angles in CH_3NCO and CH_3NCS are 125 ± 5° (electron diffraction) and 142° (microwave), respectively (160,161). In addition, one of the germanium analogs, GeH_3NCO, has also been shown to have a nonlinear GeNCO skeleton, although the magnitude of the angle has not been accurately determined (ir and microwave) (162). The heavy-atom skeleton in GeH_3NCS is most probably nonlinear also. The linearity of the SiH_3- derivatives has been ascribed to the presence of $(p \rightarrow d) \pi$ bonding in the silicon–nitrogen bond. In a simple orbital model of the nitrogen atom in these compounds, two of the five valence electrons of nitrogen are involved in σ-bonds and one is involved in a normal $(p—p) \pi$ bond. One σ-bond is with the M atom of the MH_3- group; the remaining σ- and π-bonds are with the carbon atom of the NCO– group. The hybridization of the nitrogen atom can then be described as sp^2, the remaining lone pair of electrons occupying one of the hybrid orbitals. This model accounts for the bent structure of the CH_3- and GeH_3- derivatives, and to account for the linear structures of the SiH_3- derivatives, it is suggested that the lone pair of electrons on nitrogen is involved in a $(p \rightarrow d) \pi$ bond with silicon. This results in a change of hybridization associated with nitrogen from sp^2 to sp and accounts for the linear structures of the SiNCO, SiNCS, and SiNCSe linkages. Although $(p \rightarrow d) \pi$ bonding is also possible in the Ge–N linkage, if it is present, it does not alter the structure of the molecule appreciably. A number of investigations have revealed that the ability for germanium to participate in $(p \rightarrow d) \pi$ bonding with first-row donor elements is less than that of silicon (162–166). However, predictions of structure based solely on this concept must be made with caution. For example, in contrast to the linear heavy-atom skeletons present in the SiH_3- derivatives, both $(CH_3)_3SiNCO$ and $(CH_3)_3SiNCS$ have substantial deviations from linearity with Si–N–C bond angles of 150 ± 3° and 154 ± 2°, respectively (electron diffraction) (167). In addition, the structure of SiH_3N_3, which is isoelectronic with SiH_3NCO, does not contain a linear SiN_3 skeleton as might be expected, but exists as an asymmetric top molecule with a nonlinear SiN_3 skeleton (ir and microwave) (120,168). The structural difference between the two isoelectronic molecules has been rationalized on the basis of Linnett's "double quartet" modification of the octet rule (169). It suggests that the π-bonding capability of the nitrogen atom with silicon in these compounds is highly dependent on the nuclear charge of the atom at the other end of the grouping. However, it also has been pointed out that the nonlinear structure of SiH_3N_3 does not preclude the possibility of $(p \rightarrow d)$ π bonding in the molecule, at least in theory (120). Nonlinear heavy-atom skeletons have also been observed for $(CH_3)_3SiN_3$ (ir and microwave (170)) and GeH_3N_3 (Raman-infrared (171)).

The SiH_3– pseudohalides, in general, are less thermally stable than the SiH_3–halides. The rates of thermal decomposition for the compounds vary depending on the particular derivative, and it appears that in most cases trace amounts of impurities catalyze the decompositions. Both SiH_3CN and SiH_3NCO are stable under vacuum at room temperature for several weeks; however, SiH_3NCS, SiH_3NCSe, and SiH_3N_3 decompose slowly at room temperature (5,116–118,120). The decomposition reactions have not been investigated thoroughly, but the products include hydrogen, SiH_4, Si_2H_6, and an uncharacterized liquid from the SiH_3NCS decomposition (116); SiH_4 and an uncharacterized solid from the SiH_3N_3 decomposition (120); and a brick-red solid with a trace of SiH_4 from the SiH_3NCSe decomposition (118). On heating the latter compound for 1 hr at $80°C$, a pale-orange solid is formed, together with small quantities of SiH_4, SiH_3CN, $(SiH_3)_2Se$, and HCN. Both SiH_3NCO and SiH_3NCSe decompose rapidly in the presence of the silver salts from which they are made. In fact, to prepare these compounds by this method successfully, the SiH_3I used in the conversion must be diluted with dry nitrogen (117,118). From the photodecomposition of SiH_3N_3 in solid argon matrices near $4°K$, iminosilicon, HNSi, has been detected by infrared spectroscopy (172).

Triorganosubstituted silyl pseudohalides are more stable thermally than the parent or partially organosubstituted derivatives. Trimethylsilyl azide is remarkably stable and can be held at $200°C$ for 8 hr without decomposition (170,173). A temperature of $500°C$ is required to induce thermal decomposition.

Diborane and the haloboranes (F, Cl) form simple 1:1 addition compounds with SiH_3CN at low temperatures, which decompose on heating to give SiH_4 or a halosilane and polymeric materials (174,175). Identical types of reactions occur with $(CH_3)_3SiCN$ (174,175).

$$SiH_3CN + \tfrac{1}{2}\, B_2H_6 \xrightarrow{35°C} SiH_3CN.BH_3 \xrightarrow{35°C} (BH_2CN)_n + SiH_4 \qquad (51)$$

$$SiH_3CN + BX_3 \rightarrow SiH_3CN.BX_3 \rightarrow BX_2CN + SiH_3X \qquad (52)$$

Although various triorganosilyl cyanides react readily with sulfur, forming the corresponding isothiocyanate derivative (156,176), SiH_3CN does not add sulfur in an analogous way, at least at room temperature (153). At higher temperatures, complex decomposition reactions occur. The addition of sulfur has been taken as support for the presence of the isocyanide isomer in equilibrium with the normal cyanide isomer in the triorgano derivatives as suggested by the infrared studies (5,155,156).

$$(CH_3)_3SiCN \rightleftharpoons (CH_3)_3SiNC \overset{S}{\rightarrow} (CH_3)_3SiNCS \qquad (53)$$

Supporting evidence for this is found in the reaction between $(CH_3)_3SiCN$ and $Fe(CO)_5$ (177).

$$(CH_3)_3SiCN + Fe(CO)_5 \rightarrow (CH_3)_3SiNCFe(CO)_4 + CO \qquad (54)$$

B. OXYGEN AND OTHER GROUP VI DERIVATIVES

Preparations and Reactions of Silanols, Siloxanes, and Alkoxysilanes. *Silanols.*
The simplest silanol, SiH_3OH, has never been isolated, although it is thought to be an
intermediate in the hydrolysis of silyl compounds (see equation 45). Likewise,
$SiH_2(OH)_2$ and $SiH(OH)_3$ have never been isolated, nor have any partly substituted
organic derivatives of the type CH_3SiH_2OH, $CH_3SiH(OH)_2$, or $(CH_3)_2SiHOH$. Completely substituted organic derivatives of the above silanols have been isolated, usually
being prepared by the careful hydrolysis of the corresponding chlorides, although other
derivatives have also been used in many cases (7,8). Even the organosilanols have a
strong tendency to undergo condensation to the corresponding siloxane (ether)
derivatives. The stability of silanols with respect to condensation decreases as the
number of –OH groups on the silicon increases and only those silanols which contain
large bulky organic groups are resistant to condensation. Thus, attempts to prepare
$CH_3Si(OH)_3$ have failed (178); however, $C_6H_5Si(OH)_3$ has been isolated and is stable
at room temperature and neutral pH (179).

The silanols are slightly less basic, but much more acidic than their carbon
analogs (180) and undergo chemical reactions which are very similar to those of the
alcohols (7,8).

Siloxanes (Ethers). The hydrolysis of practically any SiH_3– or organosilyl compound leads to the formation of the corresponding siloxane ($\equiv$Si–O–Si$\equiv$) derivative
(4–6). Disilyl ether, $(SiH_3)_2O$ (disiloxane), has been most commonly prepared by the
hydrolysis of an SiH_3– halide, although better yields can be obtained if $(SiH_3)_2S$ is used
(137). Hydrolysis of amine derivatives is not used for the synthesis of ethers containing
Si–H bonds since the solution becomes basic on hydrolysis and the Si–H bonds are
readily destroyed. Treatment of halide derivatives with metal salts such as ZnO, AgO,
or Ag_2CO_3 also leads to the formation of siloxane derivatives (4–8). Bisdisilanyl ether,
$(SiH_3SiH_2)_2O$ (1,2-disilyldisiloxane), and silyl disilanyl ether, $SiH_3OSiH_2SiH_3$ (1-silyl-
disiloxane), have been prepared by the hydrolysis of SiH_3SiH_2I and a mixture of SiH_3I
and SiH_3SiH_2Br, respectively (57,109). The unsymmetrical siloxane $(CH_3)_3SiOSiH_3$
has been prepared by the direct interaction of $(CH_3)_3SiOH$ with SiH_3I (109). Both
$(CH_3)_3SiOSiH_3$ and $SiH_3OSiH_2SiH_3$ tend to undergo a redistribution reaction in the
liquid phase, giving an equilibrium system of the unsymmetrical siloxane and the symmetrical siloxanes derived therefrom. Partially halogenated derivatives of $(SiH_3)_2O$ are

$$2 \ SiH_3OSiH_2SiH_3 \rightleftharpoons (SiH_3)_2O + (SiH_3SiH_2)_2O \qquad (55)$$

known; $(HSiCl_2)_2O$ and $(H_2SiCl)_2O$ are prepared by the controlled hydrolysis of $HSiCl_3$-
and H_2SiCl_2, respectively (181), and $(H_2SiF)_2O$ and $H_2SiFOSiH_3$ are formed in the
reaction of PF_5 with $(SiH_3)_2O$ (182).

$$(SiH_3)_2O + 2 \ PF_5 \xrightarrow{-78°C} (H_2SiF)_2O + 2 \ HPF_4 \qquad (56)$$

The di- and trisubstituted siloxy derivatives of SiH_4, ie, $(SiH_3O)_2SiH_2$ and $(SiH_3O)_3$-
SiH, have been prepared by the low-temperature, liquid-phase, base-catalyzed condensation of $(SiH_3)_2O$ (183).

$$2 \ (SiH_3)_2O \xrightarrow{NH_3} (SiH_3O)_2SiH_2 + SiH_4 \qquad (57)$$

Alkoxysilanes. Most of the simple alkoxysilanes which contain Si–H bonds cannot
be conveniently prepared by the direct reaction of an alcohol with an appropriate silyl
or partially substituted organosilyl halide because of secondary reactions which occur

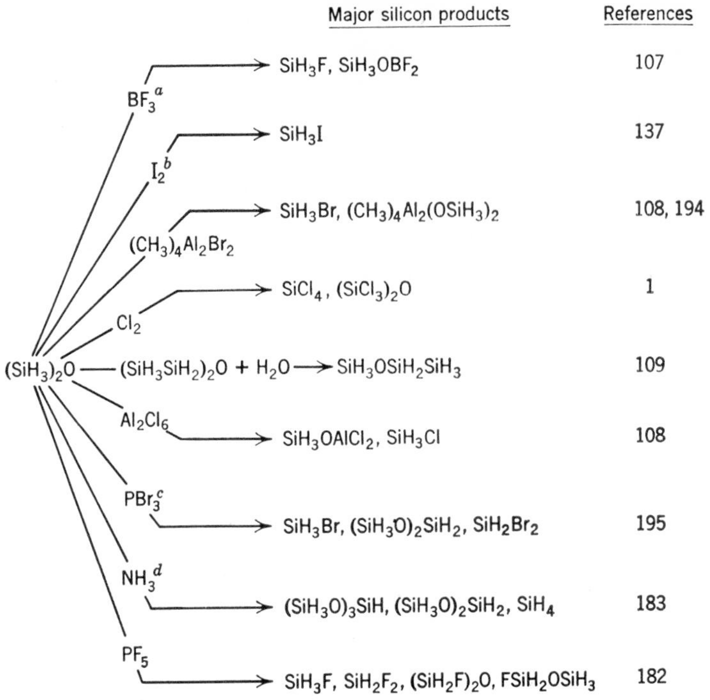

	Major silicon products	References

$(SiH_3)_2O$ reactions (Fig. 3):

- $BF_3{}^a$ → SiH_3F, SiH_3OBF_2 — 107
- $I_2{}^b$ → SiH_3I — 137
- $(CH_3)_4Al_2Br_2$ → SiH_3Br, $(CH_3)_4Al_2(OSiH_3)_2$ — 108, 194
- Cl_2 → $SiCl_4$, $(SiCl_3)_2O$ — 1
- $(SiH_3SiH_2)_2O + H_2O \longrightarrow SiH_3OSiH_2SiH_3$ — 109
- Al_2Cl_6 → SiH_3OAlCl_2, SiH_3Cl — 108
- $PBr_3{}^c$ → SiH_3Br, $(SiH_3O)_2SiH_2$, SiH_2Br_2 — 195
- $NH_3{}^d$ → $(SiH_3O)_3SiH$, $(SiH_3O)_2SiH_2$, SiH_4 — 183
- PF_5 → SiH_3F, SiH_2F_2, $(SiH_2F)_2O$, $FSiH_2OSiH_3$ — 182

Fig. 3. Some reactions of disiloxane. [a]Identical reaction with BCl_3. [b]No reaction with HI. [c]No reaction with PF_3 or PCl_3. [d]Other Lewis bases can also be used, eg, PH_3, $(CH_3)_2NH$, or LiH.

at the Si–H bond. Methoxysilane, CH_3OSiH_3 (silyl methyl ether), has been prepared by the interaction of dry CH_3OH with either the $(CH_3)_3N$ adduct of SiH_3I (125) or with $(SiH_3)_2S$ (184). The latter procedure is quite general and has been used to prepare

$$SiH_3I \cdot N(CH_3)_3 + CH_3OH \rightarrow SiH_3OCH_3 + (CH_3)_3N \cdot HI \tag{58}$$

$SiH_3SiH_2OCH_3$ (185) and other partially or fully substituted organic derivatives of this type (186,187). Other alcohols have also been employed in the reaction (188).

$$(SiH_3SiH_2)_2S + 2 CH_3OH \rightarrow 2 SiH_3SiH_2OCH_3 + H_2S \tag{59}$$

$$(SiH_3)_2S + 2 CF_3CH_2OH \rightarrow 2 SiH_3OCH_2CF_3 + H_2S \tag{60}$$

The higher-substituted methoxy derivatives of SiH_4 can be prepared by the liquid-phase, base-catalyzed condensation of SiH_3OCH_3 (189), by the reaction at room temperature of SiH_4 with CH_3OH (54), or by the reaction of methoxychlorosilanes with $LiBH_4$ (190). Alkoxychlorosilanes which contain Si–H bonds can be prepared by the

$$SiHCl(OCH_3)_2 + LiBH_4 \rightarrow LiCl + \frac{1}{2} B_2H_6 + SiH_2(OCH_3)_2 \tag{61}$$

reaction of $HSiCl_3$ with dialkyl sulfites or alkyl nitrites (190). Tri- and tetraalkoxy-

$$SiHCl_3 + 2 SO(OC_2H_5)_2 \rightarrow 2 C_2H_5Cl + SiHCl(OC_2H_5)_2 + 2 SO_2 \tag{62}$$

$$SiHCl_3 + 2 CH_3ONO \rightarrow SiHCl(OCH_3)_2 + 2 NOCl \tag{63}$$

silanes have also been prepared by the reaction of alcohols with $HSiCl_3$ and $SiCl_4$, respectively (191). In the latter reaction, alkoxychlorosilanes of the type CH_3OSiCl_3, $(CH_3O)_2SiCl_2$ can be obtained (192).

An unusual reaction occurs between formaldehyde and SiH_3Cl, $HSiCl_3$, or $SiCl_4$, yielding $ClCH_2OSiH_3$, $ClCH_2OSiHCl_2$, and $ClCH_2OSiCl_3$, respectively (193).

A summary of some of the reactions of $(SiH_3)_2O$ is given in Figure 3. The cleavage of the Si–O bond by covalent halides is common to both $(SiH_3)_2O$ and SiH_3OCH_3 and, in fact, to all siloxanes and alkoxysilanes (4–8). For the boron, aluminum, and phosphorus halides, the initial step of the reaction is thought to involve the formation of a weak four-center transition complex as shown below for $(SiH_3)_2O$ and BCl_3 (107). The complex is not stable and does not dissociate into the original reactants, but decom-

$$(SiH_3)_2O + BCl_3 \rightarrow \begin{array}{c} SiH_3-O-SiH_3 \\ \downarrow \ \vdots \ \uparrow \\ ClB-Cl \\ Cl \end{array} \rightarrow SiH_3Cl + SiH_3OBCl_2 \qquad (64)$$

poses with cleavage of an Si–O bond. Although SiH_3OBCl_2 is reasonably stable at room temperature, SiH_3OBF_2 disproportionates as shown in equation 65.

$$3 SiH_3OBF_2 \rightarrow 3 SiH_3F + BF_3 + B_2O_3 \qquad (65)$$

When an equimolar quantity of $(SiH_3)_2O$ and $(SiH_3SiH_2)_2O$ is allowed to react with a deficit of BCl_3 at $-78°C$, preferential reaction of the $(SiH_3SiH_2)_2O$ occurs (109). In a related reaction, when $SiH_3OSiH_2SiH_3$ is treated with BCl_3, preferential cleavage of the SiH_3SiH_2–O bond occurs, although appreciable cleavage of the SiH_3–O bond is also detected (109). These observations have been explained by considering that the two silicon atoms in the SiH_3SiH_2- group can more effectively accept the negative charge of the chlorine atom in the transition complex than one silicon atom, perhaps through some degree of $(d \rightarrow d)$ π bonding between adjacent silicon atoms.

Although HI does not react with $(SiH_3)_2O$, it does react with $(CH_3SiH_2)_2O$, forming CH_3SiH_2I (106). On mixing GeH_3F and $(SiH_3)_2O$ in an attempted exchange reaction, SiH_3F is formed, together with SiF_4; however, no $(GeH_3)_2O$ is obtained (192).

The Si–O bond of SiH_3OCH_3 is quantitatively cleaved by PCl_3; however, no reaction occurs on allowing PCl_3 and $(SiH_3)_2O$ to react under the same experimental condi-

$$SiH_3OCH_3 + PCl_3 \rightarrow SiH_3Cl + CH_3OPCl_2 \qquad (66)$$

tions (195). Bond cleavage and disproportionation reactions occur with both $(SiH_3)_2O$ and SiH_3OCH_3 when PBr_3 is used.

Methoxysilane and most alkoxysilanes in general hydrolyze rapidly to the corresponding symmetrical siloxane derivatives (4–8, 125). In the liquid phase, SiH_3OCH_3

$$2 SiH_3OCH_3 + H_2O \rightarrow (SiH_3)_2O + 2 CH_3OH \qquad (67)$$

reacts with CH_3OH to yield various methoxysilanes and hydrogen (125). It also reacts with I_2 to form SiH_3I, and with BF_3 to form SiH_3F and CH_3OBF_2. With PF_5, Si–O bond cleavage also occurs with the formation of SiH_3F and an unstable solid material believed to be CH_3OPF_4 (182).

Structures and Basicities of Siloxanes and Alkoxysilanes. There is a considerable amount of experimental evidence and discussion in the literature which indicates that the bonding in the Si–O linkage is not of the normal σ type as found in the analogous C–O linkage. For example, the 1.634 ± 0.002 Å Si–O bond length in $(SiH_3)_2O$ is considerably shorter than the 1.77 Å normal silicon–oxygen single-bond length estimated from the radius sum for oxygen and silicon, which includes a correction for the ionic character of the bond (196). The results have been explained by invoking a certain amount of π-bonding between silicon and oxygen, giving "double-bond character" to the Si–O bond. The π character arises from the fact that the vacant $3d$ orbitals of Si and the filled $2p$ orbitals of O are of π symmetry and can overlap to form a dative π-bond if the relative energies of the orbitals are appropriate (Fig. 1).

The involvement of oxygen's lone pairs of electrons in $(p \rightarrow d)$ π bonding is also apparent in the magnitude of the angles formed by bonds to the oxygen atom in these ether systems. In $(CH_3)_2O$, the C–O–C bond angle is $111.7 \pm 0.3°$ (microwave) in accord with an approximately sp^3 hybrid orbital about oxygen with two lone pairs of electrons occupying hybrid orbitals (197). In $(SiH_3)_2O$, Si–O–Si bond angle should be of a similar magnitude in the absence of appreciable $(p \rightarrow d)$ π bonding. However, if both lone pairs of electrons on oxygen are completely involved in π-bonding, the Si–O–Si bond angle should be $180°$ with an sp hybrid orbital system at oxygen. The actual Si–O–Si bond in $(SiH_3)_2O$ is $144.1 \pm 0.8°$ (electron diffraction), indicating that there is considerably less p character in the oxygen hybrid orbital of the silicon ether than there is in the carbon ether, although it is not completely of the sp type (196). It has been concluded that each of the two lone electron pairs of oxygen are about 50% involved in π-bonding with silicon (196). The Si–O–Si angle in $((CH_3)_3Si)_2O$ is $130 \pm 10°$ (electron diffraction) (198). Infrared studies of SiH_3OCH_3 show that the molecule is definitely nonlinear, but a quantitative measure of the Si–O–C angle has not been made (184).

The results of base-strength studies of organic ethers, siloxanes, and alkoxysilanes are also consistent with appreciable $(p \rightarrow d)$ π bonding in the Si–O linkage. For example, B_2H_6 forms an acid-base adduct with $(CH_3)_2O$ at $-78°C$, but it does not form an adduct with either $(SiH_3)_2O$ or SiH_3OCH_3, even though silicon is more electropositive than carbon (125). In addition, from hydrogen-bonding studies, SiH_3OCH_3 has been shown to act as a weaker base than $(CH_3)_2O$ but stronger than $(SiH_3)_2O$ (185). The base properties of SiH_3OCH_3 and $SiH_3SiH_2OCH_3$ are identical. Detailed studies of organosilicon derivatives confirm the general order or basicities as, organic ethers > alkoxysilanes > siloxanes (199). With the lone pairs of electrons of oxygen involved in $(p \rightarrow d)$ π bonding, they are not as available for donation to Lewis acids for complex formation or hydrogen bonding. For the alkoxysilanes, a model has been proposed where only one pair of electrons in a p orbital on oxygen is involved in π-bonding, with the second lone pair of electrons localized in a hybrid orbital (approximately an sp^2 hybrid orbital) at the oxygen (199). The lone pair of electrons in the hybrid orbital would not have the correct symmetry to form appreciable overlap with the d orbitals of silicon, and hence, the molecule would have some, but reduced overall base character. An orbital model for the $(p \rightarrow d)$ π bond in the Si–O–C linkage of alkoxysilanes is shown in Figure 4. Substitution of CH_3- groups for hydrogen atoms in the SiH_3- derivatives increases the basicity of the siloxane or alkoxysilane (186).

The dipole moments of $(SiH_3)_2O$ (0.24 D) and SiH_3OCH_3 (1.166 D) are also consistent with the above oxygen valence angle, base strength, and π-bonding discussion and have been studied in detail (200).

Very few spectroscopic, dipole-moment, or base-strength studies have been carried out on germanium ethers. The most recent infrared study of $(GeH_3)_2O$ suggests a Ge–O–Ge bond angle of $139 \pm 6°$ (201). Hydrogen-bonding studies indicate that GeH_3OCH_3 and $((CH_3)_3Ge)_2O$ are stronger Lewis bases than $(CH_3)_2O$ and $((CH_3)_3C)_2O$ respectively, in accord with the more electropositive character of germanium compared to carbon (163,165). It appears that although $(p \rightarrow d)$ π bonding may be present in the Ge–O linkage of germanium ethers, it does not appreciably alter their electron-donor character.

An attempt has been made to determine the relative inductive effects of the CH_3-, SiH_3-, and GeH_3- groups by measuring the relative Lewis basicities of compounds of the type $MH_3CH_2OCH_3$ (M = C, Si, and Ge) (163, 187). In these compounds, $(p \rightarrow d)$ π bonding involving adjacent atoms as discussed previously is eliminated and the normal inductive effects of the MH_3- groups should be apparent. However, hydrogen-bonding studies indicate that both $SiH_3CH_2OCH_3$ and $GeH_3CH_2OCH_3$ act as weaker Lewis bases than $CH_3CH_2OCH_3$, contrary to what would be expected from simple electronegativity considerations (163,187). In organosilicon compounds, it has been

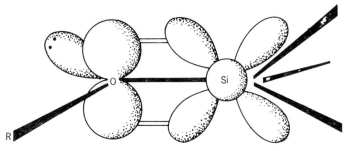

Fig. 4. Orbital model for the $(p \rightarrow d)$ π bond in the Si–O–C linkage of alkoxysilanes.

reasonably well established that the $(CH_3)_3Si-$ group has a greater $+I$ effect (electron-releasing) than the $(CH_3)_3C-$ group as expected in most systems (7); however, again the relative Lewis basicities of $(CH_3)_3CCH_2OCH_3$ and $(CH_3)_3SiCH_2OCH_3$ as determined by an NMR dilution shift study indicate that the latter compound acts as the weaker base (202). It has been suggested that the low basicities of these compounds may be due to an interaction between the p orbitals on oxygen and the d orbitals on silicon or germanium through an intervening $-CH_2-$ group, ie,

$$SiH_3 \longleftarrow O$$

Dipole moment and proton NMR data for the compounds SiH_3CH_2X (X = Cl, Br, I) are also consistent with an interaction of this type (148).

Sulfur Derivatives. Compared to the wealth of information known about compounds which contain Si–O bonds, little is known about compounds containing Si–S linkages. Three types of compounds have been characterized, ie, the analogs of the thiols ($\equiv$Si–SH), the mercaptosilanes or alkylthiosilanes ($\equiv$Si–SR), and the silthianes or sulfides ($\equiv$Si–S–Si$\equiv$).

The simple sulfhydryl derivative of SiH_4, SiH_3SH ("silyl mercaptan"), has been prepared and isolated from the equilibrium reaction between $(SiH_3)_2S$ and hydrogen sulfide at room temperature (137). Preparations of the corresponding organosilicon

$$(SiH_3)_2S + H_2S \rightleftharpoons 2 \, SiH_3SH \tag{68}$$

derivatives have made use of other reactions as shown in equations 69 and 70 (7).

$$(CH_3)_3SiNH(phenyl) + H_2S \rightarrow (CH_3)_3SiSH + NH_2(phenyl) \tag{69}$$

$$(CH_3)_3SiCl + LiSH \rightarrow (CH_3)_3SiSH + LiCl \tag{70}$$

Although information about the acidity of SiH_3SH is not available, organosilanethiols are known to act as stronger acids than the analogous carbon compounds (203).

Disilyl sulfide, $(SiH_3)_2S$ (disilthiane), and bisdisilanyl sulfide, $(SiH_3SiH_2)_2S$, have been prepared by passing the vapors of SiH_3I and SiH_3SiH_2I, respectively, over red mercuric sulfide at room temperature (137,204).

$$2 SiH_3I + HgS \rightarrow (SiH_3)_2S + HgI_2 \qquad (71)$$

This method has also been applied to the preparation of organosubstituted derivatives, although other procedures are available such as the direct reaction of an organosilicon halide with hydrogen sulfide in the presence of a base (7,8).

The preparations of some alkylthiosilanes which contain the SiH_3- group are given in equations 72–74. No analogous SiH_3SiH_2- derivatives have been prepared.

$$SiH_3I . N(CH_3)_3 + CH_3SH \xrightarrow{(205)} SiH_3SCH_3 + HI . N(CH_3)_3 \qquad (72)$$

$$2 SiH_3I + (CF_3S)_2Hg \xrightarrow{(131)} 2 SiH_3SCF_3 + HgI_2 \qquad (73)$$

$$2 SiCl_3SCH_2CH_3 \xrightarrow[(206)]{LiAlH_4} SiH_3SCH_2CH_3 \qquad (74)$$

Sulfur derivatives of the silanes are reasonably stable thermally, provided the samples are pure. For example, SiH_3SCF_3 is thermally stable at room temperature in a clean glass apparatus, but decomposes even at $-46°C$ in the presence of $(CF_3S)_2Hg$ in a dirty apparatus (131). Pure $(SiH_3)_2S$ does not undergo any detectable decomposition when stored for four days at room temperature in the dark, and even on heating the sample to $100°C$ in a sealed tube for several hours, only slight decomposition has been noted (137). It is spontaneously flammable in moist, but not dry air. In the presence of $(CH_3)_3N$, both $(SiH_3)_2S$ and SiH_3SCF_3 decompose according to equations 75 and 76 (131,207). The products of these reactions (except for SiH_4) have been isolated as their

$$x (SiH_3)_2S \rightarrow (SiH_2S)_x + x SiH_4 \qquad (75)$$

$$x SiH_3SCF_3 \rightarrow (CF_2S)_x + x SiH_3F \qquad (76)$$

$(CH_3)_3N$ adducts. Disilyl sulfide and NH_3 form a 1:2 adduct at low temperatures which can be sublimed, although at higher temperatures the adduct decomposes to SiH_4 and a solid which corresponds to the condensation product adduct SiH_3SSiH_2-$SSiH_3 . 3NH_3$ (207). The Si–S bond in $(SiH_3)_2S$ is not cleaved by BF_3 (107); the results of various other reactions of $(SiH_3)_2S$ are summarized in Figure 5.

The donor properties of the sulfur atom in SiH_3- and organosilyl sulfides are less than they are in analogous carbon systems (106,107,205). The relative Lewis basicities of $(SiH_3)_2S$ and SiH_3SCH_3 have not been distinguished because neither compound shows any donor properties toward B_2H_6 or phenol (205,208). In addition, $(SiH_3)_2S$ does not form an adduct with BF_3 (107), nor does it form sulfonium compounds with CH_3I or SiH_3I (137). These properties and others are consistent with $(p \rightarrow d)$ π bonding in the Si–S linkage, although it appears that the ability of sulfur to form π-bonds with silicon is lower than that of oxygen (3–6). The alteration of the Si–S–Si bond angle due to $(p \rightarrow d)$ π bonding is not as great as it is in the Si–O–Si linkage because the sulfur valence angles of $(CH_3)_2S$ and $(SiH_3)_2S$ are $98.9 \pm 0.2°$ (microwave) (209) and $97.4 \pm 0.7°$ (electron diffraction) (210), respectively. The corresponding angle in $((CH_3)_3Si)_2S$ is $104°$ (Raman-infrared) (211).

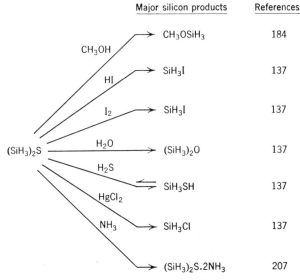

Fig. 5. Some reactions of disilyl sulfide.

It also appears that π-bonding is present in the Ge–S linkage of simple germanium sulfides and that it is important enough to lower the basicities of compounds of this type below the basicities of analogous organic sulfides (208,212). The relative basicities of the sulfur derivatives of SiH_4 and GeH_4 have not been determined. The Ge–S–Ge bond angle of $(GeH_3)_2S$ is approx $108°$ (Raman-infrared) (213).

Selenium and Tellurium Derivatives. Disilyl selenide and $(SiH_3)_2Te$ have been prepared by the interaction of SiH_3I with Ag_2Se and Li_2Te, respectively (137,143). On allowing $(CF_3Se)_2Hg$ and $(C_3F_7Se)_2Hg$ to interact with SiH_3I, the compounds SiH_3-$SeCF_3$ and $SiH_3SeC_3F_7$, respectively, are obtained (144). The latter compound has been found to react with $HgBr_2$ at room temperature to give almost quantitative yields of SiH_3Br. Although SiH_3SeCF_3 is more stable thermally than SiH_3SCF_3, $(SiH_3)_2Se$ is less stable thermally than its sulfur analog. Disilyl selenide reacts with water, I_2, and HI in a manner analogous to $(SiH_3)_2S$ (137). Disilyl telluride reacts with oxygen to form $(SiH_3)_2O$ and tellurium (143). No structural or base-strength studies of these compounds have been reported.

C. NITROGEN AND OTHER GROUP V DERIVATIVES

Preparations and Reactions of Amine and Hydrazine Compounds. The reaction of SiH_3– and SiH_3SiH_2– halides with ammonia or various primary or secondary amines has been the most common way to prepare amine derivatives of the silanes (4–6,214).

$$3\,SiH_3Cl + 4\,NH_3 \rightarrow (SiH_3)_3N + 3\,NH_4Cl \tag{77}$$

$$2\,SiH_3Br + 3\,CH_3NH_2 \rightarrow (SiH_3)_2NCH_3 + 2\,CH_3NH_3Br \tag{78}$$

$$3\,SiH_3SiH_2I + 4\,NH_3 \rightarrow (SiH_3SiH_2)_3N + 3\,NH_4I \tag{79}$$

Tetrasilylhydrazine has also been prepared by an analogous reaction (132).

$$4\,SiH_3I + 5\,N_2H_4 \rightarrow (SiH_3)_4N_2 + 4\,N_2H_5I \tag{80}$$

For good yields of $(SiH_3)_3N$ from SiH_3Cl and ammonia, the reaction must be carried out in the gas phase, since secondary reactions occur in the liquid phase, producing

SiH_4, polymeric materials and, under certain conditions, the heterocyclic compound N,N',N''-trisilylcyclotrisilazane, $(SiH_3NSiH_2)_3$ (6,214). The latter compound is also produced in the decomposition of liquid $(SiH_3)_3N$ in the presence of bases such as ammonia, LiH, and other amines (6).

The reaction in systems where more than one N–H bond is replaced presumably proceeds in a stepwise manner. Although SiH_3NH_2 has not been isolated, disilylamine, $(SiH_3)_2NH$ (disilazane), can be prepared as shown in equation 81, provided a deficit of ammonia is used (215). Disilylamine reacts with SiH_3I to give $(SiH_3)_3N$ and rapidly

$$2 \ (C_6H_5)_2NSiH_3 + NH_3 \xrightarrow{-46°C} 2 \ (C_6H_5)_2NH + (SiH_3)_2NH \qquad (81)$$

decomposes in the presence of ammonia with the formation of SiH_4 and a polymeric material. The compound is very stable in the gas phase, being unaffected by heating

$$4 \ (SiH_3)_2NH + SiH_3I \rightarrow 3 \ (SiH_3)_3N + NH_4I \qquad (82)$$

$$(SiH_3)_2NH \xrightarrow{NH_3} 1/x \ (SiH_2NH)_x + SiH_4 \qquad (83)$$

to 150°C for 3 hr. In the liquid phase it undergoes a condensation reaction forming $(SiH_3)_3N$.

$$3 \ (SiH_3)_2NH \rightarrow 2 \ (SiH_3)_3N + NH_3 \qquad (84)$$

In the triorganosubstituted silicon derivatives, the tendency for condensation decreases as the size of the groups attached to silicon (or nitrogen) increases (7,8). Thus, $(CH_3)_3SiNH_2$ has not been isolated and the only organosilicon product in the reaction of $(CH_3)_3SiCl$ with NH_3 is hexamethyldisilazane, $((CH_3)_3Si)_2NH$ (216–218). Even at 500°C with pyridine as solvent, the trisubstituted amine is not formed. Two preparations of $((CH_3)_3Si)_3N$ are given in equations 85 and 86 (217,219).

$$(CH_3)_3SiCl + ((CH_3)_3Si)_2NNa \rightarrow ((CH_3)_3Si)_3N + NaCl \qquad (85)$$

$$3 \ (CH_3)_3SiCl + Li_3N \rightarrow ((CH_3)_3Si)_3N + 3 \ LiCl \qquad (86)$$

Although amino derivatives of SiH_4, ie, $SiH_{4-n}(NH_2)_n$, have not been isolated and appear to be unstable, the corresponding dimethylamino derivatives, $SiH_{4-n}(N(CH_3)_2)_n$ ($n = 1$–4), are known, being prepared by the general reaction

$$SiH_{4-n}X_n + 2n \ NH(CH_3)_2 \rightarrow SiH_{4-n}(N(CH_3)_2)_n + n \ NH_2(CH_3)_2X \qquad (87)$$

where X = Br ($n = 1$), I ($n = 2$), or Cl ($n = 3$ or 4) (135,220).

Most of the tertiary SiH_3– and SiH_3SiH_2– amines are reasonably inert to thermal decomposition at room temperature. Trisilylamine undergoes only slight thermal decomposition, forming SiH_4 and a polymeric material when stored at room temperature for several months (5); $(SiH_3SiH_2)_3N$ undergoes no thermal decomposition when heated to 90°C for several hours (204). Both compounds are spontaneously flammable in air. The N-alkyl SiH_3– amines are less stable thermally than $(SiH_3)_3N$, with SiH_3N-$(CH_3)_2$ decomposing appreciably at its melting point (3°C) (135). In the pyrolysis of the latter compound (200°C for 20 hr), the main reaction is disproportionation about silicon (134).

$$3 \ (CH_3)_2NSiH_3 \rightarrow SiH(N(CH_3)_2)_3 + 2 \ SiH_4 \qquad (88)$$

A similar conclusion can be made about the thermal stabilities of the SiH_3SiH_2– amines, and from the reaction of SiH_3SiH_2Br with $(CH_3)_2NH$ (the latter in slight excess) the compound 1,1-*bis*(dimethylamino)disilane, $SiH_3SiH(N(CH_3)_2)_2$, was iso-

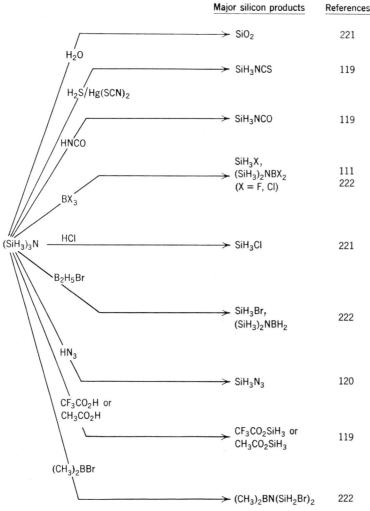

Fig. 6. Some reactions of trisilylamine.

lated, in addition to $SiH_3SiH_2N(CH_3)_2$ and Si_2H_6 (110). The disubstituted derivative is thought to arise from the base-catalyzed condensation of $SiH_3SiH_2N(CH_3)_2$.

$$2\ SiH_3SiH_2N(CH_3)_2 \rightarrow SiH_3SiH(N(CH_3)_2)_2 + Si_2H_6 \tag{89}$$

The Si–N bond in SiH_3– and organosilylamines is susceptible to cleavage by water, alcohols, and various acids. Although $((CH_3)_3Si)_3N$ is relatively inert to hydrolysis, the reaction of $((CH_3)_3Si)_2NH$ with water has been used for the preparation of $(CH_3)_3$-SiOH (7,8). The alcoholysis of $((CH_3)_3Si)_2NH$ results in the formation of alkoxytri-

$$((CH_3)_3Si)_2NH + 2\ H_2O \rightarrow 2\ (CH_3)_3SiOH + NH_3 \tag{90}$$

methylsilanes (7,8). Corresponding reactions with SiH_3– and partially substituted organosilylamines have not been successful, due to the attack on the Si–H bonds by the alkaline solution produced from the liberated ammonia. Some important reactions of $(SiH_3)_3N$ are summarized in Figure 6. In many cases analogous reactions occur with other silylamines with organic groups on either the nitrogen or silicon atoms (4–6).

In the reaction of $(SiH_3)_3N$ with the boron halides (F and Cl), addition compounds are first formed at $-78°C$, which decompose on warming to give $(SiH_3)_2NBX_2$ and the corresponding SiH_3- halide (111,222). Both $(SiH_3)_2NBCl_2$ and $(SiH_3)_2NBF_2$ decompose further on standing.

$$3 \ (SiH_3)_2NBF_2 \rightarrow (SiH_3NBF)_3 + 3 \ SiH_3F \qquad (91)$$

The $(SiH_3)_2NBH_2$ formed in the reaction of $(SiH_3)_3N$ with B_2H_5Br has been shown to react with B_2H_6, producing $(SiH_3)_2NB_2H_5$. This compound is thought to have a hydrogen bridge structure similar to that found in B_2H_6 (222).

Although $(SiH_3)_3N$ and $(SiH_3)_2NCH_3$ do not react with CO_2, CS_2, or COS even at temperatures up to $100°C$ and pressures of 30 atm, $SiH_3N(CH_3)_2$ does react with these reagents to form silyl N,N-dimethylcarbamate, $(CH_3)_2NC(O)OSiH_3$, the corresponding thio derivative, and O-silyl-N,N-dimethylmonothiocarbamate, $(CH_3)_2NC(S)OSiH_3$, respectively (223). Dimethylaminosilane also reacts with SiH_3I to form a 1:1 adduct which rapidly decomposes on heating at $100°C$ to give a complex mixture of liquid and solid products (129). Treatment of the products with $HgCl_2$ gives a more volatile mixture which can be separated into $(CH_3)_2NSiH_2Cl$, $((CH_3)_2N)_2SiHCl$, and SiH_2Cl_2. The decomposition of the $(CH_3CH_2)_2NSiH_3 \cdot SiH_3I$ adduct yields $(CH_3CH_2)_2NSiH_2I$ and SiH_4. Silyl iodide adducts with other compounds which contain the $=N-SiH_3$ grouping decompose in a similar manner (129).

Other Nitrogen Derivatives. Treatment of SiH_3I or SiH_3Br with silver(I) cyanamide yields the compound $(SiH_3)_2CN_2$ which has the carbodiimide structure $SiH_3NCNSiH_3$, rather than the previously assumed $(SiH_3)_2N \cdot CN$ structure (139,224). The compound reacts with hydrogen chloride according to equation 92 and forms an

$$SiH_3NCNSiH_3 + 4 \ HCl \rightarrow 2 \ SiH_3Cl + H_2NCCl_2NH_2 \qquad (92)$$

unstable addition compound with BF_3.

One of the first pentacoordinate silicon compounds to be reported is the liquid 1:1 adduct formed between $CHF_2CF_2SiH_3$ and trimethylamine (225). From infrared and NMR measurements, the adduct is believed to have a trigonal bipyramidal structure with the Si–H bonds directed toward the three equatorial positions.

Other compounds with Si–N linkages, ie, the pseudohalogen (NCO, NCS, NCSe, and N_3) derivatives and nitrogen-base adducts of the SiH_3- halides are discussed in section 5A, p. 181.

Structures and Basicities of Silyl Amines. As in the case of the Si–O bond, $(p \rightarrow d) \ \pi$ bonding has been used to explain the shorter-than-expected Si–N bond lengths, wide nitrogen valence angles, and low basicities of silyl amines. The 1.738 ± 0.020 Å Si–N bond length (electron diffraction (226)) in $(SiH_3)_3N$ is shorter than the 1.80 Å estimated normal single Si–N bond length and in contrast to the well-known pyramidal structure of $(CH_3)_3N$, $(SiH_3)_3N$ has a planar structure (zero dipole moment (136)) with $119.6 \pm 1.0°$ Si–N–Si bond angles (electron diffraction) (226). In the carbon compound, the nitrogen hybrid orbital can be described as approximately sp^3 with a lone pair of electrons occupying one of the hybrid orbitals. In the analogous silicon compound, if the lone pair of electrons of nitrogen is involved in $(p \rightarrow d) \ \pi$ bonding with silicon, the hybridization at the nitrogen atom should approach or be sp^2, as indeed the planar structure indicates. From a theoretical calculation, the mean Si–N $(p \rightarrow d) \pi$ bond energy in $(SiH_3)_3N$ has been estimated to be approx 16 kcal/mole (227). The Si–N–Si bond angles in $((CH_3)_3Si)_2NH$, $(SiH_3)_2NH$, and $(SiH_3)_2NBF_2$ are 125.5

± 1.8, 127.9 ± 0.2, and 125.6 ± 2.6°, respectively (electron diffraction) (228). The C–N–C angle in $(CH_3)_2NH$ is 112.2° (microwave) (229).

The base properties of silicon amines are also consistent with the presence of $(p \rightarrow d) \pi$ bonding in the Si–N linkage. Considering the relative electronegativities of carbon (2.5) and silicon (1.8), amines with Si–N linkages should act as stronger Lewis bases than analogous amines with C–N linkages. However, the opposite is true with the electron-donor properties of the following series of amines increasing as shown (111,230).

$$(SiH_3)_3N < (SiH_3)_2NCH_3 < SiH_3N(CH_3)_2 < N(CH_3)_3$$

The more SiH_3- groups present, the more the lone pair of electrons on nitrogen can be delocalized through π-bonding. This results in progressively reduced base properties of the molecules. Trisilylamine does form an adduct with the very strong Lewis acid $((CH_3)_3Al)_2$, but not with $(CH_3)_3B$, B_2H_6, or $(CH_3)_3Ga$ (230). The last three amines in the above series form adducts with B_2H_6, $((CH_3)_3Al)_2$, and $(CH_3)_3Ga$; however, only $SiH_3N(CH_3)_2$ and $(CH_3)_3N$ form adducts with $(CH_3)_3B$ (230). Organosilicon amines, in general, act as stronger Lewis bases than the analogous parent SiH_3- amines.

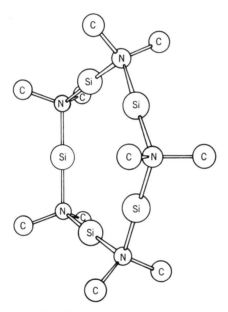

Fig. 7. Stereoview of the $SiH_3N(CH_3)_2$ pentamer. The hydrogen atoms (not shown) about each silicon are presumed to be trigonally arranged in a plane perpendicular to ihe N–Si–N bonds. The molecules pack in parallel planes.

Both $CH_3SiH_2N(CH_3)_2$ and $(CH_3)_3SiN(CH_3)_2$ react with CH_3I to form stable solids which are believed to be ionic quaternary ammonium compounds of the type $[\equiv SiN-(CH_3)_3]^+I^-$ (231). Although adducts are formed between CH_3SiH_2I and $CH_3SiH_2N-(CH_3)_2$ or $(CH_3)_3SiN(CH_3)_2$, they are completely dissociated in the vapor state (231). In similar amines which contain two or three silicon atoms, complex formation with CH_3I or CH_3SiH_2I is not observed (5,231).

Several physical characteristics of $SiH_3N(CH_3)_2$ are unusual and have suggested that intermolecular dative bonding is present in the crystalline state of the compound.

For example, $SiH_3N(CH_3)_2$ melts at about $3°C$, whereas the related compounds $(SiH_3)_3$-N, $CH_3SiH_2N(CH_3)_2$, and $SiH_3N(CH_2CH_3)_2$ melt at -105.6, -150, and $-149°C$, respectively (1,134,135,231). In addition, the solid- and gas-phase infrared spectra of $SiH_3N(CH_3)_2$ are radically different (232). An x-ray diffraction analysis indicates that in the crystalline state the compound is pentameric, composed of ten-membered slightly skewed rings of alternating silicon and nitrogen atoms (21). The association involves the lone pair of electrons of nitrogen on one $SiH_3N(CH_3)_2$ molecule with the empty d orbitals of silicon on an adjacent molecule. The silicon atoms are penta-coordinated in a trigonal bipyramidal arrangement with the two Si–N bonds in apical directions. A stereoview of the $SiH_3N(CH_3)_2$ pentamer is shown in Figure 7.

The structures of $(SiH_3)_2NN(SiH_3)_2$ and the deuterated derivative have been interpreted in terms of a staggered (D_{2d}) molecular skeleton configuration (Raman-infrared) (233).

Phosphorus, Arsenic, and Antimony Derivatives. The chemistry of silane derivatives which contain the lower group V elements has not been investigated in much detail. Trisilylphosphine, $(SiH_3)_3P$, has been prepared by the reaction of SiH_3Cl or SiH_3Br with KPH_2 at low ($-100°C$) temperatures (234–236).

$$3\ SiH_3Cl + 3\ KPH_2 \rightarrow (SiH_3)_3P + 2\ PH_3 + 3\ KCl \qquad (93)$$

Silylphosphine, SiH_3PH_2, has been prepared by heating a mixture of SiH_4 and PH_3 to about $400°C$ (92) or by subjecting the mixture to an ozonizer type of silent electric discharge (78). Although the isomeric compounds $(SiH_3)_2PH$ and SiH_3SiH_2-PH_2 have also been obtained in the SiH_4–PH_3 discharge system (79), each can be specifically prepared by the discharge of SiH_4–SiH_3PH_2 and Si_2H_6–PH_3 systems, respectively (80). Both SiH_3PH_2 and $SiH_3SiH_2PH_2$ have also been prepared from the reaction of $LiAl(PH_2)_4$ with SiH_3Br and SiH_3SiH_2Br, respectively (237). This reaction has also been used to prepare several organosilicon and germanium–PH_2 derivatives (237,238). From the reaction of SiH_3I with white phosphorus, SiH_3PI_2 is obtained, together with $(SiH_3)_2PI$ and possibly $(SiH_3)_3P$, although the latter two compounds were not purified (127). The reaction of $LiP(CH_2CH_3)_2$ with SiH_3Br results in the formation of $SiH_3P(CH_2CH_3)_2$ together with some $H_2Si(P(CH_2CH_3)_2)_2$ and $HSi(P(CH_2$-$CH_3)_2)_3$ (239). The latter compound undergoes a metalation reaction with LiP-$(CH_2CH_3)_2$, forming $LiSi(P(CH_2CH_3)_2)_3$. This compound in turn undergoes a number of interesting coupling reactions, one of which is shown in equation 94.

$$LiSi(P(CH_2CH_3)_2)_3 + SiH_3Br \rightarrow SiH_3Si(P(CH_2CH_3)_2)_3 + LiBr \qquad (94)$$

Both $(SiH_3)_3As$ and $(SiH_3)_3Sb$ have been prepared by allowing SiH_3Cl or SiH_3Br to react with suspensions of Li_3As or Li_3Sb in dimethylether at $-80°C$ (236,240). In the reaction of K_3As with SiH_3I, $(SiH_3)_2AsH$ and $(SiH_3)_3As$ are apparently formed, but could not be purified (127). Trisilylarsine has also been prepared by the reaction of SiH_3Br with $KAsH_2$ (236). Monosilylarsine has been prepared by subjecting an equimolar mixture of SiH_4 and AsH_3 to a silent electric discharge (78). Compounds having compositions Si_2AsH_7 and $SiAs_2H_6$ have also been detected in the system. The direct reaction between SiH_3I and arsenic produces SiH_3AsH_2 and, in addition, $(SiH_3)_2AsI$ and SiH_3AsI_2, although only the latter compound has been purified and characterized (127).

Both SiH_3PH_2 and SiH_3AsH_2 form 1:1 adducts with BCl_3 and B_2H_5Br at $-78°C$ which decompose on warming (241,242). The overall reactions are shown in equations

95 and 96.   With BBr$_3$, the compounds undergo a reaction which is similar to that with

$$SiH_3MH_2 + BCl_3 \rightarrow SiH_3Cl + 1/n \ (BCl_2MH_2)_n \tag{95}$$

$$SiH_3MH_2 + B_2H_5Br \rightarrow SiH_3Br + \tfrac{1}{2} B_2H_6 + 1/n \ (BH_2MH_2)_n \tag{96}$$

BCl$_3$, except that higher brominated silanes, ie, SiH$_2$Br$_2$ and SiHBr$_3$, are produced in major amounts, presumably because BBr$_3$ is an effective brominating agent for systems containing Si–H bonds (242).   In the B$_2$H$_5$Br reactions, two adducts are apparently formed: an initial adduct having the composition SiH$_3$MH$_2$B$_2$H$_5$Br decomposes to a second adduct, with the liberation of B$_2$H$_6$.   The SiH$_3$AsH$_2$ adducts are less ther-

$$SiH_3MH_2B_2H_5Br \rightarrow SiH_3MH_2BH_2Br + \tfrac{1}{2} B_2H_6 \tag{97}$$

mally stable than their phosphorus analogs.   Diborane reacts with SiH$_3$PH$_2$ under pressure to form a "triple mixed hydride" adduct, SiH$_3$PH$_2$BH$_3$, which has been studied by NMR spectroscopy (243).   The analogous reaction between B$_2$H$_6$ and SiH$_3$AsH$_2$ results in the formation of (SiH$_3$)$_3$As (242).   The mechanism of the latter reaction has been rationalized in terms of an SiH$_3$AsH$_2$BH$_3$ intermediate.

Trigermylphosphine has been prepared in high yield by the reaction of (SiH$_3$)$_3$P with GeH$_3$Br at 0°C (244).

The structures of the silyl derivatives of phosphorus, arsenic, and antimony are particularly interesting since they should show the stereochemical effects which result from $(p \rightarrow d)$ π bonding involving silicon and donor atoms in the lower rows of the periodic table.   Although Raman and infrared spectral data on (SiH$_3$)$_3$P and (SiH$_3$)$_3$As were first interpreted in terms of planar Si$_3$P and Si$_3$As skeletons (235,240), electron diffraction data have now revealed that the heavy-atom skeletons of the compounds are nonplanar (245).   The phosphorus and arsenic valence angles of (SiH$_3$)$_3$P and (SiH$_3$)$_3$As are 95 ± 2° and 91.5 ± 2°, respectively.   Trigermylphosphine is also believed to have a nonplanar heavy-atom skeleton (Raman-infrared) (244).   No conclusions could be made about the structure of (SiH$_3$)$_3$Sb from its Raman and infrared spectra (240).

The above structural data, together with the structural information about (SiH$_3$)$_2$S cited previously, indicate that although $(p \rightarrow d)$ π bonding may be present in Si–X linkages where X is a second- or third-row donor group V or VI atom, the structures of the compounds derived therefrom are not affected as much as when X is a first-row group V or VI element.

D. GROUP IV DERIVATIVES

Organosilicon Compounds.   The vast field of organosilicon chemistry has been surveyed in a number of excellent reference books (7,8,94,246,247) and will not be discussed here except for considering organosilanes of the type RSiH$_3$, R$_2$SiH$_2$, and R$_3$SiH. These derivatives are generally prepared by the following methods:

1.   The reduction of an organohalo- or organoalkoxysilane with LiAlH$_4$ or another suitable hydride (27).

$$4 \ CH_3SiCl_3 + 3 \ LiAlH_4 \xrightarrow{\text{ether}} 4 \ CH_3SiH_3 + 3 \ LiCl + 3 \ AlCl_3 \tag{98}$$

$$(SiCl_3)_3CH + 9 \ LiH \xrightarrow[\text{(236)}]{\text{LiAlH}_4} (SiH_3)_3CH + 9 \ LiCl \tag{99}$$

2. The reaction between an unsaturated hydrocarbon and SiH_4 or alkylsilanes which contain at least two Si–H bonds (7,8,246). However, in many cases all Si–H bonds may undergo reaction.

$$SiH_4 + CH_2{=}CH_2 \xrightarrow[\text{(95)}]{450°C} CH_3CH_2SiH_3 + \text{other organosilanes} \qquad (100)$$

3. The reaction between an organometallic compound (usually a Grignard reagent) and a silane or halosilane.

$$2\ SiH_3Br + BrMgC{\equiv}CMgBr \xrightarrow{\text{(248)}} SiH_3C{\equiv}CSiH_3 + 2\ MgBr_2 \qquad (101)$$

$$Si_2H_6 + CH_3Li \xrightarrow{\text{(73)}} CH_3SiH_2SiH_3 + LiH \qquad (102)$$

4. The reaction of alkali metal derivatives of silane or certain organosilanes with organic halides.

$$CH_3I + SiH_3K \xrightarrow{\text{(63,64)}} CH_3SiH_3 + KI \qquad (103)$$

Although cyclic compounds of the parent silanes have not been isolated, many compounds are known which contain $-SiH_2-$ or $-SiH-$ units as part of an organic ring system. Examples of these compounds include $(CH_2)_4SiH_2$, $(CH_2)_3SiH_2$, and $(CH_2-$

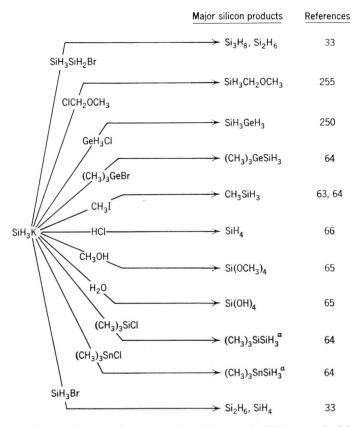

Fig. 8. Some reactions of silylpotassium. (Original references should be consulted for solvents employed and the reaction conditions.) [a]See discussion for secondary reactions.

$SiH_2)_3$, although many more complex systems have also been reported (7,246,249). The latter compound, like cyclohexane, exists mainly in the chair form (246).

The chemistry of the Si–H bond in organosilanes and the parent silanes previously discussed is for the most part identical, but the former compounds are generally less reactive than the latter compounds. The derivatives formed from both series of compounds also have similar chemical properties. The organic-substituted compounds are generally more stable thermally than those derived from the parent silanes.

Germanium and Tin Derivatives. Silicon–germanium hydrides of the type $Si_xGe_yH_{2x+2y+2}$ have been prepared by several methods. The first member of the series, SiH_3GeH_3, can be prepared from the coupling reactions between SiH_3K and GeH_3Cl (250) or GeH_3K and SiH_3Br (251). This compound and various other higher members of the series have also been prepared by the acidic hydrolysis of MgGeSi alloys or SiO–GeO mixtures and from applying a silent electrical discharge to mixtures of GeH_4 and SiH_4 (and Si_2H_6) (11,13–16,77). The high-molecular-weight compounds have been partially characterized by their chemical reactions and gas-chromatographic behavior. Pyrolysis of mixtures of silanes and germanes at about 290–350°C also produce mixed silicon–germanium hydrides (15). For example, the pyrolysis of a Ge_3H_8–n-Si_4H_{10} mixture produces n- and iso-Si_4GeH_{12}, the latter compound being [Si–Si(Ge)Si–Si]H_{12}. No unsaturated or cyclic silicon–germanium hydrides have ever been obtained in these reactions. The isomeric triple mixed hydrides, $SiH_3CH_2GeH_3$ and $CH_3SiH_2GeH_3$, have been prepared by the reaction of GeH_3K with SiH_3CH_2Cl and CH_3SiH_2Cl, respectively (252).

The first member of the mixed silicon–tin hydride derivatives, ie, SiH_3SnH_3, has recently been prepared by the reduction of either $Cl_3SiSnCl_3$ or the corresponding hexa-acetate derivative with $LiAlH_4$ (253). The related compound, GeH_3SnH_3, was prepared in a similar manner. Both compounds are stable only in dilute ether solutions below −80°C and decompose according to equation 104.

$$MH_3SnH_3 \xrightarrow{\text{M = Si, Ge}} MH_4 + Sn + H_2 \qquad (104)$$

A number of completely or partially organosubstituted compounds which contain Si–Ge or Si–Sn bonds have also been reported. They have normally been prepared by a coupling reaction (see Fig. 8) (4,5,7).

E. ALKALI METAL AND GROUP III DERIVATIVES

The preparation of alkali metal derivatives of the silanes is discussed in section 4C, p.178. Although the sodium, potassium, rubidium, and cesium SiH_3– metal derivatives have been prepared, most of the work with derivatives of this type has been with the potassium salt. There is also evidence for the existence of $KSiH_2SiH_3$ and KSi_3H_7 (70).

Silylpotassium can be obtained as a white crystalline solid (of the NaCl structure (254)), although most of its reactions have been carried out in solvents in which it is made. Solid $KSiH_3$ is remarkably stable thermally, decomposing in vacuum at 240°C (66). Some of the reactions which it undergoes are shown in Figure 8.

The coupling reactions have been extremely useful for the preparation of various SiH_3– derivatives of boron, aluminum, and the group IV elements.

$$SiH_3K + ClB(N(CH_3)_2)_2 \xrightarrow{\text{(255a)}} SiH_3B(N(CH_3)_2)_2 + KCl \qquad (105)$$

$$3\,SiH_3Na + AlCl_3 \xrightarrow{\text{(255b)}} (SiH_3)_3Al + 3\,NaCl \qquad (106)$$

Stability is imparted to SiH_3–boron compounds when B–N bonds are present. The one SiH_3–aluminum compound reported, $(SiH_3)_3Al$, is not very stable thermally (255b).

In the reaction of SiH_3K with $(CH_3)_3SiCl$ or $(CH_3)_3SnCl$, the expected SiH_3–derivatives are formed; however, $((CH_3)_3Si)_2SiH_2$, $((CH_3)_3Si)_3SiH$, $((CH_3)_3Sn)_3SiH$, and $((CH_3)_3Sn)_4Si$ are also formed, presumably by a metal-exchange reaction followed by additional coupling (64).

$$(CH_3)_3SiSiH_3 + SiH_3K \rightarrow (CH_3)_3SiSiH_2K + SiH_4 \tag{107}$$

$$(CH_3)_3SiSiH_2K + (CH_3)_3SiCl \rightarrow ((CH_3)_3Si)_2SiH_2, \text{ etc} + KCl \tag{108}$$

F. TRANSITION METAL DERIVATIVES

Preparations. Most of the investigations of transition-metal complexes which contain Si–metal bonds have developed only since 1965, although the first compound of this type, $(CH_3)_3Si$–$Fe(CO)_2(\pi C_5H_5)$, was synthesized in 1956 (256). The majority of investigations reported thus far have involved derivatives of cobalt, manganese, and iron. The first SiH_3– transition-metal complex to be reported was silylcolbalt tetra-carbonyl, $SiH_3Co(CO)_4$, prepared by the low-temperature reaction of SiH_3I with an ether solution containing the $[Co(CO_4)]^-$ ion (142). Other known SiH_3– derivatives include $SiH_3Mn(CO)_5$, prepared from the reaction of SiH_3I with $NaMn(CO)_5$ (145,257), and $(SiH_3)_2Fe(CO)_4$ and $(SiH_3)HFe(CO)_4$, both of which have been isolated from the reaction of SiH_3I with $Na_2Fe(CO)_4$ (138). Similar coupling reactions have also been widely used to prepare organosilicon derivatives of the transition metals (258). Some examples of other preparations which have been employed for organo- or halosilicon derivatives of this type are summarized by equations 107–111 (259–263).

$$2 R_3SiH + Co_2(CO)_8 \xrightarrow{\text{R = organic group, F, Cl}} 2 R_3SiCo(CO)_4 + H_2 \tag{109}$$

$$R_3SiH + HCo(CO)_4 \xrightarrow{\text{R = organic group, F, Cl}} R_3SiCo(CO)_4 + H_2 \tag{110}$$

$$(CH_3)_3SiN(CH_3)_2 + HCo(PF_3)_4 \rightarrow (CH_3)_3SiCo(PF_3)_4 + (CH_3)_2NH \tag{111}$$

$$2 (CH_3)_3SiH + Mn_2(CO)_{10} \rightarrow 2 (CH_3)_3SiMn(CO)_5 + H_2 \tag{112}$$

$$(CH_3)_3SiH + HMn(CO)_5 \rightarrow (CH_3)_3SiMn(CO)_5 + H_2 \tag{113}$$

Thermal Stability. The SiH_3- and organosilyl transition-metal complexes are generally more stable thermally than their corresponding carbon analogs. For example, $CH_3Co(CO)_4$ decomposes rapidly above $-30°C$, whereas 30% of a sample of $SiH_3Co(CO)_4$ is recovered unchanged after being heated at $100°C$ for 0.5 hr (142). The greater stability of the silicon derivative has been attributed to the presence of $(d \rightarrow d)$ π bonding in the Si–metal bond (142). However, a reversal in the relative stabilities of the two series of compounds is noted for the perfluoro derivatives. Thus, $CF_3Co(CO)_4$ can be distilled at its boiling point $(91°C)$ without decomposition, whereas $SiF_3Co(CO)_4$ undergoes complete decomposition after 18 hr at room temperature (261).

$$8 SiF_3Co(CO)_4 \rightarrow 6 SiF_4 + 4 CO + 2 Si + Co_4(CO)_{12} + 2 Co_2(CO)_8 \tag{114}$$

Silylmanganese pentacarbonyl can be stored under vacuum at room temperature for long periods of time without decomposition (145) and thermal studies of $(CH_3)_3$-$SiMn(CO)_5$ and $(CH_3)_3SiCo(CO)_4$ indicate that the former is more stable than the latter (261). Disilyliron pentacarbonyl decomposes at about $110°C$ yielding hydrogen, SiH_4, and $(SiH_3)HFe(CO)_4$ (138).

Chemical Properties. Four general types of reactions have been observed for silyl metal carbonyls.

1. Substitution reactions can occur at the Si–H bond, as shown in equation 115 (145). However, in the reaction of hydrogen chloride with $SiH_3Co(CO)_4$, $(SiH_3)_2Fe$-

$$SiH_3Mn(CO)_5 + xHCl \xrightarrow[x = 1-3]{75°C} SiH_{3-x}Cl_xMn(CO)_5 + xH_2 \tag{115}$$

$(CO)_4$, or $(SiH_3)HFe(CO)_4$, the Si–metal bond is cleaved (see equations 117–120) (138,142). The reaction at room temperature between $CH_3SiH_2Co(CO)_4$ and PF_5 produces $CH_3SiF_2Co(CO)_4$ (264).

2. Tertiary amines form adducts with the compounds. For example, trimethylamine forms 1:2 (acceptor:base) adducts with $SiH_3Co(CO)_4$, $SiH_3Mn(CO)_5$, and $(SiH_3)_2Fe(CO)_4$ (138,257), although a 1:1 adduct is formed with $(CH_3)_3SiCo(CO)_4$ (261). Pyridine also forms a 1:2 (acceptor:base) adduct with $SiH_3Co(CO)_4$ and $SiH_3Mn(CO)_5$, and the latter compound forms a 1:1 adduct with the bidentate ligand, 2,2′-bipyridyl (257). In most instances, these adducts are more chemically reactive than the parent derivatives (see equation 119). From infrared studies, they appear to contain the carbonylmetallate anion in the solid state and have been formulated as $[SiH_3 \cdot 2base$ or $(CH_3)_3Si \cdot base]^+$ $[M(CO)_n]^-$ (257,261). In the $(SiH_3)_2Fe(CO)_4 \cdot 2$-$(CH_3)_3N$ adduct, chemical evidence indicates that one trimethylamine molecule is bonded to each SiH_3- group, rather than both being attached to one SiH_3- group (138).

3. Substitution reactions can occur at the metal atom. For example, treatment of $SiH_3Co(CO)_4$ or $SiH_3Mn(CO)_5$ with triphenylphosphine results in the elimination of CO (145).

$$SiH_3Co(CO)_4 + P(phenyl)_3 \rightarrow SiH_3Co(CO)_3(P(phenyl)_3) + CO \tag{116}$$

4. The Si–metal bond can be cleaved by various reagents. For example, gaseous hydrogen chloride cleaves the Si–metal bond of both $SiH_3Co(CO)_4$ and $(SiH_3)_2Fe(CO)_4$, with the latter compound undergoing stepwise cleavage (138,142). The hydrolysis of

$$SiH_3Co(CO)_4 + HCl \rightarrow SiH_3Cl + HCo(CO)_4 \tag{117}$$

$$(SiH_3)_2Fe(CO)_4 + HCl \rightarrow SiH_3Cl + SiH_3(H)Fe(CO)_4 \tag{118}$$

$$SiH_3(H)Fe(CO)_4 + HCl \rightarrow SiH_3Cl + H_2Fe(CO)_4 \tag{119}$$

$SiH_3Co(CO)_4$ proceeds in a similar manner, forming $(SiH_3)_2O$ and $HCo(CO)_4$ (142).

Treatment of $SiH_3Mn(CO)_5$ or $SiH_3Co(CO)_4$ with ammonia also cleaves the Si–metal bond (145). In the $SiH_3Co(CO)_4$ reaction, some of the $(SiH_3)_2NH$ undergoes

$$2 SiH_3Mn(CO)_5 + NH_3 \rightarrow 2 HMn(CO)_5 + (SiH_3)_2NH \tag{120}$$

decomposition, giving SiH_4, $(SiH_3)_3N$, and polymeric products. Although the Si–Mn bond in $SiH_3Mn(CO)_5$ is inert to cleavage by hydrogen chloride, the bond in the 1:2 pyridine adduct is rapidly and quantitatively cleaved at $-80°C$ (145).

$$SiH_3Mn(CO)_5 \cdot 2\, py + 3\, HCl \rightarrow SiH_3Cl + HMn(CO)_5 + 2\, py \cdot HCl \tag{121}$$

Three additional reactions of $SiH_3Co(CO)_4$ have been studied (142). Alkaline hydrolysis leads to the quantitative evolution of hydrogen free from CO while bromine causes the complete breakdown of the compound with the formation of $SiBr_4$, HBr, CO, $COBr_2$, and $CoBr_2$. An equilibrium reaction occurs with HgI_2, as shown in equation 120, which is displaced well to the right.

$$2\, SiH_3Co(CO)_4 + HgI_2 \rightleftharpoons 2\, SiH_3I + Hg(Co(CO)_4)_2 \tag{122}$$

Silicon–transition metal carbonyls show no tendency to undergo CO or SO_2 insertion reactions into the Si–metal bond, even at high pressure; this type of reaction is

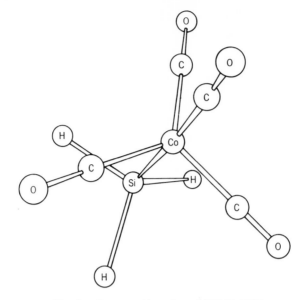

Fig. 9. A perspective view of $SiH_3Co(CO)_4$.

very well known in compounds containing carbon–transition metal bonds (145). It has been suggested that this might be related to $(d \rightarrow d)$ π interaction in the Si–metal bond (145).

Structures and Bonding. The structures of $SiH_3Co(CO)_4$ and related silicon-substituted derivatives have a trigonal bipyramidal configuration of ligands about the cobalt, with the silicon groups exclusively in an axial position (ir, x-ray, electron diffraction) (265–267). A perspective view of $SiH_3Co(CO)_4$ is shown in Figure 9. The analogous carbon compounds which have been studied also have this structural arrangement (ir) (268,269).

Although structural information about $SiH_3Mn(CO)_5$ is not available, the structure of the corresponding $(CH_3)_3Si-$ derivative is known to have an octahedral configuration of ligands about the manganese (x-ray) (270).

The structures of $(SiH_3)_2Fe(CO)_4$ and $(SiH_3)HFe(CO)_4$ are also believed to be octahedral with the silicon groups (or hydrogen) in cis positions (ir, ^{57}Fe Mössbauer effect) (138,267). For $(SiCl_3)_2Fe(CO)_4$, both the cis and trans forms have been isolated (269).

Infrared and chemical data on silicon–transition metal complexes have been interpreted on the basis of partial double-bond character, ie, $(d \rightarrow d)$ π bonding, in the Si–metal bond (265). Shorter-than-expected bond lengths in the Si–Co and Si–Mn linkages in certain derivatives also give support to this. For example, the observed Si–metal bond lengths in $SiCl_3Co(CO)_4$ and $(CH_3)_3SiMn(CO)_5$ are 2.254 ± 0.003 Å and 2.497 ± 0.005 Å, respectively (x-ray) (266,270). Calculated values for single-bond lengths are subject to some uncertainty but are estimated to be 2.33–2.37 Å for the Si–Co bond and 2.62 Å for the Si–Mn bond (265,266,270). The Si–Co distance in $SiH_3Co(CO)_4$ is 2.381 ± 0.007 Å (electron diffraction) (267).

A rather unusual structural distortion has been observed in many of these derivatives; the equatorial CO groups are bent out of the equatorial plane toward the silicon atom. Some typical $\equiv Si-M-CO_{eq}$ angles are 81.7, 85, and 84.3° for SiH_3Co-

$(CO)_4$, $SiCl_3Co(CO)_4$, and $(CH_3)_3SiMn(CO)_5$, respectively (x-ray, electron diffraction) (266,267,270). Possible reasons for this include crystal-lattice distortions (in the solid state), axial-equatorial CO electron-pair repulsions, and possibly a bonding interaction between the d orbital of the group IV atom and orbitals of appropriate symmetry on the equatorial CO groups (261). Structural determinations of analogous carbon compounds will be awaited with interest.

6. Physical Properties of Some Selected Derivatives of the Silanes

A. MELTING AND BOILING POINTS

The melting and boiling points of a number of representative SiH_3- and SiH_3SiH_2- derivatives are listed in Table 2. Except for SiH_3I, the SiH_3- halides and pseudohalides all boil at lower temperatures than the corresponding CH_3- derivatives even though the silicon compounds are heavier molecules than the carbon analogs. However, the SiH_3SiH_2- halides all boil at higher temperatures than their CH_3CH_2- analogs. An empirical relationship between the boiling points of the two sets of derivatives has been

Table 2. Some Representative Silyl and Disilanyl Compounds

Compound	Melting point, °C	Boiling point, °C	Compound	Melting point, °C	Boiling point, °C
halides and pseudo-halides			group V derivatives		
			$(SiH_3)_3N$ (1)	−105.6	52
SiH_3F (111,113)		−88.1	$(SiH_3)_2NCH_3$ (135)	−124.1	32.3
SiH_3Cl (1)	−118.1	−30.4	$SiH_3N(CH_3)_2$ (134,135)	2.2 (3.3)	
SiH_3Br (1)	−94	1.9	$(SiH_3)_2NB_2H_5$ (222)	−69	54
SiH_3I (56)	−57.0	45.4	$(SiH_3N)_2C$ (139)	−74.8	84.7
SiH_3CN (116)	32.4	49.6	$(SiH_3)_2NN(SiH_3)_2$		
SiH_3NCO (117)	−88.6	18.1	(132)	−24	109
SiH_3NCS (116)	−51.8	84.0	$(SiH_3)_3P$ (236)		114
SiH_3NCSe (118)	−15.1	111	$(SiH_3)_3As$ (236)		120
SiH_3N_3 (120)	−81.8	25.8	SiH_3PI_2 (127)	−1.8	190
SiH_3SiH_2F (110)	−100.3	−10.0	SiH_3AsI_2 (127)	−4.0	210
SiH_3SiH_2Cl (121)	−111.6	40.1	$(SiH_3)_3Sb$ (236)		255
SiH_3SiH_2Br (122)	−97.2	69.5	$(SiH_3SiH_2)_3N$ (204)	−97.1	176
SiH_3SiH_2I (57)	−86.1	102.8	$SiH_3SiH_2N(CH_3)_2$		
group VI derivatives			(110)		65.8
$(SiH_3)_2O$ (1)	−143.6	−15.2	group IV derivatives		
SiH_3OCH_3 (125)	−98.5	−21.1	CH_3SiH_3 (272)	−156.8	−57.5
HCO_2SiH_3 (119)	−60.4	31.4	$C_6H_5SiH_3$ (27)		120
$CH_3CO_2SiH_3$ (119)	−62.4	56.2	$H_3SiC{\equiv}CSiH_3$ (248)	−59	43
$(SiH_3)_2S$ (137)	−70.0	58.8	$H_3SiC{\equiv}CH$ (141)	−90.7	−22.4
SiH_3SCH_3 (205)	−116.7	46.8	$HC(SiH_3)_3$ (236)		57.1
SiH_3SCF_3 (131)	−127	13.6	SiH_3GeH_3 (77)	−119.7	7.0
SiH_3SH (137)	−134	14.2	$SiH_3CH_2GeH_3$ (252)	−134.8	29.9
$(SiH_3)_2Se$ (137)	−68.0	85.2	$SiH_3SiH_2CH_3$ (81)	−134.9	16.6
SiH_3SeCF_3 (144)	−125.8	35	transition metal derivatives		
$(SiH_3)_2Te$ (143)		49	$SiH_3Co(CO)_4$ (142)	−53.5	112
		(50 Torr)	$(SiH_3)_2Fe(CO)_4$ (138)	52	145
$(SiH_3SiH_2)_2O$ (57)	−111.7	94.8	$SiH_3Mn(CO)_5$		
$SiH_3SiH_2OCH_3$ (185)	−52.2	42.3	(145,257)	25.5	134
$(SiH_3SiH_2)_2S$ (204)	−70.4	144			

given, together with a discussion of the factors which could be responsible for the differences (110,271).

<h2 align="center">B. SPECTRAL PROPERTIES</h2>

Reference has been made throughout this article to various spectral measurements which have been made on derivatives of the silanes. Space does not permit a detailed discussion of all spectral parameters; however, a few pertinent comments should be made. The presence of an Si–H bond in a molecule can easily be detected by the strong Si–H stretching vibration which occurs in the infrared region at about 2100–2200 cm^{-1}. Other characteristic absorptions due to the SiH_2– and SiH_3– groupings also appear in the 650–1000 cm^{-1} region. It has been observed that the SiH_3– symmetrical deformation frequencies (about 900–1000 cm^{-1}) of various SiH_3– compounds are roughly related to the electronegativity of the atom to which silicon is bound (273). A similar correlation is found with CH_3– and GeH_3– compounds. Other characteristic absorptions of silicon compounds can be found in various infrared reference books (274).

Many proton NMR measurements have been carried out on the silanes and their derivatives. Several papers with collective and comparative NMR data have appeared (40,275–279), although data for most derivatives reported since 1963 have been presented as a part of the general characterization of the compounds. In the series of SiH_3– derivatives there is a general shift of the proton resonance to low fields as the electronegativity of the substituent increases, although the relationship is not linear (40). A similar trend is found for the α protons of SiH_3SiH_2– compounds (277). In analogous carbon and silicon compounds, the position of the Si–H proton resonance is normally to the low field of the C–H proton resonance. Because naturally occurring silicon contains approx 5% of the magnetic isotope ^{22}Si (spin $\frac{1}{2}$), directly bound ^{22}Si–H coupling constants are easily obtained from NMR studies of the silanes. The magnitude of this coupling generally falls in the 200–400 cps range, and attempts have been made to relate the values with the degree of s character in the silicon hybrid orbital (225,275). Interpretation of NMR data based on the presence (or absence) of $(p \rightarrow d)$ π bonding in silicon compounds has, in general, not been successful (3,5,280).

The equilibrium reactions in various two-component hydrogen halide, SiH_3–, or GeH_3– systems have been quantitatively studied by NMR techniques (192). In the halide systems, equilibrium constants favor the heavier halogen bound to germanium and the lighter ones bound to silicon.

Very few electron-spin-resonance (ESR) studies have been carried out on the silanes. The spectra of CH_3, SiH_3, GeH_3, and SnH_3 free radicals, produced in a krypton matrix at 4.2°K by γ irradiation of the parent hydrides, have been studied, and it has been concluded that unlike the CH_3 radical, the SiH_3 radical is not planar (88). Most likely, the GeH_3 and SnH_3 radicals are also not planar. ESR measurements have also identified the novel anion radical $(CH_3)_{12}Si_6{}^-$ formed by the reaction of the cyclic compound $(CH_3)_{12}Si_6$ with Na–K alloy at −90°C (281). The odd electron interacts equally with all the protons, and ^{29}Si and ^{13}C satellite resonances show that all the silicon atoms are equivalent, as are all the carbon atoms. The results are of theoretical significance, since the electron delocalization which is occurring over the entire ring system is almost certain to involve a $3d$ π orbital system.

Mass spectral measurements of the silanes and their derivatives have mainly been carried out to obtain structural and thermochemical information. Some representa-

Table 3. Some Thermochemical Data Derived from Mass Spectral Measurements[a]

Compound	Heat of formation (gas), kcal/mole	R_3Si-X bond dissociation energy, kcal/mole	Reference
SiH_3-H	7.8	94 ± 3	282, 283
$H_3Si-SiH_3$	15.1	81.3, 83.7	284–286
$H_3Si-GeH_3$	7.5[b]	99.9	287
H_3Si-PH_2	1.9	88.2	286
$H_3Si-AsH_2$	37	73	289
H_3Si-CH_3	-4 ± 4	86 ± 4	283
$H_3Si-C_2H_5$	-15 ± 4	89 ± 3	283
$H_3Si-iso-C_3H_7$	-14 ± 4	79 ± 3	283
$H_3Si-t-C_4H_9$	-11 ± 4	65 ± 3	283
$F_3Si-Co(CO)_4$	-490 ± 10	105 ± 12	290
$CH_3(F)_2Si-Co(CO)_4$	-437 ± 12	127 ± 15	291
$(CH_3)_3Si-Si(CH_3)_3$	-118 ± 2	67 ± 2	292
$(CH_3)_3Si-H$	-55 ± 2	81 ± 2	292

[a] It is assumed that measured appearance potentials do not include excess kinetic or excitation energy.

[b] 27.8 kcal/mole from calorimetric measurements (288).

tive bond dissociation energies and heats of formation which have been obtained from appearance-potential measurements are given in Table 3.

The electronic absorption spectra of $(SiH_3)_2O$, $(SiH_3)_3N$, SiH_3Cl, and $(SiH_3)_2NCH_3$ in the vacuum ultraviolet are much more diffuse than the spectra of the corresponding carbon compounds (293). Of particular interest is the fact that the absorption maxima of SiH_3- derivatives are found at lower wavelengths than the maxima of the corresponding CH_3- derivatives. The difference is large ($\sim$0.5 to several eV) and it suggests that the SiH_3- compounds possess considerably higher first ionization potentials than the CH_3- compounds. Although this order is not that expected from the relative electronegativities of carbon and silicon, it can be rationalized in terms of the previously mentioned $(p \rightarrow d)$ π delocalization in the various Si–X linkages.

Bibliography

"Silicon Compounds" in *ECT* 1st ed., Vol. 12, pp. 365–392, by E. G. Rochow, Harvard University.

1. A. Stock, *Hydrides of Boron and Silicon*, Cornell University Press, Ithaca, N.Y., 1933.
2. R. T. Sanderson, *Vacuum Manipulations of Volatile Compounds*, John Wiley & Sons, Inc., New York, 1948.
3. E. A. V. Ebsworth, "Physical Basis of the Chemistry of the Group IV Elements," *Organometallic Chemistry of the Group IV Elements*, Vol. I, Marcel Dekker, Inc., New York, 1968, Chap. 1.
4. A. G. MacDiarmid, *Advan. Inorg. Chem. Radiochem.* **3**, 207 (1961).
5. E. A. V. Ebsworth, *Volatile Silicon Compounds*, The Macmillan Co., New York, 1963.
6. F. G. A. Stone, *Hydrogen Compounds of the Group IV Elements*, Prentice-Hall, Inc., Englewood Cliffs, N.J., 1962.
7. C. Eaborn, *Organosilicon Compounds*, Butterworths Scientific Publications, London, 1960.
8. V. Bažant, V. Chvalovský, and J. Rathouský, *Organosilicon Compounds*, Academic Press, Inc., New York, 1965.
9. L. H. Sommer, *Stereochemistry, Mechanism, and Silicon*, McGraw-Hill Book Co., Inc., New York, 1965.
10. S. D. Gokhale and W. L. Jolly, *Inorg. Chem.* **3**, 946 (1964).

11. T. D. Andrews and C. S. G. Phillips, *J. Chem. Soc.* **A1966**, 46.
12. K. Borer and C. S. G. Phillips, *Proc. Chem. Soc.* **1959**, 189.
13. C. S. G. Phillips and P. L. Timms, *Anal. Chem.* **35**, 505 (1963).
14. C. S. G. Phillips, P. Powell, J. A. Semlyen, and P. L. Timms, *Z. Anal. Chem.* **197**, 202 (1963).
15. P. L. Timms, C. C. Simpson, and C. S. G. Phillips, *J. Chem. Soc.* **1964**, 1467.
16. P. Royen and C. Rocktäschel, *Angew. Chem.* **76**, 302 (1964).
17. F. Fehér and H. Strack, *Naturwissenschaften* **50**, 570 (1963).
18. B. E. Douglas and D. H. McDaniel, *Concepts and Models of Inorganic Chemistry*, Ginn and Co., Publishers, Boston, 1965, p. 58.
19. K. S. Pitzer, *J. Am. Chem. Soc.* **70**, 2140 (1948).
20. E. J. Crane, *Chem. Eng. News* **24**, 1233 (1946).
21. R. Rudman, W. C. Hamilton, S. Novick, and T. D. Goldfarb, *J. Am. Chem. Soc.* **89**, 5157 (1967).
22. F. G. A. Stone and D. Seyferth, *J. Inorg. Nucl. Chem.* **1**, 112 (1955).
23. T. L. Cottrell, *The Strengths of Chemical Bonds*, 2nd ed., Butterworth and Co. Ltd., London, 1958.
24. H. J. Emeléus and A. G. Maddock, *J. Chem. Soc.* **1946**, 1131.
25. W. C. Johnson and S. Isenberg, *J. Am. Chem. Soc.* **57**, 1349 (1935).
26. F. Fehér and W. Tromm, *Z. Anorg. Chem.* **282**, 29 (1955).
27. A. E. Finholt, A. C. Bond, Jr., K. E. Wilzbach, and H. I. Schlesinger, *J. Am. Chem. Soc.* **69**, 2692 (1947).
28. H. S. Gutowsky and E. O. Stejskal, *J. Chem. Phys.* **22**, 939 (1954).
29. W. Sundermeyer, *Pure Applied Chem.* **13**, 93 (1966).
30. H. L. Jackson, F. D. Marsh, and E. L. Muetterties, *Inorg. Chem.* **2**, 43 (1963).
31. H. G. Weiss and H. D. Fisher, *Inorg. Chem.* **2**, 880 (1963).
32. A. D. Craig and A. G. MacDiarmid, *J. Inorg. Nucl. Chem.* **24**, 161 (1962).
33. R. C. Kennedy, L. P. Freeman, A. P. Fox, and M. A. Ring, *J. Inorg. Nucl. Chem.* **28**, 1373 (1966).
34. E. J. Spanier and A. G. MacDiarmid, *Inorg. Chem.* **1**, 432 (1962).
35. S. D. Gokhale, J. E. Drake, and W. L. Jolly, *J. Inorg. Nucl. Chem.* **27**, 1911 (1965).
36. F. Fehér, H. Keller, G. Kuhlborsch, and H. Lunleich, *Angew. Chem.* **70**, 402 (1958).
37. G. W. Bethke and M. K. Wilson, *J. Chem. Phys.* **26**, 1107 (1957).
38. W. B. Steward and H. H. Nielsen, *Phys. Rev.* **47**, 828 (1935).
39. C. H. Tindal, J. W. Straley, and H. H. Nielsen, *Phys. Rev.* **62**, 151 (1942).
40. E. A. V. Ebsworth and J. J. Turner, *J. Phys. Chem.* **67**, 805 (1963).
41. E. A. V. Ebsworth and J. J. Turner, *Trans. Faraday Soc.* **60**, 256 (1964).
42. J. E. Drake and W. L. Jolly, *J. Chem. Phys.* **38**, 1033 (1963).
43. H. Niki and G. J. Mains, *J. Phys. Chem.* **68**, 304 (1964).
44. H. J. Emeléus and K. Stewart, *Trans. Faraday Soc.* **32**, 1577 (1936).
45. G. A. Gibbon, Y. Rousseau, C. H. Van Dyke, and G. J. Mains, *Inorg. Chem.* **5**, 114 (1966).
46. G. Schott, W. Herrmann, and E. Hirschmann, *Angew. Chem.* **68**, 213 (1956).
47. G. Schott and W. Herrmann, *Z. Anorg. Chem.* **288**, 1 (1956).
48. G. Schott and E. Hirschmann, *Z. Anorg. Chem.* **288**, 9 (1956).
49. A. Stock and F. Zeidler, *Ber.* **56B**, 986 (1923).
50. M. Schmeisser and M. Schwarzmann, *Z. Naturforsch.* **11b**, 278 (1956).
51. R. Schwarz and F. Heinrich, *Z. Anorg. Chem.* **221**, 277 (1935).
52. L. R. Harper, S. Yolles, and H. C. Miller, *J. Inorg. Nucl. Chem.* **21**, 294 (1961).
52a. R. Müller and G. Meier, *Z. Anorg. Chem.* **337**, 268 (1965).
53. H. J. Emeléus and K. Stewart, *J. Chem. Soc.* **1935**, 1182; **1936**, 677.
54. B. Sternbach and A. G. MacDiarmid, *J. Am. Chem. Soc.* **81**, 5109 (1959).
55. J. S. Peake, W. H. Nebergall, and Y. T. Chen, *J. Am. Chem. Soc.* **74**, 1526 (1952).
56. H. J. Emeléus, A. G. Maddock, and C. Reid, *J. Chem. Soc.* **1941**, 353.
57. L. G. L. Ward and A. G. MacDiarmid, *J. Am. Chem. Soc.* **82**, 2151 (1960).
58. M. Abedini, C. H. Van Dyke, and A. G. MacDiarmid, *J. Inorg. Nucl. Chem.* **25**, 307 (1963).
59. H. E. Opitz, J. S. Peake, and W. H. Nebergall, *J. Am. Chem. Soc.* **78**, 292 (1956).
60. C. H. Van Dyke and A. G. MacDiarmid, *J. Inorg. Nucl. Chem.* **25**, 1503 (1963).
61. J. E. Drake and N. Goddard, *Inorg. Nucl. Chem. Letters* **4**, 385 (1968).

62. J. E. Drake and J. Simpson, *J. Inorg. Nucl. Chem. Letters* **2**, 219 (1966).
63. S. Cradock, G. A. Gibbon, and C. H. Van Dyke, *Inorg. Chem.* **6**, 1751 (1967).
64. E. Amberger and E. Mühlhofer, *J. Organometallic Chem.* **12**, 55 (1968).
65. E. Amberger, R. Römer, and A. Layer, *J. Organometallic Chem.* **12**, 417 (1968).
66. M. A. Ring and D. M. Ritter, *J. Am. Chem. Soc.* **83**, 802 (1961).
67. Sr. S. P. Garrity and M. A. Ring, *Inorg. Nucl. Chem. Letters* **4**, 77 (1968).
68. D. S. Rustad and W. L. Jolly, *Inorg. Chem.* **6**, 1986 (1967).
69. J. A. Morrison and M. A. Ring, *Inorg. Chem.* **6**, 100 (1967).
70. M. A. Ring, L. P. Freeman, and A. P. Fox, *Inorg. Chem.* **3**, 1200 (1964).
71. R. P. Hollandsworth, W. M. Ingle, and M. A. Ring, *Inorg. Chem.* **6**, 844 (1967).
72. R. P. Hollandsworth and M. A. Ring, *Inorg. Chem.* **7**, 1635 (1968).
73. E. A. Groschwitz, W. M. Ingle, and M. A. Ring, *J. Organometallic Chem.* **9**, 421 (1967).
74. W. J. Bolduc and M. A. Ring, *J. Organometallic Chem.* **6**, 202 (1966).
75. R. N. Meals, *J. Am. Chem. Soc.* **68**, 1880 (1946).
76. N. B. Bhatt and S. K. K. Jatkar, *J. Indian Inst. Sci.* **20A**, 34 (1937).
77. E. J. Spanier and A. G. MacDiarmid, *Inorg. Chem.* **2**, 215 (1963).
78. J. E. Drake and W. L. Jolly, *Chem. Ind. (London)*, **1962**, 1470.
79. S. D. Gokhale and W. L. Jolly, *Inorg. Chem.* **3**, 1141 (1964).
80. *Ibid.*, **4**, 596 (1965).
81. M. Abedini and A. G. MacDiarmid, *Inorg. Chem.* **5**, 2040 (1966).
82. D. White and E. G. Rockow, *J. Am. Chem. Soc.* **76**, 3897 (1954).
83. M. A. Nay, G. N. C. Woodall, O. P. Strausz, and H. E. Gunning, *J. Am. Chem. Soc.* **87**, 179 (1965).
84. O. P. Strausz, K. Obi, and W. K. Duholke, *J. Am. Chem. Soc.* **90**, 1359 (1968).
85. R. Schaeffer and L. Ross, *J. Am. Chem. Soc.* **81**, 3486 (1959).
86. P. P. Gaspar, B. D. Pate, and W. Eckelman, *J. Am. Chem. Soc.* **88**, 3878 (1966).
87. F. J. Adrian, E. L. Cochran, and V. A. Bowers, "Free Radicals in Inorganic Chemistry," *Advan. Chem. Ser.* **36**, 50 (1962).
88. R. L. Morehouse, J. J. Christiansen, and W. Gordy, *J. Chem. Phys.* **45**, 1751 (1966).
89. G. Fritz, *Z. Naturforsch.* **7b**, 507 (1952).
90. A. Stock and C. Somieski, *Ber.* **56**, 247 (1923).
91. H. J. Emeléus and C. Reid, *J. Chem. Soc.* **1939**, 1021.
92. G. Fritz, *Z. Naturforsch.* **8b**, 776 (1953); *Z. Anorg. Chem.* **280**, 332 (1955).
93. C. H. Lewis, H. C. Kelly, M. B. Giusto, and S. Johnson, *J. Electrochem. Soc.* **108**, 1114 (1961); J. M. Wilson, *Research* **12**, 91 (1959).
94. R. J. H. Voorhoeve, *Organosilanes—Precursors to Silicones*, American Elsevier Publishing Co., New York, 1967.
95. G. Fritz, *Z. Naturforsch.* **7b**, 207 (1952).
96. *Ibid.*, **6b**, 116 (1951).
97. A. G. MacDiarmid, in W. L. Jolly, ed., *Preparative Inorganic Reactions*, Vol. I, Interscience Publishers, a division of John Wiley & Sons, Inc., New York, 1964, p. 165.
98. B. J. Aylett and I. A. Ellis, *J. Chem. Soc.* **1960**, 3415.
99. G. Fritz and D. Kummer, *Z. Anorg. Chem.* **306**, 191 (1960).
100. *Ibid.*, **304**, 322 (1960).
101. *Ibid.*, **310**, 327 (1961).
102. *Ibid.*, **308**, 105 (1961).
103. G. Fritz and D. Kummer, *Ber.* **94**, 1143 (1961).
104. R. D. Verma and L. C. Leitch, *Can. J. Chem.* **41**, 1652 (1963).
105. L. G. L. Ward, *Inorg. Syntheses* **11**, 159 (1968).
106. H. J. Emeléus and M. Onyszchuk, *J. Chem. Soc.* **1958**, 604.
107. M. Onyszchuk, *Can. J. Chem.* **39**, 808 (1961).
108. W. A. Kriner, A. G. MacDiarmid, and E. C. Evers, *J. Am. Chem. Soc.* **80**, 1546 (1958).
109. C. H. Van Dyke and A. G. MacDiarmid, *Inorg. Chem.* **3**, 747 (1964).
110. M. Abedini and A. G. MacDiarmid, *Inorg. Chem.* **2**, 608 (1963).
111. S. Sujishi and S. Witz, *J. Am. Chem. Soc.* **79**, 2447 (1957).
112. H. S. Booth and W. D. Stillwell, *J. Am. Chem. Soc.* **56**, 1531 (1934).
113. H. J. Emeléus and A. G. Maddock, *J. Chem. Soc.* **1944**, 293.

114. S. Cradock, E. A. V. Ebsworth, and A. G. Robiette, *Trans. Faraday Soc.* **60**, 1502 (1964).

115. U.S. Pat. 2,627,451 (1953), C. E. Erickson and G. H. Wagner; *Chem. Abstr.* **48**, 1420b (1964). U.S. Pat. 2,735,861 (1956), C. E. Erickson and G. H. Wagner; *Chem. Abstr.* **50**, 13986b (1956).

116. A. G. MacDiarmid, *J. Inorg. Nucl. Chem.* **2**, 88 (1956).

117. E. A. V. Ebsworth and M. J. Mays, *J. Chem. Soc.* **1962**, 4844.

118. E. A. V. Ebsworth and M. J. Mays, *J. Chem. Soc.* **1963**, 3893.

119. E. A. V. Ebsworth and J. C. Thompson, *J. Chem. Soc.* **A1967**, 69.

120. E. A. V. Ebsworth and M. J. Mays, *J. Chem. Soc.* **1964**, 3450.

121. A. D. Craig, J. V. Urenovitch, and A. G. MacDiarmid, *J. Chem. Soc.* **1962**, 548.

122. L. G. L. Ward and A. G. MacDiarmid, *J. Inorg. Nucl. Chem.* **20**, 345 (1961).

123. H. J. Campbell-Ferguson, *J. Inorg. Nucl. Chem.* **27**, 2121 (1965).

124. E. Wiberg and W. Simmler, *Z. Anorg. Chem.* **283**, 401 (1956).

125. B. Sternbach and A. G. MacDiarmid, *J. Am. Chem. Soc.* **83**, 3384 (1961).

126. H. J. Campbell-Ferguson and E. A. V. Ebsworth, *J. Chem. Soc.* **A1966**, 1508.

127. B. J. Aylett, H. J. Emeléus, and A. G. Maddock, *J. Inorg. Nucl. Chem.* **1**, 187 (1955).

128. H. J. Campbell-Ferguson and E. A. V. Ebsworth, *J. Chem. Soc.* **A1967**, 705.

129. J. Emsley, *J. Chem. Soc.* **A1968**, 1009.

130. B. J. Aylett, *J. Inorg. Nucl. Chem.* **15**, 87 (1960).

131. A. J. Downs and E. A. V. Ebsworth, *J. Chem. Soc.* **1960**, 3516.

132. B. J. Aylett, *J. Inorg. Nucl. Chem.* **2**, 325 (1956).

133. B. J. Aylett and J. Emsley, *J. Chem. Soc.* **A1967**, 1918.

134. B. J. Aylett and J. Emsley, *J. Chem. Soc.* **A1967**, 652.

135. S. Sujishi and S. Witz, *J. Am. Chem. Soc.* **76**, 4631 (1954).

136. R. Varma, A. G. MacDiarmid, and J. G. Miller, *J. Chem. Phys.* **39**, 3157 (1963).

137. H. J. Emeléus, A. G. MacDiarmid, and A. G. Maddock, *J. Inorg. Nucl. Chem.* **1**, 194 (1955).

138. B. J. Aylett, J. M. Campbell, and A. Walton, *Inorg. Nucl. Chem. Letters* **4**, 79 (1968).

139. E. A. V. Ebsworth and M. J. Mays, *J. Chem. Soc.* **1961**, 4879.

140. U. Wannagat, Lecture, *Second International Symposium on Organosilicon Chemistry, Bordeaux, France, July 1968*.

141. E. A. V. Ebsworth and S. G. Frankiss, *J. Chem. Soc.* **1963**, 661.

142. B. J. Aylett and J. M. Campbell, *Chem. Commun.* **11**, 217 (1965).

143. H. Bürger and U. Goetze, *Inorg. Nucl. Chem. Letters* **3**, 549 (1967).

144. E. A. V. Ebsworth, H. J. Emeléus, and N. Welcman, *J. Chem. Soc.* **1962**, 2290.

145. B. J. Aylett and J. M. Campbell, *Inorg. Nucl. Chem. Letters* **3**, 137 (1967).

146. B. Bak, J. Bruhn, and J. Rastrup-Anderson, *Acta Chem. Scand.* **8**, 367 (1954).

147. D. P. Craig, A. Maccoll, R. S. Nyholm, L. E. Orgel, and L. E. Sutton, *J. Chem. Soc.* **1954**, 332.

148. J. M. Bellama, Ph.D. Dissertation, University of Pennsylvania, Philadelphia, 1967.

149. A. P. Cox and R. Varma, *J. Chem. Phys.* **44**, 2619 (1966).

150. R. D. Nelson, D. R. Lide, Jr., and A. A. Maryott, "Selected Values of Electric Dipole Moments for Molecules in the Gas Phase," *Publ. NSRDS-NBS 10*, National Bureau of Standards, Washington, D.C., 1967.

151. N. Muller and R. C. Bracken, *J. Chem. Phys.* **32**, 1577 (1960).

152. J. Sheridan and A. C. Turner, *Proc. Chem. Soc.* **1960**, 21.

153. H. R. Linton and E. R. Nixon, *Spectrochim. Acta* **10**, 299 (1958).

154. T. D. Goldfarb and B. P. Zafonte, *J. Chem. Phys.* **41**, 3653 (1964).

155. T. A. Bither, W. H. Knoth, R. V. Lindsey, Jr., and W. H. Sharkey, *J. Am. Chem. Soc.* **80**, 4151 (1958).

156. M. F. Lappert and H. Pyszora, *Advan. Inorg. Radiochemistry* **9**, 133 (1966).

157. M. C. L. Gerry, J. C. Thompson, and T. M. Sugden, *Nature* **211**, 846 (1966).

158. E. A. V. Ebsworth, R. Mould, R. Taylor, G. R. Wilkinson, and L. A. Woodward, *Trans. Faraday Soc.* **58**, 1069 (1962).

159. D. R. Jenkins, R. Kewley, and T. M. Sugden, *Proc. Chem. Soc.* **1960**, 220; *Trans. Faraday Soc.* **58**, 1284 (1962).

160. E. H. Eyster, R. H. Gillette, and L. O. Brockway, *J. Am. Chem. Soc.* **62**, 3236 (1940).

161. C. I. Beard and B. P. Dailey, *J. Am. Chem. Soc.* **71**, 929 (1949).

162. J. E. Griffiths and A. L. Beach, *Chem. Commun.* **19**, 437 (1965); K. R. Ramaprasad, R. Varma,

and R. Nelson, *J. Am. Chem. Soc.* **90**, 6247 (1968); J. E. Griffiths, *J. Chem. Phys.*, **48**, 278 (1968).

163. G. A. Gibbon, J. T. Wang, and C. H. Van Dyke, *Inorg. Chem.* **6**, 1989 (1967).
164. J. E. Griffiths and M. Onyszchuk, *Can. J. Chem.* **39**, 339 (1961).
165. E. W. Abel, D. A. Armitage, and D. B. Brady, *Trans. Faraday Soc.* **62**, 3459 (1966).
166. R. West and R. H. Baney, *J. Phys. Chem.* **64**, 822 (1960).
167. K. Kimura, K. Katada, and S. H. Bauer, *J. Am. Chem. Soc.* **88**, 416 (1966).
168. E. A. V. Ebsworth, D. R. Jenkins, M. J. Mays, and T. M. Sugden, *Proc. Chem. Soc.* **1963**, 21.
169. J. W. Linnett, *Nature* **199**, 168 (1963).
170. J. S. Thayer and R. West, *Inorg. Chem.* **3**, 889 (1964).
171. S. Cradock and E. A. V. Ebsworth, *J. Chem. Soc.* **A1968**, 1420.
172. J. F. Ogilvie and S. Cradock, *Chem. Commun.* **12**, 364 (1966).
173. J. W. Connolly and G. Urry, *Inorg. Chem.* **1**, 718 (1962).
174. E. C. Evers, W. O. Freitag, J. N. Keith, W. A. Kriner, A. G. MacDiarmid, and S. Sujishi, *J. Am. Chem. Soc.* **81**, 4493 (1959).
175. E. C. Evers, W. O. Freitag, W. A. Kriner, A. G. MacDiarmid, and S. Sujishi, *J. Inorg. Nucl. Chem.* **13**, 239 (1960).
176. J. J. McBride, Jr., and H. C. Beachell, *J. Am. Chem. Soc.* **74**, 5247 (1952).
177. D. Seyferth and N. Kahlen, *J. Am. Chem. Soc.* **82**, 1080 (1960).
178. S. W. Kantor, *J. Am. Chem. Soc.* **75**, 2712 (1953).
179. L. J. Tyler, *J. Am. Chem. Soc.* **77**, 770 (1955); T. Takiguchi, *J. Am. Chem. Soc.* **81**, 2359 (1959).
180. R. West and R. H. Baney, *J. Am. Chem. Soc.* **81**, 6145 (1959).
181. R. West, *J. Am. Chem. Soc.* **75**, 1002 (1953).
182. C. H. Van Dyke and E. W. Kifer, *Abstracts, 156th National Meeting, American Chemical Society, Atlantic City, N.J., Sept. 1968*, Paper 115 (Inorg. Sect.).
183. A. G. MacDiarmid and T. Yoshioka, *Abstracts, 149th National Meeting, American Chemical Society, Detroit, Mich., April 1965*, p. 5M.
184. G. S. Weiss and E. R. Nixon, *Spectrochimica Acta* **21**, 903 (1965).
185. C. H. Van Dyke and A. G. MacDiarmid, unpublished results.
186. N. Viswanathan and C. H. Van Dyke, *J. Chem. Soc.* **1968**, 487.
187. J. T. Wang and C. H. Van Dyke, *Inorg. Chem.* **6**, 1741 (1967).
188. J. T. Wang and C. H. Van Dyke, unpublished results.
189. T. Yoshioka and A. G. MacDiarmid, unpublished results.
190. O. J. Klejnot, *Inorg. Chem.* **2**, 825 (1963).
191. H. Reuther, *Chem. Tech. (Berlin)* **2**, 331 (1950); D. F. Pebbard, W. G. Brown, and W. C. Johnson, *J. Am. Chem. Soc.* **68**, 70 (1946).
192. S. Cradock and E. A. V. Ebsworth, *J. Chem. Soc.* **A1967**, 1226.
193. R. E. Frost and E. G. Rochow, *J. Inorg. Nucl. Chem.* **5**, 201, 207 (1958).
194. J. F. Salmon and E. C. Evers, *J. Inorg. Nucl. Chem.* **28**, 2787 (1966).
195. C. H. Van Dyke, *J. Inorg. Nucl. Chem.* **30**, 81 (1968).
196. A. Almenningen, O. Bastiansen, V. Ewing, K. Hedberg, and M. Traetteberg, *Acta Chem. Scand.* **17**, 2455 (1963).
197. U. Blukis, P. H. Kasai, and R. J. Myers, *J. Chem. Phys.* **38**, 2753 (1963).
198. K. Yamasaki, A. Kotera, M. Yokoi, and Y. Ueda, *J. Chem. Phys.* **18**, 1414 (1950); M. Yokoi, *Bull. Chem. Soc. Japan* **30**, 106 (1957).
199. R. West, L. S. Whatley, and K. J. Lake, *J. Am. Chem. Soc.* **83**, 761 (1961).
200. R. Varma, A. G. MacDiarmid, and J. G. Miller, *Inorg. Chem.* **3**, 1754 (1964).
201. S. Cradock, *J. Chem. Soc.* **A1968**, 1426.
202. E. W. Abel, D. A. Armitage, and S. P. Tyfield, *J. Chem. Soc.* **A1967**, 554.
203. R. M. Salinger and R. West, *J. Organometallic Chem.* **11**, 631 (1968).
204. L. G. L. Ward and A. G. MacDiarmid, *J. Inorg. Nucl. Chem.* **21**, 287 (1961).
205. B. Sternbach and A. G. MacDiarmid, *J. Inorg. Nucl. Chem.* **23**, 225 (1961).
206. M. Schmeisser and H. Müller, *Angew. Chem.* **69**, 781 (1957).
207. A. G. MacDiarmid, *J. Inorg. Nucl. Chem.* **25**, 1534 (1963).
208. J. T. Wang and C. H. Van Dyke, *Chem. Comm.* **18**, 928 (1967).
209. L. Pierce and M. Hayashi, *J. Chem. Phys.* **35**, 479 (1961).

210. A. Almenningen, K. Hedberg, and R. Seip, *Acta Chem. Scand.* **17**, 2264 (1963).
211. H. Kriegsmann, *Z. Elektrochem.* **61**, 1088 (1957).
212. J. T. Wang and C. H. Van Dyke, *Inorg. Chem.* **7**, 1319 (1968).
213. T. D. Goldfarb and S. Sujishi, *J. Am. Chem. Soc.* **86**, 1679 (1964).
214. B. J. Aylett, in W. L. Jolly, ed., *Preparative Inorganic Reactions*, Vol. II, Interscience Publishers, a division of John Wiley & Sons, Inc., New York, 1965, p. 93.
215. B. J. Aylett and M. J. Hakim, *Inorg. Chem.* **5**, 167 (1966).
216. R. O. Sauer and R. H. Hasek, *J. Am. Chem. Soc.* **68**, 241 (1946).
217. J. Goubeau and J. Jiménez-Barberá, *Z. Anorg. Chem.* **303**, 217 (1960).
218. U. Wannagat and H. Niederprüm, *Angew. Chem.* **71**, 574 (1959).
219. W. L. Lehn, *J. Am. Chem. Soc.* **86**, 305 (1964).
220. B. J. Aylett and L. K. Peterson, *J. Chem. Soc.* **1964**, 3429.
221. A. Stock and C. Somieski, *Ber.* **54**, 740 (1921).
222. A. B. Burg and E. S. Kuljian, *J. Am. Chem. Soc.* **72**, 3103 (1954).
223. E. A. V. Ebsworth, G. Rocktäschel, and J. C. Thompson, *J. Chem. Soc.* **A1967**, 362.
224. E. A. V. Ebsworth and M. J. Mays, *Spectrochim. Acta* **19**, 1127 (1963).
225. D. I. Cook, R. Fields, M. Green, R. N. Haszeldine, B. R. Iles, A. Jones, and M. J. Newlands, *J. Chem. Soc.* **A1966**, 887.
226. K. Hedberg, *J. Am. Chem. Soc.* **77**, 6491 (1955).
227. P. G. Perkins, *Chem. Commun.* **6**, 368 (1967).
228. A. G. Robiette, G. M. Sheldrick, W. S. Sheldrick, B. Beagley, D. W. J. Cruickshank, J. J. Monaghan, B. J. Aylett, and I. A. Ellis, *Chem. Commun.* **15**, 909 (1968).
229. J. E. Wollrab and V. W. Laurie, *J. Chem. Phys.* **48**, 5058 (1968).
230. J. M. Manasevit, Ph.D. Thesis, Illinois Institute of Technology, Chicago, Ill., 1959.
231. E. A. V. Ebsworth and H. J. Eméleus, *J. Chem. Soc.* **1958**, 2150.
232. T. D. Goldfarb and B. N. Khare, *J. Chem. Phys.* **46**, 3384 (1967).
233. B. J. Aylett, J. R. Hall, D. C. McKean, R. Taylor, and L. A. Woodward, *Spectrochim. Acta* **16**, 747 (1960).
234. E. Amberger and H. Boeters, *Angew. Chem.* **74**, 32 (1962).
235. G. Davidson, E. A. V. Ebsworth, G. M. Sheldrick, and L. A. Woodward, *Chem. Commun.* **7** 122 (1965).
236. E. Amberger and H. D. Boeters, *Ber.* **97**, 1999 (1964).
237. A. D. Norman, *Chem. Commun.* **14**, 812 (1968).
238. D. C. Wingleth and A. D. Norman, *Chem. Commun.* **23**, 1218 (1967).
239. G. Fritz and G. Becker, *Angew. Chem., Internatl. Ed.* **6**, 1078 (1967).
240. G. Davidson, L. A. Woodward, E. A. V. Ebsworth, and G. M. Sheldrick, *Spectrochim. Acta* **23A**, 2609 (1967).
241. J. E. Drake and J. Simpson, *Inorg. Chem.* **6**, 1984 (1967).
242. J. E. Drake and J. Simpson, *J. Chem. Soc.* **A1968**, 1039.
243. J. E. Drake and J. Simpson, *Chem. Commun.* **6**, 249 (1967).
244. S. Cradock, E. A. V. Ebsworth, G. Davidson, and L. A. Woodward, *J. Chem. Soc.* **A1967**, 1229.
245. B. Beagley, A. G. Robiette, and G. M. Sheldrick, *Chem. Commun.* **12**, 601 (1967).
246. A. D. Petrov, B. F. Mironov, V. A. Ponomarenko, and E. A. Chernyshev, *Synthesis of Organosilicon Monomers*, Consultants Bureau, New York, 1964.
247. C. Eaborn and R. W. Bott, "The Formation and Reactions of Silicon–Carbon Bonds," in A. G. MacDiarmid, ed., *Organometallic Compounds of the Group IV Elements*, Vol. 1, Marcel Dekker, Inc., New York, 1968, Chap. 2.
248. R. C. Lord, D. W. Mayo, H. E. Opitz, and J. S. Peake, *Spectrochim. Acta* **12**, 147 (1958).
249. J. Laane, *J. Am. Chem. Soc.* **89**, 1144 (1967).
250. R. Varma and A. P. Cox, *Angew. Chem.* **76**, 649 (1964).
251. W. A. Dutton and M. Onyszchuk, *Inorg. Chem.* **7**, 1735 (1968).
252. G. A. Gibbon and C. H. Van Dyke, *Abstracts, 155th National Meeting American Chemical Society, San Francisco, Cal., April 1968*, p. M-114.
253. E. Wiberg, E. Amberger, and H. Cambensi, *Z. Anorg. Chem.* **351**, 164 (1967).
254. M. A. Ring and D. M. Ritter, *J. Phys. Chem.* **65**, 182 (1961).

255. R. Varma, *Abstracts, 151st Meeting American Chemical Society, Pittsburgh, Pa., March 1966*, p. H-26.

255a. E. Amberger and R. Römer, *Z. Anorg. Chem.* **345**, 1 (1966).

255b. P. Hagenmuller and M. Pouchard, *Société chimique de France* (Bulletin), 1187 (1964).

256. T. S. Piper, D. Lemal, and G. Wilkinson, *Naturwissenschaften* **43**, 129 (1956).

257. B. J. Aylett and J. M. Campbell, *Chem. Commun.* **4**, 159 (1967).

258. D. J. Cardin, S. A. Keppie, B. M. Kingston, and M. F. Lappert, *Chem. Comm.* **20**, 1035 (1967).

259. Y. L. Baay and A. G. MacDiarmid, *Inorg. Nucl. Chem. Letters* **3**, 159 (1967).

260. A. J. Chalk and J. F. Harrod, *J. Am. Chem. Soc.* **87**, 1133 (1965).

261. A. G. MacDiarmid, unpublished observation.

262. D. J. Cardin and M. F. Lappert, *Chem. Commun.* **15**, 506 (1966).

263. W. Jetz and W. A. G. Graham, *J. Am. Chem. Soc.* **89**, 2773 (1967); W. Jetz, P. B. Simons, J. A. J. Thompson, and W. A. G. Graham, *Inorg. Chem.* **5**, 2217 (1966).

264. A. G. MacDiarmid, S. K. Gondal, F. E. Saalfeld, and M. V. McDowell, *Abstracts, 155th Meeting American Chemical Society, San Francisco, Cal., April 1968*, p. M-79.

265. A. P. Hagen and A. G. MacDiarmid, *Inorg. Chem.* **6**, 686 (1967).

266. W. T. Robinson and J. A. Ibers, *Inorg. Chem.* **6**, 1208 (1967).

267. B. J. Aylett and J. M. Campbell, *Abstracts, 2nd International Symposium Organosilicon Chemistry, Bordeaux, France, 1968*, p. 8; A. G. Robiette, G. M. Sheldrick, R. N. F. Simpson, B. J. Aylett, and J. M. Campbell, *J. Organometallic Chem.* **14**, 279 (1968).

268. L. Markó, G. Bor, G. Almásy, and P. Szabó, *Brennstoff-Chem.* **44**, 184 (1965).

269. O. Kahn and M. Bigorgne, *J. Organometallic Chem.* **10**, 137 (1967).

270. R. S. Hamilton and E. R. Corey, *Abstracts, 156th National Meeting American Chemical Society, Atlantic City, N.J., Sept. 1968*, Paper 25 (Inorg. Sect.).

271. A. G. MacDiarmid, *Quart. Rev. (London)* **10**, 208 (1956).

272. S. Tannenbaum, S. Kay, and G. F. Lewenz, *J. Am. Chem. Soc.* **75**, 3753 (1953).

273. W. L. Jolly, *J. Am. Chem. Soc.* **85**, 3083 (1963).

274. L. J. Bellamy, *The Infrared Spectra of Complex Molecules*, 2nd ed., John Wiley & Sons, Inc., New York, 1958.

275. E. A. V. Ebsworth and J. J. Turner, *J. Chem. Phys.* **36**, 2628 (1962).

276. E. A. V. Ebsworth and S. Frankiss, *Trans. Faraday Soc.* **59**, 1518 (1963).

277. C. H. Van Dyke and A. G. MacDiarmid, *Inorg. Chem.* **3**, 1071 (1964).

278. H. J. Campbell-Ferguson, E. A. V. Ebsworth, A. G. MacDiarmid, and T. Yoshioka, *J. Phys. Chem.* **71**, 723 (1967); T. Yoshioka and A. G. MacDiarmid, *J. Mol. Spectroscopy* **21**, 103 (1966).

279. E. A. V. Ebsworth and G. M. Sheldrick, *Trans. Faraday Soc.* **63**, 3282 (1966).

280. E. A. V. Ebsworth and S. G. Frankiss, *J. Am. Chem. Soc.* **85**, 3516 (1963).

281. G. R. Husk and R. West, *J. Am. Chem. Soc.* **87**, 3993 (1965).

282. F. E. Saalfeld and H. J. Svec, *Inorg. Chem.* **2**, 46 (1963).

283. W. C. Steele, L. D. Nichols, and F. G. A. Stone, *J. Am. Chem. Soc.* **84**, 4441 (1962).

284. F. E. Saalfeld and H. J. Svec, *Inorg. Chem.* **2**, 50 (1963).

285. W. C. Steele and F. G. A. Stone, *J. Am. Chem. Soc.* **84**, 3599 (1962).

286. F. E. Saalfeld and H. J. Svec, *Inorg. Chem.* **3**, 1442 (1964).

287. F. E. Saalfeld and H. J. Svec, *J. Phys. Chem.* **70**, 1753 (1966).

288. S. R. Gunn and J. H. Kindsvater, *J. Phys. Chem.* **70**, 1750 (1966).

289. F. E. Saalfeld and M. V. McDowell, *Inorg. Chem.* **6**, 96 (1967).

290. F. E. Saalfeld, M. V. McDowell, A. P. Hagen, and A. G. MacDiarmid, *Inorg. Chem.* **7**, 1665 (1968).

291. F. E. Saalfeld, M. V. McDowell, S. K. Gondal, and A. G. MacDiarmid, *Inorg. Chem.* **7**, 1465 (1968).

292. S. J. Band, I. M. T. Davidson, C. A. Lambert, and I. L. Stephenson, *Chem. Commun.* **14**, 723 (1967).

293. S. Bell and A. D. Walsh, *Trans. Faraday Soc.* **62**, 3005 (1966).

CHARLES H. VAN DYKE
Carnegie-Mellon University

SILICON ETHERS AND ESTERS

Probably the oldest organic silicon compound known, the silicon orthoester, tetraethyl orthosilicate, was first prepared by Von Ebelman (1) in 1846 by the reaction of silicon tetrachloride with ethyl alcohol. This is the same reaction, incidentally, by which it is produced commercially today. Following Von Ebelman's discovery, nearly all of the known alcohols have since been reacted with silicon tetrachloride or other silicon halides, forming the corresponding esters of orthosilicic acid (2,3). These compounds have the formula $Si(OR)_4$, where the R's may be the same or different. They are often referred to as organic ethers of silicon in organic literature; for example, tetraethyl orthosilicate can be called tetraethoxysilane. This usage, as should be, is becoming more prevalent in modern chemical technology. The older terms, alkyl silicates and alkyl orthosilicates, are unfortunately still used in industry and will be briefly referred to here.

Preparation

The laboratory synthesis of alkoxy- and aryloxysilanes (alkyl and aryl silicates) can be carried out by a variety of methods and from several different raw materials. A few of these methods are indicated by the equations given below. All of these reactions occur rapidly at room temperature except equations 4 and 6.

$$SiCl_4 + 4 C_2H_5OH \rightarrow (C_2H_5O)_4Si + 4 HCl \tag{1}$$

$$SiS_2 + 4 C_2H_5OH \rightarrow (C_2H_5O)_4Si + 2 H_2S \tag{2}$$

$$SiH_4 + 4 C_2H_5OH \rightarrow (C_2H_5O)_4Si + 4 H_2 \tag{3}$$

$$Si + 4 CH_3OH \xrightarrow[\Delta]{Cu} (CH_3O)_4Si + 2 H_2 \tag{4}$$

$$SiCl_4 + 4 C_2H_5ONa \rightarrow (C_2H_5O)_4Si + 4 NaCl \tag{5}$$

$$H_4SiO_4 + 4 C_4H_9OH \xrightarrow{\Delta} (C_4H_9O)_4Si + 4 H_2O \tag{6}$$

The most common method, reacting a silicon halide with alcohol, works well with primary and secondary alcohols, but not with tertiary alcohols (2). The reaction proceeds stepwise, the first stage being endothermic and the latter exothermic.

$$SiCl_4 + ROH \rightarrow Cl_3SiOR + HCl$$

$$Cl_3SiOR + ROH \rightarrow Cl_2Si(OR)_2 + HCl$$

$$Cl_2Si(OR)_2 + ROH \rightarrow ClSi(OR)_3 + HCl$$

$$ClSi(OR)_3 + ROH \rightarrow Si(OR)_4 + HCl$$

In addition to the above, various higher alkyl and aryl derivatives can be produced from the more readily available methoxides and ethoxides by the interchange reaction between an alcohol and the silicon alkoxide (5).

$$Si(OR)_4 + 4 R'OH \rightleftharpoons Si(OR')_4 + 4 ROH$$

These reactions are normally slow, but the presence of a catalyst, such as acids or bases, and the continuous removal of the alcohol as it is formed, bring the reactions to equilibrium favoring the desired product.

The alkyl and aryl thiosilanes (orthothiosilicates) can also be prepared by the action of a silicon tetrahalide on the desired sodium mercaptide (4).

$$4 RSNa + SiCl_4 \rightarrow Si(SR)_4 + 4 NaCl$$

Alkaminosilanes are also known and are prepared via one of the following reactions:

$$SiCl_4 + 4\ LiNR_2 \rightarrow Si(NR_2)_4 + 4\ LiCl$$

$$SiCl_4 + ClMgNR_2 \rightarrow Si(NR_2)_4 + 4\ MgCl_2$$

$$SiCl_4 + RNH_2 \rightarrow ClSi(NHR)_3 + 3\ HCl$$

The last reaction does not go to completion, probably due to steric hindrance (5a).

The silicon esters of organic acids, or silicon carboxylates, are also known and are prepared by the reaction of the acid with silicon halides; ie, the reaction of silicon tetrachloride with acetic acid gives tetraacetoxysilane (silicon tetraacetate).

$$SiCl_4 + 4\ CH_3COOH \rightarrow (CH_3COO)_4Si + 4\ HCl$$

The acetate can also be prepared by the action of acetic anhydride on silicon tetrachloride.

$$SiCl_4 + 4\ (CH_3CO)_2O \rightarrow (CH_3COO)_4Si + 4\ CH_3COCl$$

The tetraacetoxysilane is a colorless crystalline product boiling at 148°C (5–6 mm). The acetoxy group also reacts with alcohols to produce silicon alkoxides and the organic acid (6). The acetates have some applications as crosslinkers in room-temperature-vulcanizing (RTV) silicones and as adhesion promoters. The chloroalkoxysilanes are interesting, but have achieved no commercial significance. They are synthesized according to the following equation (7):

$$SiCl_4 + H_2C\overset{\displaystyle O}{\overbrace{\qquad\qquad}}CH_2 \rightarrow Si(OC_2H_4Cl)_4$$

Physical and Chemical Properties

The silicon alkoxides and aryloxides are characterized by an etherlike odor, and are in general, clear, colorless liquids or colorless solids. They exhibit excellent thermal stability, particularly the aryloxy derivatives, but are generally unstable to water. The boiling points increase with molecular weight (see Table 1). They react readily with alkylating agents such as Grignard reagents, zinc alkyls, aluminum alkyls, etc, and can be used as solvents for Grignard reactions.

Table 1. Boiling Points of Silicon Alkoxides

Formula	Boiling point, °C	Formula	Boiling point, °C
$(CH_3O)_4Si$	121	$(C_4H_9O)_4Si$	275
$(C_2H_5O)_4Si$	166.5	$(C_8H_{17}O)_4Si$	204[a]
$(C_3H_7O)_4Si$	227		

[a] At a pressure of 3 mm Hg.

Production and Uses

Only two alkoxysilanes are produced commercially, although several alkyl and aryl alkoxysilanes such as methyl- and phenyltriethoxysilane, $CH_3Si(OC_2H_5)_3$, $C_6H_5Si(OC_2H_5)_3$, and dimethyldiethoxysilane, $(CH_3)_2Si(OC_2H_5)_2$, etc are produced. The latter have major applications in the silicone field (see under Silicones). Of the numerous tetraalkoxy- and aryloxysilanes investigated by, and made available to, industrial

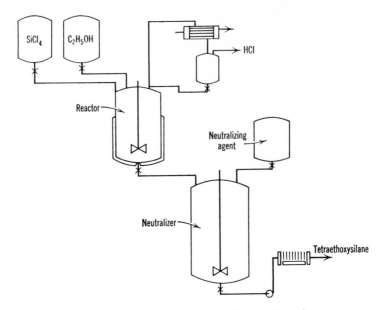

Fig. 1. Tetraethoxysilane batch production flow chart.

and governmental research and development groups since World War II, only two have made the grade as full-time industrial chemicals. These are tetraethoxysilane (ethyl silicate) and tetra(2-ethylbutoxy)silane (2-ethylbutyl silicate) plus their hydrolysis products, the alkoxysiloxanes.

Tetraethoxysilane, $(C_2H_5O)_4Si$. As mentioned previously, tetraethoxysilane ("ethyl silicate") is produced commercially by the same process that was used by its discoverer, Von Ebelman, in 1846, ie, the reaction of ethyl alcohol with silicon tetrachloride (equation 1).

As would be expected there have been many refinements of the process. These have been principally concerned with the removal of hydrogen chloride from the reaction in order to reduce hydrolysis by-products, and thus improve yields of the tetraethoxysilane. The by-product reactions are hydrogen chloride acting on the alcohol to give ethyl chloride and water; and excess silicon tetrachloride catalyzing alcohol to form ethers and water (8,9). The water which is formed can then react with nearly all of the intermediates in the reaction mass.

$$C_2H_5OH \xrightarrow{SiCl_4} C_2H_5OC_2H_5 + H_2O$$

$$C_2H_5OH + HCl \rightarrow C_2H_5Cl + H_2O$$

$$2\ H_2O + SiCl_4 \rightarrow SiO_2 + 4\ HCl$$

$$H_2O + 2\ Si(OC_2H_5)_4 \rightarrow (C_2H_5O)_3SiOSi(OC_2H_5)_3 + 2\ C_2H_5OH$$

$$H_2O + 2\ (C_2H_5O)_3SiCl \rightarrow (C_2H_5O)_3SiOSi(OC_2H_5)_3 + 2\ HCl$$

A great many methods have been proposed for continuous removal of the hydrogen chloride as it is formed. A few of the methods are (*1*) addition of amines to neutralize the HCl (10); (*2*) blowing dry nitrogen, air, or carbon dioxide through the reaction mixture (11,12); (*3*) the use of sodium alkoxides (13,14); (*4*) the use of hydrocarbon solvents and azeotroping agents (15); (*5*) applying vacuum (8,16); and (*6*) reaction in vapor phase (17). All of these methods can be used more or less successfully, depending on the product and production method.

Tetraethoxysilane is produced both by batch and continuous processes, depending upon volume (see Fig. 1).

A polymeric siloxane form of tetraethoxysilane is also marketed. This is known in the trade as ethyl silicate "40," so named because it contains 40% silicon dioxide equivalent. This is actually a polysiloxane containing an average of about five silicon atoms in the molecule. This grade is usually produced by simply using alcohol containing the necessary equivalent of water in the reaction (17). It can also be produced by the controlled hydrolysis of the tetraethoxysilane.

Three commercial grades of tetraethoxysilane are presently marketed in the U.S., pure tetraethyl orthosilicate, ethyl silicate condensed, and ethyl silicate "40." All three grades are manufactured and sold by Stauffer Chemical Company and Union Carbide Corporation. Prices in bulk quantities are quoted at $0.62/lb for the pure tetraethyl orthosilicate, $0.355/lb for the condensed ethyl silicate, and $0.47/lb for ethyl silicate "40." Production and sales are on the order of 2.5–3 million lb/yr.

These commercial ethyl silicates have two major applications in industry. They are used extensively in the nonferrous metallurgical industry as mold binders for investment casting (18) (sometimes referred to as the lost wax process) (19–21). Both the condensed and "40" grades are used in this application.

The next largest application is in corrosion-resistant coatings (22–25) primarily as a binder for zinc dust paints. Miscellaneous applications include the production of white-light bulbs (26), the preparation of soluble silicas, catalyst preparation and regeneration, and as a crosslinker and intermediate in silicones (27).

Tetra(2-ethylbutoxy)silane, $(C_6H_{13}O)_4Si$. This material, and more importantly, the disiloxane derivative, gained commercial significance late in the 1950s as high-temperature synthetic lubricants and hydraulic fluids for military application (18). The tetrasilicate was used as a machine-gun lubricant, and the disiloxane as a hydraulic fluid for type III aircraft hydraulic systems.

They are produced commercially by Union Carbide Corporation. Manufacturing processes are similar to those for the ethyl silicates, using 2-ethylbutanol and silicon tetrachloride as raw materials.

Specialty Alkoxysilanes and Siloxanes. Although the above are the only commercially produced compounds, there are many that have small specialty applications and are produced in mini-plant and pilot-plant quantities. *Tetra-n-butoxysilane,* $(C_4H_9O)_4Si$, is used in making sealants for the aircraft industry.

Tetrakis(2-methoxyetoxy)silane (2-methoxyethyl silicate), $(CH_3OC_2H_4O)_4Si$, has the advantages of a high flash point plus hydrolysis rates equal to those of the ethyl silicates, and thus finds use in high-temperature and corrosion-resistant coatings.

Tetracyclohexoxysilane (cyclohexyl silicate), $(C_6H_{11}O)_4Si$, is a waxlike product which blends well with organic waxes and silicones for improved water repellency, oil retention, etc, and has application in fish fly treatments, specialty waxes, mold releases, etc.

Diisopropoxydiacetoxysilane, $(iso-C_3H_7O)_2Si(OOCCH_3)_2$, is an excellent coupling agent for certain elastomers and also is an adhesion promoter for coatings.

Triethoxysilane, $(C_2H_5O)_3SiH$, can act as a blowing agent by liberating hydrogen in the presence of weak bases. Use is made of this in making certain foamed silicas. It is also used as an intermediate for silicone products such as aminopropyltriethoxysilane, which finds application as a glass sizing agent. Triethoxysilane is produced by and used internally by the silicone producers. All of the above compounds are produced by the Anderson Development Company.

Physiological Properties

Unlike the silicones, which are noted for their physiological inertness, the alkoxysilanes, particularly those with short-chain alkyl groups, have some toxic properties. Tetraethoxysilane is readily absorbed with resultant hemolytic effect similar to ether and chloroform (28). Inhalation of air containing 9–20 mg/l is fatal to experimental animals. However, at lower concentrations no silicosis or similar effects due to silica content have been found (29). A peculiarity of tetramethoxysilane, and standing completely alone in this respect, is its effect on the eye. Sporadic reports that it causes severe irritation and even ulceration of the cornea have been noted.

Similar experience by the author with four workers who were exposed in April 1959 revealed (via slit microscopy, carried out the first day after exposure) that the epithelium had a superficial granular type of "cast" to it and that there were fine lipoidlike particles in the superficial stroma. There was a definite edema of the corneal stroma, and in one case, necrosis of the epithelium and the development of a corneal ulcer. All cases responded to treatment and there was no permanent damage resulting. This experience led to an investigation of the effects of various alkyl and higher alkoxymethoxysilanes on the eyes of rabbits (30). This work revealed that the substitution of one alkyl group for a methoxy group in tetramethoxysilane (ie, methyltrimethoxysilane) significantly reduced or eliminated this effect on the eye. A similar effect was noted when two higher alkoxy groups were introduced into tetramethoxysilane (ie, diethoxydimethoxysilane).

Bibliography

"Silicon Esters and Ethers" treated under "Silicon Compounds" in *ECT* 1st ed., Vol. 12, pp. 371–372, by E. G. Rochow, Harvard University.

1. J. Von Ebelman, *Ann. Chem.* **57**, 319 (1845).
2. J. R. Wright, R. O. Bolt, A. Goldschmidt, and A. D. Abbott, *J. Am. Chem. Soc.* **80**, 1733 (1958).
3. H. W. Post, *The Chemistry of the Orthoesters*, Reinhold Publishing Corp., New York, 1943, p. 120.
4. H. Bacher and F. Stienstra, *Rec. Trav. Chim.* **54**, 38 (1935).
5a. H. Breederweld and H. I. Waterman, *Res. Correspondence* **6**, 48s (1953).
5. Ger. Pat. 285,285, (Nov. 22, 1914), L. Knorr and W. Weyland.
6. B. N. Bolgov, V. P. Davydova, and M. G. Voronkov, *J. Gen. Chem.* **27**, 1593 (1957).
7. U.S. Pat. 2,381,138 (Aug. 7, 1945), W. I. Patnode and R. O. Sauer (to General Electric Co.).
8. R. E. Gessner, R. L. Schank, and C. F. Schubert, *Proc. West Va. Acad. Sci.* **33**, 62 (1961).
9. A. P. Kreshkov and G. D. Nesronova, *Zh. Obshch. Khim.* **19**, 660 (1949).
10. C. Miner and L. Bryan, *Ind. Eng. Chem.* **39**, 1385 (1947).
11. W. C. Schumb and D. F. Holloway, *J. Am. Chem. Soc.* **63**, 2753 (1941).
12. O. Peppard, W. Brown, and W. Johnson, *J. Am. Chem. Soc.* **68**, 70 (1946).
13. A. Ladenburg, *Ann. Chem.* **173**, 151 (1874).
14. B. Helferich and J. Hausen, *Chem. Ber.* **57**, 759 (1924).
15. M. Kalinin, *Compt. Rend. Acad. Sci. URSS* **18**, 433 (1938).
16. U.S. Pat. 3,008,975 (June 24, 1958), C. F. Schubert (to Union Carbide Corp.).
17. H. G. Emblem, K. Hargreaves, and N. A. Hurt, *Ind. Chemist* **39**, 576 (Nov. 1963).
18. A. R. Anderson, *Chem. Week* **87**, 55 (Sept. 17, 1960).
19. A. Dunlop, *Foundry Trade J.* **75**, 107 (1945).
20. A. E. Focke, *Metal Progr.* **49**, 489 (1945).

21. J. W. Glaser, *Iron Age* **157**, 52 (1945).
22. U.S. Pat. 1,809,755 (June 9, 1931), G. King and R. T. Welfall.
23. U.S. Pat. 2,524,357 (Oct. 3, 1950), P. Robey (to Socony-Vacuum Oil Co.).
24. U.S. Pat. 3,056,684 (Oct. 2, 1962), S. L. Lopata and W. E. Keithler (to Carboline Co.).
25. U.S. Pat. 2,450,327 (Sept. 28, 1948), H. D. Cogan (to Carbide and Carbon Chemicals Corp.).
26. U.S. Pat. 2,545,896 (March 20, 1951), M. Pipkin (to General Electric Co.).
27. U.S. Pat. 2,485,928 (Oct. 25, 1949), P. C. Servais (to Dow Chemical Co.).
28. Kasper, McCord, and Fredrick, *Ind. Med.* **6**, 660–664 (1937).
29. Holzapfel, *Z. Ver. Deut. Ingr.* **87**, 605 (1943).
30. Unpublished work by C. Benz at Adrian, Mich., J. R. Walter of University of Michigan Medical School, and C. G. Neuroth of Anderson Chemical Co.

A. R. ANDERSON
Anderson Development Company

SILICONES

The name "silicone" denotes a polymer,

$$(R_nSiO_{(4-n)/2})_m$$

where n is between 0 and 3 and m is 2 or larger. It contains a repeating silicon–oxygen backbone and has organic groups, R, attached to a significant proportion of the silicon atoms by silicon–carbon bonds. From the gray area surrounding this definition we have chosen to include in this discussion some industrially important or interesting copolymers with organic and inorganic components and to exclude polysilicate esters and organosilicon polymers without industrial importance. Some word is needed to describe the family of commercial products based on these polymers, and "silicone" fills that need very well. It has no place in scientific nomenclature, although it was originally introduced, before polymers were understood, under the supposition that compounds of the empirical formula R_1R_2SiO were analogous to ketones (1). Only much later was it used to cover related polymers (2). In commercial silicones most of the R groups are methyl; longer alkyl, fluoroalkyl, phenyl, vinyl, and a few others are substituted for specific purposes. Some of the R groups in the polymer may also be hydrogen, chlorine, alkoxy, acyloxy, or alkylamino, etc. These polymers are combined with fillers, additives, and solvents to make products that are still loosely classed as silicones.

The methyl silicones, which for both economic and technical reasons dominate the commercial situation, have an unusual combination of properties. They were chosen for investigation and development because they are stable and inert, but in addition they turned out to have low surface tension, to be water-repellent and generally incompatible with organic materials, and to be nonconductors of electricity, Also, their properties change less on going to either high or low temperatures than do those of most materials. They are useful because of their stability in unfavorable environments, or because of their flexibility at low temperatures, or because of their surface properties, or for some combination of such characteristics.

Scientific interest in silicones can be traced back to the nineteenth century (3) but industrial interest did not begin until the early 1930s. In the United States the Corning Glass Works pioneered in work on organosilicon polymers, both in their own laboratories and at the Mellon Institute. Their objective was to develop resins both as varnishes and as partners for glass fiber in high-temperature electrical insulation. In the same period the General Electric Company had similar interests, but first chose to work with silicate esters. Somewhat later Union Carbide Corporation began a program on organometallic research which included organosilicon chemistry. In Russia work on organosilicon chemistry began in the early 1930s and led to silicone resins in that decade. Expansion to pilot-plant production by Corning and General Electric was followed by the formation of Dow Corning in 1943, a joint effort by Corning and Dow Chemical Company. In the United States military uses dominated early product development. Silicone fluids were used for damping in aircraft instruments, for antifoams in petroleum oils, and for making greases used as ignition sealing compounds. Silicone resins were used as components of insulation for motors. Silicone rubber was used for making gaskets for searchlights and turbosuperchargers. After the war civilian uses followed these patterns but expanded gradually to include release agents for molding rubber; water repellents for textiles, paper, and masonry; and ingredients for paints, lubricants, and automobile and furniture polishes.

There were the following four basic manufacturers of silicones in the United States in 1968: Dow Corning, General Electric Company, Union Carbide, and Stauffer Chemical. There are also major producers in Great Britain, France, Germany (East and West), Japan, and Russia, and smaller manufacturers in Belgium, Italy, Czechoslovakia, and elsewhere. Production and consumption of silicone resins and rubbers in the United States is estimated annually (4), and in 1966 the production estimates were 4514 and 6696 tons, respectively. The third major class of product, the fluids, is of comparable size. There is no reliable way to estimate the total world production, but the general range of estimates for 1966 was about 30–40 thousand tons.

Average prices per lb in 1966 were estimated (4) to be \$3.66 for rubber and \$1.90 for resins. The price of dimethyl silicone fluid in the United States was \$6.80 in 1942, \$3.80 in 1952 (3), and had dropped to \$1.55 in 1968.

Nomenclature. Polymer nomenclature is inherently complex and difficult to use, and as a result that of silicones was very early simplified by the use of the letters M, D, T, and Q to represent monofunctional, difunctional, trifunctional, and quadrifunctional monomer units (5). Primes, eg D′, are used to indicate substituents other than methyl. This notation, plus Me for methyl, Ph for phenyl, and Vi for vinyl, is used here. Equivalent symbols are shown in Table 1.

Obviously the primes must be specifically identified in the context. Proper nomenclature follows IUPAC rules (6,7), but, again, in the written or spoken language of the industry it is much more common, for example, to hear "methyl tetramer" or simply "tetramer," than the proper "octamethylcyclotetrasiloxane." Table 2 shows the various ways of identifying siloxanes.

Once the meaning of the primes (see Tables 1 and 2) is defined, the MDTQ nomenclature can identify polysiloxanes with as little ambiguity as the more conventional

Table 1. Formulas and Symbols for Silicones

Formula	Equivalent formula	Symbol
$(CH_3)_3SiO_{0.5}$	$Me_3SiO_{0.5}$	M
$(CH_3)_2SiO$	Me_2SiO	D
$CH_3SiO_{1.5}$	$MeSiO_{1.5}$	T
$CH_3(C_6H_5)SiO$	$MePhSiO$	D′
$(C_6H_5)_2SiO$	Ph_2SiO	D′
$(CH_3)HSiO$	$MeHSiO$	D′
SiO_2	SiO_2	Q

Table 2. Identification of Siloxanes

Structural formula[a]	MDT formula	Systematic name[b]	Common usage
Me$_3$SiOSiMe$_3$	MM	hexamethyldisiloxane	mono
Me$_3$SiOSiMe$_2$OSiMe$_3$	MDM	octamethyltrisiloxane	
Me$_3$SiO(SiMe$_2$O)$_2$SiMe$_3$	MD$_2$M	decamethyltetrasiloxane	
Me$_2$Si—O—Si—Me$_2$ $\qquad$ $\mid\qquad\mid$ $\qquad$ O $\quad$ O $\qquad$ $\mid\qquad\mid$ Me$_2$Si—O—SiMe$_2$	D$_4$	octamethylcyclotetra-siloxane	methyl tetramer
Ph$_2$Si—O—Si—Ph$_2$ $\qquad$ $\mid\qquad\mid$ $\qquad$ O $\quad$ O $\qquad$ $\mid\qquad\mid$ Ph$_2$Si—O—Si—Ph$_2$	D$'_4$	octaphenylcyclotetra-siloxane	phenyl-tetramer
MePhSi—O—Si—MePh $\qquad$ $\mid\qquad\mid$ $\qquad$ O $\quad$ O $\qquad$ $\mid\qquad\mid$ MePhSi—O—Si—MePh	D$'_4$	1,3,5,7 tetramethyl-1,3,5,7-tetraphenyl-cyclotetrasiloxane	methylphenyl-tetramer
(Me$_3$SiO)$_3$SiMe	M$_3$T	1,1,1,3,5,5,5-heptamethyl-3-trimethylsiloxy-trisiloxane	
Me$_3$SiOSiHMeOSiMe$_3$	MD$'$M	1,1,1,3,5,5,5-heptamethyl-trisiloxane	
Me$_2$PhSiOSiMePhOSiPhMe$_2$	M$'$D$'$M$'$	1,1,3,5,5-pentamethyl-1,3,5-triphenyltrisiloxane	

^{a} Abbreviated.　　　　^{b} IUPAC.

systems. For example, Me$_3$Si—O—SiMe$_2$—O—SiPh—(OSiMe$_3$)$_2$ becomes MDT$'$M$_2$, where T$'$, in this case, is C$_6$H$_5$SiO$_{1.5}$.

Chemical Properties

The two kinds of bonds most characteristic of silicones are those of silicon to oxygen and silicon to carbon. The nature of the SiO bond is influenced by the electropositive character of silicon (1.7 in Pauling's scale of electronegativities) and by the availability of the vacant d orbitals in silicon for dative bonding. The SiO bond is about 50% ionic, with silicon the positive member. It has a high heat of formation (108 Kcal/mole) and is very resistant to homolytic cleavage. But it is susceptible to heterolytic cleavage, ie, to attack by acids and bases. In this respect the SiO—SiO backbone of silicones is very different from the C—C—C—C backbone of hydrocarbon polymers. The oxygen atom, with two electrons involved in ($p \rightarrow d$) π dative bonds with the silicon, is less basic than that in ethers, and the hydrogen in the SiOH group is more acidic than in COH (7a).

The SiC bond is slightly ionic (12% on the basis of Pauling's electronegativity), again with silicon positive. The heat of formation is about 76–85 kcal/mole, almost as great as for the CC— bond. It may or may not be susceptible to heterolytic cleavage, depending upon the substituents on the carbon. Chloromethyl, cyanomethyl, or even phenyl groups are more easily cleaved from silicon by water, acids, or bases than methyl groups are .

The siloxane bond flexes and rotates fairly freely about the SiO axis, especially with small substituents, such as methyl, on the silicon atoms (8). Rotation is also free about the SiC axis in methylsilicon compounds. As a result of the freedom of motion, intermolecular distances between methylsiloxane chains are greater than is the case with hydrocarbons, and intermolecular forces are smaller (9).

Polysiloxanes are formed by the condensation of silanols. This is a reversible reaction, and is catalyzed by acids or bases:

$$2 \equiv\!\text{SiOH} \leftrightarrows \equiv\!\text{SiOSi}\!\equiv + \text{H}_2\text{O}$$

Equilibrium generally lies far to the right, and this is especially true of methylsilicon compounds. Thus, in the hydrolysis of dimethyldichlorosilane the silanols initially formed react very rapidly to yield mixtures of linear and cyclic polysiloxanes. Hydrochloric acid by-product hastens this process:

$$\text{Me}_2\text{SiCl}_2 + \text{H}_2\text{O} \rightarrow \begin{array}{ll} \text{Me}_2\text{Si(OH)}_2 & \text{dimethylsilanediol} \\ \downarrow & \\ \text{HO(Me}_2\text{SiO)}_n\text{H} & \text{linear polymers} \\ \text{(Me}_2\text{SiO)}_n & \text{cyclic polymers} \end{array}$$

Compounds of the type $\text{Me}_2\text{Si}\!=\!\text{O}$ are not formed because silicon does not form double bonds with any element.

It is not true in all cases that hydrolysis or condensation occur this readily. For example, the reaction $\text{Ph}_2\text{SiCl}_2 + \text{H}_2\text{O} \rightarrow \text{Ph}_2\text{Si(OH)}_2 + 2\text{HCl}$ is easily arrested at the monomer diol stage, and conversion to polymers, such as the cyclic $(\text{Ph}_2\text{SiO})_4$, occurs only slowly, and in the presence of active catalysts.

Very important to the manufacture of silicone fluids and elastomers are the siloxane rearrangement reactions which occur in the presence of acids or bases. An example is the reaction of hexamethyldisiloxane with octamethylcyclotetrasiloxane in the presence of sulfuric acid, which gives a mixture of linear and cyclic polymers (10).

$$\text{MM} + \text{D}_4 \xrightleftharpoons{\text{H}_2\text{SO}_4} \text{MD}_n\text{M} + \text{D}_m$$

This reaction involves numerous equilibria. It has been shown that in the equilibrium $\text{MD}_x\text{M} + \text{MD}_y\text{M} \leftrightarrows \text{MD}_{x-w}\text{M} + \text{MD}_{y+w}\text{M}$ the equilibrium constant is close to the theoretical value of unity, and in the equilibrium $\text{MD}_x\text{M} \leftrightarrows \text{MD}_{x-w}\text{M} + \text{D}_w$ the constant is 11×0.4^w where w is 4 or larger (ie, no cyclic smaller than D_4 was observed). Since the cyclic trimer is known, its small concentration in this system is believed to be due to ring strain, which causes it to be very reactive (11). In a solvent, such as carbon tetrachloride, the ratio of cyclics to linears increased, and the ratio of low-molecular-weight linears to high-molecular-weight linears also increased. As the ratio of M to D increased, the proportion of cyclics decreased (12).

Other acids can be used, for example, hydrogen chloride, or Lewis-type acids or sulfuric acid on Fuller's earth. Ferric chloride and HCl act in conjunction, as if the catalyst were HFeCl_4 (13).

Acids attack the more strongly basic M unit more rapidly than they do the D unit, but the strained trimer ring most rapidly of all. The order of reactivity is

$$\text{D}_3 > \text{MM} > \text{MDM} > \text{MD}_2\text{M} > \text{D}_4$$

Bases, on the other hand, attack the D unit more rapidly, and the order of decreasing reactivity is

$$\text{D}_3 > \text{D}_4 > \text{MD}_2\text{M} > \text{MDM} > \text{MM}$$

In the base-catalyzed polymerization of octamethylcyclotetrasiloxane, equilibria analogous to those described above have been observed. When M is absent or very low the equilibrium mixture contains about 85% linears and 15% cyclics. The cyclics form a continuous population at least to D_{400}, and those larger than D_{12} make up 2–3% of the total polymer in silicone oils and gums. Tetramer is the major cyclic component (14). The distribution of linears is random as in the case of acid catalysis.

The rate of alkali-catalyzed polymerization is proportional to the concentration of the cyclic siloxane and to the square root of the concentration of alkali (15,16). Activity of the group 1 hydroxides as catalysts increases from lithium to cesium. It is affected by solvents and Lewis-base solvents, such as dimethyl sulfoxide, tetrahydrofuran, and hexamethylphosphoramide increase the rate of reaction. Various substances have been reported to retard the polymerization of tetramer by potassium hydroxide, such as anisole, diphenylamine, and sodium and lithium hydroxide (17). Retardation by alkalis is surprising but has been corroborated. Hypotheses to explain this observation are speculative and the reactions require further study before they can be understood.

Methyl-3,3,3,-trifluoro-n-propylsiloxane trimer, $[(CH_3)(CF_3CH_2CH_2)SiO]_3$, reacts rapidly in the presence of NaOH at 150°C to give linear polymer, which rapidly depolymerizes under these conditions to give the cyclic tetramer. At equilibrium the polymer is made up of 86% cyclics and 14% linears (18). Therefore, to make high polymer, reaction of the trimer must be stopped at the proper time. Special catalysts, such as the sodium derivative of sodium acetate, $NaCH_2COO$ Na, have been reported to facilitate this operation.

Copolymerization is important because many fluids and most gums are copolymers containing groups such as methylvinyl-, methylphenyl-, or diphenylsiloxane units. These do not react at the same rate as dimethylsiloxane, and copolymerization involves reactivity ratios analogous to the Mayo-Lewis ratios (19) developed for vinyl monomers. (See Vinyl compounds and polymers.) In the copolymerization of octaphenylcyclotetrasiloxane and octamethylcyclotetrasiloxane, the phenyl tetramer polymerizes first (20) and then suppresses the rate of polymerization of the methyl siloxane.

Polymerization of dimethyl silicone cyclics with base catalysts proceeds as outlined above to produce linear polymers by an anionic mechanism (15):

$$(Me_2SiO)_4 + KOH \leftrightarrows HO(Me_2SiO)_4^- + K^+$$

$$HO(Me_2SiO)_4^- + (Me_2SiO)_4 \leftrightarrows HO(Me_2SiO)_8^-$$

If the concentration of chain-stopper, including KOH, is small, polymers with thousands of tetramer units are produced. Since this is a reversible process, depolymerization can occur in the presence of the same catalyst.

In addition to these important reactions of silanols and siloxanes, several other reactions are important in the manufacture and use of commercial silicones. Compounds containing SiH are especially interesting. The SiH bond is only slightly ionic (according to the Pauling values) and it has fairly high energy (76 kcal/mole). But it is easily solvolyzed by water or alcohols, easily oxidized, and, under the influence of catalysts, can be added across C—C multiple bonds to form SiC bonds. Siloxanes containing SiH can be crosslinked or modified by such reactions.

Alkoxy and acyloxy groups attached to silicon are susceptible to hydrolysis, but the rates vary widely depending upon the number, size, and nature of the alkyl, aryl, or acyl groups on the silicon or oxygen. Bonds between silicon and negative elements, such as nitrogen or chlorine, are also easily hydrolyzed. The silicon–nitrogen bond is thermally stable (77 kcal/mole) and polymers based on the silicon–nitrogen backbone have been made (21).

CHARACTERISTICS OF POLYSILOXANES

Dimethyl Silicones. Linear polydimethylsiloxanes, dimethyl silicones, have been extensively studied. The SiOSiO backbone has a zigzag form, with rotation occurring freely about both the SiO and SiC axes. Because intermolecular forces are weak, the polymers have low melting points and second-order transition temperatures. For dimethyl silicone rubber polymers these are -60 and $-123°F$, respectively. They are, therefore, noncrystallizing polymers under ordinary conditions. The low intermolecular forces also lead to low boiling points, low activation energy for viscous flow, high compressibility, small change of viscosity with temperature, and general physical weakness despite high molecular weights. There are reasons for believing that these polymers prefer to assume a helical structure with about 6 or 7 siloxane units per turn (22). This helical type of structure is unusual for bulk-liquid polymers without strong intermolecular attractions, such as hydrogen bonds (23); there is not complete agreement on this subject (7,24).

Volatile oligomers, such as MDM and D_4, in the products of equilibration of MM and D_4 can be separated and purified by fractional distillation. Study of their properties shows the effects of molecular size and structure in these systems. The technique has been extended to include related oligomers, such as M_4Q and TM_3. The mixture of D and MD oligomers is useful principally in the manufacture of gums and fluids, and the compounds are ordinarily not separated and used as silicone fluids. Properties of some of these compounds are shown in Table 3.

Table 3. Properties of MD_nM and D_n

Symbol	Melting point, °C	Boiling point, °C	Density, d^{20}	Refractive index, n_D^{20}	Viscosity, η, at 25°C, cSt	Flash point, °F
MM	-67	99.5	0.7636	1.3774	0.65	15
MDM	-80	153	0.8200	1.3840	1.04	98
MD_2M	-76	194	0.8536	1.3895	1.53	158
MD_3M	-80	229	0.8755	1.3925	2.06	202
MD_4M	-59	245	0.8910	1.3948	2.63	245
MD_5M	-78	270	0.9012	1.3965	3.24	272
MD_6M	-63	290	0.9099	1.3970	3.88	292
MD_7M		307.5	0.9180	1.3980	4.58	318
D_3	64.5	134				
D_4	17.5	175.8	0.9561	1.3968	2.30	156
D_5	-44	210	0.9593	1.3982	3.87	
D_6	-3	245	0.9672	1.4015	6.62	
D_7	-32	154^a	0.9730	1.4040	9.47	
D_8	31.5	290	1.1770^b	1.4060	13.23	

^{a} At 20 mm Hg. ^{b} Crystals.

In higher linear dimethyl silicone polymers the number-average molecular weight is related to the bulk viscosity by the relationship log (viscosity in cSt at 25°C) equals $(1.00 + 0.0123 M_n^{0.5})$ where $M_n > 2500$. The intrinsic viscosity, $[\eta]$, arrived at by the extrapolation of the viscosity to zero concentration, ie $[\ln \eta_r/c]_{c=0}$, has the following values in toluene and methyl ethyl ketone, respectively (25,26):

$$[\eta] = 2 \times 10^{-4} M_n^{0.66} \quad \text{and} \quad [\eta] = 8 \times 10^{-4} M_n^{0.5}$$

Branched polymers can be made by introduction of T or Q units (see Table 1), or by irradiation of linear polymers. For polymers of the same average molecular weight, branched molecules have lower bulk or intrinsic viscosities than linear molecules. Even a small amount of branching causes considerable decrease in the bulk viscosity (27).

Network silicone polymers may also be obtained from condensation of mixtures containing larger proportions of T and Q units, or by crosslinking chains of D units. Silicone resins are in the first class, while silicone rubber is in the second. In condensing mixtures of T and D units to make resins, however, much of the potential crosslinking is consumed in making cyclic polymers. A silicone resin is pictured not as a complex network but as knots of T-D polymers connected by chains of D polymers.

Effects of Substitution on Properties. If some of the methyl groups are replaced by longer alkyl chains, the unique properties of the methyl silicones are lost. The activation energy for viscous flow, E_{visc}, and the rates of change of viscosity with temperature and pressure increase (22). Oxidative stability decreases (see below under Changes in properties with time, p. 250). On the other hand, compatibility with organic compounds becomes greater, and lubricity improves (28).

Phenyl substitution in fluids and elastomers, which may be made either as methyl phenyl or diphenyl silicone, has some of the same effects as increasing the size of the alkyl group, but increases rather than decreases thermal or oxidative stability. Introduction of about 7.5 mole % methylphenylsiloxane into the dimethylsiloxane polymer lowers the stiffening temperature from -40 to $-112°C$ (29). This is believed to be due to interference of the bulky groups with crystallization of the methyl polymer. E_{visc} for MD'M (D' Ph$_2$SiO) is 4553 cal compared to 2446 cal for MDM, showing how the bulky phenyl groups interfere with motion.

Chlorinated phenyl groups, such as tetrachlorophenylsiloxy copolymerized into dimethyl silicone fluids, increase lubricity. In the case of MD''M polymers, where D'' is (chlorophenyl)methylsiloxane, the change is a function of the number of chlorine atoms per phenyl and of the proportion of such groups in the copolymers (30).

Vinyl groups are used in elastomers to provide reactive centers for peroxide and silane–olefin type cures (see below, p. 229). They are added either as chain-stopper or as chain-extender. The latter provides for crosslinks along the chain, while the terminal vinyl groups act to minimize the formation of useless dangling chain ends. Vinyl constituents are not added in concentrations high enough to affect physical properties of the uncured polymers.

Methyl-3,3,3-trifluoro-n-propyl silicone $[(CH_3)(CF_3CH_2CH_2)SiO]_3$, has a solubility parameter of about 9.5 (31) compared to about 7.5 for Me$_2$SiO. Solubility parameter is the square root of cohesive energy density, a measure of intermolecular forces. This siloxane may swell much less than Me$_2$SiO in octane or toluene. It also has improved lubricity (32,33) and greatly increased change of viscosity with temperature. 2-Cyanoethyl and 3-cyanopropyl substituents give copolymers with a solubility parameter of about 9.0–9.5, which is similar to that of fluoro silicone.

Polyethers have been introduced as substituents by various methods (34,35). The copolymers are in general water-soluble, and have higher viscosity-temperature coefficients, and better load-carrying capacity as lubricants than Me$_2$SiO polymers.

They are of practical interest because of the effect they have on polyurethan foams (see under Commercial silicones, p. 232).

Incorporation of SiH-containing monomer units, particularly $(CH_3)HSiO$, changes the physical properties of fluids, but the most important change is the increase in reactivity (see below, pp. 230, 241). Water repellency remains good and ability to cross-link readily increases the usefulness of the polymer in textile treatment.

Physical properties of several oligomers with various substituents are shown in Table 4. A great many such oligomeric compounds have been prepared and described (36,37), and several are employed industrially as intermediates in the preparation of polymers.

Table 4. Properties of Siloxane Oligomers

Formula	Boiling point at mm Hg, °C	Density, d^{20}	Refractive index, n_D^{20}	Melting point, °C
$(Ph_2SiO)_4$	335_1			200
$(CH_3PhSiO)_4$	$237_{1.5}$	1.183	1.5461	99
$CH_3SiOSiPh_2OSiCH_3$	172_{18}	0.984	1.4927	
$[(CF_3CH_2CH_2)CH_3SiO]_4$	134_3	1.255	1.3724	
$[(CH_2{=}CH)(CH_3)SiO]_4$	111_{10}	0.9875	1.4342	-43.5
$(CH_3)_3Si[OSi(CH_3)H]_2OSi(CH_3)_3$	177	0.8559	1.3854	
$(CH_3HSiO)_4$	134	0.9912	1.3870	-69

Silicone Rubber. See also Vol. 7, p. 698. To convert silicone elastomer gum—a viscous (10–30 million cSt) fluid—into a rubber, it must be crosslinked, and to make the rubber strong it must be reinforced, because the tensile strength of cured dimethyl silicone rubber gum is only about 50 psi. See also Rubber compounding.

An alternate approach to the use of reinforcing fillers is that of putting crystallizing segments into the polymer. For example, block polymers containing "silphenylene" segments, $+Me_2SiC_6H_4SiMe_2O+$, may have gum tensile strengths of 1000–2700 psi (38). The usual method of increasing strength, however, is to add reinforcing fillers, and the usual reinforcing agents for silicone rubber are finely divided silicas made by either the fume process or the wet process. Fume-process silicas, such as Cab-O-Sil (Godfrey L. Cabot Div. of Cabot Corp.) give the highest degree of reinforcement of silicone rubber. Wet-process silicas or aerogels, such as Santocel (Monsanto Chemical Co.) are also used. See Amorphous silica under Silica.

The silica filler used must be of small particle size to be a good reinforcing agent. It should have a diameter about the length of a fully extended polymer chain (1 μ) to be semireinforcing, and 0.01–0.05 μ to be highly reinforcing. Fine particle size does not necessarily lead to good reinforcement, because finely divided fillers tend to agglomerate and are extremely hard to disperse. This tendency can be countered by treating the filler to give it an organic or a silicone coating before mixing it with gum. Such treatment reduces agglomeration and prevents premature crepe hardening.

Where physical strength is not required of the finished product, nonreinforcing fillers are used. They may stabilize the product, as in the case of iron oxide or titanium dioxide, or color it, or simply lower the cost per unit volume. Carbon black can be used to make the product conduct electricity.

Silicone rubber can be cured by heating the reinforced polymer with a free-radical generator, such as benzoyl peroxide. In the case of dimethyl silicone elastomers the predominant mechanism appears to be one in which hydrogen is abstracted from methyl groups and the resulting free radicals couple to form $Si-CH_2CH_2-Si$ bridges, as follows:

$$(C_6H_5COO)_2 \rightarrow 2\,C_6H_5COO\cdot$$

$$C_6H_5COO\cdot + (CH_3)_2SiO \rightarrow \cdot CH_2(CH_3)SiO + C_6H_5COOH$$

$$2\cdot CH_2(CH_3)SiO \rightarrow -O(CH_3)\underset{|}{Si}-CH_2CH_2-\underset{|}{Si}(CH_3)O-$$

When the polymer contains vinyl groups, the peroxide radical fragment adds to the double bond to give a radical which couples, as illustrated by the following equation:

$$C_6H_5COO\cdot + CH_2{=}CH\underset{|}{Si}(CH_3) \rightarrow \underset{\underset{OOCC_6H_5}{|}}{CH_2}{-}\underset{|}{\dot{C}H}{-}\underset{|}{Si}(CH_3) \rightarrow \begin{array}{l} -\underset{|}{O}\\ -\underset{|}{Si}(CH_3)\\ CH{-}CH_2OOCC_6H_5\\ |\\ CH{-}CH_2OOCC_6H_5\\ |\\ -O\underset{|}{Si}(CH_3) \end{array}$$

There are three differences of practical importance. The vinyl-based cure (1) does not generate a benzoic acid by-product, which can catalyze decomposition or rearrangement of the siloxane polymer; (2) it functions with less peroxide and (3) works with types of peroxides that do not abstract hydrogen from methyl groups, such as 2,5-dimethyl-2,5-di(t-butylperoxy) hexane.

Several peroxides are used commercially to catalyze these reactions. One of the most common of these is benzoyl peroxide. About 1.5–2% is used for nonvinyl gums and about 1% for vinyl gums (based on weight of gum). Curing temperature is about 120°C. Bis(2,4-dichlorobenzoyl) peroxide, 2,5-dimethyl-2,5-di(t-butylperoxy)hexane, t-butyl peroxybenzoate, and dicumyl peroxide are also commonly used to obtain special effects (see Peroxides and peroxy compounds, organic). For example, bis(2,4-dichlorobenzoyl) peroxide permits rapid cure in air at 600°F without the development of porosity which would be caused by the volatilization of lower-boiling catalysts.

Cure is also brought about by γ or high-energy-electron radiation, which causes scission of all types of bonds, including SiO, but the reactions important to cure are those involving SiC and CH. Hydrogen, methane, and ethane are evolved, and bridges between chains are formed by recombination of the radicals generated. These bridges are $Si-CH_2-Si$ and $Si-Si$ and perhaps $Si-CH_2CH_2-Si$ (39). An absorbed dose of 3–5 million roentgens is required to obtain an effective cure. This type of cure leaves no acidic fragments in the polymer. γ Radiation effects cures of thick sections, but high-energy electrons penetrate only a few mm of the compound (40).

The addition of SiH to $SiCH{=}CH_2$ in the presence of platinum, chloroplatinic acid, or other metallic catalysts, can also be used to cure silicone rubber or encapsulating resin (41). This reaction creates $Si-CH_2CH_2-Si$ bridges between polymer chains. Cure occurs slowly (days) at room temperature, but is generally run at somewhat higher temperatures (50–100°C). Control of the environment is important because the catalyst can be poisoned, and because water or alcohols can react with SiH in the presence of these catalysts, as shown by the following equation:

$$\equiv SiH + H_2O \xrightarrow{\text{catalyst}} \equiv SiOH + H_2$$

Several routes to room-temperature cure of silicone rubber are used in practice, and each has its advantages. Reaction of SiOH with SiH generates crosslinking SiOSi bonds and hydrogen as a by-product, which can be used to produce foamed rubber or resin. Reaction of SiOH with SiOR evolves the alcohol ROH, for example ethanol. This occurs at room temperature after the addition of a catalyst (42). The rate of cure depends upon the catalyst used, the concentration of catalyst, and the temperature. Reaction of SiOH with an acetoxysilane, and reaction of the resulting polymer with atmospheric moisture, provides another method (43,44), which is reported to proceed in the following steps (45):

$$HO(SiMe_2O)_nH + MeSi(OAc)_3 \rightarrow (AcO)_2SiMe(OSiMe_2)_nOSiMe(OAc)_2 + 2\ HOAc$$

$$\equiv SiOAc + H_2O \rightarrow \equiv SiOH + HOAc$$

$$\equiv SiOAc + \equiv SiOH \rightarrow \equiv SiOSi\equiv + HOAc$$

Cure is hastened by use of catalysts (46) in two-part as well as one-part RTV (room temperature vulcanizing) systems. Many hydrolyzable groups other than acetoxy have been suggested for this type of cure. For example, the ketoxime group is of interest because the product of hydrolysis is not acidic (47).

$$2 \equiv Si{-}ONC(CH_3)(C_2H_5) \xrightarrow{H_2O} \equiv SiOSi\equiv + 2\ HONC(CH_3)(C_2H_5)$$

Still another approach involves methoxysiloxanes, catalyzed by titanium chelates, to bring about rapid reaction with atmospheric moisture (48).

Despite the commercial importance of the products using RTV systems, little has been published concerning the chemistry of the processes. It has been shown that in the RTV system involving silanols and ethyl silicate (a) ethanol is evolved and siloxanes are formed; (b) the reaction does not take place in the absence of an initiator (tin compound); and (c) the latter reacts with ethyl silicate to form SiOSn compounds (49). The other types effect the cure by relatively straightforward hydrolysis and condensation reactions, or by silane–olefin additions.

Silicone Resins. Reinforcing fillers do not perform the same function in resins as they do in rubbers. Particulate reinforcing agents are not as widely used, for they do not lead to a product of higher tensile strength. They are used to fill and harden some molding compounds. Random fibers or woven cloth (usually glass) are used to increase physical strength. Mica plates are used to increase electric strength and resistivity.

In distinction to the cure of rubber, the cure of silicone resins and many RTV silicone elastomers occurs entirely through the formation of siloxane linkages by condensation of silanols. In resins this is a continuation of the overall condensation process by which the resin is prepared. As condensation continues in the system, the rate decreases, owing to diminishing silanol concentration, increasing steric hindrance, and decreasing mobility. For final cure, therefore, the reaction must be speeded up by heat and catalysts. Even so, some silanols remain, and slow cure continues for the life of the resin. The reaction is reversible, and water must be removed from the system to permit a high degree of cure.

Many substances catalyze silanol condensation, including acids, bases (50), soluble organic salts of lead, cobalt, tin, iron, and other metals (51), and also organotin compounds, such as dibutyltin dilaurate (52), or tetramethylguanidine salts (53).

The properties of a silicone resin are related to the degree of cure and this in turn is a function of the conditions (temperature, concentration, and catalyst) and of the types of substituents (methyl or phenyl) on the silicon. The modulus of the resin increases with cure time, and that of hard resins increases more rapidly than that of soft resins (9,54). A silicone resin or rubber has a transition temperature above which the polymer is rubbery and below which it is hard and relatively brittle. The slope of the Young's modulus vs temperature curve is steep at this temperature, which varies from below $-60°C$ for silicone rubber to 25, 125, or over $200°C$ for various kinds of silicone resins. The transition temperature is a function of the extent of cure of the resin.

Copolymers of silicones and organic polymers have offered the hope of achieving low cost and physical strength while retaining the durability and surface properties of silicones. Two approaches have been used (excluding that of making simple blends without tying the polymers together by chemical bonds). The easier and less expensive approach is to react siloxanes containing silanols or alkoxysilanes with the hydroxy groups of organic polymers, to give silicon–oxygen–carbon links between the polymers, as illustrated by the formation of silicone alkyds:

$$
\begin{array}{ll}
& \overset{|}{O} \\
\text{RSiOH} + \text{CH}_2\text{OH} & \overset{|}{O} \\
\overset{|}{O} \quad \overset{|}{\text{CHOCOR}'} & \rightarrow \text{RSiO—CH}_2 \qquad + \text{H}_2\text{O} \\
\overset{|}{} \quad \overset{|}{\text{CH}_2\text{OCOR}'} & \overset{|}{O} \quad \overset{|}{\text{CHOCOR}'} \\
& \overset{|}{\text{CH}_2\text{OCOR}'}
\end{array}
$$

Alternatively, $\equiv$SiOCH$_3$ compounds can react, giving methanol as a by-product and the same copolymer as obtained with silanol. The same types of reactions can be used for polyesters, epoxies, phenol–formaldehyde, and acrylic resins. The SiOC bond offers a potential (hydrolytically) weak point, but in practice the polymers are satisfactorily stable.

This is also true of siloxane–polyether copolymers, which were originally made by transalkoxylation (34), as follows:

$$\text{EtSi(OEt)}_3 + 3\,(\text{Me}_2\text{SiO})_4 \rightarrow \text{EtSi((OMe}_2\text{Si)}_4\text{OEt)}_3$$

The ethoxy groups on this branched polymer can be replaced by HO(CH$_2$CH$_2$O)$_n$-C$_4$H$_9$ polymers:

$$\text{\textasciitilde Me}_2\text{SiOEt} + \text{HO(CH}_2\text{CH}_2\text{O)}_n\text{Bu} \xrightarrow{\text{acid catalyst}} \text{\textasciitilde Me}_2\text{SiO(CH}_2\text{CH}_2\text{O)}_n\text{Bu} + \text{EtOH}$$

Other approaches have been developed, for example, the reaction of SiH groups in polysiloxanes with the polyether alcohols, yielding hydrogen as a by-product (55).

The SiOC link can be avoided in many ways, since organofunctional silanes and siloxanes of so many kinds are available. For example, carboxyalkyl-functional or hydroxyalkyl-functional silicones might be used in making copolymers with polyesters, epoxy or amine-functional silicones with epoxy resins, and vinyl- or methacrylate-functional silicones with acrylic or polyvinyl resins. The vinyl siloxanes do not have favorable monomer-reactivity ratios, but those having groups such as OSi(CH$_3$)CH$_2$-CH$_2$OCOC(CH$_3$)$=$CH$_2$ should have the same vinyl activity as other methacrylate esters.

Polyethers have been linked to siloxanes as OSi(CH$_3$)CH$_2$O(CH$_2$CH$_2$O)$_n$R, using the Williamson synthesis (56), or by adding SiH to olefins to make OSi(CH$_3$)CH$_2$CH$_2$-(OCH$_2$CH$_2$)$_n$OR (57).

Polyimide silicones have been made by reaction of ethanolamine derivatives with polyacids, such as 1,2,4,5-benzenetetracarboxylic acid (pyromellitic acid, see Vol. 15, p. 480), or from aminoalkyl silicones, as shown below:

$$-\text{OMe}_2\text{Si} - \text{OCH}_2\text{CH}_2\text{NH}_2 \; + \; \begin{matrix} \text{HOOC} \\ \text{HOOC} \end{matrix} \bigcirc \begin{matrix} \text{COOH} \\ \text{COOH} \end{matrix} \; \longrightarrow \; \text{polyimide silicone}$$

$$-\text{OMe}_2\text{SiCH}_2\text{CH}_2\text{CH}_2\text{NH}_2 \; + \; \begin{matrix} \text{HOOC} \\ \text{HOOC} \end{matrix} \bigcirc \begin{matrix} \text{COOH} \\ \text{COOH} \end{matrix} \; \longrightarrow \; \text{polyimide silicone}$$

Another type of copolymer has metal atoms in the siloxane chain. Reaction of titanium esters with silanols leads to the following titanoxysiloxane copolymers:

$$\sim\sim\text{Me}_2\text{SiOH} + \text{EtOTi}\equiv \rightarrow \sim\sim\text{Me}_2\text{SiOTi}\equiv + \text{EtOH}$$

A great many such "metalloxane" copolymers containing aluminum, titanium, boron, phosphorus, iron, and other elements have been made by Andrianov and his co-workers (58). Improvements in polymer strength have been reported, but the hydrolytic instability of the copolymers appears to be a major fault.

Silicone–carborane copolymers with in-chain or pendent carboranyl groups have been synthesized. The former type can be made by the following reaction (59):

$$(\text{CH}_3\text{O})\text{SiMe}_2-\text{CB}_{10}\text{H}_{10}\text{C}-\text{SiMe}_2(\text{OCH}_3) + \text{Me}_2\text{SiCl}_2 \xrightarrow{\text{FeCl}_3}$$

$$-\!\!\left[\text{Me}_2\text{SiO}-\text{Me}_2\text{Si}-\text{CB}_{10}\text{H}_{10}\text{C}-\text{SiMe}_2\text{OSiMe}_2\text{O}\right]\!- \; + \; 2\,\text{CH}_3\text{Cl}$$

This copolymer is called "SiB-2." Vinyl groups attached to pendant carboranyl groups can be readily introduced to provide cure points.

Copolymers in which the silicon is present to provide RTV cure to organic polymers can, in principle, be made with almost any organic polymer. A few such compounds have been reported, for example, polysulfide polymers terminated by reaction with glycidoxy or (3-methacryloxypropyl)trimethoxysilane, resulting in the following endings:

$$\overset{\displaystyle \text{OH}}{\underset{\displaystyle |}{}}$$

$$(\text{MeO})_3\text{SiCH}_2\text{CH}_2\text{CH}_2\text{OCH}_2-\text{CH}-\text{CH}_2\text{S}\sim\sim \; \text{or} \; (\text{MeO})_3\text{SiCH}_2\text{CH}_2\text{CH}_2\text{OCOCH}(\text{CH}_3)\text{CH}_2\text{S}\sim\sim$$

Such polymers appear to offer a method of making copolymers with each other or with silicone RTV as the other component (60).

Preparation and Properties of Commercial Silicones

A modern silicone plant produces many kinds of silicone polymers and many hundreds of products, and may be integrated back to manufacture of raw materials, such as methyl chloride, silicon, and reinforcing-grade silica. A simplified overall flowsheet is shown in Figures 1a and 1b.

Methylchlorosilanes are the starting materials for making methyl silicones. They are made industrially by the highly exothermic reaction of methyl chloride with silicon, catalyzed by copper (61), at about 300°C. To avoid side reactions, which occur at high temperatures, provisions must be made for the removal of heat. Stirred or fluidized beds are satisfactory for keeping the temperature under control (62–64).

This reaction has been thoroughly studied, and many observations made on various effects of temperature, pressure, particle size, and impurities of silicon and copper, additives, diluents, hydrogen chloride, hydrogen, and poisons for the catalyst. Ex-

Table 5. Properties of Methylchlorosilanes

Compound	Boiling point, °C	Density, d^{20}	Refractive index, n_D^{20}	Assay, %
$(CH_3)SiCl_3$	66.4	1.273	1.4088	95–98
$(CH_3)_2SiCl_2$	70.0	1.067	1.4023	99–99.4
$(CH_3)_3SiCl$	57.9	0.854	1.3893	90–98
CH_3SiHCl_2	41.0	1.110	1.3982	95–97
$(CH_3)_2SiHCl$	35.0	0.854	1.3820	
$(CH_3)_2Si_2Cl_4{}^a$	113–155			

^{a} With other disilanes.

cellent reviews of small-scale or pilot-plant studies are available (6,65–68). Very little has been published regarding industrial apparatus, performance, or economics.

The reaction produces both chlorosilanes and chlorodisilanes, together with many hydrocarbons and some complex silicon compounds. Under proper control the major product is dichlorodimethylsilane and trichloromethylsilane is the major by-product. There have been reports of 85–90% yields of dichlorodimethylsilane at high utilization of silicon in laboratory operations.

A list of the major components of the product stream and their properties is given in Table 5.

For various reasons it is impractical to balance the production of the individual compounds in this complex reaction mixture with demand. There are several inter-conversion processes which can be used to achieve a balance, such as redistribution, cleavage, and methylation, as shown in the following examples:

$$(CH_3)SiCl_3 + (CH_3)_3SiCl \underset{}{\overset{\text{catalyst, 150°C}}{\rightleftharpoons}} 2\,(CH_3)_2SiCl_2$$

$$(CH_3)_2Si_2Cl_4 + HCl \xrightarrow{\text{catalyst}} CH_3SiCl_3 + CH_3SiHCl_2$$

$$CH_3SiCl_3 + CH_3MgCl \rightarrow (CH_3)_2SiCl_2$$

Aluminum chloride catalyzes the redistribution reaction, and SiH compounds promote catalysis (69). At equilibrium the mixture contains about 70% $(CH_3)_2SiCl_2$. Amines catalyze cleavage of disilanes by HCl. The Grignard reaction (qv) can also be used; methylaluminum dichloride or dimethylaluminum dichloride can be used in place of magnesium compounds.

Other Chlorosilanes. The direct process can also be used to make *phenylchlorosilanes*. In this case chlorobenzene reacts with silicon at about 550°C and the catalyst is either silver or copper. The two major products are phenyltrichlorosilane and diphenyldichlorosilane. *Ethylchlorosilanes* can be made by reaction of ethyl chloride with copper–silicon. Except for these three systems the direct process is inefficient for the reaction of organic chlorides with silicon to make organochlorosilanes.

There are several other ways to manufacture phenylchlorosilanes, including the Grignard and related organometallic processes, or condensation of $SiHCl_3$ with benzene or with chlorobenzene (70,71), as shown below:

$$SiCl_4 + C_6H_5MgCl \rightarrow C_6H_5SiCl_3 + MgCl_2$$

$$HSiCl_3 + C_6H_6 \xrightarrow[300°C]{BCl_3} H_2 + C_6H_5SiCl_3$$

$$HSiCl_3 + ClC_6H_5 \xrightarrow{500°C} HCl + C_6H_5SiCl_3$$

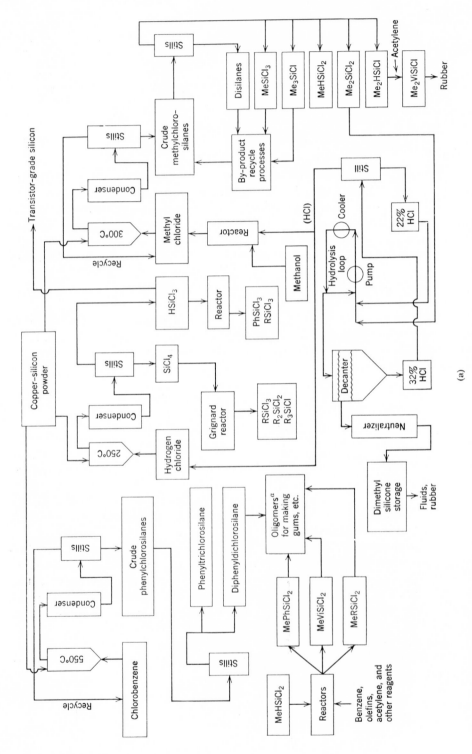

(a)

[a] These oligomers correspond to the ones shown below (b) (upper left). The preparation is the same for both.

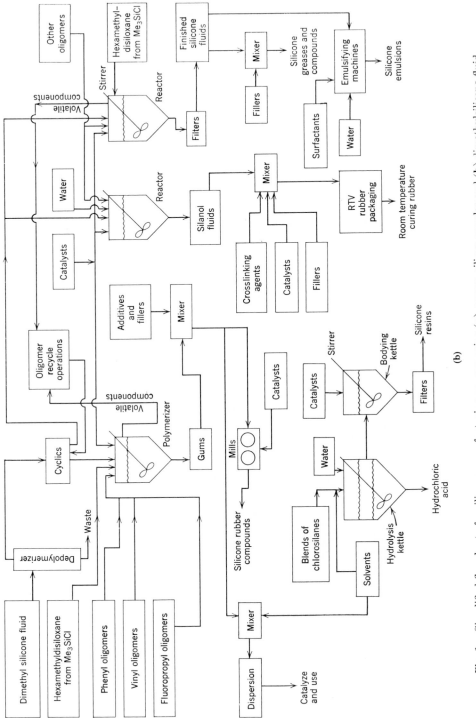

Fig. 1. Simplified flowsheet of a silicone manufacturing process using (**a**) copper–silicon powder and (**b**) dimethylsilicone fluid.

Use of MeSiCl$_3$ in the first reaction, and of MeHSiCl$_2$ in the other, results in the production of (CH$_3$)(C$_6$H$_5$)SiCl$_2$.

Vinylchlorosilanes can be made by the catalyzed addition of SiH compounds to acetylene, by condensation with vinyl chloride in a hot tube without catalyst (72), or from vinyl Grignard reagent, as follows:

$$(CH_3)SiHCl_2 + HC\!\equiv\!CH \xrightarrow{Pt} (CH_3)(C_2H_3)SiCl_2$$

$$(CH_3)SiHCl_2 + ClCH\!=\!CH_2 \xrightarrow{500°C} HCl + (CH_3)(C_2H_3)SiCl_2$$

Processes for making other organochlorosilanes are described above under Silanes. Properties of several industrially important organochlorosilanes are given in Table 6.

Table 6. Properties of Organochlorosilanes

Compound	Boiling point, °C	Density, d	Refractive index, n_D	Assay,[b] %
(C$_6$H$_5$)SiCl$_3$	201.5	1.3185[25]	1.5245[25]	95–98
(C$_6$H$_5$)$_2$SiCl$_2$	305	1.218[25]	1.5765[20]	93–96
(CH$_3$)(C$_6$H$_5$)SiCl$_2$	205	1.174[25]	1.5180[20]	96
(CH$_3$)$_2$(C$_6$H$_5$)SiCl	193.5	1.032[20]	1.5082[25]	
(CH$_3$)(C$_6$H$_5$)$_2$SiCl	295.5	1.1277[20]	1.5742[20]	97
(CH$_3$)(C$_2$H$_3$)SiCl$_2$	93	1.085[25]	1.4200[25]	93
(C$_2$H$_3$)SiCl$_3$	92	1.265[25]	1.4330[25]	95
(CF$_3$CH$_2$CH$_2$)(CH$_3$)SiCl$_2$	122[a]	1.2611[20]	1.3817[25]	
CNCH$_2$CH$_2$SiCl$_3$	224	0.9699[20]	1.4103[20]	

[a] At 737 mm Hg.   [b] Commercial grades.

In all cases the crude mixtures from the reactors are separated by fractional distillation. In the case of the methylchlorosilanes this is done in a system of continuous columns, supplemented by batch columns for minor products. The order of separation is not critical, but a typical scheme is shown in Figure 2 (73,74).

Dichlorodimethylsilane is required in purities above 99.5%, and for the final stage three 150-ft columns are used.

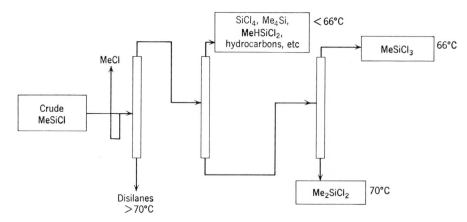

Fig. 2. Separation scheme for methylchlorosilanes.

The separated methylchlorosilanes (Table 5) are pumped to drums or storage tanks. Here they must be protected from moisture and air to avert corrosion of the tanks and danger of fire.

Conversion to Siloxanes. The subsequent stages of manufacture are concerned first with converting these chlorosilanes to siloxanes and then with controlling the molecular size and composition of the silicone polymers. The conversion to siloxanes is done by hydrolysis, and there are the following three primary processes for this: (*1*) continuous hydrolysis to make Me_2SiO and $MeHSiO$ fluids, (*2*) batch hydrolysis of Me_3SiCl and other special small-volume materials; and (*3*) hydrolysis of solutions of chlorosilanes to make resins.

The production of silicone fluids and elastomers—in excess of 20,000 tons annually —is based on the hydrolysis product of dichlorodimethylsilane. Batch or continuous processes are available, but the latter is preferable on a large scale. In one such process the chlorosilane (99% pure, with trichloromethylsilane as the major impurity) is mixed with 22% (azeotropic) aqueous hydrochloric acid in a pump and forced through a loop of glass pipe in a heat exchanger (75). A mixture of fluid and acid is bled off the loop to a separator; here 32% hydrochloric acid is removed from the bottom and silicone fluid from the top. The acid is distilled to generate hydrogen chloride and 22% aqueous hydrochloric acid, and the latter is recycled to the hydrolysis loop.

The silicone fluid is washed, separated, and neutralized. It is a mixture of roughly equal proportions of linear and cyclic polymers (see p. 224). The major cyclic component is the tetramer, octamethylcyclotetrasiloxane. This and other volatile cyclics are useful in the manufacture of silicone fluids and elastomers because they are free of the T component in the starting dichlorodimethylsilane. The yield of cyclics can be increased by depolymerizing the fluid by heating it with strong alkali (76).

$$HO(Me_2SiO)_nH \xrightarrow[200°C]{KOH} (Me_2SiO)_3 + (Me_2SiO)_4 + (Me_2SiO)_5 + \dots$$

Dichloromethylsilane, CH_3SiHCl_2, can also be converted to silicone fluid by hydrolysis with 22% hydrochloric acid in a similar fashion. A few % of chlorotrimethylsilane may be added before hydrolysis, because the SiH is too reactive to permit subsequent use of the catalytic equilibration techniques employed for introducing chainstoppers into other silicone fluids.

Chlorotrimethylsilane is hydrolyzed in glass-lined kettles to produce hexamethyldisiloxane. The product, impure because of hydrocarbons, $SiCl_4$, and other chlorosilanes in commercial Me_3SiCl, can be purified by distillation. The yield can be improved by depolymerizing MQ copolymers by heating with alkalis.

Silicone Fluids. Dimethyl silicone fluids are made by reacting dimethyl silicone stock (the crude fluid or distilled cyclics) with hexamethyldisiloxane. As described above (see p. 224), this reaction produces mixtures of MD_nM and D_m polymers. The ratio of M to D in the charge controls the average molecular weight and the viscosity of the product. For relatively low-viscosity fluids the process is run for several hours at 180°C in glass-lined kettles with acid clay catalysts or, at lower temperatures, with sulfuric acid.

Alkaline catalysts are used for the production of high-viscosity fluids or gums. These polymers can be processed batchwise in kettles, or continuously in a heated tube with stirring (77). Polymerization is continued in the case of gums to make polymers of over 500,000 average molecular weight and 10-million-cSt viscosity. Most gums

Table 7. Properties of Silicone Fluids

Type of fluid		Viscosity at 25°C, cSt	VTC	d^{25}	n^{25}_D	Pour point, °F	Flash point, °F	Surface tension, at 25°C, dyn/cm	Thermal conductivity at 150°F, Btu/(hr)(ft²)(°F/ft)	Electric strength, kV/mil	electric const	Vol resistivity, Ω-cm × 10^{-4} (min)
Me₂SiO, Mole%	Copolymer silicone											
100	none	10	0.56	0.940	1.399	−100	410	20.0	0.075	35.0	2.60	1
100	none	100	0.59	0.968	1.4030	−67	575	20.9	0.090	35.0	2.75	1
100	none	1,000	0.60	0.974	1.4035	−58	600	21.1	0.092	35.0	2.75	1
100	none	10,000	0.60	0.975	1.4035	−53	600	21.3	0.090	35.0	2.75	1
100	none	100,000	0.60	0.978	1.4035	−40	600	21.3	0.090	35.0	2.75	1
50	MePhSiO	125	0.76	1.07	1.495	−50	575	24.7	0.082	32.5	2.88	1
91.2	MePhSiO	50	0.62	0.99	1.425	−100	540	25.0	0.085	32.5	2.79	1
91.2	MePhSiO	100	0.62	0.99	1.425	−100	560	24.1	0.088	32.5	2.80	1
95.6	Ph₂SiO	100	0.62	1.00	1.421	−100	575	24.0		35.0	2.78	1
>90	tetrachlorophenyl siloxane	70	0.69	1.045	1.428	−100	550	21	0.087		2.90	
0	MeHSiO	25	0.50	0.98	1.397			20			2.88	
0–10ᵃ	(CF₃CH₂CH₂)-(CH₃)SiO	300	0.90	1.25		−55		26				
92	MeSiO₁.₅	50	0.57	0.972	1.403	−120	600	21.0	0.087	35.0	2.74	1

ᵃ Aproximate value.

contain vinyl substituents, which are introduced by copolymerizing Me_2SiO with a little $(MeViSiO)_n$ or $(MeViSi)_2O$ or both. The conditions are similar to those used for making dimethyl gums.

Phenyl substituents are added as $+Ph_2SiO+_n$ or $+MePhSiO+_n$ to fluids and gums; alkaline catalysis is used to equilibrate these with $+Me_2SiO+$. Diffusion-pump fluids are special cases, consisting of trisiloxanes with four or five phenyl groups, for example $MePh_2SiOSiMePhOSiMePh_2$, and are unusual silicones, being actually the pure compounds. They can be made by special techniques, such as condensation of $MePh_2SiOH$ with $MePhSiCl_2$, catalyzed by amines, and followed by neutralization and fractional distillation.

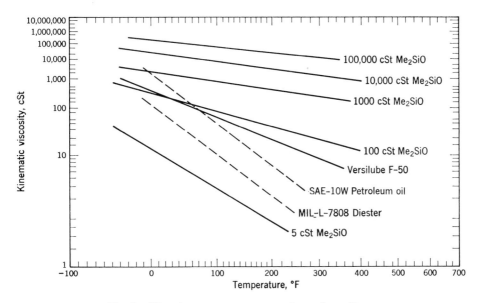

Fig. 3. Viscosity–temperature curve for various silicones.

Methyl trifluoropropyl fluids and gums (of proprietary composition) require special techniques because, as explained above, the cyclic tetramer is more stable than either the trimer or the linear polymers. The necessary rearrangement reactions are therefore run with catalysts such as $NaCH_2COONa$, or the reaction is stopped by the addition of carbon dioxide before conversion to tetramer occurs. Patents are available describing both homopolymers and copolymers with dimethyl silicone (77a); the actual composition of commercial trifluoropropyl methyl silicones is proprietary.

Stabilization of the equilibrated polymer usually requires the removal or neutralization of the catalyst. Acid clay can be filtered off; sulfuric acid or potassium hydroxide can be washed out with water. Neutralizing agents, such as phosphite esters, carbon dioxide, or iodine, can be used in the case of alkaline catalysis. Tetramethylammonium hydroxide or tetrabutylphosphonium hydroxide may also be used as catalyst (77–79). They decompose at higher temperatures to give neutral products, and are especially useful in continuous processes where washing or neutralizing would be difficult. After removal of the catalyst in one of these ways, the polymer is heated in vacuo to remove low-molecular-weight, volatile products. These may be recycled to the equilibration processes.

Fluids are sometimes blended in order to make fluids of intermediate viscosities. Since the properties of a polymer depend upon molecular-weight distribution, as well as upon average molecular weight, blending can affect properties appreciably. Blends of fluids of widely different viscosities are less Newtonian in behavior than those of normal molecular-weight distribution.

Some properties of commercial silicone fluids are shown in Table 7. The dimethyl silicone fluids have unusual rheological behavior, reflected in the viscosity-temperature coefficient, VTC, of Table 7. VTC is defined as follows:

$$\frac{\text{viscosity at 100°F} - \text{viscosity at 210°F}}{\text{viscosity at 100°F}}$$

where viscosities are in cSt.

A broader picture of the relationship is given in Figure 3 where viscosity is shown as a function of temperature (80), as follows:

$$\log \log (\eta + 0.8) = A \log T + C$$

where A and C are constants.

Two nonsilicone fluids are plotted here to illustrate the steeper slopes characteristic of such materials. Silicones with phenyl, trifluoropropyl, or larger alkyl substituents also show steeper slopes when plotted in this way.

Changes in pressure cause unusually large changes in volume (81) and in viscosity (82). The flow of methyl silicone fluids is Newtonian (meaning that the viscosity is constant over a broad range of rates of shear) for fluids of less than 1000 cP, but the apparent viscosity decreases with the shear rate for higher viscosity fluids (22). The fluids are stable to shear stress, however, and return to original viscosity after being passed through small orifices under pressure. Thermal expansion of the volume is about 0.1 per %°C (3). Specific heat ranges from 0.33 to 0.37 cal/g between 0 and 100°C, increasing with viscosity (3).

When the fluids are spread over water to form monomolecular films, and then the films are compressed laterally, the ratio of stress to strain undergoes several changes associated with changes in the order and orientation of the molecules (83,84). The force required for compression is also a function of the pH. The interfacial tension against water is about 42 dyn/cm. Spread on glass, the fluids repel water, forming a contact angle of about 103°, roughly the same as for paraffins.

The dimethyl silicone fluids are good hydrodynamic lubricants, but poor for sliding friction. For steel on steel the coefficient of friction is about 0.3–0.5. For some metal combinations, such as brass on steel, the fluids are fair lubricants for medium loads (85).

The dimethyl silicone fluids are transparent to light and to ultraviolet radiation having wavelengths greater than 280 nm. There are many strong selective bands in the infrared region.

The velocity of sound at 30°C is 873.2 and 987.3 m/sec for 0.65-cSt and 1000-cSt fluids, respectively (86). It decreases as the temperature is raised and is significantly higher for methyl phenyl silicones.

The dielectric constant (see Table 7) decreases with temperature. For example, a 1000-cSt fluid has a constant of 2.76 at 30°C and 2.54 at 100°C (87). The power factor is low, but increases with temperature, and behaves irregularly with frequency. Resistivity decreases with temperature. γ Radiation causes decreases in resistivity and dielectric strength (88). The latter is also lowered by moisture (89).

Gases are soluble in dimethyl silicone polymers. The solubilities of air, nitrogen, and carbon dioxide are 0.17, 0.17, and 1.00 cm³ (STP) per cm³ at 25°C and 1 atm, respectively (3). The solubility of oxygen in 26,000-cSt fluid at 1 atm is 0.0002 g/g, that of hydrogen in D_4 is 0.00007g/g (90). Water is almost insoluble in dimethyl silicone (91). The fluids are miscible with benzene, dimethyl ether, methyl ethyl ketone, carbon tetrachloride, or kerosene. They are somewhat soluble in acetone, dioxane, ethanol, and butanol, and are insoluble in water, methanol, ethylene glycol, and Cellosolve (Union Carbide, 2-ethoxyethanol) (22).

Methyl phenyl silicone fluids (with, for example, 8–50% MePhSiO) have higher viscosity–temperature coefficients, lower pour points, and lower flash points than dimethyl silicone fluids of the same viscosity. They are less compressible and change viscosity more rapidly with pressure than methyl fluids (therefore show up well in the Ryder Gear Test for lubricity, Fed Spec 791, method 6508). Their principal advantage is their greater stability to oxidation and γ radiation. Three such fluids are described in Table 7.

Fluids with chlorinated phenyl groups attached to silicone (Table 7) have improved lubricating properties. For example, Versilube F-50 (General Electric Co.) was shown by the Shell 4-ball wear test to be comparable to mineral oil or ester lubricants, and much better than dimethyl or methyl phenyl silicone (92).

Methyl trifluoropropyl silicone fluid (Table 7) also changes viscosity rapidly with pressure, and for this reason can show good lubricating properties (93). The methyl alkyl fluids, where alkyl is octyl to tetradecyl, likewise are good lubricants but have higher viscosity-temperature coefficients and poorer oxidative stability than methyl fluids (28).

Methyl alkyl silicone fluids are better prepared by the addition of olefins to methyl hydrogen (MeHSiO) fluids than by the condensation of methylalkylsilanols or rearrangements of siloxanes. Platinum-type catalysts are suitable for these additions. The fluids have higher viscosity–temperature coefficients, lower compressibility, better lubricating properties, and greater compatibility with organic materials than have the dimethyl silicones.

Silicone Rubber. Heat-curing types of silicone rubber are made up of gums, fillers, additives, and catalysts (94). They are commercially available as gums, reinforced gums (gum and a portion of the filler), uncatalyzed compounds, dispersions, and catalyzed compounds. The last mentioned are compositions, ready for use by the purchaser, which contain a catalyst. The following types of gums are available: general-purpose (methyl and vinyl); high and low temperature (phenyl, methyl, and vinyl); low compression set (methyl and vinyl); low shrink (devolatilized); and solvent resistant (fluorosilicone). Some gum properties are shown in Table 8.

Table 8. Properties of Silicone Gums

Type	Density, d^{25}	$T_g{}^a$,°C	Mp, °C	ASTM-D926 Williams plasticity
$(CH_3)_2SiO$	0.98	−123	−60	95–125
$CH_3C_6H_5$—SiO	0.98	−113	none	135–180
$(CH_3)(CF_3CH_2CH_2)SiO$	1.25	−65		
SiB-2 carborane		−34	+5	

^{a} Glass-transition temperature.

Fillers are finely divided silica (fume silica, etc), diatomaceous earth, mined silica, titanium dioxide, calcium carbonate, ferric oxide, and others. Catalysts are discussed above (p. 229). Detailed information on formulations is available from manufacturers of silicones (95).

The ingredients are mixed in equipment, such as doughmixers or Banbury mills. Peroxide catalysts are added on water-cooled rubber mills. (See Rubber compounding.) These can be used for the whole process in small-scale operations. To make dispersions or pastes, solvents, such as xylene, are stirred with the mixture.

The uncured rubber mixtures range from a tough putty to a hard deformable plastic in consistency. Those with reinforcing fillers tend to become stiff (develop structure) on storage unless structure-control additives, such as water, diphenylsilanediol, pinacoxysilanes, or silicone fluids are added to the mixture (96–98).

It is common practice in the industry to prepare specific or custom mixtures for specific product applications. Hundreds of formulations have been compounded and in such complex systems the potential number is enormous. In general, a formula is designed to achieve some special operating or processing requirement, and formulations are classified accordingly. Some types of particular importance or interest are listed in Table 9 (40,99–101).

Table 9. Properties of Classes of Silicone Elastomers

Class	Hardness, Durometer	Tensile strength, psi	Elongation, %	Compressive set, at 300°F for 22 hr, %	Useful temp range, °F min	Useful temp range, °F max	Tear strength, psi
general purpose	40–80	700–1,000	100–400	15–50	−75	500	50
low compression set	50–80	700–1,000	80–400	10–15	−75	500	50
extreme low temp	25–80	800–1,500	150–600	20–50	−150	500	175
extreme high temp	40–80	700–1,100	200–500	10–40	−75	600	
wire and cable	50–80	600–1,500	100–500	20–50	−150	500	
solvent resistant	50–60	850–1,000	170–225	20–30	−90	450	75
high-strength flame retardant	40–50	1,400–1,600	500–700				160–220

The properties of fabricated rubber depend on the type of "compound" (mixture), ie, upon the gum, filler, catalyst, additives, and solvents (if any) used. They also depend on the relative proportions of these ingredients. A high proportion of filler (high loading) leads to greater hardness, less elongation, and greater solvent resistance.

The properties also depend upon the thoroughness of mixing, and the degree of wetting of the filler by the gum. The properties change as cure progresses, and are stabilized by "post-cure" heating to remove volatiles (devolatilization). To a very large extent they are affected by the environment and also by aging. Since one of the principal advantages of silicone rubber is its durability, the effects of environment are of special importance; these will be discussed below (see p. 250).

Before use silicone rubber mixtures are "catalyzed and freshened" (ie, catalyst is added and the mixture is freshly milled) on rubber mills until they band into smooth continuous sheets that are easily worked. The freshened (freshly mixed) compound is molded at a temperature from 225–350°F and a pressure from 800–1500 psi. The molds are lubricated by a 1–2% aqueous solution of a household detergent, such as Dreft (Proctor & Gamble). The rubber is charged into the mold, and the press closed and bumped several times to let the trapped gases escape, after which the rubber is cured for a selected time and temperature. It can be used as press cured, or it can be postcured by heating in an oven at temperatures at or above the expected operating temperature, to drive off volatile catalyst decomposition products and to stabilize properties (40).

To make insulated wire, rods, channels, tubing, etc, the compounds are extruded in standard rubber extrusion equipment. The extruded rubber is heated briefly to set its properties; for this, hot air vulcanization at 300–450°C or steam at 40–100 psi for several minutes is sufficient. Final properties can be developed by oven curing or by continuous steam vulcanization.

To coat silicone rubber on a fabric, such as glass cloth, rubber dispersed in a solvent is used. The cloth may be dip-coated, then dried and cured in heated towers. It may also be calendered using high-penetration, soft silicone stocks on standard three- and four-roll calenders. (See Coated fabrics, also Vol. 5, p. 684.) Ducts and hoses

Table 10. Permeability of Silicone Rubber (103,104)

Type of compound	Temp, °C	Gas	Permeability, $cm^3/(sec)(cm^2)$ (cm Hg/mm)
Me_2SiO	26	CO_2	59.2
	26	CO_2	10.4
fluorosilicone	25	CO_2	304
	25	CO_2	59
	25	air	33
nitrile silicone	31	CO_2	178
	31	O_2	30
Me_2SiO	30	butane	1.53
	70	butane	1.29

can be built up from dip-coated or calendered cloth, and complex structures can be formed on mandrels followed by wrapping and curing to produce large ducts (40), or by extrusion. Sponging of silicone rubber is normally accomplished by the use of nitrogen blowing agents, which produce closed-cell sponge. Silicone rubber foam or sponge is made in densities of about 0.015–0.035 lb/in.³ (see Foamed plastics).

When silicone rubber must be bonded to other materials, such as metals, ceramics, or plastics, primers are generally used. These may be silicate esters or silicone pastes. After evaporation of solvent from the primed surface, silicone rubber compounds can be applied and cured under pressure. There are also self-bonding silicone rubber stocks requiring no primer.

Some of the properties of the cured compound are shown in Table 9. The properties of rubber change with temperature as, for example, Young's modulus decreases from about 10^4 to 2×10^2 in going from −60°F to room temperature, and then remains fairly constant to 500°F. Resistivity decreases, electric strength does not change greatly; dielectric constant increases for 60-cycle current, decreases for 10^4 cycles and above; power factor increases considerably. Tensile strength decreases from about 1000 psi at 0°C to 300 psi at 300°C.

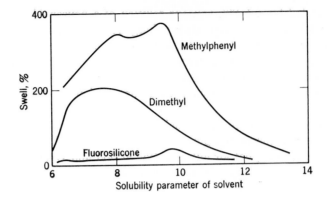

Fig. 4. Swelling of silicone rubber by solvents.

Thermal conductivity of silicone rubber is about 0.006 W/(in.²)(°F/in.) or 0.08–0.10 Btu/(hr)(ft²)(°F/ft), which is about twice that of organic rubbers (see reference 37, p. 477).

Silicone rubber (gum) films are permeable to gases and hydrocarbons, in general about 10 or 20 times as permeable as organic polymers (40). Water diffuses through lightly crosslinked gum as monomer, dimer, and trimer, with diffusion coefficients of 10.5, 3.6, and 3.1×10^{-5}, respectively, at 65°C (102). Silicone rubber compounds are permeable to gases, as shown in Table 10.

Solvents diffuse into silicone rubber and swell, soften, and weaken it. The degree of swelling depends upon the solvent, and has been correlated with the solubility parameters of solvent and rubber, as illustrated in Figure 4. The correlation is improved if electrostatic interactions are considered (31). The solubility parameter is the square root of the energy of vaporization per cm³ (102a). (See also Solvents.)

Aqueous solutions interact with silicone rubber, with varying effects. Water itself has little effect though at higher temperatures it causes a little softening and weakening, and if the rubber is heated with it in a sealed tube, reversion to a sticky polymer occurs. Concentrated solutions of acids and bases are more damaging (40).

Heat alone can cause depolymerization and volatilization, with the rate increasing appreciably above 600°F, even in decatalyzed (neutral) compounds.

Bouncing putty (a mixture based on polydimethylsiloxane polymer modified by boric acid, with special additives, fillers, and plasticizers) flows on slow application of pressure like a very viscous liquid, but on shock behaves like a very elastic solid and may even shatter.

Room Temperature Vulcanizing Rubber, RTV. The silicone polymers used in making RTV are silicone fluids with silanol end groups. These can be made by depolymerizing linear polydimethylsiloxane with water at 150–175°C with KOH (42) or with ammonia or amines (105) as catalysts.

Polymers with phenyl, trifluoropropyl, or cyanoethyl substituents are used to make low-temperature-, heat-, radiation-, or solvent-resistant products. Fillers are used in much the same way as in heat-cured rubber, but must be compatible with the curing agent, which means they must usually be dry.

For some types of RTV, the polymer is mixed with the filler and ethyl silicate. A catalyst, such as dibutyltin dilaurate, is stirred in just before using the material. Polymerization begins immediately, with elimination of ethyl alcohol. The pot life and the work life depend upon the type and concentration of the catalyst and on the temperature, so the pot life can be prolonged by refrigeration. Pot life is generally on the order of a few hours at room temperature. The time required to obtain a firm cure is about a day at room temperature, and an hour or so at 150°C (106).

Another type of RTV rubber is made by mixing polymer, filler, crosslinking agent, and curing catalyst, and packaging the mixture to protect it from moisture. Contact with air brings about reactions which cure the polymer. The time required for cure depends upon the temperature, the humidity, and the thickness of the silicone layer. Under typical ambient conditions the surface is tackfree in 15–30 min, and a $\frac{1}{8}$ in. thick layer cures through in less than a day. Acetic acid or methyl ethyl ketoxime are typical by-products of the curing systems. Cure progresses and strength is developed slowly for about 3 weeks (107).

The original viscosity of either type of RTV can be varied by adjusting that of the polymer, from 10 to 10^4 P. Some products are compounded to be pourable, others are thixotropic. These properties are controlled by fillers and additives.

Some physical properties of cured RTV rubber are shown in Table 11 (35). The electrical properties are listed in Table 12 (23).

Table 11. Physical Properties of RTV's

Specific gravity	Durometer hardness, Shore A	Tensile strength, psi	Elongation, %
1.18	45	350	180
1.30	50	450	140
1.37	55	550	120
1.45	60	650	110
1.33	50	500	200
1.48	65	700	110
1.45	60	750	160

Table 12. Typical Electrical Properties of RTV's

Type	Vol resistivity, Ω-cm	Electric strength, V/mil	Dielec const at 60 cps	Dielec const at 1 Mc	Power factor at 60 cps	Power factor at 1 Mc
A	6×10^{14}	630	3.6	3.4	0.019	0.005
B	5×10^{13}	650	3.6	3.1	0.011	0.003
C	1.3×10^{14}	600	4.0	3.7	0.200	0.003
D	1×10^{15}	670	4.5	3.7	0.010	0.002
E	1×10^{14}	550	4.6	3.7	0.023	0.002
F	1.3×10^{14}	600	4.0	3.7	0.020	0.003

Thermal conductivity of cured RTV is on the order of 0.15–0.18 Btu/(hr)(ft²)-(°F/ft). Other properties in regard to solvents, chemicals, stability, etc, are comparable to those of heat-cured rubber. RTV's can also be made to foam (108).

As with the case of heat-cured rubber, RTV must often be applied after priming the surface of the substrate if adhesion to the latter is needed. Some types of RTV, however, are self-bonding to many substrates. For example, to unprimed aluminum, bonds with 200-psi shear strength or 20-lb/in. peel strength are reported, and good bonds are formed with copper, glass, and acrylic resins.

Silicone encapsulating RTV systems have been described (see Embedding). They are free-flowing fluids, some of which have filler and some not. They consist of two parts, which are mixed just before use. They have excellent electrical properties (109).

Silicone Resins are highly crosslinked siloxane systems, the crosslinking components being introduced as trifunctional or tetrafunctional silanes in the first stage of manufacture. For example, a solution of MeSiCl₃, Me₂SiCl₂, PhSiCl₃, and Ph₂SiCl₂, or MePhSiCl₂ in toluene is hydrolyzed to form a complex copolymer mixture, which remains in solution in toluene. The aqueous hydrochloric acid is separated from this, and the resin solution is washed and then heated in the presence of a mild condensation catalyst to body the resin to the proper viscosity and cure time. It is finally adjusted to specifications by distilling off or adding solvents. For molding resins, fillers, such as glass fibers, may be added and solvent removed to yield a solid resin or resin-glass mixture. This is also the procedure for preparing silicone–resin intermediates used for making silicone–organic copolymers.

The properties of the finished silicone resin depend upon the choice of chlorosilanes, the degree of cure, and, to some extent, on the processing conditions. The general effects of the most commonly used monomers on the properties of a film are listed in Table 13.

Table 13. Effect of Monomers on the Properties of Silicone-Resins Films

Property	MeSiCl₃	PhSiCl₃	Me₂SiCl₂	Ph₂SiCl₂	MePhSiCl₂
hardness	increased	increased	decreased	decreased	decreased
brittleness	increased	greatly increased	decreased	decreased	decreased
stiffness	increased	increased	decreased	decreased	decreased
toughness	increased		decreased	decreased	decreased
cure speed	much faster	some increase	slower	much slower	slower
tack	decreased	some decrease	increased	increased	increased

Phenyl and alkyl (other than methyl) groups increase the compatibility with organic materials. Water-repellent resins are generally based on methyl or longer alkyl monomers. Processing conditions vary from hydrolysis in strong acid, to dilute acid, or to buffered aqueous systems; alkoxysilanes can be also used to avoid generation of acid systems. The choice of solvent can affect the result, and so can temperature, concentration, and choice of catalyst for bodying and curing. An interesting illustration of effects of conditions is provided by the "ladder" polymer, as shown below:

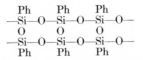

where M_n (number-average molecular weight) = 14,000 and M_w (weight-average molecular weight) = 26,000.

Such a polymer is obtained by heating the hydrolyzate of PhSiCl₃ with alkali in a high-boiling solvent (110). A tough infusible resin is obtained which can be cast from solvents to clear films.

Dipping or impregnating varnishes used to bond and insulate electrical coils and glass cloth are usually supplied as 50 or 60% silicone resin in an organic solvent. Components are dipped, drained, baked, and then again dipped, drained, and baked repeatedly to build up the required thickness of insulation. They are then finally cured with a somewhat longer bake, with time and temperature determined by the resin used and the complexity of the component structure. The final bake is usually for several hours at 400–500°F, although lower temperatures can be used (7).

Silicone laminating resins are used first to coat glass cloth and this coating is cured to a nontacky partially cured stage. Stacks of cloth so treated are pressed at about 1000 psi and heated to cure (high-pressure laminates), or are bag-molded or vacuum-formed at 100 psi or less (low-pressure laminates) before cure. See Laminated and reinforced plastics.

Mica paper may be impregnated by silicone resin solution and cured. Asbestos fibers or paper are also used with silicone resins. Some resins, for example those used to make masonry or ceramics water repellent, cure on air-drying at room temperature. Most silicone resins require heat and catalysts for curing. During the life of the product curing continues and properties change with time (see p. 250).

Table 14. Properties of Silicone Impregnating Resins

Property	Value	
heat endurance at 250°C, hr		
flexure life[a]	250	
craze life[b]	750	
thermal life,[c] hr		
at 300°C	500	
at 275°C	1500	
at 250°C	4500	
weight loss, after 3 hr at 250°C, %	4	
	dry	*wet*
electric strength,[d] V/mil	1500	1000
power factor at 25°C		
at 100 cycles	0.0084	0.0085
at 10^6 cycles	0.0043	0.0047
dielectric const at 25°C		
at 100 cycles	3.0	3.0
at 10^6 cycles	2.9	2.9

[a] Hours after which a film on a copper strip cracked, when bent around a small rod.

[b] Hours after which cracking was visible and evident without bending.

[c] Hours of aging to reduce electric strength of a glass cloth impregnated with silicone varnish to 50% of its initial value.

[d] Electrodes 2 in. in diam.

Typical properties of a freshly cured impregnating resin are shown in Table 14 (9). Properties of molded silicone resins have been described (see Insulation, electrical). Laminates range rather broadly in properties (111), as shown in Table 15 (9).

Pressure-sensitive adhesives are made by compounding silicone elastomer gums with silicone resins which are not completely compatible with the elastomer. They are available as solutions in volatile solvents, and are applied to the backing by conventional knife-coating techniques. When the solvent evaporates, a sticky film is left. This is cured, to develop strength and reduce tack, by heating with a peroxide. Fillers can be used to increase cohesive strength and decrease tack (112).

Water-repellent resins applied to masonry surfaces coat the pores and act by repelling water which otherwise would wet the walls of these pores. Sufficient hydrostatic pressure head can overcome this surface activity. There is not a continuous film to bar passage of water or water vapor.

Silicone films deposited on glass from solutions of carbonfunctional alkoxysilanes improve adhesion of the glass to organic resins.

Release resins are baked on metal surfaces to prevent materials from sticking to these surfaces. See Abherents.

Paints are made from silicone resin solutions by mixing with stable pigments, such as aluminum flakes. Silicone paints are very stable, and even after oxidation the residual polymer bonds the pigment. Silicone–aluminum paint is serviceable to 500°F. Silicone paints with TiO_2 or other pigments resist discoloration due to heat or weathering, and have good gloss retention, good hardness, mar resistance, flexibility, and resistance to soap, fat, and fruit juices. The baking time is longer and the temperature higher than required for curing organic resins.

Table 15. Properties of Silicone–Glass Laminates

Property	Value
tensile strength, psi	30,000–35,000
elongation at break, %	1–2
flexural strength, psi	20,000–45,000
compressive strength, psi	20,000
modulus, psi	
flexure at 25°C	$2 \times 10^6 – 3.5 \times 10^6$
at 260°C	$1.9 \times 10^6 – 2.5 \times 10^6$
tension	$1.5 \times 10^6 – 2.8 \times 10^6$
impact, Izod, ft-lb/in.	5–25
distortion temperature, °C	>200
electric strength, V/mil	250–400
power factor, %	
at 10^3 cps	0.5
at 10^6 cps	0.001–0.002
arc resistance, sec	220–350

Sodium methyl siliconate is made by dissolving $CH_3SiO_{1.5}$ polymer in aqueous NaOH. It behaves like a solution of $CH_3Si(OH)_2(ONa)$ monomer. On acidification the methyl silicone resin reprecipitates at a rate dependent upon dilution and pH. Methyl siliconic acid, $CH_3Si(OH)_3$, is a weak acid, and even carbon dioxide decomposes the sodium salt and leads to precipitation of the polymer.

Products Based on Silicone Fluids. Several types of greases are made from mixtures of silicone fluids and fillers. For insulating and water-repellent greases silica filler is used, and the fluid may be dimethyl, dimethyl copolymerized with methyl phenyl, or methyl trifluoropropyl silicone. For lubricating grease the fillers are generally lithium soaps, and the preferred fluids are methyl phenyl, chlorinated phenyl methyl, or methyl trifluoropropyl silicones. Other fillers, such as carbon black, Indanthrene Blue, or aryl ureas have also been used in such greases. The temperature limit for soap-filled greases is set by the melting point of the soap. The dielectric greases (or "compounds") show less than 10% bleed even for 24 hr at 400°F and they have low evaporation loss. Their electric strength is high, arc resistance is over 100 sec, and dissipation factor is less than 0.0025. They are workable at low temperatures and they do not have a "dropping point," as soap-filled greases do.

Lubricating greases vary in properties, depending on the type of fluid and thickener used. They have wide service-temperature ranges (from -100 to $450°F$), dropping points in the range of $400–500°F$ (depending on the soap used), low bleed, and low evaporation rate and weight loss in vacuum. Those based on fluids with good lubricating properties are good lubricants, capable of prolonged performance up to $400°F$. Those based on other fluids are suitable for roller bearings or light loads (113,114). Greases filled with carbon black are similar in terms of dropping point, useful temperature range, and lubricity to those based on silica. See Lubrication.

Emulsions of silicone fluids in water are made for convenience in applying small amounts of silicone to textiles, paper, or other surfaces. Concentrations are usually in the range of 20–40% silicone, except for foam control agents, which may contain as little as 10% silicone. Various emulsifying agents are used, in general nonionic. The emulsified silicone fluids may be of any type, but are usually dimethyl silicone. Those based on methyl hydrogen fluid (MeHSiO) can react with water to generate hydrogen and must be stabilized by buffers when stored.

Antifoams are made from fluids of 350–12,000 cSt viscosities, which may be compounded with fillers and dispersing agents. Fluorosilicone and dimethyl silicone fluids are used in antifoams. Emulsified fluids are especially convenient as antifoams, because they disperse rapidly. See Foams.

Copolymer Products. There are two industrially important types of silicone–organic copolymers, the silicone resin–organic resin protective coatings, and the silicone fluid–polyether fluid foam-control agents.

Silicone–alkyds are made by heating mixtures of phthalic anhydride, glycerol, fatty acids, and silanol or methoxysilane-containing silicone resin in solvent (115). Usually about 25–50% of the product is silicone. Silicone-alkyd paints and enamels have original gloss values of about 85, which decline only to about 72 after a 400-hr exposure in the twin-arc weatherometer. They have good outdoor weatherability, and retain their integrity at high temperatures (to $700°F$). They may be air-dried, or baked at about $300–350°F$.

Silicone–epoxies and silicone–acrylics are prepared either by blending or copolymerizing, as is also the case with silicone–alkyds or polyesters. They likewise have good color and gloss retention, and weatherability.

Resinous or rubbery polymers can be made by copolymerizing dimethyl silicone with polycarbonate (qv) (116,117). Typical properties are shown in Table 16.

The siloxane–polyether copolymers are made from several types of silicones and polyethers. The properties of the products depend upon the composition of both components. The copolymers are tailor-made to perform in specific polyurethan foam

Table 16. Properties of Resinous or Rubbery Copolymers (Silicone Polycarbonate)

Me$_2$SiO, %	Softening temp, °C	Tensile strength, psi	Elongation, %
9		12,000	
10	120–160	9,200	10
25	145–160	8,400	10
50	75–130		
53		2,000	360

systems (see under Uses, p. 255) and many types have been developed for this purpose alone. It is sufficient here to describe the preparation of one such copolymer (34).

Cyclic Me_2SiO oligomers were heated with ethyltriethoxysilane in the presence of KOH, yielding a 1500-cP fluid with 8.8% ethoxy groups. This was then mixed in toluene with a butoxylated polyether alcohol, $C_4H_9(OCH_2CH_2)_n(OCH(CH_3)CH_2)_mOH$ of molecular weight 1530, having 50 wt % poly(ethylene oxide) and 50 wt % poly(propylene oxide). Trifluoroacetic acid was added to catalyze transesterification, and ethanol–toluene azeotrope was stripped off. The product was neutralized with $NaHCO_3$. It was a fluid of 880 cSt viscosity, which was completely miscible with water below 95°F, but not completely miscible above 95°F.

Changes in Properties with Time

Fluids. Oxidation of methyl silicones yields formaldehyde and formic acid. Each molecule of either of these formed represents a carbon cleaved from silicon and results in the formation of a siloxane linkage. Thus, D units are converted to T or Q units and the polymer is branched or crosslinked.

Prolonged heating of silicone fluids can result in devolatilization and cracking and therefore in loss of weight and change in viscosity. Heated under nitrogen at 300°C, a 100-cSt dimethyl silicone fluid decreased 47% in viscosity in 480 hr (9). Heating under air causes loss in weight, and gelation occurs in about 200 hr at 250°C. Stability is improved by antioxidants, such as phenyl-α-naphthylamine, to the extent of a 45-fold increase in life at 300°C. Compounds of titanium, iron, and cerium (118) have also been reported to increase life; 0.02% cerium is said to do so by preventing "unzipping" and being converted into cyclics. Preoxidation, combined with the use of iron catalysts, results in fluids which do not gel in 500 hr at 600°F.

Copolymer fluids containing Me_2SiO and either MePhSiO or Ph_2SiO are more stable at high temperatures than dimethyl silicone, and heat aging is further improved when the end groups are phenyl-substituted (119).

Diethyl silicone fluids are less stable at high temperatures than dimethyl, but can be stabilized by chelate-type inhibitors such as copper ethyl acetoacetate (120).

Methyl alkyl silicone fluids are in general less stable than dimethyl fluids; it is the methyl group that is unique, the longer alkyls being roughly equivalent to each other in oxidation stability (28).

Ozone and electrical corona discharge, which degrade organic polymers, do not attack silicone fluids or elastomers.

Dimethyl silicones crosslink when subjected to γ or electron radiation. Small radiation doses increase the viscosity of the fluids, and branched molecules are formed (39). The G value (energy yield) is about 2.5 ± 0.4 crosslinks per 100 electron V of energy absorbed (121–123). With increased radiation dose, the fluid gels when there is an average of one crosslink per molecule; actually only about 2% of the monomer units are crosslinked but these form a network which prevents flow (39). Further radiation increases the insoluble fraction. Fluids containing MePhSiO or Ph_2SiO are more stable to radiation; methyl fluid is attacked 35 times more rapidly than phenyl fluid, and phenyl groups also protect silicone rubber (124,125).

Rubber. Heat aging causes various changes in cured silicone rubber which can be noted in the properties either at elevated temperature, or after return to room temperature. Heating in hot air at 125°C causes decrease in % of elongation and increase

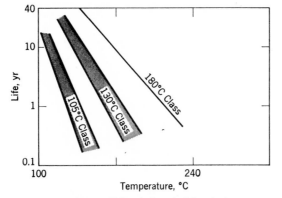

Fig. 5.   Life of electrical insulation.

in hardness, but no great change in tensile strength (40). The time to reduce "elongation at break" to 50% has been suggested as a criterion for heat aging studies (126). Compounds are known which can withstand a week or two of aging at 315°C before undergoing this much deterioration.

Permanent deformation occurs when rubber is compressed or stretched at high temperature. This is due in large part to relaxation of stress by rearrangement of chemical bonds. In the case of silicone it is the Si—O—Si bonds that break and reform. The rate at which this occurs depends upon the temperature, upon the presence of rearrangement catalysts, and also upon the presence of water. A common measure of the ability to undergo or withstand this type of change is a test for compression set. The percentage of permanent set varies with time and temperature. Values for several types of silicone rubber were shown in Table 9. Low compression set was at one time achieved by the use of additives but is now achieved by the use of vinyl gums and noncatalytic components.

Heating silicone rubber in a confined space with water can cause reversion to a sticky mass. As in the case of compression set this change is minimized by the use of neutral components. Water alone is not particularly harmful, even at 125–175°C. However, seal material, good at 500°F in air, is good only up to 250°F in steam (127).

Silicone rubber can burn, but the residue is siliceous rather than carbonaceous, and tends to have some structural integrity, as well as to be a nonconductor of electricity. This makes it valuable for electrical insulation on ships, especially naval vessels.

Electron or γ radiation causes damage to cured silicone rubber. Elongation is decreased, but tensile strength is not greatly affected. Antirads decrease crosslinking, and are more effective at higher temperatures (128). On the whole, methyl silicone rubbers are not very resistant to γ radiation. Phenyl-containing silicone rubber is more resistant, in direct proportion to the phenyl content (129).

Some of the effects of heat aging on silicone resins are indicated in Tables 14 and 15. The general effect is gradual embrittlement and crazing; electrical properties do not change greatly (9). The overall effectiveness of silicone insulations, including rubber and resin, is evident from temperature-life charts, such as shown in Figure 5.

Resins. Silicone resins change little on exposure to weather, ie, to humidity, heat, and sunlight. Weather resistance is carried over into silicone–organic copolymers and blends, provided the ratio of silicone to organic component is high enough. A modified silicone-varnish film shows a flexure life of 1000 hr at 200°C, 150 hr at 250°C, and craze life (see p. 247) of 2000 hr and 800 hr, respectively (9). Its thermal life (see p. 247) varies from 35 hr at 300°C to 2200 hr at 225°C. The color and gloss retention of silicone and modified silicone paints on aging are excellent.

Greases. Silicone greases are also resistant to heat aging. Those filled with soap are limited by the oxidative stability of the soap. Those based on methyl phenyl fluids are particularly good with respect to heat aging, and are superior to methyl or fluorosilicone-fluid based greases in radiation resistance.

Copolymers. Vinylcarboranyl-modified SiB-2 (silicone carborane) is very stable to heat aging. An experimental rubber compound containing this polymer, silica, and 5% ferric oxide antioxidant, changed on heating, as shown in Table 17 (130).

Table 17. Stability of Silicone Carborane, Tested at Ambient Conditions, after Heat Aging

Time, hr	Temperature, °F	Hardness, Shore A	Elongation, %	Tensile strength, psi
0		65	110	252
24	600	71	51	171
24	800	51	105	102
2	900	47	194	104

Below 600°C (1112°F) these polymers are susceptible to oxidation reactions similar to those of dimethyl silicones, but they show much lower volatility losses (131).

Silphenylene polymer, $-(OMe_2SiC_6H_4SiMe_2-)_n$ likewise has a much lower volatility loss than dimethyl silicone on aging at 250–300°C (132). The future availabilities of carborane and silphenylene copolymers are uncertain, however.

Analytical and Test Methods

Qualitative identification of silicones can be made through their infrared (133) or ultraviolet spectra. The SiMe and SiMe_2 groups show absorption at 1259 and 800 cm^{-1}, and SiOSi at 1010–1110 cm^{-1}. The ratio of methyl to phenyl groups in the polymers can be determined by measuring the intensity of the MeSi and PhSi bands at 1263 and 1435 cm^{-1} (134). Phenyl silicones also show absorption at 260, 265, and 272 nm in the ultraviolet spectrum.

Quantitative determination, for example, on paper, textiles, or in formulations, can be done by ashing and determination as silica, or by extraction with solvents and measurement by infrared absorption.

Special groups are determined by specific reactions. For example, chlorosilanes can be hydrolyzed and the halogen determined by titration with alkali or silver nitrate. Other types of halogen substitution may require more drastic methods of decomposition. SiH is determined by infrared absorption at 2100–2250 cm^{-1} or by evolution of hydrogen on hydrolysis or alcoholysis catalyzed by bases. Silanol can be determined by measurement of methane evolved with methyl Grignard reagent; water is corrected for by reaction with calcium hydride, which, unless specially prepared, does not react with silanol. Water and silanol can also be determined separately by infrared techniques.

Gel-permeation chromatography has been used to determine the distribution of molecular weights in silicone gums (135). Gas chromatography is satisfactory for separation and determination of smaller linears and cyclics. Mass spectrometry and gas chromatography are useful in identifying and measuring volatile silicones and intermediates (136–138).

The general analytical chemistry of silicones has been reviewed by McHard (139) and by Kreshkov (140).

Biological, Health, and Safety Factors

Methyl silicones are biologically inert (141) and this is manifested in many ways. They do not react with body fluids, they do not cause coagulation of blood in contact with them, they do not adhere to body tissues, and they do not show irritating or toxic effects. These properties are no doubt due to the molecular weight and incompatibility, as well as the stability, of the polymers; in contrast, the dimer, hexamethyldisiloxane, has some toxic properties (142).

These qualities of the methyl polymers are by and large true of phenyl-, alkyl-, and fluoroalkyl-substituted polymers also. Trifluoropropyl silicones, however, evolve toxic materials when heated above 550°F (143).

Formulated silicones contain ingredients which may be irritating or toxic. For example, some of the metallic or organometallic catalysts in RTV or resin are irritating or toxic, but they are used at very low levels in silicones. By-products of peroxide or RTV cure may be irritating. Emulsifiers in silicone emulsions, or bactericides used to keep these or silicone RTV from deterioration, are potential hazards. Many such products, however, are formulated to meet specific Federal (FDA) or other safety standards. Silicone resins are sold in solvents, and these may be hazardous with regard to health or fire. Those solvents causing air pollution difficulties can be replaced by less hazardous solvents.

Methylchlorosilanes are flammable, and are corrosive because of HCl liberated on hydrolysis; other chlorosilanes are less flammable, but all are hazardous chemicals. Volatile oligomeric siloxanes are somewhat flammable, and can be generated by decomposition of siloxane polymers. Compounds containing SiH liberate hydrogen on hydrolysis or alcoholysis, and this is a hazard both in capacity to generate pressure and in flammability.

A few other silicon compounds are known to be toxic. For example, methyl and ethyl orthosilicates have some toxicity. (See Silicon ethers and esters under Silicon compounds.) Products of this type are used in formulating silicones, such as RTV. It should not be assumed that because silicone polymers are physiologically inert, silicone products are completely harmless, though this is usually the case.

Silicone rubber is in general resistant to bacterial or fungus growth, but attack has been noted in a few cases (144,145). This attack is very probably upon nonsilicone components, such as fatty acids, but the net result is some ability to support growth.

Uses

The thousand or so silicone products now commercially available have uses in many industries, in medicine and surgery, and in the home (146). The following brief summary is intended to be illustrative over a broad spectrum.

Electrical. Fluids, greases, rubbers, resins, and adhesives are all used as electrical insulators where resistance to prolonged heating and to other unfavorable factors, such as corona, ozone, or humidity, are involved, or where reliability is very important (147).

Dielectric fluids are used in transformers and capacitors, and for arc-quenching in switch gear. They are also used as dielectric coolants or heat-transfer media for electronic components, such as power tubes, rectifiers, and magnetrons. They are used as coolants in electrical discharge machining.

Greases are used for potting, sealing, and protecting electrical components. Applied to high-voltage insulators, grease protects from contamination. An early use of this type of product was a filler for high-voltage conduits on aircraft, to seal out moisture and eliminate corona discharge.

Impregnating and dipping varnishes were used for insulation of motors for shipboard use by the Navy, in order to permit use of thinner insulation and therefore construction of smaller motors to operate at higher temperatures. These varnishes fill all the air spaces and voids within the windings, and bond and protect, as well as insulate. They are also used on transformers and coils. Other varnishes are used as protective coatings on printed circuits. Silicone insulation can introduce a special problem due to more rapid wear of commutator brushes in enclosed motors (9).

Silicone rubber is used to insulate wire and cable. For power cable, particularly underground, it provides for dissipation of heat, and increases current-carrying capacity. It improves the reliability of shipboard cable. Rubber and resin are also used to coat glass cloth, or other fabric, which is then used as sleeving to cover insulated wire. Silicone rubber is used for spark-plug boots, and insulation for ignition harness in automobiles.

Two-part room-temperature curing rubber is used for potting, encapsulating, and embedding electrical and electronic devices, circuits, or systems. It is also used to make dip or conformal coatings for such devices and systems. Examples are the encapsulation of aircraft transformers or of assemblies of power supplies, to protect them from environment and from shock. A clear RTV may be used for embedding or potting where the assembly may have to be repaired. RTV is also used as insulation around connectors and contacts. The one-part types of RTV are general-purpose adhesives and sealants for bonding, environmental protection, and protection against shock and vibration. Flowable one-part RTV is used to make conformal coating for printed circuit boards. See Embedding.

Resins are used to make rigid glass-cloth laminates for electrical panel boards, printed circuit boards, and slot wedges for motors, and to bond mica segments for commutator cones, motor slot liners, and coil forms.

Mechanical. Laminates are also used for aircraft firewalls and ducts, and filled molded resins for electrical connectors and brake shoes. Silicone sponge resin can also be used to fill voids and act as a firewall and insulation.

Silicone fluids and greases are used as lubricants (148). Methyl and phenyl fluids are useful for long-term light service as in instruments, or as thread lubricants. Chlorinated phenyl fluids are used for heavy service, as in high-temperature aircraft turbine pumps and in jet engines. The corresponding greases are used where the lubricant must remain in place.

Fluids are used for hydraulic power transmission, as pressure hydraulic fluids, or in fluid clutches. They are also useful for vibration damping, as in dash-pot dampers and torsional vibration dampers for automobiles and aircraft. Rubber is also useful to dampen vibration. Fluid may be used as a "fluid spring" to replace conventional helical steel springs.

Oligomeric compounds, such as $Ph_2MeSiOSiMePhOSiMePh_2$, are used as diffusion-pump fluids.

Silicone rubber is made into O-rings, gaskets, and aerodynamic seals which are used as mechanical seals. Examples are transmission oil seals for fluid drive transmissions, or seals for aircraft doors. It is combined with glass or other cloth to make heater ducts, for example, jet starter hose or deicer ducts.

Processing. Silicone fluids and emulsions are used in mold-release agents in making automobile tires, and as release agents in ingot molds and glass molds. (See Abherents.) In automotive work methyl alkyl silicone fluids are used for release because dimethyl silicone can cause problems in subsequent painting operations. Resins are used in making ceramic cores for metal casting. RTV is used to make molds for casting epoxy coatings on transistors. Paper, used as interleaving for stacks of rubber or plastics, is made nonadherent, even to common pressure-sensitive adhesives, by treatment with silicone fluids. The spouts of paper milk cartons are treated to make them open readily.

Textiles are treated with fluids to provide water repellency, oil and stain resistance, soft finish, and antistatic properties. Silicones are also components of crease-proofing formulations. Leather is treated with fluid to separate the fibers, soften the leather, and provide water repellency.

Glass is treated with fluids to improve strength, reduce breakage, and make the surface water repellent.

Antifoams (see Foams) are used in food processing, in fermentation of wine, and in frying oil. They are also used in chemical processing to increase effective kettle capacity, in making paint resins, etc, and in the petroleum industry.

Fluids are used to control the formation of foam in foamed polyurethan (polyether and polyester types). The silicone–polyether copolymer fluids are used in one-shot polyurethan foam, where they act to give control of pore size and to guide toward closed- or open-cell types of foam. They make bubble formation easier, promote uniform cell size, and prevent bubble coalescence (149).

Fluids are added to paints to improve flowing, spreading, and leveling, and as antifloat agents for pigments.

Fluids are used for heating baths and for sterilizers, for example, for dental instruments.

Polyethylene and polypropylene pellets for injection molding can be treated with a little silicone fluid to make them flow more easily.

Copolymer fluids are used as coagulants for rubber latex, as components of fungicides and insecticides, and in ball-milling and dispersing pigments.

Fluids with SiH are useful to help prevent corrosion, as reduction sensitizers in silver halide emulsions, and as reducing agents in laboratory processes.

Aerospace. Besides uses in electrical insulation, sealants, and gaskets, silicones (foam rubber) are used as ablative coats for missiles. (See Ablation.) Rubber is used for tubing for in-flight feeding, and for making oxygen masks. Specially formulated pastes or putties, made from solvent-resistant polymers, are used as channel sealants in aircraft wings.

Construction. Masonry walls and highways are made water-repellent by surface treatment or by mixing silicone with cement. Resins in organic solvents and aqueous solutions of sodium methyl siliconate are used for such purposes.

RTV is used to seal spaces between masonry, and between masonry and window frames, etc. It is also used to seal glass into window-wall construction. It is applied to the surface of roofs to make a continuous membrane coating impervious to water and weather. It is also used over wood or masonry to provide a water-repellent, durable "traffic topping," for example on patios or around swimming pools.

Silicone paint or copolymer paints are used on smokestacks, building sidings, space heaters, ovens, and other appliances. Weather-resistant silicone–acrylic paints are used for coil coatings for making aluminum siding.

Medical, Surgical, and Cosmetic. Silicone fluids are used as baths in the treatment of burns, as lubricants for artificial eyes, for gastric disorders, and for storage of antibiotics. Wound dressings are treated to prevent them from adhering to tissue. Plasma bottles are treated to prevent coagulation of blood and to keep the blood from wetting the bottle, thus making it drain more completely.

Rubber parts are used for surgical tubing, for heart valves, for prosthetic parts and contact lenses. RTV is also used for prostheses and for encasing "pacemakers" for heart patients. It has been used as a dental mold material.

Medical uses are related to pharmaceutical and cosmetic uses (150), such as skin lotions for dermatitis, sun tan lotions, coatings for razor blades to prevent skin irritation, shaving cream, and hair treatment. Greases are used to protect soldiers' feet when immersed in water for long periods.

The Dow Corning Center for Aid to Medical Research, founded in 1959 in Midland, Mich., is an excellent source of information on medical as well as surgical uses for silicones (151).

Consumer Products. Early consumer products included paper treated with fluid used to clean eyeglasses. Home-applied treatments for leather are also available.

Many furniture and automobile polishes contain silicone fluids which make them rub out more easily, give more brilliant shine, and permit easy removal of liquids spilled on the polished surface. Some automobile polish fluids, designed to resist the action of detergents, contain special silicones.

Household equipment, such as baking or frying pans, may be treated with silicone so that the food releases from them more easily. Ovens may be treated similarly to aid in cleaning. Ironing spray containing silicone fluid makes the iron slip more easily over cloth.

RTV rubber is used as an adhesive and sealant, for example, to caulk around bathtubs, or to repair broken dishes or plastic parts, and to insulate ignition wires in automobiles.

Bouncing putty is used as a toy, but also as a means of providing exercise to people suffering from partial paralysis.

In the laboratory, silicone grease is used for stopcocks, and silicone gums are used as the stationary phase in gas chromatographs.

Bibliography

"Silicones" in *ECT* 1st ed., Vol. 12, pp. 393–413, by R. R. McGregor, Mellon Institute of Industrial Research.

1. F. S. Kipping and L. L. Lloyd, *J. Chem. Soc.* **1901,** 79, 449.
2. U.S. Pat. 2,258,218 (Oct. 1941), E. G. Rochow (to General Electric Co.).
3. R. R. McGregor, *Silicones*, McGraw-Hill Book Co., Inc., New York, 1954.
4. *Chemical Statistics Handbook*, Manufacturing Chemists' Association, Washington, D.C., 1966.
5. C. B. Hurd, *J. Am. Chem. Soc.* **68,** 364 (1946).

6. *Chem. Eng. News* **30**, 4517 (1952).
7. R. N. Meals and F. M. Lewis, *Silicones*, Reinhold Publishing Co., New York, 1959.
7a. L. Alfred, E. G. Rochow, and F. G. A. Stone, *J. Inorg. Nucl. Chem.* **2**, 416 (1956); R. West and R. H. Barney, *J. Inorg. Nucl. Chem.* **7**, 297 (1958).
8. P. J. Flory, V. Crescenzi, and J. E. Mark, *J. Am. Chem. Soc.* **86**, 146 (1964).
9. E. G. Rochow, *An Introduction to the Chemistry of the Silicones*, John Wiley & Sons, Inc., New York, 1951.
10. W. Patnode and D. F. Wilcock, *J. Am. Chem. Soc.* **68**, 358 (1946).
11. D. W. Scott, *J. Am. Chem. Soc.* **68**, 2294 (1946).
12. D. F. Wilcock, *J. Am. Chem. Soc.* **69**, 480 (1947).
13. T. C. Kendrick, *J. Chem. Soc.* **1965**, 2027.
14. J. F. Brown and G. M. J. Slusarczuk, *J. Am. Chem. Soc.* **87**, 931 (1965).
15. W. T. Grubb and R. C. Osthoff, *J. Am. Chem. Soc.* **77**, 1405 (1955).
16. K. Vesely and M. Kucera, *Symposium über Makromolecule in Wiesbaden, DBR, Kurzmitteilungen 4, B3, 1959.*
17. M. Kucera, M. Jelinek, J. Lanikova, and K. Vesely, *J. Polymer Sci.* **53**, 311 (1961).
18. E. D. Brown and J. B. Carmichael, *J. Polymer Sci.* **B3**, 473 (1965).
19. F. R. Mayo and F. M. Lewis, *J. Am. Chem. Soc.* **66**, 1544 (1944).
20. Z. Laita and M. Jelinek, *Vysokomolekul. Soedin.* **5**, 1268 (1963).
21. C. R. Kruger and E. G. Rochow, *J. Polymer Sci.* **A2**, 3179 (1964).
22. A. J. Barry and H. N. Beck, "Silicone Polymers," in F. G. A. Stone and W. A. G. Graham, eds., *Inorganic Polymers*, Academic Press, Inc., New York, 1962.
23. A. V. Tobolsky, *J. Polymer Sci.* **C9**, 157 (1965).
24. P. J. Flory and J. A. Semlyen, *J. Am. Chem. Soc.* **88**, 3209 (1966).
25. A. J. Barry, *J. Appl. Phys.* **17**, 1020 (1946).
26. P. J. Flory, L. Mandelkern, J. B. Kinsinger, and W. B. Shultz, *J. Am. Chem. Soc.* **74**, 3364 (1952).
27. A. Charlesby, *J. Polymer Sci.* **17**, 379 (1955).
28. E. D. Brown, Jr., *Am. Soc. Lubric. Eng. Trans.* **9**, 31 (1966).
29. K. E. Polmanteer and M. J. Hunter, *J. Appl. Polymer Sci.* **1**, 3 (1959).
30. T. V. Koroleva, T. A. Krasovskaya, M. V. Sobolevskii, L. V. Gornets, and Yu. E. Raskin, *Soviet Plastics* **28** (Jan. 1967).
31. K. B. Yerrick and H. N. Beck, *Rubber Chem. Technol.* **37**, 261 (1964).
32. H. M. Schiefer and J. VanDyke, *Am. Soc. Lubric. Eng. Trans.* **7**, 32 (1964).
33. H. M. Schiefer, *Am. Soc. Lubric. Eng. Trans.* **9**, 36 (1966).
34. U.S. Pat. 2,834,748 (May 1958), D. L. Bailey and F. M. O'Connor (to Union Carbide Co.).
35. R. N. Meals, *Ann. N.Y. Acad. Sci.* **125**, 137 (1964).
36. V. Bazant, V. Chvalovsky, and J. Rathousky, *Organosilicon Compounds*, Academic Press, Inc., New York, 1965.
37. *Gmelins Handbuch der anorganischen Chemie*, 8th ed., System Nummer 15, Silicium, Teil C, Organische Siliciumverbindungen, Verlag Chemie G.m.b.H., Weinheim, West Germany, 1958.
38. R. L. Merker, *J. Polymer Sci.* **A2** (1), 31 (1964).
39. A. Charlesby, *Atomic Radiation and Polymers*, Pergamon Press, Inc., New York, 1960, Chap. 16.
40. F. M. Lewis, *Rubber Chem. Technol.* **35**, 1222 (1962).
41. U.S. Pat. 3,020,260 (Feb. 1962), M. E. Nelson (to Dow Corning Corp.).
42. U.S. Pat. 2,843,555 (July 1958), C. A. Berridge (to General Electric Co.).
43. Fr. Pat. 1,198,749 (Dec. 1959), L. Ceyzeriat (to Société des Usines Chimiques Rhône Poulenc).
44. U.S. Pat. 2,615,861 (Oct. 1952), P. P. Peyrot and L. J. Dumoulin.
45. U.S. Pat. 3,077,465 (Feb. 1963), L. B. Bruner (to Dow Corning Corp.).
46. U.S. Pat. 3,082,527 (March 1963), S. Nitzsche and M. Wick (to Wacker-Chemie, G.m.b.H.).
47. Fr. Pat. 1,314,649 (Dec. 1962), E. Sweet (to Dow Corning Corp.).
48. U.S. Pat. 3,334,067 (Aug. 1967), D. R. Weyenberg (to Dow Corning Corp.).
49. J. Nagy and A. Borbely-Kaszmann, *International Symposium on Organosilicon Chemistry, Scientific Communications, Prague, 1965*, p. 201.
50. C. Eaborn, *Organosilicon Compounds*, Butterworths Scientific Publications, London, 1960.
51. U.S. Pat. 2,449,572 (Sept. 1948), C. E. Welsh (to General Electric Co.).

52. Brit. Pat. 841,825 (July 1960), to Wacker-Chemie G.m.b.H.
53. Belg. Pat. 685,439 (Feb. 1967), to Dow Corning Corp.
54. J. R. McLoughlin, *Insulation (Libertyville)* **2** (11), 28 (1956).
55. Fr. Pat. 1,313,814 (Nov. 1962), to Imperial Chemical Industries, Ltd.
56. Fr. Pat. 1,326,879 (April 1963), W. Simmler and H. W. Kauczor (to Farbenfabriken Bayer, A.G.).
57. Fr. Pat. 1,327,546 (April 1963), L. A. Haluska (to Dow Corning Corp.).
58. K. A. Andrianov, *Metalorganic Polymers*, Interscience Publishers, a div. of John Wiley & Sons, Inc., New York, 1965.
59. H. Schroeder, O. G. Schaffling, T. B. Larchar, F. F. Frulla, and T. L. Heying, *Rubber Chem. Technol.* **39**, 1184 (1966).
60. U.S. Pat. 3,317,461 (May 1967), E. P. Plueddemann (to Dow Corning Corp.).
61. U.S. Pat. 2,380,995 (Aug. 1945), E. G. Rochow (to General Electric Co.).
62. U.S. Pat. 2,449,821 (Sept. 1948), J. E. Sellers and J. L. Davis (to General Electric Co.).
63. U.S. Pat. 2,389,931 (Nov. 1945), C. E. Reed and J. T. Coe (to General Electric Co.).
64. D. G. Weaver and R. J. O'Connors, *Ind. Eng. Chem.* **50**, 132 (1958).
65. V. Bazant, *Pure Appl. Chem.* **13**, 313 (1966).
65a. V. Bazant, J. Joklik, and J. Rathousky, *Angew. Chem. Intern. Ed. Engl.* **7** (2), 112 (1968).
66. J. J. Zuckerman, "The direct Synthesis of Organosilicon Compounds," in H. J. Emeleus and A. G. Sharpe, eds., *Advanced Inorganic Chemistry and Radiochemistry*, Vol. 6, Academic Press, Inc., New York, 1964, p. 383.
67. R. J. H. Voorhoeve, *Organohalosilanes, Precursors to Silicones*, Elsevier Publishing Co., New York, 1967.
68. A. D. Petrov, V. F. Mironov, V. A. Ponomarenko, and E. A. Chernyshev, *Synthesis of Organosilicon Monomers*, Consultants Bureau, New York, 1964.
69. B. A. Bluestein and H. R. McEntee, *Advan. Chem. Ser.* **23**, 233 (1959).
70. U.S. Pat. 2,557,931 (June 1951), A. J. Barry (to Dow Corning Corp.); *Advan. Chem. Ser.* **23**, 246 (1959).
71. U.S. Pat. 2,511,820 (June 1950), A. J. Barry, D. E. Hook, and L. DePree (to Dow Corning Corp.).
72. U.S. Pat. 2,770,634 (Nov. 1956), D. R. Weyenberg (to Dow Corning Corp.).
73. U.S. Pat. 2,563,557 (Aug. 1951), A. E. Schubert and C. E. Reed (to General Electric Co.).
74. S. Fordham, *Silicones*, Philosophical Library, New York, 1960.
75. R. Gutoff, *Ind. Eng. Chem.* **49**, 1807 (1957).
76. Brit. Pat. 843,273 (Aug. 1960), A. N. Pines (to Union Carbide Corp.).
77. N. Kirk, *Ind. Eng. Chem.* **51**, 515 (1959).
77a. U.S. Pat. 3,179,619 (April 1965), E. D. Brown (to Dow Corning Corp.); U.S. Pat. 3,050,492 (Aug. 1962) K. E. Polmanteer and E. D. Brown (to Dow Corning Corp.).
78. S. W. Kantor, W. T. Grubb, and R. C. Osthoff, *J. Am. Chem. Soc.* **76**, 5190 (1954).
79. U.S. Pat. 2,443,353 (June 1948), J. F. Hyde and W. Daudt (to Dow Corning Corp.).
80. *Physical Properties of Lubricants*, American Society for Testing Materials, Philadelphia, Pa., 1949.
81. P. W. Bridgman, *Proc. Am. Acad. Arts Sci.* **77**, 129 (1949).
82. *Ibid.*, 115 (1949).
83. W. Noll, *Kolloid-Z.* **211**, 98 (1966).
84. H. W. Fox, P. W. Taylor, and W. A. Zisman, *Ind. Eng. Chem.* **39**, 1401 (1947).
85. A. A. Bondi, *Physical Chemistry of Lubricating Oils*, Reinhold Publishing Co., New York, 1951.
86. A. Weissler, *J. Am. Chem. Soc.* **71**, 93 (1949).
87. E. B. Baker, A. J. Barry, and M. J. Hunter, *Ind. Eng. Chem.* **38**, 1117 (1946).
88. F. Clark, *Insulating Materials for Design and Engineering Practice*, John Wiley & Sons, Inc., New York, 1962.
89. *Silicone Dielectric Fluids and Compounds*, S-24A, The General Electric Company, Waterford, New York, 1963.
90. P. Cannon, L. E. St. Pierre, and A. A. Miller, *J. Chem. Eng. Data* **5**, 236 (1960).
91. G. E. Vogel and F. O. Stark, *J. Chem. Eng. Data* **9**, 599 (1964).
92. *Versilube Silicone Lubricants*, S-10B, The General Electric Company, Waterford, New York, 1966.
93. D. Tabor and W. D. Winer, *Am. Soc. Lubric. Eng. Trans.* **8**, 69 (1965).

94. R. A. Labine, *Chem. Eng.* **67** (14), 102 (1960).

95. *Silicone Rubber Handbook*, The General Electric Company, Waterford, New York, 1963.

96. U.S. Pat. 2,890,188 (June 1959), G. M. Konkle, J. A. McHard, and K. Polmanteer (to Dow Corning Corp.).

97. Brit. Pat. 791,169 (Feb. 1958), Imperial Chemical Industries, Ltd.

98. Fr. Pat. 1,379,242 (Oct. 1964), J. F. Hyde (to Dow Corning Corp.).

99. J. C. Caprino, *Mater. Symp. Natl. SAMPE Symp., 7th, Los Angeles, 1964,* sect. 14.

100. W. Brenn, D. Lum, and M. W. Riley, *High Temperature Plastics*, Reinhold Publishing Co., New York, 1962.

101. W. Postelnek, *Ind. Eng. Chem.* **50,** 1602 (1958).

102. J. A. Barrie and B. Platt, *Polymer* **4,** 303 (1963).

102a. J. H. Hildebrand and R. L. Scott *"The Solubility of Non-Electrolytes,"* Reinhold Publishing Co., New York, 1950.

103. R. M. Barrer, J. A. Barrie, and N. K. Raman, *Rubber Chem. Technol.* **36,** 642, 651 (1963).

104. C. J. Major and K. Kammermeyer, *Mod. Plastics* **39** (11), 135 (1962).

105. U.S. Pats. 3,046,293 and 3,046,294 (July 1962), R. A. Pike (to Union Carbide Corp.).

106. *RTV Silicone Rubber*, S-3C, The General Electric Co., Waterford, New York, 1964.

107. *Silicone Rubber Adhesive/Sealants for Industrial Applications*, S-2D, The General Electric Co., Waterford, New York, 1967.

108. *Silicone Thermal Barriers for Aerospace Applications*, S-30, The General Electric Co., Waterford, New York, 1966.

109. F. J. Modic, *Proc. 6th Elec. Insul. Conf. (Sept. 1965)*, The Institute of Electrical and Electronics Engineers, Inc., New York, 1966, pp. 131.

110. J. F. Brown et al., *J. Am. Chem. Soc.* **82,** 6194 (1960).

111. H. C. Smith, D. L. Sweeney, and E. G. Bittner, *Insulation (Libertyville)* **13** (7), 257, 268 (1967).

112. F. J. Modic, *Adhesives Age* **5** (Dec. 1962).

113. N. Pilpel, *Chem. Process Eng.* **45,** 492 (1964).

114. *Silicone Greases*, S-21, The General Electric Co., Waterford, New York, 1965.

115. *Silicone Resin Intermediate for Copolymer Vehicles*, S-22, The General Electric Co., Waterford, New York, 1967.

116. E. P. Goldberg, *J. Polymer Sci.* **B2** (8), 835 (1964).

117. U.S. Pat. 3,189,662 (June 1965), H. A. Vaughn (to General Electric Co.).

118. H. R. Baker, R. E. Kagarise, J. G. O'Rear, and P. J. Sneigoski, *J. Chem. Eng. Data* **11,** 110 (1966).

119. M. V. Sobolevskii, et al., *Plasticheskie Massy* **1962** (3), 13.

120. I. Lipovetz and A. Borbely, *Periodica Polytech.* **2,** 259 (1958).

121. E. L. Warrick, *Ind. Eng. Chem.* **47,** 2388 (1955).

122. A. M. Bueche, *J. Polymer Sci.* **19,** 297 (1956).

123. L. E. St. Pierre, H. A. Dewhurst, and A. M. Bueche, *J. Polymer Sci.* **36,** 105 (1959).

124. A. Chapiro, *Radiation Chemistry of Polymeric Systems*, Interscience Publishers, a div. of John Wiley & Sons, Inc., New York, 1962.

125. R. K. Jenkins, *J. Polymer Sci.* **A1** (4), 2161 (1966).

126. W. J. Bobear, *Rubber Age* **95,** 71 (1964).

127. R. Harrington, *Rubber Age* **84,** 798 (1959).

128. D. J. Fischer, R. G. Chaffee, and V. Flegel, *Rubber Age* **87,** 59 (1960).

129. S. D. Gehman and G. C. Gregson, *Rubber Rev.* **33** (5), 1429 (1960).

130. H. Schroeder, O. G. Schaffling, T. D. Larchar, F. F. Frulla, and T. L. Heying, *Contract Nobs* 92143 (1966).

131. A. D. Delman, A. A. Stein, J. J. Kelly, and B. B. Simms, *J. Appl. Polymer Sci.* **11,** 1979 (1967).

132. R. L. Merker and M. J. Scott, *J. Polymer Sci.* **A2,** 15 (1964).

133. L. J. Bellamy, *The Infra-Red Spectra of Complex Molecules*, 2nd ed., John Wiley & Sons, Inc., New York, 1958.

134. J. H. Lady, G. M. Bower, R. E. Adams, and P. F. Byrne, *Anal. Chem.* **31,** 1100 (1959).

135. F. Rodriguez, R. A. Kulakowski, and O. K. Clark, *Ind. Eng. Chem. Prod. Res. Develop.* **5,** 121 (1966).

136. N. N. Sokolov, K. A. Andrianov, and S. M. Akimova, *J. Gen. Chem. USSR (Engl. Transl.)* **25,** 647 (1955).

137. C. A. Hirt, *Anal. Chem.* **33**, 1786 (1961).

138. N. A. Palamarchuk, S. V. Syavtsillo, and N. M. Turkel'taub, *Gaz. Khromatogr. Akad. Nauk SSSR, Tr. Vtoror Vses Konf. Moscow 1962*, pp. 303–306; *Chem. Abstr.* **62**, 7117 (1965).

139. J. A. McHard, "Silicones" in G. M. Kline, ed., *Analytical Chemistry of Polymers*, Interscience Publishers, Inc., New York, 1959.

140. A. P. Kreshkov et al., *Manual for the Analysis of Monomeric and Polymeric Siliconorganic Compounds*, Moscow, 1962 (in Russian); *Chem. Abstr.* **58**, 10735^d, 1963.

141. V. K. Rowe, H. C. Spencer, and S. L. Bass, *J. Ind. Hyg. Toxicol.* **30**, 332 (1948).

142. L. C. Clark and F. Gollan, *Science* **152**, 1755 (1966).

143. *Fluids and Lubricants, FS-1265 Fluid*, Bull. 05-168, Dow Corning Corporation, Midland, Mich., 1967.

144. O. H. Calderon and E. E. Staffeldt, *Intern. Biodeterioration Bull.* **1** (2), 33 (1965).

145. S. H. Ross, *U.S. Dept. Comm. Office Tech. Serv. AD 429476* (1963).

146. W. Noll, *Chemie und Technologie der Silicone*, Verlag Chemie G.m.b.H., Weinheim, West Germany, 1960; for translation of 2nd German ed. (1965), see W. Noll, *Chemistry and Technology of Silicone*, Academic Press, Inc., New York, 1968.

147. J. H. Davis and D. E. W. Rees, *Proc. Inst. Elec. Engrs.* **112**, 1607 (1965).

148. R. W. Awe and H. M. Schiefer, "Silicones," in R. C. Gunderson and A. W. Hart, eds., *Synthetic Lubricants*, Reinhold Publishing Corp., New York, 1962.

149. R. J. Boudreau, *Modern Plastics*, **44** (5), 133 (1967).

150. D. Pail and C. W. Todd, *Am. Perfumer* **77**, 62 (1962).

151. S. A. Braley, Jr., *Am. Chem. Soc. Div. Org. Coatings, Plastics Chem., Preprints* **24** (2), 189 (1964).

ROBERT MEALS
General Electric Co.

SILYLATING AGENTS

This article deals with silylating agents (methylsilylating agents) and with organofunctional silylating agents (silane coupling agents).

Methylsilylating agents convert mineral surfaces to water-repellent, low-energy surfaces useful in water-resistant treatments for masonry, electrical insulators, and packings for gas chromatography, and in noncaking fire extinguishers. As an analytical tool, methylsilylation of active hydrogens in polar molecules converts many complex natural products to tractable fluids that can be separated and analyzed by distillation, gas chromatography, or mass spectrometry.

Silane coupling agents modify the interface between mineral surfaces and organic resins to improve the adhesion between resin and surface, thus improving physical properties and water resistance of reinforced plastics. Suitable coupling agents are now available for any of the common plastics with metal, glass, or many other inorganic reinforcements. Major applications for these coupling agents are in reinforced plastics for boats, storage tanks, pipes, and architectural structures. Newer applications are being found in treatment of mineral fillers and pigments for paint and rubber, in primers to improve the adhesion of paints and plastics to metals and other mineral surfaces, and in tarnish- and corrosion-inhibitors for silver, copper, aluminum, and steel.

Methylsilylating Agents

Surface Modification. The discovery by Patnode (1) in 1940 that methylchlorosilanes in the vapor phase will react with many types of surfaces to produce water-repellent films has led to one of the most important developments in the organosilicon field. Methylchlorosilanes react with surface water, hydroxyl groups, or other active hydrogen groups of the surface to liberate HCl and deposit a very thin film of methylpolysiloxanes which has a very low critical surface tension (2) and is therefore not wetted by water. Ceramic insulators may be treated with methylchlorosilane vapors or solutions in inert solvents to maintain high electrical resistivity under humid conditions (3). The corrosive action of the evolved HCl can be avoided by prehydrolyzing the chlorosilanes in an organic solvent and applying as organic solutions of organopolysiloxanols. Hydrolyzed methylchlorosilanes are also dissolved in aqueous alkali and applied as aqueous solutions of sodium methylsiliconates. The siliconates are neutralized by carbon dioxide in the air to form an insoluble, water-resistant methylpolysiloxane film within 24 hr. Treatment of brick, mortar, sandstone, concrete, and other masonry protects the surface from spalling, cracking, efflorescence, and other types of damage caused by water. The total annual market in the U.S.A. for silane water repellents is more than a million dollars at $1–3/lb of applied silicon compounds.

In recent years a number of reactive monomeric silylating agents have been marketed for treatment of polar materials. These materials are supplied as reagent-grade chemicals or as silylating kits in appropriate solvents, selling for $6–35 per 100 g of reactive silane. Although they find important applications in analytical procedures, they have not found a market as industrial chemicals. Commercially available silylating agents are shown in Table 1.

Table 1. Silylating Agents as Analytical Reagents

Chemical name	Formula
trimethylchlorosilane (with amines)	$(CH_3)_3SiCl$
n-trimethylsilyldimethylamine	$(CH_3)_3SiN(CH_3)_2$
hexamethyldisilazane	$(CH_3)_3SiNHSi(CH_3)_3$
n-trimethylsilylacetamide	$CH_3CONHSi(CH_3)_3$
bis(trimethylsilyl)acetamide	$CH_3C\begin{smallmatrix}\diagup OSi(CH_3)_3 \\ \diagdown NSi(CH_3)_3\end{smallmatrix}$
bis(trimethylsilyl)trifluoroacetamide	$CF_3C\begin{smallmatrix}\diagup OSi(CH_3)_3 \\ \diagdown NSi(CH_3)_3\end{smallmatrix}$
dimethylchlorosilane	$(CH_3)_2HSiCl$
tetramethyldisilazane	$(CH_3)_2HSiNHSiH(CH_3)_2$
bromomethyldimethylchlorosilane	$BrCH_2(CH_3)_2SiCl$
chloromethyldimethylchlorosilane	$ClCH_2(CH_3)_2SiCl$
di(chloromethyl)tetramethyldisilazane	$ClCH_2(CH_3)_2SiNHSi(CH_3)_2CH_2Cl$

The chlorosilanes react rapidly with active hydrogens in the presence of amines to form silylated derivatives and amine hydrochloride:

$$ROH + (CH_3)_3SiCl \xrightarrow{\text{pyridine}} ROSi(CH_3)_3 + \text{pyridine.HCl}$$

Silylamines and silazanes are somewhat more convenient to use since they generate volatile by-products. A trace of hydrogen chloride or chlorosilane is added to catalyze the reaction.

$$ROH + (CH_3)_3SiN(CH_3)_2 \rightarrow ROSi(CH_3)_3 + (CH_3)_2NH\uparrow$$

$$2\,ROH + (CH_3)_3SiNHSi(CH_3)_3 \rightarrow 2\,ROSi(CH_3)_3 + NH_3\uparrow$$

Molecular Modification. Trimethylsilyl (TMS) derivatives of polyols were proposed by Sprung and Nelson (4) as convenient heat-stable derivatives for isolation by distillation. TMS derivatives are easily prepared, are stable toward heat and oxygen, have considerably lower boiling points than the corresponding polyols, and are quantitatively hydrolyzed to yield the original material.

A method of silylating biologically active compounds like heparin, penicillin, and erythromycin with a mixture of trimethylchlorosilane and hexamethyldisilazane was first reported by Speier (5) in 1956. Certain undesirable properties of the compounds, like bitter taste and rapid elimination from the body, were changed without reducing their biological activities.

TMS derivatives of phenols were prepared by Langer, Patages, and Wender (6) for identification of parent phenols by gas–liquid chromatography (GLC).

In a significant study of wide scope, Bentley, Sweeley, and co-workers (7) established trimethylsilylation as the most versatile and important derivatization for the gas–liquid partition chromatography of carbohydrates.

Similar techniques have been used to prepare volatile products from such intractable materials as amino acids (8), peptides (9), steroids (10), flavonoid compounds (11), bile (12), and Krebs cycle acids (13).

Bis(trimethylsilyl)acetamide (14) and bis(trimethylsilyl)trifluoroacetamide (15) are the most reactive silylating agents and are used for the preparation of TMS derivatives of amides, ureas, amino acids, hindered phenols, carboxylic acids, and enols.

It is possible to use halogen-sensitive detectors in gas-chromatographic analysis of acidic or phenolic pesticides by silylating them with halogenated silylating agents like chloromethyldimethylchlorosilane, bromomethyldimethylchlorosilane, or di(chloromethyl)tetramethyldisilazane (16).

Many siliceous supports for packing of gas-chromatography columns have adsorptive properties that result in "tailing" in the detection of volatile molecules. The common silylating agents are used to deactivate active sites such as Si—OH, Al—OH, and Fe—OH on siliceous supports (17).

Mass Spectrometry. TMS derivatives of alcohols cleave in the α position in a mass spectrometer yielding intense peaks allowing unambiguous assignment of the hydroxyl position (18). Unsaturated acids were oxidized by OsO_4 and Na_2SO_3 to dihydroxy compounds that were converted to TMS derivatives and identified by mass spectrometry (19).

Silicate Modifications. A method was described by Lentz (20) in which silicate minerals were simultaneously acid-leached and trimethylsilyl end-blocked to yield specific trimethylsilyl silicates having the same silicate structure as the mineral from which they were derived. Olivine, hemimorphite, sodalite, natrolite, laumontite, and sodium silicates were converted to TMS derivatives of orthosilicates, pyrosilicates, cyclic polysilicates, etc, making it possible to classify the minerals according to their silicate structure. The same technique was used to analyze the silicate structure of hydrated portland-cement paste (21), and also to show the effect of carbon dioxide on silicate structures in portland-cement pastes (22).

Organofunctional Silylating Agents

The concept that two dissimilar materials may be held together by a third intermediate material as coupling agent was used by Plato to explain how a universe made up of four elements—earth, air, fire, and water—could exist as a homogeneous whole. "It is not possible for two things to be fairly united without a third, for they need a bond between them which shall join them both ..., that as the first is to the middle, so is the middle to the last ... Then all will be unity."

Since organofunctional silicones are hybrids of silica and of organic materials related to resins, it is not surprising that they were tested as coupling agents to improve the bonding of organic resins to mineral surfaces. A major need for coupling agents arose in 1940 when glass fibers were first used as reinforcement in organic resins. The specific strength-to-weight ratios of early glass-reinforced plastics were higher than aluminum or steel, but they lost much of their strength during prolonged exposure to moisture.

Although glass treated with methylsilylating agents is resistant to water it does not provide good adhesion of organic resins. The sizing of glass with allyl silanes (23) or with unsaturated chrome complexes (24) was patented as a means of improving the wet-strength retention of glass-reinforced polyesters. Vinyltrichlorosilane, applied to glass from vapor or from a solvent, was claimed to be more effective than the allylsilane treatment (25). All treatments with chlorosilanes required a water rinse to remove HCl. It was postulated that the coupling agents, deposited on the glass surface, reacted in some way with the resins during their cure. All successful coupling agents have in one way or another fulfilled the requirements of this concept.

A universal finish (NOL-24) for glass reinforcements in polyesters, epoxies, phenolics, etc, was developed at the Naval Ordnance Laboratories from alkenyltri-

Table 2. Commercial Silane Coupling Agents

No.	Name	Formula	Application
1.	vinyltriethoxysilane	$CH_2{=}CHSi(OC_2H_5)_3$	unsaturated polymers
2.	vinyltris(β-methoxyethoxy)silane	$CH_2{=}CHSi(OCH_2CH_2OCH_3)_3$	unsaturated polymers
3.	vinyltriacetoxysilane	$CH_2{=}CHSi(OOCCH_3)_3$	unsaturated polymers
4.	γ-methacryloxypropyltrimethoxy-silane	$CH_2{=}C(CH_3)COO(CH_2)_3Si(OCH_3)_3$	unsaturated polymers
5.	γ-aminopropyltriethoxysilane	$H_2NCH_2CH_2CH_2Si(OC_2H_5)_3$	epoxies, phenolics, nylon
6.	γ-(β-aminoethyl)aminopropyl-trimethoxysilane	$H_2NCH_2CH_2NH(CH_2)_3Si(OCH_3)_3$	epoxies, phenolics, nylon
7.	γ-glycidoxypropyltrimethoxy-silane	$\overset{O}{\overset{\displaystyle\triangle}{CH_2CHCH_2}}O(CH_2)_3Si(OCH_3)_3$	almost all resins
8.	γ-mercaptopropyltrimethoxy-silane	$HSCH_2CH_2CH_2Si(OCH_3)_3$	almost all resins
9.	β-(3,4-epoxycyclohexyl)ethyl-trimethoxysilane	$\text{(epoxycyclohexyl)}{-}CH_2CH_2Si(OCH_3)_3$	epoxies
10.	γ-chloropropyltrimethoxysilane	$ClCH_2CH_2CH_2Si(OMe)_3$	epoxies

chlorosilanes and resorcinol (26). Practice in the reinforced plastics industry, however, has been to use specific coupling agents with different resins rather than to standardize on one universal finish for all resins.

All commercial silane coupling agents are of the general structure $X_3Si(CH_2)_nY$, where n is 0–3, X is a hydrolyzable group on silicon, and Y is an organofunctional group selected for compatibility with a given resin (Table 2).

Since silane coupling agents are generally applied to glass from water solutions, the hydrolyzable groups are only essential for generating intermediate silanols:

$$X_3Si(CH_2)_nY + 3\ H_2O \rightarrow (HO)_3Si(CH_2)_nY + 3\ HX$$

Essentially equivalent performance was obtained from aqueous vinylsilane coupling agents derived from all common hydrolyzable vinylsilanes (27).

Commercial silane coupling agents are soluble in water, or become soluble as the alkoxy groups hydrolyze from silicon. The resulting aqueous solutions are stable in water for at least several hours, but may become insoluble as the silanols condense to siloxanes. Freshly prepared aqueous solutions of the silane coupling agents are therefore applied to glass filaments by the fiber manufacturer along with a polymeric substance, a lubricant, and an antistatic agent as a complete size for glass roving (28). Glass cloth woven from glass roving with a starch–oil size may be heat-cleaned to burn off the organic size and treated with a dilute solution of the desired silane coupling agent. This operation is accomplished by the glass weaver, or by the reinforced-plastics fabricator. The total amount of silane coupling agent applied is generally 0.1–0.5% of the weight of glass.

Laboratory application of silane coupling agents is most readily accomplished with heat-cleaned glass roving or glass cloth available from the weavers. The silanes may be applied from water or from organic solvents. When the silane is neither alkaline nor acidic in its own right, 0.1% acetic acid is added to the finishing solution to promote hydrolysis of the hydrolyzable silane. The glass is dipped in a 0.5% solution of finishing agent, air-dried for about 1 hr at room temperature, and then dried for 7 min at 230°F (110°C). In the case of chlorosilanes applied from an organic solvent, the finished glass is washed with water between the air-dry and final-drying operations.

The U.S. market for silane coupling agents in 1968 was several million dollars at $2.00–8.00/lb. The major applications were on glass fiber for reinforced plastics and insulation.

Performance of Silane Coupling Agents. Although silane coupling agents were first introduced to improve the water resistance of reinforced plastics it was soon observed that they also imparted significant improvement to initial properties of laminates. The degree of improvement obtained even under optimum conditions varied with the resin, the glass content, and the severity of the test. The improvement in laminate properties imparted by silane coupling agents in typical glass-cloth laminates are summarized in Table 3. All results are based on compression-molded test samples containing 60–70% glass in the laminate. Heat-cleaned glass cloth treated with 0.5% silane coupling agent in each case was compared with untreated heat-cleaned glass. Wet-strength tests differ for different resins since water resistance varies markedly with the chemical nature of the resin. Epoxy, polyester, phenolic, melamine, poly(styrene-*co*-acrylonitrile), and nylon laminates were tested after 2 hr in boiling water (29). Buton (a butadiene–styrene copolymer) and styrene–divinylbenzene co-

Table 3. Silane Performance in Glass-Cloth-Reinforced Laminates

Resin	Silane coupling agent (Table 2)	Flexural strength improvement, %	
		Dry	Wet
epoxy (anhydride)	7,9	10	10
epoxy (aromatic amine)	5–7,10	30	80
polyester	1–4	50	150
buton	1–4	50	300
phenolic	5–7	40	150
melamine	5,6	100	250
styrene–divinylbenzene (cast)	4	90	300
poly(styrene–acrylonitrile)	7	50	150
nylon	5–7	110	100
polypropylene	4 (plus peroxide)	150	250

polymers were boiled for seven days in water (30), while polypropylene was tested after 16 hr in water at 120°F (48°C) (31).

Certain trends are clear in comparing the response of different resins to the presence of coupling agents. Epoxy–anhydride resins are unique in initial bonding and in resistance to water. An epoxide–anhydride reaction at the glass surface is ideal for scavenging surface moisture. At the same time the moisture provides a resin with a high hydroxyl content at the interface. Amine-cured epoxies also have a high hydroxyl content, but they are not as effective as anhydrides in scavenging water from the surface. With the proper silane coupling agent the epoxy–amine laminates rate among the best in absolute strength, both dry and wet.

Condensation polymers (phenolics, melamine) that eliminate volatile by-products during cure benefit greatly from silane coupling agents. Although the resin intermediates are highly polar, they become less polar during cure, and polar volatiles are deposited at the interface. Silane coupling agents on glass withstand attack by these volatiles and, by reacting with the resin, they provide a silanol-bonded interface with glass.

Nonpolar resins benefit most from coupling agents in both dry- and wet-strength. Although the resins themselves are very resistant to water, they have only weak van der Waals bonding to the glass and therefore are least capable of competing with water for the surface.

Absolute values of dry- and wet-strength of laminates of various resins with silane-treated glass are surprisingly uniform at about 80,000 psi. This suggests that silane coupling agents eliminate the major cause of failure at the glass-resin interface and that the ultimate strength is determined by the strength of the resin itself.

The use of silane coupling agents as integral-blend additives often gives performance comparable to that obtained by separate treatment of the reinforcement (32). As additive, the necessary reactive silane is dissolved directly into the resin system prior to putting it in contact with the inorganic filler, reinforcement, or substrate to be bonded. Under these conditions the silane migrates to the hydrophilic surface where it reacts with absorbed moisture to produce silanol groups which bond to the surface. However, because the process involves migration of the silane to the surface, it is necessary to permit sufficient time for reaction to occur at the surface, and larger amounts (1%) of silane are required. Integral blends are especially convenient in composites of resins with particulate fillers. This technique was used by Vanderbilt (33) and by Ziemianski (34) to study the effect of silane coupling agents on various mineral surfaces. The improvement in physical properties observed by optimum addition of silane coupling agent to polymer mixes with finely divided fillers is summarized in Table 4. It appears that silica and alumina are most responsive to silane coupling agents, silicate minerals differ in their response, and certain minerals like calcium carbonate show no response. The more responsive minerals are converted by silane coupling agents into strong reinforcing fillers.

Table 4. Silane Performance with Particulate Fillers

Resin	Filler	Silane coupling agent (Table 2)	Flexural strength improvement, %	
			Dry	Wet
buton	silica	2 (vinyl)	200	250
buton	alumina	2 (vinyl)	180	200
buton	hydrated alumina	2 (vinyl)	100	100
buton	glass flakes	2 (vinyl)	150	500
buton	ASP-400 clay	2 (vinyl)	55	65
buton	talc	2 (vinyl)	80	80
buton	calcium carbonate	2 (vinyl)	none	none
epoxy	silica	5 (aminopropyl)	20	150
epoxy	Al-needles	5 (aminopropyl)	100	200
epoxy	Al-powder	9 (epoxy)	50	
epoxy	Fe-powder	9 (epoxy)	40	
epoxy	wollastonite	7 (epoxy)	20	50
epoxy	ASP-400 clay	7 (epoxy)	5	10
polyester	silica	2 (vinyl)	50	50
polyester	wollastonite	4 (methacrylate)	18	50

Many of the silane coupling agents designed for application with glass reinforced thermosetting resins (Table 2) were also found to be effective on glass cloth when molded with thermoplastic resins (35–37). It was postulated that coupling agents were reactive with certain thermoplastics (nylon, polyvinylchloride), but that they functioned by solution compatibility with the inert thermoplastics (polystyrene, polyethylene).

New high-temperature resins (polyimides and polybenzimidazoles) with useful properties to temperatures above 300°C required new heat-stable coupling agents on glass. A new class of thermally stable coupling agents was developed from organofunctional aromatic silanes (38). These materials are stable to at least 100°C higher temperatures than the coupling agents of Table 2. It may be concluded that effective silane coupling agents can be provided for any new resins as the need arises.

Although it might be expected that addition of any polar reactant to a resin system would improve its adhesion to a mineral surface it has been shown that silanes and chrome complexes are uniquely effective with glass and are the only known true coupling agents. Since the methacrylate-functional silane (no. 4 of Table 2) is known to be one of the most effective coupling agents for glass to polyesters and since many organofunctional methacrylates are available, it was convenient to compare these materials as integral blends (2%) with a polyester resin on heat-cleaned glass cloth (29).

Carboxyl, hydroxyl, amide epoxy, acid phosphate ester, and titanate-functional methacrylates used as additives gave a slight improvement in properties (up to 10–20%) to polyester laminates, but at this level did not function as true coupling agents (50–150% improvement).

The amount of silane coupling agent required on a surface is so small that the threshold concentration for coupling cannot be observed by ordinary analytical means. Pickup of coupling agent has been examined in a very sensitive manner by the use of C^{14}-labeled silane coupling agents (39,40). Very light application of coupling agent, or removal of all but a fraction of a monolayer of coupling agent with a solvent from silica or from glass, still allowed for adequate bonding between resin and treated glass.

The silane-coupling-agent concept has been extended to many other applications as adhesion promoters. Particulate mineral- or glass-fiber reinforcement for rubber is improved greatly by the use of amino-, methacryloxy-, epoxy-, or mercapto-functional silane coupling agents (41–43) (nos. 4, 5, 6, 7, and 8 of Table 2). Adhesion of polysulfide or urethane sealants to mineral surfaces is improved by priming the surface with an appropriate organofunctional silane or by adding the silane to the sealant as an integral blend (44). Similar applications are found for silane coupling agents with metal adhesives and with paint films on metal. Thin films of hydrolyzed organofunctional silane coupling agents (nos. 5–8 of Table 2) deposited on silver, copper, aluminum, and steel have been shown to protect the metal against tarnishing or corrosion (45). Amino-functional silanes (nos. 5 and 6 of Table 2) alone, or as copolymers with other silanes or with organic resins, are especially resistant against sulfide tarnish on silver and high-temperature oxidation of copper (46,47). It appears that the organofunctional groups form chelate complexes with surface metal since thin films on copper are stable to temperatures that would cause rapid oxidation of the neat resin.

Bibliography

1. U.S. Pat. 2,306,222 (1940), W. I. Patnode (to General Electric Co.).
2. E. G. Shafrin and W. A. Zisman, "Contact Angle, Wettability and Adhesion," *Advan. Chem. Ser.* No. 43, American Chemical Society, Washington, D.C., 1964, p. 145.
3. O. K. Johannson and J. J. Torok, *Proc. Inst. Radio Engrs.* **34**, 296 (1946).
4. M. M. Sprung and L. S. Nelson, *J. Org. Chem.* **20**, 1750 (1955).
5. U.S. Pat. 2,746,956 (May, 1956), J. L. Speier (to Dow Corning Corp.).
6. S. H. Langer, P. Patages, and I. Wender, *Chem. Ind. London* **1958**, 1664 (1958).
7. C. C. Sweeley, R. Bentley, M. Makita, and W. W. Wells, *J. Am. Chem. Soc.* **85**, 2497 (1963).
8. L. Birkhofer and A. Ritter, *Chem. Ber.* **93**, 424 (1960).
9. L. Birkhofer, A. Ritter, and P. Neuhausen, *Ann.* **659**, 190 (1962).
10. T. Luukainen, W. J. A. Vanden Heuvel, and E. C. Horning, *Biochem. Biophys. Acta* **62**, 153 (1962).
11. A. J. Waiss, Jr., R. E. Lundin, and D. J. Stern, *Tetrahedron Letters* **10**, 573 (1964).
12. M. Makita and W. W. Wells, *Anal. Biochem.* **5**, 523 (1963).
13. Z. Horii, M. Makita, and Y. Tamura, *Chem. Ind. London* **1965**, 1494 (1965).
14. J. F. Klebe, H. Finkbiner, and D. M. White, *J. Am. Chem. Soc.* **88**, 3390 (1966).
15. D. L. Stalling, C. W. Gehrke, and R. W. Zumwalt, *Biochem. Biophys. Res. Commun.* **31** (4), 616 (1968).
16. C. A. Bache, L. E. St. John, Jr., and O. J. Lisk, *Anal. Chem.* **40** (8), 1241 (1968).
17. R. H. Perrett and J. H. Purnell, *J. Chromatog.* **7**, 455 (1962).
18. A. G. Sharkey, Jr., R. A. Friedel, and S. H. Langer, *Anal. Chem.* **29**, 770 (1957).
19. P. Capella and C. M. Zorzut, *Anal. Chem.* **40**, 1458 (1968).
20. C. W. Lentz, *Inorg. Chem.* **3**, 574 (1964).
21. C. W. Lentz, *Spec. Rept. 90*, Highway Research Board, Washington, D.C., 1966.

22. C. W. Lentz, *Papers 36th Congr. Intern. Chim. Ind., Brussels, Sept. 1966.*
23. U.S. Pat. 2,563,289 (1951), R. Steinman (to Owens Corning Fiberglas Corp.).
24. U.S. Pat. 2,611,718 (1952), R. Steinman (to Owens Corning Fiberglas Corp.).
25. J. Bjorksten and L. C. Yaeger, *Mod. Plastics* **29,** 124 (July 1952).
26. U.S. Pat. 2,720,470 (1955), P. W. Erickson and I. Silver (to U.S.A. Secy. of Navy).
27. E. P. Plueddemann, H. A. Clark, L. E. Nelson, and K. R. Hoffman, *Mod. Plastics* **39,** 139 (Aug. 1962).
28. U.S. Pat. 3,207,623 (Sept., 1965), A. Marzocchi and N. S. Janetos (to Owens Corning Fiberglas Corp.).
29. E. P. Plueddemann, *J. Paint Technol.* **40** (516), 1–9 (1968).
30. B. M. Vanderbilt, *Paper XXIII-1 Soc. Plastics Engrs. 22nd. Ann. Tech. Conf., 1966.*
31. S. Sterman and J. G. Marsden, *Mod. Plastics* **43,** 3 (July 1966).
32. S. Sterman and J. G. Marsden, *Plastics Technol.* **9** (5), 38–41 (1963).
33. B. M. Vanderbilt and J. J. Jaruzelski, *Ind. Eng. Chem. Prod. Res. Develop.* **1** (3), 188 (1962).
34. L. P. Ziemianski, *Paper XVII-2, Soc. Plastics Engrs. 22nd. Ann. Tech. Conf., 1966.*
35. E. P. Plueddemann, *Paper 19-A, Soc. Plastics Engrs. 20th. Ann. Tech. Conf., 1964.*
36. S. Sterman and J. G. Marsden, *Paper VII-3, Soc. Plastics Engrs. 21st. Ann. Tech. Conf., 1965.*
37. R. V. Viventi, *Paper IV-3, Soc. Plastics Engrs. 26th. Ann. Tech. Conf., 1968.*
38. E. P. Plueddemann, *Paper 9-A, Soc. Plastics Engrs. 22nd. Ann. Tech. Conf., 1966.*
39. O. K. Johannson, F. O. Stark, G. E. Vogel, and R. M. Fleischmann, *J. Composition Mater.* **1,** 278 (1967).
40. M. E. Schrader, I. Lerner, and F. J. D'Oria, *Mod. Plastics* **45,** 195 (Sept. 1967).
41. B. M. Vanderbilt and R. E. Clayton, *Ind. Eng. Chem. Prod. Res. Develop.* **4,** 18 (March 1965); *Rubber Age N.Y.* (July 1964), 575.
42. U.S. Pat. 3,390,120 (June 1968), J. Iannicelli (to J. M. Huber Corp.).
43. U.S. Pat. 3,364,059 (Jan. 1968), A. Marzocchi (to Owens Corning Fiberglas Corp.).
44. S. Sterman and J. B. Toogood, *Adhesives Age* **8** (7), 34 (1965).
45. Brit. Pat. 1,102,251 (Feb. 1968), A. N. Pines, J. G. Marsden, and S. Sterman (to Union Carbide Corp.).
46. U.S. Pat. 3,175,921 (March 1965), R. C. Hedlund (to Dow Corning Corp.).
47. U.S. Pat. 3,085,908 (April 1963), E. L. Morehouse and A. N. Pines (to Union Carbide Corp.).

EDWIN P. PLUEDDEMANN
Dow Corning Corporation

SILICONES.   See Silicon compounds.

SILICONIZING.   See Vol. 13, p. 314.

SILICOSIS.   See Vol. 7, p. 459.

SILK

Silk is a textile fiber produced by the larvae of various species of moths, the most important being *Bombyx mori*, or mulberry worm. This and certain other species are carefully bred. Tussah ("wild") silk can be produced by *Antheraea pernyi* and by other species, including *Antheraea mylitta*, which are not domesticated. The silk fibers resulting from the solidification of secretions of the worm are converted into yarns used for clothing and other textiles. Like wool (qv), and unlike the vegetable fibers, silk is a protein fiber.

According to legend, in about 2698 BC Empress Si-Lung Chi of China discovered that silk from the silkworm could be reeled continuously from cocoons immersed in hot water, and that cloth could be made out of this silk.

It is believed that the secret of producing silk was learned by the Japanese about AD 300, and that it was learned in India at about the same time or a little later. Since then Japan and India have rivaled China in producing raw silk and silken fabrics. Because of quick adaptation to modern methods of reeling, biological control, and marketing, Japan became the leading silk-producing country and maintained her position until World War II. India produces chiefly tussah or wild silk.

The Chinese sold silk to the Persians, who in turn resold it to nations of the West, particularly to the Roman Empire. About AD 555, however, two monks smuggled a supply of eggs and mulberry tree seeds out of China in their hollow bamboo canes and introduced sericulture to Europe. Furthermore, as a result of the Arab conquests sericulture spread to Sicily, along the coast of Africa into Spain, and later into Italy and France. From France Flemish weavers carried the secret to England.

In 1622, King James I of England tried to establish a silk industry in Virginia, but after several unsuccessful attempts the enterprise was abandoned. At about the time of the American Revolution there was a large development of silk culture in colonial Georgia, the Carolinas, and Connecticut. Later, in the nineteenth century, mulberry trees became the object of widespread speculation and were sold to farmers as far west as the Mississippi valley. Since then comparatively recent attempts have been made to propagate silk in Michigan, California, Florida, and in the region near Mineral Wells, Texas. The most important reason for the concentration of silk culture in China and Japan is the very low cost of labor in those countries; the farmers raise the silkworms and harvest the cocoons.

Sericulture

Silkworms may be classified biologically according to the number of generations per year. The monovoltine is a worm that in a year yields only one generation, while the bivoltine gives two generations, and the polyvoltine, many generations. The first two types spin a silk superior to that of the last, the reason possibly being their longer hibernation or rest period.

In the life cycle of a typical breed, the eggs as just laid by the moth are of a grayish-cream color if fertile, and white if infertile. During the incubation period, which lasts about seven days, the color of the eggs darkens; immediately before hatching they are dark blue. Optimum conditions of temperature and relative humidity are about 70°F and 80–85%, respectively.

When just hatched, the worm is about $\frac{1}{8}$ in. long and weighs approx 0.5 mg. It goes through four growth periods, called "instars," each of which lasts about three days. The worm molts after each instar. During these periods the silkworm eats constantly, feeding on leaves from the mulberry tree (preferably the *Morus alba*), and grows rapidly. Upon reaching maturity, the worm is about 10,000 times as large as when first born and about 14,000 times as heavy. This unusually rapid growth necessitates the shedding of skin four times. With certain breeds there is a fifth molt. The fifth period of growth, requiring about five days, includes growth up to the completion of spinning of the cocoon. In the spinning, which consists of extrusion through the highly specialized spinneret, the colloidal spin solution stored in the silk gland is converted into a solid filament.

After the completion of spinning, the larva changes into a pupa or chrysalis. This period, known as the transition stage, requires about two days. During the inert pupa stage, which lasts about a week, biological changes take place within the organism; the color of the pupa turns from cream to dark brown, and the body becomes rather stiff.

When ready to come out of the cocoon, the moth secretes a solution which sufficiently softens the silk on the thin end of the cocoon to permit exit. Immediately upon emerging the moth mates and then, if a female, lays eggs and dies. The mating, which lasts about a day, completes the cycle.

Physical and Chemical Properties

PHYSICAL PROPERTIES

The three principal types of cocoons are classified according to color: white, green, and yellow.

Under microscopic examination domestic raw silk appears to be tubular; the fibers are not entirely smooth, due to the presence of silk gum on the surface. Degummed silk appears smoother, but occasionally small splotches of gum may be seen if the fibers are magnified 500 times. Cross sections of both raw and degummed silk fibers appear to be triangular, although a few are oval.

Domestic silk is a hygroscopic fiber capable of absorbing as much as 22.7% moisture at 95% rh and 75°F. However, it has a standard moisture regain (standard moisture regain is the amount of atmospheric moisture a fiber regains at 70°F and 65% rh, after drying to constant weight) of 11%; this regain is the same as those of viscose and cuprammonium rayon, greater than those of cotton, acetate, rayon, and nylon, and less than that of wool. In dry tensile strength, silk has a tenacity of about 3.5 to 5.0 g/den; this compares favorably with many of the synthetic fibers. Even regular-tenacity nylon is only about 0.5 g/den stronger. (The denier of a fiber is the weight in g of 9000 m; for silk, skeins of 450 m are weighed in units of 0.05 g.) See Acetate and triacetate fibers; Polyamides; Rayon.

Another favorable property of silk is its toughness, that is, its ability to endure permanent deformations without rupture. In this respect it ranks close to nylon. Other favorable qualities are its high resilience, its low elasticity, and its warmth of feel; it has good crease resistance and fine draping qualities.

CHEMICAL COMPOSITION

Raw silk is made up principally of two proteins: sericin and fibroin, both of which are insoluble in cold water. Unlike wool keratin, the silk proteins contain no sulfur.

Sericin ("silk gum") is present in raw silk on the surface of the fibers to the extent of 15–25 wt %, depending upon the type of silkworm and upon the locale.   It may be hydrolyzed with mineral acids, principally sulfuric, to form a mixture of at least twelve amino acids, the principal ones being alanine, tyrosine, glycine, and leucine.   Serine was discovered by Cramer in 1865 in the hydrolyzate obtained by treating a sample of sericin with sulfuric acid.

Fibroin, the fiber proper, consists of long parallel chains of amino acid units or residues held together lengthwise by peptide linkages, and probably held together sidewise by hydrogen bonding.   Each chain of fibroin is actually a zigzag; the partial structure below is shown as straight for simplicity.   Glycine (R = H), alanine (R =

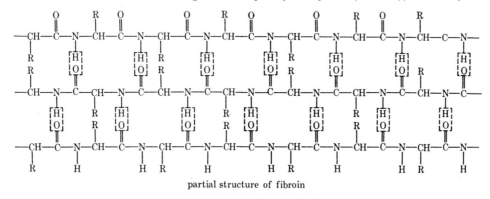

partial structure of fibroin

CH_3), serine (R = CH_2OH), and tyrosine (R = $CH_2C_6H_4OH$) are the principal amino acid units present in the chains (there are smaller amounts of other residues).   The sequential spacing of these constitutes a definite pattern.

Table 1.   Analysis of Silk Fibroin

Amino acid	Moles of acid/10^5 g	Substituent R in acid of formula $NH_2CHRCOOH$
glycine	567.2	H—
alanine	385.7	CH_3—
leucine	6.2	$(CH_3)_2CHCH_2$—
isoleucine	6.9	$CH_3CH_2CH(CH_3)$—
valine	26.7	$(CH_3)_2CH$—
phenylalanine	8.0	$C_6H_5CH_2$—
serine	152.0	CH_2OH—
threonine	12.5	$CH_3CH(OH)$—
tyrosine	62.3	$HOC_6H_5CH_2$—
aspartic acid	17.6	$HOOCCH_2$—
glutamic acid	11.8	$HOOCCH_2CH_2$—
arginine	5.6	$NH_2C(NH)NH(CH_2)_3$—
lysine	3.8	$NH_2(CH_2)_4$—
histidine	1.9	NH—CH≡N—CH≡CCH₂—
proline	5.1	NH—CH_2—CH_2—CH_2—CHCOOH[a]
tryptophan	2.5	

[a] This is the complete formula of the acid.

When silk fibroin is hydrolyzed with strong acids a mixture of amino acids is formed (1a). This includes principally the following:

glycine	41.2%	serine	16.0%
alanine	33.0%	tyrosine	11.4%

x-Ray analysis shows a high degree of crystallinity. The polypeptide chains constituting the silk filaments are packed in such a way as to form crystalline regions whose molecular atoms exert natural forces of attraction. These forces hold the chains tightly to one another. Unlike wool, silk has fully extended polypeptide chains (the zigzag chain is not compressed). This highly extended nature of the fiber molecules and a high degree of orientation explain the low elasticity of silk. Only a relatively small amount of molecular chain slippage can take place when the fiber is stretched. In the case of wool, however, the folded molecular chains can unfold and become fully extended. The great strength of the silk filament is due largely to close packing of the molecules, a high degree of crystallinity, and the natural forces of attraction.

Schroeder and Kay (quoted in reference 2) give the analysis of silk fibroin (*Bombyx mori*) presented in Table 1.

Analyses of silk as given by Silbermann (in ref. 3) are shown in Table 2. It is believed that the wax and fat in silk aid in water repellency. The salts are present in the small amount of mineral matter in the fibers.

Table 2. Chemical Components of Silk, %

Component	White[a]		Yellow[a]	
	Cocoons	Raw silk	Cocoons	Raw silk
fibroin	73.59	76.20	70.02	72.35
ash of fibroin	0.09	0.09	0.16	0.16
sericin	22.28	22.01	24.29	23.13
wax and fat	3.02	1.36	3.46	2.75
salts	1.60	0.30	1.92	1.60

[a] Due to pigmentation, or lack of it, occurring principally in the sericin gum. Sericin can be removed by degumming.

CHEMICAL PROPERTIES

In dilute solutions of acid, silk behaves like wool in that a certain amount of the acid combines with the protein fiber. There is practically no loss of tensile strength. In strong acids, however, silk is more readily attacked than wool. For example, silk may be separated from wool in a fabric by treating the fabric with cold concentrated hydrochloric acid for a short time; the silk dissolves, leaving the wool behind.

Silk is more resistant than wool to alkalis, even to a hot dilute (1%) solution of caustic soda. However, silk appears to dissolve in a hot concentrated solution (5+%) of either caustic soda or caustic potash. Table 3 gives the action of the most common acids, bases, and salts. Table 4 gives the solvent action of certain miscellaneous chemicals on silk.

Oxidizing agents such as sodium dichromate, potassium permanganate, and sodium and calcium hypochlorites destroy silk unless used with considerable care in very dilute solutions. Chlorine and the hypochlorites yellow and weaken silk.

Table 3. Action of Chemicals on Silk

Action of acids	Action of alkalis	Action of salts
Concentrated	*Concentrated*	
1. H_2SO_4: dissolves.	1. Hot NaOH: dissolves.	1. Salts of heavy metals: readily absorbed. If too much of the metallic salt is absorbed, rapid deterioration may occur. The principal metallic salt used in weighting silk is $SnCl_4$.
2. HCl: dissolves.	2. Hot KOH: dissolves.	
3. HNO_3: turns yellow. Color may be removed by boiling solution of $SnCl_2$.	3. NaOH + glucose or glycerol: sericin removed without dissolving the fibroin appreciably.	
4. HCO_2H (90%): swells, contracts, and gelatinizes.	*Dilute*	
Dilute	1. NaOH or KOH: luster reduced, but fibers are generally more resistant than wool.	2. NaCl solution: Fibers tendered over a period of time, especially if they have been treated with a salt of a heavy metal such as $SnCl_4$.
1. HCl (28%): shrinks approx ⅓ with no appreciable loss in tensile strength. Above 28% concn, fiber disintegrates; below, no shrinkage occurs.		
2. Dilute acids generally: readily absorbed, with increase in luster and acquisition of scroop.	2. NH_4OH + soap: gum removed without injury to the fibroin.	
3. Cold H_2SiF_6 and HF (5%): any inorganic weighting material present removed without injury to fibers.	3. Hot boiling soap solution: fibers somewhat injured over an extended period.	
4. Tannic acid: absorbed by silk up to 25% of its weight from a hot solution.	4. $Ca(OH)_2$: sericin somewhat softened; fibroin swells to a certain extent.	

Table 4. Miscellaneous Solvents for Silk

Solvent	Conditions
ammoniacal nickel oxide	boiling solution
basic zinc chloride	concentrated solution
copper sulfate + glycerol	alkaline (with NaOH) solution
Schweitzer's reagent	reagent alkaline with ammonia
stannic chloride	concentration
zinc chloride	acidulated solution

Processing

Cocoons from which moths have emerged are unfit for reeling because the silk fiber is broken by the moth. Therefore the cocoons (except those from which the moth is allowed to emerge for the next generation) are steamed or heated to kill the insect.

Reeling. The unruptured cocoons are first graded as to size and color, after which they are placed in basins of warm water containing a little soap. Soon it is possible to unwind a continuous filament from each cocoon. Several filaments are taken together, put on a small brush, and passed through porcelain guides of a reel, where the fibers are given a slight twist to form a thread. The product in this form is known as *raw silk*. The filaments from five cocoons, on an average, will give a thread of 13/15 den (the *denier*, which cannot be precisely controlled, ranges from 13 to 15); seven cocoons are used for 20/22-den thread. These threads, although they are made up of several filaments, are referred to as *singles*. In Japan, after reeling, the silk is rereeled into standard-size skeins. The reeling operation is carried out in a plant called a *filature*.

Throwing. For some textile operations, such as the manufacture of hosiery (although hardly any silk hosiery is made at present), the threads from the filature can be used, but for the weaving of most silk fabrics the threads are converted to commercial yarns of the required size (denier). This operation is called "throwing"; the person who carries it out is called a "throwster." Several threads may be combined with larger or smaller amounts of twist, according to the product required.

Spinning (4). Silk from ruptured cocoons, and other waste silk, is first treated with hot water and soap (degumming, or boiling off) to remove sericin and other impurities which amount to about 30% of the total weight. For a description of the degumming process, see Vol. 7, p. 520. In this process sericin is removed from the surface of the fiber. Although all the sericin can be removed, partial degumming is sometimes used; complete degumming results in a silk that tangles badly. The sericin acts as a natural finishing agent for the silk. A series of degumming baths may be used, the number depending on the extent of degumming desired.

After thorough rinsing, the material is dried and conditioned. It is then spun into yarn by methods that are, on the whole, similar to those used with other fibers such as cotton or wool.

Testing. The International Silk Association has adopted a series of quality tests for raw silk. Visual inspection with special apparatus is used to test for such things as evenness and the absence of defects (of which a very great variety are possible in the natural product). Instrumental methods are used for tenacity and elongation (see Textile testing). The Association has adopted grades as follows, in decreasing order of merit: 6A, 5A, 4A, 3A, 2A, A, B, C, D, E, F, and G for raw silk of 33 den or finer, and 4A–G for raw silk of 34 den or coarser (5).

Weighting. Weighting, formerly one of the most important finishing operations but now seldom done, usually precedes dyeing. In the degumming of silk before dyeing there is a loss in weight of about 22–25%. For example, 1 lb of raw silk gives 12 oz of degummed silk. The purpose of weighting, therefore, is to make up for this loss; the dyer does this by using suitable metallic salts. "Par" weight denotes the amount of chemical weighting added to the degummed silk to bring it back to the original weight of raw silk. Often, in order to obtain a heavier fabric with better draping qualities, a great deal more weighting material is added than is necessary to bring it back to par. This weighting may vary from 50 to as high as 300% above par. Weighting for ordinary purposes ranges from 24 to 28 oz; that is, 1 lb of raw silk is brought up to this weight.

There are two general methods of weighting silk; one for black fabrics, the other for white and fancy colors. Tannin and iron salts are the materials used for black-dyed goods. The degummed silk is steeped in a strong tannic acid bath, which the fiber readily absorbs. Then the excess liquor is squeezed out and the goods are placed in a bath of an iron salt, such as basic iron sulfate. An insoluble grayish-black precipitate of iron tannate is formed in the fiber. A treatment with potassium ferrocyanide gives a desirable bluish tone to the finished black and also adds weight to the silk. A final treatment in a weak alkaline bath or with soap ensures complete precipitation and fixation of the metallic compounds. Additional increases in weight may be obtained by repeating the operations as many times as necessary. Then the silk may be dyed with logwood to obtain a very desirable final black, or it may be dyed with a mordant–acid dye mixture. However, since the advent of modern coal tar synthetic dyes, the use of iron compounds as weighting agents for blacks has been almost altogether superseded by that of tin salts (9).

For white or colors other than black, the method of weighting silk with tin silico-phosphate is generally used. The degummed silk is treated with an acid solution of stannic chloride until the fiber is saturated with it. Then the excess uncombined liquor is hydroextracted, and the silk is washed thoroughly with cold water to convert the stannic chloride to hydrochloric acid, which washes out, and the oxide, which remains deposited in the fiber. The silk is then treated in a hot solution (140–160°F) of disodium phosphate; the phosphate radical so introduced enables the silk to absorb more of the stannic chloride and subsequently more of the phosphate compound. In this manner weighting may be carried on almost indefinitely by repeating the rounds. Every completed round is known as a "pass"; hence, silk can be termed one, two, three, or four pass silk. A final treatment in a hot solution of sodium silicate further increases the weight and adequately fixes the tin salts in the goods. The final tin silicophosphate weighting substance acts as a mordant for many of the dyes, giving faster colors than if the silk had not been weighted. Tin weighting imparts luster and body to the fiber in addition to giving it a good firm feel and a high degree of scroop.

Besides replacing the loss of weight caused by degumming, weighting has been used to increase the density of silk (1b). Because silk is very expensive, it is not often made into heavy fabrics. Accordingly, an increase in density brought about by metallic salt absorption greatly enhances the hand (feel) of the fabric. Silk weighted moderately will contain 25–50% of the salt. Cook (1b) states that a crepe-de-Chine is normally weighted with 25–45% tin salt, satin may have 50%, and georgette 30%. Tie fabrics contain as much as 60%.

It is generally known that weighted silk fabrics are not as strong as unweighted pure silk (1a), because heavily weighted fabrics deteriorate rapidly in the presence of light and air. Also, perspiration causes weighted silk to rot, and for this reason such silk should not be made into underwear. Because weighting decreases the life of the fiber, it is no longer practiced to any appreciable extent, "pure-dye" silk is much more common at present.

Dyeing, Printing, and Finishing. In order to obtain luster and to ensure even penetration of color and of finishing materials, degumming of either skeins or fabric is essential. The naturally green and yellow silks may be whitened without too much difficulty by degumming and subsequently bleaching with hydrogen peroxide. The golden-brown tussah silk, on the other hand, is difficult to bleach. As a protein material, silk is amphoteric; hence it has good affinity for both acid and basic colors. Acid colors are applied at temperatures considerably below the boiling point in an acidulated boiled-off liquor, which serves as a leveling and protective agent. Basic dyes combine very readily with silk and should be applied at 160–180°F to prevent a superficial and uneven deposition of color. Addition of a small amount of acetic acid or acetin (glycerol monoacetate) increases the solubility of the basic colors, there-by promoting evenness and penetration. Silk can also be dyed with substantive or direct colors either in a neutral bath or in one acidulated with acetic acid at 160–180°F. However, the dyes must be carefully selected, as many dyes will not dye silk. Mordant colors are not often employed on silk. Logwood black has been the only mordant dye used on both weighted and unweighted yarn and piece goods. Metalized acid dyes, soluble-type vat dyes for light shades, and certain developed colors may be employed.

Silk is dyed both as skein yarn and in woven piece goods. One purpose of yarn dyeing is to produce "shot" effects in weaving where a particular fabric design calls for the filling to be of a different color from the warp, eg, in tie fabrics and different-colored brocades. Another aim is to dye warp and filling yarns the same color, black, to produce silk facings for men's evening dress material. Yarn dyeing usually costs more than dyeing in the piece. Woven and knitted fabrics are usually dyed in the piece. Colored designs may be produced on silk by direct contact printing, by discharge printing, or by resist printing (a carry-over from the original Javanese batik printing), and the printing method used may be block, screen, or roller.

Trotman (6a) states that dyeing is usually started at a temperature of 105°F, and that during the entire process the temperature should not exceed 185°F, in order to prevent lowering the tensile strength and luster of the fibers. Some acid colors require acid in the dyebath, and accordingly the boiled-off liquor may be "broken" with sulfuric acid until it is barely acid. In dyeing with neutral-dyeing acid colors, acetic acid is substituted. Sometimes these colors are applied in a soap bath containing about 10 or 20% sodium sulfate. In the case of basic, or cationic, colors, silk is dyed in a broken degumming bath containing, for example, 25 gal of boiled-off liquor plus 75 gal of soft water. After just enough acetic acid is added to barely redden litmus, the temperature of the bath is raised to about 100°F, the dye solution added, and the silk dyed at about 180°F for 30 min. If the dye tends to go on too fast, the color may be added to the bath in several portions. Sometimes dyeing can be carried out either in a neutral soap bath or in a bath more highly acidulated with acetic acid (for example: 8 oz of acetic acid/100 gal of water). According to Trotman (6a), the fastness of cationic dyes on silk may be increased by aftertreating the dyed goods with tannic acid. Further improvement in fastness may be obtained by subsequent treatment with tartar emetic (potassium antimonyl tartrate); this will also add weight and body to silk, thereby enhancing "hand."

For exceptional wetfastness a more modern class of dyes, namely the reactives (6b), can be used (see Vol. 7, p. 630). These dichlorotriazinyl colors may be applied cold in a bath containing the dye and 10 lb of either sodium chloride or anhydrous sodium sulfate per 100 gal of liquor. The goods are allowed to remain in the cold bath for 20 min, more salt is added, the temperature is slowly raised to 122°F, and dyeing is continued for 15 min longer. Fixation of color is obtained by adding about 2 lb of anhydrous sodium carbonate per 100 gal of water, and allowing the goods to remain in this bath for 40 min at 122°F. To prevent crocking (color coming off one fabric and onto another, in laundering), the dyed silk is then soaped at a temperature between 185 and 203°F to remove the uncombined dye from the fiber. These dyes may also be applied in a bath acidulated with 0.5% (of the weight of the goods) formic acid (85%). After the temperature of the bath is brought to 104°F the silk is entered and the temperature slowly raised to 185°F. Then 3.5% more acid is added in several portions over a 30-min period. Dyeing is continued for another half hour, after which time the bath is dropped, and the goods are rinsed, soaped, rinsed again, and dried.

Reactive dyes containing only one active chlorine atom (or monochlorotriazinyl) are rarely used to dye silk because of the difficulty of getting deep shades. The so-called "hot"-dyeing colors may be applied in very much the same manner as the cold-dyeing ones, except that the temperature should be increased to 160 or 195°F, depending on the dye used (7).

Unweighted natural silk is dyed, usually in skein form, with indigoid vat colors (8a) for use in making articles requiring a high degree of light- and wetfastness, such as slip covers, curtains, embroidery yarns, etc. Effect threads for dress goods and suitings are also dyed with vat colors. To prevent damaging the silk all dyeings are carried out in a weakly alkaline bath containing sodium hydroxide, hydrosulfite, and a protective colloid such as glue or gelatin. When dyeing with the strongly alkaline-requiring anthraquinone vat colors caustic concentration is kept at 0.5 oz/gal, and the temperature is held constant at 100–110°F.

Silk can also be dyed with soluble-type vat colors, known as leuco esters of vat dyes, in either an acid or a neutral bath (8b). An acid bath usually requires 3–5% acetic acid (28%) to exhaust the dyebath. About 1–2% sodium or zinc sulfoxylate is used to prevent premature oxidation. The goods are entered in the bath cold, the temperature is raised to 180°F, and the dyeing is carried out at this temperature for half an hour. After dyeing, the silk is rinsed and treated in a bath containing 1–2% ammonium thiocyanate and 0.3–2.5% sodium bichromate. If a neutral dyebath is used, 10–40% sodium sulfate is added, depending upon shade depth. Development is carried out with 7 oz of 66°Bé sulfuric acid in 10 gal of lukewarm liquor; the temperature is raised to 185°F over a 30-min period, and then held there for 30 min. The silk is then rinsed, neutralized with ammonium hydroxide, soaped at 180–190°F, and given a final rinse to complete the operation.

After either the dyeing or the printing, the silk piece goods must pass through the desired finishing process. Certain finishes impart firmness, fullness, dullness, luster, softness, or draping quality. For example, if it is desired to impart a property known as "scroop" (a rustling sound) to silk evening dress goods, after dyeing or printing, the material can be aftertreated with a solution of an organic acid, such as tartaric acid, and dried without rinsing. Such treatment will impart not only scroop, but also added luster. There are also finishes that will increase softness.

World Production

Table 5 (10a) shows the world production of raw silk in 1965. The unit is bales; a bale of silk weighs 60 kg. Japan leads all other countries, followed by mainland China, India, and South Korea.

Table 5. World Production of Raw Silk in 1965, bale

China	125,000	Italy	6,667
South Korea	14,183	Japan	318,438
Spain	817	Yugoslavia	833
France	100	total	548,331
India	21,400		

World production for various years is given in Table 6 (10a). It is apparent from this table that between 1938 and 1965 the total world production dropped about 42%, probably due to the increasing importance and use of synthetic fibers.

Table 7 (10b) shows imports of raw silk to the United States between 1956 and 1967.

Table 8 (10b) shows price per lb of raw silk. From $7.75/lb early in 1967 the price skyrocketed to the September 1967 level of $10.40/lb.

Table 6. World Production of Raw Silk, bale

1938	1958	1960	1962	1964
940,944	563,918	522,832	549,998	544,998

Table 7. U.S. Imports of Raw Silk

Year	Imports			
	Total	Japanese	Italian	Others
1956	59,510	55,068	313	4,129
1958	35,020	31,710	1,953	1,357
1960	49,537	46,515	740	2,282
1962	43,641	39,851	1,257	2,533
1964	37,103	26,031	3,356	7,716
1965	30,458	16,738	5,693	8,027
1966	28,117	9,367	7,747	11,003

Table 8. Price for Raw Silk (20/22) in New York, $/lb

1964	1965	1966	1967
5.50–5.76	5.95–7.34	7.33–8.88	7.75–0.00

Competition with man-made fibers is not the only reason for a marked decline in the use of silk in the United States. Hans Vaterlaus (11), Executive Vice-President of the International Silk Association, stated that the consumption of raw silk in the United States had dropped very drastically recently because of an abnormally high price. Therefore, many manufacturers had to change to mixed fabrics and blends with synthetic fibers.

A marked increase in domestic consumption of silk in Japan, chiefly for kimonos and for silk fabrics to be exported (11), is largely responsible for the sharp price rise. Consequently, for the first time Japan now imports more silk than she exports. What little raw silk is consumed in the United States is for the most part being imported from South Korea and Italy. Since the beginning of 1967 imports of Japanese silk have dropped down to practically nothing.

According to Tsukasa Furukawa (12) the Japanese are considering synthetics because of prohibitively high silk prices. Several Nippon companies now market a variety of fabrics made of new synthetic filaments resembling silk. Among these newer synthetics are Vilon (Nihon Vinylon Company of Japan), a 30-den yarn selling for $2.80/lb; a polyvinyl alcohol fiber (40 den) with a dry touch resembling that of silk, selling for $2.90/lb; polyester ether; and others. These silklike fabrics are finding a growing market in the United States, Europe, and Australia.

Bibliography

"Silk" in *ECT* 1st ed., Vol. 12, pp. 414–452, by A. C. Hayes, North Carolina State College School of Textiles.

1. J. Gordon Cook, *Handbook of Textile Fibers*, 3rd ed., Merrow Publishing Co., Ltd., Watford, Herts., England, 1964.
   a. pp. 154, 155; b. pp. 163, 164.
2. R. H. Peters, *Textile Chemistry*, Vol. 1, The American Elsevier Publishing Co., New York, 1963, p. 305.
3. H. R. Mauersberger, ed., *Matthews' Textile Fibers*, 6th ed., John Wiley & Sons, Inc., New York, 1954, p. 791.
4. J. Lewis, *The Silk Book*, The Silk and Rayon Users' Association, London, 1951, p. 19.

5. International Silk Association, *Standard Method of Raw Silk Testing and Classification*, Perreaud, Lyons, France, 1950; Technology and Research Committee, *Standard Manual of Raw Silk Testing and Classification*.

6. E. R. Trotman, *Dyeing and Chemical Technology of Textile Fibers*, 3rd ed., Charles Griffin, & Co., Ltd., London, 1964.
   a. pp. 331, 332, 363; b. p. 505.

7. R. L. Denyer et al., "Dyeing of Non-Cellulosic Fibers with Procion Dyes," in Knight and Forster, *Procion Dyestuffs in Textile Dyeing*, Imperial Chemical Industries Ltd., Dyestuffs Division, Leeds, Great Britain, 1962, p. 329.

8. American Assoc. of Textile Chemists and Colorists, *The Application of Vat Dyes*, Mack Printing Co., Easton, Pa., 1953.
   a. pp. 169–170; b. p. 282.

9. J. T. Marsh, *An Introduction to Textile Finishing*, 6th rev. impression, Chapman and Hall, Ltd. London, 1957, p. 304.

10. The Japan Public Relations Assoc. of Silk Industry, *Silk Statistics* (special issue of *Silk Digest*), Tokyo, 1967.
   a. pp. 18, 19; b. pp. 20, 21.

11. Hans Vaterlaus' letter, dated September 15, 1967, to Mrs. Davora Nielson, Librarian of the School of Textiles, North Carolina State University, Raleigh, N.C.

12. Tsukasa Furukawa, "Japanese Eyeing Synthetics Due to High Silk Prices," *Daily News Record*, *No. 32* ((whole no. 22698) (Feb. 14), Fairchild Publications, Inc., New York, 1968, p. 15.

A. C. HAYES
School of Textiles
North Carolina State University

SILLIMANITE, $Al_2O_3 \cdot SiO_2$.   See Refractories.

SILVER AND SILVER ALLOYS

Silver (Ag), at. no. 47, is the whitest and has the highest electrical and thermal conductivities of all the metals. It is relatively corrosion resistant. It appears in the periodic table in group IB in the 5th period; the other elements of the group are copper and gold and the neighboring elements of the period are palladium and cadmium. It has been known and prized since prehistoric times.

Silver was formerly used primarily for coinage, jewelry, tableware, and decorative articles. In recent years coinage has declined sharply, and technical industrial uses for silver, such as photography, electrical contacts, brazing alloys, and batteries, have surpassed the aesthetic uses for the metal. See also Silver compounds.

Physical Properties

Some of the physical properties are given in Table 1. Optical reflectance and the neutron-absorption characteristics are shown in Figures 1 and 2, respectively.

Yield Strength (2). This property varies, depending on the sensitivity of the test. Annealed material may show a crude yield strength (0.2% offset) of 7900 psi, a 0.01% proof stress of 1100 psi, and a proportional limit of 670 psi. The crude yield strength of heavily cold-worked silver will approach 80–90% of the tensile strength.

Malleability and Ductility. Silver is second only to gold in this quality. The pure metal can be rolled into foil or beaten to leaf and can be drawn into fine wire. Extensive working is done between anneals (if any are used). In high-purity metal the heat generated by cold working may suffice to recrystallize the metal.

Table 1. Physical Properties

Properties	Value
density (1), g/cm³	
as annealed at 20°C	10.491
hard drawn at 20°C	10.434
at 976°C	9.285
melting point (1), °C	960.8[a]
vol increase on melting (2), %	5
boiling point, °C	2187–2259 (1)
	2212 (3)
vapor pressure (p = mm Hg)	$\log p = -13340/T + 8.342$ for liquid (1)
	$\log p = -14020/T + 8.887$ for solid (3)
thermal expansion (3), per °C	
-190–0°C	17.0×10^{-6}
0–100°C	19.68×10^{-6}
0–500°C	20.61×10^{-6}
$l_t = l_0(1 + 19.494 \times 10^{-6}t - 1.0379$ $\times 10^{-9}t^2 + 2.375 \times 10^{-12}t^3)(1)$	
specific heat (1), cal/(g)(°C)	
solid $C_p = 0.055401 + 0.14414 \times 10^{-4}T - 0.16216 \times 10^{-8}T^2$	
gaseous	0.046
heat of fusion (1), cal/g	25
heat of vaporization (1), cal/g	565
heat of sublimation (1), cal/g	593–627[b]
thermal conductivity,	
cal/(sec)(cm²)(°C/cm)	
at 0°C	0.999 (4)
at 100°C	0.998 (4)
	0.934 (1)
at 200°C	0.896 (1)
at 300°C	0.864 (1)
at 400°C	0.844 (1)
at 500°C	0.870 (1)
electrical resistivity (1)	
for high-purity vacuum-annealed	
silver at 20°C, $\mu\Omega$-cm	1.59
temperature effect (4)	
R_t/R_0 (ratio to R at 0°C)	
at 20.4°K	0.01
at -78°C	0.684
at 100°C	1.41
at 200°C	1.83
at 400°C	2.71
at 800°C	4.62
at 960.5°C (solid)	5.14
at 960.5°C (liquid)	10.8
electrical conductivity (1)	
% of IACS	
for high-purity silver at 20°C,	108.4
ordinary 99.9% pure silver,	104
temperature coefficient of resistance (1)	
from 0–100°C, per °C	0.004098
diamagnetic properties (1) at 20°C, cgs units	-0.181×10^{-6}
electronic work function (1), eV	
thermionic work function	3.09–4.31
photoelectric work function	3.67–4.81
contact potential method	4.21–4.47

Table 1 (*continued*)

Properties		Value
surface tension (1) at 1268°K, dyn/cm		920
viscosity (1) at 1043°C, P		0.03697
crystallography (1)		
habit		face-centered cubic
lattice constant at 20°C, Å		4.086
atomic radius, Å		1.442
thermoelectric force vs Pt (1), mV		
at −100°C		−35
at 0°C		0
at 100°C		0.74
at 300°C		3.05
mechanical properties of commercially pure silver (99.9+%)		
elastic modulus tension, psi		
at 20°C		11.7×10^6 (1)
		11.0×10^6 (3)
at 30°C		10.6×10^6 (4)
torsion or shear modulus, psi		3.86×10^6 (1)
tensile properties (1) of 0.091-in. diam wire at 20°C	*Ultimate tensile strength, psi*	*Elongation, in 2 in. %*
annealed	25,000	52
cold worked 50%	44,000	5
tensile strength at 320°C (short time), psi		15,000

[a] A fixed point on the international temperature scale, revised in 1949. The 1927 scale used 960.5°C.

[b] Or 64.1–67.7 kcal/mole.

Recrystallization Temperature (1). This varies, depending on purity and amount of cold work. Softening begins at about 65°C for heavily worked material and lightly worked metal may require 250°C. A nominal, practical annealing temperature is 350°C.

Chemical Properties

The electron configuration of silver is 2 : 8 : 18 : 18 : 1. The primary valence is 1, although evidence exists for a higher valence state in "divalent" silver oxide (see p. 302) and other higher-valence compounds.

The Commission on Atomic Weight of the International Union of Pure and Applied Chemistry (IUPAC) in 1965 proposed 107.868 on the unified scale (^{12}C = 12) to replace the value used up to then of 107.880 (O = 16).

There are two stable isotopes weighing 107 and 109, with an abundance ratio of 1.075 to 1. Twenty-five radioactive isotopes are known with weights from 102 to 117 inclusive, and half-lives of from 5 sec to 253 days.

The standard electrode potential is +0.7978 V. In the convention used the potential of hydrogen is assigned the value of 0 and the more positive the value of the voltage the more noble the metal is. Copper has the value of 0.52 V and gold of 1.68 V. Silver is thus more noble than copper and much less noble than gold. Both copper and

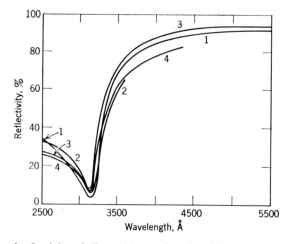

Fig. 1. Change of reflectivity of silver with wavelength. After Coblentz and Stair (5).

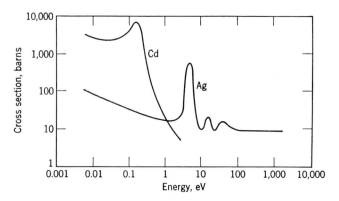

Fig. 2. Total neutron cross sections of silver and cadmium. From Bleuler and Goldsmith (6). Copyright 1952 by Ernst Bleuler and George J. Goldsmith. Courtesy Holt, Rinehart and Winston, Inc.

silver are tarnished by sulfur compounds in the atmosphere, but silver is not oxidized; for this reason silver is a generally useful electrical contact material.

Silver is unique among all the metals for its ability in the molten condition to dissolve large quantities of oxygen and for liberating much of it upon solidification. In air, at temperatures just above the melting point, silver dissolves about ten times its own volume of oxygen, or about 0.32%. During cooling the rapid liberation of oxygen gives rise to the familiar phenomenon of spitting (1).

As temperature increases above the melting point the oxygen solubility decreases slightly. The solubility increases with the partial pressure of O_2 in accordance with the relationship $\sqrt{P}/S = 0.135$, where P = pressure of O_2 in mm Hg and S = solubility in cm^3 O_2 (STP) per 100 g Ag.

High-purity solid silver at just below the melting point contains 0.006% O_2 at equilibrium with air. This drops to 0.001% below 600°C. However, the presence of small amounts of copper, lead, etc, nearly always found in commercial fine silver, makes silver have an apparently higher dissolving power for oxygen. In silver at equilibrium with air, these metals are present as oxides and, on annealing such metal in hydrogen, water vapor is generated internally, causing it to blister and embrittle. This is usually combatted by deoxidizing the melt with a stronger oxide former, such as phosphorus or lithium.

Although consideration has been given to the use of the high solubility of oxygen in molten silver for the separation of oxygen from air, little of practical value has resulted (4).

Oxygen diffuses rapidly through silver at elevated temperatures (4):

$$D = 1.71/10^{43} \times \sqrt{P}/d \times T^{14.62}$$

where D = rate of diffusion in cm³ (STP)/(m²)(hr)
P = O_2 pressure in mm Hg
d = thickness of silver in mm
T = absolute temperature

Thus at 800°C and 0.10-mm foil thickness, and a pressure difference of 2 atm of oxygen, the rate of diffusion is 225 cm³/(m²)(min) (4). The rate is not attractive for the amount of silver required.

The ability of silver to diffuse oxygen is used in the internal oxidation of AgMg and AgCd alloys (see p.294). The solubility and diffusibility of oxygen are also related to the catalytic activity of silver (see p. 292). For other than these cases, oxygen in silver is more of a nuisance than a useful characteristic. Besides embrittlement, another adverse evidence of oxygen diffusion is the separation of silver plate from base metals by the formation of a layer of base metal oxide at the interface when plated metal is heated in air and oxygen diffuses to the interface.

Silver is rather inert to many substances as would be expected from the noble solution potential. The principal chemical reaction of silver for the production of chemical compounds of silver is its reaction with nitric acid, which gives silver nitrate and a mixture of NO and NO_2. Nitric acid attacks silver at all concentrations. The reaction is most used at about 50:50 HNO_3/H_2O, hot, for etching silver and for producing silver nitrate solution, and is the starting point for the preparation of most other chemical compounds of silver (see Silver compounds).

At elevated temperatures silver and the halogens combine quickly and quantitatively with liberation of heat. Thus molten silver chloride is prepared for use in batteries by the direct reaction of chlorine gas on silver at temperatures above 455°C (the melting point of AgCl).

Silver metal is dissolved by alkali metal cyanide solutions either as anode, or in the presence of oxygen to form $NaAg(CN)_2$ or $KAg(CN)_2$:

$$Ag + 2\ NaCN \rightarrow NaAg(CN)_2 + Na^+ + e$$

$$2\ Ag + 4\ NaCN + H_2O + \tfrac{1}{2}\ O_2 \rightarrow 2\ NaAg(CN)_2 + 2\ NaOH$$

This reaction is of commercial importance in electroplating, and was formerly used in the extraction of silver from its ores.

Most other reactions of the metal are of importance primarily from the standpoint of corrosion. The following is a partial list of substances causing corrosive attack on silver: alkali metal cyanides; alkali metal, alkaline earth metal, and hydrogen peroxides; alkali metal and ammonium sulfides; bromine, wet or hot; chlorine oxygen acids; chlorine, hot; chromic acid; ferric sulfate; glass (molten) including borax; hydrogen sulfide; mercuric and mercurous salts; mercury; nitric acid; peroxysulfates; permanganates; sodium thiosulfate; sulfur; and sulfuric acid (concd).

The reader is referred especially to reference 4, pages 357–400, for a comprehensive list of corrosive materials. Whether or not silver is attacked by a particular reagent depends, in many cases, on temperature, or the presence of moisture or of sulfur, etc; hence a simple and comprehensive list is not possible.

Occurrence, Extraction, and Refining (1)

Silver is found as native silver (rather rarely) and as mineral species, such as cerargyrite (AgCl), argentite (Ag_2S), several complex sulfides containing antimony and/or arsenic, and tetrahedrite (($CuAg)_3(SbAs)S_3$), the main silver mineral of the most important silver mine in the United States, the Sunshine Mine in the Coeur d'Alene district, Idaho. Silver is also found in seawater in amounts on the order of 80–280 parts per trillion (10^{-12}). Most silver of commercial value is associated with copper, lead, and zinc. It is an economic fact of critical importance that silver is primarily a by-product of the mining of nonferrous base metals. Table 2 shows this relationship as it existed in the United States in 1963.

Table 2. United States Mine Production of Silver in 1963, According to Recoverable Value of Ore (Excludes Mines with Annual Production below 100,000 Oz)

Class of ore (percentage of total value contributed by silver)	Silver produced, troy oz[a]	Percentage of U.S. total		
		By classes	Cumulative %	
			0–100	100–0
0–10	10,190,763	30.40	30.40	100.00
10–20	6,958,367	20.76	51.16	69.60
20–30	1,924,452	5.75	56.91	48.84
30–40	252,555	0.75	57.66	43.09
40–50	3,586,952	10.70	68.36	42.34
50–60			68.36	31.64
60–70			68.36	31.64
70–80	267,853	0.80	69.16	31.64
80–90	9,841,311	29.36	98.52	30.84
90–100	494,827	1.48	100.00	1.48
0–100	33,517,080	100.00		

SOURCE: *U.S. Bur. Mines Inform. Circ. 8257* (1965).

[a] Troy oz = 31.103 g.

Even where the value of silver exceeds that of associated base metals, the weight of the base metals will usually exceed the silver. The Sunshine tetrahedrite contains six times as much copper as silver, by weight.

EXTRACTIVE METALLURGY

The extractive metallurgy of silver is essentially that of copper, lead, and zinc extraction, and silver follows these metals through the concentrating and smelting processes (7). The occurrence of silver in high concentrations independently of these base metals was once sufficiently widespread to support broad use of direct treatment by cyanidation or amalgamation, processes now used mainly on gold ores (Vol. 10, p. 628). A process of historic interest was the patio process in which silver minerals were first ground and then treated with salt, copper sulfate, and mercury; mixing and mulling were accomplished by driving mules over the flat heap. The silver amalgamated with the mercury and was recovered by retorting the amalgam (8).

Silver from Copper Extraction (7). In the refining of copper, fire processes do not return the silver values; thus when the copper contains appreciable silver, the electrolytic process is used (see Copper). The silver first separates from the main stream of the copper in the anode slimes of the copper electrolytic refining process. These slimes, which are the insoluble residues from the anodic dissolution of blister copper, usually contain 3000–6000 troy oz (1 oz = 31.103 g) of silver per ton, ie, 10–20% Ag, about 50–300 oz Au, 10–30% Cu, a few percent of Se, Te, Sb, As, and up to 20% Pb. The dry weight of the raw slimes is about 5–25 lb/ton of copper anodes dissolved (1).

The slimes are leached with hot dilute sulfuric acid with aeration to dissolve copper and some selenium and tellurium; roasting may follow for high-selenium and -tellurium materials. The treated slimes then contain 6000–12,000 oz Ag per ton, 2–4% Cu, 6–25% Pb, 2–7% Se, 3–14% Fe, and a few percent of antimony and arsenic together with the gold and platinum group metals.

The treated slimes are smelted in a doré furnace, a small reverberatory, together with fluxes such as $CaCO_3$, SiO_2, $Na_2B_4O_7$, CaF_2, etc. ("Doré" denotes an alloy of gold and silver.) Most of the base metals appear as silicates in the slags, which also contain important amounts of gold and silver, and are returned to the copper smelting process (the copper anode furnace). Alternatively, if the lead content is high, they may be sent to a lead smelter for the blast furnace.

On cooling somewhat from this stage, Se and Te separate out as a matte which is treated in situ with soda ash and niter to form a slag containing the Se and Te as water-soluble compounds. This is skimmed off for separate treatment. The remaining bullion is further oxidized to remove other impurities and is then cast into doré anodes which contain 94.0–98.5% Ag, 1.0–5.0% Au, 0.3–1.3% Cu, plus platinum group metals up to $\frac{1}{10}$ the amount of gold. Doré anodes are electrolyzed in a nitrate solution containing 40–140 g/l Ag and 5–80 g/l Cu, at 3.8–6.0 pH. Anode current density is on the order of 40–60 amp/ft². Silver of better than 99.9% purity is deposited in needlelike crystals at the cathode, is harvested perhaps twice per day, washed, melted, and cast into commercial bars weighing about 1100 troy oz.

The gold and platinum metals do not dissolve but report in the anode slimes or gold mud which is caught in the anode bag or diaphragm. The base metals accumulate in the electrolyte, which is partially replaced periodically.

The cells are of two types. The Moebius cell is about 30 × 30 × 24 in. deep and the anodes and cathodes hang vertically in alternate arrangement. The anodes are enclosed in cloth bags to catch the gold mud. A "windshield wiper" between each anode and cathode scrapes the crystals off the cathode sheet from where they fall into a basket on the bottom. This facilitates the removal and drainage of the crystals.

In the Balbach-Thum cells the cathode is on the floor of the cell and the anodes rest in a shallow tray suspended on the edge of the cell. The tray has a filter-cloth bottom which acts as a diaphragm to catch the gold mud. Silver crystals are shoveled or raked from the bottom cathode.

The Moebius cells require less floor space and less voltage. The Thum cells require less labor and the anode stubs do not have to be remelted; they are consumed completely.

Silver from Lead Extraction. In the smelting of lead (qv) the silver content may leave the main stream of the lead at any one of several places. The abbreviated flow diagram in Figure 3 shows the possible silver routes.

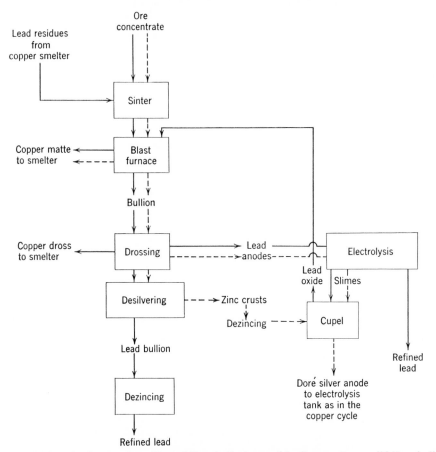

Fig. 3. Silver from lead extraction. Dotted lines indicate possible silver routes; solid lines indicate lead routes. From Schack and Clemmons (7).

Besides the route shown, the lead blast furnace, when being used to smelt large amounts of secondary silver (scrap metals containing silver), may operate in a closed cycle with the cupel. Scrap recovery may produce lead bullion with as much as 30% of silver. It follows that the blast furnace slag from this operation is also rich and it is therefore carefully saved for a separate campaign in the lead blast furnace with silver-lean lead.

The rich lead bullion goes directly to the cupel, a furnace similar to the doré furnace. The cupel is provided with air jets to blow directly onto the surface of the molten metal to oxidize the lead more or less continuously. The lead oxide makes a molten flux to carry off other impurities. The end result is doré bullion containing approx 98% or more of silver. The lead oxide from the cupel is recycled to the lead blast furnace.

STANDARDS AND SPECIFICATIONS

Commercial fine silver contains a minimum of 999.0 pts per thousand of silver as measured by the Volhard-Gay-Lussac method. The balance is mostly copper and/or lead. Following are typical analyses (in %):

Ag	Cu	Pb	Bi	Fe	Mn	Au	Pd
99.94	0.05	0.001	0.001	0.001	0.001		
99.91	0.06	0.020	0.001	0.001		0.0005	0.0005

Prior to 1964, there was no industry standard other than 999.0 minimum fineness. Many brands of bullion, however, were consistently of good quality for many technical uses. In 1964, ASTM issued a tentative specification for fine silver which was revised in 1966 to include a purer grade. ASTM B 413-66 T provides for grade 99.90 with 0.08% max Cu, 0.001% max Bi, 0.002% max Fe, and 0.025% max Pb; grade 99.95 has 0.04% max Cu, 0.001% max Bi, 0.001% max Fe, and 0.015% max Pb. The 99.90 grade has been adopted as the standard for trading on the Commodity Exchange in New York.

Assaying and Analysis

The presence of silver in large amounts of miscellaneous foreign matter, such as in ores, concentrates, ashes, sweepings, buff dust, etc, is almost invariably determined by the fire assay method. In this method the sample is fused with fluxes, litharge, and reducing agents and the metal values are gathered into a lead button from which other base metals are oxidized away by heating with more fluxes in a shallow dish called a scorifier. The purified lead button is further oxidized on a cupel (a crucible of a porous refractory material) to convert all the lead to lead oxide which is absorbed into the cupel leaving a silver bead substantially free of base metal and containing only gold and the platinum metals when these were present in the sample (12).

Silver in noninterfering base-metal alloys is usually determined by first dissolving the sample in nitric acid and then precipitating silver as the chloride. The chloride may be weighed, or the whole determination may be done volumetrically. The reader is referred to reference 12 for details on the Gay-Lussac and Volhard methods. The precision of the volumetric method is on the order of 0.2–0.4 pts per thousand, the gravimetric about 1.0 pts, and the fire assay about 1.5–2.0 pts on bullion samples and about 0.3–0.5% of the amount present in a pulp sample of sweeps, etc. See also Silver compounds.

Safety Aspects

There are few hazards in the melting, handling, and working of silver and silver–copper alloys in massive form. There is, however, an industrial disease peculiar to silver called argyria (13) that results from the absorption of chemical or colloidal silver into the system and its precipitation to form an irreversible and permanent pigmentation of the skin—slate gray, blue gray, or sometimes purplish—that is quite disfiguring but without any other physiological effect. The disease most often results from the habitual ingestion or inhalation of chemical or colloidal silver, or its injection or application to body cavities or mucous surfaces. It is therefore prudent that those habitually exposed to silver dusts and other silver wastes, including condensed vapor and spray from melting operations, should maintain a good standard of industrial hygiene including the ventilation of melting pots (which should be done anyway to save silver!) and of buff wheels, daily bathing, washing before eating, and the use of masks where ventilation does not keep the air clean.

The hazard is much more pronounced in the handling and habitual use of silver pharmaceuticals. Nevertheless, those responsible for the safety of workers in silver are urged to consult reference 13, p. 118.

There are also hazards in the melting of silver alloys containing cadmium (see Cadmium).

History and Economics (1)

The first metals to be used by man were probably gold, copper, and silver, in that order. Gold was first because it is very often found in the native state. Copper was next because it was so widespread, and silver not until later because it was much less widespread, was nearly always hidden as a sulfide, and was frequently associated with lead. It is possible that man's domestic fires accidentally reduced the first argentiferous galena, or perhaps a forest fire smelted an outcropping of the ore. From there it would be a simple matter for the lead to have been oxidized away (cupeled) to leave a mass of pure silver which could be worked into ornaments.

The earliest traditional records, as well as archeological evidence, showed that man in southern Europe and Asia Minor used silver both for ornament and as a medium of exchange; the predecessors of the Hittites in Cappadocia at least as far back as the fourth millennium BC are known to have done substantial work on silver production. By 2000 BC merchants in Cappadocia were exporting silver to Assyria. By 500 BC the important silver mines of Laurium in Greece had been opened and were said to have been the chief support of Athens in the Persian Wars. These mines lasted until the first century AD, by which time silver was being widely sought and produced, often by slaves and convicts. The Spanish silver–lead mines were a case in point, first developed by the Carthaginians and then taken over by the Romans after the Punic Wars.

The early spice trade with India was financed in part with silver from the Spanish mines, stopped in the eighth century by the Moorish invasion. From then until the fifteenth century there was some mining development in Bohemia and Transylvania, but the greatest silver discoveries of all time were the Spanish discoveries in their new Western Empire, chiefly in Mexico, Bolivia, and Peru. The patio process, mentioned before, came into wide use during the 300 years following the mid-sixteenth century.

Wars in Mexico interfered with silver production in the first half of the nineteenth century, and shortly thereafter the great deposits in the Sierra Nevada—the Mother Lode—were opened; these placed the United States first in the production of silver until about 1900. Heretofore silver was produced primarily from ore having silver as the principal value, but after this date silver became more and more a by-product of copper and lead mining as the rich silver deposits became exhausted.

The modern history of silver in Western Europe and the United States has three important facets: the development of silversmithing, the political-monetary aspect, and the rise of technical industrial applications of the metal. In the arts, the fine white appearance, the workability, and the scarcity have made it desirable both for ornamentation and as a store of wealth. Pure silver, however, is too soft for durability and this has been remedied by the addition of copper in amounts usually less than 10%. The best-known and still the widest used is the *English sterling* alloy made of 925 pts of silver to 75 pts of copper. This was started about 1200 AD. The term sterling is a contraction of the word Easterling derived from the free cities of eastern Germany that formed the Hanseatic League. The quality of their coin was much liked by the English in the twelfth century and was adopted by them for their silversmithing.

Every piece of silverware was sent to an assay office to be assayed and then stamped with a mark indicating sterling fineness, and where assayed, a mark designating the maker, and a mark designating the year. In London this was done at the guild hall of the goldsmiths; hence the term "hallmarked."

Although various vessels and decorative objects have been used for eating since Roman times or before, the thirteenth-century spoon was the first item of tableware as we know it, together with salt shakers and bowls; then came silver dinner plates. Tankards with lids came in the sixteenth century together with bowls, ladles, candle-sticks, tea services, etc, until by the eighteenth century "the table was so fully furnished that the food could be brought to it only one course at a time" (1).

As silverware became more widely used, more and more mass-production manu-facturing practices replaced hand-smithing during the nineteenth and twentieth cen-turies. Silver-clad copper came into use in the eighteenth century as *Sheffield plate*, which is sterling clad onto a slab of copper that is then rolled down to sheet. Later silver electroplate applied to nickel brass replaced Sheffield, as it was amenable to thinner coatings and did not show copper at exposed edges.

Political and Monetary Aspects in the United States

From 1793 to 1873 the United States was officially on a bimetallic standard under which the Mint accepted both silver and gold for coinage at a fixed monetary ratio of about 16 to 1.

The flood of silver from new sources in the West during the last half of the nine-teenth century resulted in silver being overpriced by the Mint, and the Government was rapidly gaining silver and losing gold; hence the change in 1873. With the decline

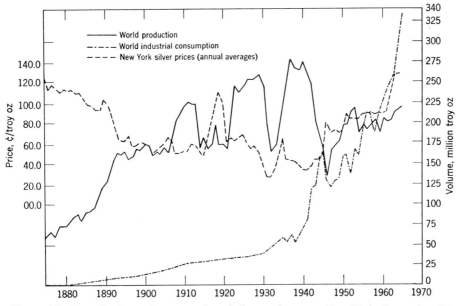

Fig. 4. World production and consumption of silver and average New York silver prices (9).

in its use as a monetary base (as distinguished from subsidiary coin) and with the general oversupply as a by-product of other metals, silver prices sank until World War I (see Fig. 4).

The mining interests were not idle during this time, and sought Government support of silver. The Bland-Allison Act of 1878 and the Sherman Silver Purchase Act of 1890 provided for purchase of silver by the Treasury. Nevertheless the price dropped persistently until the onset of World War I, when inflation drove the price to its then all-time high of $1.385 per troy oz in November of 1919, creating a monetary crisis in India.

Table 3. World Silver Consumption, Excluding Communist-Dominated Areas, million troy oz (10)

Uses	1963	1964	1965	1966	1967
industrial					
United States	110.0	123.0	137.0	150.0	145.0
Canada	4.6	5.0	5.3	5.5	5.4
Mexico	3.2	4.1	4.7	5.1	5.0
United Kingdom	20.0	23.0	25.0	25.0	24.0
France	13.9	14.8	14.0	14.7	14.7
West Germany	40.5	46.3	54.6	48.2	48.2
Italy	25.0	30.0	35.0	35.0	33.0
Japan	20.0	20.0	25.0	27.0	31.1
India	2.5	12.0	16.0	16.0	15.0
other countries	21.0	26.0	30.0	30.0	30.0
total industrial	260.7	304.2	346.6	356.5	351.4
coinage[a]					
Canada	13.0	13.7	20.4	14.7	8.2
France	12.2	10.7	7.2	10.6	9.6
Italy	0.5	1.4	2.4	2.5	1.6
Japan	4.2	17.3	5.8	5.0	
other countries	25.0	21.0	24.5	20.0	15.0
total coinage	54.9	64.1	60.3	52.8	34.4
total consumption	315.6	368.3	406.9	409.3	385.8

[a] Consumption of silver for U.S. coinage has been excluded from this table. Supplies needed for this purpose are obtained entirely from Treasury stocks and have never been part of market demand. The amounts consumed for the past five years have been as follows (in million troy oz):

1963	1964	1965	1966	1967
111.5	203.0	320.3	53.6	43 8

During the 1920s and early 1930s the price declined and reached its all-time low of 24.5¢ in 1932, at which point the Government again intervened. There followed a series of silver-purchase acts which only temporarily elevated the price, but under which the Government acquired 2 billion ounces of silver in seven years. It issued silver certificates against much of it. Increased demand in World War II and further Government silver purchase started the price up again in 1945 and the trend has been up since that time until this writing in January, 1968. During this interval the Government changed from being a buyer of silver in a surplus market to a seller of silver in a scarcity market, largely because of the increased demand for industrial uses. The Treasury's silver bullion holding was reduced to 348,000,000 oz by the end of 1967. The Government continues to sell up to 2,000,000 oz weekly at going prices, about $2.10 per troy oz at this writing.

Table 4. World Silver Supplies, Excluding Communist-Dominated Areas, million troy oz (10)

Source	1963	1964	1965	1966	1967
new production					
Mexico	42.7	41.7	40.3	43.0	38.3
United States	35.2	36.3	39.8	43.7	31.0
Canada	29.8	29.9	31.9	33.4	37.1
Peru	36.8	37.0	35.3	37.0	37.0
Bolivia	4.9	4.8	4.1	5.0	5.0
other South and Central American					
countries	9.1	9.4	10.2	10.0	10.0
total Western Hemisphere	158.5	159.1	161.6	172.1	158.4
outside the Western Hemisphere	56.1	51.6	53.7	55.0	55.0
total new production	214.6	210.7	215.3	227.1	213.4
other supplies					
U.S. Treasury silver	25.2	151.0	80.4	142.5	195.2
stocks of foreign governments	10.0	20.0	17.0	10.0	5.0
demonitized coin	15.0	20.0	30.0	28.0	35.0
sales by U.S.S.R.			9.4	9.6	8.0
liquidation of speculative holdings					
and inventory reductions	40.0		35.0		
salvage and other miscellaneous					
sources	10.8	36.6	19.8	32.1	49.2
total other supplies	101.0	227.6	191.6	222.2	292.4
total world supplies	315.6	438.3	406.9	449.3	505.8
less additions to speculative					
holdings and inventory					
accumulations		70.0		40.0	120.0
available for consumption	315.6	368.3	406.9	409.3	385.8

Until 1965 the coinage of the United States was of coin silver (90% Ag–10% Cu) for the dollar, the half dollar, quarter, and dime. The silver dollar contained a dollar's worth of fine silver when silver was priced at $1.29 per troy oz. One dollar in subsidiary coins contained a dollar's worth of silver at $1.38 per troy oz and thus in early 1968 silver dimes, quarters, and half dollars (nonlaminated) are worth considerably more than face value. The only silver still being minted is the laminated half dollar averaging 40% Ag. It consists of 80% Ag–20% Cu cover plates laminated to a core metal containing 21.5% Ag–78.5% Cu. The new 25¢ and 10¢ subsidiary coins are of cupronickel laminated to copper, with no silver.

It was estimated that approx $2,700,000,000 of subsidiary coins were in circulation up to 1965, which are now (1968) being hoarded by individuals and retired by the Treasury. Melting by the public is still prohibited.

Tables 3 and 4 show how world use exceeds world new production. Since very little of the world's silver has ever been really lost (the amount used in photography, and not recovered, is comparatively small), there are large hoards of the metal available, such as the old coinage of the United States and other countries, the private hoards of long standing, as in India, and the recent speculative hoards, from which the deficit between new production and use could be supplied for some time.

Uses of Pure Silver

In 1965 the industrial use of silver in the United States was about 140 million oz divided as follows: photography (qv), 32%; electrical and electronic, 31%; silverware and jewelry, 17%; brazing alloys and solders, 13%; all other 7%.

Among the electrical uses of pure silver are electrical contacts, printed circuits, and batteries. However, contacts also comprise a major use for silver alloys. There are three special virtues of silver for electrical contacts: high electrical conductivity, high thermal conductivity, and good corrosion or oxidation resistance. Adverse properties are a tendency to weld with heavy currents, which can be abated by alloying; softness and lack of mechanical durability, also remediable by alloying; and susceptibility to tarnishing which is important mainly in microcurrent circuits, and for which there is no deterrent other than the use of a tarnishproof metal, such as either gold or platinum.

In silver batteries pure silver is the cathode, and the cathode depolarizer is usually silver oxide (divalent), while the anode is usually zinc or cadmium (see Batteries, primary). The silver–zinc cell can provide 40 Wh/lb, the silver–cadmium cell 27 Wh/lb, and the industrial lead–acid battery 10 Wh/lb. The silver cells are capable of a very high discharge rate. At equivalent capacity they cost roughly five times as much as the lead cell (based on $1.29 silver). The silver electrode reaction in a caustic electrolyte is

$$2\ AgO + H_2O + 2\ e \underset{\text{charge}}{\overset{\text{discharge}}{\rightleftharpoons}} Ag_2O + 2\ OH^-$$

$$Ag_2O + H_2O + 2\ e \underset{\text{charge}}{\overset{\text{discharge}}{\rightleftharpoons}} 2\ Ag + 2\ OH^-$$

In the seawater-activated Ag–AgCl–Mg cell, AgCl is reduced to silver while the cathode is depolarized, and Mg is converted to $MgCl_2$ which is washed out (see Vol. 3, pp. 132–134). The principal use is in torpedo propulsion.

In the electronics industry, pure silver powder pigments are used in special paints for putting electrodes onto capacitor dielectrics, such as mica, glass, and titanate ceramics. Similar paints are used for stenciling printed circuits onto ceramics. These paints usually incorporate low-melting glass frits for bonding to ceramics.

Electroplating (qv) for both technical and esthetic purposes is nearly always done with pure silver, and the alkali cyanide–silver cyanide bath is almost universally used.

Mirror coatings, whether applied by the chemical mirroring technique or by hot metallic vapor in vacuum, are of pure silver.

Pure silver in the form of wire screens or as loosely packed electrolytic "needles" is used as the catalyst for the oxidation of methanol to formaldehyde. For the ethylene to ethylene oxide reaction, a porous silver powder coating on ceramic balls serves as the catalyst.

Alloys

The most important alloy system, by all odds, is that of silver and copper. It forms a eutectic at 72% Ag, melting at 779°C with two terminal solid solutions—the silver-rich, containing 8.8 wt% copper, and the copper-rich, containing 8.0% silver at the eutectic temperature. The solubility in both phases drops off to negligible amounts at room temperature (see Fig. 5).

Coin silver contains 10% copper and was the alloy for United States coinage. It is used for electrical applications, particularly where strength and hardness are required. The eutectic alloy is also used for electromechanical parts.

The strength of the silver copper alloys as a function of copper content and cold work is shown in Figure 6. With heavy cold work, the strength of the eutectic alloy can be raised to over 100,000 psi. Copper has a relatively small effect on the electrical conductivity of silver and vice versa.

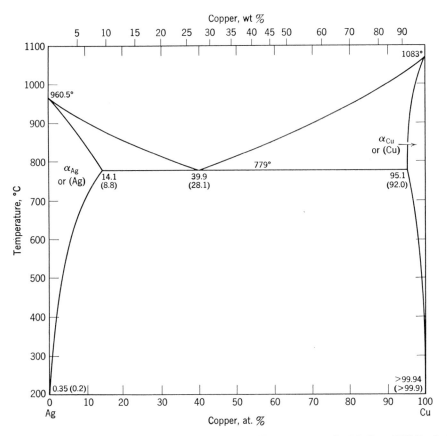

Fig. 5. The silver–copper system. From Hansen (11). Copyright 1958 by McGraw-Hill Book Co., Inc. Courtesy McGraw-Hill Book Co., Inc.

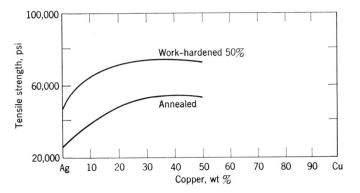

Fig. 6. Variation of tensile strength with composition for annealed and cold-worked silver–copper alloys (1). Copyright 1967 by D. Van Nostrand Co. Courtesy D. Van Nostrand Co.

The eutectic alloy is used as a silver solder or brazing alloy and also as a base for many other lower-melting-point solders or brazing alloys. Additions of zinc, of zinc and cadmium, and of tin are used to lower the melting temperature of silver–copper alloys. See Solders and brazing alloys.

Other silver alloys of commerce are those used in electrical contacts, and some of these are not true alloys but are mixtures of silver and substances not miscible with silver by melting. The more important of these contain 10 or 15% CdO (balance silver); 10–75% W (balance silver); 10–40% Ni (balance silver); and 0.5–2% graphite (balance silver).

The effect of CdO is to reduce the tendency of silver contacts to weld closed and to increase arc-erosion resistance. The W and Ni sintered mixtures are used in heavy-current, high-voltage devices to resist arcing and improve the mechanical durability against battering. Silver–graphite is used for sliding contacts. There are many other alloys, mixtures, and modifications, too numerous to mention here. However, of growing importance because of the increasing price of silver are the bimetals in which silver or its alloys are clad onto copper or other base metals and from which parts are fabricated in such a way as to have the silver only at the critical area of electrical contact.

Silver solders or brazing alloys make joints that are much stronger and more durable than soft-solder (Pb–Sn alloy) joints. Most refrigeration system copper tubing is silver soldered or brazed as is much industrial and commercial piping. Brazing alloys are much used in hard goods manufacture, such as in bicycles, automotive parts, and in military goods, such as artillery shells, firearms parts, rocket tubing, aircraft subassemblies, etc.

Bibliography

"Silver and Silver Alloys" in *ECT* 1st ed., Vol. 12, pp. 426–438, by E. H. Konrad and F. A. Meier (Analysis), The American Platinum Works.

1. A. Butts and C. Coxe, *Silver—Economics, Metallurgy, and Use*, D. Van Nostrand Co., Inc., Princeton, N.J., 1967.
2. *Edelmetall Taschenbuch*, Degussa, Frankfurt, Germany, 1967.
3. *Metals Handbook*, 8th ed., American Society for Metals, New York, 1961.
4. L. Addicks, *Silver in Industry*, Reinhold Publishing Corp., New York, 1940.
5. W. W. Coblentz and R. Stair, *Natl. Bur. Standards J. Res.* **2**, 243 (1929).
6. E. Bleuler and G. J. Goldsmith, *Experimental Nucleonics*, Holt, Rinehart and Winston, Inc., New York, 1952.
7. C. H. Schack and B. H. Clemmons, "Review and Evaluation of Silver-Production Techniques," *U.S. Bur. Mines, Inform. Circ. 8266* (1965).
8. F. R. S. Gowland, *The Metallurgy of the Non-Ferrous Metals*, Griffin and Co. Ltd., London, 1921.
9. *The Silver Market in 1966*, Handy & Harman, New York, 1967.
10. *The Silver Market in 1967*, Handy & Harman, New York, 1968.
11. Max Hansen, *Constitution of Binary Alloys*, 2nd ed., McGraw-Hill Book Co., Inc., New York, 1958.
12. O. C. Shepard and W. F. Dietrich, *Fire Assaying*, McGraw-Hill Book, Co., Inc., New York, 1940.
13. W. R. Hill and D. H. Pillsbury, *Argyria—The Industrial Pharmacology of Silver*, Williams and Wilkins Co., Baltimore, Md., 1934.

C. D. Coxe
Handy & Harman

SILVER COMPOUNDS

Silver belongs to group IB of the periodic table and has a $4d^{10} 5s^1$ outer electronic configuration. The standard electrode potentials show that oxidation of the metal leads most easily to the $+1$ oxidation state:

$$\text{Ag} \xrightarrow[3]{-0.799\text{V}} \text{Ag}^+ \xrightarrow[4]{-1.98\text{V}} \text{Ag}^{2+} \xrightarrow{\text{Ca}-2.1\text{V}} \text{AgO}^+$$

Of the three oxidation states only silver(I) exists in solution. The only two stable binary Ag(II) compounds are the fluoride and oxide; Ag(III) exists only when stabilized through complex formation. Silver subfluoride, Ag_2F, has also been prepared.

Silver forms a number of colored salts with colorless anions, such as Br^-, I^-, and certain oxygenated anions, even though Ag^+ ions themselves are colorless. This is considered evidence for the partially covalent nature of these silver salts. Only three simple silver salts, the fluoride, nitrate, and perchlorate, are soluble to the extent of one mole per liter. The acetate, chlorate, nitrite, and sulfate are partially soluble; all other silver salts are considered insoluble in water. Most of the insoluble salts dissolve in water when complexes are formed with excess ammonia, cyanide, thiosulfate, and the halides. The fluoride, periodate, and perchlorate are the only hydrated silver salts known.

Most silver compounds are prepared from silver nitrate which is invariably produced from metallic silver. Unlike many other industrial chemicals, silver compounds are offered on the market in small quantities and are generally of high purity.

Commercial specifications of silver compounds are not always readily available because in many instances they are produced captively from the metal by a few manufacturers. Silver chloride, oxide, and sulfate are available in a technical grade; silver nitrate and nitrite are available in a technical grade, as well as in a USP XVII grade. Several silver compounds are available as reagent-grade chemicals; each lot is analyzed and the silver content is usually at least 99.5% of theory.

Most silver compounds are shipped in brown glass bottles or jars from 1 oz to 5 gal. In most instances a poison class B label is required. Oxidants, such as silver nitrate and perchlorate, also need a DOT (formerly ICC) yellow label.

Silver(I) Compounds

SILVER ACETATE AND SILVER ORGANIC ACID SALTS. Silver acetate, $AgC_2H_3O_2$, is prepared by the reaction of a soluble acetate and silver nitrate. The solubility is 11.1 g/liter at 25°C. Slightly soluble or insoluble silver salts are precipitated when virtually all mono- and dicarboxylic acids, or their anions, are allowed to react with silver nitrate solutions. Some of the salts of the higher fatty acids have found limited commercial use. Silver oxalate, $Ag_2C_2O_4$, decomposes explosively when heated to elevated temperatures.

SILVER ARSENATE AND ARSENITE. When arsenate ions are added to a solution of silver nitrate, a dark-red precipitate of silver arsenate is formed. Silver arsenite, formed by the reaction of a soluble arsenite with silver nitrate, is yellow when freshly precipitated, but rapidly turns brown. Both salts decompose upon heating to yield metallic silver.

SILVER CARBONATE.   Addition of an alkaline carbonate solution to one of silver nitrate produces silver carbonate, Ag_2CO_3.   A concentrated solution of silver nitrate should be employed, under strict pH and temperature control, to minimize silver oxide formation.   The freshly prepared precipitate is white, but turns yellow upon washing or heating.   Its solubility in pure water is 0.033 g/liter at 25°C;   1.15 g dissolves in one liter of water under 0.9 atm pressure of carbon dioxide.

Silver carbonate is slightly photosensitive.   Owing to extensive hydrolysis, a suspension of the solid in water appears basic.   Upon heating, the solid decomposes to Ag_2O and CO_2, a reaction which goes to completion at 218°C.

SILVER CHROMATE AND SILVER DICHROMATE, Ag_2CrO_4 and $Ag_2Cr_2O_7$, are prepared by the reaction of solutions of silver nitrate with the corresponding soluble chromium salt.   The solubility of the chromate is 0.036 g/liter at 25°C;   that of the dichromate is 0.083 g/liter at 15°C.   Boiling water converts the dichromate to chromate.

Formation of the characteristic brick-red silver chromate color is used as a qualitative test for chromate ions and as an indicator in the classic Mohr titrations of halides with silver nitrate.

SILVER CYANIDE.   Addition of equimolar quantities of cyanide ion to a silver nitrate solution precipitates silver cyanide, AgCN.   The solubility in water is 0.070 g/liter at 25°C;   in cyanide solutions it is greatly increased because of complex formation.   The structure of the solid, as indicated by x-ray diffraction analysis, consists of infinite chains of alternating cyanide groups and silver atoms arranged in a hexagonal lattice with silver atoms at the apixes of a tetrahedron.   The silver atoms are joined to the cyanide groups by bonding through both carbon and nitrogen.   For the —Ag—C$\equiv$N—Ag— arrangement the Ag—Ag distance is 5.26×10^{-8} cm (1).

SILVER HALIDES AND OTHER HALOGEN SALTS.   **Silver chloride,** AgCl, separates as a white precipitate when chloride ions are added to a solution of silver nitrate.   It can also be formed by the direct reaction of the elements at elevated temperatures and by the reaction of metallic silver, hydrochloric acid, and oxidizing agents at room temperature.   It occurs in nature as the mineral cerargyrite (horn silver).

Silver chloride has a cubic structure; the distance between each ion in the lattice is 2.77×10^{-8} cm.   Silver chloride is the most ionic of the halides; the covalent radii of the elements Ag:Cl are in the ratio 1.26:0.99.   The salt melts at 455°C and boils at 1550°C.

The solubility of silver chloride is 0.00193 g/liter at 25°C; the solubility product, K_{sp}, is 1.8×10^{-10} at 25°C.   The order of solubility of the three silver halides is Cl > Br > I.   Silver chloride is soluble in cyanide, thiosulfate, ammonia, and chloride solutions through complex formation.   It is insoluble in nitric and dilute sulfuric acid; concentrated sulfuric acid converts it to the sulfate.

The stability of silver chloride in the dark and its ease of reduction after exposure to light are the basis for its use in photography.   With sufficient intensity and time, the solid can be completely decomposed into its elements.

All silver halides are reduced to silver by treating an aqueous suspension of the salt with active metals, such as magnesium, zinc, aluminum, copper, mercury, iron, or lead.   Alternatively, the dry salt can be heated with turnings or powder of the above metals to accomplish the reduction. Mild reducing agents, including ferrous sulfate, sulfurous acid, and stannous chloride, do not attack silver chloride, but treatment with more powerful reagents, such as sodium stannite and sodium hyposulfite, produces metallic silver. Photolyzed silver chloride and bromide are reduced by organic agents, such as hydroquinone and p-aminophenol, in the photographic development reaction.

Treatment of an ammoniacal solution of silver chloride with sulfide ions yields silver sulfide. With zinc, mercuric, or lead sulfide simple metathesis occurs, but, upon treatment with cuprous sulfide, some metallic silver is also formed. At high temperature bromine and iodine react with silver chloride to form silver bromide and silver iodide.

Silver chloride is very ductile and can be rolled into large sheets; individual crystals of up to 10 lb have been prepared. For the preparation of high-purity silver halide crystals, see reference 2.

Silver bromide, AgBr, separates as a light yellow to green-yellow precipitate, when bromide ions are added to a silver nitrate solution. Direct synthesis from the elements is difficult. It occurs in nature as the mineral bromyrite.

Like silver chloride, silver bromide has a cubic structure; the interion distance is 2.88×10^{-8} cm. The yellow color is due to ionic deformation, an indication of its partially covalent character. The covalent radii of the elements Ag:Br are in the ratio $1.26:1.14$. The salt melts at $434°C$ and decomposes at $700°C$. The crystal structure of photographic grains is generally octahedral. Cubic crystals are produced only when exact stoichiometric amounts of silver nitrate and potassium bromide are mixed. If an excess of either ion is present, octahedral crystals tend to be formed.

The solubility of silver bromide is 0.00013 g/liter at $25°C$; the solubility product, K_{sp}, is 3.3×10^{-13} at $25°C$. It is less soluble in ammonia than silver chloride, but is easily dissolved by the other complexing agents.

Silver bromide is far more sensitive to photoreduction than the chloride or iodide and is therefore used extensively in photographic products. When heated above $500°C$, it begins to dissociate into the elements. Solidification of melted silver bromide yields a malleable transparent yellow solid. Silver bromide is more difficult to reduce with hydrogen than is silver chloride. Even if elevated temperatures are used, the reaction is incomplete due to its reversibility. Most silver chloride reducing agents also reduce the bromide. Treatment with hot concentrated sulfuric acid yields silver sulfate.

Silver iodide, AgI, precipitates from solution as a yellow solid when a soluble iodide salt is added to a silver nitrate solution. Preparation from the elements is quantitative only at elevated temperatures. It occurs in nature as the mineral iodyrite.

Silver iodide is trimorphic. The yellow α form is cubic and stable above $145.8°C$. Below $145.8°C$, the green-yellow hexagonal β form is produced, while the γ form, "cold cubic," exists below $137°C$. The covalent radii of the elements Ag:I are in the ratio $1.26:1.33$. Silver iodide melts with decomposition at $552°C$.

Silver iodide smoke is obtained by vaporizing the solid at a high temperature, and suddenly cooling it. The unit cell of these smoke crystals differs by only 1% from ice crystals. They are therefore useful for the seeding of clouds.

The solubility of silver iodide is 2.6×10^{-6} g/liter at $25°C$; its solubility product, K_{sp}, is 8.5×10^{-17} at $25°C$. Even in concentrated ammonia, silver iodide is only slightly soluble; it dissolves slowly in cyanide and thiosulfate solutions. Owing to formation of complex salts as AgI_2^-, it is quite soluble in iodide solutions.

Silver iodide is the least photosensitive of the three halides. It is difficult to reduce by metals, but zinc and iron reduce it quantitatively in the presence of sulfuric acid. When heated with concentrated ammonia, silver iodide turns white because of the formation of crystalline $AgI \cdot \frac{1}{2}NH_3$.

Silver fluoride, AgF, is prepared by the reaction of hydrofluoric acid with silver oxide or carbonate. The anhydrous salt is colorless; the dihydrate (unstable above 42°C) and the tetrahydrate (unstable over 18°C) are yellow. At 25°C, 1000 g of a saturated solution contains 642 g of silver fluoride. Ultraviolet radiation decomposes it to the subfluoride, Ag_2F, and fluorine.

Hypohalites. The hypochlorite, AgClO, hypobromite, AgBrO, and hypoiodite, AgIO, have all been prepared, but only silver hypochlorite is moderately stable at room temperature and even it decomposes slowly to silver chloride and silver chlorate.

Halates. Three silver halate salts, $AgClO_3$, $AgBrO_3$, and $AgIO_3$, have been prepared. Silver chlorate is soluble in water but silver bromate and iodate are not. Silver chlorate is best prepared by the reaction between silver sulfate and a soluble chlorate. The halates may decompose explosively if heated.

Perhalates. Silver perchlorate, $AgClO_4$, and periodate, $AgIO_4$, have been prepared; silver perbromate is not known. Silver perchlorate is prepared from silver oxide by its reaction with perchloric acid or by treating silver sulfate with barium perchlorate. The colorless monohydrate decomposes above 43°C to yield the anhydrous salt. Silver perchlorate crystallizes at ordinary temperatures in the rhombic system and changes to the rock-salt type at higher temperatures. It has a markedly lower transition temperature, 155°C, than the other perchlorates. One kilogram of a satd solution at 25°C contains 845 g of silver perchlorate. Silver perchlorate is one of the few silver salts that are appreciably soluble in organic solvents, such as glycerol, chlorobenzene, nitromethane, and benzene. The benzene–silver perchlorate adduct appears to be polymeric (3).

Silver tetrafluoroborate, $AgBF_4$, is formed by the reaction of silver borate with sodium borofluoride or bromine trifluoride. Like silver perchlorate, it is soluble in hydrocarbon solvents.

SILVER NITRATE, $AgNO_3$, is the most important commercial silver salt. Because it is stable, freely soluble in water, and can be prepared in high purity, it serves as the commercial starting material for virtually all other silver compounds. In the classic method of preparation metallic silver is dissolved in nitric acid. Heavy-metal impurities, such as copper, lead, and iron, are precipitated by raising the pH to 5.9 with silver oxide and then boiling the solution. To effect crystallization, the silver nitrate solution is made slightly acid, heated, evaporated, and then poured into pans to cool. The crystals are washed on a centrifuge and dried. If a purer product is required, the solid is recrystallized from water.

The Kestner-Johnson dissolver is now used to prepare silver nitrate solutions in a number of plants both in the United States and in Europe (4). Special purification processes have been developed using treatment with silver oxide combined with activated charcoal or alumina (5,6). Ultraviolet radiation is sometimes used to reduce noble metal impurities to the metallic state for easy removal (7). Flowsheets for the Kestner-Johnson dissolver, an Englehard Industries plant incorporating the dissolver, and some of the Du Pont purification techniques are available (8). In most commercial plants the nitrous oxide liberated by the reaction is oxidized and absorbed in water for recovery and reuse.

High-purity silver nitrate, such as is used in photography, is made from bars of fine silver (99.97%). At Eastman Kodak Company, where a substantial share of the total U.S. production is manufactured, the silver bars are dissolved in nitric acid in three continuous tanks connected in parallel. The resulting solution, containing 65% silver nitrate, is then passed through a clean-up tank which removes all but a trace of nitric acid. The crude crystals are isolated by centrifugation. After recrystallization from hot water, the crystals are again centrifuged and dried in a rotary dryer. All equipment used in this process is made of either AISI 309 or 310 stainless steel. This continuous process supersedes the old batch process and not only saves labor, but produces a more uniform product (9).

Silver nitrate consists of colorless rhombic crystals. It is dimorphic and the transition to the hexagonal rhombohedral form occurs at 159.8°C (10). The solubility increases with the temperature as follows:

Temperature, °C	g $AgNO_3$/ kg satd soln	Temperature, °C	g $AgNO_3$/ kg satd soln
0	548	60	815
25	710	100	880

The alchemist's name, lunar caustic, is still applied to the fused salt.

Solid silver nitrate is stable when heated to 350°C, provided a trace of nitric acid is present; at 440°C it decomposes to metallic silver, nitrogen, and oxides of nitrogen. Solutions of the salt are neutral. In the absence of organic matter, it is not photosensitive. Anhydrous halogen halides do not react with it, but all the halogen acids, except hydrogen fluoride, precipitate the silver halide. It is easily reduced to the metal by many organic compounds, such as glucose, tartaric acid, and formaldehyde. Hydrogen gas reduces silver nitrate above 80°C. At elevated temperatures powdered graphite also reduces silver nitrate.

SILVER NITRITE, $AgNO_2$, is prepared by the reaction between silver nitrate and a soluble nitrite or silver sulfate and barium nitrite. The yellow crystals exist in two tautomeric forms. Its solubility in water is 1.55 g/liter at 0°C and 4.2 g/liter at 25°C.

SILVER OXIDE. Dark-brown to black crystals of silver oxide, Ag_2O, are formed when an excess of hydroxide ions is added to a silver nitrate solution. It is also prepared by heating the metal in the presence of oxygen. The completely pure anhydrous oxide is difficult to prepare; it invariably contains either some water or free silver (11).

A composite value calculated from a number of determinations indicates the solubility of silver oxide to be 0.022 g/liter 25°C (12). It is freely soluble in most silver-complexing agents. Dissolution in ammonia may produce highly explosive fulminating silver or Bertholet's silver (13), containing silver imide or silver nitride.

The solid, which is stable at room temperature, begins to decompose into its elements when heated to 100°C, and is completely decomposed above 300°C. Aqueous suspensions are basic to litmus. It reacts with sulfur to form silver sulfide and absorbs carbon dioxide from the air to form silver carbonate. Reaction with thiosulfate ions yields a mixture of the sulfide and sulfate. Moist silver oxide is used in organic synthesis as a mild oxidant and to replace bromide and iodide groups with hydroxide.

There is no evidence for the existence of silver hydroxide; all reactions intended to produce it yield the brown oxide.

SILVER PHOSPHATE. Silver orthophosphate, commonly known as silver phosphate, Ag_3PO_4, is a bright yellow crystalline material. Silver pyrophosphate, $Ag_4P_2O_7$, is white. Each is prepared by treating a silver nitrate solution with a soluble ortho- or pyrophosphate; use of phosphoric acid yields the orthophosphate salt. Silver orthophosphate is produced when silver pyrophosphate is allowed to react with sulfuric or nitric acid. Phosphoric acid converts Ag_3PO_4 into Ag_2HPO_4, but the dihydrogen phosphate, AgH_2PO_4, has not been prepared. Both the ortho and pyro salts are photosensitive; silver pyrophosphate turns red upon exposure to light.

SILVER SULFATE, Ag_2SO_4, consisting of white rhombic crystals, is prepared industrially by treating metallic silver with hot sulfuric acid. It can also be obtained by acidifying silver nitrate with sulfuric acid and removing the nitric acid by evaporation.

The solubility of silver sulfate in water is 8.3 g/liter at 25°C; it is more soluble in sulfuric acid than in water because of formation of $AgHSO_4$.

The thermal stability of silver sulfate permits the direct oxidation and recovery of the silver contained in sulfide minerals. Only when heated above 1085°C, does it decompose to silver, sulfur dioxide, and oxygen. It is reduced to the metal by a variety of agents, including hydrogen, carbon, carbon monoxide, zinc, and copper.

SILVER SULFIDE, Ag_2S, is precipitated as a finely divided black powder when most silver salts are treated with an alkaline sulfide or hydrogen sulfide. Silver and sulfur combine even in the cold to form silver sulfide. The material is dimorphic, and transition from the rhombohedral to cubic form occurs at 175°C. Both forms, argentite (cubic) and acanthite (rhombic), are known in nature. There are also a number of double sulfide minerals, notably those with arsenic and antimony.

Silver sulfide is one of the most insoluble silver compounds known. The solubility product, K_{sp}, at 25°C, is 3.8×10^{-52} (14) or 5.9×10^{-52} (15). Nonoxidizing mineral acids do not attack it, but it is soluble in nitric acid, concentrated sulfuric acid, and alkaline cyanide solutions.

Silver tarnish consists of silver sulfide. It occurs readily only when a trace of moisture is present. For its removal, silver polishes contain high levels of chloride plus an abrasive or rely on complex formation with such materials as thiourea. Although silver sulfide is exceptionally stable in air and sunlight, it readily decomposes when heated at 810°C. It is heated with the oxide or sulfate to produce metallic silver. Moss silver (filiform silver), consisting of long hairlike growths of pure silver, is formed by prolonged heating of silver sulfide below 810°C.

Silver sulfide is very ductile, and can be cast and drawn into strips or wires. The pure material conducts electricity like a metal of high specific resistance, yet has a zero temperature coefficient. The metallic conduction is believed to be due to the fact that a few of the atoms exist in the divalent state and thus free electrons are present to transport the current. If the silver sulfide is not pure and contains an excess of either sulfur or silver, the conduction is greatly decreased.

Other Silver(I) Compounds

A variety of other silver(I) compounds have been prepared but they have limited commercial application.

SILVER ACETYLIDE or silver carbide, Ag_2C_2, is formed by bubbling acetylene through an ammoniacal silver nitrate solution. It is sensitive to detonation on contact.

SILVER AZIDE, AgN_3, is another explosive silver salt formed by treating a silver nitrate solution with hydrazine or hydrazoic acid.

SILVER PERMANGANATE, $AgMnO_4$, is a violet solid that is formed by the reaction of solutions of potassium permanganate and silver nitrate. It is decomposed by heating, upon exposure to light, or by reaction with alcohol.

SILVER SELENATE, Ag_2SeO_4, is produced by the reaction of solutions of silver carbonate and selenic acid. It is about as soluble in water as is silver sulfate.

SILVER SELENIDE, Ag_2Se, is known as the mineral naumannite. It is formed by reacting silver nitrate with metallic selenium. When heated above 300°C, it decomposes to form moss silver.

SILVER SILICATE, Ag_2SiO_3, precipitates as a yellow solid when a soluble metasilicate is reacted with a solution of silver nitrate. Upon drying it becomes brownish in color. When heated above 500°C, the salt decomposes to metallic silver, oxygen, and silica.

SILVER SULFITE, Ag_2SO_3, is formed by bubbling sulfur dioxide through a silver nitrate solution. The white solid is unstable to light, heat, and boiling water.

SILVER TELLURIDE occurs in nature as hessite, Ag_2Te, or stutzite, Ag_4Te.

SILVER THIOCYANATE, $AgSCN$, is formed by reaction of equimolar quantities of silver ion and a soluble thiocyanate.

SILVER THIOSULFATE, $Ag_2S_2O_3$, precipitates when a soluble thiosulfate reacts with an excess of silver nitrate, but the product invariably contains some silver sulfide. This is minimized by complexing the silver before addition of the thiosulfate. The formation of soluble thiosulfate complexes is one of the essential reactions of photography.

SILVER(I) COMPLEXES

Silver forms a number of complexes both with π-bonding and non-π-bonding ligands. Many ligands form linear polynuclear complexes. Although silver complexes up to AgL_4 are known, usually the AgL and AgL_2 species are most stable.

AMMONIA AND AMINE COMPLEXES. Silver ion forms the complexes $Ag(NH_3)_2{}^+$ and $Ag(NH_3)_3{}^+$ when allowed to react with excess ammonia. These complexes should not be prepared from silver oxide suspensions containing strong bases to avoid formation of fulminating silver. Highly explosive fulminating silver, believed to consist of either silver nitride or silver imide, may detonate spontaneously when silver oxide is heated with ammonia or when alkaline solutions of a silver amine complex are allowed to stand. Such solutions are rendered harmless by the addition of hydrochloric acid. Stable silver complexes are also formed from many aliphatic and aromatic amines, including quinoline, pyridine, aniline, and ethylamine (16).

CYANIDE COMPLEXES.   Insoluble silver cyanide, AgCN, is readily dissolved by addition of an excess of alkali cyanide.   The predominant species is $Ag(CN)_2^-$, although the tri- and tetracyanato complexes are also formed.   Virtually all silver salts, including the very insoluble silver sulfide, dissolve in cyanide solutions because of the low dissociation of the complex, as shown below:

$$K = \frac{[Ag^+][CN^-]^2}{[Ag(CN)_2^-]} = 4 \times 10^{-19}$$

HALIDE COMPLEXES.   Silver halides form soluble complex ions of the formula AgX_2^- with chloride, bromide, and iodide.   The stability increases in the order $I > Br > Cl$.   The solubilizing effect of halide complex formation is shown by the fact that silver chloride is more than a hundred times as soluble in $1N$ hydrochloric acid as in pure water.

OLEFIN COMPLEXES.   Silver forms weak complexes with most olefins and many aromatic compounds.   Most of these compounds are stable only in solution.   The stability of olefin complexes generally decreases as more hydrogens of the ethylene group are substituted by alkyl groups.   The nature of these complexes is summarized by Cotton and Wilkinson (17).

SULFUR–BONDED COMPLEXES.   Next to the cyanide complexes, the most stable silver complexes are those involving sulfur bonding.   The photographically important silver thiosulfate–sodium thiosulfate–water system has been extensively studied (18).   When insoluble silver thiosulfate, $Ag_2S_2O_3$, is dissolved in excess thiosulfate, a variety of silver complexes are formed.   At low concentrations of $S_2O_3^{2-}$, the principal species is $Ag_2(S_2O_3)_2^{2-}$, but at high $S_2O_3^{2-}$ concentrations, species such as $Ag_2(S_2O_3)_6^{10-}$ may be present (19).   Most silver compounds, except the sulfide, dissolve in excess thiosulfate.

   A series of stable soluble complexes is also formed with thiourea and its derivatives (20).   Silver forms stable, slightly ionized salts with aliphatic and aromatic thiols.

Other Oxidation States

   Silver Subfluoride.   The existence of silver subfluoride, Ag_2F, is well established. It is a compound, not a mixture of metal and salt, as many other subvalence compounds have been found to be (21).   The bright-yellow solid is prepared from silver fluoride, AgF, by electrolysis, ultraviolet irradiation, or reaction with a suspension of silver in hydrofluoric acid.

   Silver(II) Compounds.   *Silver(II) fluoride*, AgF_2, a black amorphous, hygroscopic material, is obtained by the treatment of silver chloride with fluorine gas at 200°C (22).   It is useful as a powerful oxidant or fluorinating agent.   When heated above 450°C, it decomposes into AgF and fluorine.

   Silver(II) oxide, AgO, was first prepared more than 100 years ago (23).   Long thought to be a silver(I) peroxide, it is now recognized as a true oxide of silver(II). It is prepared by the anodic or alkaline–peroxysulfate oxidation of silver(I) salts of nonreducing anions.   Oxidation of neutral or acid silver(I) salt solutions yields silver (II) oxy salts (24).   Silver(II) oxide is a strong oxidant; its reactions in alkaline medium have been studied extensively (25).   Both silver(II) oxide and fluoride decompose in aqueous solution unless stabilized with concentrated nitric acid.

Silver(II) is also stabilized by coordination with some nitrogen heterocyclic bases, such as pyridine and dipyridyl. These complexes are cationic and involve hybrid dsp^2 bonds (26). They are prepared by the peroxysulfate oxidation of silver(I) solutions, in the presence of an excess of the ligand. Numerous silver(II) oxy salts, such as $Ag(Ag_3O_4)_2NO_3$, $Ag(Ag_3O_4)_2ClO_4$, and $Ag(Ag_3O_4)_2F$, have also been prepared. An extensive review of the higher oxidation states of silver is available (27).

Silver(III) Compounds. No simple silver(III) compounds exist. Transitory silver(III) compounds are formed when silver(I) salts are used as catalysts in oxidation reactions. The relatively stable complex of silver(III)–ethylene biguanide appear to be 4-coordinate and diamagnetic (28). Salts such as $KAgF_4$ have also been prepared (27).

Analysis

Qualitative Detection. As little as 100 pts per billion of silver can be detected by using emission spectrography; two sensitive arc-emission lines for silver occur at 3280.683 and 3382.891 Å. Silver compounds can be identified from their crystallographic pattern by x-ray diffraction. A number of selective spot tests are known for silver, such as reaction with p-dimethylaminorhodanine, dithizone in carbon tetrachloride, ceric ammonium nitrate, or pyrogallol red. The application, interferences, and detection limits of these tests and many others is given by Feigl (29). A new spot test for silver ions is based on the oxidation of manganous ion in the presence of pyridine (30).

Quantitative Determination. Silver is determined gravimetrically by precipitation with chloride, sulfide, chromate, or a variety of organic reagents, such as 1,2,3-benzotriazole. It can be precipitated as the metal by electrodeposition or by using chemical reducing agents. Numerous excellent volumetric methods exist for the determination of silver in the semimicro to macro range. The classic Dénige method, based on complex formation with cyanide, is not only highly accurate but can be applied directly for the analysis of silver halides. Precipitation-titration methods with halide, thiocyanate, and thioacetamide are also known. Diethyldithiocarbamate and diphenylthiocarbazone (dithizone) are two well-known reagents used to determine silver colorimetrically through formation of complexes extractable by organic solvents. Goulden (31) has described these and other colorimetric procedures for silver. Microgram to milligram quantities of silver in solution can be determined electrochemically by amperometric, coulometric, and polarographic techniques. In industry instrumental techniques, such as emission spectrography, atomic absorption, and x-ray fluorescence, have found wide application in the analysis of silver compounds in various matrix materials. A comprehensive summary of all the methods of analysis of silver compounds is given in the Kolthoff and Elving treatise (32).

Toxicology

The soluble silver salts are poisonous. The fatal dose by injection varies from 30 gr (1 gr (grain) = 0.065 g) to 1 oz. Insoluble silver salts appear much less toxic. Prolonged contact with silver compounds may produce "argyria," a slate-gray to bluish or even black pigmentation of the skin, produced by the accumulation of absorbed silver in the corium of the skin. It becomes visible only upon exposure to sunlight. Although apparently harmless, once developed the condition is permanent.

Economic Aspects

The largest single use of silver compounds is for the manufacture of photographic products. The *U.S. Bureau of Mines Minerals Yearbook* (33) lists the distribution of silver compounds used in 1966 as follows (1 troy oz = 31.10 g):

Distribution	1000 troy oz	Distribution	1000 troy oz
photography	48,435	mirrors	2,946
electroplating	21,486	catalysts	2,683
batteries	12,517	total	88,067

This accounts for almost half of the total 183,696,000 troy oz of silver consumed in the United States in 1966.

The use of silver for batteries has become increasingly important because of the space program; in 1960 only 3,500,000 troy oz were used for this purpose.

The price of silver compounds is directly related to the price of the metal. Up to the end of 1966, the price of silver metal was stabilized at $1.293/troy oz; the price in Feb. 1968 was $1.75/troy oz. Because demand has consistently exceeded production, a drastic decline in this price seem as unlikely.

Applications

Batteries. Although silver batteries have been known for more than 100 years, only recently have they found industrial use (see Vol. 3, p. 128).

Controversy still exists as to the mechanism involved in the alkaline silver oxide–zinc battery, but it is generally considered to involve both silver(I) and (II) oxide (34). The Wh/lb output of this battery is four times that of a conventional industrial lead–acid battery, but, because of its relatively high cost and short life, it is used primarily by the military for torpedoes, missiles, aircraft, and submarines. The Ranger, Mariner, and Surveyor space programs employ sealed silver oxide–zinc batteries.

Alkaline silver oxide–cadmium batteries are still under development. They offer moderate current densities and life and have found limited use in cordless appliances.

The silver chloride–magnesium battery is a primary battery and cannot be recharged. It is used principally for torpedos and sonobuoys. It can easily be activated by immersion in seawater.

A lithium–silver chloride battery has recently been constructed and may find use in space systems (35). A rechargeable solar-energy cell employs a silver chloride membrane (36).

Catalysts. Both metallic silver and silver compounds are used in industry as catalysts in oxidation, reduction, and polymerization reactions.

Silver oxide has been patented as a catalyst in the production of aldehydes (37) and phthalic anhydride (38) and for many mild oxidation vapor-phase reactions. It is reported that silver nitrate catalyzes the conversion of methanol to formaldehyde (39) and of ammonium nitrate to nitrous oxide (40). The conversion of ethylene into ethylene oxide is catalyzed by silver thiocyanate (41). Sulfur dioxide is oxidized to SO_3 by using a silica catalyst containing silver sulfate (42).

Silver nitrate catalysts may be employed in the polymerization of polytetrafluoroethylene (43) and polyacrylonitrile (44). Silanes can be formed directly from the elements by using a silver sulfide catalyst (45).

Combinations of silver and copper oxides are reported to be useful as air purifiers (46) and engine exhaust-gas combustion catalysts (47). Hopcalite, a mixture of oxides of silver, copper, manganese, and cobalt in the weight ratio of $1:6:10:3$ has been used since World War I in gas masks to prevent carbon monoxide poisoning (48).

Many oxidations are accelerated by adding a trace of silver ion; this catalytic effect is used in analytical chemistry in the oxidation of chloride with cerium (IV) (49) and manganous ion with peroxysulfate (50).

Electroplating (qv). The most important and widely used silver-plating baths employ alkaline solutions of silver cyanide. An excess of cyanide over that required to form the $Ag(CN)_2^-$ complex is employed to control the concentration of silver ions in solution and provide for a more uniform deposit. The silver in the bath can be supplied either by addition of silver cyanide or by dissolution of the silver rod anode. Baths containing from 40 to 140 g of silver cyanide per liter have been employed (51). Although repeated attempts have been made, to date no way has yet been found to obtain uniform adherent deposits from a commercial plating bath employing a nitric acid solution of silver nitrate (52).

Fungicides. The "oligodynamic effect" (Greek: *oligos* = few, *dynamos* = power) refers to the germicidal properties exerted by minute quantities of many heavy-metal ions in solution. Next to copper, silver is the most oligodynamic material; less than 10 ppm in water has a pronounced bactericidal effect. Silver oxide mixed with silver zeolite can be used to deionize and purify sea- or brackish water. Silver bromide crystals are patented for use in a water-sterilization process (53). Silver compounds are claimed to be effective as slimicides and in antifouling paints (54). Silver metharsonate acts as an algicide. Incorporation of 10 ppm of silver butylphosphate in jet fuels is claimed to inhibit bacterial growth (55).

Medical Preparations. Silver compounds, either in the form of soluble silver salts, colloidal silver suspensions, or as powders, are used in medicine as germicides, antiseptics, and caustics. Silver ions precipitate protein; thus the activity of the preparation depends on their concentration in solution. The introduction of sulfa drugs and antibiotics has reduced, but not eliminated, the use of medicinal silver compounds. Unlike the "miracle drugs," silver preparations are not likely to lead to sensitization of the patient; they also have a broad spectrum of activity, and organisms have not developed strains resistant to their action (56).

Silver nitrate is used in medicine in the form of sticks or solutions of varying concentrations. Aqueous solutions containing 10–20% silver nitrate or solid sticks are highly corrosive, and are applied locally to remove warts and to stimulate the healing of wounds. Compresses are saturated with 0.05–0.1% aqueous solutions of silver nitrate for direct application to severe burns. In addition to the powerful germicidal effect, a membrane is created which protects against fluid loss and reduces formation of scar tissue. Solutions of 0.01–0.1% concn are effective antiseptics for mucous membranes. Acute eczema and athlete's foot are treated with wet dressings of 0.1–0.25% silver nitrate. One drop of 1% silver nitrate is placed in the eyes of new-born infants as a prophylactic against opthalmia neonatorum. An isotonic wash of sodium chloride is commonly used to interrupt the astringent action of silver nitrate preparations. Ammoniacal silver nitrate is applied locally to the teeth to arrest the progress of dental caries.

Silver picrate (silver 2,4,6-trinitrophenoxide.H_2O), known as Picragol (registered trademark Wyeth Laboratories), is used at 1% concn in powdered talc for the treatment of vaginitis. Silver arsphenamine is the disodium salt of silver 3,3′-diamino--4,4′-dihydroxyarsenobenzene; a 0.5% solution is used in the treatment of syphilis. Silver neoarsphernamine (the disodium salt of silver 3,3′-diamino-4,4′-dihydroxyar-senobenzene-*N*-methanolsulfoxylate) is also commercially available (57). Silver phe-nolsulfonate, silberol, has antiseptic properties but is not corrosive.

Colloidal silver preparations are employed as antiseptics. Because of the low concentration of silver ion, they lack the corrosive and astringent properties of the soluble silver salts. The concentration of ionic silver is not sufficient to precipitate chlorides or proteins and therefore they penetrate the tissues more readily than soluble silver salt solutions. Both silver halide and silver protein colloidal solutions are commercially available.

Neo-Silvol (registered trademark, Parke, Davis & Company) consists of 18–22% colloidal silver iodide in gelatin. Colloidal silver chloride, known as Lunosol (registered trademark, Hille Laboratories), contains 10% silver nitrate stabilized by sucrose or another protective colloid. These aqueous dispersions are used as bactericides for in-fections of accessible mucous membranes.

The two classes of silver proteins, mild and strong, are distinguished by their differ-ing antiseptic action. The strong silver proteins possess a lower total silver content, but release a higher concentration of ionic silver and are thus more germicidal and irritating. Mild silver protein contains 19–23% silver. It is prepared from moist silver oxide reacted with either a casein, alkaline gelatin, or serum albumin solution. Mild protein solutions should be freshly dispensed as they decompose with time to pro-duce more ionic silver and become increasingly astringent. Strong silver proteins, such as Protargol (registered trademark, Winthrop Laboratories), contain 7.5–8.5% silver and are prepared by the reaction between a silver salt and a purified protein. Strong silver proteins are intermediate in activity between mild proteins and silver nitrate solutions.

An aqueous colloidal suspension containing 0.5% metallic silver, Colsargen (regis-tered trademark, Crooke Laboratories), is used as a mucous membrane antiseptic.

Mirrors. Large quantities of silver are employed annually in the production of mirrors. Mirroring processes employ two separate solutions: one contains silver ion, usually as the ammonia complex, and the other contains a reducing agent, such as formaldehyde, rochelle salts (sodium potassium tartrate), sugar, or hydrazine. Special precautions are observed in recovering silver from used mirror solutions because of the formation of fulminating silver (58) (see page 301).

Office Copying Systems. (See Reprography; also reference 59.) Many office copying systems are based on formation of silver images and employ light-sensitive silver halides in diffusion-transfer, gelatin-transfer, or stabilization processes. Thermo-graphic systems have also been described, combining organic reducing agents and silver salts of fatty acids (60,61). The use of silver benzenesulfinate is claimed in print-out coatings (62). Photoconductographic developers for silver-image products incor-porate a silver–ethylenethiourea complex (63). For lower cost, a nickel-image photo-conductographic developer has a soluble nickel salt plus a trace of silver acetate as an initiator (64).

Photography (qv). As previously mentioned, the largest single use for silver compounds remains the production of photographic products. Silver nitrate is the starting compound for the production of the light-sensitive silver halides. The silver halide usually accounts for 30–40% of the total emulsion weight. Many different silver halide emulsions are manufactured; the ratio of the halides and preparation details are adjusted according to the specific properties desired. For photographic papers and other emulsions of low sensitivity, the chloride, chlorobromide, or bromide is employed. Emulsions of high sensitivity are primarily bromide plus up to 5 mole % silver iodide. Pure silver iodide emulsions are not commercially important and silver fluoride has no comparable photographic use. The role of silver halides in photography is discussed in detail by James and Higgins (65) and by Mees (66).

New methods of image-recording seek to avoid the high cost of silver. Few offer the combination of high image-density, exceptional resolution, permanence, and tricolor recording. In color recording, dyes comprise the finished image, and all the silver coating is liberated during processing and can potentially be recovered. A large portion of the silver in black-and-white products is also available for recovery, principally in the fixing bath. Several diverse methods have been developed for recovering silver from various commercial processing solutions (67).

Other Uses. A variety of silver compounds have been added to and impart unusual properties to glass. A recent patent claims that automobile glass can be made shatter-resistant by the presence of silver fluoride or silver fluoroborate (68). Incorporation of 0.05–0.3% silver chloride plus a reducing agent in a formulation for auto glass is indicated to give a product that prevents daylight glare yet provides normal light vision (69). The formulas for photosensitive glasses include silver chloride (70) or silver molybdate (71).

It has been found that off-flavors in wine, due principally to tartaric acid, are removed by adding finely divided silver chloride and filtering (72). Silver chloride is also used as an ionization detector for cosmic rays, radar screens, and infrared radiation windows. Silver iodide, well known for its use in the seeding of clouds, requires special preparation for this purpose (73). Silver perchlorate can be used as an accelerant in rocket propellants (74).

Olefins can be purified by using silver tetrafluoroborate to remove acetylenes (75) and aromatic hydrocarbons (76). Silver sulfide, iodide, and bromate are claimed to be effective special-purpose lubricants (77,78). A novel application involves spraying an acetone slurry of silver carbide and silver nitrate on a work piece, drying it, and detonating it to form small intricate shapes (79).

Numerous other uses of silver compounds have been developed throughout the years; many are described in the annual series by Rook (80).

Bibliography

"Silver compounds" in *ECT* 1st ed., Vol. 12, pp. 438–443, by F. A. Meier, The American Platinum Works.

1. C. D. West, *Z. Krist.* **90**, 555–556 (1935).
2. N. R. Nail, F. Moser, P. E. Goddard, and F. Urbach, *Rev. Sci. Instr.* **28**, 275–278 (1957).
3. H. G. Smith and R. E. Rundel, *J. Am. Chem. Soc.* **80**, 5075 (1958).
4. U.S. Pats. 2,581,518 and 2,581,519 (Feb. 17, 1948), T. Critchley (to Johnson and Sons' Smelting Works, Enfield, England).
5. U.S. Pat. 2,543,792 (Nov. 2, 1949), M. Marasco and J. A. Moede (to E. I. du Pont de Nemours & Co., Inc.).
6. U.S. Pat. 2,614,029 (Feb. 21, 1951), J. A. Moede (to E. I. du Pont de Nemours & Co., Inc.).
7. U.S. Pat. 2,940,828 (Oct. 29, 1957), J. A. Moede (to E. I. du Pont de Nemours & Co., Inc.).
8. *Chem. Eng.* **70**, 86–88 (Aug. 1963).
9. *Ibid.* **59**, 217–219 (Oct. 1952).
10. J. Zawidzki, *Z. Physik. Chem.* **43**, 313 (1903).

11. A. F. Wells, *Structural Inorganic Chemistry*, Oxford University Press, London, 1945, p. 316.
12. W. F. Linke, *Solubilities of Inorganic and Metal-Organic Compounds*, Vol. I, 4th ed., American Chemical Society, Washington, D.C., 1958. (This reference provides many useful solubility data on a wide variety of materials. All solubility data given in this section have been obtained from this source.)
13. F. Raschig, *Ann. Chem.* **233**, 93 (1886).
14. S. F. Ravitz, *J. Phys. Chem.* **40**, 61–70 (1936).
15. A. F. Kapustinski and I. A. Korschunov, *J. Phys. Chem.* (*U.S.S.R.*) **14**, 134 (1940).
16. A. E. Martell and M. Calvin, *Chemistry of the Metal Chelate Compounds*, Prentice-Hall, Inc., New York, 1952, p. 160.
17. F. A. Cotton and G. Wilkinson, *Advanced Inorganic Chemistry*, Interscience Publishers, a div. of John Wiley & Sons, Inc., New York, 1962, p. 642.
18. H. H. Bassett and J. T. Lemon, *J. Chem. Soc.* **1933**, 1423–1427.
19. H. Brintzinger and W. Eckhardt, *Z. Anorg. Allgem. Chem.* **231**, 327–341 (1937).
20. S. Ahrland and J. Chatt, *Chem. Ind.* (*London*), **1955**, 96.
21. H. Terrey and H. Diamond, *J. Chem. Soc.* **1928**, 2820.
22. H. F. Priest, *Inorg. Syn.* **3**, 176 (1950).
23. J. Schiel, *Ann. Chem.* **132**, 322 (1864).
24. J. McMillan, *J. Electrochem. Soc.* **106**, 1072 (1959).
25. T. P. Dirkse, *J. Electrochem. Soc.* **106**, 920 (1959).
26. R. Nyholm, *Quart. Rev.* (*London*), **7**, 392 (1953).
27. J. McMillan, *Chem. Rev.* **62**, 65–80 (1962).
28. P. Ray, *Nature* **151**, 643 (1943).
29. F. Feigl, *Spot Tests in Inorganic Analysis*, 5th ed., Elsevier Publishing Co., New York, 1958, pp. 58–64.
30. N. S. Poomia and H. Gupta, *J. Chem. Educ.* **44**, 480 (1967).
31. R. Goulden, *Ind. Chemist* **34**, 137, 200 (1958).
32. E. P. Przybylowicz and C. W. Zuehlke, "Silver," in I. M. Kolthoff and P. J. Elving, eds., *Treatise on Analytical Chemistry*, Part II, Vol. IV, Interscience Publishers, a div. of John Wiley & Sons, Inc., New York, 1966, pp. 3–63.
33. *U.S. Bureau of Mines, 1966 Minerals Yearbook*, Vol. I, U.S. Govt. Printing Office, Washington, D.C., 1967, p. 352.
34. J. F. Donahue, "Silver Batteries," in A. Butts and C. D. Coxe, eds., *Silver-Economics, Metallurgy and Use*, D. Van Nostrand Co., Inc., Princeton, N.J., 1967, pp. 153–180.
35. E. Chilton, Jr., et al., *NASA Accession N65-21557, Report AD-612189*, Washington, D.C., 1965.
36. U.S. Pat. 3,114,658 (Oct. 22, 1959), S. Zaromb (to Philco Corp.).
37. Belg. Pat. 657,745 (April 30, 1965), Dynamit Nobel A.G.
38. Belg. Pat. 661,854 (Sept. 30, 1965), H. Nonnenmacher (to Badische Anilin- und Soda-Fabrik A.G.).
39. U.S.S.R. Pat. 175,043 (Sept. 21, 1965), I. Kushnarenko.
40. Brit. Pat. 510,889 (1939), E. I. du Pont de Nemours & Co., Inc.
41. Ger. Pat. 1,200,263 (Aug. 14, 1965), W. Friedricksen (to Badische Anilin- und Soda-Fabrik A.G.).
42. Ger. Pat. 1,133,350 (July 19, 1962), K. Wimmer (to Badische Anilin- und Soda-Fabrik A.G.).
43. Belg. Pat. 629,806 (Oct. 21, 1963), M. Ragazzini, et al. (to Sicedison Società per Azioni).
44. P. Pickhart, "Silver Catalysts," in reference 34, p. 190.
45. Japan. Pat. 21,507 (Nov. 9, 1959), K. Tachiki and Y. Yamashita.
46. U.S. Pat. 3,034,947 (April 25, 1956), J. R. Conlisk, et al.(to U.S. Army).
47. Brit. Pat. 1,040,295 (Aug. 24, 1966), D. DeRyche (to Peter Spence and Sons, Ltd.).
48. A. B. Lamb, W. C. Bray, and J. Frazer, *Ind. Eng. Chem.* **12**, 213 (1920).
49. H. Goto and T. Thiokawa, *Sci. Rept. Res. Inst. Tohoku Univ. Ser. A* **2**, 446 (1950).
50. A. L. Underwood, A. M. Burrill, and L. B. Rogers, *Anal. Chem.* **24**, 1597 (1952).
51. M. A. Orr, "Electroplating," in reference 34, p. 185.
52. A. G. Gray, *Modern Electroplating*, John Wiley & Sons, Inc., New York, 1953, p. 368.
53. U.S. Pat. 3,257,315 (June 21, 1966), D. B. Pall (to Pall Corp.)
54. Brit. Pat. 953,753 (April 2, 1964), H. B. Beer.
55. U.S. Pat. 3,226,210 (Dec. 28, 1965), J. N. Baptist, et al. (to W. R. Grace & Co.).
56. M. Y. Crannel, "Silver in Medicine," in reference 34, pp. 227–235.

57. G. L. Jenkins, W. H. Hartung, K. E. Hamlin, and J. B. Data, *The Chemistry of Organic Medicinal Products*, 4th ed., John Wiley & Sons, Inc., New York, 1957, pp. 305–307.

58. J. C. Rice, *J. Chem. Educ.* **11**, 231 (1939).

59. *Chem. Eng. News* **42** (28), 115 and (29), 84 (1964).

60. Belg. Pat. 663,112 (Oct. 27, 1965), D. A. Morgan (to The Minnesota Mining and Manufacturing Company).

61. Brit. Pat. 954,198 (April 21, 1960), The Minnesota Mining and Manufacturing Company.

62. U.S. Pat. 3,152,904 (June 29, 1964), D. P. Sorensen and J. W. Shephard (to The Minnesota Mining and Manufacturing Company).

63. U.S. Pat. 3,165,456 (Nov. 21, 1960), D. A. Morgan (to The Minnesota Mining and Manufacturing Company).

64. U.S. Pat. 3,076,752 (Oct. 17, 1958), C. O. McMaster (to The Minnesota Mining and Manufacturing Company).

65. T. H. James and G. C. Higgins, *Fundamentals of Photographic Theory*, Morgan and Morgan, Inc., New York, 1960.

66. T. H. James, ed., C. E. K. Mees, *The Theory of the Photographic Process*, 3rd ed., The Macmillan Co., New York, 1966.

67. M. L. Schreiber, *Soc. Motion Picture Television Eng.* **74**, 505–513 (1965).

68. Belg. Pat. 660,196 (Aug. 24, 1965), Imperial Chemicals Industries, Ltd.

69. Belg. Pat. 643,613 (Aug. 10, 1964), D. N. Brown and T. O'Leary (to Corning Glass Works).

70. U.S. Pat. 3,252,374 (Feb. 15, 1962), S. D. Stookey (to Corning Glass Works).

71. Belg. Pat. 644,989 (Sept. 10, 1964), L. C. Sawchuk and S. D. Stookey (to Corning Glass Works).

72. J. Schneyder, *Mitt. Klosterneuburg Ser. A* **16**, 63–66 (1965).

73. F. Anyz and L. Sramek, *Proc. Natl. Conf. Aerosols 1st, Liblice, Czechoslovakia, 1962*, p. 559.

74. U.S. Pat. 3,000,716 (June 20, 1955), R. W Lawrence and G. A. Zimmerman (to Aerojet-General Corp.).

75. U.S. Pat. 3,101,381 (Aug. 20, 1963), W. N. Baxter (to E. I. du Pont de Nemours & Co., Inc.).

76. Brit. Pat. 969,312 (Sept. 8, 1964), (to Farbwerke-Hoechst A.G.).

77. V. Hopkins and D. Gaddis, *Lubrication Eng.* **21**, 52 (1965).

78. Ger. Pat. 1,116,335 (Nov. 2, 1961), C. S. Oliver and A. J. Haltner (to General Electric Co.).

79. W. Baker and F. Hoese, *Chem. Eng. News* **43** (49), 46 (1965).

80. H. S. Rooke, ed., *Reports on the Progress of Applied Chemistry*, Vol. I, 1961, to Vol. L, 1965, Society of Chemical Industry, London, 1961–1965.

General References

J. Kleinberg, W. J. Argersinger, and E. Griswold, *Inorganic Chemistry*, D. C. Heath & Co., Boston, 1960, pp. 589–607.

J. W. Laist, "Silver," in M. Sneed, J. Maynard, and R. Brasted, eds., *Comprehensive Inorganic Chemistry*, Vol. II, D. Van Nostrand Co., Princeton, N.J., 1954, pp. 114–183.

T. Moeller, *Inorganic Chemistry*, John Wiley & Sons, Inc., New York, 1952, pp. 818–844.

H. Remy, *Treatise on Inorganic Chemistry*, Vol. II, Elsevier Publishing Co., Amsterdam, 1956, pp. 397–409.

THOMAS N. TISCHER
Eastman Kodak Company

SILVER PLATING. See Vol. 8, p. 64.

SILYLATING AGENTS. See Silicon compounds.

SINK–FLOAT SEPARATION. See Vol. 10. p. 701.

SINTERED METALS. See Powder metallurgy.

SISAL. See Vol. 9, p. 179.

SIZE MEASUREMENT OF PARTICLES

Measurement of the sizes of fine particles has advanced greatly in recent years. Many methods have been perfected to measure fineness or to estimate it from some related property. The techniques are applied to the coarse products of crushing machines, to the finer ranges of pulverized materials, to precipitates and fumes, and to emulsions and colloids. A few of the major industrial materials for which the control of particle size is important are: abrasives, cements, ceramic materials, dusts, dyes, emulsions, fertilizers, fuels, metal powders, mineral fillers, muds, ores, photographic emulsions, pigments, plastics, and soils. See also Dust; Sedimentation; Size reduction; Size separation.

What Is a Particle? Materials which are the subject of particle-size measurement consist of a multiplicity of particles, often of greatly differing size and shape. In order to evaluate the fineness of such material, the product must be resolved into the individual units of which it is composed. This basic unit, known as the individual particle, must be differentiated from groups or clusters of such units and from crystal units of which the individual particle may be composed. The first distinction may be illustrated by drying a fine clay mud. It forms a cake which breaks into pieces because of shrinkage. Each of these pieces consists of many individual particles held together by cohesive forces between particulate surfaces in contact with each other. They may be dispersed into individual particles again by adding water and stirring. However, the separation is not a sharp one. Metal-powder particles, if sintered in a furnace, develop similar-type clusters, which are knit together by recrystallization and crystal growth. If the sintering is only light, the particles may be broken down to finer sizes resembling the original individual particles, whereas if the sintering has been done at a higher temperature they may shrink together into a more coherent mass. At some point in this process the unit which was originally designated as the "individual" particle has permanently lost its identity.

A close examination of an individual particle, to determine whether it meets the definition internally, may reveal that it consists of a group of tightly bound crystals, as in granite. On the other hand, the bond may be very loose, as with mica schist and crushed particles. There is yet another form of particle, exemplified by silica gel or active carbon, which is itself porous, so that there may be many times more surface inside of the particle than would be expected from its external dimensions. It is necessary to give an interpretive judgment in some of these borderline cases. However, most cases are simpler, and it is easy to differentiate the individual particles as an entity.

Because size measurement is most usually directed toward the individual particle, it is of particular importance that groups of particles be dispersed so that the individual particles may display their specific properties. There are, however, some commercial materials in which aggregates or clusters of particles, rather than individual particles, determine the properties of the final product.

Particle Shape and Dimensions. Shapes of particles range from spheres (formed by cooling or evaporating liquids in sprays or by emulsification) through natural geometric crystals and their variants, ragged material derived from easily cleaved minerals, to the irregular forms found as the result of crushing and grinding operations. There is often a wide variation in particle shape within a sample. Particle shape in a quantitative sense has often not been adequately defined, and the selection of dimensions to define size has varied considerably.

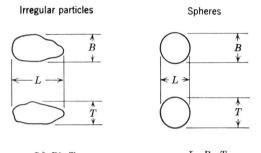

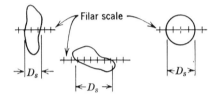

Fig. 1. Dimensions of particles.

The three major dimensions of length, breadth, and thickness may be designated as L, B, and T (Fig. 1). A few examples of parameters that have been used to characterize particles are: *(1)* B is taken as average diameter, since it is the intermediate dimension. It is generally the controlling dimension in sieving, and it is almost always visible under the microscope, whereas, for a platelike particle, which tends to be flat, T is not visible. *(2)* $(L + B)/2$ is an average of the intermediate and large dimensions. It reflects the general impression of size as a particle generally appears in the microscope. For such particles as needlelike crystals, it is an improvement over B alone; but its use generally results in assigning too large a size to the particle. *(3)* $\sqrt{LB}$ more nearly approaches a measure of the area of particles. Its use involves more work in figuring the size of each particle. *(4)* $(L + B + T)/3$ is an arithmetic mean of three dimensions, each of which needs to be measured. T is generally more difficult to measure, since it falls in the axis of vision of the microscope and needs to be measured in depth. *(5)* $\sqrt{[2(LB) + 2(BT) + 2(LT)]/6}$ represents the side of a cube of surface equal to that of a particle. *(6)* $\sqrt[3]{LBT}$ is more comprehensive than *(3)*, and it represents the side of a cube having the volume of the particle. *(7)* $3LBT/(LB + LT + BT)$ is the harmonic mean of the dimensions and is related to the specific surface of the material. *(8)* Statistical mean diameter (Fig. 1) is a term applied to a dimension measured by microscope. A filar scale is employed to split the particle into halves of equal area above and below the line, and the distance between particle edges is measured. It can be seen that when a narrow particle is vertical in the field, it will have a small dimension across its middle, whereas, when it lies across the field, that same particle has a large dimension assigned to it. When many particles are randomly oriented, the statistical mean diameter of those of the same size and shape is a suitable mean of L and B.

A great many particles must be evaluated in order to secure a truly representative distribution; hence the simplest measure of each individual particle becomes important. The choice varies also with the method of test. In sieving, the B and T cross section is passed or retained in relation to an aperture. Under the microscope the B dimension is generally the smaller visible one and is simple and representative; in other tests the surface or the diameter of equivalent sphere may be the criterion. For spheres these values will all be alike, whatever the method of test. For needles and platelike shapes the results differ greatly, depending on the diametral criterion employed, and it is important to define which form of average diameter is being used.

Distribution of Particle Size. There are a number of ways of expressing the particle-size distribution of a sample, and each has merit for some application. The value of materials used as paint pigments, for example, is related to the amount of surface that will absorb and reflect light. If they are employed in thin coatings, it is also important that they do not possess coarse grits, whether as individual units or flocculates; otherwise the film may have a roughness that is undesirable. In this case, as in many others, there is a preferred size range for the material and also a limiting size that is acceptable.

A good overall presentation of the particle size lies in a distribution curve, wherein the range of particle diameters, or an equivalent, is divided into a suitable number of class intervals of properly selected width, and some measure of amount—number, surface, or weight—of particles falling in each class interval is expressed, preferably as a percentage of the total. This takes the form of a curve which expresses the particle-size characteristics of the material.

Representation of Data. The application of particle-size measurement in many specialized and relatively unconnected fields has given rise to the development of a vast miscellany of methods for expressing the results of such measurements. Some are basic, and some are crude; and each of them serves some purpose. Out of them, a group of methods may be selected which are both basic and useful.

Table 1. Size Distribution of Particles

Size range (diameter), μ	Percent by weight	Size range (diameter), μ	Percent by weight
0–5	2.3	40–80	21.1
5–10	2.7	80–160	34.5
10–20	9.1	160–320	15.6
20–40	13.3	320–640	1.4

Tabulation of Size Distribution. This is simply a statement of the amounts of material falling within each of several ranges of diameter which comprise the range of the sample. Such an example is given in Table 1. It will be observed that the size ranges or class intervals are bounded by diameters which increase by a ratio of 2. Little material falls within the smallest range which, incidentally, is not further subdivided. The largest particle is about 350 μ, and the upper limiting range is not filled. However, the intervening values present a discernible distribution. If another series of size ranges had been selected for this same material, the values might have been so different as to be unrecognizable as pertaining to the same material. It is a simple matter to place two such sets of data on a common base in which the selection of class interval is unimportant, except that there must be a sufficient number of points to define a true curve. Some of the succeeding methods will do this.

Table 2. Cumulative Size Distribution

Diameter, μ	Cumulative percent plus	Cumulative percent minus
5	97.7	2.3
10	95.0	5.0
20	85.9	14.1
40	72.6	27.4
80	51.5	48.5
160	17.0	83.0
320	1.4	98.6
640	0.0	100.0

Cumulative Curve of Distribution. The preceding data may be converted to a cumulative plot, in which the total percent coarser (or finer) than each of several diameters is calculated. Since the 2.3% falling in the 0–5 μ range is finer than 5 μ, the total amount above 5 μ is 97.7%, and the other points may be similarly derived, as shown in Table 2.

When plotted against the logarithm of diameter, these figures give an S curve; any other set of class intervals properly chosen will fall upon this curve. The actual curve obtained on plotting the cumulative percent plus figures is curve 4 in Figure 2, which shows typical distributions of a number of materials. If the vertical scale of cumulative percent were to read from zero downward, the same curves would be cumulative percent undersize. Other methods of plotting may be employed: The cumulative percent may be plotted on a logarithmic scale, or on a probability scale, and the diameter may be plotted linearly, or as reciprocal diameter.

Percent per Unit Interval vs Diameter. Another basic type of distribution curve eliminates the selected class intervals by dividing each percentage by the width of its respective class interval. If, then, each unit of diameter in a class interval is said to have this resulting percentage, a plot of percentage vs diameter becomes a rectangular block in any one class interval, the area of which is the percentage in that interval, while a series of such blocks becomes the basis for a curve whose area is 100%.

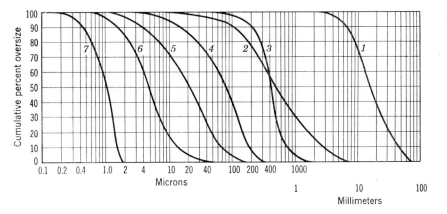

Fig. 2. Particle size distribution curves for typical materials. Curves: (*1*) coarse aggregate; (*2*) fine aggregate; (*3*) filter sand; (*4*) powdered coal; (*5*) portland cement; (*6*) mineral fillers; (*7*) pigments.

The usual practice of converting such a block plot or histogram to a curve may be followed; a trial plot is first made through centers of block tops, and smoothing is carried out visually or by the aid of running averages and curve-fitting techniques. Taking the same data as just presented and calculating to percent per micron, one obtains the results shown in Table 3.

These data have been plotted in Figure 3 as a block plot or histogram.

In order to determine additionally the influence of dimensions measured upon the diameter, data other than those given above have been used (see Fig. 4). A sample of ground quartz was measured in the microscope, the length L and the breadth B of each particle being recorded. Although only one histogram is shown and curve 1 is

Table 3. Weight Percentage per Unit Interval

Diameters		Percent	
Range, μ	Interval, μ	By wt in interval	By wt per micron
0–5	5	2.3	0.46
5–10	5	2.7	0.54
10–20	10	9.1	0.91
20–40	20	13.3	0.67
40–80	40	21.1	0.53
80–160	80	34.5	0.43
160–320	160	15.6	0.097
320–640	320	1.4	0.005

drawn through it to give distribution based on B diameter, curve 2 (using the arithmetic mean of length and breadth) and curve 3 (using the length) were similarly plotted as blocks and then converted to curves. The importance of stating the dimension employed becomes very evident.

The percent per unit diameter curves are sensitive, since each percentage is but a part of the whole and delineates the character of only a small portion of the material. They may be enlarged in desired areas by the use of logarithmic instead of linear scales. Other functions such as percent surface or percent particle frequency may be employed in lieu of percent by weight.

Specific Surface. Often it is more useful to determine the surface of material which may be expressed as square meters per gram or other convenient unit of the same dimensions. This may be derived from the distribution curves by numerical or graphical means. If graphical, the Gates and the Roller diagrams may be employed (Figs. 5a and 5b). The former is a plot of distribution as cumulative percent undersize vs reciprocal diameter, and the latter is a plot of distribution as percent by weight per unit diameter vs logarithm of diameter. The area beneath each of them is a measure of the specific surface of the size distribution represented by the curves.

Figure 5a shows the form of the Gates diagram and the manner of its integration. Since specific surface, that is, area per unit weight, is a function of diameter squared over diameter cubed, it is a reciprocal diameter relation. Surface is proportional to the integral of differential weights multiplied by reciprocal diameter over the weight range of the sample. Without destroying the proportionality, percentages based on number

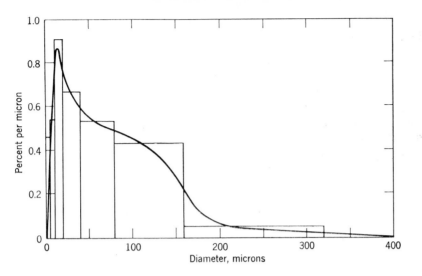

Fig. 3. Block plot (histogram) of size distribution of particles.

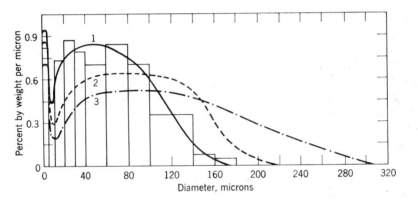

Fig. 4. Distribution curves of ground quartz using different diametral criteria. Curves: (1) histogram and curve, B diameter; (2) curve, $L + B/2$ diameter; (3) curve, L diameter.

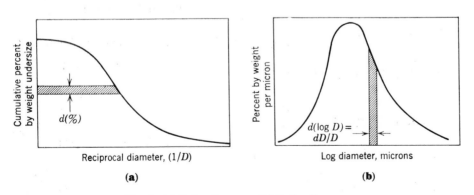

Fig. 5. (a) Gates diagram; (b) Roller diagram.

of particles may be substituted for percentages based on weight, giving the following relation:

$$\text{surface} \sim \int_0^{100} d(\%)/D$$

where the differential percentage $d(\%)$ over the diameter D is represented as an infinitely slender horizontal bar on the Gates diagram; and the summation between 0 and 100% represents the specific surface of the sample.

The Roller diagram may be considered in somewhat the same manner, as shown in Figure 5b. The expression given above may be multiplied and divided by differential diameter within the integral. Then,

$$\text{surface} \sim \int \frac{d(\%)}{dD} \times \frac{dD}{D} \quad \text{or} \quad \int_0^{D_{max}} \frac{d(\%)}{dD} \times d(\log D)$$

wherein $d(\%)/dD$ corresponds to the percent per micron. The expression within the integral represents an infinitely slender vertical bar on the Roller diagram, and the summation of the area beneath the diagram, between zero and maximum diameter, represents surface.

In addition to the methods for calculating surface, there are several methods for the direct measurement of surface. Some of these give a good measure of external surface, while others include internal or interstitial surface as well as the external. Since very great differences may exist between external and total surface for many substances, the surface measured, or the method employed, should always be stated.

Average Diameter. A knowledge of the size distribution affords a basis for calculating an "average diameter" of all the particles in a sample. Some methods of testing give only an average diameter, not a size distribution. There are many average diameters, such as weight mean and surface mean. The choice of the type of mean value employed depends on which property of the whole mass of particles is of interest.

In the following summary of a number of types of mean value, d represents diameter and the subscript denotes the particular diameter being considered, as, for example, the maximum d_1 and minimum d_2 diameters of a range of particle sizes, while n is the number of particles.

1. Arithmetic mean: $\dfrac{d_1 + d_2}{2}$

2. Geometric mean: $\sqrt{d_1 d_2}$

3. Taschinger's mean: $\dfrac{d_1 - d_2}{\log_e d_1 - \log_e d_2}$

4. Mellor's mean: $\sqrt[3]{\dfrac{(d_1 + d_2)(d_1{}^2 + d_2{}^2)}{4}}$

5. Mean of form: $\dfrac{4}{5}\dfrac{d_1{}^5 - d_2{}^5}{d_1{}^4 - d_2{}^4}$

6. Von Reytt's mean: $0.435(d_1 + d_2)$

7. Number mean: $\dfrac{\Sigma nd}{\Sigma n}$

8. Length mean: $\dfrac{\Sigma nd^2}{\Sigma nd}$

9. Surface mean: $\dfrac{\Sigma nd^3}{\Sigma nd^2}$

10. Volume mean (= weight mean, for particles all of the same density): $\dfrac{\Sigma nd^4}{\Sigma nd^3}$

11. Surface diameter: $\sqrt{\dfrac{\Sigma nd^2}{\Sigma n}}$

12. Volume diameter: $\sqrt[3]{\dfrac{\Sigma nd^3}{\Sigma n}}$

Of these, the first six were derived on the assumption that the distribution of sizes in the interval considered is uniform and that it may be expressed in terms derived from maximum and minimum sizes. In any ordinary material that is not the case, and these means are therefore of dubious value. When the size range is narrow, as the products between sieves, these means may be employed; in such cases it is probable that the simple arithmetic mean will suffice.

The remaining averages, being in the form of summations, take into account whatever irregularities in size distribution may occur. In general, the mean that refers to the property which is of greatest significance should be employed. The differences between them are substantial, hence the type of mean employed should always be stated.

Uniformity Coefficients. It is evident that there can be any number of size distributions giving the same average diameter. A given average may result from the occurrence of an overwhelming predominance of particles of almost exactly the same size, or from the presence of amounts of widely different sizes equally distributed on either side of the median. Obviously no average diameter can state all there is to be known about a given collection of particles. In order to offset this difficulty while still preserving simplicity of expression, a distribution factor, or uniformity coefficient, expressing the shape of the distribution curve is often given along with an average diameter. Its function is to give some indication of the breadth of the size-distribution curve.

One simple method of expressing the distribution is to state maximum, minimum, and average sizes. As the exact maxima and minima are often difficult to locate, 10 and 90% points on the cumulative curve are often used. Some prefer to distribute the curve in terms of quadrants, giving the 25, 50, and 75% points, while still others use values closer to the exact maxima and minima as, for example, the 5 and 95% points, including also the 50% point. Some indication may be had from the general slope of the cumulative percent curve. Since the line is not often straight over a range of diameters, the slope is more easily determined from a plot on probability paper.

Another type of uniformity coefficient can be obtained by calculating the moments of the blocks in a block plot, using the tallest central block as an axis. Yet another calculation of uniformity coefficient V_l may be made using the equation:

$$V_l = d_l \sqrt{\frac{\Sigma n}{2\Sigma n(d_e - d)^2}}$$

where d_l is $\Sigma nd/\Sigma n$ and d is the average diameter of each size interval. A variant of this is:

$$V_s = d_s \sqrt{\frac{\Sigma W}{2\Sigma W(d_s - d)^2}}$$

where W is weight in size fraction, d_s is $\Sigma nd^3/\Sigma nd^2$, and d is average diameter of each size interval.

Skewness factors and spread of size may be employed in accordance with good statistical practice. Some of the relations pertaining to the laws of size reduction may also be considered. In various fields of work, surface factors and fineness moduli have been empirically derived and used as uniformity coefficients.

Table 4. Comparison of Testing Sieves

Tyler standard[a]			U.S. Bur. Standards[b]					British standard[c]				IMM sieves[d]		
Mesh	Aperture in.	mm	Mesh double Tyler series	Mesh	Aperture in.	mm	Toler-ance, %	Mesh	Aperture in.	mm	Toler-ance, %	Mesh	Aperture in.	mm
	0.312	7.925	2½	2½	0.315	8.00	3							
3	0.263	6.680		3	0.265	6.73	3							
	0.221	5.613	3½	3½	0.223	5.66	3							
4	0.185	4.699		4	0.187	4.76	3							
	0.156	3.962	5	5	0.157	4.00	3							
6	0.131	3.327		6	0.132	3.36	3	5	0.1320	3.34	3			
	0.110	2.794	7	7	0.111	2.83	3	6	0.1107	2.81	3			
8	0.093	2.362		8	0.0937	2.38	3	7	0.0949	2.41	3	5	0.100	2.54
	0.078	1.981	9	10	0.0787	2.00	3	8	0.0810	2.05	3			
10	0.065	1.651		12	0.0661	1.68	3	10	0.0660	1.67	3	8	0.062	1.574
	0.055	1.397	12	14	0.0555	1.41	3	12	0.0553	1.40	3			
14	0.046	1.168		16	0.0469	1.19	3	14	0.0474	1.20	3	10	0.050	1.270
	0.039	0.991		18	0.0394	1.00	3	16	0.0395	1.00	3	12	0.0416	1.056
20	0.0328	0.833	16	20	0.0331	0.84	5	18	0.0336	0.85	5	16	0.0312	0.792
	0.0276	0.701	24	25	0.0280	0.71	5	22	0.0275	0.70	5	20	0.025	0.635

Tyler mesh	Aperture (in.)	Aperture (mm)	Mesh	Mesh	Aperture (in.)	Aperture (mm)	Ratio	Mesh	Aperture (in.)	Aperture (mm)	Ratio	Mesh	Aperture (in.)	Aperture (mm)
28	0.0232	0.589		30	0.0232	0.59	5	25	0.0236	0.60	5	25	0.020	0.508
	0.0195	0.495	32	35	0.0197	0.50	5	30	0.0197	0.50	5	30	0.0166	0.421
35	0.0164	0.417		40	0.0165	0.42	5	36	0.0166	0.421	5	35	0.0142	0.361
	0.0138	0.351	42	45	0.0138	0.35	5	44	0.0139	0.353	5	40	0.0125	0.317
48	0.0116	0.295		50	0.0117	0.297	6	52	0.0116	0.295	6	50	0.01	0.254
	0.0097	0.246	60	60	0.0098	0.250	6	60	0.0099	0.252	6	60	0.0083	0.211
65	0.0082	0.208		70	0.0083	0.210	6	72	0.0083	0.211	6	70	0.0071	0.180
	0.0069	0.175	80	80	0.0070	0.177	6	85	0.0070	0.177	6	80	0.0062	0.157
100	0.0058	0.147		100	0.0059	0.149	6	100	0.0060	0.152	6	90	0.0055	0.139
	0.0049	0.124	115	120	0.0049	0.125	6	120	0.0049	0.125	6	100	0.0050	0.127
150	0.0041	0.104		140	0.0041	0.105	8	150	0.0041	0.105	8	120	0.0042	0.107
	0.0035	0.088	170	170	0.0035	0.088	8	170	0.0035	0.088	8	150	0.0033	0.084
200	0.0029	0.074		200	0.0029	0.074	8	200	0.0030	0.076	8	200	0.0025	0.063
	0.0024	0.061	250	230	0.0024	0.062	8	240	0.0026	0.065				
270	0.0021	0.053		270	0.0021	0.053	8	300	0.0021	0.053				
	0.0017	0.043	325	325	0.0017	0.044								
400	0.0015	0.037												

a The base of the Tyler series is the 200-mesh screen with aperture equal to 0.0029 in. or 0.074 mm. The ratio between apertures of consecutive screens is the square root of 2. For closer sizing a series of intermediate screens is available, the ratio between apertures of consecutive screens in the double Tyler series being the fourth root of 2.

b The base of the U.S. Bureau of Standards series is the 18-mesh screen with 1.00-mm aperture. The ratio between apertures of consecutive screens is the fourth root of 2.

c The ratio between apertures of consecutive British standard screens is only approximately equal to the fourth root of 2 because wire diameters are limited to those occurring in the SWG (Standard Wire Gauge) series.

d In IMM (Institution of Mining and Metallurgy) screens, wire diameter equals aperture, and aperture in inches equals 1 divided by twice the mesh number.

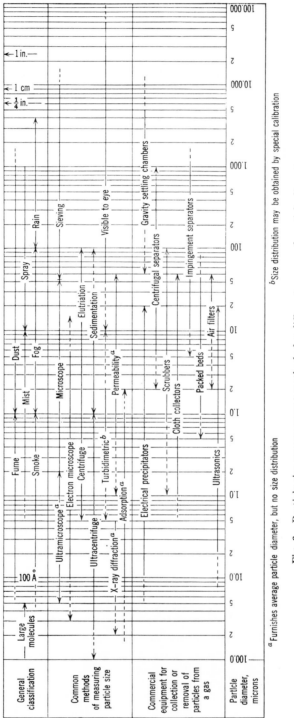

Fig. 6. Particle size measurement methods for different ranges of particle diameter.

Methods for Size Measurement

The determination of particle size or of a size characteristic may be done by any of several methods, each of which is most applicable to a particular range of particle size. See Figure 6.

A brief description of the more important methods of particle-size measurement is given below. See also reference 1.

Sieving. Probably the simplest and most widely used method of determining particle-size distributions is sieving. The method involves shaking the sample through a pair, or more commonly a stack, of pans, each with a wire-cloth bottom of successively smaller size openings. The sample is separated into a series of fractions on the individual sieves.

Sieve analyses can be completed in a relatively short time, require little operator skill, and involve relatively inexpensive equipment.

A thorough study of the physical laws that govern the sieving of fine particles has been published by Whitby (2).

Table 4 compares four systems of standard sieves. Micromesh sieves (3) extend the range of measurement to as low as 10 mm (0.01 m).

Microscopy. Microscopy is the most direct method for particle size distribution measurements. Theoretically, its range of applicability is unlimited; but practical limitations and availability of more expedient techniques make microscopy a less desirable tool in certain size ranges. Table 5 shows the regions of applicability of microscopic techniques.

Table 5. Regions of Applicability of Microscopic Techniques

Method	Normal size range, μ	Equipment required[a]
white light	0.4–100	ordinary microscope, white light
ultraviolet	0.1–100	microscope equipped with quartz optics, monochromatic light source
ultramicroscopy	0.01–0.2	microscope equipped for dark-field illumination, arc light source
electron microscopy	0.001–5	Philips, RCA, Hitachi, Zeiss, Metropolitan-Vickers, or Siemens electron microscope

[a] Several automatic and semiautomatic scanning devices are available for counting and sizing particles. Although they are rather expensive, the manpower saved can justify the expense in some cases.

The Flying Spot Particle Resolver is based on the work of Roberts and Young and associates (4–6). It uses flying-spot scanning, a method of converting a two-dimensional density distribution into a varying voltage-time relation. The results from the instrument correlate well with the ASTM E20-51T (1951) method (7).

The Casella Automatic Particle Counter and Sizer utilizes track scanning (8) for counting and sizing particles.

A microscope method of measuring thicknesses of fine particles has been described by Robbins (9).

Table 6. Miscellaneous Techniques for Particle Size Determination

Technique	Size distribution[a]	Useful on	Normal size range, μ	Equipment required	Approx elapsed time[b]	Reference
permeametry	no	powders	0.5–50	(a) Fisher Sub-Sieve Sizer (b) Blaine Permeameter (c) other special equipment	15 min	20–24
adsorption	no	powders	0.01–10	(a) BET gas adsorption apparatus or Perkin-Shell Sorptometer (b) common laboratory equipment for adsorption from soln (c) calorimetric apparatus for heat of immersion	1–2 hr	see Adsorption
light scattering	difficult	powders, emulsions, suspensions	0.05–1.0	photometer; for example, Brice-Phoenix	hr	25,26
change in electrolytic resistivity	yes	powders, bubbles, emulsions, suspensions	2–100	Coulter Counter (marketed by Coulter Industrial Co., Elmhurst, Ill.)	1 hr	27–30
cascade impactor	no	air-borne particles, aerosols	0.1–100	Casella-Sonkin (marketed in U.S. by Mine Safety Appliance Co.)		31–33
x-ray low-angle scattering	no	powders	0.01–10	x-ray diffraction equipment plus special attachment	hr	34
sonic vibrations	possible	powders, liquid contaminants	limited	sonic generator	min	35
bulk density and rate of packing	no	powders	limited	common laboratory equipment	min	36–38
magnetochemistry	no	powders	0.005–10	equipment for magnetic measurements	hr	39
precipitation of charged particles	no	aerosols	0.2–1.5	home-made precipitator, voltmeter, potentiometer		40
reflectance	no	colored emulsions, emulsion kinetics	1–60	special cells, pulse generator, dual-beam cathode-ray oscillograph		41–43
light scatter decay	no	aerosols, fine powders	1–10	home-built		44

[a]"No" means only an average size is obtainable.   [b] Per determination (estimated).

Another method for measuring particle thickness utilizes stereophotogrammetric procedures (10). Best results, however, are obtained only with particles larger than 100 μ.

Equipment for direct photomicrography of aerosol particles has been described by Cadle and Wiggens (11).

Sedimentation and Related Techniques. Numerous techniques are related to sedimentation, including centrifugation, and elutriation, which is the reverse of sedimentation. See Sedimentation; also references 1, 12–19.

Other Techniques. Some other techniques for particle-size measurement are summarized in Table 6 (1).

Bibliography

"Size Measurement of Particles" in *ECT* 1st ed., Vol. 12, pp. 472–497, by K. T. Whitby, University of Minnesota.

1. R. R. Irani and C. F. Callis. *Particle Size: Measurement, Interpretation, and Application,* John Wiley & Sons, Inc., New York, 1963.
2. K. T. Whitby, "The Mechanics of Fine Sieving," Ph.D. Thesis, University of Minnesota, 1954; "Symposium on Particle Size Measurement," *ASTM Spec. Tech. Publ. No. 234* (1958).
3. H. W. Daeschner, E. E. Seibert, and E. D. Peters, "Symposium on Particle Size Measurement," *ASTM Spec. Tech. Publ. No. 234* (1958).
4. F. Roberts and J. Z. Young, *Nature* **167,** 1231 (1951).
5. F. Roberts, *Nature* **169,** 518 (1952).
6. F. Roberts and J. Z. Young, *Proc. Inst. Elec. Engrs. (London) Pt A3* **99,** 747 (1952).
7. D. P. Ames, R. R. Irani, and C. F. Callis, *J. Phys. Chem.* **63,** 531 (1959).
8. D. G. W. Hawksley, *Brit. J. Appl. Phys.,* Suppl. No. 3, 125 (1954).
9. W. H. M. Robbins, *Brit. J. Appl. Phys.,* Suppl. No. 3, 189 (1954).
10. B. C. Aschenbrenner, *Photogrammatic Eng.* **21,** 376 (1955).
11. R. D. Cadle and E. J. Wiggens, *Chem. Eng. News* **31,** 3074 (1953).
12. A. I. Michaels, T. L. Weaver, and R. C. Nelson, *ASTM Bull. No. 247,* 140 (1960).
13. A. H. M. Andreasen, *Chim. Ind. (Paris)* **70,** 863 (1953).
14. R. H. Lester, *Am. Ceram. Soc. Bull.* **37,** 129 (1958).
15. K. T. Whitby, *Heating, Piping and Air Conditioning* **61,** 449 (1955).
16. D. P. Ames, R. R. Irani, and C. F. Callis, *J. Phys. Chem.* **63,** 531 (1959).
17. A. K. Gupta, *J. Appl. Chem. (London)* **9,** 487 (1959).
18. K. T. Whitby, A. B. Algren, and J. C. Annis, *ASTM Spec. Tech. Publ. No. 234,* 117 (1958).
19. V. K. La Mer, R. H. Smellie, and P. K. Lee, *J. Colloid Sci.* **12,** 566 (1957).
20. F. B. Hutto and D. W. Davis, *Offic. Dig. Federation Paint Varnish Prod. Clubs* **31,** 429 (1959).
21. S. S. Ober and K. J. Frederick, *ASTM Spec. Tech. Publ. No. 234,* 279 (1958).
22. R. M. Barrer and D. M. Grove, *Trans. Faraday Soc.* **47,** 826 (1951).
23. G. Kraus and J. W. Ross, *J. Phys. Chem.* **57,** 330 (1953).
24. R. T. Johansen, P. B. Lorenz, C. G. Dodd, F. D. Pidgeon, and J. W. Davis, *J. Phys. Chem.* **57,** 40 (1953).
25. C. T. O'Konski, M. D. Bitron, and W. I. Higuski, *ASTM Spec. Tech. Publ. No. 234,* 180 (1958).
26. R. M. Tabibian and W. Heller, *J. Colloid Sci.* **13,** 6 (1958).
27. R. H. Berg, *ASTM Spec. Tech. Publ. No. 234,* 245 (1959).
28. H. E. Kubitschek, *Res. Appl. Ind.* **13,** 128 (1960).
29. R. R. Irani, *Anal. Chem.* **32,** 1162 (1960).
30. E. S. Palik, *Anal. Chem.* **33,** 956 (1961).
31. J. A. Brink, *Ind. Eng. Chem.* **50,** 645 (1958).
32. R. I. Mitchell and J. M. Pilcher, *Ind. Eng. Chem.* **51,** 1039 (1959).
33. H. Binark and W. E. Ranz, *Ind. Eng. Chem.* **51,** 701 (1959).
34. W. J. Marculaitis, *J. Colloid Sci.* **12,** 581 (1957).
35. R. C. Cadle, *Particle Size Determination,* Interscience Publishers, New York, 1955, p. 293.
36. F. S. Sinnat and L. Slater, *Fuel* **2,** 142 (1932).

37. H. E. Rose, *The Measurement of Particle Size in Very Fine Powders*, Chemical Publishing Co., New York, 1954.
38. J. J. Hermans, *Flow Properties of Disperse Systems*, North-Holland Publishing Co., Amsterdam, 1953.
39. P. W. Selwood, *Magnetochemistry*, 2nd ed., Interscience Publishers, Inc., New York, 1956, pp. 91, 122–126, 389–396.
40. F. G. Drozin and V. K. La Mer, *J. Colloid Sci.* **14**, 74 (1959).
41. A. Kahn and D. R. Lewis, *J. Phys. Chem.* **58**, 801 (1954).
42. H. Benoit, *Ann. Phys.* **6**, 561 (1951).
43. C. T. O'Konski and B. Zimm, *Science* **11**, 113 (1950).
44. R. L. Dimmick, M. T. Hatch, and J. Ng, *A.M.A. Arch. Ind. Health* **18**, 23 (1958).
45. R. D. Cadle, *Particles in the Atmosphere and Space*, Reinhold Publishing Corp., New York, 1966.
46. R. D. Cadle, *Particle Size; Theory and Industrial Applications*, Reinhold Publishing Corp., New York, 1965.
47. C. N. Davies, *Recent Advances in Aerosol Research*, The MacMillan Co., New York, 1964.
48. C. N. Davies, ed., *Aerosol Science*, Academic Press, Inc., New York, 1966.
49. N. A. Fuchs, *The Mechanics of Aerosols*, The MacMillan Co., New York, 1964.
50. H. L. Green and W. R. Lane, *Particulate Clouds: Dusts, Smokes, and Mists*, 2nd ed., D. Van Nostrand Co., Inc., Princeton, N.J., 1964.
51. J. Happel and H. Brenner, *Low Reynolds Number Hydrodynamics*, Prentice-Hall, Inc., Englewood Cliffs, N.J., 1965.
52. G. Herdan, *Small Particle Statistics*, American Elsevier Publishing Co., New York, 1953.
53. C. Junge, *Air Chemistry and Radioactivity*, Academic Press, Inc., New York, 1963.
54. C. Orr, Jr., *Particulate Technology*, The MacMillan Co., New York, 1966.
55. F. A. Zenz and D. F. Othmer, *Fluidization and Fluid-Particle Systems*, Reinhold Publishing Corp., New York, 1960.

SIZE REDUCTION

It is necessary to reduce the size of solid or semisolid pieces of matter for many reasons; the most important objectives are (*1*) to liberate the desired constituent in a mixture from unwanted components, such as ore from rock; (*2*) to create a large surface area per unit mass in order to improve utilization, as is the case in the pulverization of coal for combustion; and (*3*) to produce a material in an acceptable form for a desired purpose, as for cement, fertilizer, and paint pigments (see Pigments (Dispersed pigment concentrates)).

Size reduction may be accomplished by cutting, tearing, impacting, rubbing, compressing, and explosive disintegrating. In industry the machines employed are described as shearers, shredders, defiberizers, hullers, disintegrators, mills, crushers, grinders, and pulverizers. Shearers and shredders find application with sheets of material, for example, metal, paper, rubber. Defiberizers, hullers, and disintegrators are utilized principally in the processing of grain and other commodities. The remaining machines—the mills, crushers, grinders, and pulverizers—are employed to reduce the size of solid matter mechanically, achieving a wide variety of properties in the products, which are intended for a host of uses. The mode of action of representative machines, their particular fields of application, and size reduction in general are the subjects of this article.

Comminution is a general term describing size reduction, without regard to the mechanism involved. *Crushing* is usually applied to the breaking of relatively coarse chunks of solids, ranging in size from several feet in diameter to less than an inch, where the breaking is brought about by a relatively slow compressive action concentrated mostly on individual pieces. *Grinding* denotes reduction to the finer sizes and implies a shearing or rubbing action, some of which occurs between individual pieces. There is not a clear distinction between crushing and grinding in many instances, for some current equipment accomplishes fine grinding largely through the mechanisms of impaction and compression. *Pulverizing* is employed broadly to describe any operation producing a fine powder; sometimes it is applied to the breaking apart of the weak interparticle bonds of a caked precipitate.

The nature of the feed and the desired product size dictate to a great extent the type of machine or machines that must be employed. Of prime concern, however, are the hardness, abrasiveness, homogeneity, toxicity, purity, melting or softening point, and, if wet grinding is contemplated, the solubility of the material. The physical structure of solids and the characteristics of fracture must be examined before these factors can be adequately evaluated.

Characteristics of Solids

Solids may be homogeneous or heterogeneous, crystalline or amorphous, hard or soft, brittle or plastic. By far the greater quantity of commercially important materials which require crushing are heterogeneous. Iron ore, for example, is typically composed of relatively pure iron oxide particles intermixed with silica. Interfacial regions or boundaries generally involve less energetic bonding and thus fracture is most likely to occur along such boundaries. The entire mass is also likely to be permeated with pores.

Even crystals of pure substances, unless grown under carefully controlled conditions, have internal weaknesses due to missing atoms or ions in their lattice structure and cracks and flaws arising from thermal stress or mechanical shock (1). A perfect crystal, if pressed with an increasing force, would presumably distribute the load uniformly throughout its structure until it eventually disintegrated into a dust of crystallites or elementary building blocks of the crystal. Actual crystals fail under much less than the theoretically required force and break into a spectrum of particle sizes. Such imperfections make crushing easier, at least down to certain sizes. As blemishes are eliminated, the remaining material tends to be stronger and more energy must be supplied to reduce it further in size.

Noncrystalline materials such as glass contain microscopic cracks and flaws extending from their surface inward to various depths. These faults, known as Griffith cracks from their discoverer (2), serve to multiply an applied force by an amount that increases with crack length and to focus the stress at the crack vertex. Many materials that are considered to be amorphous develop crystallites under strain (3). Since these crystallites are embedded in an amorphous matrix and are more rigid than the amorphous material, they tend to promote crack formation and fracture.

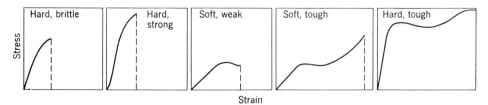

Fig. 1. Stress-strain behavior of typical materials.

Stress-strain curves such as those portrayed in Figure 1 reveal the characteristic behavior of typical solids. The initial straight-line portion of each curve defines the Hooke's law region, ie, the region where stress is proportional to strain. The ratio of stress to strain is Young's modulus and its magnitude is a measure of stiffness or softness. The stress at the knee of a curve, as in the three curves on the right, is the yield point and is a measure of the resistance to permanent deformation. Beyond this point is the failure region where nonrecoverable plastic deformation is exhibited. The total area under the stress–strain curve represents the energy of fracture; it is also a rough measure of the toughness or impact strength of the material. A stress–strain curve cannot present the entire picture, however. The rapidity of application of a force and external conditions can greatly influence the fracture process. An ordinary rock, for example, will flow if force is applied slowly over a period of years, but a vigorous blow will shatter it. Certain brittle materials, on the other hand, fracture at lower stresses when the force is applied slowly than when application is rapid (4). Ambient conditions influence the behavior of many substances. Rock salt, for example, can be bent under water but behaves as a very brittle substance in dry air.

Nature of Fracture

A material such as steel exhibits a stress-strain curve which is nearly reversible in the elastic Hooke's law region, but few materials for which size reduction is required do so. If these materials are unloaded and reloaded, an elastic looping or hysteresis occurs in the stress-strain cycle. The area of the loop represents a dissipation of energy, usually as heat. Although this loss of energy amounts to a net work input, it produces no fracture. Likewise, when a force is applied and released, resulting in permanent deformation, energy has been expended but negligible size reduction is achieved. However, cracks may have been initiated. For fracture to occur a crack has to be propagated through the material.

Crack extension, or fracture, really begins when the release of elastic energy in a material is sufficient to make the crack self-propagating and therefore independent of an external source of energy. The tip or furthest extension of a crack is the region of greatest stress when a force is applied in a manner acting to open the crack. The applied force distorts the material having the crack and thus feeds energy into the system. When the stored energy of elastic deformation exceeds that needed to form fresh surface and to cause plastic deformation at the crack tip, the crack opens. The strain energy which is released causes the crack to expand without further external force being required. The expansion rapidly attains a terminal velocity which varies from material to material but amounts to a progression rate approximately half that of transverse waves in the solid (5). Stress waves released by the initial fracture pulse interfere and produce other regions of high stress from which new fractures can begin. Branching of cracks also occurs.

Energy Utilization

Energy expended in size reduction follows a number of paths, but most of it ultimately appears as heat. It can go into actual reduction in the size of the material, into friction in the equipment, or into interparticle effects, being released as sound or as frictional electricity. Within the material, the energy may also be utilized in producing elastic and plastic deformation, atomic lattice rearrangements, and surface energy. Figure 2 depicts the several conversions which the energy may undergo (6).

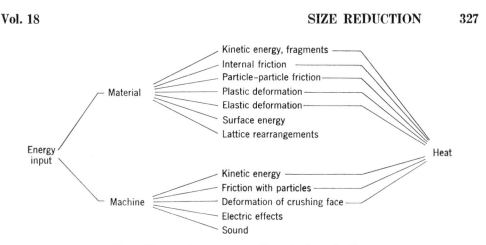

Fig. 2. Routes of energy expenditure in size reduction.

Size reduction is a very inefficient process if the surface area production as represented by the surface energy of the product is taken as the only useful energy expenditure. Actual materials will not fracture, however, unless they are deformed. Deformation should therefore be looked upon as a necessary prerequisite for fracture, or even as an activation step (1). From this viewpoint, size reduction is reasonably efficient. Friction between fragments accounts for a considerable portion of the required energy, especially in fine grinding (7). For this reason, if for no other, fines should be removed from a pulverizer as rapidly as possible.

Fracture Mechanisms

There are three basic mechanisms by which solids are mechanically reduced in size. A load of sufficient magnitude applied normally to the surface of a homogeneous, isotropic object and directed toward its center results in the formation of two or more—most likely more—fragments or particles. This is spoken of as a *compression* or *impact fracture*, depending on whether the load was applied slowly or rapidly. When the load is applied off-center the process is known as *chipping*. Ordinarily, fewer particles are formed by chipping than by impact. The grinding mechanism is termed *abrasion* when the load is applied parallel to the surface of the solid. Extremely fine particles are produced by abrasion.

The relative frequency of occurrence of impact, chipping, and abrasive fracture determines the distribution of fragment sizes in actual comminution devices, each mechanism being associated with a characteristic distribution function (8,9). Thus comminution can be treated as an "averaging process" or as a "summation of comminution events" (10).

Distribution of Fragment Sizes

Single-event impact fracture has been described theoretically and the predicted distribution function tested experimentally. Chipping and abrasion distribution functions have been determined experimentally but corresponding functions have not been derived from models of the processes. Nevertheless, it is useful to consider each single-event behavior separately, because appropriate combinations of them lead to the complex-event, or actual, distribution that results from a grinding operation. The relative proportions of the three fracture processes reveal a great deal about a grinding process.

Single-Event Impact Fracture. Of the various single-event, impact-fracture distribution functions that have been proposed on theoretical grounds (11–14), the following (15) is perhaps the most sound. This equation for a brittle, homogeneous, and isotropic solid may be written

$$M = 1 - \left(1 - \frac{x}{x_0}\right)^r \qquad (1)$$

where M is the cumulative weight fraction finer than size x, x_0 is the characteristic dimension of the parent solid prior to fracture, and r is a measure of the number of breaks in the parent solid. The derivation assumes that fracture takes place randomly and that each break is an independent event. Theoretically, the equation applies equally well if the solid is a long thin rod, if the cross-sectional area of the solid is proportional to its characteristic dimension squared, or if the length of the intercept along any line passing through the solid is proportional to its characteristic dimension. Some direct experimental verification of equation 1 has been obtained (10) but its chief value at the present time is that for small values of x it reduces to a form that resembles the better verified (16,17), but empirical, equation (18),

$$M = (x/k)^\alpha \qquad (2)$$

where α is the distribution modulus, ie, the slope of the straight line resulting from a plot on log-log paper of the cumulative weight fraction fines against size, and k is the size modulus, when α is near unity. The distribution modulus α has been found to be close to unity for single-event impact fracture, so this stands as a criterion for fracture by impact. The dotted curve of Figure 3 (10) illustrates the data expected from a repeated impact fracture test.

Single-Event Abrasion. The mechanism of abrasion is easily described; it is simply surface wear such as occurs when chalk is rubbed against a blackboard. Two distinct sizes of particles are produced. The parent particle, the chalk, is slightly reduced in size and many small fragments are created. A discontinuity thus exists between the two modes on a size distribution plot. Distribution functions have not been derived theoretically because single-event abrasion is difficult to define realistically.

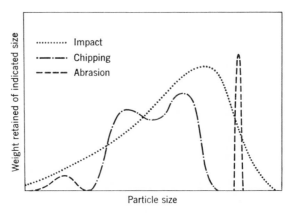

Fig. 3. Hypothetical single-event fracture size distributions.   After Mular (10).

The broken-line curve of Figure 3 shows data that might be obtained from a single abrasion event.

Single-Event Chipping. Chipping is akin to both coarse abrasion and incomplete impact fracture. It also is difficult to define in terms of a single event, but, clearly, it will result in a particle-size distribution bearing a strong resemblance either to incom-

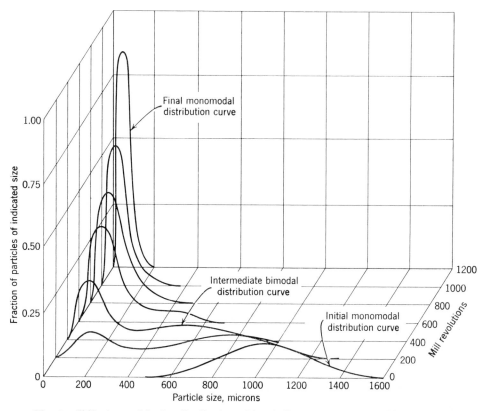

Fig. 4. Shifts in particle-size distribution with grinding progress. After Kelleher (19).

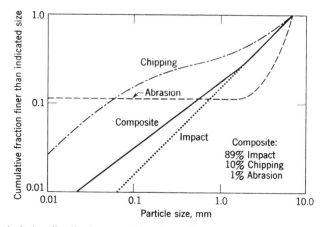

Fig. 5. Hypothetical size distributions resulting from three fracture mechanisms and the resulting composite size distribution. After Mular (10).

plete impact fracture or to abrasion. The long and short dashed curve of Figure 3 shows the hypothetical result of a single chipping event.

Summation-of-Events, or Complex, Fracture. As grinding proceeds in actual devices the size distribution of the fragments changes. This is illustrated by the three-dimensional plot of Figure 4 (19) where the size distribution of the material being crushed is presented as a function of revolutions of the mill. The relative rates for impact-, abrasion-, and chipping-grinding are established at any one time by various factors, including particle size, shape, density, and hardness, the number of particles, the cleavage habit of the solid, the density and viscosity of the suspending medium, and the characteristics of the grinding device. A given grinder tends to break fragments in a systematic way. If the various breakage rates are constant relative to one another, a characteristic weight fraction of the total mass of material undergoing grinding will conform to an impact-type distribution function; another weight fraction will follow an abrasion distribution function; and another will be described by a chipping distribution function. In Figure 5 (10) are plotted, as the logarithm of the cumulative weight fraction finer than the indicated size vs the logarithm of size, hypothetical results for a test in which 89% of the total feed (initial size, 6.68 mm) was presumed to have been broken by impact, 10% by chipping, and 1% by abrasion (10). The respective distribution functions are shown, the impact-crushing contribution being represented by a line with a distribution modulus of unity. The composite curve as represented by equation 2 with an α value of 0.8 is also indicated and shown to compare well with typical experimental results.

Size-Distribution Relationships

Experimental methods of particle-size measurement are numerous (20–22); most of them depend strongly upon the size of the particles involved. By using standard mesh sieves, it is possible to determine particle diameters over essentially the entire comminution size range with comparative ease and reproducibility. The following discussion presumes the use of the sieving technique which is widely employed in size-reduction analysis, although the method of treating particle-size distribution data does not depend on the measurement procedure.

A size determination is made using a stack of sieves, with the size of the openings decreasing from top to bottom. A sample of material is placed on the upper sieve. The entire stack is then shaken until the sample distributes itself on the individual sieves according to the size of the particles and the size of the openings. The weight of material on each sieve is then determined. The results can be tabulated either as the mass fraction equal to and greater than, or equal to and less than, the size of the sieve openings. Sieve openings usually progress in the ratio $1:\sqrt{2}$; every second sieve, therefore, will have openings in the ratio $1:2$.

For convenience and simplicity, a single particle size is often employed to characterize size reduction, a favorite one being the sieve opening size through which 80% (by weight) of the material will pass. Equation 2, as presented before, is most often used as the starting point for an analysis. If it applies, the data plot on a log-log grid as a line which is approximately straight, as shown by Figure 5. Deviations from linearity are usually most pronounced for the coarser sizes. Figure 6 (16) presents a plot of typical data obtained by subjecting quartz to successive size reductions in a roll mill. The abscissa is a logarithmic scale, although it may not appear so upon first examination.

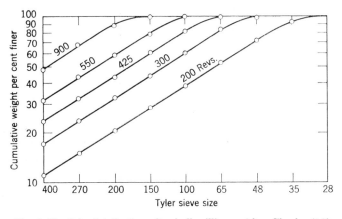

Fig. 6. Particle distribution after ball milling.   After Charles (16).

Another of the more widely employed equations for testing size-reduction processes (23) is

$$M = 1 - \exp\left(-Bx^m\right) \tag{3}$$

where M and x are defined as before and B and m are other constants.   The constant B tends to be characteristic of the solid material while the value of m shifts according to the spread of the distribution.   Graphically, distribution data are tested by writing equation 3 in the form

$$\log \ln \left(\frac{1}{1 - M}\right) = m \log x + \log B \tag{4}$$

and plotting $\ln \left(\frac{1}{1 - M}\right)$ vs x on a log-log grid.   If a straight line results, the slope is m and the intercept is B.

A useful method of analyzing size-distribution data is by means of the log normal-distribution equation (24).   One form of this equation is

$$\Delta M = \frac{1}{\sqrt{2\pi} \ln \delta} \int_{\ln x_1}^{\ln x_2} \exp\left\{-\left[\ln \frac{x}{X}\Big/\left(\sqrt{2} \ln \delta\right)\right]^2\right\} d \ln x \ldots \tag{5}$$

where ΔM is the weight fraction of particles between sizes x_1 and x_2, X the geometric mean size, and δ the geometric standard deviation.

Calculating the several parameters of equation 5 can become laborious.   Fortunately, the job is greatly simplified by the use of logarithmic probability paper.   Particle size (or sieve-opening dimension) is plotted on the ordinate and weight percent under-size along the abscissa.   The 50% point on the best straight line through the data points is the geometric mean particle size.   The spread, or range, of particle sizes is indicated by the geometric standard deviation, this measure being numerically equal to the 84.13% size divided by the 50.00% size, or to the 50.00% size divided by the 15.87% size.

The particular advantage of this method of data presentation is that once the mean diameter on a specified basis (eg, weight) and the geometric standard deviation are found, other mean diameters—number mean, surface-area mean, etc—can be calculated easily (6,25,26). Mean diameters are useful because they represent the entire distribution. The surface-area mean particle diameter, for example, is that diameter which, upon division into $6W/\rho$, where W is the weight of a quantity of powder and ρ its density, gives the total surface area of the quantity of powder.

When the distribution is bimodal, a good fit of data is usually obtained with the relationship (27)

$$M = 0.5 + f \operatorname{erf} \left(\ln \frac{x}{X_1} \middle/ \ln \delta_1 \right) + (1 - f) \operatorname{erf} \left(\ln \frac{x}{X_2} \middle/ \ln \delta_2 \right) \ldots \tag{6}$$

where X_1 and δ_1 are the geometric mean size and geometric standard deviation, respectively, for the peak of the distribution nearest the smallest size; X_2 and δ_2 are similar quantities for the peak nearest the largest size; f is the weight fraction at which occurs the transition between the two modes; and erf denotes "the error function of."

Size-Reduction Theories

At the present time the only sure means for determining the size reduction that can be accomplished in a particular comminution device is to make full-scale tests with a sufficient quantity of the actual material to obtain reliable data. Nevertheless, considerable success has been achieved in describing comminution processes theoretically, and some of the newer mathematical matrix methods now awaiting experimental verification portend even greater success for developing true comminution laws.

Energy Input. The cost of the energy required is a major factor in the economic success of any size-reduction operation. Accordingly, much effort has been devoted to relating the magnitude of the energy input to the size reduction accomplished.

Energy-size relationships basically derive from the proposition that the energy necessary to change the size of a particle infinitesimally is inversely proportional to the particle size raised to some power n, or that

$$dE = -K(dD/D^n) \tag{7}$$

where E is the energy, K a constant, and D the particle diameter. When n is 2, equation 7 becomes upon integration

$$E = K\left(\frac{1}{D_2} - \frac{1}{D_1} \right) \tag{8}$$

where D_1 and D_2 are, respectively, the particle diameters before and after size reduction. Equation 8 written in terms of specific surface areas is

$$E = k_1(A_2 - A_1) \tag{9}$$

where k_1 is a new constant incorporating the relation between particle surface and particle diameter, and A_1 and A_2 are, respectively, the specific surface areas before and after size reduction.

Equation 9 is a statement of Rittinger's (28) expression, apparently formulated axiomatically, that the energy required for reduction is proportional to the new surface area created. The relation would be expected to apply precisely if all crushing energy were transferred into surface energy and if the crushing energy required per unit of surface were independent of particle size. It should be most applicable to the fine grinding of brittle materials, for in this situation a minimum of strain energy is involved and elastic and plastic deformations are minimal. The relationship does indeed describe certain grinding data of this type, but there are many other sets of data that it does not fit.

An expression formulated by Kick (29) states that the expenditure of equivalent amounts of energy should result in equivalent geometrical changes in the size of a material. This amounts to saying that, if one unit of energy reduces a certain mass of equal-size particles to particles of half the size, one additional unit of energy must reduce the half-size particles again by half, or to one-quarter of their original size. A mathematical statement of the postulate is obtained by integrating equation 7 with $n = 1$. It is

$$E = k_2 \log (D_1/D_2) \tag{10}$$

if $k_2 = 2.303K$.

This postulate, in effect, assumes that the material being reduced is either homogeneous or has faults uniformly distributed throughout its structure. In the case of coarse material undergoing a limited size reduction, uniformity of faults may indeed prevail. Likewise, uniformity may exist with very small particles because faults will have been eliminated. Equation 10 is often applicable to coarse and to very fine grinding, but, as in the previous instance, only a portion of the available data is adequately described by it.

Integration of equation 7 with n equal to $3/2$, a value midway between previous selections, leads to

$$E = 2K\left(\frac{1}{\sqrt{D_2}} - \frac{1}{\sqrt{D_1}}\right) \tag{11}$$

the expression of Bond (30). The latter indicates that the energy usefully applied in breakage must be inversely proportional to the square root of particle diameters, which is in general agreement with much crushing and grinding data. Practically, equation 11 can be written

$$W = W_t\left(\sqrt{\frac{100}{P}} - \sqrt{\frac{100}{F}}\right) \tag{12}$$

where P and F are, respectively, the product and feed particle sizes measured as the sieve-opening dimension (in microns) through which 80% by weight of the product and feed material will pass, W_t is a "work index" representing theoretically the work input required to crush from an infinitely large particle size down to 80% passing a sieve with 100-μ openings, ie,

$$W_t = K/\sqrt{100} \tag{13}$$

and W is the work required to crush from size F to size P in the same units as W_t. The work index would be a true constant if the breaking characteristics of materials remained the same over all size ranges and if the efficiencies of all grinding machines were equal. Unfortunately, this is not often the case. The value of W_t is subject to change with shifts in particle-size distribution and with the structural characteristics of the material to be crushed. The most satisfactory use can be made of the index when it is determined under conditions closely approximating those of the final operation. Standard laboratory tests (31) have been devised for its evaluation, however. Dry-grind W_t values are usually about 1.3 times wet-grind ones. Average work index

Table 1. Average Wet-Grind Work Indexes, Closed-Circuit Operations (32)

Material	Specific gravity	Work index (W_i), kWh/short ton
barite	4.28	6.2
basalt	2.89	20.4
bauxite	2.38	9.5
dolomite	2.82	11.3
flint	2.65	26.2
glass	2.58	3.1
gypsum rock	2.69	8.2
limestone	2.69	11.6
phosphate rock	2.66	10.1
quartz	2.64	12.8
silicon carbide	2.73	26.2

values as measured using more or less standardized crushers and grinders are listed in Table 1 for some of the more common materials (32). The specific gravity is included as an aid in determining the similarity of a material to one for which a value is listed.

If n in equation 7 is replaced by $(1 + n)$ and the equation integrated, the result (33,34) in terms defined for equation 12 is

$$W = W_i \left[1 - \left(\frac{1}{F/P} \right)^n \right] \left(\frac{100}{P} \right)^n \tag{14}$$

Both W_i and n are now found experimentally to be essentially constant for a given material over a considerable particle-size range. Work-index values are as given above and n varies from about 0.25 to 0.73, depending on the material. The work index may be considered a true constant in equation 14 while n becomes a deviation exponent expressing the variation in the resistance to crushing with changes in particle size and with shifts in crusher efficiency which may also be influenced by particle size.

It is to be noted that the W_i values as listed apply to closed-circuit operation. In this method of size reduction the grinder discharges to a separating device which removes the fraction of feed that has been reduced to the desired fineness and returns the oversize, called the "circulating load," to the grinder. Open-circuit grinding is that method of size reduction in which the desired reduction, for example to a size where 95% passes a sieve with 100-μ openings, is obtained by a single passage of the material through the grinder.

Conversion of W_i values from closed-circuit to open-circuit operation, either wet or dry, is accomplished by multiplying W_i values as given in Table 1 by the factor of Table 2 (32). To determine the appropriate value for the factor, the percentage of product passing for both the closed-circuit and open-circuit operations must be identical. As indicated previously, the W_i values of Table 1 apply to an operation where 80% of the product is of the desired fineness. These particular values can be converted, therefore, only to open-circuit grinding when 80% of the product passes a 100-μ opening sieve. Of course, W_i values can be obtained at other percentages passing and these could then be converted to open-circuit operation at the same percent passing.

Choosing from among the above expressions, or from others that have been proposed (35–41) for purposes of analyzing and predicting performance, necessarily has to be made pragmatically at the present time. Estimating mill size and the number

Table 2. Closed-Circuit to Open-Circuit Conversion Factors (32)

Product passing reference sieve, %	Multiplication factor	Product passing reference sieve, %	Multiplication factor
50	1.035	90	1.40
60	1.05	92	1.46
70	1.10	95	1.57
80	1.20	98	1.70

of mills necessary to handle a particular job requires a relationship between net horsepower requirements and mill dimensions in addition to work-index information. The gross horsepower of a ball mill, for example, is roughly 1.2–1.3 times the net horsepower. The net horsepower H_n for a ball mill of length L (ft) and diameter D (ft) has been given (42) as

$$H_n = 2.5 \left[\left(\frac{L}{2} - 1 \right) K + 1 \right] \left(\frac{D}{2} \right)^{2.5} \left(\frac{S}{S_c} \right) \tag{15}$$

where K is 0.90 for mills less than 5 ft in length and 0.85 otherwise, S the mill speed, and S_c the critical mill speed, ie, the speed at which the charges and balls begin to ride without tumbling and therefore produce no grinding.

To allow for the breakage characteristics of different materials, the work index W_t, defined as the kilowatt-hours per short ton required to break from an infinite size to a fineness where 80% passes 100 μ, may be written, following equation 13, as

$$W_t = 0.8 W_p \left(\frac{x_t}{100} \right)^{\frac{1}{2}} \tag{16}$$

where W_p is the kilowatt-hours per short ton of material passing necessary to reduce to product size x_t.

The gross horsepower H for a single mill then becomes

$$H = (M_t/t_r) W_p \tag{17}$$

where M_t is the tons of product less than size x_t and t_r is the retention time in the mill. Because the number of mills N required to produce J tons of fines per unit of time is equal to $J t_r/M_t$, equation 17 can be written

$$N = \frac{0.8 W_p J}{2.5 \left[\left(\frac{L}{2} - 1 \right) K + 1 \right] \left(\frac{D}{2} \right)^{2.5} \left(\frac{S}{S_c} \right)} \tag{18}$$

when allowance is made for H_n being about $0.8H$. Since J and W_p are presumably fixed by the requirements of the process, the length, diameter, and speed of rotation of the mill are most important in determining N. Available space, future expansion plans, the size of commercially available mills, etc, must also enter into the final selection.

Rate. Size-reduction theories involving rate consider the mass of the particles being crushed, particle size, and the residence time of the particles in the mill as fundamental quantities. The results have been described as being in accord with a zero-order, a first-order, or even a second-order rate law, depending on the grinder and conditions.

For short grinding periods in an impact mill, for example, zero-order behavior should be observed. After a period of grinding, impact-reduction of a given size of particles will follow a first-order law if there has been no interference from product particles. The actual number N of particles that survive breakage must be the product of the number present at the start N_0 and the probable fraction surviving breakage after time t, ie,

$$N = N_0 \exp(-\lambda t) \tag{19}$$

where λ is a decay constant. Taking the average mass of a particle in a given size range as constant, then the ratio N/N_0 is equivalent to the ratio M/M_0, where M is the mass of particles as yet unbroken and M_0 the initial mass. The differential grinding rate is therefore

$$dM/dt = -\lambda M \tag{20}$$

On the other hand, when t is small the survival probability is approximately $(1 - \lambda t)$, and the most probable fraction of the initial feed broken is $1 - (1 - \lambda t)$ or λt. The weight of undersize formed is now expressed by

$$M_0 - M = M_0 \lambda t \tag{21}$$

A number of recent rate theories consider size reduction to be analogous to radioactive decay processes. Parent particles are broken (they decay), producing daughter particles which themselves decay, producing second-generation daughter particles which also decay, and so on. Analyses of data have employed a set of first-order differential equations (43), a finite difference equation in conjunction with digital computer solution (44), an integrodifferential equation (45), and matrix algebra methods also requiring computer solution (46–51). No theory has yet been developed to a point where it is possible to take a given feed size-mass distribution and to calculate the mill size required to give a desired product size-mass distribution at a specified rate of output. Such a goal will be within the realm of possibility, however, when system-characterizing parameters are more completely understood and evaluated and digital computers are utilized fully. When finally realized, the approach may well be to set up an appropriate differential equation representing a size-mass balance along the following lines (52) and then to utilize numerical computation.

If P is the percentage by weight of a charge to a mill that is less than sieve size x, P becomes a function of x and R, the revolutions of grinding, ie, $P = P(x,R)$. The weight percentage w present in a differential size element dx is then

$$w = \left[\frac{\partial P(x,R)}{\partial x} \right] dx \tag{22}$$

and the quantity dw broken in an increment of grinding dr is given by

$$\frac{dw}{dr} = -\left[\frac{\partial^2 P(x,R)}{\partial x \partial r} \right] dx \tag{23}$$

The fractional weight of particles of size x broken out per revolution may be written $S(x)$ and defined as a selection function, ie

$$S(x) = \left(\frac{dw}{dr} \right) \bigg/ w = -\left[\frac{\partial^2 P(x,R)}{\partial x \partial r} \right] \bigg/ \left[\frac{\partial P(x,R)}{\partial x} \right] \tag{24}$$

A distribution function $B(y,x)$ may also be defined as the fractional weight of particles less than size y produced from breakage of size x. As an example, $B(10,500) = 0.02$ means that when particles of 500-μ size are broken, 2% of the mass falls below 10 μ in size. Considering then the breakage of particles in the size range x to $x + dx$, the amount broken in dr revolutions of the mill is dw and, from the definition of $B(y,x)$, the amount of dw falling below y is given by

$$B(y,x)\ dw = \left[\frac{\partial P(x,R)}{\partial x}\right] S(x)\ B(y,x)\ dx\ dr \tag{25}$$

As a first approximation, S and B might be assumed constant with the feed size or the degree of grinding. Then the size-distribution function $P(y,R)$ at a stage of grinding will be the percent of material less than size y originally, plus the percent of material produced from the material larger than y after R revolutions of grinding. $P(y,0)$ is thus the percent of material less than size y originally. The percent of material produced from the material larger than y after R revolutions is the sum of the amounts of equation 25 with respect to R and x, from $x = y$ to $x = x_{max}$. Thus the full differential equation representing a basic law of batch grinding is

$$P(y,R) = P(y,0) + \int_0^R \int_y^{x_{max}} \left[\frac{\partial P(x,R)}{\partial x}\right] S(x)\ B(y,x)\ dx\ dr \tag{26}$$

Experimentally, the terms of equation 26 may be evaluated using radioactive tracer techniques (44,53) or monosize particles for fracture (52). Mathematically, the equation can be adapted to a variety of milling conditions, including closed-circuit grinding with a classifier.

Dimensional Analysis. When the performance of prototype comminution devices needs to be predicted from models, dimensional analysis affords a powerful tool. Most frequently dimensional analysis is used in determining the size of the components of a mill in relation to power input (54) for the purpose of scaling up grinding mills, but the process of grinding as a function of mill parameters has also been studied (55).

Using specific surface area per unit volume A as a measure of the extent of grinding, A may be said for a ball mill, for example, to depend on mill diameter D, ball diameter d, mean particle diameter x, ball density ρ, the charge (slurry) density ρ_c, gravity g, mill speed S, exit port diameter e, energy necessary to change the surface by a unit amount E, grinding time t, fraction of the mill volume occupied by balls and adjacent free spaces J, and the volume occupied by the powder and voids expressed as a fraction of the volume of the charge (slurry) V (55). Since J and V are already dimensionless, they are excluded from consideration according to the Buckingham Pi theorem. There are then eleven variables, and eleven minus three or eight dimensionless groups must be obtainable. Using fundamental units of mass, length, and time in conjunction with experimental data, the significant groups can be arranged into

$$\frac{A}{t} = K\left(\frac{D^{1/2}\rho}{E}\right)\phi_1\left(\frac{d}{D}\right)\phi_2\left(\frac{x}{D}\right)\phi_3\left(\frac{S}{S_c}\right)\phi_4\left(\frac{\rho_c}{\rho}\right)\phi_5\ (J)\phi_6(V)\phi_7\left(\frac{e}{D}\right) \tag{27}$$

where S_c is the critical mill speed and ϕ symbolizes "function of." The constant K has a value of 0.02 $\pm$ 50% for a ball mill.

The dependent variable on the left of equation 27 may be considered as an integral rate of production of surface if the initial surface area was small. Curves based on experimental data must be employed to evaluate the several functional relationships.

Thermodynamics. For the most part, thermodynamic treatments have been applied to comminution systems in attempts to determine how fracture, fracture propagation, input energy, surface energy, and heat are interrelated. Unfortunately, there has been confusion about the precise meaning of surface tension, surface stress, and surface energy in the case of solids, so many results must be viewed with caution.

Basically, thermodynamic analyses have succeeded in showing (*1*) that the work to fracture a particle is dependent on surface energy (56); (*2*) that yield stress is dependent on strain rate, temperature, and the kind of fluid filling particle pores (57); and (*3*) that breakage processes should be more efficient at elevated temperatures (58).

Open- vs Closed-Circuit Operation

As noted above, grinding can be accomplished by the open-circuit procedure or by the closed-circuit method with various degrees of recirculation. The percentage circulating load is defined as the weight of material returned from the separator to the mill divided by the weight of new feed entering the mill, multiplied by 100. A grinding operation usually proceeds most economically when the material of acceptable size is removed and the oversize recirculated, even though a considerable investment in extra equipment is required. Circulating loads up to 500% are sometimes employed. Grinding equipment that will produce, for example, 1000 lb/hr of a product, 98.5% of which passes a 200-mesh sieve, will probably produce 2000 lb/hr or more of a product, 90% of which passes a 200-mesh sieve. If adequate separation is carried out, closed-circuit operation will provide 1800 lb/hr of desired product whereas open-circuit operation will produce only 985 lb/hr. Closed-circuit calculations involve the solution of numerous simultaneous equations and are conveniently made by matrix algebra (51,59) or with the aid of charts (60).

Influence of Conditions

When the material to be ground is received wet, ie, with water associated, it is usually desirable to grind it as a fluid pulp, especially if a finely divided product is required. In wet-grinding, the particles remain dispersed to finer sizes and grinding energy is more efficiently applied. This is evident from lower work indexes, as noted previously. The inclusion of chemical additives promotes grinding in many cases, permitting both more rapid grinding and grinding to smaller particle sizes. Electrolytes and surface-active agents apparently nullify the electrical forces created when bonds are broken and incipient cracks are formed, thereby preventing a rewelding or healing of the cracks. Water vapor, possibly with oxygen, from the atmosphere probably serves the same function in so-called "dry" grinding. Inorganic sulfates, chlorides, and carbonates, oleic acid, and triethanolamine salts of lignosulfonic acids are among the additives used. Salts having a multivalent cation and a complex anion are especially effective with metallic materials (61,62).

Heating a material prior to crushing decreases the crushing energy expenditure when the binding energy of the material decreases with increasing temperature more than plasticity increases. The absolute mechanical efficiency for wet-grinding limestone, quartz, and several ores at temperatures between 32 and 130°F apparently increases about 1% for every 10°F increase, but some of this gain is undoubtedly accounted for by a decrease in fluid viscosity. Heating rock to 1000°C prior to fracture is reported (63) to give both a marked reduction in the crushing energy required and an increase in the uniformity of product size. More importantly, fracture seemed to occur more frequently along intergranular boundaries or in a manner that would suggest more complete separation of valuable mineral components, if the same result were to hold true for an ore. Differences in the expansion coefficients of the various constituents may account for some of this effect. Whether the expense of generating the additional heat and the concomitant structural problems associated with the grinding machine is justified by the increase in comminution rate must be decided by considering the economics of each particular case.

Special Techniques

When difficult-to-grind materials must be reduced to fine particles and also dispersed in a liquid, one method that may be applied is to dry-grind the material admixed with another solid which is soluble in the liquid to be utilized as the dispersant for the desired particles. The extra solid is dissolved and removed by filtering after the grinding has proceeded to the required degree (64,65).

The heat generated in reducing the size of certain materials sometimes raises their temperature beyond tolerable limits. Plastics, for example, are very tough yet have relatively low softening or melting points, while insecticides have heat-sensitive components. Chilling prior to and during grinding in cases such as these is thus often necessary. Mixing with dry ice just before the material enters the grinder is one common solution. The dry ice is ground along with the feed material, but it evaporates rapidly, leaving only the desired product. Storing the material in a cold environment and then piping chilled gas through the crusher along with the feed is also employed. Even liquid nitrogen is occasionally used as a coolant. A word of caution is necessary, however. Cast iron becomes quite brittle at these low temperatures, so for safety stainless steel or another cold-resisting alloy should compose critical grinder components intended for such use.

At the other extreme, it is advantageous to heat certain types of materials during grinding. Carbon-paper ink, certain processed foods, and wax and paraffin products are more easily handled if they can be treated as liquids in which solid particles are suspended to be ground, dispersed, or both. Certain grinders are therefore surrounded by jackets for steam or hot water circulation. Finally, some materials are pyrophoric, easily oxidized, or subject to other characteristic reactions if exposed to ambient air. These situations are handled by introducing the proper inert atmosphere and, perhaps, maintaining it throughout subsequent processing.

Equipment

Each type of comminution equipment operates most satisfactorily on a material having particular size, hardness, toughness, and moisture-content characteristics. Indeed, the equipment was designed with these factors being considered. A pulverizing plant to produce a fine product will generally utilize one or more coarse or primary crushers, intermediate or secondary crushers, and fine grinders. The following sections review the types of equipment commercially available in each of these categories; Table 3 (66) presents the performance characteristics of the major types of equipment in summary form.

Coarse Size Reduction. Coarse-stage size reduction, ie, the crushing of pieces 2–4 in. in diameter and larger and of materials having a Mohs hardness of 4 or more

Table 3. Performance Characteristics of Typical Size Reduction Equipment (66)

Type	Action	Typical feed sizes	Typical product sizes	Capacity range, ton/hr	Power required, hp-hr/ ton	Used extensively for	Not usually used for	Remarks
jaw crushers	compression	6–72 in.	4–11 in.	10–1000	0.3–1	medium and hard rock	soft, sticky materials	gives few fines; reduction ratio 4:1
gyrators large	compression	6–72 in.	1–11 in.	35–3500	0.2–0.7	medium and hard rock	soft, sticky materials	gives few fines; reduction ratio up to 8:1
small	compression and impact	1–10 in.	¼–1½ in.	10–600	0.5–3			
roll crushers smooth	compression	¼–3 in.	¼–⅝ in.	3–150	1–1½	medium and tough, abrasive feeds	large slippery lumps	
toothed	shear, attrition, impact	3–20 in.	2–8 in.	5–1000	0.2–0.5	friable feeds	hard rock	
revolving mills rod	attrition (impact)	½–1 in.	4–28 mesh	3–120	0.5–4	pregrinding abrasive feeds	fine grinding	
ball, pebble, tube, compartment	attrition and impact	30 mesh –1 in.	20–200 mesh	0.5–75	10–20	fine grinding abrasive feeds	soft materials	often used for mixing and blending
hammer mills impactors	impact	10 mesh –10 in.	48 mesh –⅛ in.	0.2–600	0.5–10	abrasive feeds	fine grinding	handles damp feeds
swing	impact and attrition	20 mesh –40 in.	–325 mesh –2 in.	0.05–400	1–200	almost any nonabrasive material	abrasive feeds	coarse to ultrafine reduction
ring roll mills, bowl mills	rolling compression	20 mesh –1 in.	–325– 20 mesh	0.02–20	5–200	soft to fairly hard materials	abrasive feeds	large amount of fines products; mill usually air-swept
attrition mills	attrition	⅜–1 in.	–200– 20 mesh	0.2–5	15–200	soft, fibrous materials	hard, abrasive feeds	
fluid energy mills	impact (attrition)	100 mesh –½ in.	1–30 μ	0.1–10	a	moderately hard, friable feeds	soft, sticky materials	ultrafine reduction

a One to 4 lb of steam or 6–9 lb compressed air per lb of product.

Fig. 7. Jaw crusher.   Courtesy Sturtevant Mill Company.

is usually accomplished with jaw or gyratory crushers. The *jaw crusher*, Figure 7, applies a pressure on the pieces to be crushed through the mechanism of one fixed and one movable plate or jaw. The cast-steel jaws are supported on a frame of the same material and are further protected by an abrasion-resistant liner. Jaw movement is accomplished through an eccentric, pitman, and toggles. Since crushing can occur only as the movable jaw approaches the fixed one, power is supplied intermittently. One or two heavy flywheels are provided to help equalize the power demand.

While the crushing action of a gyratory crusher is similar to that of a jaw crusher, its construction is quite different. In a typical *gyratory crusher*, Figure 8, a heavy crushing member shaped somewhat like a stubby baseball bat is suspended by what would correspond to the grip end of a bat so as to rotate or, as the name would indicate, to gyrate in a horizontal plane inside the confines of a heavy-walled, conical chamber that is larger at the top than in its lower portions. The bottom of the conical chamber is open and the moving crusher partially blocks the opening. As the crushing member (the gyratory head) moves, large pieces of material dumped into the conical chamber at the top are caught and crushed against the chamber's steel walls. The crushed products and other small pieces fall through the space between the crushing member and the outer shell into a discharge chute.

Materials softer than a Mohs hardness of 4, such as ice or coal, are broken with hammer or toothed roll mills. The essential feature of a *hammer mill* is an element rotating at high speed to which a number of rigid (Figure 9) or pivoting (Figure 10) rods, rings, or links are attached; these hammer into the incoming feed, breaking some of it directly and driving some against a stationary breaker plate where further disruption occurs. The outstanding feature of a toothed *roll mill* for coarse crushing is a cylinder, Figure 11, or cylinders, Figure 12, with protruding teeth; the cylinders rotate in a horizontal plane. A single roll mill having spiked teeth crushes with the aid of a breaker plate by pressing its teeth into the larger feed lumps and causing disintegration,

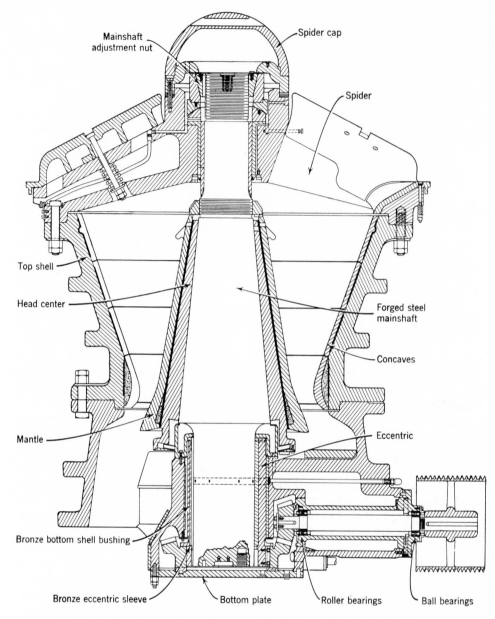

Fig. 8. Gyratory crusher.   Courtesy Allis-Chalmers Manufacturing Co.

somewhat in the manner of ice broken manually with an ice pick.   Relatively little
fine material is produced by this method of breaking.

Intermediate Size Reduction.   Crushing in the range from a very few inches to
fractions of an inch in diameter is intermediate size reduction.   The most widely used
and, indeed, the standard for this size range is the *cone crusher*, Figure 13.   In several
respects it is the reverse of a gyratory crusher.   In the cone crusher, the moving member is generally a conical or umbrella-shaped piece mounted with its apex upward and
with heavy bearings at its base.   The stationary grinding surface is in the form of a

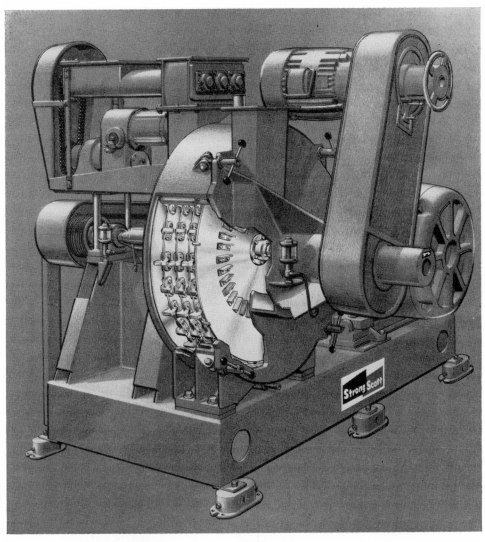

Fig. 9. Rigid hammer mill.   Courtesy Strong-Scott Manufacturing Co.

hollow section of a cone somewhat larger and with a lesser flare than the moving member and mounted in an inverted position over the moving member. By means of an eccentric journal the inner core is sometimes made to rotate on a short radius within the outer cone. Thus the distance between any two points opposite each other on the two crushing surfaces increases and decreases during each revolution. When the distance increases, pieces fall into the channel between the surfaces. They are crushed as the separation narrows again. During the opening cycle the crushed pieces fall clear of the crushing surfaces while other larger pieces fall in, so that the process can be repeated. Pieces discharged can never be larger than the greatest separation between the two crushing surfaces, hence this distance is made adjustable, within limits, by a mechanism which raises or lowers the stationary crushing cone.

Roll mills for intermediate-range reduction consist of two heavy cylinders, Figure 14, mounted in juxtaposition and made to rotate so that their upper surfaces move

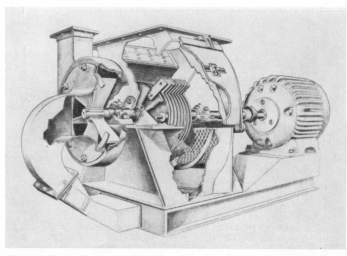

Fig. 10. Swing hammer mill.   Courtesy Sprout, Waldron & Co., Inc.

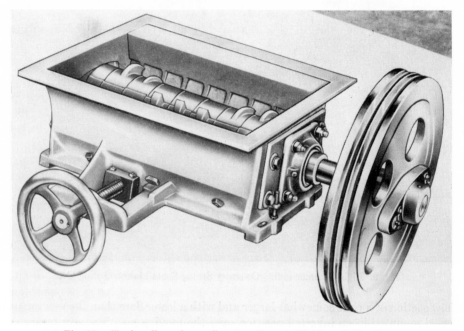

Fig. 11.   Single-roll crusher.   Courtesy Sprout, Waldron & Co., Inc.

toward each other.   Feed material is caught, or nipped, and pulled between the rolls where it is crushed.   Both the roll diameters and the separation between them can be varied, permitting considerable flexibility in operation.   The reduction that can be accomplished in one pass is, however, comparatively small; average product diameters are rarely less than about one-quarter of feed diameters.   Greater reduction ratios are obtained by employing multiroll mills (Fig. 15).

Fine Size Reduction.   Among the first mills producing a moderately fine powder were those for grinding wheat and corn into flour and meal.   These generally consisted of a block which rubbed against another stationary block;   both blocks were usually

Fig. 12. Double-shaft sawtooth crusher. Courtesy The Bauer Bros. Co.

Fig. 13. Cone crusher. Courtesy Sturtevant Mill Company.

Fig. 14. Paired-roll crusher.   Courtesy Sturtevant Mill Company.

Fig. 15. Three-pair roll crusher.   Courtesy Sprout, Waldron & Co., Inc.

Fig. 16. Attrition mill. Courtesy The Bauer Bros. Co.

stone. Size reduction resulted largely from the application of shearing forces. Modern mills that utilize shearing forces predominantly are generally called *attrition mills* (Fig. 16). They basically consist of one hardened plate which rotates at a relatively high speed in close proximity to a similar stationary plate. The space between the plates is adjustable to permit alteration of the product size as well as adjustment for wear.

Where large outputs are required, these frictional or shear-type mills have been superseded by *roller mills*, also called *bowl mills*. The crushing mechanism in the latter is a combination of compression, shear, and impact. Fracture is accomplished in roller mills as particles pass between rollers or heavy balls and a crushing ring (Figs. 17 and 18). The crushing ring forms a part of the vertical wall of a pan or bowl into which the material to be ground is fed. Either the rollers or the bowl may be rotated. If the bowl is driven, the rollers are pulled against the crushing ring by powerful springs. In designs making use of a stationary bowl, the rollers are mounted on a spider attached to a main shaft so that centrifugal force presses the rollers against the ring during operation. Roller mills are commonly fitted with sizing devices, such as screens or steady streams of air, which allow particles to escape only when a predetermined particle size has been attained.

A preponderance of fine powder is produced by means of *ball, tube, or rod mills*, collectively described as tumbling mills. These mills (Figs. 19–21), are composed of a cylindrical, conical, or spheroidal shell that rotates about an axis (generally horizontal) while partly filled with steel or porcelain balls, flint pebbles, or, in the case of the rod mill, steel rods. The latter serve as the grinding media by impacting with and rolling over the feed material as both media and feed tumble down after being lifted up the rotating chamber wall. Small mills may be operated batchwise; most larger mills are designed to run continuously. The feed usually enters through a hollow supporting shaft, or trunnion, at one end and discharges through another trunnion or through a

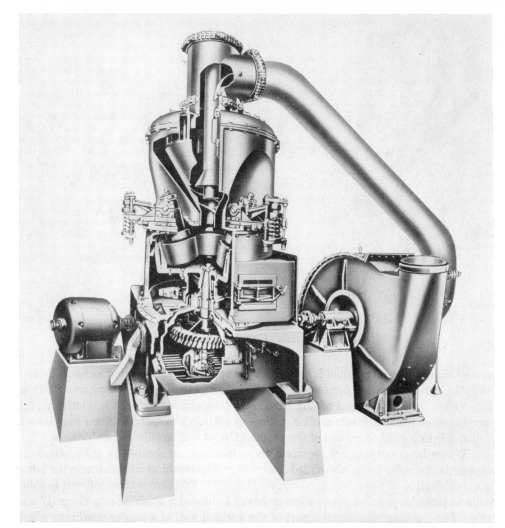

Fig. 17. Bowl mill.   Courtesy Raymond Div., Combustion Engineering Co.

grate—a metal plate with holes or slots too small for balls to pass—at the other end.   A few mills are supported by means of peripheral steel tires that ride on metal rollers. Product discharge in this case is through a grate and the open end of the mill.   Simple ball mills (Fig. 19) are about as large in diameter as they are long; they are usually constructed with alloy steel liners that may be replaced when wear becomes excessive.

As a general rule, the most effective size reduction is accomplished when the balls or pebbles are just large enough to break the largest particles they encounter.   Since particle size decreases as the feed progresses through the mill, two systems may be employed to maintain a more acceptable ball-to-particle size ratio.   One, the *compound mill* (Fig. 20), consists of two to four compartments separated by grates.   The compartments in the direction of particle progression may or may not decrease in diameter, but they are charged with smaller and smaller balls to make for maximum efficiency as finer particles are produced.   In effect, a compartmented mill is a series of mills operated as one unit.   The second system may be described as a cylindroconical

Fig. 18. Roller mill.   Courtesy Williams Patent Crusher and Pulverizer Co., Inc.

mill, ie, one having a cylindrical shell portion at the feed end followed by a section that tapers from the cylinder to the trunnion of the discharge end somewhat like the left-hand compartment of Figure 20.   Balls in a variety of sizes make up the grinding media.   Under ideal conditions, the larger balls segregate in the larger diameter, or cylindrical, portion of the mill where the coarse feed enters, while balls of lesser size congregate toward the discharge, or lesser diameter, end where the finer product is encountered.   Table 4 (66) gives the capacity and power requirements of ball mills.

A *tube mill* differs from a ball mill primarily in that its body is longer in proportion to its diameter; in some cases the ratio of length to diameter is as large as 10:1.   Although both tube and ball mills utilize spherical grinding bodies, the tube mill is often lined with ceramic sections and charged with flint pebbles; it is used primarily in those cases where iron cannot be tolerated in the product, as for example in face powder.   A rod mill (Fig. 21) is even more different in that the grinding media are steel rods and not balls.   Here both mill and rod lengths are always greater than the mill diameter to ensure that the rods will lie in the mill parallel to the axis of rotation.   Because the main impact of the rods is most likely to be received by the largest piece finding its way between two rods, the smaller pieces are protected, with the result that a rod mill produces a more closely sized product than do ball or tube mills.   Rod mills are more

Table 4. Capacity and Power Requirements of Mills (66)

Size (diam × length), ft	Approx ball load, lb	Approx rpm	Approx av capacity, ton/24 hr			Motor hp
			½ in. to 48 mesh	¼ in. to 65 mesh	¼ in. to 100 mesh	
Ball mills						
3 × 2	1,000	35	12	9	5	6–8
3 × 4	2,000	35	24	18	10	12–15
4 × 4	3,300	30	42	30	20	20–25
5 × 4	5,000	29	80	55	30	30–40
5 × 6	7,500	29	120	85	50	40–50
6 × 3	6,000	25	125	85	50	50–60
6 × 5	10,000	25	210	150	90	75–100
6 × 6	12,000	25	250	175	100	90–120
6 × 12	24,000	25	500	340	200	150–200
7 × 6	21,000	23	500	350	200	110–160
8 × 6	28,000	22	620	450	260	150–225
10 × 9	74,000	17	1,500	1,100	650	550–600
Cylindroconical mills						
2 × ⅔	600	40	4	3	2	2
3 × ⅔	1,100	35	12	10	9	5–8
3 × 2	2,000	35	17	15	13	10
5 × 3	9,500	28	100	80	60	40–50
6 × 3	15,000	24	180	120	90	60–75
7 × 4	27,000	23	300	220	150	125
8 × 4	38,000	21	480	350	270	175–200
12 × 6	110,000	16	1,800	1,400	1,000	700–800

Fig. 19. Ball mill.   Courtesy Allis-Chalmers Manufacturing Co.

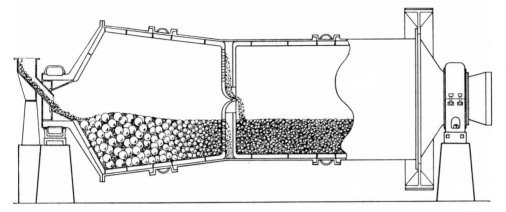

Fig. 20. Cone and compartmental ball mill. Courtesy Hardinge Co., Metal Products Div., Koppers Co., Inc.

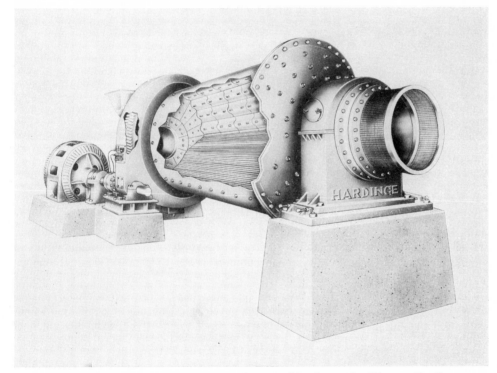

Fig. 21. Rod mill. Courtesy Hardinge Co., Metal Products Div., Koppers Co., Inc.

costly to operate than other tumbling mills; they are used when a smaller proportion of fines is desired in the product and when attaining this condition justifies the extra cost.

All minerals, rocks, ores, and brittle solids will grind themselves when tumbled without balls or rods being present; this is called autogenous grinding (67). Since the grinding rate has a strong dependence on the solids density, production is generally not as great under this situation as when heavy balls or other media are included. An *autogenous grinder*, sometimes called a *cascade mill*, is shown in Figure 22.

Fig. 22. Autogenous (cascade) crusher. Courtesy Hardinge Co., Metal Products Div.,
Koppers Co., Inc.

Ball, tube, and rod mill capacity is directly proportional to the speed of rotation.
The energy required to produce a unit quantity of product remains reasonably constant from about 55 to 90% of the critical speed, the speed at which particles and balls
are held by centrifugal force against the walls of the mill and do not fall, tumble, or
slide. At the critical speed, therefore, no grinding occurs. The mill is said to be centrifuging and must necessarily be operated at a lower rate of revolution. For a small
particle to ride against the wall without slipping, geometric and dynamical considerations show that the critical speed S_c in revolutions per minute is given by $76.6/D$,
where D is the mill diameter measured in feet. Since the center of mass of the balls or
rods composing the grinding charge is somewhat less than the total mill diameter,
critical speed is customarily defined as

$$S_c = \frac{76.6}{D - d} \tag{28}$$

where d is the ball or rod diameter, also measured in feet. When the grinding charge
shows no appreciable cohesion, as for a very dry or a thoroughly wet pulp, highest ball
mill capacity is usually obtained just below the critical speed, perhaps at 0.80 to 0.90
S_c. The greatest energy absorption by a mill occurs (68) at about $0.84S_c$. Under
these conditions some of the balls are cataracting, ie, they are being thrown into the air
from the portion of the charge that is riding highest up the mill wall with just enough
energy to land on the toe, or lower portion, of the charge where the largest and toughest

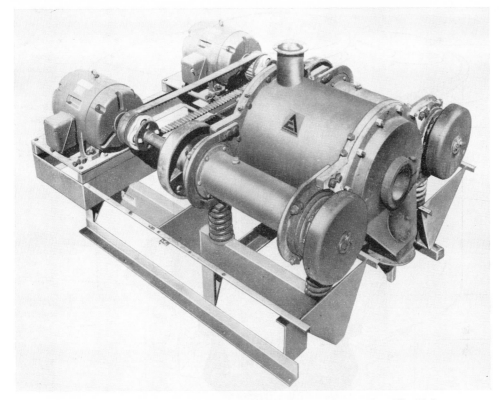

Fig. 23. Vibrating mill. Courtesy Process Equipment & Systems Div., Allis-Chalmers Manufacturing Co.

pieces are usually found. For grinding wet feeds that have no large pieces, highest efficiency (69,70) is obtained at a somewhat slower speed, and without cataracting. Apparently fine grinding can be accomplished efficiently in a noncataracting (NC) ball mill because the rolling-sliding interaction between balls is sufficiently energetic to break any particle; the quiescent character of the charge permits the finer particles to come to the top for discharge and the heavier ones to settle for maximum grinding. Partially wet feeds and those that for other reasons show a tendency to adhere to the mill shell or to the balls must be operated at still slower rates of rotation, perhaps 0.65 S_c, to prevent the feeds from being carried around with the mill. Rod mills normally run at about 85% of the speed of a ball mill of the same diameter. Metal liners and grinding media both wear more per unit mass of product as speed increases. For this reason it may be cheaper to install a mill somewhat larger than required and run it at a slower speed.

Where space is at a premium, a *vibrating ball mill* is conveniently employed. In terms of energy expended, these mills are generally less efficient, at least down to product particle diameters of some $50\,\mu$; for smaller particles they become increasingly efficient. Vibrating ball mills require more frequent maintenance than other types of mills, however, in all product size ranges. Vibrating mills will often grind to finer sizes than other mills, eg, ball mills (71).

One vibrating mill, shown in Figure 23, consists of a spring-mounted grinding chamber which is given vigorous, high-speed vibration by an eccentric mechanism.

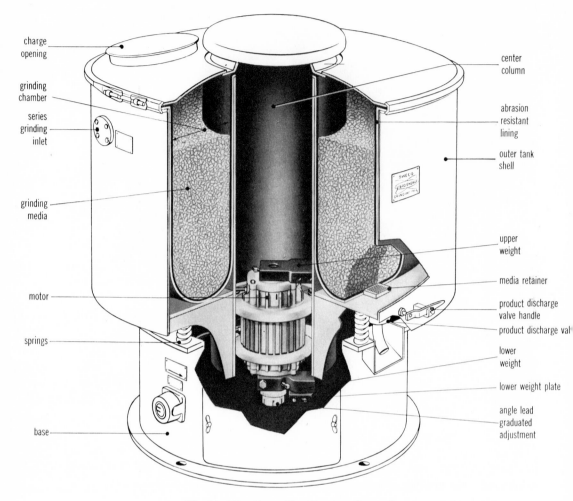

charge opening

grinding chamber

series grinding inlet

grinding media

motor

springs

base

center column

abrasion resistant lining

outer tank shell

upper weight

media retainer

product discharge valve handle

product discharge val

lower weight

lower weight plate

angle lead graduated adjustment

Fig. 24. Vibrating mill.   Courtesy Sweco, Inc.

The chamber is partially filled with balls or rods which strike the walls and each other, producing size reduction in the feed material as it comes within the impact zone.   All parts subject to wear are replaceable.   In another type of machine, pictured in Figure 24, the grinding chamber, shaped like an annulus, is mounted on springs with its axis vertical.   An electric motor eccentrically weighted at either end is attached to the chamber.   The actual movement of the chamber that results when the motor is energized is a vertical planetary gyration superimposed upon a horizontal planetary gyration.   As a result, the particles of the grinding media impact rapidly with one another, while rotating slowly.   The rotation provides a small amount of shear force, which is useful for dispersing agglomerates in some materials.

Most solids behave like brittle materials if struck at a sufficiently high speed. High-velocity impacts thus are the basis for a large class of mills, called *impact mills*. Perhaps the most familiar is the rotary hammer mill, which was described in a previous section dealing with coarse size reduction.   The mill is quite similar when employed as a fine grinder except that higher speeds are utilized and the airstream produced by the

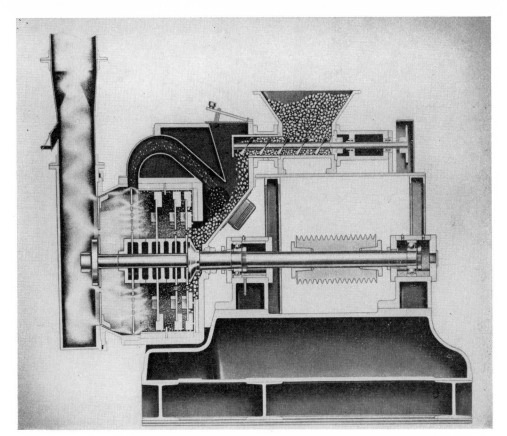

Fig. 25. Air-swept pulverizer.   Courtesy Schutz-O'Neill Company.

rotating beaters is now employed to effect the removal of the pulverized product by deflecting it toward the delivery end of the mill. A unit can, in addition, be air-swept for product removal.

In the air-swept pulverizer, shown in Figure 25, precrushed dry or semidry solids enter the mill from an adjustable feeder device together with a controlled volume of air via the air inlet (A). Drawn into the mill chamber, the solids encounter a series of discs rotating at peripheral velocities up to 25,000 ft/min on a dynamically-balanced rotor. Forward discs have perimeter beaters rigidly affixed for precision clearance of the corrugated or perforated chamber liners. Rear classifier discs have openings near rims serving as discharge ports for the fines-bearing airstream. On entering the chamber, the solids are thrown centrifugally to the disc perimeters and impacted and sheared between the beaters (B) and liner (C), producing both coarse and fine particles progressively from one beater disc to the next. Turbine action within the mill alternately compresses and expands the air between the discs, producing a turbulence which, with centrifugal force, ensures maximum contact of the material with the beaters plus simultaneous attritional reduction by frictional collision of material in the turbulent air.

Heavier coarse particles are held in grinding contact longest, while fines are swept forward on the airstream. At the primary classifier plate (D), finer particles pass while oversize particles are deflected on the recirculatory positive airstream into the tailings

Fig. 26. Cage mill (counterrotating).   Courtesy Stedman Foundry & Machine Co., Inc.

recycle housing (E).   Fines passing primary classification are again classified at the final classifier plate (F), where conical tapering of the housing and whizzer blades on the disc give the final sharp cut-point, oversize particles being recycled through (E) while fines of desired size are swept into the discharge housing (G) and onward to the collecting equipment.

The adjustable secondary air inlet (H) maintains air velocity balance within the mill.   The plate magnet (I) removes tramp iron from the feed.   The resilient vibration dampener (J) mounted on the mill base is cemented to the plant floor to isolate vibration, already minimal by dynamic balancing of the rotor and the heavy cast mill base. Material enters through a screw-type feeder (rotary and vibratory feeders are also available).

A variant of this type of grinder is the *cage mill*, Figure 26, which has rotors which turn in opposite directions concentrically within one another.   When feed is admitted into the central region it is thrown outward by the rotation and subjected to a beating action by the bars mounted on the rings of the rotors.

In all versions of impact mills feed material is accelerated to a high velocity by a rapidly spinning rotor and ejected against a target.   A particle thus has as its grinding force only its kinetic energy at the moment of impact.   If the gap between rotor and

Sand-Mill Operation

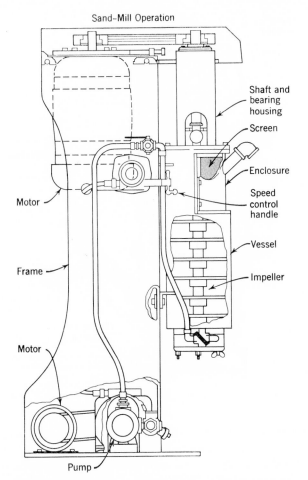

Fig. 27. Sand grinder. Courtesy Morehouse-Cowles, Inc.

target is wide enough for the largest piece to be completely suspended at some point in its traverse, attritional and frictional forces will be negligible. The capacity of a true impact mill thus varies almost exactly as the inverse square of the rotor peripheral velocity.

Impact mills operate with a minimum of product heating. If, however, heating effects are critical, passing air through the mill can hold temperatures to quite low levels. Because the chief difficulty in operating impact mills has always been wear, present mills are not recommended for use with hard and abrasive materials. In mills such as these, which use rapidly rotating parts, wear is especially critical because stresses are ordinarily high and a little weakening can lead to failure. Present mills use carbide coatings and roll forgings to give a maximum of strength and wear resistance. Because inertial forces vary with mass as the inverse cube of diameter, when velocity is constant small particles impact with much less kinetic energy than large ones. The chance of particles below a certain size shattering decreases rapidly, causing impact mills to produce a rather sharp size distribution with a minimum of fines. Breaking by impact, particularly at a high velocity, tends to produce particles which are more nearly cubical than those obtained from most other methods (72).

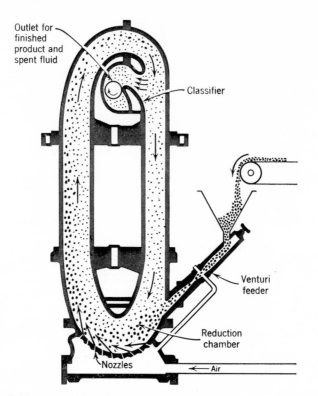

Fig. 28. Fluid energy mill.   Courtesy Fluid Energy Processing & Equipment Co.

The *sand grinder* mill, which is radically different from any other yet described, uses 20- to 30-mesh Ottawa sand particles as the grinding media.   The primary use of the mill is in grinding and dispersing a variety of pigments for inks, paints, and fillers (73).   Basically, the sand grinder (74) consists of a motor-driven spindle, on which are arranged a number of flat discs mounted, usually vertically, inside a cylindrical chamber (Fig. 27).   The chamber contains the sand.   The particles to be ground enter in a slurry at the top of the chamber and pass out at the bottom through a screen of size opening just sufficient to prevent the sand from being discharged.   Instead of depending on tumbling to produce disruptive forces, the rotating discs create circulating patterns within the mixture of sand, vehicle, and solid particles.   A small particle caught between two relatively large sand particles moving at different velocities is subject to considerable compressive and shearing forces.

Under proper conditions of operation, disc and sand wear is almost negligible. After a few hours, new sand is polished free of surface irregularities and there is no appreciable change after months of use.   Likewise, discs, the only other parts subject to wear, have been found to have long life if harder than 40 Rockwell C.   The proper ratio is approximately one volume of sand to one of slurry or pulp.   Smaller amounts result in gaps between the sand particles which are too large for grinding to occur efficiently, while greater amounts give a more rigid sand structure that stifles attrition. The most common operating temperature is between 120 and 150°F, this being the temperature at which a mill stabilizes with a moderate flow of water in a jacket surrounding the mill's grinding chamber.

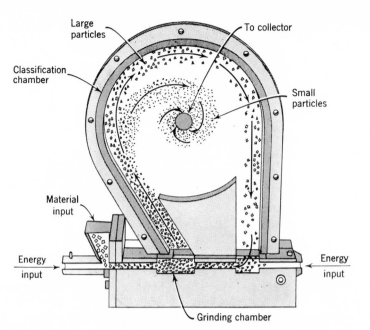

Fig. 29. Fluid energy mill. Courtesy Trost Jet Mill Div., Helme Products, Inc.

Limitations in mechanical mills as previously described become evident when a powder finer than one for which 95% will pass a 325-mesh sieve (44-μ openings) is desired. The underlying principle of all *fluid energy mills* is that particles are caused to collide with sufficient force for one or more of them to be broken into smaller bodies (Fig. 28). Such collisions are produced by exposing the material to be pulverized to a high-velocity fluid stream within the mill. The fluid, usually air or steam (in the case of heat-insensitive powders) under pressure, is introduced through nozzles designed to convert as much as possible of the fluid pressure energy into kinetic energy. Particles, upon being swept into the resulting violent turbulence, beat against one another and are pulverized. If the particles are not broken immediately they circulate around within the mill until their size is reduced to the desired limit.

The entraining of materials in a fluid jet to be blasted against a wall or anvil situated in the path of the jet, although often tried, has never been commercially successful because of nozzle and anvil wear. The problem is largely overcome by utilizing two opposed straight channels, permitting the particles to undergo protracted acceleration and then to suffer direct collisions (Fig. 29). Unbroken particles are recirculated.

Because fluid energy mills require considerable energy for their operation, it is often most economical to grind as fine as possible with conventional mills and then feed the product to a fluid energy mill for final pulverizing. In no case should the feed be larger than minus 4 mesh. Table 5 (66) presents a general guide to fluid energy mill sizes and energy requirements.

True colloids are not obtained until dispersions at least on the order of 0.1-μ diameter are reached, but a mill capable of reducing solids in a liquid phase to 1-μ diameter and less and of emulsifying and homogenizing fluids is called a *colloid mill* (Fig. 30). Two types, a smooth-surface and a rough-surface mill, are representative.

Table 5. Size and Grinding Energy Requirements of the Fluid Energy Mill (66)

Mill size, in.	Air operation,[a] ft³/min	Steam operation,[b] lb/hr
2	20	
4	40	
8	100	250
12	225	600
15	350	900
20	550	1500
24	1000	2600
30	1500	4000

[a] Volume of free air at 60°F and 14.7 psi.   Compressed to 100 psi.

[b] Steam supplied at 150 psi and 550°F.

Smooth-surface mills depend upon hydraulic shearing forces for their action; they consist of a smooth moving surface that passes a fixed or counterrotating smooth surface at a high velocity. Separation between the surfaces may be as small as 0.001 in. Great stresses are thus developed in any fluid film between the surfaces and these disrupt solid particles or another fluid phase suspended therein. The working surfaces may be either a truncated cone rotating within a fixed cone or flat plates. Usually the rotating member is allowed to act as a centrifugal pump, drawing the material through the mill continuously and with great force. The rough-surface mill differs only in that

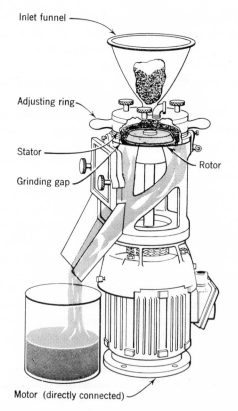

Fig. 30. Colloid mill.   Courtesy Premier Mill Corporation.

Table 6. U.S. Comminution Equipment Manufacturers, by Type (76)

Manufacturer	Type of equipment
Abbé Engineering Co., New York, N.Y.	a, k, l, v
Paul O. Abbe, Inc., Little Falls, N.J.	k, l
Allis-Chalmers Mfg. Co., Milwaukee, Wis.	a, b, e, f, j, k, l, m, p, r, v
Alpine American Corp., Saxonville, Mass.	g, i
American Pulverizer Co., St. Louis, Mo.	f, j, r
Babcock & Wilcox Co., New York, N.Y.	k
Bacon, Greene & Milroy, New Haven, Conn.	a, e
Ball & Jewell, Inc., Brooklyn, N.Y.	g
Bartlett & Snow Co., Cleveland, Ohio	d, e
Bauer Brothers Co., Springfield, Ohio	d, e, f, i, j, r, t
Bird Machine Co., South Walpole, Mass.	w
Bonnet Co., Canton, Ohio	c
Bradley Pulverizer Co., Allentown, Pa.	p
Braun Corp., Los Angeles, Calif.	a, i
Buffalo Hammermill Co., Buffalo, N.Y.	f, j, r
Jabez Burns & Sons, Inc., New York, N.Y.	d, e, i, n
Chemicolloid Laboratories, Garden City Park, N.Y.	s
Clearfield Machine Co., Clearfield, Pa.	a, c
Cog Corp., Chicago, Ill.	j, r
Crossley Machine Co., Trenton, N.J.	k
J. H. Day Co., Cincinnati, Ohio	d, e, m
Denver Equipment Co., Denver, Colo.	a, e, k
J. P. Devine Manufacturing Co., Pittsburgh, Pa.	k, m
Dorr-Oliver, Inc., Stamford, Conn.	h
Farrell-Birmingham Co., Ansonia, Conn.	l, m
W. J. Fitzpatrick Co., Chicago, Ill.	a, e, k
Fluid Energy Processing & Equipment Co., Philadelphia, Pa.	u
Foster Wheeler Co., New York, N.Y.	k, l
Ralph W. Fry, Easton, Pa.	d, e, i, j
Gifford Wood Co., Hudson, N.Y.	d, s
Gruendler Crusher & Pulverizer Co., St. Louis, Mo.	a, d, e, f, g, j, n, r
B. G. Gump Co., Chicago, Ill.	e, k, l, n
Hardinge Co., York, Pa.	k, l, n
Hutchison Manufacturing Co., Houston, Tex.	u
Jacobson Machine Works, Minneapolis, Minn.	f, j
Jeffrey Manufacturing Co., Columbus, Ohio	d, e, f, j
Jet Pulverizer Co., Palmyra, N.J.	u
Kennedy Van Saun Manufacturing & Engineering Co., Danville, Pa.	a, b, k, l
J. M. Lehmann Co., Lyndhurst, N.J.	m
Link Belt Co., Chicago, Ill.	d, e
Majac, Inc., Pittsburgh, Pa.	u, w
Manton Gaulin Co., Everett, Mass.	s
Mead Mill Co., Detroit, Mich.	i
Franklin P. Miller & Son, East Orange, N.J.	d, e, f, i, j, o, r
Mine Smelter & Supply Co., Denver, Colo.	k, l
Morehouse Industries, Los Angeles, Calif.	s
Mueller Machine Co., Trenton, N.J.	k
Munson Mill Machinery Co., Utica, N.Y.	i, j, o, r
National Engineering Corp., Chicago, Ill.	c
New England Road Machinery Co., Boston, Mass.	a
New Holland Machine Co., New Holland, Pa.	d, e, f, j

(continued)

Table 6 (*continued*)

Manufacturer	Type of equipment
Nordberg Manufacturing Co., Milwaukee, Wis.	b, k, l
Pallmann Pulverizer Co., Hoboken, N.J.	i
Patterson Foundry & Machine Co., East Liverpool, Ohio	k, l
Pennsylvania Crusher Co., West Chester, Pa.	a, b, d, e, f, j
Posey Iron Works, Lancaster, Pa.	a, c
Prater Pulverizer Co., Chicago, Ill.	d, e, f, j, r
Premier Mill Co., New York, N.Y.	s
Pulva Corp., Perth Amboy, N.J.	j, r
Pulverizing Machinery Co., Summit, N.J.	r, t
Raymond Pulverizer Div., Combustion Engineering Corp., Chicago, Ill.	g, n, p, q, r, t
Reduction Engineering Corp., Newark, N.J.	u
Rietz Manufacturing Co., Santa Rosa, Calif.	d, j
Charles Ross & Son Co., Brooklyn, N.Y.	i, p, t
Safety Industries, Entoleter Div., New Haven, Conn.	j
Schutz-O'Neill Co., Minneapolis, Minn.	e, j, k, t
J. B. Sedberry Co., Tyler, Tex.	f, j, r
Sharples Corp., Philadelphia, Pa.	w
F. L. Smidth & Co., New York, N.Y.	k, l
Smith Engineering Works, Milwaukee, Wis.	a, b, e, f
Sonic Engineering Co., Norwalk, Conn.	s
Southwestern Engineering Corp., Los Angeles, Calif.	k, v
Sprout, Waldron & Co., Muncy, Pa.	d, e, f, i, j
Stedman Foundry & Machine Co., Aurora, Ind.	f, g, j
F. J. Stokes Co., Philadelphia, Pa.	j, r
Straub Manufacturing Co., Oakland, Calif.	a, b, k, l
Strong-Scott Manufacturing Co., Minneapolis, Minn.	t
Sturtevant Mill Co., Boston, Mass.	a, e, f, h, j, n, o, r, t, u
Traylor Engineering & Manufacturing Div., General American Transportation Corp., Allentown, Pa.	a, b, e, k, l
Tri Homo Corp., Salem, Mass.	o, s
Trost Jet Mill Co., Moorestown, N.J.	u
U.S. Stoneware Co., Akron, Ohio	k
Universal Engineering Corp., Cedar Rapids, Iowa	a
Universal Road Machinery Co., Kingston, N.Y.	a
Urshel Laboratories, Valparaiso, Ind.	h
Williams Patent Crusher & Pulverizer Co., St. Louis, Mo.	a, f, j, p
Young Machinery Co., Muncy, Pa.	f, i, j

LEGEND

a. jaw
b. gyratory and cone
c. edge runners, dry pans, and chaser mills
d. roll crushers, single roll
e. roll crushers, double rolls
f. hammer mills, heavy duty
g. cage disintegrators
h. rotary crushers
i. disc mills
j. hammer mills
k. ball, pebble, and rod mills

l. continuous tube, compartment, and conical mills
m. roll flakers
n. ring-roll mills
o. buhrstone mills
p. low- and high-side roller mills
q. bowl mills
r. hammer mills (fine grinding)
s. colloid mills
t. pulverizers
u. fluid energy mills
v. vibrating mills

shallow grooves or corrugations add intense eddy currents, turbulence, and impaction of particles on hardened surfaces to the hydraulic shearing action. Many colloid mills are supplied with a jacket to permit either heating or cooling.

For dry-grinding fine chemicals and delicate biological materials in the 1–10-μ-diameter range, a smooth-surface, high-speed mill has been tested (75). Essentially like a colloid mill, except that particles are ground in a gaseous medium, the mill utilizes a rotor 6 in. in diameter encased in a smooth-surfaced housing with 0.015 in. clearance between the rotor periphery and the housing. Feed in the form of an air- or gas-borne dust is delivered to the mill at the rate of about $1\frac{1}{2}$ ft^3/min. The device is driven by an electric motor of about 5 hp, and grinding surface speeds up to 65,000 ft/min were attained. The housing is jacketed for circulating a cooling fluid.

Table 6 presents a listing of U.S. manufacturers and the type of equipment each produces.

Bibliography

"Size Reduction" in *ECT* 1st ed., Vol. 12, pp. 498–520, by L. T. Work, Consulting Engineer.

1. E. L. Piret, "Fundamental Aspects of Grinding," *Chem. Eng. Prog.* **49,** 56–63 (1953).
2. A. A. Griffith, "The Phenomena of Rupture and Flow in Solids," *Phil. Trans. Roy. Soc. London, Ser. A* **221,** 163–198 (1921).
3. A. Turner, Jr., *Mechanical Behavior of High Polymers,* Interscience Publishers, New York, 1948.
4. H. E. Galanty, "The Size Reduction Paradox," *Ind. Eng. Chem.* **55,** 46–52 (1963).
5. H. T. Corten and F. R. Park, "Fracture," *Intern. Sci. Technol.* 24–36 (March 1963).
6. C. Orr, Jr., *Particulate Technology,* The Macmillan Co., New York, 1966, p. 47.
7. R. W. Bown, "Energy Distribution of Pulverizing," *Trans. Inst. Mining Met., Sect. C* **75,** C173–178 (1966).
8. D. D. Crabtree, R. S. Kinasevich, A. L. Mular, T. P. Meloy, and D. W. Fuerstenau, "Mechanisms of Size Reduction in Comminution Systems. Part I. Impact, Abrasion, and Chipping Grinding," *Trans. AIME* **229,** 201–206 (1964).
9. D. D. Crabtree, R. S. Kinasevich, A. L. Mular, T. P. Meloy, and D. W. Fuerstenau, "Mechanisms of Size Reduction in Comminution Systems. Part II. Interpreting Size Distribution Curves and the Comminution Event Hypothesis," *Trans. AIME* **229,** 207–210 (1964).
10. A. L. Mular, "Comminution in Tumbling Mills," *Can. Met. Quart.* **4,** 31–74 (1965).
11. J. J. Gilvarry, "Fracture of Brittle Solids. I. Distribution Function for Fragment Size in Single Fracture (Theoretical)," *J. Appl. Phys.* **32,** 391–399 (1961).
12. J. J. Gilvarry and B. H. Bergstrom, "Fracture of Brittle Solids. II. Distribution Function for Fragment Size in Single Fracture (Experimental)," *J. Appl. Phys.* **32,** 400–410 (1961).
13. J. G. Bennett, "Broken Coal," *J. Inst. Fuel* **10,** 22–39 (1936).
14. A. M. Gaudin and T. P. Meloy, "Model and a Comminution Distribution Equation for Single Fracture," *Trans. Soc. Mining Engrs. AIME* **223,** 41–43 (1962).
15. T. P. Meloy, "A Three Dimensional Derivation of the Gaudin Size Distribution Equation," *Trans. AIME* **226,** 447–448 (1963).
16. R. J. Charles, "Energy-Size Reduction Relationships in Comminution," *Trans. AIME* **208,** 80–88 (1957).
17. R. J. Charles and P. L. de Bruyn, "Energy Transfer by Impact," *Mining Eng.* **8,** 47–53 (1956).
18. R. Schuhmann, Jr., "Principles of Comminution, II. Size Distribution and Surface Calculations," *Mining Technol.* **4,** Tech. Publ. No. 1189 (1940).
19. J. Kelleher, "Comminution Theory and Practice," *Brit. Chem. Eng.* **4,** 472 (1959).
20. C. Orr, Jr., and J. M. DallaValle, *Fine Particle Measurement,* The Macmillan Co., New York, 1959.
21. R. D. Cadle, *Particle Size,* Reinhold Publishing Corp., New York, 1965.
22. *Particle Size Measurement,* Spec. Tech. Publ. No. 234, American Society of Testing Materials, Philadelphia, 1958.

23. P. Rosin and E. Rammler, "The Laws Governing the Fineness of Powdered Coal," *J. Inst. Fuel* **7**, 29–36 (1933).

24. T. Hatch and S. P. Choate, "Statistical Description of the Size Properties of Non-Uniform Particulate Substances," *J. Franklin Inst.* **207**, 369–387 (1929).

25. J. M. DallaValle, *Micromeritics: The Technology of Fine Particles*, Pitman Publishing Co., New York, 1948.

26. G. Herdan, *Small Particle Statistics*, Academic Press, New York, 1960.

27. R. Irani and C. Callis, *Particle Size: Measurement, Interpretation, and Application*, John Wiley & Sons, Inc., New York, 1963.

28. P. R. vonRittinger, *Lehrbuch der Aufbereitungskunde*, Berlin (1867).

29. F. Kick, *Das Gesetz der proportionalen Widerstände und seine Anwendung*, Leipzig (1885).

30. F. C. Bond, "The Third Theory of Comminution," *Mining Eng.* **4**, 484–494 (1952).

31. F. C. Bond, "Standard Grindability Tests Tabulated," *Trans. AIME* **183**, 313–329 (1949).

32. F. C. Bond, *Crushing and Grinding Calculations*, Allis-Chalmers Manufacturing Co., Milwaukee, Wisconsin, 1961, pp. 13, 14.

33. J. A. Holmes, "A Contribution to the Study of Comminution in a Modified Form of Kick's Law," *Trans. Inst. Chem. Engrs. (London)* **35**, 125–140 (1957).

34. G. C. Harris, "Comminution: A Modified Logistic Growth Function," *Nature* **197**, 371 (1963).

35. A. H. M. Andreason, "Zur Kenntnis des Zerkleinerungsvorganges," *Kolloid-Z.* **78**, 148–156 (1937).

36. I. Evans, "The Breakage of Bulk Solids: A Rational Index and Its Practical Use," *Trans. Inst. Chem. Engrs. (London)* **40**, 309–314 (1962).

37. J. Kelleher, "Comminution Theory and Practice, Part II," *Brit. Chem. Eng.* **5**, 773–783 (1960).

38. Y. Nakagawa and K. Matsui, "Relation Between Number of Blows, Mill Revolutions, New Work Input to Crushing, Surface Increment, and Size Distribution of Crushed Products," *Chem. Eng. (Tokyo)* **24**, 500–507 (1960).

39. H. Rumpf, "Problemstellungen und neuere Ergebnisse der Bruchtheorie," *Materialpruefung* **3**, 253–264 (1961).

40. F. X. Tartaron, "Comminution Theory," *Trans. Soc. Mining Engrs. AIME* **223**, 64–66 (1962).

41. F. X. Tartaron, "A General Theory of Comminution," *Trans. Soc. Mining Engrs. AIME* **226**, 183–190 (1963).

42. A. M. Gow, M. Guggenheim, A. B. Campbell, and W. H. Coghill, "Ball Milling," *Am. AIME Inst. Mining Met. Engrs.*, Tech. Publ. No. 517, 52 pp. (1934).

43. K. Sedlatschek and L. Bass, "Contribution to the Theory of Milling Processes," *Powder Met. Bull.* **6**, 148–153 (1953).

44. R. P. Gardner and L. G. Austin, "A Chemical Engineering Treatment of Batch Grinding," *Proc. 1st European Size Reduction Symposium, Zerkleinern*, H. Rumpf and D. Behrens, eds., Verlag Chemie, Weinheim, 1962, pp. 217–231.

45. K. J. Reid, "A Solution to the Batch Grinding Equation," *Chem. Eng. Sci.* **20**, 953–963 (1965).

46. A. M. Gaudin and T. P. Meloy, "Model and a Comminution Distribution Equation for Repeated Fracture," *Trans. Soc. Mining Engrs. AIME* **223**, 43–50 (1962).

47. S. R. Broadbent and T. G. Callcott, "Coal Breakage Processes. I. A New Analysis of Coal Breakage Processes," *J. Inst. Fuel* **29**, 524–528 (1956).

48. S. R. Broadbent and T. G. Callcott, "Coal Breakage Processes. II. A Matrix Representation of Breakage," *J. Inst. Fuel* **29**, 528–539 (1956).

49. S. R. Broadbent and T. G. Callcott, "Coal Breakage Processes. III. The Analysis of a Coal Transport System," *J. Inst. Fuel* **30**, 13–17 (Jan. 1957).

50. S. R. Broadbent and T. G. Callcott, "Coal Breakage Processes. IV. An Exploratory Analysis of the Cone Mill in Open-Circuit Grinding," *J. Inst. Fuel* **30**, 18–21 (1957).

51. S. R. Broadbent and T. G. Callcott, "Coal Breakage Processes. V. Analysis of Closed-Circuit Grinding," *J. Inst. Fuel* **30**, 21–25 (1957).

52. L. G. Austin and R. R. Klimpel, "The Theory of Grinding Operations," *Ind. Eng. Chem.* **56** (11), 18–29 (1964).

53. R. P. Gardner and L. G. Austin, "Use of Radioactive Tracer Techniques and Computer in Study of Batch Grinding of Coal," *J. Inst. Fuel* **35**, 173–177 (1962).

54. H. E. Rose and D. E. Evans, "The Dynamics of the Ball Mill," *Proc. Automobile Div. Inst. Mech. Engrs. (London)* **170**, 773–792 (1956).

55. H. E. Rose and R. M. E. Sullivan, *A Treatise on the Internal Mechanics of Ball, Tube, and Rod Mills*, Constable, London, 1958.

56. R. A. Zeleny and E. L. Piret, "Dissipation of Energy in Single-Particle Crushing," *I&EC Process Design and Development* **1**, 37–41 (1962).

57. G. D. Boozer, K. H. Hiller, and S. Serdengecti, "Effects of Pore Fluids on the Deformation Behavior of Rocks Subjected to Triaxial Compression," *Proc. 5th Symp. Rock Mechanics*, C. Fairhurst, ed., Pergamon Press, New York, 1963, pp. 579–625.

58. L. E. Djingheuzian, "Development of the Science of Grinding," *Can. Min. Met. Bull.* **45**, 658–663 (1952).

59. S. R. Broadbent and T. G. Callcott, "A Matrix Analysis of Processes Involving Particle Assemblies," *Phil. Trans. Roy. Soc. London, Ser. A* **249**, 99–123 (1956).

60. K. Fujino and H. Taniguchi, "A Study of Performance of Classifier and Mill Capacity in Closed Circuit Grinding," *Chem. Eng. (Tokyo)* **24**, 93–98 (1960).

61. M. Quatinez, R. J. Schafer, and C. R. Smeal, "The Production of Submicron Metal Powders by Ball-Milling with Grinding Aids," *NASA Tech. Note D-879* (March 1962).

62. M. Quatinez, R. J. Schafer, and C. R. Smeal, "The Production of Submicron Metal Powders by Ball-Milling with Grinding Aids," *Trans. Met. Soc. AIME* **221**, 1105–1110 (1961).

63. J. H. Brown, "Intergranular Comminution by Heating," *Mining Engr.* **10**, 490–496 (1958).

64. J. L. Moilliet, "The Role of Surface Active Agents in Processes for Dispersing Solids in Liquid Media," *Proc. Intern. Congr. Surface Activity 2d*, Butterworth & Co. Ltd., London, 1957, pp. 162–167.

65. H. Neugebauer, "The Preparation of Colloidal System by Trituration," *Kolloid-Z.* **43**, 65–67 (1927).

66. R. V. Riley, "Theory and Practice of Crushing and Grinding," *Chem. Process Eng.* **46**, 189–195 (1965).

67. R. T. Hukki, "Fundamental Study of Grinding Characteristics of Tumbling Mills," *Intern. Mining Proc. Congr. (London)*, Preprint, 6–9 (1960).

68. A. Masson, "Contribution to the Study of the Optimum Loading Charge in Dry-Ball Mills," *Rev. Mater. Construct. Trav. Publ.* **531**, 303–312 (1959).

69. F. M. Lewis and J. R. Goodman, "Grinding Practice at the Tennessee Copper Company's Isabella Mill," *Trans. AIME* **208**, 1253–1255 (1957).

70. J. F. Myers, "Study of the Noncataracting (N-C) Ball Mill," *Trans. Can. Inst. Mining Met.* **61**, 269–278 (1958).

71. R. Barta and Z. Bruthans, "Thermographic Study of Activation by Vibration Grinding," *Silikaty* **6**, 9–15 (1962).

72. F. C. Bond, "Control Particles Shape and Size," *Chem. Eng.* **61**, 195–198 (August 1954).

73. I. L. Feld, T. N. McVay, H. L. Gilmore, and B. H. Clemmons, "Paper-Coating Clay from Coarse Georgia Kaolin by a New Attritio-Grinding Process," *U.S. Bureau of Mines*, Washington, D.C., Rept. Investigations 5697 (1960).

74. D. G. Bosse, *Development and Use of the "Sand Grinder," Papers Philadelphia Convention Federation Paint and Varnish Clubs, 1957*.

75. H. G. Tanner, "New Type of Mill for Refined Chemicals," *Ind. Eng. Chem.* **49**, 170–173 (1957).

76. A. L. Stern, "A Guide to Crushing and Grinding Practice," *Chem. Eng.* **69**, 129–146 (1962).

CLYDE ORR, JR.

Georgia Institute of Technology

SIZE SEPARATION

Size separation as here defined covers the operation of separating mixtures of particles of various sizes into two or more products so that the majority of particles in one product will fall into a size range coarser or finer than that in the next product. This is an important feature of ore concentration where fine grinding is required to free small particles of valuable mineral from the rock matrix. (For sizing in connection with concentration see Gravity concentration.)

Size separation is important in many industries, particularly mining, rock products, and coal, and also in the production of ceramics, portland cement, pigments, and abrasives, where the raw materials must be broken down by crushing and/or grinding operations prior to separation into fine or graded sizes suitable for further processing or marketing. Size separations may be performed by either wet or dry methods, which have developed concurrently with those of size reduction. See also Sedimentation; Size measurement of particles; Size reduction.

In current practice, sizing is accomplished either by screening or by classification; classification may be performed either by hydraulic or by pneumatic processes. Which of these methods is finally selected depends upon the type of material and to some extent on how fine a separation is to be made.

Although screening is the simplest and most effective method of separating particles of different sizes, a limit is reached as the size of separation desired decreases. This limitation results not only because it is impractical to make screens having more than 300–400 openings to the linear inch, and difficult to prevent "blinding" of the openings due to the wedging of particles, corrosion, and sometimes chemical precipitation, but also because even at considerably coarser meshes, screening capacities fall off rapidly.

For large-tonnage operations in the mining and metallurgical field, screening is seldom carried below 6–8 mm (2.5–3.5 mesh). In smaller operations and for the production of some finished products, screening at 1–2 mm (9–16 mesh) is entirely satisfactory; this is extended down to 0.3 mm (48 mesh) in certain cases. Only in a very limited number of industries (grain and carbon flours) are 300–400 mesh (0.04 mm) screens or bolting cloths found in use.

On the other hand, classification methods which make use of the differential rates of settlement of different size particles under gravitational or centrifugal forces are capable of handling particles of a size range extending from 5 to 6 mm down to a few thousandths of a millimeter. As in the case of screens, classifier capacities tend to fall off as the fineness of separation increases, and the effectiveness of the operation is influenced by such factors as the temperature, the state of chemical or physical dispersion of the particles, and the nature of the medium used.

The definition of particle size is largely arbitrary since it depends upon whether screening or classification methods are used. Customarily classification products are

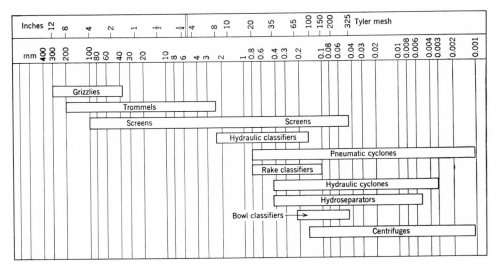

Fig. 1. Normal sizes of separation obtained with various machines.

evaluated by screen analysis down to 325 mesh and below this by subsieve sizing techniques. In the case of screening, the "size" of a particle is determined by whether it will pass through or be retained on a screen having openings of known dimensions, whereas in pneumatic or hydraulic sizing procedures the "size" is the diameter of an equivalent sphere of the same specific gravity that will settle at the same rate. Since most of the particles found in nature or produced by crushing and grinding are of irregular shape, it is apparent that size as such has no fixed dimensional meaning. From microscopic or other methods of measurement it is possible to calculate a theoretical "average" or limiting particle diameter, surface area, or volume for any screened or classified product, the practical value of which will depend upon the material involved and its subsequent processing.

With respect to the choice of a particular piece of equipment for a specific size separation, it should be noted that in addition to the size-range and tonnage considerations mentioned above, the proper selection will depend upon such factors as the physical properties of the material, whether it is wet or dry; the sharpness of the separation desired; the space available; and the investment, operating costs, and maintenance involved. Figure 1 indicates the range of particle-size applications of sizing devices.

Screen Sizing

Screening (1–4) is the operation of separating a mixture of various sized particles into two or more portions by means of screens. This is accomplished commercially by using a surface containing a large number of openings of specified size. The material which remains on a given screen is the *plus or oversize* of that screen while that passing is the *minus or undersize*. Screening can be considered a mechanical system of measuring the size of individual particles.

Percentage of opening is the ratio of the combined area of the openings to the total area of the screening surface. It is equal to 100 × the open area divided by the total area of the screen surface. *Aperture*, or screen size, is defined as the minimum clear space contained within the meshes of the screen. The interrelation between the aperture A, mesh M, and wire diameter D for square woven screens is shown in the following equation in which P is the percentage of opening:

$$P = A^2/(A + D)^2 = (1 - MD)^2 \qquad (1)$$

A screen scale (1–3) is a series of test screens having successively larger or smaller openings. See Size measurement of particles.

The *probability of passage through openings* by particles, which is influenced by a great many factors such as size of openings, relative particle size, and deflection of particles on wires, is too detailed to be more than briefly discussed in this article (see refs. 3,5,6). When the particle is small as compared with the diameter of the hole, the probability is infinitely great, but as the diameter of the particle approaches that of the hole it becomes infinitely small. This illustrates the great difficulty of screening out particles with diameters only slightly less than those of the holes in the screen, and also shows that a screen must be very long to pass all the grains it should pass theoretically.

Effect of Variables. In considering the ordinary screening operation, no uniform method has yet been devised for calculating screen efficiency. Generally, the ratio of weight of undersize actually obtained to weight of screen undersize in the feed as determined by standard screening procedure is used for this purpose, but the method leaves much to be desired. Efficiencies will vary widely depending upon such factors as mesh of separation, characteristics of the feed, and loading of the screens. To increase recovery of undersize, certain operators use screens of larger mesh than the desired separation, depending upon experience or experiment in choosing the proper size.

The *shape of particles* being treated greatly affects the operation of a screen because the difference in fracture or cleavage among minerals causes a variation in the ratio of the mass to the minimum dimensions of the particles. In a mass of broken ore very few particles are of exactly the same shape. They tend to be oval, flat, cubical, or prismatic, making the real sizes and quantities that will pass a hole of given diameter quite different for different materials.

The *proportions of coarse and fine particles* directly affect the rate of screening. An ore containing little fine material requires less screening surface or less time to remove the material under, say, 0.5 in. in size, than another ore which contains a much larger percentage of fines. In general the difficulties of screening increase rapidly as the size of the screen holes decreases. Small screen holes blind more readily because of the wedging of small particles in the holes and agglutination, or because of the tendency of small particles to stick to the wires and to each other.

The *moisture content* is important because it tends to make fine material sticky, and there is a range of moisture contents where screening may be difficult or impossible. However, screening operations may be performed wet instead of dry.

Shape of Screen Holes. Circular, square, slotted, or rectangular holes may pass different amounts of the same material. If the screening surface is to make a separation of a coarse size, circular or square openings are the rule; for fine separations square, rectangular, and slotted openings are used. Slotted openings produce a separation at a size equivalent to that obtained with round openings of a diameter slightly larger than the width of the slot. Surfaces with rectangular openings present a significantly larger open area, 28–36% over surfaces with square or round openings.

The *slope of the screen* has a considerable bearing on the rate of screening and the size of the products. A particle that is just small enough to pass vertically through a hole in a horizontal screen may not pass through when the screen is inclined, because only the horizontal projection of the opening presents itself (see under Hi-Prob screen, p. 374). The steeper the slope the smaller is the maximum grain that will pass through. In practice, an optimum angle of inclination is selected to prevent blinding; for vibrating screens the angle usually increases as feed size decreases, but this is not true for oscillating screens. Generally speaking, slope must be coordinated with speed and stroke of vibration in order to secure the best results.

The *temperature* of the moving particles and of the screen surface also affects the screening speed. Hot dry ore such as that from a roasting furnace separates into sizes faster than ore at atmospheric temperatures. Other factors affecting screening rates are *velocity of flow, coefficient of friction* between screen and material, and *motion of the screen*.

Screen Surfaces. The three general types of screening surfaces (1–3,5) are (*1*) parallel bars or rods, (*2*) punched plates, and (*3*) woven wire and silk. Generally speaking, parallel rods are used for the coarsest sizing and woven wire for the finest.

Bar or rod screens made from steel, cast iron, or alloy bars have been used over a long period for stationary scalping screens, and modifications of these types are employed in vibrating screens for coarse sizing. Many specially shaped bars are used, the most popular being wedge-shaped in cross section with the broad edge uppermost to reduce clogging of the screen. In all of these, the spaces between the bars form long narrow openings for the undersize to pass through. The bars are placed either parallel to, or at right angles to the flow of material, depending on the type of screen used.

Punched-plate screens are made of sheet steel punched by dies in various patterns. The openings are circular, square, or slot-like. Slotted openings make a separation equivalent to that made by round holes having a diameter slightly larger than the width of the slot. The principal drawback of slotted plate is its generally low percentage of open space as compared with woven-wire cloth. It has been demonstrated that for the average crushed material the maximum size of particles passing a round hole of given diameter is about 81% of those passing a square hole of the same side dimension.

Woven-wire screens are made with either square or rectangular openings and in a number of different forms intended to lengthen their life or to avoid displacement of the wires in service. Rectangular openings give the advantage of greater percentage of apertures in ratio to the area of the screen, while square openings make a more rigid cloth and are consequently preferred for very coarse screening.

Silk bolting cloth is used mainly in the screening of very fine mesh materials such as graphite, abrasives, and grain flours. Silk screens are made with openings comparable to those of wire screens. The principal producers are Simpson-Orville Co. and Sprout, Waldron & Co., Inc.

Types of Screens. Several different types of screens have been developed to suit varied conditions of size separation. Screens are classified according to their method of support or operation as *fixed* and *moving*.

Fixed screens are usually flat and set at an angle which may vary from 0 to 50° from the horizontal, an exception being the DSM or sieve-bend screen (see below), the surface of which is curved, the curvature varying from 50 to 300° of a complete circle. Moving screens may be divided into four main classes: revolving, traveling-belt, shaking, and vibrating. Stationary screens are usually run dry, except for the DSM screen which operates with a wet feed; moving screens are operated either wet or dry.

In wet screening, water sprays are applied above the screen deck to assist in washing particles through the screen openings.

Stationary gravity screens, called "grizzlies" in ore dressing, have a fixed surface set at an angle sufficiently great to allow the material being screened to travel over it by gravity. Inverted railroad rails are frequently used as bars. Their economical use is limited to coarse screening with spacing 1½ in. and greater. Many variations in construction, material used, and modes of operation may be found in the mining and kindred industries (see p. 373).

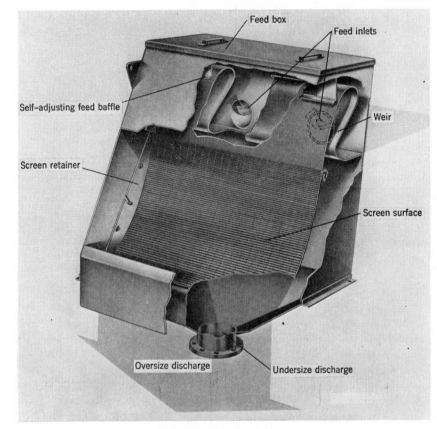

Fig. 2. 50° DSM screen. Courtesy Dorr-Oliver Co., Inc.

The *DSM screen* consists of a stationary screen-housing equipped with a concaved wedge-bar-type screen with provisions for introducing feed and withdrawing undersize and oversize product. Figure 2 is a cutaway drawing of the DSM screen illustrating the component parts, using a 50° screen surface and gravity feed.

The feed chamber is fitted with a flanged inlet pipe. The parabolic curved weir together with the self-adjusting flow baffle assures the proper distribution of the feed to the screen surface. The screen surface is constructed of wedge-shaped bars mounted in a frame at right angles to the direction of feed. Both screen and frame form an arc of a circle and are rigidly clamped to the screen housing. The screen box is an integral part of the housing and provides the means for collecting undersize fraction. An open spout at the lower end of the screen surface carries away the oversize fraction.

In operation, slurry enters the feed box and is fed tangentially over the weir onto the upper surface of the screen. Flowing down the concave surface at right angles to the openings between the wedge bars, the undersize fraction and liquid pass through these apertures and are collected in the screen box. Dewatered oversize material flows down the screen surface to the oversize discharge. Size separation is controlled solely by the size of the opening between the wedge bars. This separation is unique in that the largest undersize particles are considerably smaller than the size of the openings between the bars. Slurry feed passing over the screen surface is deflected from its path. This is caused by the underside of the flow being retarded by coming in contact with the surface of the wedge bars. A layer of liquid and solid particles, the thickness of the desired undersize fraction, strikes the side of the following bar and is sliced off and directed downward through the slot into the screen box.

In *revolving screens*, often called "trommels," the screening surface forms the envelope of a revolving cylinder whose axis is tilted at an angle with the horizontal. Occasionally, the trommels are composed of screens having openings of varying size running throughout their length; the feed enters at the end with the finest screen. Also available is a compound trommel having two or more concentric screens, with openings of different size, mounted on the same shaft with the coarsest screen innermost. Revolving screens are most efficient for material ranging from $\frac{1}{4}$ to $2\frac{1}{2}$ in. in size, and they have wide applications in ore dressing and in sand and gravel sizing.

Crushed material fed into a trommel is first carried up inside by the revolving envelope and then rolls down the slope. This movement continues until the undersize passes through holes in the screen and the oversize is discharged at the lower end. The disadvantages of this type of screen are the relatively large floor space needed for a given tonnage and the comparatively high amount of maintenance required, particularly on the screening surface.

Revolving screening devices which are hexagonal in cross section and use silk or metal bolting cloth as the screening surface are generally called "reels." They are driven at relatively high speed and depend largely on centrifugal force to drive the particles through the screen. This action may be assisted by brushes inside the reel. Their chief applications are in the flour-milling industry and for sizing nonabrasive materials such as graphite.

Traveling-belt screens (3) include all those that travel continuously around end pulleys as a conveyor belt, with the belt itself forming the screening surface. The Callow screen used frequently in the mining industry is typical of this class. Usually the whole belt is a continuous screen cloth; belts have also been made of endless chains or of individual, hinged sections each containing a screen. They have been used extensively for fine wet-screening of ores, as in the Callow screen. The feed is delivered to the outside of the screen and the undersize is removed from inside the screen. The oversize travels on the belt until it passes over the end pulley, where a water spray washes it off, frees the clogged meshes, and prepares the cloth to take on a new load.

Shaking screens (4) include a number of types, depending upon construction and kind of imparted motion. The most common among these are listed below.

Straight-line vibrating screens consist of either a flat or slightly sloped surface which is given a reciprocating or oscillating motion, causing the material to move from feed to discharge end. A number of different mechanical movements have been introduced by means of off-center and eccentric drive mechanisms in order to vary the path of travel over the screen surface. These screens are employed to the greatest

Fig. 3. Deister three-deck vibrating screen. Courtesy Deister Machine Co., Inc.

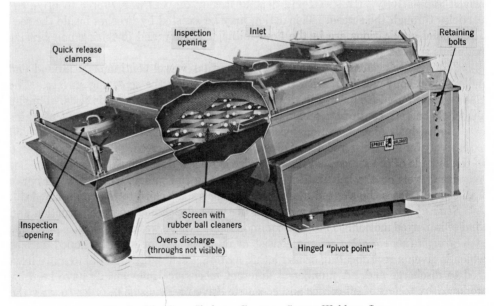

Fig. 4. The Gyro-Shaker. Courtesy Sprout-Waldron, Inc.

extent in the treatment of various metallic ores, coal, and industrial minerals such as phosphate rock and asbestos. An example is the Deister screen (Deister Machine Co., Inc.) shown in Figure 3, which illustrates the use of woven wire as a screening medium. Wire-mesh screens over a wide range of sizes in single, double-, and triple-deck designs are also widely used. Other vibrating screens of the same general type are the Symons (Nordberg Mfg. Co.) and those made by Link-Belt Corp., Allis-Chalmers Mfg. Co., Kennedy-Van Saun Manufacturing and Engineering Co., and Simplicity Engineering Co.

Gyratory rotary screens have a motion that varies from circular at the feed end to reciprocal at the discharge end. Counterbalanced eccentrics impart a rotary motion about a vertical axis at the feed end. At the discharge end a mechanism which includes a slide bearing is usually provided. The Gyro-Shaker (Sprout-Waldron Co.) (Fig. 4) and the Rotex (Simpson-Orville Co.) are examples of this type of screen.

Circular rotary screens are usually built to hold stacks of screen surfaces which are given a horizontal motion in a perfect circle at about 300 rpm. A great variety of multideck arrangements for multiple separations or to increase the surface area for two-size separations are possible with these screens. The screen body is supported by flexible steel "reeds" but the drives are mounted on the floor. The Gyro-Whip Sifter (Sprout-Waldron Co.) is a well-known screen of this type.

Circular vibrators are typified by the Sweco Vibro-Energy Separator (Southwestern Engineering Co.). In this machine a double set of eccentrics gives the unit both a rotary and a vibrating motion that results in a spiral screening pattern. The screen is built in single- and multideck units.

High-speed vibrators are operated either mechanically or electromagnetically at 1200–3000 pulsations/min, but at a low amplitude, in a direction perpendicular to the screen surface, which is set at a fairly steep angle. The Hum-mer screen (W. S. Tyler & Co.) and units made by The Jeffrey Manufacturing Co. vibrate the entire screen body, while other manufacturers use a design that vibrates only the screen surface, the body remaining stationary.

Developments in Screening. The art of screen sizing has made considerable progress over the years, with a trend toward larger screens and higher capacities; for example, screens as large as 6 ft wide and 20 ft long are now in use, while better alloys and bearings have made possible the use of higher speeds in mechanically vibrated screens.

The *differential-angle step-deck* screen, in which the screen surface has three or more sections, each at a different angle to the horizontal, is of interest. The feed section has the greatest inclination to assist in moving the load; then, as the load decreases, the inclination of the successive sections is decreased to facilitate more accurate sizing of the near-mesh particles. In wet-screening each section is sometimes equipped with washing, or pulping, troughs where the scrubbing action tends to release fines that can be eliminated through the screen in the next section.

For dewatering, washing, and sizing, considerable use is made of horizontal, rather than sloping, screens, of which the Horizontal Straightline screen (Link-Belt Co.) is an example. The vibrating mechanism is designed to move the material without the assistance of gravity, and the advantage of a horizontal screen is that it will give more accurate sizing and take up less headroom than a sloping screen.

Another growing tendency is toward the adoption of bar-type screens used with vibrating mechanisms, even for fine screening. In these screens the screen surface is made up of shaped bars or rods which are joined together in such a manner as to give

Fig. 5. Hi-Prob sizer. Courtesy Mine & Smelter Supply Co.

a long, narrow slot for the actual screening. The Symons vibrating rod and bar grizzlies are examples of this development. The chief advantage of this type of screen-deck construction is that these screens are more resistant to wear and thus reduce the cost. There is, of course, some sacrifice in the accuracy of the screening, but for many applications this is relatively unimportant. Furthermore, by proper selection of the screen opening and bar design, quite accurate sizing and good screening efficiency can be obtained.

A recent development of considerable interest is the Hi-Prob sizer (6), manufac-tured by the Mine & Smelter Supply Co. It has the appearance of a standard vibrating screen but operates on a very different principle. The unit (Fig. 5) consists of five superimposed screen decks, each with a slightly steeper slope than the one above. The screen meshes used are no less than twice the size of the desired separation. Two out-of-balance motors transmit a linear vibration to each deck and the resultant action serves to fluidize the feed so that the particles can be separated by the probability principle discussed on page 368 (3). The screen can handle material from 2 in. to 150 mesh, and because of the ratio of size of opening to size of separation, high capacity is obtained with far less blinding than for conventional screens, even on materials with small amounts of moisture. Single- or multiple-product separations can be made.

Another development in wet-screening is the Rapifine DSM screen (Dorr-Oliver,

Inc.) (7) in which a 60° DSM screen (see p. 370) is fitted with a motorized rapping device that periodically raps the underside of the screen surface to prevent blinding and ensure full capacity. This piece of equipment has extended the effective range of wet-screening down to 325 mesh with high tonnage capacity. It provides more efficient size separation than a cyclone or other wet-classification device, because the separation is determined by particle dimensions rather than specific gravity. An important application is in closed-circuit fine grinding where it is desired to remove from the circuit released heavy mineral, and to return to the mill only the mixed, unliberated larger particles which are generally the lighter particles.

Electrically heated screens (Fig. 6) for dry-screening operations find considerable application, especially for material which tends to be slightly damp or sticky. Low-voltage electric current is passed through the screen surface, so that the screen wires are maintained at a temperature of 75–100°F. This relatively low heat is sufficient to keep the wires clean and to prevent blinding.

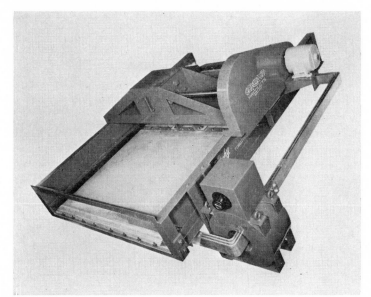

Fig. 6. The Leahy electrically heated vibrating screen. Courtesy The Deister Concentrator Co.

Ball Trays. To reduce the tendency of fine screens to blind, some manufacturers use a ball tray (of larger mesh) below the separating screen to support a large number of 1–1½-in. rubber balls. The shaking motion of the screen causes the balls to bounce against the underside of the separating screen, thereby loosening material that may have become attached to, or wedged in, the wire mesh.

Aqueous Classification

Classification (1–3,5,8), in the terminology of mineral dressing, refers to the process of sorting mixtures of particles into two or more fractions, each containing particles of a more or less limited size range. The separation is rarely, if ever, complete due mainly to variations in the shape and density of the particles. The measure of its completeness is determined by sizing the products on a standard series of screens down to 325 mesh/in. (0.043-mm opening) and below this by various subsieve sizing techniques based on Stokes' law for rates of settling of solid particles in a fluid. See Sedimentation.

This section is limited to a discussion of classification in an aqueous medium, where the size separations referred to are accomplished by taking advantage of the difference in the rates of settlement in water between particles of different sizes. These rates follow Stokes' law of viscous resistance in the case of very small particles and Newton's law of eddying, or turbulent resistance, for particles above about 1 mm in diam (sp gr 2.65) in water. The intermediate rates can be found by a dimensionless equation devised by Castleman (3), from which it is possible to predict the behavior of a particle of any size (see also ref. 9).

Where conditions are such that the particles are relatively far apart, their movement is said to be *free settling;* where crowding occurs and the particles are interfering with one another, the state is described as one of *hindered settling*. Under ideal conditions the relative diameter of two particles for constant conditions of viscosity, flocculation, etc, determines their relative rate of fall, but in practice particle shape and density are also involved. The *settling ratio* (both free and hindered) is defined as the ratio of the diameter of the light particle to that of the heavy particle which is equal-settling with it; where heterogeneous mixtures are involved, this becomes a factor of importance in making size separations on a commercial basis.

When a body falls in a liquid medium, it meets a resistance that is a function of its velocity, which increases until the resistance force equals the gravitational pull. Thereafter the body falls at this constant *terminal velocity*.

The state of flocculation of the very small (-200 mesh (0.074 mm)) particles in a pulp has a great effect on their classification characteristics if the flow rates and detentions involved permit the formation of groupings or clusters, since these settle at rates very much higher than those of the individual particles of which they are composed. For the most efficient classification of such fines, pulp which has been well dispersed by either chemical or mechanical means is generally desirable, and sometimes essential. For a detailed discussion, see chapter 8, "Movement of Solids in Fluids," in reference 5.

Aqueous classification (10) may be accomplished in a number of wet-type mechanical devices such as the reciprocating rake and spiral classifiers for separations in the coarser size ranges, and by the use of machines such as the bowl classifier, centrifuge, hydroseparator, or liquid cyclone for finer sizes. Nonmechanical hydraulic classifiers are also used to a certain extent.

Classification is affected by the following factors: (*1*) specific gravity of particles; (*2*) size of particles; (*3*) shape of particles; (*4*) possible selective attachment of air bubbles; (*5*) magnetism of particles; (*6*) density of fluid medium; and (*7*) viscosity of medium. Thus it seems that unless the material to be sized is uniform in shape and specific gravity, there is little chance of obtaining a true size separation by classification methods alone. Screening, however, will give a size separation which is independent of the above factors, although particle shape, magnetism, and viscosity of the fluid may have some effect, especially when the finer sizes of screens are used.

The most common application of classifiers is in the dressing of metallic and nonmetallic ores, where the machines are operated in closed circuit with grinding mills to separate the mill discharge into a product having the required fineness for subsequent processing and an oversize fraction to be returned to the mill for further reduction. Another important use is in the washing and dewatering of granular products such as phosphate rock, ground silica, concrete sand, fine coal, limestone, precipitated alumina, and mineral concentrates from flotation. Other applications are in degritting and leaching, in which the main object is the dissolving and removal of substances from granular material by washing.

Classifiers have been designed and built in a wide variety of types which may be divided into two main groups, hydraulic and nonhydraulic, depending on whether or not an upward current of "hydraulic" water is used as a sorting column. The latter may be further subdivided into mechanical and nonmechanical classifiers.

In addition to the above there is also centrifugal classification and pneumatic classification.

NONMECHANICAL, NONHYDRAULIC CLASSIFIERS

The simplest type of classifier consists of a tank (usually conical in form) placed in a stream of pulp with the feed flowing in on one side and overflowing on the other. The overflow contains the fine material, which does not settle, while the coarser material drops to the bottom of the tank and is discharged by a spigot. Several of these tanks may be placed in a series of increasing size from which may be obtained a series of graded products determined by the velocity of the stream in each tank and the law of equal falling particles. Rittinger's Spitzkasten is such a series. Devices of this type were at one time widely used for desliming operations in ore dressing.

Among the other nonmechanical classifiers is the Caldecott cone which gave results considered satisfactory before the advent of more efficient mechanical classifiers. It consists of a sheet-iron conical tank with a central feed pipe and a peripheral overflow launder, the sides of the cone sloping 60 or 70° from the horizontal. Similar to the Caldecott is the Allen cone, which is distinguished by an automatic discharge. It has been used to a considerable extent in the Southern phosphate rock washing plants. Other cone classifiers are the Callow, Boylan, Wuensch, and Nordberg-Wood. For a discussion of nonmechanical classifiers see reference 3, which includes illustrations of all types. Cone classifiers range in size from 4 to 8 ft in diam and up to 8 ft in depth. They have capacities ranging from 100 to 1000 tons/24 hr depending upon the character of the feed. At the present time their use is restricted to special applications, usually of limited size.

MECHANICAL CLASSIFIERS

Functions (8). Primarily, a classifier must function as a container in which the solids segregate. This could be a tub or tank of almost any shape. Although batch separations can be made in such a container, for modern commercial operation the classifier should fulfill one or more, and in many cases all, of the following functions: (1) It must collect the undersize and convey it to a convenient point by means of a launder. (2) It must separate the oversize from the undersize and dewater it as much as possible. This is usually accomplished by rakes or screws in inclined troughs whereby the oversize is removed from the pool of overflow pulp and drained. (3) In closed-circuit grinding, which is the principal application of classifiers, the oversize must be conveyed from the discharge to the feed end of the mill. This is performed by the rakes or screws. (4) Changing operating conditions of tonnage, temperature, and character of solids necessitate some flexibility of control in obtaining the separation desired. Within limits, this can be done by moisture control, but it is also advantageous to control both the actual and effective area of the classifier pool. In certain

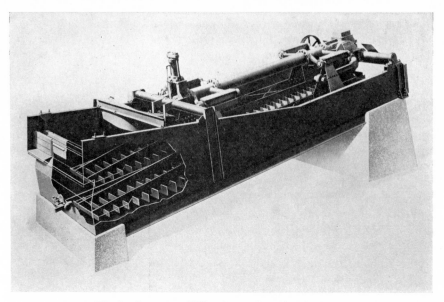

Fig. 7. Dorr type-HX reciprocating rake classifier.

classifiers this can be done by changing the overflow weir, the slope, and the raking speed.

With correct dilution and rake speed, a pulp fed to the classifier segregates rapidly into (1) the coarse, quick-settling material, larger than the mesh of separation, and (2) the fine, slow-settling material, finer than the mesh of separation. The coarse portion sinks to the bottom of the pool and is transported up the inclined deck by the action of the rakes. The fine portion, held in suspension by the specific gravity of the pulp and the degree of agitation of the rakes, flows to the overflow lip and leaves the classifier.

With the proper size and type of classifier, the mesh of separation can be controlled by means of various adjustments including pulp dilution, tank slope, and rake speed. Broadly speaking, the greater the rake speed, the higher is the concentration of solids in the pulp; and the steeper the slope, the coarser is the mesh of separation and vice versa. All factors, including speed, dilution, slope, separation mesh, and nature of materials, remaining the same, the overflow and raking capacity are proportional to the classifier width. The finer the material to be raked, the slower must be the raking speed and the smaller the tank slope, resulting in reduced capacity.

Reciprocating rake classifiers are exemplified by the Dorr classifier (see Fig. 7), which is essentially an inclined rectangular settling tank in the form of a trough open at the upper end for the discharge of oversize grains and provided with a weir at the lower end where fine particles and slimes are overflowed. In various installations the inclination of the bottom of the tank is 1½ in. or more per foot, depending on the size at which a separation is to be made. A reciprocating raking mechanism carries settled solids up the inclined deck to the sand-discharge lip. Feed enters through either end of a transverse launder located near the overflow, which is equipped with splitter vanes for obtaining an even distribution across the width of the tank.

The modern type-H mechanism is supported at only three points. At the discharge end it is carried by the support tube which spans the tank and rests on two pedestal bearings. A support shaft and bearing attached to the hydraulic lifting device by a hanger rod provides the third point of support near the overflow end. All bearings are above the pulp level. The machine is designated as simplex for one rake, duplex for two rakes, and quadruplex for four rakes. The type-H mechanism may be driven by a constant- or variable-speed drive, connected by conventional V-belts to a pinion shaft. Integral with this shaft are two helical pinions of opposite hand which drive the gears and crankshafts. To each crankshaft is mounted a connecting rod, which drives the rakes forward and backward.

The vertical lifting of the rakes at the end of each stroke and subsequent lowering at the beginning of the next is activated by a cam, cam roller arm, and pivot shaft contained in an oiltight housing at the head end of the unit. The pivot shaft is bolted to the upper rocker arm, so that the oscillation of the cam roller causes the entire torque tube, rocker arm, and slide assembly to rock from side to side on its centerline axis. This motion alternately raises and lowers each set of rakes in synchronization with their forward and backward movement. The motion of the reciprocating rakes facilitates the release of undesired fines from the sand bed through agitation and slight attrition. Natural drainage, which may be assisted by water sprays applied above the pulp level, further aids in the removal of fines and entrained liquid. A considerable portion of accompanying free moisture is removed from the sands by compression at the upper end of the inclined drainage deck above the pulp level.

Rake-type classifiers are divided roughly into three groups—light-, medium-, and heavy-duty—depending upon the amount and characteristics of the materials which they are to handle and the mesh of separation.

Light-duty machines range in size from $1\frac{1}{2} \times 18$ ft to 5×30 ft and their raking capacities vary from 100 tons/24 hr for a 2.70 sp gr ore at 200 mesh to 2800 tons for a 4.50 sp gr ore at 28 mesh. The mechanisms are built in simplex and duplex units. Medium-duty classifiers range in size from 6×18 ft to 16×30 ft with an extreme variation in raking capacity from 750 to 10,500 tons/24 hr, depending upon the above-mentioned conditions. For heavy-duty machines, the corresponding figures are 5×24 ft to 16×32 ft with rake capacities ranging from 2200 to 25,000 tons/24 hr. The medium- and heavy-duty classifiers are made in duplex and quadruplex units.

The Dorr bowl classifier consists essentially of a straight Dorr classifier which has a shallow circular bowl with a revolving raking mechanism superimposed on the lower end. Feed enters through a central loading well; overflow takes place across a peripheral weir. Coarse solids are raked to an opening in the center of the bowl and pass through into the reciprocating rake compartment below. Bowl-type classifiers are also made by the Hardinge Company. Bowl classifiers are used when a cleaner rake product is desired, where the overflow product is to be of extremely fine size, and where the overflow capacity is large in comparison to the raking capacity. Bowls for these classifiers range in diameter from 6 to 25 ft, depending upon the size of the reciprocating raking mechanism.

Another reciprocating rake classifier is the Geco made by General Engineering Co. In this machine two sets of blades act independently, one moving up the slope as the other is traveling back over it. Thus, the raking movement is practically continuous; the sands are not allowed to slip back and the pulp is agitated continuously. The design allows a steeper rise, which facilitates the return of sands to the mill in closed-circuit grinding and reduces floor space. The slope is adjustable.

Spiral rake classifiers (3) belong to another group of mechanical classifiers which have applications similar to those of reciprocating rake machines, the largest fields being closed-circuit grinding and minerals washing. A typical model is the Akins (Mine & Smelter Supply Co.) (see Fig. 8) which consists of the usual sloping trough where the pulp is kept gently agitated by one or more spiral ribbons mounted on a shaft. When a mixture of water or solution and solids is fed into the settling pool at the lower end of the trough, the coarse particles settle out and are carried up the incline by the revolving spiral. Drainage is effected at the upper end of the inclined trough or deck, while at the lower end fine particles carried in suspension with slime and water are discharged by an overflow weir. The mesh of separation, the capacity, power consumption, and other functions of the Akins are controlled by the same factors as those for the Dorr classifier. The slope is usually from 3 to 4 in./ft, and several sizes in both the "high weir" and "submerged spiral" types are furnished. Wash sprays can be used above the pulp level to aid in the removal of entrained fines from the sand load. Spiral raking classifiers similar to the Akins are manufactured by Denver Equipment Co. and the Hardinge Co.

Fig. 8. Akins duplex spiral classifier. Courtesy Mine & Smelter Supply Co.

The Hardinge countercurrent classifier differs from the regular type of spiral classifiers in that the continuous spiral rake is rigidly attached to the inside of a rotating drum which is mounted on tires and rollers at a slight slope from the horizontal. The material to be classified is fed at the lower end of the drum and, as the machine revolves, the coarse particles that settle out are carried up the slope and are discharged at an elevation above the pulp bath level. The fines are held in suspension and washed back toward the overflow end by the wash water introduced at the sand or oversize discharge end. Control of size separation is obtained through the speed of rotation, pulp dilution, and depth of pulp pool. Its principal application is in the closed-circuit grinding of ores.

Power consumption by classifiers is notably low compared to that of other process machinery. It will range from 1-hp motors for the smallest light-duty machine to 15–20 hp for medium-duty and 30 hp for the largest heavy-duty machines. The bowl mechanisms will require from 1 to $7\frac{1}{2}$-hp motors over the extreme range of sizes.

Hydroseparators (10) in action are essentially overloaded thickeners in that (*1*) all of the feed particles are not settled out, and (2) the portion of the feed solids carried off in a cloudy supernatant liquid will be composed of the finest particles in the original feed. The practice of deliberately overloading a thickener so that it classifies the feed particles roughly according to their size is known as "hydroseparation." In practice, the mechanism for hydroseparation does not differ substantially from that suitable for thickening (see Sedimentation). The main points of difference between sedimentation machines functioning as hydroseparators (classifiers) and thickeners are discussed briefly below.

Hydroseparators have a higher ratio of overflow to underflow capacity. *Thickeners* are usually rated on the basis of unit areas—square feet of settling area per ton of solids per 24 hr. On the other hand, hydroseparator capacities are expressed as overflow that is, vertical upward displacement. For example, to produce a fine overflow product (98.5% − 325 mesh) on a water-floated clay, a hydroseparator has to provide space to overflow a 26.1:1 (water:solids) pulp at the rate of 3 ft/hr. On a thickener basis, this is equivalent to a unit area of 11.6 ft²/(tons/24 hr). The underflow must be removed at a higher dilution than in other types of classifiers, which means not only that more water must be subsequently removed from the product, but also that the hydroseparator underflow will carry a larger amount of undersize as void solids. This may necessitate an additional machine, such as a rake classifier, if a clean product is required.

When hydroseparation is made at about 60–200 mesh, as in sand or phosphate rock washing plants and in many other industrial applications, the amount of settled material to be raked can be much greater in relation to the size of the machine than with thickeners operated as such. Moreover, the action of hydroseparation itself removes from the sands most of the slime normally acting as lubricant so that the rake product is difficult to handle. To meet these conditions, heavier mechanisms rotating at a higher than normal speed must be used in place of the standard thickener mechanisms. The field for the application of hydroseparators may be divided roughly into three classes: (1) for extremely fine separations where large areas and quiescent settling conditions are essential; (2) for rough sloughing off of slimes before subsequent treatment, where the expense of bowl classifiers is not warranted; and (3) for rough removal of fines and dewatering a very dilute, large-volume feed. Slush from anthracite coal breakers is a typical feed where the hydroseparation step is primarily for dewatering but the elimination of high-ash-content fine slimes is also accomplished.

The principal makes of hydroseparators are the Dorr hydroseparator, the Hardinge hydroclassifier, and the Denver hydroclassifier.

Washers, although not ordinarily rated as classifiers, are included in this section because they are widely used for the separation of valuable minerals from fine wastes. They might be termed rough washing classifiers. The two main functions of a log washer are to disintegrate lump material and to separate the fines. Washers usually consist of one or more "logs" or shafts, carrying metal blades at the surface, which are placed in an inclined trough at a slope of about 1–1½ in./ft.

The Dorr washer is a standard classifier, adapted for breaking up a tenuous bonding of dissimilar grains such as a sand–clay mixture. It is substantially a single-stage Dorr classifier with a perforated washing trommel partially submerged in the classifier bath across its overflow end. This arrangement makes it possible to obtain three products from a mixed feed: (1) a scrubbed coarse oversize as trommel discharge, which may be used as coarse concrete aggregate; (2) a granular rake product (fine aggregate); and (3) a fine overflow consisting of silt and slime.

HYDRAULIC CLASSIFIERS OR SIZERS

These classifying devices are characterized by the use of water, in addition to that of the feed pulp, introduced so that its course of flow opposes that of the settling particles. It is termed hydraulic water. Its quantity and resultant velocity constitute the principal means of controlling operations and results.

Hydraulic classifiers are of two types, the grouping being based on the degree of crowding of the grains in the separating zone. If this zone is relatively uncrowded so that collision between particles is relatively infrequent, the machine is free-settling. If the zone is crowded, so that no particle can pass through without material hindrance, the device is hindered-settling.

Free-Settling Hydraulic Classifiers. The fundamental principle of free-settling hydraulic classifiers is the utilization of the settling rates of grains of different sizes or densities in order to obtain a series of graded products. The particles, during their forward movement by the carrying current, are subjected to a series of rising hydraulic currents or eddies which usually decrease in velocity through a series of pockets. The grains which are sufficiently heavy to settle against the upward current in the first pocket do so and are withdrawn through an orifice at the bottom, while the lighter grains are carried on to the pockets with successively lower velocities, where in turn they are collected and withdrawn.

Typical of free-settling hydraulic classifiers is the Richards deep-pocket or launder-vortex machine which consists of a shallow trough with four pockets of successively increasing cross section. Each pocket is provided with a 9-in. long sorting column composed of a section of 3-in. pipe with a vortex fitting at the bottom. The vortex imparts a whirling motion to the entering hydraulic water which carries light grains upward into the next pocket and allows the heavy ones to drop into the spigot. This classifier will handle about 60 tons/24 hr of pyrite ore containing about 75% of quartz gangue ground to $\frac{3}{16}$-in. size and in a 10:1 pulp of water and solids. Other machines of this type are the Evans, Calumet, and Richards annular vortex.

Hindered-Settling Hydraulic Classifiers (3). (See also Gravity concentration.) Among the most widely used classifiers of this type are the Dorrco sizer, and its later development, the Dorrco Jet sizer. The Dorrco sizer, which is a modernization of its prototype, the Fahrenwald sizer, consists of a trapezoidal tank divided into three or more communicating pockets, each with its individual controls and valves.

The pockets, which are separated from each other by submerged baffle plates, are provided at the bottom with constriction plates which have holes with diameters and spacing planned to produce a teeter condition (alternate rapid rising and falling) in each pocket correlated with the approximate size and gravity of the particles to be retained in that pocket. Water under hydraulic pressure from a header is introduced through an adjustable pinch valve into the hydraulic compartment under each pocket. The water flowing upward through a constriction plate furnishes a uniform rising current in the sorting zone of each compartment. A discharge valve which is automatically controlled by a special mechanism is provided for each pocket. The automatic control mechanism functions in accordance with conditions of pulp density in the sorting compartment. Associated with the control mechanism is an indicator which enables the operator to inform himself easily and at all times of the pocket density conditions. Feed is introduced at the narrow end of the sizer into the feed compartment which is equipped with a constriction plate, and in which preliminary sorting occurs. When the machine is adjusted, the position of the discharge mechanism in

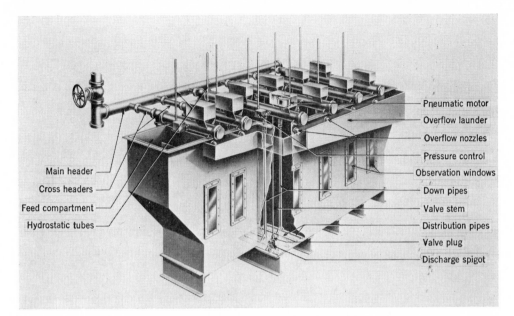

Pneumatic motor
Overflow launder
Overflow nozzles
Pressure control
Observation windows
Down pipes
Valve stem
Distribution pipes
Valve plug
Discharge spigot

Main header
Cross headers
Feed compartment
Hydrostatic tubes

Fig. 9.   Dorrco Jet sizer (9½ pocket unit).

each pocket reaches a balance determined by the hydrostatic pressure established by the control instrument. Whenever a change occurs in the size distribution or rate of the feed, the machine adjusts automatically to such new conditions, and the discharge is again continuous until a further change in feed takes place.

The Dorrco Jet sizer, illustrated in Figure 9, was developed to provide greater flexibility, higher capacity than the largest of the standard Dorrco sizers, and less expensive construction. The sizer is built up of a number of interconnecting square pockets of the same size (30 in. on each side) which may be arranged in a number of configurations to suit the size distribution of the feed. Constriction plates are dispensed with and the hydraulic water is supplied to the bottom of each compartment through distribution pipes provided with nylon nozzles. The same type of automatic control of the discharge valves is used on this machine as on the standard sizer. A typical 21½-pocket unit can size up to 90 tons/hr of specification sand.

The classifier cleaner made by the Wilmot Engineering Co. is a partially hindered-settling machine which is used almost exclusively for coal cleaning (see Fig. 10). It differs from the previously mentioned devices in that it has a hindered-settling zone at the bottom which supplements a free-settling zone at the top of the classifier. These zones are not brought about by a constriction of the bottom of the classifier, but by an increase in velocity of flow in the bottom zone without an increase in the top zone. The cardinal feature is the continuous circulation through the machine of a relatively large quantity of fine mineral particles, accomplished by the use of an outside pump discharging through an arrangement similar to that of a revolving lawn sprinkler. Discharge of the sediment occurs whenever the pulp density exceeds a predetermined figure. The latest design includes a two-electrode probe liquid-level control and a hydraulic valve operator for the butterfly valve refuse discharge.

The classifying Siphonsizer made by the Dorr-Oliver Co. is a comparatively new, two-product hydraulic classifier that combines free settling and hindered settling in a

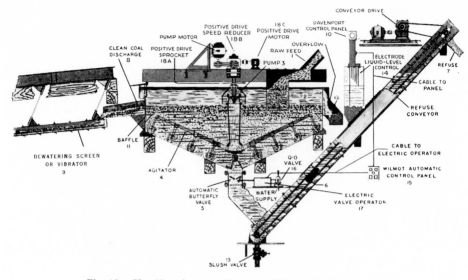

Fig. 10. Classifier cleaner. Courtesy Wilmot Engineering Co.

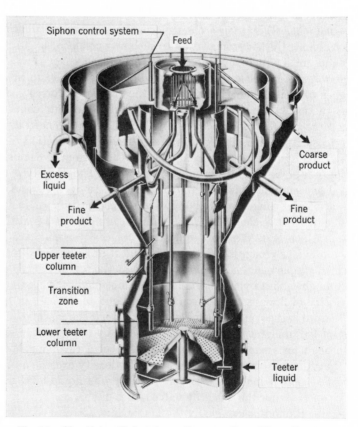

Fig. 11. Classifying Siphonsizer. Courtesy Dorr-Oliver Co., Inc.

single unit (see the cutaway drawing shown in Fig. 11). Among various novel features, the unit includes an inner and outer sorting column, an upper and lower teeter column, and provision for the removal of the coarse fraction by means of one or more syphons, the operation of which is automatically controlled by float valves. Since the discharge of the syphons is near the top of the unit, the total head loss is reduced to a minimum. Because virtually all of the fines and critical-size material is stripped from the coarse product before it enters the teeter bed, the sizing is rapid and efficient.

Also in commercial use are a number of other hindered-settling classifiers, one of the best known of which is the Concenco classifier, made by the Deister Concentrator Co. This unit consists of a series of sorting compartments of uniform size; by regulating the amount of hydraulic water to each compartment and the size of the spigot opening, a series of products is obtained, grading from coarse at the feed end to fine at the overflow end. The same company also makes the Concenco SuperSorter, a multicompartment hydraulic sizer used mainly in the coal industry. In this machine each compartment is provided with a conical bottom into which the sized solids pass and from which they are removed by a water ejector controlled automatically by the volume of solids present. The Dorr Hydroscillator, which combines the features of both mechanical and hydraulic classification, is used to a limited extent in closed-circuit grinding. In appearance it resembles a rake classifier upon which is superimposed a shallow bowl with an oscillating bottom perforated with holes for the introduction of hydraulic water. The separation is sharp and the coarse (rake) product is exceptionally free of slime. The machine operates with as little as 0.7 ton hydraulic water per ton of solids.

Centrifugal Classification (Hydraulic)

The theory and operation of the various types of centrifugal machines have been discussed (see Centrifugal separation), and only the functioning of centrifugals in the field of hydraulic classification will be considered here. They have the advantage of requiring a much smaller ground area than gravity machines, since the effective settling area under centrifugal force, which may reach 1000 times gravity, is greatly increased. However, all types of centrifuges have a high first cost, and relatively high power and maintenance requirements.

A representative machine of this type is the Bird continuous centrifugal, which consists of a truncated cone fixed to and rotating at high speed on a horizontal shaft. Rotating at a slightly slower speed is an internal spiral to remove continuously the solids deposited on the inner surface of the cone or "bowl." Feed enters the cone by means of the hollow center shaft; overflow leaves the cone or bowl through ports at the large end, and oversize solids, moved by the spiral, exit through ports at the small end of the cone.

The continuous centrifugal functioning as a classifier is used in the processing of very fine-grained pigments such as titanium dioxide and lithopone, which require sizing at 100% below 5 μ. Other materials such as clay, calcium carbonate, and fillers are similarly classified. Also, in closed-circuit grinding in the cement industry it can handle a thick slurry ground to 85% below 200 mesh which is suitable for direct blending and calcination.

Liquid Cyclones (11,12). Also within the category of nonmechanical hydraulic classifiers are liquid cyclones, which operate on the same general principle as the familiar dust-collecting cyclone. Although there is a concentration of solids in the underflow, the

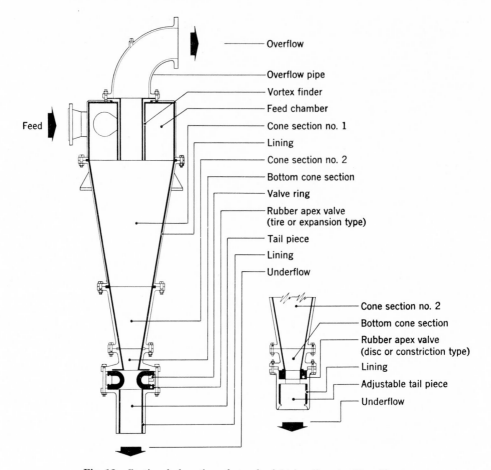

Feed

Overflow

Overflow pipe

Vortex finder

Feed chamber

Cone section no. 1

Lining

Cone section no. 2

Bottom cone section

Valve ring

Rubber apex valve
(tire or expansion type)

Tail piece

Lining

Underflow

Cone section no. 2

Bottom cone section

Rubber apex valve
(disc or constriction type)

Lining

Adjustable tail piece

Underflow

Fig. 12. Sectional elevation of standard 24-in. diameter DorrClone.

cyclone must not be confused with a thickener.   By the very nature of the high shearing forces set up within the unit it is rarely possible to produce a clear overflow.

Since their first installation in the United States in 1949, liquid cyclones have found such extensive industrial application that there are now (1968) many thousands in operation in widely diverse fields, ranging from the closed-circuit grinding of ores to the fractionation of food and pharmaceutical products.   Cyclones are especially well adapted to degritting operations in the treatment of clays, raw water, and petroleum supplies, and to desliming in the ore dressing and metallurgical fields.   The forerunner of the cyclone, the Dutch State Mines separator, now known as the DorrClone, (Dorr-Oliver, Inc.) was described in Gravity separation, Vol. 10, p. 705.   A sectional view of a typical modern DorrClone is shown in Figure 12.   Other models of hydraulic cyclones having operating characteristics similar to those of the DorrClone are manufactured in the U.S. by Equipment Engineers, Bauer Brothers, and Heyl & Paterson.

In operation, feed furnished by a centrifugal pump enters tangentially into the upper section of the cyclone at sufficient pressure to support the vortex action of the pulp within the unit.   The centrifugal forces in the vortex throw the coarser particles contained in the feed to the walls of the cone, where they collect and pass downward and out of the unit through the apex valve, which is frequently fitted with an automatic

Fig. 13. Manifolded 10-mm DorrClone separators in a starch plant.

control, and thence to the discharge, or tail pipe. Fine particles move to the inner spiral of the vortex and together with most of the water are displaced upward to the vortex finder. Depending on the design, the overflow either goes to an overflow chamber or directly to a 90° elbow attached to the vortex finder.

In relation to its small enclosed volume the liquid cyclone has a very high capacity and comparatively low first cost. The diameter of the unit is the basic factor in determining the size of separation and also the capacity. The diameter of the apex valve and vortex finder are then adjusted to suit the desired consistency of discharge and volume split between overflow and underflow. A 10-mm-diam cyclone making a separation in the range of 3 to 5 μ will have a capacity of about 1 gal/min (gpm), whereas a 24-in.-diam unit making a 48-mesh separation would have a capacity of 1500 gpm (6-ft-diam units with a capacity of 3000–4000 gpm have been built). Feed pressures vary from 60–100 psi for 10-mm cyclones to 15–20 psi (or lower) for the larger-sized units.

A number of special cyclones have been developed for use in industry, one of the most widely used being the manifolded type, where a large number (up to 300) of small cyclones operate within a single housing, thereby providing high throughput capacity. Figure 13 shows such an installation in a starch plant. The unit in the foreground has the outer casing removed to show the cyclone arrangement. Multiple cyclones of this general design operate in parallel with common feed, overflow, and discharge chambers.

Table 1. Operating Characteristics and Fields of Application for Aqueous Classifiers

Type of classifier	Normal size range			Classification		Normal feed tonnage range, tons/hr[a]	Max oversize	Normal overflow % solids
	Width	Diameter	Max length	Average separation ranges	Relative classifier efficiency			
straight or unit type	14 in.–20 ft		40 ft	20–150 mesh	medium	1–350	1–1½ in.	5–65
bowl classifier	18 in.–20 ft	4–28 ft	38 ft	65–325 mesh	medium +	1–300	½ in.	5–25
bowl desiltor	4–16 ft	20–50 ft	38 ft	100–325 mesh	medium	5–250	½ in.	1–15
hydroseparator		4–250 ft		usually 100–325 mesh[b]	low	a few lb/hr to 500–700 tons/hr	½ in.	1–20
hydraulic classifiers								
sizer	varies with no. of pockets		varies with no. of pockets	8–100 mesh	high	2–100	⅛–³⁄₁₆ in.	5–20
SuperSorter	6 ft		ca 40 ft	½–150 mesh	high	40–150	½ in.	5–20
Hydroscillator	4–12 ft	4–14 ft	30 ft	20–200 mesh	high	5–250	½–1 in.	15–30
centrifugal classifiers								
cyclone		3–30 in.	9 ft	35 mesh to 3 μ	medium	10–1500 g/min	14–20 m	5–30
solid bowl centrifuge		18–54 in.	70 in.	100 mesh to 5 μ	medium +	up to 500 g/min	½ in.	5–30
cone classifier		2–12 ft		28–325 mesh	low	up to 100	½ in.	5–30
sand washer		7, 9, 12 ft		28–65 mesh	medium	25–125	1 in.	5–20

[a] Unless otherwise indicated.   [b] Special cases 35 mesh to 5 μ.

Table 1a. Operating Characteristics and Fields of Application for Aqueous Classifiers

Type of classifier	Normal feed density range, %	Underflow or rake product, % solids	Drive motor range, hp	Hydraulic water required	Typical applications
straight or unit type	not critical	80–83	½–25	spray wash optional	closed-circuit grinding; washing and dewatering; process feed control
bowl classifier	between 10–75 solids	75–83	bowl: 1–7½ rakes: 1–25	water added with feed or in classifier for correct overflow density	closed-circuit grinding—mostly in secondary circuit but sometimes in primary; washing and dewatering
bowl desiltor	not critical	75–83	bowl: 1–10 rakes: 5–25	spray wash optional	recovery fine sand, limestone, coal, fine phosphate rock from large flow volumes
hydroseparator	5–20 (not critical)	30–50	fractional to 15	all water enters with feed	for fine separation where large feed volumes are involved
hydraulic classifiers sizer	40–60	40–60	1–2 for air pressure	up to 4 tons/ton of feed	gravity concentration of metallic ores; preparation of table feed; sizing of homogeneous materials
SuperSorter	30–60	40–60	1 to operate valves	up to 4 tons/ton of feed	gravity concentration, preparation of table feed, coal; sizing of homogeneous materials
Hydrosillator	40–80	75–83	bowl: 3–10 rakes: 5–20	up to 1.5 tons/ton of feed	used where exceptionally clean rake sands are needed; closed-circuit grinding
centrifugal classifiers cyclone	1–30	55–70	power or pressure head	none	for fine separations in variety fields
solid bowl centrifuge	1–30	40–70	10–150	none	for fine size fractionating to 5 μ
cone classifier	not critical	35–60	none	none	for desliming and primary dewatering
sand washer	ca 30–35 solids	80–83 solids	5–10	none	for desliming and dewatering large tonnages of bulk material

A number of units are often arranged in series with the solids advancing countercurrent to the washing stream. Multiple cyclones may be molded into a single soft rubber block or individually cast of metal or plastic and supported in perforated metal shells. In some applications, such as for catalyst recovery, multiple cyclones are housed in massive casings held together with heavy-tension bolts to withstand high pressure.

For further details of cyclone theory, design, performance, and application see Bradley (12), which also contains an extensive bibliography.

Tables 1 and 1a show the operating characteristics and fields of application for various types of aqueous classifiers.

Pneumatic Classification

Successful air classification requires that the material be substantially dry. Since drying of ore is impractical in most mineral beneficiation plants, the process of air classification is used only for certain special applications or for high-value materials such as a few industrial minerals. The terms "pneumatic classification," "air sizing," and "air classification" are synonymous in this article.

Air sizing (1–3,13,15) is similar to water classification except that it takes place in a medium which is fifty to one hundred times less viscous, and the apparent specific gravity of any pneumatic suspension is much less than that of a water suspension of the same volumetric composition. These factors induce much higher settling velocities in air than in water, higher fluid speeds, and suspensions which are volumetrically more dilute. The same fundamental laws apply in air as in water classification although, in the case of most air suspensions, the operation is usually free-settling. See Gas cleaning and purification.

Pneumatic classification is similar to pneumatic concentration, especially if the material being handled is substantially homogeneous. In this case, separation on pneumatic tables may be according to particle size and shape rather than by specific gravity or apparent bulk density. See Vol. 10, p. 719. The chief applications of air sizing are in closed-circuit grinding in dry mills, the cleaning of fine sizes of bituminous coal, and the grading of dry materials for the consumer market.

In general, pneumatic classifiers may be divided into two forms, stream-flow and centrifugal-flow types, of which the latter are the more important.

Stream-flow, or pure-gravity-type, separation requires the simpler type of equipment; this consists of a chamber in which air or gas velocity is reduced to enable dust particles to settle out by the action of gravity. The particles thus settled must be relatively dense, having the maximum mass for the minimum surface. In practice gravity settlers are limited to collecting particles larger than about 325 mesh (43-μ diam). For removing smaller particles the required vessel size is generally too large. The Howard dust chamber is an example of a stream-flow settler which magnifies its capacity by having a number of shelves which increase the settling area and reduce the height of fall of the particles. This apparatus is used for the cleaning of sulfur dioxide from pyrites-fines calciners.

The dedusting of coal, which is essentially a pneumatic sizing operation, is practiced in many modern fine-coal cleaning plants. The various machines make use of internal fan-induced air currents flowing upward through a stream of falling coal.

The Birtley system is usually operated in open circuit with the dedusting chamber under negative pressure. The controlled inlets allow air to pass through a nozzle,

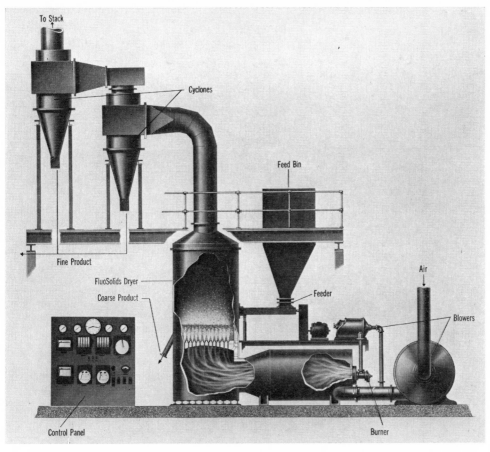

Fig. 14. Dorr-Oliver FluoSolids dryer sizer. Courtesy Dorr-Oliver Co., Inc.

aspirating the coal stream and forming a fluid mass that flows off an adjustable plate and falls into a dedusting column. Air, admitted through adjustable doors for controlling the air volume, picks up the dust from the falling coal and carries it to cyclone dust collectors.

The Simon Carves machine is a screen-type deduster in which the air passing up through the traveling bed of granular coal lifts the dust up through the layer of coal, where it is picked up and carried away by suction currents. The air is cleaned and returned to the system, thus making a closed-circuit system.

The Dorr-Oliver FluoSolids drier sizer (13) is a system which combines drying with pneumatic classification, based on the principle of fluidization. Air or gases supplied under pressure by a blower pass up through a bed of granular material, which is supported on a perforated constriction plate. The flow of the gases through the bed of material produces a turbulent mass which behaves as a fluid, hence the term fluidization. If drying is desired, hot gases from the combustion of oil or gas fuel instead of air alone are passed through the constriction plate (see Fig. 14). The stream of gas rising through the turbulent mass on the constriction plate carries off the fines at a predetermined mesh of separation into a collection cyclone, while the coarse fraction overflows in a fluidized state into a suitable receptacle or bin. The size of the solids, which

Fig. 15. Gyrotor air classifier.   Courtesy Hardinge Co. Metal Products Division, Koppers Co., Inc.

are carried out of the unit by the gases, is governed primarily by the space velocity of the gases, the specific gravity of the solids, and the shape of the particles.   Generally, this unit will have application in continuous sizing and drying of granular material up to ¼ in. in size such as iron ores, sands, coal, limestone and dolomite prior to calcination, and other minerals.

Centrifugal-flow-type pneumatic classification is applied to fine particles only, usually in conjunction with dust collectors of the cyclone type.   Dust-laden gas enters tangentially near the top and is forced down in a constantly decreasing spiral to the dust outlet at the bottom.   Dust particles are dropped at the periphery, and the separating effect increases as the apex of the cone is approached.   Relatively clean air or gas forms a vortex at the center and moves upward into the cleaned air outlet.   In some cases removal efficiencies as great as 98% have been obtained on dusts having an ultimate particle size of 0.1–2.0 μ because of the predominant effect of agglomeration and high concentration of dust.

Several commercial pneumatic machines utilize both gravity and centrifugal force to effect the classification of granular material; a typical machine is the Gayco (Universal Road Machinery Co.).   In operation, the powdered solid is fed through a hollow

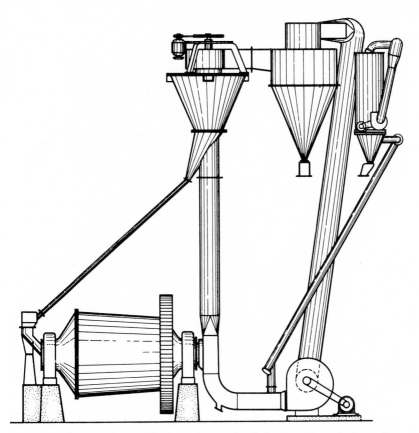

Fig. 16. A Gyrotor air classifier operating in closed circuit with a grinding mill.

vertical shaft onto a revolving disc which is bolted to the shaft. The centrifugal action of the disc throws the material radially across a rising stream of air produced by a circulating fan near the top of the cylinder. A centrifugal motion is also imparted to the air stream by a rotating fan located just above the disc. The resultant effect of these various forces acting on suspended particles is the sedimentation of the coarser grains in the inner shell while the finer grains collect in the conical portion of the outer shell. The Raymond Whizzer (Combustion Engineering Co.) and the Sturtevant Whirlwind (Sturtevant Mill Co.) classifiers operate in a similar manner.

    In the dry-grinding of ores and minerals in ball or tube mills, it is often desirable that pneumatic classifiers in closed circuit return oversize to the mills. Figure 15 shows a cutaway view of the Hardinge Gyrotor air classifier, and Figure 16 a general arrangement with Gyrotor operating in closed circuit with a grinding mill. To the right of the classifier is a product collector with an air recycling connection, and to the extreme right a vent dust collector. The entire system is operated below atmospheric pressure, preventing dust loss.

    In this system a current of air drawn through the mill picks up the partially ground mineral and carries it through a rising duct to the air classifier, where a separation of the coarse and fine particles takes place. The coarse returns to the feed end of the mill, while the fines are carried over into the cyclone product collector, where the air and finished product are separated by centrifugal force. Meanwhile, the oversize fraction is

Table 2. Operating Characteristics and Fields of Operation for Various Types of Screens and Pneumatic Classifiers[a]

	Normal size range, ft			Av separation range	Normal feed range, tons/hr	Max feed size, in.	Capacity, tons/(24 hr)(ft²) through min aperture	Power required, hp range	Typical application
	Width	Length	Diameter						
Screens (for materials coarser than 10–35 mesh)									
grizzlies, coarse	4–6	6–20		6–1½ in.	20–600	12		none	coal, crushed rock, and ores
fine (vibrating)	3–5	6–8		3¾–3/16 in.	10–100	2	1–5	none	same
trommels, coarse		8–24	2–7	2½–⅛ in.	15–500	8	0.3–2.1	5–25	sand, gravel, ores and crushed rock
fine (wet)		3–12	1–6	20–65 mesh	5–100	¼	0.79	3–5	same
shaking, coarse	2–10	6–20		6⅝–½ in.	50–500	2–6	2–80	3–7.5	coal, asbestos, phosphate rock
fine	2–4	3–4		28–150 mesh		½–1	2–20		same
vibrating, coarse	2–5	3.5–12		4½–¼ in.	10–500	4	1–60	1–10	ground ores, potash, sand, and gravel
fine	2.5–4	4–8		4–150 mesh	3–200	½	4–20	1–3	pigments, clay, cement lime, salt, sugar, powders
reels		5–8	1.5–3.5	100–325 mesh					flour, graphite, abrasives
Pneumatic classifiers (for materials finer than 200 mesh)									
FluoSolids sizer	3.5–15.5		1.2–10	20–200 mesh	1–100	¼	40 tons/(ft²) (24 hr)	2 kWh/(tons) (day)	coal, limestone, sand, phosphate rock
cyclones, coarse			3–20	100–325 mesh			1200–47,000 ft³/min	[b]	carbon, talc, metals, dust sizing and separation, sand
fine		1–6		0.1–0.001 mm			600–2500 ft³/min	same	same
air sizers			1–18	20–400 mesh	(for operating data see ref. 1, sect. 20)			1–125	barite, graphite, phosphate rock, limestone, cement, coal, closed-circuit grinding

[a] Unless otherwise indicated. [b] Hp at 50% fan efficiency = 0.3× pressure differential (in. water) (1000 ft³)/min.

returned to the mill for finish grinding. Other closed-circuit arrangements for pneumatic classification have been adapted to other types of mills such as the ring-roller, hammer, and disc mills.

The materials most frequently handled in this type of fine classification for the production of closely sized particles in the 200-mesh (72-μ) to 1.5-μ range are aluminum oxide, bronze powders, amorphous silica, tungsten, graphite, abrasive powders, lead oxide, and activated carbon. The classifiers may be installed in single or multiple units to make one or more graded products. Laboratory units are also available to supplement screen testing in the very fine ranges.

The principal operating characteristics and fields of application of the various types of screens and pneumatic classifiers are summarized in Table 2.

Classifier Design and Performance

Fundamentals of Design. Classifier design is based first upon the rate of volumetric displacement of incoming feed (solids plus fluid) and the rate of settlement of the finest particle to be retained in the coarse fraction, and second upon the rate at which the products must be discharged from the machine.

Within limits, the lower the feed dilution, the smaller the machine for a given tonnage of solids and required settling rate, but as feed dilution is lowered the viscosity and/or density of the solid–fluid mixture tends to increase, thus reducing the settling rate. A more serious disadvantage results from the fact that the voids between the particles of the coarse fraction carry a higher percentage of feed solids, thereby lowering the separating efficiency. These relationships are shown in Figure 17.

The settling rate of a solid particle in a fluid depends upon its diameter, density, and shape factor, and the density and viscosity of the fluid (see Sedimentation). The

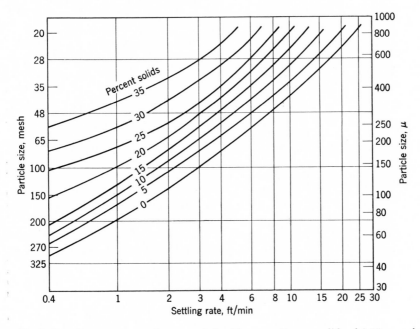

Fig. 17. Typical settling rate curves for normal classifier operation on solids of 2.65 sp gr in water at 20°C.

effect of increased numbers of particles (crowding) is roughly that of increasing the density and viscosity of the fluids. At 20°C, for instance, the settling rate of a quartz sphere (sp gr 2.65) of 0.147-mm diam is theoretically 3.0 ft/min in water, whereas in a pulp of 25% solids the rate falls to 0.4 ft/min, and under hindered-settling conditions at 40% solids (volume basis) it drops to about 0.30 ft/min, or roughly one-tenth the rate at infinite dilution.

For mechanical classifiers, in the case of metallurgical pulps, the overflow dilution should not be less than 3:1 for coarse (up to 28 mesh) separations and not less than 5:1 for 200-mesh separations. For limestone and clays twice this dilution may be necessary. Having determined the settling rate at the size of separation, usually from an actual test, a unit area (in square feet per ton of overflow solids per 24 hr) is calculated (1). This means that it is necessary to provide a certain total settling area in one or more classifiers to handle the tonnage indicated. In practice, various area factors which may range from 1.4 to 5.0, depending upon the machine, are applied in calculating "actual" as compared to the "theoretical" areas indicated. Raking capacities vary with the particular design of the machine, the rake type being available with single and multiple (up to quadruplex) raking units, so that most rake-to-feed ratios encountered in practice can be handled without difficulty.

In the case of mechanical classifiers and hydroseparators it is possible to predict with remarkable accuracy the size distribution and percentage weight of the underflow and overflow for any given feed and mesh of separation. The procedure involves applying "settling factors" to a series of size bands, or "partials," obtained from a plot of the feed-size distribution, determining the grams settled in each band from the laws of particle dynamics, and adding the overflow solids entrained as void filling in the underflow. From these weights the size distribution of the underflow is obtained and that of the overflow found by difference. For details of this calculation see Roberts and Fitch (14).

For hindered-settling classifiers, design calculations involve finding the settling rate of the average-size particle in each size band of the feed for the *void ratio* (vol of water/vol of pulp) of the mass of pulp in which the particle is settling. Richardson and Zaki (9) explain the settling behavior by means of the following general equation:

$$\frac{V_c}{V_i} = \epsilon^n \tag{2}$$

where V_c is the velocity of the particle settling in a pulp of void ratio (porosity) ϵ; V_i is the Stokes settling velocity of the particle at infinite dilution, and $n = f(Re)$ (Re is the Reynolds number):

$$Re = V_o \, \alpha\rho/\mu \tag{3}$$

where V_o is the terminal falling velocity of the particle, α is its diameter, ρ is the density, and μ the viscosity of the liquid medium. The numerical values of n are found to be as follows:

$$0 \ < Re < 0.2 \qquad\qquad n = 4.65$$
$$0.2 < Re < 1.0 \qquad\qquad n = 4.35 \times Re^{-0.03}$$
$$1.0 < Re < 500 \qquad\qquad n = 4.45 \times Re^{-0.1}$$
$$Re > 500 \qquad\qquad n = 2.39$$

From the above equations it is possible to determine the upward displacement of water required to hold particles of various diameters at the void ratios desired. For practical purposes 0.6 void ratio is about the lower limit for effective mobility (teeter) in hydraulic sizers. The sharpness of separation is to a considerable extent dependent upon the ratio of total hydraulic water to solids used, but since the areas required are proportional to the volume of hydraulic water, it is usually not economical to exceed a ratio of about 3:1, with feed dilutions in the range of 30–40% solids.

Knowing the tons of solids per hour to be handled for each size band (from a feed analysis), the ratio of hydraulic water to solids, and the upward displacement rate, the settling area required for each size fraction is readily calculated. While these areas do not usually conform exactly with manufacturers' designs, it is nearly always possible to use various combinations of standard compartments to complete the sizing. The total number of compartments will depend upon the particle-size range in the feed and the maximum particle size overflowed. However, not more than about a 2–3 mesh spread should be allowed for each compartment, or the water rate used will be too low for the coarser size and too high for the finer size. The head loss through constriction plate holes or submerged nozzles should be in the range of 2–4 ft of water.

Table 3. Tests Illustrating Differences in Size Distribution between Products from a Hydraulic Sizer and a Standard Rake Classifier[a]

(screen analyses reported as percent cumulative plus)

Sizing		Feed	Dorr classifier rake products	Dorr sizer spigots 1–5	Dorr classifier overflow	Dorr sizer spigot 6 + overflow
Mesh	Microns					
28	475	0.28	0.5	0.5		
35	336	9.65	13.5	19.4		
48	238	29.3	33.0	47.8		
65	208	46.1	63.0	73.0	2.4	2.4
100	147	66.5	86.0	95.1	22.0	9.4
150	104	80.7	94.6	99.8	47.0	47.7
200	74	86.8	97.1	100.0	62.0	72.0
wt %.................		100.0	70.3	66.2	29.7	33.8

[a] Separation in each case at 2.4% + 65 mesh.

Comparative Performance of Classifiers. In spite of the drainage decks which are a feature of mechanical classifiers, the rake—or spiral—product entrains a certain fraction of the fine solids. The hydraulic classifier, on the other hand, displaces most material below the mesh of separation and the spigot, or underflow products are slime-free. This is shown in Table 3, where the performance of a hydraulic classifier is compared with that of a mechanical classifier. Note that while the size distribution of the overflow is about the same in each case, the spigot product of the hydraulic unit is practically free of −150 mesh material. Although the hydraulic sizer can make a number of closely sized, clean products, it has less capacity than a mechanical unit of the same size, involves loss of head, and requires equipment for reclaiming and pumping hydraulic water. The cyclone has a much lower first cost and far higher capacity than either of the above, and requires the use of little, or no water, but does have a relatively high power demand for pumping.

Auxiliary Equipment and Materials of Construction

Most of the machines described in this article require for their normal operation certain items of auxiliary equipment which are discussed below.

Feeders. Many of the machines are fed directly by delivery chutes or pipes, but some of them require mechanical feeders. Many types are available, including wet, dry, proportioning, weighing, disc, chain, vibrating, screw, and belt-operated. Detailed discussions of these various types may be found in reference 3, section 18, pp. 97–107 and reference 1, section 7.

Pumps. Mechanisms such as hydroseparators, which operate continuously in tanks, usually discharge through a valve-controlled spigot, but in some instances it is desirable to have their underflows controlled by a pump which may be for either suction or pressure operation. Diaphragm pumps are most commonly used for this purpose. (See Sedimentation. Also underflow lines and density controls are covered in the same article.) Pressure pumps, usually of the centrifugal type, are required for feeding liquid cyclones such as the DorrClone and the Centri-cleaner (Bauer Bros. Co.).

Miscellaneous. There are a number of attachments for mechanical classifiers to increase their efficiency and to control their operation. Among these are a hydrometer density indicator for the control of the dilution of classifier overflow, a floating chip-removing device, and a suction box to reduce the moisture of the rake product. It is occasionally necessary to use an auxiliary sand scoop or wheel to complete the circuit between a classifier and the ball mill. For bowl classifiers there is a "critical size" control to improve classification efficiency by eliminating surging in the pool. Coarse screens are usually placed ahead of classifiers to scalp off heavy oversize.

FluoSolids sizers, cyclones, and other pneumatic classifiers are operated by fans or blowers which vary widely in capacity and pressure. Some of the limiting values are given in Table 2.

To prevent damage to drive mechanisms of hydroseparators, torque recorders and automatic overload alarms are available.

Materials of Construction. In those instances where equipment operates on dry materials, active corrosive conditions do not exist, permitting the use of iron and steel construction for the most part. In the presence of corrosive gases, stainless steel or protective coatings are used. Where severe abrasion is present, manganese steel and other hard alloy steels are employed. Also, rubber linings are installed at certain critical locations to guard against abrasion. In hydraulic classification, iron and steel construction is also the rule since water is the usual medium, but if separations are made in corrosive solutions rubber, lead-covered, stainless steel, or wooden submerged parts are employed. Abrasion is quite severe in hydraulic cyclones and its effects are minimized by using rubber or Carbofrax (The Norton Co.) at critical locations. The same practice applies to other types of sizing equipment.

Bibliography

"Size Separation" in *ECT* 1st ed., Vol. 12, pp. 520–533, by W. A. Lutz, F. L. Bosqui, and A. D. Camp, The Dorr Company.

1. J. H. Perry, *Chemical Engineers' Handbook*, 4th ed., McGraw-Hill Book Co., Inc., New York, 1963: Sect. 21, "Screening," pp. 46–52 and "Classification," pp. 52–57; Sect. 8, "Particle Size Classifier," pp. 27–32; Sect. 19, "Centrifuges," pp. 86–100; Sect. 7, "Feeders," pp. 32–34; Sect. 20, "Gas Solids Separation," pp. 62–96.

2. D. M. Liddell, *Handbook of Nonferrous Metallurgy*, Vol. I, McGraw-Hill Book Co., Inc., New York, 1945: Chap. 6, "Classification"; Chap. 5, "Screening"; Chap. 12, "Separation of Solids and Liquids from Gases."

3. A. F. Taggart, *Handbook of Mineral Dressing*, John Wiley & Sons, Inc., New York, 1945: Sect. 7, "Screen Sizing"; Sect. 19, "Screen Analysis," pp. 100–109; Sect. 8, "Classification with Water"; Sect. 9, "Air Sizing and Dust Collection."

4. S. E. Gluck, "Gyratory, Circular-Motion and Special Action Screens," *Chem. Eng.* **72**, pp. 131–146 (Oct. 25, 1965).

5. A. M. Gaudin, *Principles of Mineral Dressing*, McGraw-Hill Book Co., Inc., New York, 1939: Chap. 3, "Laboratory Sizing"; Chap. 7, "Industrial Screening"; Chap. 8, "Movement of Solids in Fluids"; Chap. 9, "Classification."

6. C. L. Stevenson, "Probability Sizing—Principles and Practice," *Papers Meeting Am. Inst. Mining Engrs., Los Angeles, Cal., 1967.*

7. J. H. Healy, A. J. Carlson, M. J. Hovland, and G. M. Marincel, "Erie Mining Co. Patents New Method for Screening Ores in Very Fine Size Ranges," *Trans. Soc. Mining Engr. AIME, April 1967.*

8. E. J. Roberts, "Sizing by Water Classification," *Papers Meeting Am. Inst. Chem. Engrs., Biloxi, Miss., March 10, 1953.*

9. J. F. Richardson and W. N. Zaki, "Sedimentation and Fluidization," Part I, *Trans. Inst. Chem. Engrs. (London)* **32**, (1954).

10. J. V. N. Door and F. L. Bosqui, "Recent Developments in Classification and Fluidization as Applications of the Principles of Particle Dynamics," in *Symposium on Mineral Dressing, Inst. Mining and Met., London, Sept. 23–25, 1952.*

11. D. A. Dahlstrom, "Fundamentals and Applications of the Liquid Cyclone," *Papers, Meet. Am. Inst. Chem. Engrs., Biloxi, Miss., March 10, 1953.*

12. D. Bradley, *The Hydrocyclone (Intern. Ser. Monographs Chem. Eng.)*, Vol. 4, Pergamon Press, London and New York, 1965.

13. C. J. Wall and W. J. Ash, "Fluid-Solid Air Sizer and Dryer," *Ind. Eng. Chem.* **41**, 1247–1249 (1949).

14. E. J. Roberts and E. B. Fitch, "Predicting Size Distribution in Classifier Product," *Trans. Soc. Mining Engr. AIME, New York, 1955.*

15. C. R. G. Treasure, "Fine Particle Classification," *Trans. Inst. Chem. Eng.* **43**, T199–T205 (1965).

F. L. Bosqui
Consultant

SLIP AGENTS. See Abherents.

SMOKES, FUMES, AND SMOG

Smokes, fumes, and smog are of growing interest because of what they do to the atmosphere and, in turn, what effects they have on all that the atmosphere surrounds—humans, plants, animals, property, goods. Atmospheric effects, however, come not only from atmospheric contaminants; even uncontaminated air has deteriorating effects on things. Oxygen and moisture corrode certain metals, while lack of moisture can cause deleterious drying of foods, fabrics, and mucous membranes. Aside from these "natural" effects of the clean atmosphere, smokes and fumes add their effects. What are smokes, fumes, and smog? What are their sources, characteristics, and effects? How can those effects be prevented or minimized?

The definition of smokes and fumes is imprecise and somewhat arbitrary. Smokes and fumes include liquid or solid particles, generally less than one micron in size, which are suspended in a gas; some metallurgical fumes may, by custom, include particles up to several microns in size. When the particle size exceeds a few microns, however, it is readily visible as an individual particle and is more commonly called a dust particle. In general, smokes are clouds made up of many particles, each of which is too small to be individually visible, which in the aggregate scatter light and are opaque to visible light. Fumes are usually not as opaque as smoke, but are translucent, or nearly so, and may have odorous or toxic gases associated with the liquid or solid particles. Smokes and fumes are generally produced by some high-temperature process, most often combustion. Some examples are tobacco smoke, coal smoke, wood smoke, smelter fume, oven fume, electric-furnace fume, etc. Smog is also an imprecise term, originally derived from the words smoke and fog, but now usually associated with the visibility-impairing mixture of liquid and solid particles and gases which appears most often in Los Angeles, but also with increasing frequency in other large cities. See also Dust (Hygienic aspects).

Sources

Smoke, fumes, and dust come from natural sources such as dust storms and volcanos, but the principal sources are man-made. Many large cities have taken action sporadically against coal smoke since London first did so in about the fourteenth century. In the United States in recent years, while coal smoke has been largely eliminated, the rapid expansion of the use of the gasoline-powered automobile and diesel-powered locomotive and truck has made transportation the largest single source of air pollution.

Figure 1 shows the relative size of sources by categories in tons per year for 1966. The largest single contaminant shown is neither a smoke or fume, but is carbon monoxide, an odorless, colorless, poisonous gas produced by automobile engines. Fortunately, this dangerous gas does not accumulate in the atmosphere, but disappears rapidly by some unknown mechanism. Also, in a few days the atmosphere rids itself of all of the pollutants in Figure 1. By contrast, carbon dioxide (a product of carbonaceous combustion), a benign gaseous "pollutant" not included in Figure 1, does not disappear, but accumulates in the atmosphere. Since the beginning of the extensive use of fuel with the Industrial Revolution, the CO_2 content of the air has increased by more than 10 percent to its present level of about 330 ppm (1). This increase is beneficial for all vegetation; in fact, many greenhouse operators now deliberately add 2000 ppm of CO_2 to the air over their plants to improve production. The rising CO_2

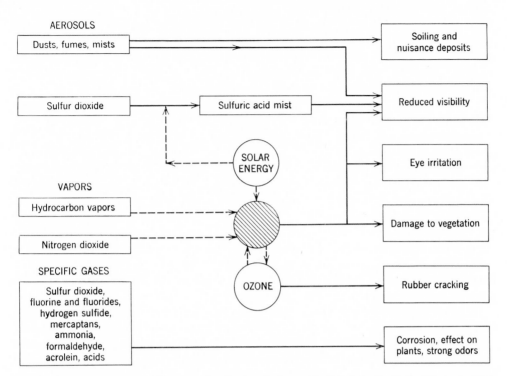

Fig. 1. Sources of the 142 million tons of pollution discharged to the air in the United States in 1966 (as estimated by the U.S. Department of Health, Education, and Welfare).

content in the atmosphere is believed to have a slight global warming effect because the sun's heat is held in the air more effectively and therefore less of that heat is radiated to outer space.   Counteracting the heating effect is the slow accumulation of fine particles in the air; these particles partially block the sun's rays and thus have a slight global chilling effect.   The ice crystals (resulting from the combustion of hydrocarbons), which form the familiar white contrails of jet aircraft usually sublimate quickly. In areas where they persist and become concentrated because of heavy air traffic, there is a marked reduction of solar radiation reaching the earth's surface.

Losses to the atmosphere from industrial processes vary as a result of different production methods.   A general idea of the losses from each of six general categories is as follows:

1. Combustion: 1–30 lb/ton of product burned.
2. Petroleum: 0.25–1.5% of the material processed or handled.
3. Chemical and allied products: 0.5–2% of the total input.
4. Metal and metal products: 0.5–2% of the basic materials put into the process.
5. Stone, sand, and glass products: 1–3% of the basic products treated in the process.
6. Food products: 0.25–1% of the basic products put into the process.

As an example of the quantities of air pollutants resulting from all sources, the air pollution concentration in one area of four million people was studied.   The combined daily total of all air contaminants discharged to the air equaled from 2000 to 2500 tons. At the same time, each foot-deep layer of air over the 150-square-mile area contains about 150,000 tons of air, or in the first 100-foot depth above the ground the weight of air over the area is 15 million tons. Thus, if the contaminants were uniformly mixed in that 100-feet-deep layer, they would constitute less than 0.02% by weight. However, this small percentage may have significant effects on visibility, and, for some individuals under certain atmospheric conditions, on health.

Combustion. Almost every combustible substance may produce smoke if burned. Magnesium produces a white smoke of finely divided MgO particles. Most carbonaceous substances and hydrocarbons produce smoke if improperly burned, that is, if some or all of the burning substance is supplied with an insufficient amount of oxygen. It is thought that the unreacted carbon molecules agglomerate as they leave the reaction zone, forming long chains of carbon particles. The accumulation of large quantities of these agglomerates and chains on the walls in the cooler parts of the combustion system are known as soot deposits. Complex organic molecules, some of which can be carcinogenic, may adhere to these soot particles produced by burning coal or oil. Thus, an ancient occupational disease of chimney sweeps was skin cancer, induced by some constituent of soot. It should be noted that, as with tobacco-induced cancer, the malady results from massive exposure, over a prolonged period; for reasons still not understood, most of those individuals so exposed never acquire the disorder.

Another diminishing pollutant from coal combustion is fly ash, the finely divided ash residue from large industrial and power-plant furnaces which burn finely ground pulverized coal or residual oil. The electric utilities have led the way in fly ash control by installing massive electrostatic precipitators which remove over 90% of that fine ash from the stack gases. Diligent research has found a few uses for this fine ash in concrete, paving materials, and other products, but most of it must be deposited as a solid waste in landfills.

Pollutants from incomplete combustion are hydrocarbons and aldehydes. Unavoidable products of combustion in air are nitrogen oxides. Sulfur-containing fuels release sulfur dioxide and small amounts of sulfur trioxide when burned.

Metallurgical Processes. Many metallurgical processes heat a mixture of raw minerals to such high temperatures that small amounts of those materials are vaporized. As soon as these vapors leave the hot zone, they condense and form opaque clouds of extremely finely divided solid particles. Thus in steelmaking, unless collection equipment is applied, brown or red iron oxide smoke is emitted from Bessemer converters, and from open-hearth, electric-arc, and basic oxygen furnaces. Ferrosilicon furnaces, calcium carbide furnaces, and lime kilns produce dense white smoke. Foundry cupolas produce tan or gray smoke. All of these smokes can be collected by elaborate and expensive equipment. In the case of the basic oxygen furnace for steelmaking, which has been widely used recently, the smoke produced is so extremely dense that operation without smoke-abatement equipment would be intolerable. Fortunately, the economic advantages of this Austrian-developed method of steelmaking are so great that the cost of highly effective, expensive collection equipment can be justified economically. See Steel. Unfortunately, this is not true of many other dirty industrial processes.

Electric furnaces emit about 5 lb of fume/ton of material charged and about 65% of this fume is less than 5 μ. Gray iron foundries emit about 16 lb of dust and fume/ton, about 40% of which is below 5 μ.

Transportation. Every 10 gallons (about 60 lb) of gasoline purchased and burned in city traffic results in the emission of the following pollutants to the air at street level (4):

	Pounds
carbon monoxide	30
hydrocarbons	3
nitrogen oxides	1
miscellaneous gas and particles	1/5

This collection of pollutants rarely creates visible smoke. However, because their aggregate volume is so enormous and they are released at street level, their contribution to total pollution is of major importance. Furthermore, photochemical reactions may occur between the pollutants in the air, producing the gases and droplets of the eye-irritating smog so evident in the atmosphere of Los Angeles, where conditions are particularly conducive to smog formation.

The diesel locomotive, truck, or car produces very little carbon monoxide, but releases 25–50% more particulates than the gasoline engine. When the diesel is heavily loaded or poorly maintained, its smoke is highly objectionable.

Measurements on jet aircraft exhaust in Los Angeles showed particle emissions up to 27 lb/ton of fuel consumed. During periods of atmospheric inversion this visible black smoke frequently accumulates in thin layers in the air above busy airports.

Petroleum Production. Petroleum refineries utilize combustion in many processes, thereby releasing many products of combustion. In addition, they circulate large quantities of hydrocarbon gases, vapors, and volatile liquids through processing apparatus which may have some leakage. Excess vapors are sometimes disposed of by burning from open flares; these can be made smokeless by using jets of steam to provide intense mixing with air. Large storage tanks for volatile liquids must be vented; the gases released should be collected to avoid contributing to smog.

Crude oil contains sulfur in varying amounts. As the crude oil is processed, the sulfur is distributed among the different fractions, tending to accumulate in the heavier materials. Cracking processes, both thermal and catalytic, convert a part of the sulfur into hydrogen sulfide, which separates out with the light gas fractions. Thiols (mercaptans) are also formed and concentrate for the most part in the gasoline fractions, from which they are removed by some type of treatment (see Gasoline; Hydrorefining under Hydroprocesses; Sulfur compounds). When the sulfur compounds are burned, sulfur dioxide is formed and emitted with the flue gases. A small proportion of the sulfur is converted to sulfur trioxide. This condenses with moisture when it cools off in the air, forming fine droplets of sulfuric acid which cause the characteristic blue haze from stacks of furnaces burning sulfur compounds.

The exhaust gases from the regeneration of catalysts used in the catalytic-cracking process contain dust. Small quantities of hydrocarbons, ammonia, and cyanide may be present. Carbon monoxide is present in sufficient concentrations to cause concern for personnel conducting tests on this equipment.

Chemical and Allied Products. The losses from chemical plants are usually odoriferous gases, vapors, and mists, depending upon the process. For example, the sulfur dioxide content of the exhaust gases of a sulfuric acid plant may be 1/4–1/2% by volume, which is sufficient to cause damage to vegetation or nuisance to the community unless the vapors are treated or emitted from a tall stack. Chemical plants dealing with soap and rubber products cause concern because of the odors associated with the operations. Paint and varnish manufacture discharges aldehydes, acrolein, and other products which may average losses as high as 120 lb/ton of material processed through the cookers. Fertilizer operations result in dust losses from grinding, mixing, and packaging of products. Losses here may be as high as 20 lb/ton of material processed. Animal-fat rendering processes cause obnoxious odors and release as much as 15 lb/ton of material cooked in the form of mists and vapors. In many of these operations solid or liquid fuels used in the process will produce contaminants, as discussed under Combustion (p. 402).

Manufacture of chemicals covers a wide range of materials and operations, with a correspondingly wide variety of possible air pollution. Products coming under this heading, in addition to those mentioned above, are coal tar derivatives, plastics, synthetic fibers, alkalis, and many others.

Mineral Earth Processing (Stone, Sand, and Glass). These processes are subject to losses of dust which may contain fluorides. Losses in rock-wool plants average 30 lb of dust/ton of process weight. Concrete-mixing plants and asphalt-paving production vary, in their discharge, with the fineness of the materials used. Some operations have shown losses in excess of 120 lb/ton of process weight. Crushing operations which utilize conveyors, screens, and rollers frequently lose large quantities of dust to the atmosphere. Glass and frit manufacturers lose only small quantities of dust, but are concerned with the gaseous or particulate fluorides which can accumulate in vegetation to damaging levels.

Food Products. Feed and flour mills emit dust which varies in quantity according to the efficiency of operation. Discharges frequently result in dust nuisances and, in some cases, strong odors. Processing of fish, meat, and coffee results in malodors. The quantities of material discharged (in cases where tests have been able to establish the value) are extremely small, but many odoriferous substances, especially organic sulfur compounds, are readily detected by the human olfactory sense in concentrations too small to be measured by instruments presently available.

Effects of Contaminants

The complex mixture of air contaminants present in the atmosphere of industrial communities produces a variety of effects. Some of the resultant nuisances are associated with chemical reactions in the atmosphere. Dusts, fumes, and mists are responsible for soiling effects and reduction of visibility. The atmospheric oxidation of sulfur dioxide to sulfur trioxide and the resulting sulfuric acid mists contribute to haze formation. When stable air conditions are such as to provide time for the oxidation of hydrocarbon vapors in the air, aerosols may be formed. The particles produced in this photochemical reaction result from the polymerization of the oxidation products of certain unsaturated hydrocarbons. Droplets of organic acids or peroxides exist at certain temperatures.

Among the vapors contained in polluted air there may be quantities of hydrocarbons. Olefinic, branched-chain, and cyclic compounds present in gasoline vapor are readily oxidized in the presence of sunlight and oxides of nitrogen to produce photochemical smog which is highly irritating to the eyes and causes damage to vegetation. A by-product of this chemical reaction is ozone, which aids in the further oxidation of the hydrocarbons and may leave residual ozone concentrations sufficiently high to lead to cracking in rubber. The gas-phase organic acids, aldehydes, and peroxides resulting from this reaction may have nuisance value or harmful effects. Some of these interrelationships are represented schematically in Figure 2.

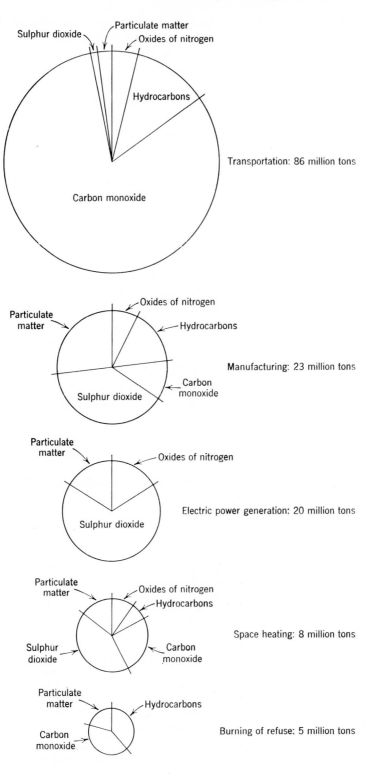

Fig. 2. Atmospheric contaminants and their effects.

Studies have been conducted which show the specific effects produced on vegetation by sulfur dioxide, oxidized hydrocarbons, fluorides, and ethylene. Distinct symptoms in plants can be ascribed for each of these gases. Eye irritation and odor evaluations are based on subjective observations.

The gaseous components associated with industrial activity, such as sulfur dioxide, hydrogen sulfide, oxides of nitrogen, and carbon monoxide, may reach concentrations which will cause damage to property. Fluorine compounds and sulfur dioxide cause specific damage to plant life. In evaluating the effects of a single contaminant or a group of contaminants in a community, the time of exposure and the concentration are important factors.

Most of the gases and vapors are colorless and not visible in the atmosphere. Their effects usually reveal their presence. At 2–3 ppm one of the most well-known contaminants, sulfur dioxide, has a noticeable odor, and it will damage certain species of vegetation at $1/4$ ppm. Sulfur dioxide concentration has been reported in different cities to vary from 0.01 to 3.00 ppm. This gas is also known to contribute to the corrosion effects found on buildings and power lines.

Research studies on other pollutants have not progressed to the stage where threshold limits in the general atmosphere are known. The concentrations in the air seldom exceed 2 ppm for any single chemical or class of air contaminant. Industrial hygiene standards may be helpful in considering the physiological effects of suspected contaminants. Table 1 lists most of the gases and vapors that can be found in a contaminated atmosphere.

The physiological effects of air pollution, of widespread concern to the general public, require additional research. Complaints show that large segments of the population in industrial areas believe that their health is being impaired. Health is such a complicated result of many positive and negative factors, however, that much more evidence is being sought to determine the effects of pollution on health. Industrial hygiene standards which are used to protect the workers against 8-hr exposures to

Table 1. Physiological Effects of Gases and Vapors Sometimes Present in Industrial Atmospheres, in ppm, by volume (10)

Substance	First effects	Threshold concentration	Dangerous or fatal concentration
acrolein	eye irritant	0.1	150–200
ammonia	throat irritant, edema	50	2,500
carbon monoxide	headache, heart effect	50	2,000
chlorine	irritation, edema	1	35–60
formaldehyde	eye irritant	5[a]	20–100
hydrogen chloride	throat irritant	5[a]	1,000
hydrogen cyanide	headache, paralysis	10[a]	100–200
hydrogen fluoride	throat irritant, mottled teeth	3	50–100
hydrogen sulfide	paralysis	10[a]	500
nitrogen dioxide	irritation, edema	5	100–150
ozone	irritation	0.1	
phosgene	lung irritant, edema	0.1	25
sulfur dioxide	throat and lung irritant	5	50–250

[a] These values are recommended as maximum concentrations for continuous 8-hr exposure with no impairment of health or well-being. "Threshold Limit Values for 1967," adopted at the 29th Annual Meeting of the American Conference of Governmental Hygienists, Chicago, May 1–2, 1967.

chemical compounds are not applicable to the general community. The relatively low concentrations of most air contaminants and the long exposure time represent different criteria to be considered in physiological studies of air contaminants. The determination of chronic or long-range hazards of low concentrations of various chemicals will require years of research. Efforts in this field are confined to a limited number of workers who are developing techniques for the experimentation. Studies are underway to evaluate the increased rate of lung cancer which may be associated with the contaminants in the general atmosphere. Table 1 gives information on the physiological effects of a number of gases and vapors sometimes present in industrial atmospheres.

Most of the effects from air contamination in industrial areas are considered to have only nuisance value. Economic losses, however, can reach tremendous figures. Although the loss of valuable compounds to the atmosphere from industrial processes represents a minor fraction of a total process, this figure, too, can reach astounding values on a national basis. The development of technology in the recovery of air waste should be explored for the recovery of critical materials or as a conservation measure. As an example, recent developments in the recovery of sulfur from refinery gas have resulted in valuable contributions of sulfur during periods of marked shortage of this valuable product. Although the cost of cleaning the atmosphere is a burden to the industrial community, the costs of corrosion, smudging, sunlight obscuration, and vegetation damage probably exceed that cost. The polluter, whether in industry or a private backyard burner, must keep in mind that when he makes the unconscious decision to pollute, he is deciding to add to his neighbor's repair and cleaning costs and perhaps to his physical discomfort as well. In a primarily agrarian society these "insults" to the neighbors were undetectable or negligible. In today's metropolitan areas waste disposal customs must be refined.

Control Measures

Control measures must be designed to reduce the detrimental effects resulting from air pollution. Smog attacks affecting an entire community can be minimized only by a control program against *all* air contaminants. Single sources are treated to relieve local nuisance conditions. Regardless of the degree of control measures required, three basic methods can be applied to reduce aerosols, vapors, and gaseous contaminants found in smoke and fumes: (*1*) Reduction at the source is accomplished by the installation of collection equipment or through operational changes which will inhibit the discharges to the atmosphere. (*2*) Dilution of the source can be accomplished by using amounts of air sufficient to make the discharge unobjectionable. (*3*) Allocating the use of the land to prevent harmful concentrations from occurring at a single source or from an area having many sources can be an effective control measure. In applying this principle, the mass rate of emission from an area is prorated over the acreage utilized by the sources. Either the acreage to be occupied or the total quantity of contaminants discharged can be regulated to avoid harmful concentrations. The mass discharged will be governed by the activity.

Before any control measures are specified, an additional factor must be evaluated. Weather plays an important role in accumulating or dispersing air contaminants. The dispersion of local concentrations of atmospheric pollution by air motion is a continuous process, but the rate at which the contaminants can be dispersed is extremely variable. The horizontal and vertical movements of the atmosphere are the primary factors in determining the rate of dispersion.

Table 2. Collection Equipment—Solid and Liquid Aerosols

| Equipment | Dust characteristics | | | Pressure drop, in. H₂O | Advantages | Disadvantages | Efficiency, % (wt basis) |
	Type	Particle size, μ	Sp gr				
		Centrifugal collectors					
simple cyclone	wood dust	50–1000	0.4–0.7	0.5–2.0	simple in construction	low efficiency	70–90
	grain dust	10–200	0.9–1.1				60–80
	mineral dust	10–500	2.0–3.0				70–90
	pulverized chemicals	10–500	1.5–3.0				70–90
high-efficiency cyclone	catalyst dust	2–80	1.5–3.5	2.0–6.0	relatively high efficiency	subject to abrasion damage	65–80
	fly ash	0.1–100	0.4–1.5				50–70
	other fine dust	5–200	1.0–3.0				85–98
impeller	foundry dust	10–300	2.5–4.0	acts as own fan	low space requirement	impeller abrasion, causing unbalance	70–90
		Electrostatic precipitators					
single-stage	gray iron cupola fume	0.5–50	3–6	0.25–0.5	high efficiency under severe conditions	high initial cost, operating difficulties	90–97
	electric-steel furnace fume	0.1–20	5–7				90–97
	open-hearth steel[a] furnace fume	0.1–3	5–7				96–99
	catalyst dust	2–80	1.5–3.5				85–98
two-stage	oil mist	10–400	~1	0.25–0.5	high efficiency for low dust loading, safe in operation	limited in use	85–99
	air conditioning	0.2–10					95–99

			Cloth filters				
tubular	metallurgical fume nonferrous ferrous	0.03–1.0 0.10–50.0	~5 3–6	0.5–6.0	high efficiency over wide particle size range	caking from moisture	98–99.5 97–99.5
screen or frame	ceramic dusts metallurgical fume	1–50 0.1–50	1–3 3–6	0.5–4.0	somewhat self-cleaning	higher stresses on filter mediums	95–99.0 94–97
reverse flow (standard cloths)	same as screen type shown above			0.5–3.0	higher dust loadings possible		
reverse jet (felt mediums)	carbon black flour dust	0.1–10 5–100	1.5 0.9	1.0–6.0	high filter ratios possible	bag wear	99.5 99.9
			Wet collectors				
spray chamber	rock dust asphalt mist acid mist	40–500 10–400 20–500	2–3 ~1 1.1–1.3	0.5–1.0	low pressure drop	high nozzle pressure required for good collection	60–75 70–80 70–90
inertial	Al and Mg grinding dust foundry dust	50–1,000 10–300	1.7–2.8 2.4–4.0	2.0–4.0	no nozzle maintenance	higher pressure drop	80–95 70–90
centrifugal spray	rock and sand dust	20–500	2–3	1.0–4.0	combined scrubbing and centrifugal action	abrasion	75–95
	acid and caustic mist	20–500	1.1–1.3				75–95
venturi scrubber	sulfuric acid mist from concentrator chemical fume	2–10 0.1–50	~1.5 1.5–3.5	10.0–15.0	high efficiency, low water rate	high power consumption	85–95 60–85

[a] Cold metal furnaces.

The effectiveness of horizontal dispersion depends upon the speed of the horizontal transport, as indicated by the wind velocity. Turbulence in this air motion affects the shape of the gas stream. Dilution takes place both in the direction of the air flow and at right angles to the flow of air. Vertical dispersion is important in relieving local concentrations. Since the horizontal air movement is usually greater at increased heights above the ground, the pollutants are more readily dispersed at higher elevations above the source. Where vertical dispersion is retarded by vertical temperature distribution, critical air-pollution conditions can prevail. The normal temperature decrease with height in the atmosphere lies between 0 and 1°C/100 m; any vertical motion brought about by the wind can take place without too much resistance under these normal conditions. When there is an increase of the temperature with height (known as an inversion of temperature), however, any appreciable vertical mixing of polluted air is suppressed. Thus, prolonged atmospheric conditions permitting the accumulation of pollution have resulted in dangerous concentrations. At Donora, Pennsylvania, in October 1948, and in the Meuse Valley, near Liège, Belgium, in December 1931, serious health hazards prevailed during prolonged periods of inversion conditions. The west coast of the U.S. and Mexico is subject to extended periods of inversions during the summer and fall months. Industrial areas in this region experience serious effects from the concentrations of air contaminants that accumulate daily when the air is incapable of dispersing the pollutants. Particularly favored locations for the accumulation of cold air, which creates strong temperature inversions, are deep narrow valleys. Thus, in judging the appropriate methods to relieve the adverse effects of pollution, the occurrences of weather phenomena which will serve to accumulate or disperse the pollution must be known.

Reduction at the Source. Equipment designed for the control of aerosols is based upon some physical mechanism of entrainment separation. The principal types of collection equipment are described below. In Table 2 are size and density data for the materials commonly associated with each type of collector. These data must, of necessity, be neither all-inclusive nor completely specific. Efficiency figures include the range in which operation may be considered feasible. See also Electrostatic precipitation; Gas cleaning.

Centrifugal Collectors. These collectors are used for the separation of the category of particulate matter normally classified as dusts. They are low in initial cost and simple in construction, and they provide dry and continuous discharge of collected material. Power consumption is low, there is little limitation on gas-stream temperature, and maintenance requirements are nominal. Collection efficiencies are definitely limited for material of small particle size. They may be used to particular advantage where dust concentrations are high or as the primary unit in a two-stage collection system.

Electrostatic Precipitators. Precipitators are of two distinct types. The single-stage or heavy-duty type is a high-voltage device in which particle charging and deposition take place simultaneously. Voltages range from 30,000 to 100,000 volts. This type is used in conjunction with electric-steel and open-hearth furnaces, gray iron cupolas, blast furnaces, nonferrous primary smelting, cement manufacturing, catalyst dust recovery, and sulfuric acid concentration, They have the advantage of high collection efficiencies over a wide particle size range, and they have large capacities. Operation may be sensitive, however, and the material to be collected must not have a high electrical resistivity.

The two-stage precipitator charges the particles in one section and collects them in another. Voltages are lower, seldom exceeding 13,000 volts. They are normally limited to light-duty air cleaning, but may be used for mists with relatively high resistivities.

Cloth Filters. These collectors are used for the high-efficiency removal of solid aerosols when an appreciable fraction of the emissions have a particle size smaller than 10 μ. The temperature of the exhaust stream must be maintained below 500°F even for the most resistant of filter mediums, and excessive humidity or entrained moisture should be avoided. High dust concentrations require increased filter area. Under these conditions cloth filters are often used as the secondary unit in a two-stage collection system.

Wet Collectors. Wet collectors are used in the control of dust, mist, and fogs. The liquid medium normally serves as a means of increasing the particle size of the contaminant aerosol to be removed, thereby facilitating separation from the exhaust stream. The liquid also may be used to remove the collected material continuously from impact surfaces and to prevent reentrainment. Efficiencies are not high for dusts except in devices with a high energy input. They may be used advantageously for soluble contaminants, or in the case of high dust loadings.

Control of specific gases, air contaminants, and vapors covers a wide range of conditions. Quantities of material vary from a few pounds of highly odoriferous material to tons of gaseous products which require collection. Furthermore, the concentration of the contaminant in the source to be controlled may range from a few parts per million to 100%. The sources, as well, vary widely to include such things as commonly observed stacks, storage tanks, stock piles, open dumps, and many others. The great variety of operations and conditions clearly indicates the need for engineering evaluations of design for each separate installation under consideration. Such classification as can be accorded to this subject is shown in Table 3. No attempt is made to show the efficiency or cost for the control of gas and vapors, because the applications vary so widely.

In addition to scrubbing with an alkaline solution as indicated in Table 3 for the absorption of sulfur dioxide from flue gases, many other methods have been attempted. Neither this method nor any other has yet been proved practical for boiler-flue gases in which the SO_2 is always very dilute, usually less than 0.3% by volume. As of this writing (1969), more research on SO_2 abatement is under way than ever before. The major effort is being applied to the reaction of SO_2 with limestone, alkalized alumina adsorption, catalytic oxidation, and adsorption by activated carbon. Many other methods have been proposed and some of these are also under research. See also Sulfur compounds (Pollution).

Careful consideration of the design of basic equipment can result in marked reductions of atmospheric pollution. Physical limitations in the equipment, imposed by economic considerations, result in restrictions which may preclude modifications in furnace designs to reduce contaminant emissions.

Studies conducted on a large installation designed for the burning of solid industrial and municipal refuse indicated that a large reduction of solid contaminants was accomplished by modification in design. The discharge from this equipment was reduced from a maximum of 8.5 lb/ton of material burned to 3.3 lb/ton of material burned. This reduction was, in general, effected through redistribution of the combustion air. Studies on similar types of equipment also indicated that the grate loading, grate design, and arch height, as a parameter of fire box dimensions, materially influenced the particulate discharge. Nevertheless, to meet some current regulations, high-efficiency dust collectors are required.

Table 3. Classification of Control Devices for Gases and Vapors

Control method	Contaminants	Sources	Remarks
absorbers (scrubbers)			
packed towers	malodors	rendering plants, chemical plants, etc	absorption solution: oxidizing agents
plate towers	hydrocarbons	oil refineries	absorption solution: absorption oil (oil is stripped and recirculated)
spray towers	acid gases		
spray chambers	H_2S	thermal and catalytic cracking plants	absorption solution: ethanolamines, potassium phosphate, Thylox, sodium phenolate, etc (the solutions are regenerated)
water jets			
	SO_2	flue gases, chemical plants	absorption solution: NAOH, $(NH_4)_2SO_2$–NH_4HSO_3, water, alkaline solution (chemicals must be replenished) dimethylamine (regenerated)
	HNO_3	chemical plants	absorption solution: alkaline solution
incineration			
flares	hydrocarbons	oil fields, refineries	venturi burners or steam injection required for smokeless combustion
fume burners	H_2S	oil refineries, chemical plants	SO_2 is product of combustion
	malodors	rendering plants, refineries, chemical plants, paint manufacturing, food processing, etc	temperature required 1400 1500°F
catalytic combustion	organic vapors	litho and enameling ovens, rubber compounding, plastics, etc	catalysts: platinum, nickel; temperature required, 500°F
	CO, oil vapors, NH_3	catalytic cracking unit regenerators	
adsorption	organic solvents	as above	mediums: activated charcoal, silica gel, activated alumina; mediums regenerated by heat and stripping; disposal of liberated odors, etc, by incineration or other means
	malodors	as above	
vapor recovery systems	gasoline, crude oil, and other volatiles	storage tanks	vapors may be compressed and liquefied or may be burned as fuel or flared
floating roofs[a]	gasoline, crude oil, and other volatiles	storage tanks	

[a] A floating roof is a cover on a vertical cylindrical type of tank which rests on the surface of the liquid within the tank and moves as the level of the liquid changes.

Modifications of oil- and gas-burning equipment, to effect a reduction in solid contaminant discharges, lie principally in the fields of ignition aids and alterations of appurtenances to facilitate operation during periods of aggravated air pollution. This is typified by modification to a large, oil-fired, brick kiln where provisions for light oil firing during the 12-hr heat-up period resulted in appreciable reduction in solid discharges. The use of electric preheaters and compressed air for oil atomization is also widespread during periods of nonavailability of steam.

Time, temperature, and turbulence are the three main factors to balance for a given air-to-fuel ratio and furnace design in order to effect complete combustion. Overfire air jets, air-distribution controls, and secondary combustion chambers represent appropriate design features to consider for the best performance. The best engineering considerations, however, cannot overcome the many deficiencies of operators in maintaining and operating the equipment.

Dilution of the Source. Theoretical mathematical equations have been derived to express the ground-level concentrations of gases downwind from a single chimney and from a row of chimneys. The results of practices which have followed these theoretical considerations agree reasonably well with the experimental work, which shows that the air contaminants reach their maximum ground concentration at a distance of approximately ten times the stack height. The concentration at that maximum varies inversely as the square of the chimney height, and its actual value is almost independent of assumptions regarding the variation of diffusion coefficient with height. At great distances the concentration at ground level falls off again until, after fifty chimney heights, the concentration varies as the inverse square of the distance and is independent of the chimney height. Thus, doubling the stack height reduces ground concentrations to one fourth, trebling to one ninth, etc.

Certain modifications of the basic studies show that, as the atmosphere approaches a more stable condition, in which there is less difference in temperature with elevation, the maximum ground concentration occurs progressively farther from the stack than the ten stack lengths. The principle involved in this consideration is that the ground concentration varies directly with the mass of contaminants emitted and inversely with wind velocity or stack height. At great distances, however, stack height has no influence on ground concentrations and the concentration tends to vary inversely as the square of the distance.

Efforts to solve air-pollution problems by these principles have been successful at smelters and other large establishments. Where nuisances are to be corrected by increasing stack height or by the discharge of hot gases at high levels, thorough studies of the average concentrations should be made and effects closely observed over long periods. After changes in the plant are made, additional field studies must be conducted to verify the results. A case in point is illustrated by studies of two smelter stacks 146 and 605 ft high, respectively. With the short stack, air measurements showed concentrations of 0.5 ppm for 30-min periods recorded 842 times during a period of seven months. During a period of fifteen months, after installation of the high stack, only one recording reached the 0.5 ppm concentration. New power plants have stacks ranging from 600 to 1200 ft high.

In areas where prolonged inversion conditions prevail, dilution cannot effectively reduce the overall pollution conditions. Dirt precipitated by the large particles in many types of processes cannot be reduced to any marked degree by the application of the principle of dilution, yet many odor problems and single-stack nuisances can be effectively corrected by this means.

A combination of dilution and operational control can be applied under certain conditions. Where adverse winds or inversions occurring at infrequent intervals facilitate the accumulation of the pollutants from a small number of sources to harmful concentrations, plant production can be curtailed. Carefully planned meteorological data are accumulated along with the information on the levels of atmospheric contamination. When the predetermined threshold values, above which harmful effects will develop, are approached, operations of the responsible sources are shut down. Automatic recording equipment is required to secure the necessary data for carrying out such a program.

Planning. The principles employed in city planning and currently applied through zoning restrictions are directed toward the best utilization of the land within the community. Industrial sites, residential areas, and the essential services should be so developed and located as to minimize all nuisance effects. As congestion increases and cities approach the population saturation point, a multitude of public problems require solution. In the foreground of the complexities of modern civilization is an increasing demand for clean air. The benefits of city planning that have been demonstrated in recent years clearly indicate that planners can do much to prevent the development of many nuisances associated with air pollution.

The location of a single industrial plant must take into account the nature of the pollution from the source, the potential effects on adjoining areas, weather conditions, and the degree of control that can be applied to the process. Techniques for evaluating these items are available. Such advance planning in growing areas can avoid costly control measures, improve public relations, and prevent litigation.

The application of air-pollution-control zoning or planning on an area basis, or to a variety of sources in an area, is an extremely complex problem. The need is apparent, however, when consideration is given to the demands that will be placed on science to safeguard the public as the use of radioactive materials for industry increases.

A basic consideration is to determine the desired air quality over an area. The land then could be occupied by a density of sources per acre to keep within the acceptable mass concentration of pollution per acre. Detailed meterorological studies of the air currents, diffusion characteristics of the contaminants for specific conditions, and threshold tolerance levels can be developed. The application of such studies by planning groups could develop useful criteria for eliminating the hazards of air pollution in critical areas.

Smokeless zones, created in selected industrial areas of England, have demonstrated the possibilities of area-wide improvement. Industries in these zones are limited to the use of certain specified fuels. Marked reduction in dustfall and sulfur dioxide levels are shown for the adjoining neighborhood as compared to unrestricted areas.

Bibliography

"Smokes and Fumes" in *ECT* 1st ed., Vol. 12, pp. 558–573, by G. P. Larson, Air Pollution Control District of Los Angeles County.

1. C. Junge, *Air Chemistry and Radioactivity*, Academic Press, Inc., New York, 1963.
2. *Proc. Third Natl. Conf. on Air Pollution*, Washington, D.C., December 1966.
3. Atomic Energy Commission, *Handbook on Aerosols*, Washington, D.C., 1950.
4. R. L. Chass, *J. Air Pollution Control. Assoc.*, **10**, 351–366 (Oct. 1960).
5. R. A. Bobrov, "The Anatomical Effects of Air Pollution on Plants," *Proc. 2nd Natl. Air Pollution Symposium*, Stanford Research Institute, Pasadena, Cal., 1952.

6. H. L. Green and W. R. Lane, *Particulate Clouds: Dusts, Smokes, and Mists*, E & F. N. Spon Ltd., London, 1957.

7. C. H. Bosanquet and J. L. Pearson, *Trans. Faraday Soc.* **1249** (April 1936).

8. *Proc. First Natl. Air Pollution Symposium*, Pasadena, Cal., 1949.

9. A. J. Haagen-Smit, C. E. Bradley, and M. M. Fox, "Formation of Ozone in the Los Angeles Smog," *Proc. 2nd Natl. Air Pollution Symposium*, Stanford Research Institute, Pasadena, Cal., 1952.

10. "Threshold Limit Values for 1964," *Arch. Environ. Health* **9**, 545–554 (Oct. 1964).

11. Manufacturing Chemists' Association, *Air Pollution Abatement Manual*, Washington, D.C., 1952.

12. A. C. Stern, ed., *Air Pollution*, Vols. 1–3, Academic Press, Inc., New York, 1968.

13. R. D. Cadle, *Particles in the Atmosphere and Space*, Reinhold Publishing Corp., New York, 1966.

14. J. W. Tukey, Chairman, *"Restoring the Quality of Our Environment,"* The White House, Washington, D.C., 1965.

RICHARD B. ENGDAHL
Battelle Memorial Institute

SOAP

Soap technology has slowly progressed from the Biblical preparations of mixed leachings from wood ashes and goat's tallow through the uncertain compositions resulting from cold mixing of refuse fats and lye solutions to the scientifically controlled full-boiled kettle process, and finally to automated continuous processes. Ironically, the successful commercial development of continuous systems occurred in a period of rapidly declining soap sales. Synthetic detergents have largely displaced soap as the active component of heavy-duty products, both solid and liquid, intended for family laundering and dishwashing. Because of their consumer acceptance, however, toilet-bar soaps and fine-laundry soap products continue to enjoy substantial popularity.

Soaps are the alkali metal salts of long-chain monocarboxylic acids represented, for example, by sodium palmitate, $CH_3(CH_2)_{14}COONa$. Sodium is the common cation of hard soaps and is combined with the paraffinlike carboxylic (fatty) acids from a great variety of animal fats, and vegetable and marine oils. These salts are strongly surface-active. The hydrophobic character of the hydrocarbonlike "tails" is expressed by (a) the formation of oriented monolayers at the surface with the tails pointing outward, and (b) by self-aggregation into micelles in the body of the solution. These phenomena are responsible for the dispersing and emulsifying powers which make soap solutions useful as detergents and emulsifiers. In hard water these soaps form a precipitate of calcium and magnesium salts, thus reducing their activity. The familiar ring around the bathtub is a manifestation of such precipitation. A host of synthetic surfactants, anionic and nonionic, have been developed whose solutions possess surface activity but which are not prone to calcium precipitation. See Surfactants. Hence, soaps have lost favor to the best of these synthetic surfactants in washing applications, notably laundry and dishwashing, where the dilute solutions used may impose high calcium-to-soap ratios. On the other hand, soaps are still preferred where soft water is available from natural sources or by treatment, and for facial and body cleansing where the soap-to-water ratio is high. See also Detergency; Laundering; Surfactants; for the soaps of heavy metals, see Driers and metallic soaps. Production in the United States and dollar value for detergents and soap from 1950 to 1967 are given in Table 1.

Table 1. Soap and Synthetic Detergents, U.S. Production and Sales[a]

Year	No. of com- panies	Amount produced and sold, 1000 lb			Sales, $ 1000		
		Synthetic detergents	Soaps	Total	Synthetic detergents	Soaps	Total
1950	101	1,093,188	2,484,931	3,578,119	222,837	463,511	686,348
1951	94	1,255,246	2,057,524	3,312,770	288,336	434,874	723,210
1952	93	1,530,119	1,870,104	3,400,223	336,663	354,631	691,294
1953	92	1,866,883	1,645,431	3,512,314	425,329	321,248	746,577
1954	80	2,063,276	1,443,313	3,506,589	475,442	317,954	793,396
1955	80	2,317,478	1,350,464	3,667,942	540,917	320,067	860,984
1956	75	2,690,327	1,285,112	3,975,439	597,441	316,091	913,532
1957	72	2,915,766	1,188,909	4,104,675	683,590	314,525	998,115
1958	67	2,951,352	1,138,148	4,089,500	715,951	324,802	1,040,753
1959	62	3,203,437	1,066,440	4,269,877	774,230	319,220	1,093,450
1960	58	3,310,650	1,056,936	4,367,586	800,673	319,211	1,119,884
1961	51	3,469,114	1,014,483	4,483,597	831,692	312,571	1,144,263
1962	45	3,752,382	1,041,882	4,794,264	900,793	317,259	1,218,052
1963	44	3,863,352	1,026,164	4,889,516	930,886	322,559	1,253,445
1964	41	4,037,070	986,854	5,023,924	961,584	319,085	1,280,669
1965	40	4,159,187	967,470	5,126,657	985,152	339,522	1,324,674
1966	40	4,298,273	967,113	5,265,406	1,014,976	353,897	1,368,873
1967	40	4,576,615	967,293	5,543,908	1,078,166	357,286	1,435,452

[a] This table covers all types of soap and synthetic detergents sold to civilians, Army, Navy, and the Government. The totals shown represent a very substantial portion of all soaps and detergents made and sold in the United States; a very small fraction is made by converters and is included. These figures do not include packaged and bulk scouring cleansers. Courtesy Soap and Detergent Association, New York.

Raw Materials

Fats and Oils. The naturally occurring fats and oils used in soapmaking are triglycerides with three fatty acid groups randomly esterified with glycerol. Each fat contains a number of long fatty acid molecules with an even number of carbon atoms ranging generally from C_{12} (lauric acid) to C_{18} (stearic acid) in the saturated series, as well as unsaturated acids of the same chain lengths. The component fatty acids found in beef tallow and coconut oil are listed in Table 2 (1). A triglyceride mixture is converted to soap by saponification with aqueous caustic soda, simultaneously releasing the glycerol in the following manner:

$$
\begin{array}{ll}
\text{RCOOCH}_2 & \text{CH}_2\text{OH} \\
\quad | & \quad | \\
\text{RCOOCH} + 3\,\text{NaOH} \rightarrow 3\,\text{RCOONa} + \text{CHOH} \\
\quad | & \quad | \\
\text{RCOOCH}_2 & \text{CH}_2\text{OH}
\end{array}
$$

Thus, the properties of the resulting soap are determined by the amounts and compositions of the component fatty acids in the starting fat mixture. The compositions of fatty acids suitable for the making of soap are restricted with respect to chain length and degree of unsaturation. In general, chain lengths of less than 12 carbon atoms are undesirable because their soaps are irritating to the skin; conversely, saturated chain lengths greater than 18 carbon atoms form soaps too insoluble for ready solution and sudsing. Similarly, too large a proportion of unsaturated fatty acids (oleic, linoleic, linolenic) yield soaps susceptible to undesirable atmospheric oxidative

Table 2. The Major Fatty Acids in Coconut Oil and Beef Tallow

Acid	Formula	Melting point, °C	Double bonds	Percent in	
				Coconut	Tallow
caprylic	$C_8H_{16}O_2$	16.5	0	8.0	
capric	$C_{10}H_{20}O_2$	31.3	0	7.0	
lauric	$C_{12}H_{24}O_2$	43.6	0	48.0	
myristic	$C_{14}H_{28}O_2$	53.8	0	17.5	2.0
palmitic	$C_{16}H_{32}O_2$	62.9	0	8.8	32.5
stearic	$C_{18}H_{36}O_2$	69.9	0	2.0	14.5
oleic	$C_{18}H_{34}O_2$	14.0	1	6.0	48.3
linoleic	$C_{18}H_{32}O_2$	−11.0	2	2.5	2.7

changes. For these reasons and the economics of price and availability, the number of fats and oils suitable for soapmaking is limited. The most important of these include the following:

Tallow (see Vol. 13, p. 183) is the principal animal fat in soapmaking. It is obtained as a by-product of the meat-processing industry by rendering the body fat from cattle and sheep. Tallows from different sources may vary considerably in color (both as received and after bleaching), titer (solidification point of the fatty acids), free fatty-acid content, saponification value (alkali required for saponification), and iodine value (measure of unsaturation). The better grades of tallow, judged principally from titer and color after a laboratory bleach, are used for the preparation of fine toilet soaps; poorer grades are used in laundry soaps. Beef or mutton fat with a titer of 40°C or higher is generally classed as tallow.

Grease is a lower grade of tallow, generally with a darker color, higher free fatty-acid content, and titer of less than 40°C.

Lard. Inedible lard (rendered hog fat) can be used as a limited replacement for tallow after partial hydrogenation to reduce its unsaturation.

Palm oil often serves as a partial substitute for tallow, particularly abroad. It is gained from a pulp of the outer fleshy fruit of the tropical palm tree (*Elaeis guineensis*). Crude palm oil has an orange-red color and is normally air bleached prior to saponification. See Fats and fatty oils.

Coconut oil is the most important vegetable oil used in soapmaking. It is obtained by crushing and extracting the dried fruit (copra) of the coconut palm tree.

Palm kernel oil is extracted from the center nuts of the same fruit cluster which yields palm oil. Since its component fatty acids resemble in kind and amount those of coconut oil, palm kernel oil can be substituted for coconut oil.

Marine oils, such as whale and menhaden oils, after partial hydrogenation, may be used in limited amounts in soapmaking.

Miscellaneons Oils. Relatively small quantities of olive, peanut, corn, sesame, babassu, and ucuhuba oil, and Chinese vegetable tallow may be used.

Foots from Oil Refining. The crude soap or "foots" obtained from refining edible oils (cottonseed, soybean, etc), as well as the foots obtained by the soapmaker in refining his fats and oils (see below under Refining) may be used in limited amounts for the preparation of low-grade soaps.

Natural Fatty Acids. A modern trend, particularly in continuous saponification operations, is to "split" or hydrolyze the oils listed above to fatty acids and glycerol prior to saponification. See Vol. 8, p. 825.

The fatty acids may then be vacuum distilled to improve the quality of the resulting soap. Saponification or neutralization proceeds so readily that sodium carbonate can be partially or wholly substituted for caustic soda.

Nonfatty Soap Stocks. Rosin (qv) and to a lesser extent tall oil (qv), and naphthenic acids (qv) are used in the preparation of laundry or textile-scouring soaps.

Alkalis. Aqueous sodium hydroxide solution (50%) is commonly used to saponify fats, oils, and fatty acids for the preparation of *hard soaps* to be finished as bars, flakes, or beads. Aqueous potassium hydroxide is used for the preparation of *soft soaps* (liquids or pastes) since the potassium soaps are more water-soluble than the sodium soaps. Blends of the two alkalis are occasionally used in order to achieve special properties.

Processing of Fats and Oils

Refining. Depending on the quality of the crude fats or oils, they may be refined and bleached prior to saponification. An amount of aqueous sodium hydroxide equivalent to the free-fatty-acid content of the oil is added with slow stirring to the hot oil. The precipitated crude soap or "foots" occludes some unwanted color bodies and, after settling, the neutral oil is filtered off. Alternatively, foots removal can be accomplished by centrifugation. The foots may be transferred to a kettle of low-quality laundry soap or acidulated to release the fatty acids for purification by distillation.

Bleaching. Further coloring matter can be removed by agitating the hot neutral oil with 1–2% bleaching clays or activated carbon, followed by filtration in plate and frame presses.

Hydrogenation. The soapmaking qualities of highly unsaturated triglycerides, such as marine oils and soft grease, can be vastly improved by hydrogenation. The elimination of some unsaturation hardens the stock and improves its odor as well as stability.

Fat and Oil Blending

The approximate percentages of the major fatty acids esterified with glycerol in coconut oil and beef tallow—the principal stocks used in most soapmaking—are listed in Table 2.

Coconut oil contains large proportions of the relatively short-chain lauric and myristic acids, while tallow is rich in the longer-chain palmitic, stearic, and oleic acids. Properties of soaps made from each of these stocks have desirable and complementary features. In general, the short-chain laurate and myristate soaps from coconut oil and the unsaturated oleate from tallow supply quick solution and foaming which is sustained by the palmitate and stearate soaps.

A sodium soap prepared from a blend of approximately 20% coconut oil and 80% tallow exhibits good properties over a broad range of solution temperatures, as well as consumer acceptance in the bar, flake, and bead end products so familiar in supermarkets. Limited substitutions for coconut oil and tallow are possible, based on similar fatty-acid distributions. Hence, most good-quality toilet soaps are saponified from a blend, whether via the mixed oils or the fatty acids therefrom.

Manufacturing Methods

Full-Boiled Kettle Method. Much of the world's soap production is still initiated batchwise in open steel "kettles" or "pans" capable of processing several thousand to several hundred thousand pounds of soap. The pans are circular or square in cross section, but taper to cones at the bottom, and are generally lagged to conserve heat. Open steam coils in the cone section supply heat and agitation; closed steam coils may also be present to supply heat without adding condensed steam. The bottom layer resulting from any stage of the boiling procedure is removed from the bottom

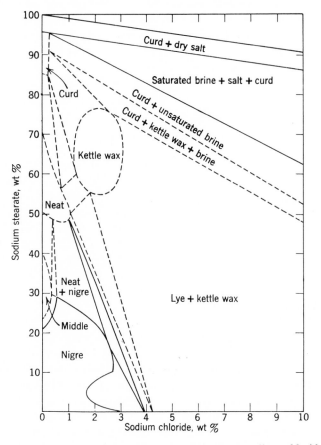

Fig. 1. Phase diagram of the ternary system sodium stearate–sodium chloride–water at 90°C. NOTE: The triangles indicate heterogeneous equilibria between the three condensed phases at the apexes of the triangle. The regions between the triangles should be filled with tie lines, each connecting two condensed phases, the tie line nearest any triangle being almost parallel to the nearest boundary of that triangle.

of the cone and transferred to storage tanks or other kettles via pumps, valves, and pipe lines. Similarly, the upper layer is removed through an adjustable swing pipe located part way down the kettle.

This process supplies completely saponified neutral soap containing approximately 30% water, a composition which—when hot—can be pumped to various finishing operations. The soap is washed free of soluble colored and odorous impurities and separated as far as possible from glycerol and from the salt added to salt out the soap. The glycerol and salt are recovered in separate concentrating and refining operations.

These objectives are accomplished by a series of saponification, washing, and "fitting" operations, which are referred to as "changes." The skilled soap-boiler, relying heavily on appearance, flow properties, feel, and even taste, obtains the desired separations, which can be best understood, however, in terms of the phase relationships.

McBains's phase diagram (2) of the ternary system sodium stearate–sodium chloride–water at 90°C, as shown in Figure 1, depicts the equilibria involved, within the limits of experimental difficulties. This diagram, involving a single pure soap, sodium stearate, is only slightly different from that of a blended commercial soap. The following five areas of variable compositions outline the regions of stability of five phases in addition to the brine: *curd soap, kettle wax soap, neat soap, middle soap,* and *"nigre."* Not too clear on the diagram is the fact that the nigre phase, containing substantial amounts of soap, is continuous along the abscissa with a "lye" of very low soap and high salt contents. Two-phase areas represent overall compositions where two immiscible phases separate. The most important two-phase separations in kettle boiling are the kettle wax on lye and neat on nigre. Within a number of triangular regions, three-phase separations occur where the compositions of the separating phases are fixed by the apexes of the triangles.

Saponification Charge. Generally, part of the weighed coconut-oil fraction of the fat charge is first run into the kettle with a little water and salt, and heated and agitated with live steam. Saponification is started by the addition of (usually) 50% caustic soda solution and the slow addition of the remaining coconut oil. The saponification of a fat can be divided into the following three broad stages: (*1*) a slow incubation period; (*2*) a rapid exothermic stage; and (*3*) gradual completion. The incubation period is largely a result of poor contact between the starting oil and water phases and can be shortened by starting a boil on a preceding nigre (see below under Fitting change), whose soap content supplies a degree of emulsification. During the slow incubation period care must be taken not to add caustic too rapidly since a large excess of unreacted alkali renders the oil and water phases even less miscible. When enough soap has formed to start emulsification, the exothermic stage begins and caustic is consumed rapidly. Steam control is necessary at this stage to prevent boiling over. A small amount of dry salt is usually added here to maintain a slight excess of electrolyte since the caustic soda content is rapidly diminishing. Some electrolyte excess is necessary to prevent "bunching," an undesired appearance of viscous middle soap (see Figure 1) which forms at low electrolyte–high water concentrations. When the coconut oil fraction is substantially all saponified, as judged by the lessening heat of reaction and the alkali consumption, the tallow fraction is pumped in and saponification continued with more alkali. It is necessary to finish the saponification stage with a bare excess (0.1% or less) of unreacted alkali since the latter, accumulating in the subsequent lye, complicates the glycerol-recovery process. Hence, the last small caustic soda additions are made slowly with the pan contents expanded by steaming to the top of the kettle on a "closed grain" and tested for alkali consumption. The grain is determined by the amount of electrolyte present. Small amounts of salt and unreacted alkali produce a soft or closed grain, the condition required during saponification since it permits maximum interaction between fat and alkali. A closed grain is readily recognized by its smooth appearance. Excess alkalinity can be simply determined by titrating a soap sample dissolved in hot neutral alcohol to the phenolphthalein end point with standard acid solution.

After completion of the saponification, dry salt is added to the boiling soap until a hard or open grain is obtained. This condition corresponds to the two-phase separation of kettle wax and lye shown in Figure 1; it is recognized by its heterogeneous appearance of soap curds and thin aqueous liquid. However, the degree of graining is a critical factor determining the volume of lye and the amount of soap left in the lye which requires considerable experience. After a short boil to equilibrate the two phases, steaming is stopped and the pan contents are allowed to separate for several hours. The lye is withdrawn and transferred to the glycerol-recovery system.

Wash Changes. Since only 30–45% of the available glycerol is removed in the saponification lye, two or more washes are made to extract as much of the remainder as economics dictate. The grained soap remaining in the pan is boiled up and water added; since most of the salt previously added was removed with the saponification lye, the soap closes again and forms a homogeneous solution. After a short boil-up, the soap is grained with salt and another glycerol-containing lye is removed after each wash.

Fitting Change. After the last wash lye is removed, the final "fit" to neat soap is begun. The grained soap from the last wash is boiled up and water gradually added to the desired fit. This composition corresponds to the two-phase neat–nigre area of Figure 1, so that on settling a thin nigre, dark with unwanted impurities, separates below the neat-soap layer. This is another critical operation since the type of fit determines the proportions of neat and nigre. Soap-boilers use a "trowel" test to determine the fit. A trowel is heated in the soap mass, then quickly withdrawn so that a thin film of soap covers it. On tilting, the soap film should slide off slowly as a sheet, leaving the trowel dry. If the film breaks up and leaves the trowel wet, the fit is too open; if the film does not slide off, the fit is too close. After several days settling, the upper neat layer is removed through the swing pipe to storage tanks. The bottom nigre layer may contain as much as one third of the fatty matter originally charged into the pan as dark-colored soap of approximately 30–35% fatty acid content. Thus it is essential to conserve the soap content while disposing of the separated impurities by various means. One procedure is to pump approximately one quarter of the nigre to an accumulation pan where, when sufficient stock has been collected, a fitting change is made and a secondary nigre dropped. The latter is usually disposed of by acidulation and the low-grade fatty acids thus obtained are sold. The upper layer is used to start another boil of low-quality soap. The remainder of the original nigre in the starting pan is washed with salt water to remove soluble impurities and settled to remove particulate impurities in the brine, which is discarded. A new boil of the same quality is started on the nigre whose soap content assists the new saponification. Alternatively, the whole of the original nigre may be transferred to the start of a new boil of lesser-quality soap.

Several variations of the soap-boiling sequence are practiced. In the direct-wash system outlined above, fresh water is used for all washes. This system requires a minimum number of kettles but produces a relatively large volume of lye for glycerol processing. In the counterwash system only the saponification lye is transferred directly to the glycerol recovery units; the remaining lyes are worked backwards through the next earlier changes in other boils. This system requires more kettles but reduces the volume of lye.

Another variation concerns the degree of completion of saponification sought in the first stage. Here either complete saponification may be sought or, in the interest of obtaining a neutral lye, only 90–95% of the fat may be saponified. In the latter case, a "strong" change is added after several wash lyes are removed for glycerol recovery. An excess of caustic soda is added in the strong change to complete saponification and the alkali-rich lye is used in the saponification stage of a new boil. In the counter-wash system, saponification is generally not complete in the first stage, but in later stages extra alkali is added which accumulates in lyes that are recycled as described.

Bleaching. The washing-stage lyes remove considerable color bodies, but further limited improvement in the color of the soap can be obtained by adding sodium hydrosulfite or sodium hypochlorite to the final washing stage. After a short boilup, the soap is grained out as usual.

Rosin. When rosin is incorporated in the soap formula, it is customary to add it to the pan in a change just prior to the fit. The rosin acids are neutralized with caustic and, after graining, the lye may be discarded since rosin contributes no glycerol.

A boil requires approximately one week from start to finish. Despite this, soap producers maintain a steady supply of neat soap for the finishing operations in holding tanks by staggering the start-up of different boils. Efforts to shorten the processing time have resulted in a number of continuous processes described below.

Cold-Process Saponification. This is the simplest of the batch saponification procedures, requiring a minimum of equipment. Since neither lyes nor nigre are separated, the glycerol and impurities from the fats remain in the soap. The fat charge is simply melted in a vessel equipped with a mechanical stirrer and the calculated amount of caustic soda solution is added with vigorous stirring. After emulsification and thickening, the mass is poured into frames where saponification is completed during cooling and solidification. The removable sides of the frame are then taken off and the soap slab is cut into bars.

Semiboiled Saponification. This is similar to the cold process save that a higher temperature is used to speed saponification and permit adjustment of the alkali content before framing. The fat charge and alkali (which may be caustic potash for soft soaps) are thoroughly mixed at 70–80°C until the soap becomes smooth. Just prior to framing, the soap may be perfumed and small amounts of sodium silicate, borax, or V. M. & P. naphtha (varnish maker and paint grade; see also Vol. 15, p. 85) may be added to laundry soaps and fine sand, pumice, etc, to abrasive hand soaps.

Jet Saponification. The Unilever process (3) for the jet saponification of fats conserves steam by withholding it during the exothermic stage of the reaction. A three-way jet uses steam to atomize proportioned feeds of fat and of caustic soda solution containing salt, thus producing the emulsion necessary to start saponification. The emulsion is sprayed into the first compartment of a receiving vessel where saponification takes place nearly to completion without benefit of added heat or agitation. After holding for a time, determined by the height of a weir, the contents spill over into a second compartment where live steam may be added to complete saponification.

Soap from Fatty Acids. Fatty acids obtained from natural oils by hydrolysis (see above under Raw materials) or by acidulation of foots are readily neutralized with caustic alkalis or carbonates to form soaps. Glycerol recovery is eliminated and, since the fatty acids are usually distilled prior to use, nigre separations may also be avoided so that the neutralization may be carried out in "crutchers" instead of kettles (a crutcher is a steam-jacketed vessel containing a sweep agitator). A number of the continuous soapmaking processes described below start with fatty acids.

CONTINUOUS PROCESSES

Efforts to shorten the processing time of the full-boiled-kettle procedure have resulted in a number of continuous processes for soap manufacture. These include both continuous splitting, distillation and neutralization of fatty acids, and continuous saponification of neutral fats, followed by continuous washing and fitting with attendant lye and nigre separations.

Procter & Gamble Process. In 1938 the Procter & Gamble Company began the manufacture of soap by a continuous process which converts raw fats to finished soaps in a matter of hours (4). The blended fats, containing zinc oxide as a catalyst, are reacted countercurrently with water in a 65-ft high stainless-steel hydrolyzing tower, maintained at 450–500°F and 600–700 psi, to yield a continuous output of fatty acid from the top and crude glycerol from the bottom. The fatty acids are distilled in vacuum and neutralized in a continuous process. This is done with proportioned caustic soda solution containing salt in a high-speed mixer. The product is neat soap ready for the various finishing operations.

Sharples Process. The Sharples system (5–8) converts fats directly to soaps and uses centrifuges to separate lyes for washing and glycerol recovery. Two stages of saponification (similar to the saponification change and the strong change of kettle boiling) are used, each making use of a mixer and a centrifuge. Washings with brine solutions are accomplished in similar mixer-centrifuge stages. The soap–salt–water balance in the final mixer can be adjusted to yield a neat–nigre separation in the final centrifuge; such fitting may not be necessary, however, since the earlier centrifugal separations remove most of the impurities found in the settled nigres.

The Mon Savon Process. This process (9) continuously converts fats and oils directly into soap and provides also for the recovery of glycerol. Hot, proportioned amounts of fat and caustic soda are first emulsified in a homogenizer to speed saponification. The emulsion is fed continuously onto the hot inner wall of a reactor where saponification is completed. Washings and lye are removed by countercurrent flows of crude soap and hot brine solutions through a multistage washing tower. Each unit of the tower is divided into mixing and settling zones. The soap discharged from the washing tower is fitted with caustic soda solution to the neat–nigre composition and settled in pans. The separated nigre is recycled through the washing tower.

The De Laval Process. In the De Laval Centripure process (10), the fats and caustic soda solution are proportioned countercurrently into a vertical reactor through which a large proportion of the saponified fat is continuously recirculated; the presence of the soap speeds saponification by emulsifying the incoming raw materials. The caustic soda addition is automatically regulated by a viscosity probe in the recirculating line. An amount of fully saponified soap equal to the raw feeds emerges from the top of the reactor for continuous countercurrent washing with brine solution, followed by centrifugal separation of soap and lye. Additions of electrolyte to the fitting stage are controlled by the viscosity. Approximately 90% of the nigre separated in the last centrifuge is returned to the last washing stage.

The Mazzoni Processes. Automated continuous systems (Mazzoni systems) are available for the saponification of fats, including the washing of the soap and the recovery of glycerol (SCN process). The SC process provides for the continuous neutralization of fatty acids by caustic soda, while the SCC process uses sodium carbonate for neutralization.

In the SCN process (11) proportioned amounts of fat, caustic soda, and brine solution are metered into a four-stage reaction autoclave, where heat, pressure, and recirculation bring about saponification to 99.5% completion. An amount of reaction mixture equivalent to the combined feeds is continuously cooled and passed into a static separator for phase separation and removal of the spent lye. The soap is washed with countercurrent lyes in several stages of mixers plus static separators. In the last stage the soap is washed with fresh brine and separated by centrifugation into soap and lye phases.

In the SC process (12) preheated fatty acids are proportioned by duplex pumps into a multistage centrifugal mixer, where they are mixed with a recirculating soap stream. An electrode is located in this soap stream which monitors the caustic feed to maintain a constant preset pH. An amount of soap equal to the feed volumes is constantly withdrawn from this system to a holding tank. Sodium chloride is either added with the caustic soda or metered in separately.

The SCC process is similar save that sodium carbonate is used for most of the fatty acid neutralization and sodium hydroxide is used only for the final adjustment.

The Crosfield Process. J. Crosfield and Sons, a Unilever subsidiary in England, began the continuous production of soap for spray-dried products in 1962 (13). The saponification unit consists of three interconnected vertical reactors with internal baffles. Metered quantities of fat and caustic soda solution are recycled through two of these reactors to maintain a high soap concentration which emulsifies the incoming feed. Saponification control is maintained automatically by regulating the feed of one reactant by means of a viscosity indicator in the recirculating loop. A bleed from the last reactor feeds a liquid–liquid extraction unit for countercurrent washing with hot brine. Fitting is done in a shallow tank with a pump-operated recirculation loop. Another viscosity control adjusts the electrolyte concentration for a neat–nigre separation obtained in a bank of centrifuges.

The Armour Process. In April 1964 the Armour Company began producing soap by an automated continuous process combining units of the Mazzoni and the De Laval systems (14).

The fat mixture is first hydrolyzed into fatty acids and water in splitting towers at high temperature and under high pressure. After distillation, the fatty acids are neutralized in a De Laval Centripure reactor and the neat soap is pumped directly to a holding tank. The finishing units consist of Mazzoni vacuum dryers, amalgamators where perfume, dye, and bacteriostat are mixed in, and Triplex plodders (G. Mazzoni, S.p.A.).

FINISHING OPERATIONS

The end product of both the kettle and continuous saponification procedures is neat soap containing approximately 30% water. Hence, the following finishing steps are customary, in one form or another, to convert neat soap to useful end products.

Drying for Bars or Flakes. The 30% water content of neat soap must be reduced to 10–15% before shaping into bars and to 5–10% before cutting into flakes. The drying is generally accomplished in cabinet, flash, or vacuum drying units. Prior to cabinet drying, the molten neat soap from storage is dropped onto a chill roll and ribbons of the solidified soap are scraped off the roll and dropped on a wire-mesh conveyor The latter moves through a hot-air cabinet where the residence time and the temperature of the air are adjusted so as to give the desired degree of drying. In flash drying, the neat soap is superheated under pressure in a heat exchanger, then released through an orifice into a vented storage tank. But in vacuum drying, the hot neat soap is sprayed onto the cold inner wall of a vacuum chamber and is then mechanically scraped off.

Mixing and Milling. Pigments, dyes, and perfumes may be added to bar- and flake-soap products, also complexing agents, such as ethylenediaminetetraacetic acid (EDTA), which retard the development of rancidity by chelating metal ions picked up during processing. These ingredients are generally coarsely worked into the dried soap flakes in a batch mixer equipped with a helical agitator. The mixture is then dumped onto a three- or five-roll mill where it is squeezed through the first two rolls, picked up by the faster roll, and passed on. The ribbons scraped from the final roll are thoroughly uniform.

Alternatively, the mixer contents may be homogenized in multistage cylindrical refiners where an internal screw forces the soap through small holes in an end plate. Pellets cut from the first plate are fed into a second refiner.

Plodding of Bar Soaps. Mill ribbons or refiner pellets are fed through a hopper into a "plodder" where an internal screw forces the soap into a compression area terminated by a tapered outlet fitted with a die through which a "log" of soap is continuously extruded. The log is cut, cooled, stamped, and wrapped.

Flakes. The soap from the mixer is passed through finishing rolls adjusted to a close tolerance to give a thin, glossy film of soap. The flake shapes are marked by rotating cutters and stripped from the final roll by a knife.

Spray-Dried Powders. Prior to spray drying, additives to complete the formulation are suspended or dissolved in hot neat soap in a crutcher. Additives may include inorganic builders, optical brighteners, and dyes. When the additives are thoroughly dispersed or dissolved, the mix is pumped to a holding tank and thence through a high-pressure pump to atomizing nozzles near the top of a spray tower. Hot air circulated through the tower evaporates water from the spray and forms beads. The soap and air streams can be either countercurrent or concurrent. Powder from the base of the tower is screened to remove off-size material which is returned to the crutcher. Then the powder can be conveyed through a zone for mist perfuming before packaging.

Heavy-duty soap powders containing inorganic builders, such as sodium tripolyphosphate, sodium pyrophosphate, sodium perborate, and sodium silicate, have been largely replaced in the United States by heavy-duty synthetic detergents containing the same additives.

Optical brighteners have enjoyed widespread consumer acceptance. These are fluorescent dyes substantive to fabrics, which function by converting ultraviolet radiation into visible blue light; the latter masks the grayness which inevitably develops in old garments. Essentially pure soap beads with only minor amounts of additives are similarly spray dried for fine-fabric laundering.

SOAP PHASES

Ternary Soap–Salt–Water Systems. Twenty years of experimentation by McBain and various associates established that a number of different phases can coexist in the three-component system of a soap kettle and that the various equilibria between the phases are rigorously governed by the phase rule. An isotherm in this system is illustrated in Figure 1 to show its application to the washing and fitting operations of kettle boiling. This ternary diagram applies equally well to the continuous procedures since the desired equilibria and phase separations are only possible within the composition limits appropriate to the chosen soap formula.

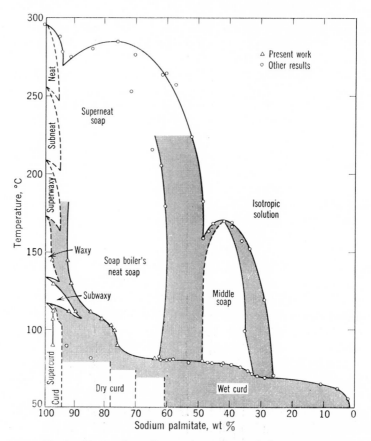

Fig. 2. Binary phase diagram for sodium palmitate–water.

Binary Soap–Water Systems. The end product of the boiling and continuous procedures, starting with either fat or fatty acid, is neat soap of approximately 69% soap and 30% water with a small residual salt content (about 0.5% or less). Hence the compositions which are finished to unbuilt bar, flake, or bead products are essentially two-component systems of soap and water. McBain and associates likewise established the equilibria in these binary systems, as far as they could be determined. The phase diagram for sodium palmitate and water is shown in Figure 2 (15). The diagrams for other soap and water systems, including a commercial soap, are generally similar (15); low salt contents only slightly distort the phase boundaries (16).

On cooling, molten neat soap of 70% soap content begins to separate at 83°C (see Figure 2) as a solid–curd phase. The boundary containing this point is known as the T_c curve and represents the temperatures at which the solid–curd phase first separates various soap and water compositions on cooling. The solid–soap area below the T_c curve is the commercially important region in which bar soaps are processed. Yet this region in Figure 2 and other McBain phase diagrams shows only a heterogeneous mixture of curd soap of indefinite composition and a dilute isotropic solution. Evidence that soap-processing methods can produce marked differences in soap properties and crystal structures in this area is discussed below under Mills work.

Solid-Soap Phases. Bodman (17) in 1940 patented a process for producing a floating soap by intensely working a semifluid soap and water mixture with air at elevated temperatures (160–225°F) followed by quick cooling without further agitation. Novel features, which distinguished this soap from prior art-milled or framed soaps of the same composition, were claimed. Hence differences in the properties of solid soaps at room temperature, dependent on their processing histories, were noted.

Similarly, Mills (18–20) discovered that the room-temperature properties of soap and water compositions were altered by working above or below a critical temperature characteristic of each composition, followed by rapid cooling without further agitation. In addition to different use properties, Mills found that soaps processed on either side of the critical temperature boundary showed different x-ray diffraction patterns at room temperature. Hence, demonstrable differences in the crystalline structures of identical compositions were shown.

In two articles related to the patents by Mills, Ferguson et al. (21,22) characterized four different phases in solid hydrous soaps by different x-ray diffraction patterns. Three of these phases were encountered in samples at room temperature of commercially important soap–water compositions. Phase transformations were induced by temperature or composition changes, particularly when assisted by the application of mechanical energy in the form of milling, plodding, or extrusion. Just as in the Mills patents, soaps of the same compositions but in different phases exhibited different solution and lathering properties. However, it was noted that the different processing conditions necessary to produce the different phases might equally well affect the use properties. Again, some detail indicative of structural difference was noted in the solid regions below the T_c boundaries of McBain's phase diagrams.

Buerger et al. (23) increased to ten the number of phases identified by x-ray short spacings in a number of individual pure soap and water compositions at room temperature. The soaps were vigorously worked (24) at fixed temperatures and compositions and then cooled to room temperature without further agitation before x-raying. The phases determined at room temperature thus descended on cooling from the worked equilibrium mixtures; hence, working temperature–composition plots of the data were called descendant phase maps.

The phase maps obtained from data at room temperature are not to be confused with phase diagrams depicting the equilibria prevailing at the actual working temperatures. However, inspection of Buerger's phase map for the sodium myristate–water system (24), shown in Figure 3, reveals striking similarities to certain features of McBain's phase diagrams. The nearly horizontal boundary between the μ and ζ fields (of different x-ray diffraction patterns) of Figure 3 agrees fairly well with McBain's "temperature of ready solubility" of 140°F (60°C) for sodium myristate (16).

The temperature of ready solubility (T_s) is defined as the temperature at which soap shows a sudden sharp increase in water solubility. In Figure 2, for example, only about 5% of sodium palmitate dissolves to a clear isotropic solution at 63°C, but about 25% is dissolved at 70°C. Similarly, the upper boundary of Figure 3 between the ζ and κ fields agrees fairly well with McBain's T_c boundary in the sodium myristate–water diagram (15), which is shown at 158°F at 50% water and 183°F at 30% water.

Hence, there is ample evidence that processing at fixed compositions on either side of McBain's boundaries produces phase discontinuities which lastingly affect the crystalline structures of subsequently solidified soap. Such structural changes can reasonably be expected to affect the use properties of the soaps.

While both Ferguson and Buerger agreed that structural differences in solid soaps could be detected by x-ray diffraction, considerable disagreement existed with respect to phase identification and nomenclature. Vold et al. (25) undertook an independent investigation which substantially confirmed Buerger's position.

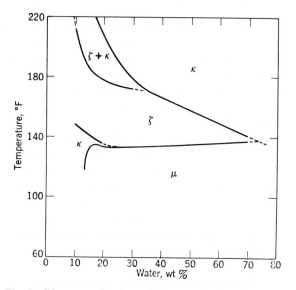

Fig. 3. Phase map for the sodium myristate–water system.

The phase changes described above were generally induced in fixed soap–water compositions upon cooling from different working temperatures. Kelly et al. (26), however, succeeded in producing a transparent soap from an ordinary soap stock containing no additives by conventional milling and plodding at about 100°F and at 20% water content. At approximately 2% less or 2% more water, the same soap stock after the same milling and plodding yielded opaque soaps. Hence, the existence of another boundary in solid soaps was indicated, this time a critical composition instead of a critical temperature boundary. Similarly, Goldwasser et al. (27) found a critical water boundary for translucency at about 15% for a modified soap stock.

Thus, it appears that solid–soap phases in the commercially important low water–low temperature area lack the mobility to establish equilibria spontaneously, in contrast to the hot-fluid phases of the kettle and the high-temperature parts of the binary diagrams. Instead, vigorous working seems necessary to establish equilibrium in relatively cold, concentrated systems. Recognition of this need and the application of x-ray diffraction have indicated fundamental differences in solid-soap structures which are not yet fully elucidated.

Specialty Soaps

Deodorant Soaps. Modern antibacterial agents (see Antiseptics) have largely supplanted the phenol ("carbolic acid") and cresylic acid formulations and resulted in greatly increased consumer demand. Vinson (28) lists the three most commonly used classes of antibacterial agents used in toilet soaps today as the bis(hydroxyphenyl)alkanes (see Vol. 2, p. 630), polybrominated salicylanilides, and halogenated carbanilides. The functional properties of these agents are the effective suppression of the growth of Gram-positive skin bacteria responsible for body odor at low concentrations and a substantivity for skin such that rinsing away is resisted. Jungermann (29) demonstrated the superior inhibition of the growth of a large number of bacteria by two deodorant soaps over a nonmedicated soap. One soap contained a combination of 0.75% hexachlorophene and 0.75% 3,4,4'-trichlorocarbanilide and the other a mixture of 0.67% 3,4,4'-trichlorocarbanilide, 0.67% 4,4'-dichloro-3-trifluoromethyl carbanilide, and 0.67% of a mixture consisting mostly of 3,4',5-tribromosalicylanilide with some 3,5-dibromosalicylanilide.

Superfatted Soaps. Many toilet soaps are superfatted with 2–6% excess of unsaponified oil or fatty acid or lanolin to produce a soft cold-cream effect by leaving a residual film on the skin after washing and rinsing.

Liquid soaps, including shampoos, are formulated with the more soluble potassium, ammonium, or triethanolamine soaps of coconut, olive, or other low-titer oils.

Shaving creams are generally formulated by saponifying a mixture of coconut oil and stearic acid with mixed caustic potash and soda. From 4 to 8% of the stearic acid may be left unneutralized to supply a pearly luster and 5–10% glycerol may be added for body.

Floating Soaps. The original floating soaps were made by beating air into molten neat soap in an open crutcher, followed by solidification in frames. These coarse air dispersions have been vastly improved by the newer methods of incorporating air under pressure in closed kneading units (17,18). Moreover, the lower water content of the new soaps (approx 20 instead of 30%) affords sufficient firmness to permit extrusion into logs for cutting and stamping after in-process cooling so that framing is no longer necessary.

Scouring soaps are manufactured in bar, paste, or powder forms and contain one or more finely-powdered insoluble abrasive materials chosen to assist a particular job, such as cleaning of mechanics' hands, pots, tile, walls, or floors. Abrasive materials used include talc, quartz, and feldspar. Alkaline builders, such as sodium silicate, sodium carbonate, or trisodium phosphate, are frequently incorporated. Soap contents in such products are generally low (5–10%) since no great amount of sudsing is desired.

Transparent soaps are usually made by the semiboiled method followed by framing. Additions of alcohol, sugar solution, and glycerol to the hot soap inhibit the growth of soap crystallites during frame cooling and promote a glassy, transparent condition. Attention has been called to milled translucent soaps made without benefit of these additives by carefully controlling the processing conditions (26,27).

Analysis

In the manufacture of soaps, certain analytical tests are performed both during and after the various processing operations. The American Oil Chemists' Society publishes a manual of sampling and analytical testing methods for soaps and soap products (30). Some of the more important analytical tests made on soaps are the following: total fatty acids, color of fatty acids, free alkalinity, salt, and glycerol. The lyes are tested for alkalinity, salt, and glycerol. Following are brief descriptions of some of the more important tests.

Total Fatty Acids. The sample is hydrolyzed with acid, the fatty acids are extracted with ether, which is evaporated, and the residue is weighed.

Color of soap is usually closely related to the color of the washed fatty acids split from the sample. The fatty acid color is compared with standard colors. For the light-colored fatty acids a $5\frac{1}{4}$-in. column is compared with color standards in a Lovibond tintometer. Darker fatty acids are compared with standard FAC color discs, which conform to specifications of the Fat Analysis Committee (FAC) of the American Oil Chemist's Society.

Free Alkalinity. A sample is dissolved in alcohol and titrated to a phenolphthalein end point with standard acid. The result is usually expressed in terms of Na_2O.

Salt is determined by titration with silver nitrate, using potassium chromate as an indicator.

Glycerol. The soap is hydrolyzed with mineral acid and a glycerol determination is made on the aqueous phase by oxidation either with potassium dichromate or with sodium periodate.

Health and Safety Factors

In the soap industry, the handling of strong caustic soda solutions is probably the greatest safety hazard. Caustic soda is usually stored and used in processing operations as a 50°Bé solution (50% NaOH by weight). At this strength, it is corrosive when in contact with the body. It may cause serious eye injuries and body burns if not washed off quickly with water. Goggles and protective clothing are worn where danger from caustic soda exists.

In some flake and powder processing operations, high dust concentrations may prove irritating to the mucous surfaces of the nasal passages and throat. Such irritation causes mild to severe discomfort but is not considered particularly injurious. New workers are chiefly affected by this dust, and almost invariably sneeze when first exposed. The discomfort arises from irritation, dryness, and soreness of mucous surfaces, sometimes accompanied by excessive mucous discharge. More experienced workers are less affected. Workers in dust areas wear masks to prevent irritation. Flakes and powders can be dedusted by dropping through a tower against a rising forced current of air. The dust is carried up and away by the air current.

Uses

Personal hygiene, domestic and commercial laundering of clothing and home, and commercial cleaning operations are the principal uses of the soluble alkali soaps. In addition, their detersive and emulsifying properties are utilized in a number of unrelated fields. The vast array of anionic, cationic, and nonionic synthetic detergents available today has undoubtedly restricted, but not eliminated, the role of soaps in some of these special applications.

Textile mills consume considerable quantities of soap in kier-boiling cotton, scouring wool, and degumming silk to remove impurities prior to finishing operations and to assist the level application of softening agents used to improve fabric feel. See Textile technology.

Soaps play a key role in emulsion-polymerization processes used in the rubber and plastic industries. In producing SBR (styrene–butadiene rubber), for example, soaps maintain an intimate emulsion between the dispersed monomers and the aqueous phase during the polymerization. Partially hydrogenated tallow soaps are generally formed in situ by dissolving the fatty acids in the monomers and adding the sodium or potassium alkali to the water phase. See Elastomers, synthetic. Soaps function similarly in the emulsion polymerizations of acrylic and vinyl monomers.

Soaps are widely used in the cosmetic industry to emulsify a variety of skin cleaners and conditioners. A partial listing of the latter includes vegetable oils, fatty acids, waxes, and mineral oil. The soaps are generally prepared in situ and the kind and amount of soap largely determines the liquid, paste, or gel forms of the end products.

Sodium and lithium soaps are extensively used to thicken mineral oil in the manufacture of lubricating greases.

Leather is degreased by hot soap solutions during processing. Finished saddles and leather goods are maintained by application of a saddle soap which usually contains a few percent of emulsified beeswax or carnauba wax.

Soaps are still used to some extent as wetting and spreading agents to improve the dispersal of insecticidal and fungicidal components of agricultural sprays.

Ammonia and alkanolamines, such as mono- and triethanolamines (see Alkanolamines), monoisopropanolamine, and 2-amino-2-methyl-1-propanol (AMP) are used to neutralize fatty acids to form specialty soaps. These soaps are good emulsifiers and are diversely employed in cosmetic preparations, soluble cutting oils used in textile processing, furniture, floor, and automobile polishes, and emulsion paints.

Bibliography

"Soap" in *ECT* 1st ed., Vol. 12, pp. 553–598, by G. W. Busby, Lever Brothers Company.

1. W. H. Mattil, *Oil Soap* **21**, 198 (1944).
2. J. W. McBain and W. W. Lee, *Ind. Eng. Chem.* **35**, 917 (1943).
3. U.S. Pat. 2,566,359 (Sept. 4, 1951), R. V. Owen (to Lever Bros. Co., Inc.).
4. G. W. McBride, *Chem. Eng.* **54**, 94 (1947).
5. U.S. Pat. 2,300,749 (Nov. 3, 1942), A. T. Scott (to Sharples Corp.).
6. U.S. Pat. 2,300,750 (Nov. 3, 1942), A. T. Scott (to Sharples Corp.).
7. U.S. Pat. 2,300,751 (Nov. 3, 1942), A. T. Scott and L. Sender (to Sharples Corp.).
8. U.S. Pat. 2,336,893 (Dec. 14, 1943), A. T. Scott (to Sharples Corp.).
9. F. Lachampt and R. Perron, in R. T. Holman, W. O. Lundberg, and T. Malkin, eds., *The Chemistry of Fats and other Lipids*, Vol. 5, Pergamon Press, Inc., New York, 1958, p. 31.
10. F. T. E. Palmqvist and F. E. Sullivan, *J. Am. Oil Chemists' Soc.* **36**, 173 (1959).
11. A. L. Schulerud, *J. Am. Oil Chemists' Soc.* **40**, 1609 (1963).
12. A. Lanteri, *Seifen-Oele-Fette-Wachse* **84**, 589 (1958).
13. F. V. Wells, *Soap Chem. Specialties* **38**, 49 (1962).
14. *Soap Chem. Specialities* **40**, 67 (1964).
15. J. W. McBain and W. W. Lee, *Oil Soap* **20**, 17 (1943).
16. J. W. McBain, R. D. Vold, and K. Gardiner, *Oil Soap* **20**, 221 (1943).

17. U.S. Pat. 2,215,539 (Sept. 24, 1940), J. W. Bodman (to Lever Bros. Co., Inc...
18. U.S. Pat. 2,295,594 (Sept. 15, 1942), V. Mills (to Procter & Gamble).
19. U.S. Pat. 2,295,595 (Sept. 15, 1942), V. Mills (to Procter & Gamble).
20. U.S. Pat. 2,295,596 (Sept. 15, 1942), V. Mills (to Procter & Gamble).
21. R. H. Ferguson, F. B. Rosevear, and R. C. Stillman, *Ind. Eng. Chem.* **35,** 1005 (1943).
22. R. H. Ferguson, *Oil Soap* **21,** 6 (1944).
23. M. J. Buerger, L. B. Smith, F. V. Ryer, and J. E. Spike, Jr., *Proc. Natl. Acad. Sci. U.S.* **31,** 226 (1945).
24. M. J. Buerger, L. B. Smith, and F. V. Ryer, *J. Am. Oil Chemists' Soc.* **24,** 193 (1947).
25. R. D. Vold, J. D. Grandine, and H. Schott, *J. Phys. Chem.* **56,** 128 (1952).
26. U.S. Pat. 2,970,116 (Jan. 31, 1961), W. A. Kelly and H. D. Hamilton (to Lever Bros. Co., Inc.).
27. U.S. Pat. 3,274,119 (Sept. 20, 1966), S. Goldwasser and F. V. Ryer (to Lever Bros. Co., Inc.).
28. L. J. Vinson, *J. Am. Oil Chemists' Soc.* **44,** 476 (1967).
29. E. Jungermann, J. Brown, Jr., F. Yackovich, and D. Taber, *J. Am. Oil Chemists' Soc.* **44,** 232 (1967).
30. *Official and Tentative Methods of the American Oil Chemists' Society,* American Oil Chemists' Society, Chicago, Ill. (Annual publication.)

F. V. Ryer
Lever Brothers Co., Inc.

SODA.   See Alkali and chlorine industries;   Sodium compounds.

SODIUM

Sodium, at. no. 11, at. wt 22.9898, is the second of the alkali metals (group IA of the periodic system).   The chemical symbol Na derives from natrium, which is the word for sodium in German and some other languages.   Elemental sodium was not isolated until 1807, when Sir Humphry Davy decomposed sodium hydroxide electrolytically to set free some bright, silvery metal beads.   A year later Gay-Lussac and Thenard reduced sodium hydroxide with iron at high temperature, but it was not until 1855 that H. Sainte-Claire Deville developed the first commercial process for the production of metallic sodium.   Deville used carbon to reduce sodium carbonate at a temperature above 1100°C.   The success of this process may be judged from the 200:1 price decrease which resulted from its operation (1).   Hamilton Y. Castner, seeking lower-cost sodium, perfected the reduction of sodium hydroxide with carbon in 1886 (2), and, in 1890, developed the electrolysis of fused sodium hydroxide (3).   The Castner electrolytic process dominated the field for ca 35 years until the advent of the Downs process for the electrolysis of fused sodium chloride (3).   The current bulk price of Downs-cell sodium is 17.75¢/lb.

The first industrial use for sodium was the reduction of sodium aluminum chloride to make aluminum.   The Hall aluminum cell replaced this process, but outlets for sodium were found in the manufacture of sodium peroxide, sodium cyanide, and antipyrin.   Many other uses developed as the industry grew, but at the present time the manufacture of tetramethyl- and tetraethyllead is the major use in the United States. See under Uses below.

The many potential advantages of sodium and sodium–potassium alloys for heat transfer in nuclear reactors led to a major advance of sodium technology beginning about 1950.   This application is expected to grow steadily over the next several decades.

and the use of sodium as an electrical conductor may achieve commercial status in the near future.

Occurrence. Sodium does not occur in the free state because of its high reactivity. The earth's crust contains 2.83 wt % and sea water 1.06 wt % of the metal in combined form (4). Many complex minerals contain sodium. Sodium chloride, sodium carbonate, sodium sulfate, sodium borate, and sodium nitrate are among the simple naturally occurring salts. Sodium salts are found in seawater, salt lakes, alkaline lakes, and mineral springs. Rock salt deposits result from the drying of salt lakes. Important U.S. sources of sodium salts are the Great Salt Lake in Utah, the Searles Lake in California, and the rock salt beds of the Gulf coast, Virginia, New York, and Michigan.

Physical and Chemical Properties

At room temperature, sodium is a soft, malleable solid easily cut with a putty knife or wire. In an inert atmosphere the freshly cut surface has a faintly pink, bright metallic lustre. Long (5) states that the true rose color of a clean sodium surface is largely masked by specular reflection. Liquid sodium has the appearance of mercury. Both solid and liquid sodium tarnish rapidly in air, the rate depending on temperature

Table 1. Physical Properties of Sodium

Property	Value[a]	Reference
melting point, °C	97.83 ± 0.02	12
heat of fusion, cal/g	27.05	13
entropy of fusion, cal/(°C)(g)	0.0729	13
vol change on melting, %	2.63	14
boiling point, °C	882	15
heat of vaporization at bp, kcal/(°C)(g)	1.127	15
entropy of vaporization at bp, kcal/(°K)(g)	0.98	15
density,[b] vapor, g/cm³		16
at 900°C	0.003	
at 1460°C	0.008	
at 1800°C	0.040	
liquid, at 210–1110°C, g/ml	$0.9453 - 0.2247 \times 10^{-3}t$	17[c]
heat capacity, vapor, at 50–1500°K,		17[c]
cal/(°C)(g-atom)	4.968	
critical temperature, °K	2570 ± 350	16
critical density, g/cm³	0.206 ± 0.041	16
critical vol, liter/g-atom	0.116 ± 0.023	16
thermal conductivity, (cal)/(sec)(cm²)(°C/cm)		
solid, at 0–97.8°C	$0.342 - 0.00040t$	14
liquid, at 97.8–512°C	$0.2166 - 0.000116t$	14
surface tension, at 98–450°C, γ, dyn/cm	$202 - 0.10t$	14
principal spectral lines, Å		4
D_1	5890	
D_2	5896	
electrochemical potential, at 25°C, V		
$Na^+ + e = Na°$	-2.7109	4

[a] Temperature, t, in °C.

[b] Values taken from plotted data.

[c] See also references 14 and 18.

and relative humidity. Exposed surfaces become white or light gray in color by formation of a coating of oxide, hydroxide, and carbonate.

Only body-centered-cubic crystals are reported for sodium at 20°C (6), the lattice constant being 4.2820 Å. The atomic radius is 1.85 Å. A low-temperature hexagonal close-packed structure and a martensitic transformation have been reported (7–9). Near the melting point the structure of liquid sodium is close packed (10), the nearest atom distance being about the same as in the solid. Pauling gives the value of 0.95 Å for the radius of the Na^+ ion (11).

In recent years the physical and thermodynamic properties of sodium have been the subject of intense study. Selected items from the voluminous literature have been assembled in Table 1. Other properties are expressed in the following equations ($T = °K; t = °C$):

vapor pressure at 1155–1735°K, atm   (18)

$$\log_{10} P = 6.67176 - \frac{5544.97}{T} - 0.61344 \log_{10} T$$

density, solid, at 0–97.8°C, g/cm³   (14)

$$d = 0.9725 - 0.2011 \times 10^{-3} t - 0.15 \times 10^{-4} t^2$$

heat capacity, cal/(°C)(g-atom)   (12,14)
    solid, at 25–97.8°C

$$C_p = 9.93555 - 0.0208053T + 0.57883 \times 10^{-4} T^2$$

liquid, at 97.8–882°C

$$C_p = 8.95811 - 0.45788 \times 10^{-2} T + 0.25409 \times 10^{-5} T^2$$

enthalpy ($Na_c{}^{298.16\ °K} = 0$), cal/g-atom   (14)
    solid, at 298.16–370.99°K

$$\Delta H = -2226.86 + 9.93555T - 1.40265 \times 10^{-2} T^2 + 1.92943 \times 10^{-5} T^3$$

liquid, at 370.99–1200°K

$$\Delta H = -1915.13 + 8.95811T - 2.2894 \times 10^{-3} T^2 + 8.46967 \times 10^{-7} T^3$$

vapor (ideal, monoatomic), at 50–1500°K

$$\Delta H = 24373.48 + 4.9680T$$

electrical resistivity, Ω-cm
    solid, at 20–97.8°C   (14)

$$r = 4.477 + 0.01932t + 0.00004t^2$$

liquid, at 100–1100°C   (17)

$$r = 6.141 + 3.505 \times 10^{-2} t + 5.689 \times 10^{-6} t^2 + 1.668 \times 10^{-8} t^3$$

viscosity, liquid, at 103–686°C, cP   (14)

$$\log \eta = -1.09127 + \frac{382}{t + 313}$$

The vapor is chiefly monoatomic; the dimer has been found spectrographically and the tetramer is reported on the basis of vapor-density data (18).

Sodium is paramagnetic. Thin films are opaque to visible light but transmit in the ultraviolet region beginning at about 2100 Å. Sodium vapor is blue but frequently a brilliant green color is observed when working with sodium at high temperature, presumably the result of color mixing of the normal blue with yellow from partial burning of the vapor. The first ionization potential is 5.14 eV. The wetting characteristics of sodium are interesting in relation to heat-transfer applications and the preparation of high-surface sodium (19). Sodium at 100–150°C readily wets and spreads over many dry solids, such as NaCl or Al_2O_3, and is highly reactive in this form. It does not easily wet stainless or carbon steel. Wetting of such structural metals is influenced by the cleanliness of the surface, the purity of the sodium, temperature, and the time of exposure. Wetting occurs more readily at 300°C or higher and, once attained, persists at lower temperatures (20).

Only ^{23}Na occurs in nature but six isotopes, having short half-lives, have been made by nuclear reactions; they are listed below.

Isotope	Half-life	Isotope	Half-life
^{20}Na	0.4 sec	^{24}Na	15.0 hr
^{21}Na	23.0 sec	^{25}Na	60.0 sec
^{22}Na	2.58 yr	^{26}Na	1.0 sec

Like other alkali metals and the alkaline earth metals, sodium forms chemically unstable solutions in dry liquid ammonia. The solvent, NH_3, and solute, Na, react slowly to form the metal amide and hydrogen in the following manner:

$$Na + NH_3 \rightarrow NaNH_2 + \tfrac{1}{2}H_2$$

This reaction is catalyzed by metals, such as iron, cobalt, and nickel, and the rate depends on the temperature of the system and the concentration of alkali metal. With very pure materials, metallic sodium can be recovered from the ammonia solution by solvent evaporation. Sodium is soluble in liquid ammonia at its boiling point to the extent of about 20% by wt. Concentrated solutions of sodium in NH_3 separate into two liquid phases when cooled below the consolute temperature, −41.6°C. The compositions of the phases are dependent on the temperature; the composition at the peak of the conjugate solutions curve is 4.15 atom % sodium. The density decreases with increasing concentration of sodium. Thus, in the two-phase region the dilute bottom phase, low in sodium concentration, is a deep blue solution; the light top phase, high in sodium concentration, has a metallic bronze appearance (21–24).

At high temperature sodium and its fused halides are mutually soluble. The consolute temperatures and corresponding Na-mole fractions are as follows: Na/NaF, 1182°C, 0.28; Na/NaCl, 1080°C, 0.50; Na/NaBr, 1025°C, 0.52; Na/NaI, 1033°C, 0.50 (25). Gaseous nitrogen has no detectable solubility in liquid sodium near the melting point, and calcium oxide and nitride are insoluble at 100–120°C (26). Solubilities of many elements and compounds in sodium are of great interest to designers of nuclear-energy and spacecraft equipment but published data are limited and conflicting. Some available data are given in Table 2.

Sodium is soluble in ethylenediamine (25,32) but solubility in other amines may require the presence of ammonia. Sodium is soluble in mixtures of ammonia and methyl- or ethylamine. Sodium dissolves in many metals to form alloys, some of which

Table 2. Solubilities in Liquid Sodium

Temperature, °C	Na$_2$O, ppm (27)	NaH, wt % (28)	Na$_2$CO$_3$, ppm (28)	NaCl, ppm (28)	Ag,[a] wt% (29)	Cu, ppm (29)	Ni, ppm (29)	C,[b] ppb[d] (29,30)	Fe,[c] ppm (31)
100	4				0.18				
150			20						
200	40		50						
250		0.005			2.50	<0.2			
300	200	0.040	160						6
325						1.0			
350		0.300							
385			270						
400	800	1.450		<9					9
445		4.290							
450						10.0	0.6	<5	
500					20.80				12
550						60.0			
600							1.4	0.1±0.05	

[a] Calculated from the following equation: $\log_{10}$ Ag, ppm $= 7.248 - 1493/°K$ (29).

[b] There is considerable doubt as to the solubility of carbon in sodium.

[c] The solubilities of iron in sodium reported in the literature vary over a wide range. Data obtained by radiochemical techniques are generally much lower than the values listed here.

[d] Parts per billion.

are liquid below 300°C (see below under Alloys). Sodium is insoluble in those hydrocarbons toward which it is chemically inert and can be dispersed in liquids, such as kerosene or mineral oil, to provide a reactive form of the metal.

In 1932 N. D. Scott and co-workers discovered a new class of complexes of ether, sodium, and polycyclic hydrocarbons (33). Sodium was found to react with naphthalene in dimethyl ether as solvent to form a soluble, dark green, reactive complex. The solution is electrically conductive. The reaction to form the complex has been described (34) as follows:

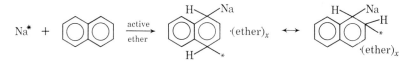

where * = unshared electron.

The addition product, C$_{10}$H$_8$Na, may be regarded as a resonance hybrid. The ether is more than just a solvent that promotes the reaction; stability of the complex depends on the presence of the ether, and sodium can be liberated from the complex by evaporation of the dimethyl ether or by dilution with an indifferent solvent, such as ethyl ether. A number of ether-type solvents are effective in this preparation, such as methyl ethyl ether, ethylene glycol dimethyl ether, dioxane, tetrahydrofuran, and others. Trimethylamine also promotes the formation of the complex. It can be called sodium–naphthalene complex or naphthalenesodium; it has also been referred to as "naphthylsodium" although this should denote C$_{10}$H$_7$Na rather than C$_{10}$H$_8$Na.

The reaction is not limited to sodium but is general for the alkali metals. Aromatic compounds other than naphthalene may also be used, for example, diphenyl, anthracene, and phenanthrene.

Some reactions of the sodium–naphthalene complex resemble those of metallic sodium. With mercury, for example, sodium amalgam is formed and the naphthalene is liberated. In other reactions dihydronaphthalene is a product and a sodium derivative of the compound supplying the hydrogen is formed. This is the case with water, alcohols, or other organics in which hydrogen can be displaced by sodium.

Sodium is a very active metal, reacting with many elements and substances (34, 35). It forms well-defined compounds with many metals, such as those in the sodium–lead system (36).

When heated in dry air, sodium ignites at approximately 120°C and burns with a yellow flame, evolving a dense white acrid smoke. Sodium reacts with air or oxygen to form a monoxide or peroxide. If the supply of the oxygen is limited and the temperature kept below 160°C, the principal reaction product is sodium monoxide, Na_2O. At 250–300°C with adequate oxygen, sodium peroxide, Na_2O_2, is formed along with very small amounts of superoxide, NaO_2 (see Peroxides). Sodium superoxide is made by the reaction of sodium peroxide and oxygen at high temperature and pressure. Sodium does not react with extremely dry oxygen or air beyond the possible formation of a surface film of transparent oxide (27).

Sodium and water react rapidly at room temperature according to the following equation:

$$Na + H_2O = NaOH + \tfrac{1}{2} H_2 + 33.67 \text{ kcal/mole}$$

The liberated heat melts the sodium and usually ignites the evolved hydrogen if the reaction is conducted in air (see below under Handling and safety). Sodium and hydrogen do not react at room temperature, but at 200–350°C sodium hydride is formed. The reaction is slow with bulk sodium but is much more rapid with either high-surface sodium (19) or sodium dispersions. The reaction using high-surface sodium is further accelerated by the use of surface-active agents (37,38), such as sodium anthracenecarboxylate and phenantrenecarboxylate.

Sodium and carbon do not react to any significant extent to form sodium carbide although the work of Guernsey and Sherman (39) is often cited as evidence of such a reaction. Sodium and Na_2CO_3 react at 500–700°C to form sodium carbide, Na_2C_2, but above 700°C free carbon is also formed (40). The reaction of sodium and sucrose at 500–700°C also produces sodium carbide but in small amounts. In these reactions the presence of the carbide was inferred from the formation of acetylene on hydrolysis of the products. Several recent investigations indicate that sodium reacts with graphite to form lamellar compounds, such as $C_{64}Na$ or $C_{96}Na$ (41–43).

Nitrogen and sodium do not react at any temperature under ordinary circumstances, but are reported to form the nitride, or the azide, under the influence of an electric discharge (20,25,44). Sodium silicide, $NaSi$, has been synthesized from the elements (45,46). When heated together sodium and phosphorus form sodium phosphide but, in the presence of air, sodium phosphate is formed with ignition. Sulfur, selenium, and tellurium react with sodium to form sulfides, selenides, and tellurides, respectively. In the vapor phase sodium reacts with all of the halogens to form halides (25). At room temperature chlorine or bromine gas react rapidly with thin films of metallic sodium (47); fluorine and sodium ignite. Molten sodium ignites in chlorine and burns to form sodium chloride.

There appears to be little reaction between sodium and carbon dioxide gas at room temperature, but on heating some sodium carbonate is formed. Under controlled conditions sodium oxalate, $Na_2(COO)_2$, may be a product. Sodium and solid carbon dioxide react explosively on impact. Above 1100°C sodium and carbon monoxide do not react, but at 600–850°C reaction occurs to produce a mixture of sodium carbide and sodium carbonate (48); in the range of 250–340°C a high yield of sodium carbonyl, $(NaCO)_6$, is obtained (49,50). Sodium reacts with nitrous oxide to form sodium oxide and burns in nitric oxide to form a mixture of nitrite and hyponitrite, $Na_2N_2O_2$. Sodium heated in nitrogen tetraoxide yields a mixture of nitrate and nitrite, while at low temperature liquid nitrogen pentoxide reacts with sodium to produce nitrogen dioxide and sodium nitrate.

Phosphorus trichloride and pentachloride react with sodium to form sodium chloride and sodium phosphide (under some conditions with detonation). Phosphorus oxychloride, $POCl_3$, reacts explosively when heated with sodium. Carbon disulfide reacts violently with sodium, forming sodium sulfide. Sodium amide, $NaNH_2$, is formed by the reaction of liquid ammonia and sodium metal or by the reaction of ammonia gas with molten sodium. Sodium reacts only superficially with liquid sulfur dioxide, but the reaction of liquid sodium at its melting point with gaseous sulfur dioxide is violent. Under controlled conditions sodium and sulfur dioxide react to yield sodium hydrosulfite, $Na_2S_2O_4$ (51). Dry hydrogen sulfide gas reacts slowly with solid sodium but, with moisture present, the reaction is very rapid with sufficient heat evolution to melt the sodium. The product is sodium sulfide.

Sodium reacts with dilute acids about as vigorously as it reacts with water. The reaction with concentrated sulfuric acid may be somewhat less vigorous.

At 300–385°C sodium and sodium hydroxide react according to the following equilibrium:

$$2\,Na + NaOH \rightleftharpoons Na_2O + NaH$$

The reaction is displaced to the right by dissociation of NaH with liberation of hydrogen. This is favored by conducting the reaction under vacuum or by sweeping the reaction zone with an inert gas to remove the hydrogen (26,52). In this manner sodium monoxide, substantially free of sodium and sodium hydroxide, may be produced. If hydrogen is not removed from the system, the equilibrium hydrogen pressure above 385°C is, for some unknown reason, less than would be predicted from the dissociation pressure of NaH. In the more complicated reaction between sodium metal and anhydrous potassium hydroxide, potassium metal and sodium hydroxide are produced in a reversible reaction (53,54) which may be expressed as follows: $Na + KOH \rightleftharpoons K + NaOH$. Superimposed on this simple equilibrium are complex reactions involving the oxides and hydrides of the respective metals. At about 400°C the metal phase, resulting from the reaction of sodium and potassium hydroxide, contains an unidentified reaction product which precipitates out of solution at about 300°C (26).

Data on the free energy of formation (55) indicate that sodium reduces oxides of group I elements, except lithium, but does not reduce oxides of group II elements, except mercury, cadmium, and zinc. Many other oxides are reduced by metallic sodium, the reduction in some cases depending on the formation of exothermic complex oxides. Iron oxide is reduced by sodium below about 1200°C, but the reaction is reversed above this temperature. Sodium reduces the fluorides of most of the elements with the notable exceptions of lithium, calcium, barium, strontium, and some of the lanthanides. It reduces most metallic chlorides, although some of the group I and group II chlorides give two-phase equilibrium systems consisting of fused salt and alloy layers (54). Some heavy metal sulfides and cyanides are reduced by sodium.

Sodium reacts with most organic compounds, particularly those which contain oxygen, nitrogen, sulfur, halogens, or carboxyl or hydroxyl groups. The reactions are violent in many cases, for example, with organic halides. Carbon may be deposited or hydrogen liberated in these reactions, and compounds containing sulfur or halogens usually form sodium sulfide or sodium halides as reaction products. Sodium reacts with alcohols to form alkoxides (qv); primary alcohols react more rapidly than secondary or tertiary, and the reactivity decreases as the number of carbon atoms of the alcohol increases. Organosodium compounds may be made by the reaction of sodium with other organometallic compounds or with active methylene compounds, by the reaction with organic halides, by cleavage of ethers, or by addition to unsaturated compounds. Some aromatic vinyl compounds and allylic compounds also react with sodium to produce sodium derivatives. Sodium forms aromatic complexes by direct reaction in suitable solvent systems (see p. 436). At moderate temperature sodium reacts with acetylene to form monosodium acetylide, $NaHC_2$; at higher temperatures sodium carbide, Na_2C_2, is formed. Sodium does not react with anhydrous ethyl ether but may react with higher ethers or with mixed ethers. Sodium may react with organic acids to give the corresponding salts with evolution of hydrogen, or it may decompose the acids. Pure, dry, saturated hydrocarbons, such as benzene, xylene, toluene, and mineral oil do not react with sodium below the hydrocarbon-cracking temperature. With unsaturated hydrocarbons, sodium may add at a double bond or cause polymerization. Sodium amalgam or the combined action of sodium and alcohol are used for organic reductions. Sodium is also used as a condensing agent in such reactions as acetoacetic ester and malonic ester syntheses, and the Wurtz and Fittig reactions.

Manufacture

Sodium can be freed from its compounds electrolytically or by chemical reduction. It was first prepared by electrolysis of fused caustic in 1807, but chemical reduction processes were used for commercial production until 1890. Electrolytic methods have been dominant since then. However, as late as 1945, the Union Carbide Corporation used existing commercial vacuum furnaces at its Spokane, Washington, plant for experimental production of sodium by reduction of sodium chloride with ferrosilicon (83% Si) (56). The pelleted charge of about 34% sodium chloride, 56% lime (or calcined dolomite), and 10% ferrosilicon, heated to 850°C at 5–0.5 mm Hg absolute pressure, gave about 85% yield on the sodium charged. A total of 22,000 lb of sodium was produced during this study. The Dow Chemical Company reports a process for making sodium by the reaction of soda ash and coke used during World War II (57,58).

The first industrial process for the manufacture of sodium was developed by Deville (59). Sodium carbonate was reduced by carbon at high temperatures to produce a mixture of carbon monoxide and sodium vapor. Success of the Deville process depended upon rapid quenching of the evolved gases to condense the sodium before a significant reversion of the reaction could occur. H. Y. Castner developed a process for the thermal reduction of sodium hydroxide with carbon (2) according to the following reaction:

$$6\ NaOH + 2\ C \rightarrow 2\ Na_2CO_3 + 3\ H_2 + 2\ Na$$

When this process is run below 1000°C, hydrogen is evolved, but no CO. There is no problem of separation, but only one third of the sodium charged is released (34, 60). Interest in thermal routes to sodium continues as indicated by current literature references (58,60–63).

Sodium amalgam, made by electrolysis of sodium chloride brine with mercury cathode cells (see Vol. 1, p. 688), has been used as a source of metallic sodium. In a low-melting fused salt-bath electrolysis cell, sodium is stripped from the amalgam anode and deposited at a steel cathode (64–66). Continued interest in this process is indicated by a U.S. patent (67). Distillation processes for recovery of sodium from amalgam have also been proposed.

Electrolysis of fused sodium chloride is the principal route to sodium today, but the older electrolysis of fused sodium hydroxide is still used in Japan and other countries where the demand for sodium is small. The electrolysis of fused sodium chloride uses a cheap, readily available raw material and produces chlorine directly as a co-product. The problems of the high melting point of sodium chloride and the corrosive nature of the bath have been largely overcome in the Downs cell (3). The technically simpler sodium hydroxide electrolysis is limited to 50% maximum current efficiency as discussed below. Another disadvantage is the necessary electrolysis of aqueous NaCl solution to produce the sodium hydroxide raw material. These difficulties offset the advantages of lower cell voltage and operating temperature, but the brine-electrolysis step does produce chlorine, the same coproduct as obtained in the Downs process.

ELECTROLYSIS OF FUSED SODIUM HYDROXIDE

The first successful electrolytic production of sodium was achieved with the Castner cell which produces sodium, water, and oxygen according to the following reactions:

$$At\ the\ cathode: \quad 4\ Na^+ + 4\ e \rightarrow 4\ Na$$

$$At\ the\ anode: \quad 4\ OH^- - 4\ e \rightarrow 2\ H_2O + O_2$$

The water formed at the anode diffuses to the cathode compartment, where it reacts with its equivalent of sodium according to the following equation:

$$2\ H_2O + 2\ Na \rightarrow 2\ NaOH + H_2$$

The net change is represented as follows:

$$2\ NaOH \rightarrow 2\ Na + H_2 + O_2$$

Since the water reacts with half of the sodium produced by the electrolysis, the current yield can never be more than 50% of theoretical. Other reactions in the cell lower this yield still more.

The Castner cell (3) was so simple in design and operation that in many years of use only minor changes were made. Castner applied for his original patent in 1890 and the first commercial plant was producing about 2 tons per week by 1893. Figure 1 shows a section of a cell used in England in the early 1950s (68). The fused caustic bath is contained in the cast-iron outer pot which rests in a brick chamber. The cylindrical copper cathode is supported on the cathode stem which extends upward through the bottom of the cell. The cathode stem is sealed and insulated from the outer pot by frozen bath. The cylindrical nickel anode, concentric with the cathode, is supported from the rim of the outer pot. The cylindrical iron-gauze diaphragm located in the 1-in. annular space between the electrodes is suspended from the inner

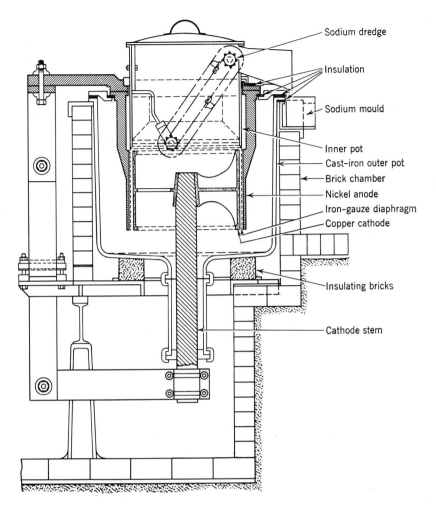

Sodium dredge

Insulation

Sodium mould

Inner pot
Cast-iron outer pot
Brick chamber
Nickel anode
Iron-gauze diaphragm
Copper cathode

Insulating bricks

Cathode stem

Fig. 1. A Castner sodium cell.

pot. Because of the difference in density, sodium rises in the hydroxide bath and collects on its surface in the inner pot. This chamber is electrically insulated from the top
anode ring which supports it. The inner pot is closed by a cover which maintains an
atmosphere of hydrogen over the sodium to prevent burning. No practical way has
been found to collect the hydrogen so it is vented into the room. The oxygen liberated
at the anode is also vented. In the operation of the Castner cells used at the Du Pont
plant at Niagara Falls until about 1925 (69), the sodium was removed by hand with a
perforated ladle. Surface-tension effects were such that the bath drained back through
the perforations but the sodium was retained in the ladle. Later cells were equipped
with mechanically driven iron-gauze buckets to remove the sodium. The cell shown in
Figure 1 may hold about a ton of molten bath, consisting primarily of mercury-cell
caustic soda with up to 10% each of sodium chloride and sodium carbonate. Some salt
is added initially to improve the bath conductivity, but the carbonate is an unwanted
impurity. After several months the chloride, carbonate, and other impurities attain
levels which seriously impair the efficiency of the cell; the bath is then removed and the

Table 3. Operating Characteristics of the Castner Cell

Property	Value
bath temperature, °C	320 ± 10
cell current, A	9000 ± 500
cell voltage, V	4.3–5.0
cathode current density, A/in.^{2}	7[a]
current efficiency, %	40[a]
sodium produced, g/Ah	0.4
g/kWh	90

[a] Approximate value.

cell restarted with fresh bath. The operating characteristics of the Castner cell are listed in Table 3.

For small cells it is necessary to supply heat externally to maintain operating temperature but large cells are heated by the electrolysis current. Of the many ingenious systems proposed to prevent the reaction of sodium with the water produced at the anode none are known to have been applied commercially. Some Castner installations are still operating in Asia (70) and possibly in parts of Europe, but in the United States the Downs process for electrolysis of fused NaCl is used exclusively. Downs plants are in operation in England, France, and Germany.

ELECTROLYSIS OF FUSED SODIUM CHLORIDE

Many cells have been developed for the electrolysis of fused sodium chloride (34,71,72), but the cell patented by J. C. Downs in 1924 (73) has been most successful. The Downs cells originally installed at the Du Pont plant at Niagara Falls, N.Y., were square, probably to suit the rectangular firebrick then available for cell lining, but improved cells of circular cross section were soon built. Those in general use by 1945 are described in detail in references 34, 70, and 74. In these cells, a single cylindrical anode (constructed of several graphite blocks) is inserted through the center of the cell bottom and is surrounded by an iron-gauze diaphragm and a cylindrical iron cathode. A major advance in cell design, introduced in the 1940s, was the replacement of the single anode and cathode with a multiple electrode arrangement consisting of four anodes of smaller diameter in a square pattern, each surrounded by a cylindrical diaphragm and cathode as shown in Figure 2, an illustration of a modern Downs cell. Without substantially increasing the overall cell dimensions, this design increases the electrode area per cell and allows increased cell amperage.

The cell consists of three chambers. The upper chamber is outside the chlorine dome and above the sodium-collecting ring. The other two chambers are the chlorine-collecting zone inside the dome and diaphragm, and the sodium-collecting zone outside the diaphragm and under the sodium-collecting ring. This arrangement serves to prevent recombination of the sodium and chlorine. As shown in Figure 2, the steel shell, i, lined with brick, g, contains the fused bath. Four cylindrical graphite anodes, m, project upward from the base of the cell, each surrounded by a diaphragm of iron gauze, j, and a steel cathode, k. The four cathode cylinders are joined to form a single unit which is supported on cathode arms projecting through the cell walls and connected to the cathode copper, l. The diaphragms are suspended from the collector assembly, h, which is supported from steel beams spanning the cell top. The collector is a complex assembly of inverted troughs and chambers arranged to collect the prod-

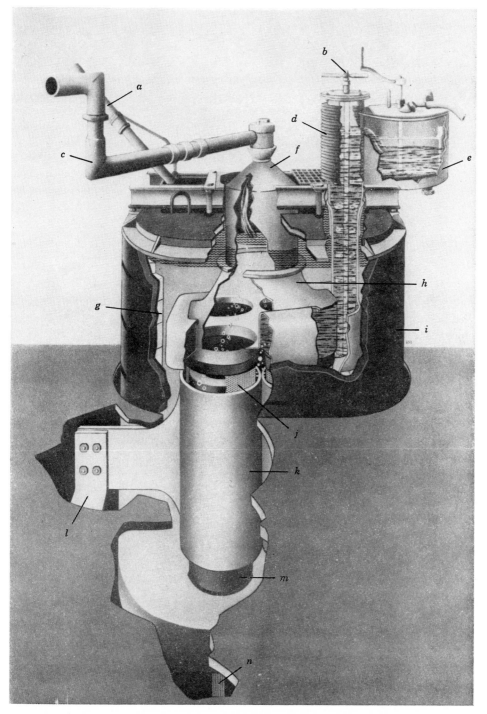

Fig. 2. A modern Downs cell. LEGEND: *a*, salt feed chute; *b*, tickler; *c*, chlorine line; *d*, air-cooled sodium riser; *e*, sodium receiver; *f*, chlorine dome; *g*, brick cell lining; *h*, product collector; *i*, steel shell; *j*, diaphragm; *k*, cathode; *l*, cathode copper; *m*, anode; *n*, anode copper.

ucts in separate compartments as they rise through the bath due to differences in density. The chlorine emerges through the nickel dome, f, and is removed through the chlorine line, c, to a header. Sodium is channeled to a "riser" pipe, d, which conducts it to a discharge point above the cell wall. The difference in level between the overflowing sodium and the cell bath occurs because of the roughly 2:1 density ratio of the fused bath and liquid sodium. The upper end of the riser pipe is fitted with cooling fins which lower the sodium temperature and thereby precipitate dissolved calcium, as discussed in more detail below. The sodium, still containing some calcium, electrolyte, and oxide, overflows into a receiver, e. The calcium precipitated in the riser pipe tends to adhere to the wall and the scraper, b, is provided to dislodge the deposit and return it to the base of the riser (see below). The cell is fitted with an insulated cover to conserve heat and protect the cell-room operators, but a small area is left uncovered for visual observation of the bath crust, for bath-level regulation, and for salt feed. Fine, dry crystalline salt is fed to the open bath through the feed chute, a.

The cell bath in early Downs cells (25,34) consisted of about 58% $CaCl_2$ and 42% NaCl by wt. This composition is a compromise between melting point and sodium content. Additional $CaCl_2$ would further lower the melting point at the expense of depletion of sodium in the electrolysis zone with resulting complications. With the above composition the cells operate at $580 \pm 10°C$, a temperature well below the range of the high solubility of sodium in the bath. The use of $CaCl_2$ in the bath causes some problems due to the following equilibrium reaction (54):

$$2 \, Na + CaCl_2 \rightleftharpoons 2 \, NaCl + Ca$$

The alloy phase contains about 5% calcium at cell conditions, an amount intolerable for most industrial uses. The bulk of this calcium is removed by precipitation in the cooled riser pipe. Any precipitated calcium which adheres to the walls of the riser most be scraped off to prevent plugging. The precipitate drops to the bath-metal interface where it reacts to reform $CaCl_2$ and sodium according to the above equilibrium. Calcium remaining in the sodium which enters the receiver is largely removed by filtration at about 110°C. The filtered sodium contains less than 0.04% Ca. The filtration operation also produces a filter cake of calcium, sodium, chlorides, and oxides which is reclaimed by utilizing the equilibrium reaction (see above) to convert the Ca metal to equivalent sodium and $CaCl_2$, the oxides and chlorides being removed with the salt phase. Several methods of recovering metallic calcium or calcium alloys from the filter cake have been proposed, but none has achieved commercial success.

Table 4. Characteristics of British and German Downs Cells

Property	Value	
	British	German
bath temperature, °C	580 ± 15	590 ± 5
cell current, A	25,000–35,000	24,000–32,000
cell voltage, V	7[a]	5.7–6.0
cathode current density, A/in.²	6.3	6.3
current efficiency, %	75–80	78
cell life, days	500–700	300–350
diaphragm life, days	20–100	20–30

[a] Approximate value.

Characteristics of Downs cells as operated in the United States have not been published; British (3) and German (74) data are listed in Table 4.

Salt, substantially free of sulfate and other impurities, is used as cell feed. This salt may be purchased from commercial salt suppliers or made on the plant site by purification of crude rock salt. Dried $CaCl_2$ or cell bath from dismantled cells is added to the bath periodically as needed to balance calcium removed with the sodium. The heat required to maintain the bath in the molten condition is supplied by the electrolysis current. Other electrolyte compositions have been proposed (75,76) in which part or all of the $CaCl_2$ is replaced by other salts. Commercial operations with such baths have demonstrated substantially improved current efficiencies and the production of crude sodium containing relatively little calcium.

Cell life is determined by the loss of graphite from the anodes. Oxygen released at the anode by electrolysis of oxides or water in the bath reacts with the graphite to form CO and CO_2. In time erosion of the anode increases the spacing between the electrodes so that the cell voltage rises to an uneconomic level. Control of the cell temperature also becomes difficult under these conditions. At this stage the cell bath is removed, the cell dismantled, and a new cell erected in its place.

Among other cells designed for the electrolysis of fused sodium chloride, three have been operated on a commercial scale. The Danneel-Lonza cell (77) was the first salt cell to be used successfully. In World War I, however, the operation of these cells was stopped and they were not operated again. The cells had no diaphragms and the sodium was confined to the cathode zone by "salt curtains" (ceramic walls). The Seward cell (78,79) was also operated in the United States for a short time before World War I. This cell used the contact-electrode principle, with the cathode immersed only a few mm in the electrolyte. The Ciba cell (80) was more successful and was used over a longer period of time. This cell was an adaptation to sodium chloride of the Castner cell for the electrolysis of fused caustic. A mixture of sodium chloride with other chlorides, molten at 620°C, was electrolyzed in rectangular or oval cells heated only by the current. Several cells have been patented for the electrolysis of fused salt in cells having molten lead cathodes (81,82,82a). The difficulty with this type of cell is the separation of the sodium from the lead.

Prices, Grades, and Forms

The price of sodium has been relatively stable for many years, as shown below.

Year	Price, $/lb	Year	Price, $/lb
1890	2.00	1953	0.16
1906	0.25	1968	0.1775
1946	0.15		(tank cars)

Sodium is one of the cheapest nonferrous metals. The low cost of sodium makes it an attractive reducing agent for the production of many metals.

Commercial sodium is an unusually pure chemical, containing about 99.95% Na. It is available in the two following grades:

Regular grade: 0.040% max calcium, 0.005% max chloride
Reactor grade: 0.001% max calcium, 0.005% max chloride

Superficial oxide, hydroxide, and carbonate are usually present, but, if necessary, sodium can be supplied with these contaminants reduced to their solubility levels.

Purification methods based on filtration and hot or cold trapping have been developed for the removal of a variety of specific impurities (27). Some typical analyses for trace elements are given in Table 5 (20, 83–85).

Table 5. Trace Elements in Commercial Sodium

Impurity	Parts per million	
	KAPL[a]	DP[b]
aluminum	8	1–4
barium	2	
beryllium	1[c]	
bismuth	10[c]	
boron	4	0.1–0.17
cadmium	1	<0.05
calcium, in regular-grade sodium	190	200
in reactor-grade sodium	2	2–8
cerium	2	
cesium	5	5
chlorides	30	30
cobalt	2	0.11–0.21
copper	2	
gold		<2
indium	2	7–13
iron	2	
lead	1	≤1
lithium	17	<0.06–0.36
magnesium	5	
manganese	2	
mercury	4[c]	
molybdenum	2[c]	
nickel	2	
nitrogen		<3[d]
palladium	5[c]	
phosphorus	10	<1
potassium	100	86–180
rare earths		4
silicon	5	
silver	1	<2
strontium	5	
sulfur	14	1–6
tin	10[c]	≤1
titanium	10[c]	
tungsten		3–7
uranium	5	
vanadium	4	
zinc	1	2–5
zirconium and hafnium		2

NOTE: This table has been adapted from reference 83.

[a] Analyses by Knowles Atomic Power Laboratory, General Electric Co., Schnectady, N.Y.

[b] Analyses by Research Laboratory, E. I. du Pont de Nemours & Co., Inc., Niagara Falls, New York.

[c] Analyses made, but no impurity detected. Values given are the sensitivity limits of the method used.

[d] Total nitrogen, ie, dissolved gas plus nitrogen compounds in reactor-grade sodium.

Sodium dispersions in inert hydrocarbons, such as white oil or kerosene, are easily prepared by heating the mixture above the melting point of sodium and subjecting it to shearing forces by agitation or any of the commonly used dispersing or homogenizing devices. Dispersion can be accelerated and finer particles produced by adding dispersing agents to the system. Oleic acid and other long-chain fatty acids, higher alcohols and esters, and some finely divided solids, such as carbon or bentonite, are effective dispersing agents.

At temperatures above 98°C the sodium is present as liquid spheres. On cooling to lower temperatures solid spheres of sodium remain dispersed in the hydrocarbon and present an extended surface for reaction. Dispersions can be made which contain up to about 50% by wt of sodium. Sodium in this form is easily handled and reacts rapidly with many reagents. For some purposes the presence of the inert hydrocarbon is a disadvantage.

High-Surface Sodium. Liquid sodium readily wets many solid surfaces, and this property may be used to provide a very reactive form of sodium without contamination by hydrocarbons. Powdered solids having high-surface area per unit volume are most suitable for making high-surface sodium, though many other powders, such as sodium chloride, sodium hydride, sodium monoxide, or sodium carbonate can be used. Completely dehydrated activated alumina powder is a very good carrier of the high-surface-to-volume ratio type.

The solid to be coated with sodium is placed in a vessel equipped with a stirrer and is heated to 110–250°C. The air is displaced with pure, dry nitrogen or another inert gas. Clean sodium is added and stirring started. If enough sodium is added to provide a monolayer or more, it is rapidly distributed over the entire available surface. Depending on the available surface, up to 10 wt % or more of sodium can be added without changing the free-flowing character of the system.

Sodium is shipped in tank cars (80,000 lb net) and in drums (230 and 420 lb net). In these forms the cars or drums are purged of air with nitrogen or other specified gas, then filled with liquid sodium. The sodium is solidified before shipment and is remelted for unloading at the point of use. Sodium is also available as molded bricks (1, 2.5, 5, or 12 lb each). Bricks are packed in soldered tins or gasketed pails or drums, depending on the amount required and the size of the bricks.

Production and End-Use Pattern

Although sodium was produced in Europe for nearly half a century before the first U.S. plant began operation in 1905, by the end of the next half-century U.S. production amounted to about 85% of the world total. The ratio today is not known with cer-

Table 6. Uses of Sodium, % of Total U.S. Production[a]

Use	1953	1959	1963	1967
gasoline additives	55	71	82	83
metals reduction		5	4	8
sodium cyanide	18	11		
sodium peroxide	4	7	6	2
ester reduction	20			
miscellaneous[b]	3	6	8	7

[a] Data compiled from *Chemical Week* and *Oil, Paint, and Drug Reporter*.
[b] Drugs, dyes, nuclear reactors, descaling, etc.

Table 7. Sodium Production, tons

Year	World	United States	Reference
1855–85	6–7		34
1905	3,600	1,200	34
1930	25,000	7,300	34
1956	150,000	130,000	86, 87
1966		165,000	88
1968		170,000[a]	89
1970		200,000[a]	89

[a] Estimated.

tainty, but U.S. production still accounts for a large share of the world total. Despite frequent and sudden shifts in the end-use pattern for sodium, as shown in Table 6, output has generally risen over the years, as shown in Table 7.

Handling and Safety

The safe handling of sodium requires special consideration because of its high reactivity with many materials. With properly designed equipment and procedures, sodium is regularly used in large and small applications without incident. The hazards of handling sodium are no greater than those encountered with many other industrial chemicals (20).

Direct contact of sodium with the skin can cause deep, serious burns due to the action of sodium with the moisture present and the subsequent corrosive action of the caustic formed. Sodium in the eye can cause blindness. For these reasons persons who work with or around sodium should wear goggles or a face shield, gloves, and other protective clothing, preferably flameproofed (83).

Perhaps the greatest hazard presented by metallic sodium stems from its extremely vigorous reaction with water to form sodium hydroxide and hydrogen with the evolution of heat. In the presence of air this combination usually results in explosion; in a closed system (with no air or oxygen present) the hydrogen evolved can cause a rapid increase in pressure. The sodium–water reaction in the absence of air has been extensively studied (20,25,90,91), with the general conclusions that (a) the rate of reaction is substantially equal to the rate of mixing the reactants, and (b) the reaction does not generally cause mechanical damage to heat-transfer equipment. The second conclusion follows from the rather considerable difficulty of rapidly mixing water and sodium due to the hydrogen liberated. The results of sodium–water reactions in the presence of air cannot be predicted since they depend on the quantities of materials, the geometry of the equipment and environment, mixing rates, etc.

Another hazard arises from the reaction of air and sodium. Liquid sodium ignites at about 120°C, though under some conditions dispersed or high-surface sodium (19) may ignite at much lower temperatures. A small local sodium fire can frequently be put out by submerging the burning mass in the remaining pool of liquid sodium with an iron blade. This is effective only if the bulk of the sodium has not reached the ignition point. Larger fires are more difficult to handle. The usual fire extinguishers (water, CO_2, carbon tetrachloride, etc) only aggravate the situation by introducing additional explosion or reaction hazards. If the vessel containing the burning sodium can be closed to exclude air or flooded with nitrogen the fire goes out and the system can be cooled. Fires which cannot be extinguished by excluding air may be quenched by large quantities of dry salt or another dry, cold, inert powder. Dry soda ash is excellent for this purpose but it tends to become damp in storage and must be carefully protected from contact with the air. To facilitate fire-fighting it is good practice to design equipment to confine any possible sodium fire.

In recent years the techniques for handling sodium in commercial-scale applications have been greatly improved (20,27,86,90,92). Contamination by sodium oxide is kept at a minimum by all-welded construction, and residual oxide is removed by cold traps and/or micrometallic filters. Leakfree electromagnetic or mechanical pumps and meters work well with clean liquid sodium (27). Corrosion of stainless- or carbonsteel equipment is minimized by keeping the oxide content at a low level.

Laboratory-scale work with sodium is best done in a glove box filled with nitrogen or another inert gas. Where this is impractical, sodium may be handled on the bench top if a few precautions are observed. Water and solutions containing water must be excluded from the area. Tools used for cutting or handling sodium should be kept clean and dry. Contact of sodium with air should be held to a minimum, since moisture in the air reacts rapidly with sodium. A metal catch pan under the equipment is desirable to contain any spills or fires. In designing equipment, provision should be made for safe removal of sodium residues at the end of the test and for cleaning of the apparatus. Residue and sodium scrap can be destroyed by burning in a steel pan in a well-ventilated hood. Equipment may be cleaned by being opened to the air and heated until any sodium present is oxidized, or by purging thoroughly with nitrogen, then slowly admitting steam to the system while maintaining the nitrogen purge.

Most reactions of sodium are heterogeneous, occurring on the surface of solid or liquid sodium. If desired, it is possible to accelerate such reactions by extending the sodium surface exposed. This can be done conveniently by dispersing the sodium in a suitable medium (93), or by spreading the sodium over a solid powder of high-surface area (19,34). Dispersions in inert hydrocarbons may be briefly exposed to air and present no special hazards as long as the hydrocarbon covers the dispersed sodium, but high-surface sodium reacts very rapidly with air and cannot be exposed without risk of fire.

Analysis

Sodium can be identified by the intense yellow color that sodium compounds impart to the flame. Identification may be confirmed spectroscopically by the presence of the characteristic sodium lines. This test is extremely sensitive and, since very many materials contain traces of sodium salts as impurities, it is not conclusive evidence of the presence of sodium in any considerable quantity.

The alkali metals are commonly separated from all elements except chlorine prior to gravimetric determination. In the absence of other alkalis, sodium may be weighed as the chloride or converted to the sulfate and weighed. Well-known gravimetric procedures employ precipitation as the uranyl acetate of sodium–zinc or sodium–magnesium. Quantitative determination of sodium without prior separations is frequently possible by emission or atomic absorption spectrometric techniques.

Metallic sodium can be determined with fair accuracy by measuring the hydrogen liberated on the addition of ethyl alcohol. Sodium amalgam can be analyzed by treating a sample with a measured volume of dilute standard acid. After the evolution of hydrogen stops, the excess acid is titrated with a standard base. In this method total alkalinity is calculated as sodium.

Calcium in commercial sodium is usually determined by precipitation as the oxalate, separation of the precipitate by filtration, and permanganate titration of the sulfuric acid solution of the precipitated oxalate. The very small amounts of calcium present in reactor-grade sodium are determined best by atomic-absorption spectrophotometry. This method detects as little as 0.5 ppm calcium. Chloride is determined as silver chloride by a turbidimetric method in which glycerol is used to stabilize the suspended precipitate. Sodium oxide is separated from sodium by treatment with mercury. The oxide is insoluble in the amalgam formed and is physically separable. The separated oxide is determined by acid titration.

Methods for the determination of impurities in sodium may be found in references 20,27,34, and 85.

Uses

The production of tetraethyl- and tetramethyllead as antiknock agents for gasoline provides the largest outlet for sodium in the United States. See Vol. 12, p. 290. Sodium is also used in the preparation of other organometallic compounds.

The manufacture of refractory metals, such as titanium, zirconium, and hafnium, by sodium reduction of their halides is a growing application. Development of this use of sodium is largely the result of increasing requirements for the refractory metals in nuclear and aerospace programs. A typical overall reaction is the following:

$$TiCl_4 + 4\,Na \rightarrow Ti + 4\,NaCl$$

Hunter prepared titanium by a bomb process in 1910 (94), and in recent years many improved processes have been described (95–98). Sodium is used to produce metallic potassium and potassium–sodium alloys by the reaction with fused KCl (34,90). These are, in turn, used as heat-transfer agents, or to produce superoxide or mixtures of superoxide and peroxide for oxygen-supply systems. The reaction of fused KOH and sodium has also been used to produce potassium (26,34). Calcium metal and calcium hydride are prepared by the reaction of $CaCl_2$ with sodium or sodium and hydrogen, respectively, at temperatures below the fusion point of the resulting salt mixtures (99,100).

Manufacture of sodium peroxide, once a major use for sodium, has declined in recent years. A number of processes have been described (101–105) but the overall reaction in any of them is the following:

$$2\,Na + O_2 \rightarrow Na_2O_2$$

Sodium monoxide, Na_2O, may be made by similar procedures by using lower temperatures and limiting the oxygen supply. Other peroxy compounds, such as calcium, magnesium, and zinc peroxides and sodium perborate, are made from sodium peroxide.

Sodium hydride is made by the following reaction of sodium and hydrogen:

$$2\,Na + H_2 \rightarrow 2\,NaH$$

Sodium hydride attains a dissociation pressure of 1 atm at about 425°C (52), but the reaction can be carried out at 250–300°C with the liquid sodium dispersed in a hydrocarbon liquid or distributed as a thin film over an inert high-surface solid, which may be preformed sodium hydride. Surface-active agents are necessary to complete the reaction (37,106). Sodium hydride is employed as catalyst or reactant in numerous organic reactions and is also used to produce other hydrides, such as sodium borohydride (107,108). Sodium is used indirectly for the descaling of metals, such as stainless steel and titanium (51). Sodium and hydrogen are fed to a molten bath of anhydrous caustic to generate sodium hydride, which dissolves in the melt and is the effective descaling agent.

Until 1961 sodium cyanide was made in the United States by the Castner process (see Cyanides, alkali metal, Vol. 6, p. 585), according to the following reaction:

$$Na + C + NH_3 \rightarrow NaCN + 1\tfrac{1}{2} H_2$$

This process, still used in some countries, has been largely superseded by a process based on the neutralization of aequeous NaOH with HCN gas made by the catalytic reaction of air, ammonia, and methane (see Vol. 6, p. 577).

Sodamide, made by the reaction of sodium and ammonia, readily forms explosive compositions on storage unless air and moisture are rigorously excluded. In chemical processes, such as the manufacture of indigo or sodium azide which require the use of sodamide, it is usually prepared as part of the process and used at once. A number of processes for the manufacture of sodium azide have been described (34), but the liquid ammonia process is preferred in the United States. In this process sodium reacts with liquid ammonia in the presence of a catalyst, such as ferric nitrate, according to the following reaction:

$$Na + NH_3 \xrightarrow{\text{catalyst}} NaNH_2 + \tfrac{1}{2} H_2$$

The slurry of NaH_2 in liquid ammonia produced by this reaction is then treated with nitrous oxide under pressure to produce the azide, as follows:

$$2\ NaNH_2 + N_2O \rightarrow NaN_3 + NaOH + NH_3$$

The reaction is carried out at about 30°C (109). The azide is separated from the caustic by recrystallization from water (110).

In the synthesis of indigo, the sodium or potassium salt of phenylglycine is fused with potassium or sodium hydroxide or a mixture of the two in the presence of sodium or sodamide. The fusion product, sodium indoxyl, is dissolved in water, hydrolyzed, and oxidized with air to indigo (see Vol. 11, p. 565). Triphenylmethane dyes (qv) are prepared by treating tetraalkyldiaminodiaryl ketones, such as tetramethyldiamino-benzophenone, with sodium and an aryl halide, eg chlorobenzene, in a hydrocarbon solvent.

Sodium is used for the preparation of a herbicide, the bisquaternary salt of bipyridyl with methyl chloride (111).

Sodium is used in the preparation of drugs and pharmaceuticals. Barbiturates (see Barbituric acid) are prepared by the condensation of substituted malonic esters with urea or a thiourea in the presence of sodium and alcohol. For example, n-butyl-ethylbarbituric acid is obtained by condensing n-butylethylmalonic ethyl ester with urea in the presence of sodium and absolute alcohol.

Acetoacetic ester (qv) is prepared by the action of sodium on ethyl acetate, and is used for preparing other compounds, for example, antipyrine (see Analgesics and anti-pyretics). High-molecular-weight alcohols, such as lauryl, cetyl, and myristyl alcohol, can be obtained by the sodium reduction of esters obtained from naturally occurring oils (112) (see Vol. 1, p. 547).

In the synthesis of perfume materials, sodium is often employed in reduction and condensation reactions. For example, phenylethyl alcohol, well known to perfume chemists for its rose odor, is prepared by the sodium reduction of the ethyl ester of phenylacetic acid in absolute alcohol (113).   See Benzyl alcohol and β-phenylethyl alcohols.

Manufacture of the mixture of dibasic acids, known as "isosebacic" acid, by a process employing sodium and butadiene has been described (114,115), but the process is not in commercial operation in the United States (see Vol. 1, p. 252).

Sodium is a catalyst for many polymerizations, two of the most familiar being the polymerization of butadiene (Buna process) and the copolymerization of butadiene–styrene mixtures (modified GR-S process).   The alfin catalysts, made from sodium, give extremely rapid or unusual polymerizations of some dienes and of styrene (116, 117). See Diene polymers; Elastomers, synthetic; Olefin polymers.

Solution of naphthalenesodium or sodium dissolved in liquid ammonia are used to treat polyfluorocarbon resins to obtain cementable surfaces (118,119).

Sodium, usually in dispersed form, is used to desulfurize a variety of hydrocarbon stocks.   The process is most useful for removal of small amounts of sulfur.

A small but expanding new use for sodium is for heat transfer in nuclear reactors. Low neutron cross section, short half-life of radioisotopes produced, low corrosiveness, low density, low viscosity, low melting point, high boiling point, and high thermal conductivity make sodium attractive for this application, particularly in fast breeder reactors (50).   Use of sodium to transfer heat in conventional fuel-fired power plants has been proposed.   Small amounts of sodium are used in miscellaneous heat-transfer applications, such as the cooling of internal combustion engine valves (34).   See also Potassium.

In addition to the metal-winning and descaling applications described above (see p. 450) numerous other metallurgical uses of sodium have been described or studied. Some of these uses are the following: preparation of powdered metals; removal of antimony, tin, and sulfur from lead; modification of the structure of silicon–aluminum alloys; the application of diffusion-alloy coatings to substrate metals (120,121); cleaning and desulfurization of molten steel; nodularization of graphite in cast iron; deoxidation of molten metals; heat treatment; and the coating of steel with aluminum or zinc.

Although its low cost and favorable electrical properties suggested sodium as an electrical conductor many years ago (122,123), only recently has a practical sodium-cored, polyethylene-sheathed cable been developed for this purpose (89).   Both primary and secondary cells have been developed which use sodium in solution, as amalgam, or as bulk metal for anode material (124,125).

Sodium is useful in the manufacture of metal carbonyls and aluminum alkyls (126,127) and a minor, but well-known use is in sodium-vapor lamps which have recently been improved to produce light of a more pleasing color than that of the original lamps (89).

Sodium Alloys

Sodium is miscible with many metals in liquid phase and may form alloys or compounds.   Important examples are listed in Table 8.

The brittleness of metals is frequently increased by the addition of sodium to form alloys.   The metals vary in their ability to dilute the natural reactivity of sodium. Most of the binary alloys are unstable in air and react with water.   Ternary and quaternary alloys are more stable.   The commercial importance of alloys of sodium with lead and potassium has already been noted; the alloy with mercury is of importance in the manufacture of sodium hydroxide by the amalgam process.

Sodium–potassium alloy is easily prepared by melting the clean metals together in an inert atmosphere or under an inert hydrocarbon. The alloy may also be prepared by reacting sodium with molten KCl, or KOH, or with solid K_2CO_3 powder.

Alloys of lead and sodium containing up to 30% sodium are obtained by heating the metals together in the proper ratio, allowing a slight excess of sodium to compensate for loss by oxidation. At about 225°C the elements react and generate enough heat to cause the temperature to rise rapidly. At this point the external heating is discontinued and the mixture is cooled and poured into molds. The brittle alloys can be ground to a powder, and should be stored under a hydrocarbon or in airtight containers to prevent surface oxidation. The 30% sodium alloy reacts vigorously with water to

Table 8. Important Metal–Sodium Systems

Metal	Alloy or compound formation	Complete	Partial	Slight	Phase diagram in reference
barium	alloys, compounds	x			128
calcium	alloys		x		6,25,46
iron	no alloys				
lead	alloys, compounds	x			6,25,46
lithium	alloys		x		6,46
magnesium	alloys			x	6,25,46
mercury	alloys, compounds		x		6,25,46
potassium	alloys, compounds[a]	x			6,20,25,46
rubidium	alloys	x			6,25,46
thorium[b]	no alloys				
tin	alloys, compounds	x			6,25
zinc	alloys, compounds		x		6,25

(Liquid phase miscibility spans Complete, Partial, Slight columns.)

[a] The only compound of potassium and sodium reported is the unstable Na_2K.

[b] The sodium–thorium diagram given in references 25 and 46 and the notation of alloy formation in references 20 and 34 appear to be erroneous (129).

liberate hydrogen and provides a convenient laboratory source of this gas. An alloy containing 10% sodium may be used in controlled reactions with organic halogen compounds that react violently with pure sodium. Sodium–lead alloys containing large amounts of sodium are used to dry organic liquids.

Sodium–lead alloys containing other metals, such as the alkaline earth metals, are hard and retain their hardness at high temperatures, being suitable for use as bearing metal. An example is "tempered lead," a bearing alloy that contains 1.3% sodium, 0.12% antimony, 0.08% tin, and the remainder lead. The German "Bahnmetall," which was used in axle bearings on railroad engines and cars, contains 0.6% sodium, 0.04% lithium, 0.6% calcium, and the remainder lead, and has a Brinell hardness of 34.

Up to about 0.6% sodium dissolves readily in mercury to form amalgams which are liquid at room temperature. The solubility of sodium in mercury is about 1% at 70°C (130) and 2% at 140°C (46). Alloys containing over 2% sodium are brittle at room temperature. Sodium-rich amalgam may be made by adding mercury dropwise to a pool of molten sodium; mercury-rich amalgam is prepared by adding small, clean pieces of sodium to clean mercury with agitation.

In either case it is necessary to maintain an inert atmosphere in the apparatus and to provide cooling to remove the considerable heat which is evolved. Solid amalgams are easily broken and powdered, but must be carefully protected against air oxidation. Amalgams are useful in many reactions in place of sodium because the reactions are easier to control. MacMullin has reviewed the preparation, properties, and uses of amalgam (130).

Sodium amalgam is commercially important in the manufacture of sodium hydroxide; sodium–potassium alloy, NaK, is used in heat-transfer applications; and sodium–lead alloy is used in the manufacture of tetraethyl- and tetramethyllead.

Sodium does not form alloys with aluminum but is used to modify the grain of aluminum–silicon alloys and aluminum–copper alloys. Sodium–gold alloy is photoelectrically sensitive and may be used in photoelectric cells. A sodium–zinc alloy, containing 2% sodium and 98% zinc, is used as a deoxidizer for other metals.

Bibliography

"Alkali Metals, Sodium" in *ECT* 1st ed., Vol. 1, pp. 435-447, by E. H. Burkey, J. A. Morrow, and M. S. Andrew, E. I. du Pont de Nemours & Co., Inc.

Special attention is called to the following references: Mellor (25) (inorganic) is comprehensive and well documented to about 1958. Sittig (34) is good on the organic chemistry of sodium. Gmelin (35) has exhaustive bibliographies. Thomson and Garelis (14) present extensive physical and thermal data in very useful forms. Jackson (20) covers heat transfer and nuclear energy aspects. Stone, et al. (18) includes a Mollier diagram for sodium. Epstein (91) is representative of the many volumes in the *Progress in Nuclear Energy Series* which collectively cover most of the areas of application of sodium in this field. Mausteller, Tepper, and Rodgers (27) review modern handling and operating techniques developed to meet a variety of problems and conditions. *The Alkali Metals* (50) collects under one cover a broad spectrum of recent research.

1. M. E. Weeks, *Discovery of the Elements*, 5th ed., Journal of Chemical Education, Easton, Pa., 1945, p. 354.
2. Alexander Fleck, *Chem. Ind.* (*London*) **66,** 515 (1947).
3. D. W. F. Hardie, *Ind. Chemist* **30,** 161–166 (1954).
4. R. C. Weast, ed., *Handbook of Chemistry and Physics*, 48th ed., Chemical Rubber Co., Cleveland, Ohio, 1967–1968.
5. C. E. Long, *J. Chem. Soc.* **13,** 122 (1861).
6. C. J. Smithells, *Metals Reference Book*, Vols. I and II, 2nd ed., Interscience Publishers, Inc., New York, 1955.
7. C. S. Barrett, *Acta Cryst.* **9,** 671–677 (1956).
8. D. Hull and H. M. Rosenburg, *Phil. Mag.* **4** (8), 303–315 (1959); *Chem Abstr.* **54,** 31b (1960).
9. C. S. Barrett, *Structure of Metals*, McGraw-Hill Book Co., Inc., New York, 1943, p. 226.
10. N. S. Gingrich, *Rev. Mod. Phys.* **15,** 90–110 (1943).
11. Linus Pauling, *The Nature of the Chemical Bond*, 3rd ed., Cornell University Press, Ithaca, N.Y., 1960, p. 514.
12. D. C. Ginnings, T. B. Douglas, and A. F. Ball, *J. Res. Natl. Bur. Std.* **45,** 23–33 (1950).
13. C. T. Ewing, J. A. Grand, and R. R. Miller, *J. Am. Chem. Soc.* **74,** 11–14 (1952).
14. G. W. Thomson and E. Garelis, *Physical and Thermodynamic Properties of Sodium*, 2nd ed., Ethyl Corporation, Research Laboratories, Detroit, Mich., 1955.
15. W. H. Evans, R. Jacobson, T. R. Munson, and D. D. Wagman, *J. Res. Natl. Bur. Std.* **55,** 83–96 (1955).
16. I. G. Dillon, P. A. Nelson, and B. S. Swanson, "Critical Temperatures and Densities of the Alkali Metals," *Argonne Natl. Lab. Rept. ANL-7025, Aug. 1965.* (Available from Clearinghouse for Federal Scientific and Technical Information, NBS, U.S. Dept. Comm., Springfield, Va.)

17. F. Teper, J. Zelenak, F. Roehlich, and V. May, "Thermophysical and Transport Properties of Liquid Metals," *Tech. Rept. AFML-TR-65-99, May, 1965, Air Force Materials Lab., Wright-Patterson Air Force Base, O.* (Defense Documentation Center, AD 464138).

18. J. P. Stone et al., "High Temperature Properties of Sodium," *NRL Report 6241, Sept. 24, 1965, U.S. Naval Research Laboratory, Washington, D.C.* (Defense Documentation Center, AD 622191).

19. *High-Surface Sodium*, Tech. Bull., National Distillers and Chemical Co., Ashtabula, O., 1953.

20. C. B. Jackson, ed., *Liquid Metals Handbook*, AEC Dept. of the Navy, Washington, D.C., 1955.

21. C. A. Kraus and W. W. Lucasse, *J. Am. Chem. Soc.* **44**, 1949–1953 (1922).

22. C. A. Kraus, *J. Chem. Educ.* **30**, 83–87 (1953).

23. J. F. Dewald and G. Lepoutre, *J. Am. Chem. Soc.* **76**, 3369–3373 (1954).

24. P. D. Schettler, Jr., P. W. Doumaux, and A. Patterson, Jr., *J. Phys. Chem.* **71** (12), 3797–3801 (1967).

25. J. W. Mellor, *Comprehensive Treatise on Inorganic and Theoretical Chemistry*, Vol. II, Suppl. II, *The Alkali Metals*, Part I, John Wiley & Sons, Inc., New York, 1961.

26. Unpublished Data, E. I. du Pont de Nemours & Co., Inc., Niagara Falls, N.Y.

27. J. W. Mausteller, F. Tepper, and S. J. Rodgers, *Alkali Metal Handling and Systems Operating Techniques*, Gordon and Breach, Science Publishers, New York, 1967.

28. D. D. Williams, J. A. Grand, and R. R. Miller, *NRL Memorandum Rept. 424, Naval Research Lab., Washington, D.C., Feb. 1, 1955.*

29. John R. Weeks, private communication, Brookhaven National Laboratory, Upton, N.Y., July 2, 1968.

30. C. Luner, A. Cosgarea, Jr., and H. M. Feder, "Solubility of Carbon in Sodium," in *Alkali Metal Coolants*, International Atomic Energy Agency, Vienna, 1967.

31. R. A. Baus et al., "The Solubility of Structural Materials in Sodium," *Proc. Intern. Conf. on the Peaceful Uses of Atomic Energy, Geneva, June 30, 1955*, International Documents Service, Columbia University Press, New York, 1955–1956.

32. S. B. Windwer, "Solutions of Alkali Metals in Ethylenediamine," *University Microfilms, Ann Arbor, Mich.*, L. C. Card No. Mic 61-707, 1960, 79 pp.

33. N. D. Scott, J. F. Walker, and V. L. Hansley, *J. Am. Chem. Soc.* **58**, 2442–2444 (1936).

34. Marshall Sittig, *Sodium: Its Manufacture, Properties and Uses*, Reinhold Publishing Corp., New York, 1956.

35. *Gmelin's Handbuch der Anorganischen Chemie*, 8th ed., Sodium (Natrium), Suppl. Part 2, Syst. Nr. 21, Verlag Chemie, Weinheim, 1965.

36. I. T. Krohn, R. C. Werner, and H. Shapiro, *J. Am. Chem. Soc.* **77**, 2110–2113 (1955).

37. V. C. Hansley and P. J. Carlisle, *Chem. Eng. News* **23** (2), 1332–1333, 1380 (1945).

38. P. V. H. Pascal, *Nouveau Traité de Chimie Minérale*, Vol. II, Masson et Cie., Paris, 1966.

39. E. W. Guernsey and M. S. Sherman, *J. Am. Chem. Soc.* **47**, 1932–1940 (1925).

40. K. J. Kelly, E. W. Hobart, and R. G. Bjork, "Studies Concerning the Chemical State of Carbon, Nitrogen and Oxygen in Alkali Metals," *U.S. Atomic Energy Commission CNLM-6337, April 14, 1965.* (Available through Clearinghouse for Federal Scientific and Technical Information.)

41. W. C. Sleppy, *Inorg. Chem.* **5** (11), 2021–2023 (1966).

42. R. C. Asher and S. A. Wilson, *Nature* **181**, 409–410 (1958).

43. A. Hérold, *Bull. Soc. Chim. France* **1955**, 999–1012.

44. G. J. Moody and J. D. R. Thomas, *J. Chem. Educ.* **43** (4), 205–206 (1966).

45. E. Hohmann, *Z. Anorg. Allgem. Chem.* **251**, 113–126 (1948).

46. M. Hansen, *Constitution of Binary Alloys*, McGraw-Hill Book Co., Inc., New York, 1958.

47. M. J. Dignam and D. A. Huggins, *J. Electrochem. Soc.* **114** (2), 117–123 (1967).

48. U.S. Pat. 2,642,347 (June 16, 1953), H. N. Gilbert (to E. I. du Pont de Nemours & Co., Inc.).

49. U.S. Pat. 2,858,194 (Oct. 28, 1958), H. C. Miller (to E. I. du Pont de Nemours & Co., Inc.).

50. "The Alkali Metals," *An International Symposium, Nottingham, England, July 1966*, Special Publication No. 22, The Chemical Society, London, 1967.

51. H. N. Gilbert, *Chem. Eng. News* **26**, 2604–2606, 2660 (1948).

52. D. D. William, "A Study of the Sodium–Hydrogen–Oxygen System," *U.S. Naval Research Lab. Memorandum Rept. No. 33, Washington, D.C.*, June 1952.

53. M. I. Klyashtornyi, *Zhur. Priklad. Khim.* **31**, 684–689 (1958); *Chem. Abstr.* **52**, 144961 (1958).

54. E. Rinck, *Ann. Chim. (Paris)* **18**, 395–531 (1932).

55. A. Glassner, "The Thermochemical Properties of the Oxides, Fluorides, and Chlorides to 2500°K.," *Argonne Natl. Lab. Rept. ANL-5750*, U.S. Govt. Printing Office, Washington, D.C., 1957.

56. D. J. Hansen, private communication, Union Carbide Corp., Niagara Falls, N.Y., April 19, 1968.

57. George L. Clark, ed., *Encyclopedia of Chemistry*, 2nd ed., Reinhold Publishing Corp., New York, 1966, p. 997.

58. U.S. Pat. 2,391,728 (Dec. 25, 1945), T. H. McConica et al. (to Dow Chemical Co.).

59. H. S-C. Deville, *Ann. Chim. Phys.* **43**, 5–33 (1855).

60. U.S. Pat. 2,789,047 (Apr. 16, 1957), Charles H. Lemke (to E. I. du Pont de Nemours & Co., Inc.).

61. *Chem. Week* **79,** 88 (Aug. 11, 1956).

62. *Chem. Eng. News* **37,** 48 (Sept. 14, 1959).

63. *Chem. Week* **92,** 57 (March 2, 1963).

64. U.S. Pat. 2,148,404 (Feb. 21, 1939), H. N. Gilbert (to E. I. du Pont de Nemours & Co., Inc.).

65. U.S. Pat. 2,234,967 (March 18, 1941), H. N. Gilbert (to E. I. du Pont de Nemours & Co., Inc.).

66. W. C. Gardiner, *U.S. Dept. Comm. Office Tech. Serv. Rept., PB-44670* (1946) (*FIAT Final Rept. 819*).

67. U.S. Pat. 3,265,490 (Aug. 9, 1966), Shiro Yoshizawa et al. (to Tekkosha Co., Ltd., Tokyo).

68. T. Wallace, *Chem. Ind. (London)* **1953,** 876–882.

69. H. N. Gilbert, *J. Electrochem. Soc.* **99**, 3050–3060 (1952).

70. C. L. Mantell, *Electrochemical Engineering*, 4th ed., McGraw-Hill Book Co., Inc., New York, 1960.

71. H. E. Batsford, *Chem. Met. Eng.* **26,** 888–894 (1922).

72. *Ibid.*, 932–935 (1922).

73. U.S. 1,501,756 (July 15, 1924), J. C. Downs (to Roessler and Hasslacher Chemical Co.).

74. W. C. Gardiner, *U.S. Dept. Comm. Office Tech. Serv. Rept., PB-44671* (1946) (*FIAT Final Rept. 820*).

75. U.S. Pat. 2,850,442 (Sept. 2, 1958), W. S. Cathcart et al. (to E. I. du Pont de Nemours & Co., Inc.).

76. U.S. Pat. 3,020,221 (Feb. 6, 1962), W. H. Loftus (to E. I. du Pont de Nemours & Co., Inc.).

77. Ger. Pat. 268,280 (Dec. 12, 1913), Elektrizitätswerk Lonza.

78. U.S. Pat. 1,043,154 (Nov. 5, 1912), G. O. Seward, F. Kügelgen, and F. Bidder (to Virginia Laboratory Co.).

79. U.S. Pat. 1,092,178 (April 7, 1914), G. O. Seward and F. Kügelgen (to Virginia Laboratory Co.).

80. U.S. Pat. 1,074,988 (Oct. 7, 1913), E. Steinbuch (to Society of Chemical Industry, Basel).

81. U.S. Pat. 623,691 (April 25, 1899), C. E. Acker.

82. E. A. Ashcroft, *Trans. Electrochem. Soc.* **9,** 123–142 (1906).

82a. *Chem. Eng.* **69** (6), 90–94 (March 1962).

83. *Sodium Handling and Properties*, E. I. du Pont de Nemours & Co., Inc., 1962.

84. W. H. Bruggeman, *J. Am. Inst. Chem. Eng.* **2,** 153–156 (1956).

85. C. H. Lemke, N. D. Clare, and R. E. DeSantis, *Nucleonics* **19** (2), 78–79 (Feb. 1961).

86. *Chem. Eng. News* **34** (17), 1991–1992 (April 23, 1956).

87. *Chem. Week* **84** (34), 76–80 (Jan. 24, 1959).

88. *U.S. Dept. Comm. Ser. M28A (65), 13* (March 20, 1968).

89. *Chem. Week* **101** (8), 79–84 (Aug. 19, 1967).

90. "Handling and Uses of the Alkali Metals," *Advan. Chem. Ser.* **19,** (1957).

91. L. F. Epstein, "Recent Developments in the Study of Metal-Water Reactions," in C. M. Nicholls, ed., *Progress in Nuclear Energy*, Ser. IV, Vol. 4, Pergamon Press, Inc., New York, 1961, pp. 461–483.

92. *Chem. Eng.* **65** (12), 63–64 (June 16, 1958).

93. I. Fatt and M. Tashima, *Alkali Metal Dispersions*, D. Van Nostrand Company, Inc., Princeton, N.J., 1961.

94. M. A. Hunter, *J. Am. Chem. Soc.* **32**, 330–336 (1910).

95. U.S. Pat. 2,890,111 (June 9, 1959), S. M. Shelton (to United States of America).

96. U.S. Pat. 2,828,119 (March 25, 1958), G. R. Findley (to National Research Corp.).

97. U.S. Pat. 2,890,112 (June 9, 1959), C. H. Winter, Jr. (to E. I. du Pont de Nemours & Co., Inc.).

98. Brit. Pat. 816,017 (July 8, 1959), (to National Distillers and Chemical Corp.).

99. U.S. Pat. 2,794,732 (June 4, 1957), P. P. Alexander (to Metal Hydrides, Inc.).

100. U.S. Pat. 2,794,733 (June 4, 1957), P. P. Alexander and R. C. Wade (to Metal Hydrides, Inc.).

101. U.S. Pat. 1,796,241 (March 10, 1931), H. R. Carveth (to Roessler and Hasslacher Chem. Co.).

102. U.S. Pat. 2,633,406 (March 31, 1953), D. S. Nantz (to National Distillers Products Corp.).

103. U.S. Pat. 2,671,010 (March 2, 1954), L. J. Governale (to Ethyl Corp.).

104. U.S. Pat. 2,685,500 (Aug. 3, 1954), R. E. Hulse and D. S. Nantz (to National Distillers Products Co.).

105. I. I. Vol'nov, *Peroxides, Superoxides, and Ozonides of Alkali and Alkaline Earth Metals*, Plenum Publishers Corp., New York (1966).

106. T. P. Whaley and C. C. Chappelow, Jr., in T. Moeller, ed., *Inorganic Syntheses*, Vol. 5, McGraw-Hill Book Co., Inc., New York, 1957, pp. 10–13.

107. H. I. Schlesinger, Herbert C. Brown, et al., *J. Am. Chem. Soc.* **75**, 186–224 (1952).

108. *Chem. Week* **88** (23), 63 (June 1961).

109. U.S. Pat. 2,373,800 (April 17, 1945), Marshall F. Acken and William F. Filbert (to E. I. du Pont de Nemours & Co., Inc.).

110. Tadao Kawakami et al., *Nagoya Kogyo Gijutsu Shikensho Hokoku (Japan)* **3** (3), 14–23 (1954); **4** (1), 24–29 (1955); **7** (6), 429–435 (1958); **7** (11), 855–861 (1958); **8** (11), 793–798 (1959); **9** (1), 33–40 (1960); **9** (2), 85–92 (1960). English translation available through Special Libraries Association Translation Center, John Crerar Library, Chicago, Ill.

111. *European Chemical News (London)* **14** (336), 34 (1968).

112. U.S. Pat. 2,915,564 (Dec. 1, 1959), V. L. Hansley (to National Distillers and Chemical Corp.).

113. H. N. Gilbert, N. D. Scott, W. F. Zimmerli, and V. L. Hansley, *Ind. Eng. Chem.* **25**, 735–741 (1933).

114. M. Sittig, *Mod. Plastics* **32** (12), 150–152, 217–218 (1955).

115. U.S. Pat. 2,352,461 (June 27, 1944), J. F. Walker (to E. I. du Pont de Nemours & Co., Inc.).

116. A. A. Morton, *Ind. Eng. Chem.* **42**, 1488–1496 (1950).

117. A. A. Morton, "Alfin Catalysis," in N. M. Bikales, ed., *Encyclopedia of Polymer Science and Technology*, Vol. 1, Interscience Publishers, a div. of John Wiley & Sons, Inc., New York, 1964, pp. 629–638.

118. U.S. Pat. 2,809,130 (Oct. 8, 1957), G. Rappaport (to General Motors Corp.).

119. U.S. Pat. 2,789,063 (April 16, 1957), Robert J. Purvis and Warren R. Beck (to Minnesota Mining & Manufacturing Co.).

120. U.S. Pat. 3,220,876 (Nov. 30, 1965), R. D. Moeller (to North American Aviation, Inc.).

121. U.S. Pat. 3,251,719 (May 17, 1966), Frederick Tepper, et al. (to M. S. A. Research Corp.).

122. K. Weedon, *Tek. Ukeblad. (Norway)* **113** (14), 238–243 (1966); *Chem. Abstr.* **65**, 3129b, 1966.

123. R. H. Boundy, *Trans. Electrochem. Soc.* **62**, 151–160 (1932).

124. R. D. Weaver, S. W. Smith, and N. L. Willmann, *J. Electrochem. Soc.* **109** (8), 653–657 (1962).

125. N. Weber and J. T. Kummer, "A Sodium–Sulfur Secondary Battery," *Proc. 21st Annual Power Sources Conf., U.S. Army, Electronics Command, Atlantic City, N.J., 1967*, pp. 37–39.

126. U.S. Pat. 2,952,524 (Sept. 13, 1960), H. E. Podall (to Ethyl Corp.).

127. Brit. Pat. 848,103 (Sept. 14, 1960), Goodrich-Gulf Chemical, Inc.

128. F. A. Kanda, R. M. Stevens, and D. V. Keller, *J. Phys. Chem.* **69** (11), 3867–3872 (1965).

129. L. R. Kelman, private communication, Argonne National Laboratory, Argonne, Ill., May 17, 1968.

130. R. B. MacMullin, *Chem. Eng. Prog.* **46**, 440–455 (1950).

CHARLES H. LEMKE
E. I. du Pont de Nemours & Co., Inc

SODIUM COMPOUNDS

SODIUM CARBONATES.   The manufacture of sodium carbonate by the ammonia–soda (Solvay) process is described in Vol. 1, p. 707. This article traces the manufacture of sodium carbonate from the natural mineral, trona. It also deals with several related compounds.

Sodium Carbonate

Sodium carbonate, Na_2CO_3, is a white, crystalline, hygroscopic powder.   In the chemical industry the terms "ash," "soda ash," "soda," and "calcined soda" are used for the anhydrous salt. Of late the term "natural ash" has been used to designate sodium carbonate produced directly from natural minerals, while "synthetic ash" denotes the product of the Solvay process. Chemically these materials are identical.

Some important properties of soda ash are: mp, 851°C; heat capacity at 25°C, 26.41 cal/(°C) (mole); heat of fusion, 8 kcal/mole; density at 20°C, 2.533 g/cm³. Solubility and phase relationships are shown in Figure 1.   Corresponding values for the solubility of pure sodium carbonate in water are given in Table 1.

During the 1960s there has been a significant shift in the technology of producing soda ash in the U.S., with the growth of Wyoming soda ash industry representing one of the major developments in the supply of inorganic chemicals.   Just as in the 1880s the advent of the Solvay process (Vol. 1, p. 712) caused the decline of the Leblanc process, so the exploitation of the Wyoming deposits of trona (sodium sesquicarbonate, $Na_2CO_3.NaHCO_3.2H_2O$) is now limiting the further growth of U.S. synthetic soda ash production.   At the end of 1968, one third of the installed U.S. production capacity was located in the vicinity of the town of Green River, Wyoming.   The trona beds in the Green River formation were brought into production in 1948, ten years after their discovery.

Occurrence.   Trona is relatively rare.   Major natural evaporite deposits containing this mineral are found near Searles Lake and Owens Lake, California;   Magadi Lake, Kenya;   Lake Texcoco, Mexico;   and Lagunillas, Venezuela (1).   The Wyoming

Table 1. Solubility of Pure Na_2CO_3 in Water

Area	Na_2CO_3, % From	Na_2CO_3, % To	Temperature, °C At and below	Temperature, °C From	Temperature, °C To	Solid phases	Liquid phase, % Na_2CO_3 in solution From	Liquid phase, % Na_2CO_3 in solution To	Transition points Na_2CO_3, %	Transition points °C
1	0	5.9		0	−2.1	ice	0	5.9		
2	0	37.0	−2.1			ice + $Na_2CO_3.10H_2O$	none		5.9	−2.1
3	5.9	37.0		−2.1	+32.0	$Na_2CO_3.10H_2O$	5.9	31.3		
4	37.0	45.7	+32.0			$Na_2CO_3.10H_2O$ + $Na_2CO_3.7H_2O$	none		31.3	+32.0
5	31.3	45.7		+32.0	+35.4	$Na_2CO_3.7H_2O$	31.3	33.2		
6	45.7	85.5	+35.4			$Na_2CO_3.7H_2O$ + $Na_2CO_3.H_2O$	none		33.2	+35.4
7	30.8	85.5		+35.4	109.0	$Na_2CO_3.H_2O$	33.2	30.8		
8	85.5	100.0	109.0			$Na_2CO_3.H_2O$ + Na_2CO_3	none		30.8	109.0
9	30.8	100.0		109 and above		Na_2CO_3	30.8			

deposits are the residue of Gosiute Lake which covered western Wyoming for four million years during the early and middle Eocene age. The evaporite beds of essentially pure trona, and trona mixed with halite (NaCl), are located in the Green River Basin of the Green River formation, which is above the Wasatch formation and below the Bridger formation. The exact depositional mechanism which formed these beds is not known (2). The Green River formation also contains extensive deposits of oil shale (see Shale oil). However, pure trona is found only in the Green River Basin. Other sodium carbonate salts such as nahcolite ($NaHCO_3$) and dawsonite ($NaAl(OH)_2CO_3$) have been found in the Uinta and Piceance Creek Basins.

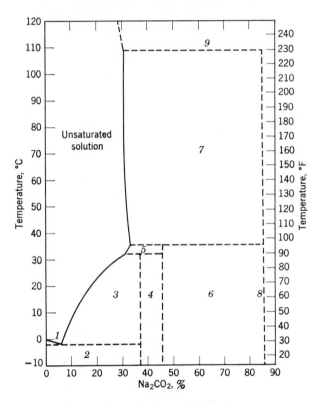

Fig. 1. Solubility of pure Na_2CO_3 in water.

The absence of chloride in many of the beds has caused considerable speculation. Sodium chloride is usually the most plentiful constituent in evaporating water and coprecipitates with most salts, for example, with sylvinite—a mechanical mixture of potassium and sodium chlorides (see Potassium and compounds). A recent theory proposed that a low reef in Gosiute Lake partially isolated an area in the central and south central region of the Green River Basin. Concentrated lake water from other portions of the lake flowed into this isolated area. In the semistagnant basin deposition took place, but no deposition occurred in the other portions of the lake because fresh-water streams diluted the water sufficiently to prevent it. This semistagnant portion of the Gosiute Lake deposits is now called the saline deposit of the Wilkins Peak Member of the Green River formation. An outline of Lake Gosiute as it may have existed during the depositional stage is shown in Figure 2.

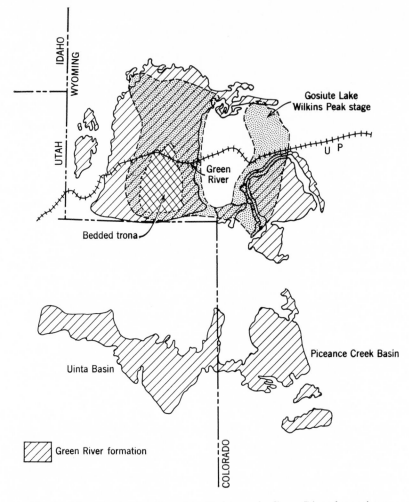

Fig. 2. Map showing location of bedded trona in Green River formation.

The Green River trona beds were discovered in 1938 when the Mountain Fuel Supply Company drilled the John Hay No. 1 well eighteen miles west of Green River, Wyoming. When the U.S. Geological Survey made borings at 1500 ft, expecting to find oil or natural gas, trona was identified in the samples taken. The Union Pacific Railroad, which under the Land Grant Act of 1862 still retains all mineral rights under all odd-numbered square mile sections along its 40-mile-wide right-of-way, confirmed this finding in five core holes drilled during the years 1940–1942. This drilling revealed many trona beds, ranging in thickness from a few inches to a major bed varying in thickness from 7 to 11 ft at about 1500 ft. Westvaco Chlorine Products, since acquired by FMC Corporation, cored the deposit in 1945 and sank its first mine shaft in 1947. Stauffer (Wyoming) is operating a bed at 800 ft, while Allied Chemical Company is developing a mine at the 1500-ft level. Exploration activities have become more extensive and additional mineable beds have been found in other areas of the basin. The deposit is now known to be at least 900 sq miles in area, containing at least 17 billion tons of trona. The several trona beds are approximately horizontal and are found dispersed throughout the 300-ft-thick Green River formation. The U.S. Geological Survey of the Department of the Interior has established a Sodium Withdrawal Area over the deposit. This means that mining leases for sodium-bearing minerals in the area are auctioned to the highest competitive bidder.

A sodium carbonate deposit is normally a massive brown matrix of trona containing other alkaline minerals, as well as shales. Thin beds of clear material, so-called spar trona in which the crystals are aligned perpendicular to the bed, have been found. A typical analysis of massive trona shows the ore to be 95% sodium sesquicarbonate.

Constituent	Percent	Constituent	Percent
Na_2CO_3	45.11	Na_2SO_4	0.01
$NaHCO_3$	35.85	Fe_2SO_4	0.11
H_2O	15.32	insolubles	3.75
$NaCl$	0.03		

The extremely low chloride and sulfate content distinguishes this trona deposit from other alkali deposits throughout the world. The insolubles are primarily dolomite shales and clays. The alkaline minerals found associated with the deposit are shown in Table 2. Many of these minerals were first described by analysis of materials found in the various cores.

Table 2. The Chemical Composition of the Alkaline Minerals

Mineral	Chemical composition
shortite	$Na_2CO_3 \cdot CaCO_3$
nahcolite	$NaHCO_3$
northuptite	$Na_3MgCl(CO_3)_2$
bradleyite	$Na_3Mg(PO_4)(CO_3)$
pirssonite	$Na_2Ca(CO_3)_2 \cdot 2H_2O$
gaylussite	$Na_2Ca(CO_3)_2 \cdot 5H_2O$
dawsonite	$NaAl(OH_2)CO_3$

Other Sources. Natural soda ash is also produced from the saline deposits at Searles Lake and Owens Lake, California, and other dry saline lakes.

Consideration has also been given to mining the nahcolite and dawsonite deposits associated with the oil shale in the Uinta and Piceance Creek Basins. So far the only deposits located have not been of sufficient extent, purity, and mineability to warrant direct exploitation. The suggestion has been made that these minerals be coproduced with oil-shale petroleum, thus reducing the production costs of both petroleum and soda ash. Since economic oil-shale conversion is still some time away and since the richest oil-shale reserves do not necessarily coincide with the richest Na-bearing minerals, these sodium reserves will probably not be tapped within the next decade.

Mining. Mining of the sedimentary trona required the solving of many problems (3–6). The ore is the strongest rock in the formation and its removal permits the roof and floor of the mine to move under the pressure of the overburden. Mechanical properties (3) are shown in Table 3.

The initial approach to mining was based on coal-mining practice; equipment was modified to suit the special conditions of the trona formation. The workings are normally carried out at a tunnel or room height of 8 ft. Thin seams of trona which are

Table 3. Modulus of Elasticity and Compressive Strength of Rocks around Mine Opening

Material	Modulus of elasticity, psi	Uniaxial compressive strength, psi
trona	3.3×10^6	7500
roof shale	0.7×10^6	3500
floor shale	0.3×10^6	3200

present above and below the major bed are not recovered. The mines are worked by conventional room-and-pillar technique. Initially blasting was used throughout, but continuous miners were introduced in the 1950s, and a large percentage of the ore is now mined this way.

Conventional mining at the face is with equipment, primarily designed for coal mining, which has been modified to suit the heavier and harder trona. Equipment includes universal cutters, face drills, loading machines, shuttle cars, and roof-bolting machines. The face is prepared with a narrow, horizontal cut at midface. The cut varies from 4 to 6 ft, depending on room size, and is 10 ft deep. Drilling is with hydraulically operated auger bits. Blasting is done with a mixture of ammonium nitrate and fuel oil prepared and placed by special equipment. The broken ore is mucked with loading machines to cable shuttle cars.

Continuous-mining equipment also evolved from coal-mining equipment. The rough trona proved to be more than a match, causing excessive wear. Modifications have improved the equipment. After mining, the ore is transported to the hoisting shaft by conveyor belts, and lifted to the surface.

Trona Purification Processes. Several processes are available for removing the impurities present in trona. The processes can be separated into two groups; either the trona is purified and the resulting sodium sesquicarbonate crystals are calcined to soda ash or the trona is calcined to impure soda ash which is then purified.

Sodium Sesquicarbonate Process (7,8). In this process (Fig. 3), trona is fed into a series of well-agitated dissolvers where boiling mother liquor is saturated with trona. The dissolver effluent is pumped to Dorr-type clarifiers for sedimentation. The insolubles, consisting of shale, clay, and certain complex salts containing calcium carbonates, settle out. Flocculating agents, such as natural gums or polymeric electrolytes, are used to speed the settling of the fines. The waste solids containing almost all the insolubles are fed with makeup water to a second clarifier. The insolubles from this vessel are pumped to a waste pond. Contacting the makeup water with the insolubles in the second clarifier precipitates the calcium and magnesium salts, which is beneficial for growing better sesquicarbonate crystals.

The clarified liquor is further treated before crystallizing. Carbon is added to remove organic compounds found associated with the trona. Unless these compounds are removed, they will cause foaming in the crystallizer and modify the action of the growth-control reagents. The carbon, now loaded with organics and any remaining insolubles, is removed in a battery of Sweetland pressure filters (Dorr-Oliver, Inc.) using diatomaceous earth as a filter aid. Since the mother liquor is corrosive to steel, a low concentration of sulfide ion is maintained to control attack on the materials of construction, as well as to reduce contamination of the product with heavy metals.

The clear feed liquor is now ready for crystallization. To assist crystal growth a surfactant is added to modify the habit of the sodium sesquicarbonate as it crystallizes from the mother liquor in a series of three Struthers-Wells crystallizers. These vacuum

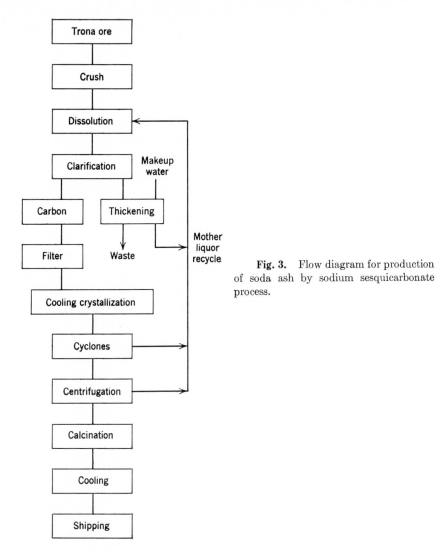

Fig. 3. Flow diagram for production of soda ash by sodium sesquicarbonate process.

crystallizers, of conventional design, concentrate the solution by evaporation and cooling. Growth occurs on the crystals suspended in the circulating magna. The crystallizers are operated with a suspended crystal slurry having a density of 20–30%. The temperature of the mother liquor in passing through the system is reduced in stages to 40°C. The needle-shaped, monoclinic sesquicarbonate crystals grow up to 1 cm in length. The condensate vapor from the crystallizer is used to reheat the mother liquor. Any sulfide lost from the solution by the evaporative process is also recovered.

The crystal slurry is concentrated in liquid cyclones (see Vol. 10, p. 340) and then separated in continuous centrifuges. The mother liquor is recycled to the dissolvers. The crystals are washed with makeup water, and are then conveyed to the calciners for decomposition of the sesquicarbonate to sodium carbonate.

$$2 \, Na_2CO_3 \cdot NaHCO_3 \cdot 2H_2O \rightarrow 3 \, Na_2CO_3 + 5 \, H_2O + CO_2$$

Calcination is carried out in steam-tube rotary calciners or gas-fired rotary calciners. In the steam tubes the calcination temperatures are as low as 200°C. The gas-fired units achieve higher temperatures in the product. The bulk density of the product is about 50 lb/ft³.

Some material is double calcined to heat-densify it to a bulk density of 60 lb/ft³ or higher. Fluid-bed calcination has also been proposed.

After calcination, the soda ash is cooled and stored, ready for shipment.

Monohydrate Process. The sodium carbonate monohydrate process (9,10) is also used commercially. The ore is first crushed, then calcined to produce a crude soda ash which is much more soluble than raw trona. The sesquicarbonate decomposes completely to Na_2CO_3 at 150–200°C. If higher-temperature calcination is used, organics are burned off, but soluble sodium silicates are produced by the reaction between soda ash and the clays. The crude soda ash is leached with water. The sodium carbonate solution is then settled, clarified, and filtered. The solution is passed through carbon columns to remove soluble organics produced in the low-temperature calcination. The clear carbonate liquor is then evaporated to produce crystals of sodium carbonate monohydrate. The crystallization must be carried out in a series of three evaporative units at about 100°C, because the retrograde solubility of the carbonate would cause the salt to go back into solution on cooling. The crystal slurry is concentrated and centrifuged. The mother liquor is returned to the evaporators and the crystals are calcined to soda ash (anhydrous sodium carbonate).

Other Processes. As an alternative to using sesquicarbonate or monohydrate as an intermediate alkali in the refining process, sodium bicarbonate or anhydrous sodium carbonate can be produced (11). High pressure and temperature equipment would be required for the crystallization of anhydrous Na_2CO_3 above the monohydrate transition point, 107°C. Various patents have described methods for carrying this out, but as yet none have been commercialized.

Solution-mining of the trona deposits has also been proposed. The process is not as simple as is the case with solution-mining of halite because of the complex solubility relationships in the system containing sodium sesquicarbonate and sodium bicarbonate. The latter tends to precipitate from dissolved trona and clog the dissolving face.

Product Quality. Soda ash produced from trona is chemically equivalent to that produced by the synthetic ash process. It contains fewer impurities, primarily because the raw material, trona, contains less chloride than the raw materials for the Solvay process. Representative analyses are shown in Table 4.

Soda ash is marketed in several bulk densities. The traditional grades of the synthetic ash produced are light ash (30 lb/ft³) and dense ash (60 lb/ft³). The first soda ash from the sesquicarbonate process averaged about 50 lb/ft³. The glass industry, the major user of Wyoming ash, has traditionally used a 60 lb/ft³ material. Heat-densification techniques have been developed to meet this demand. The monohydrate

Table 4. The Analysis of Soda Ash

Assay	Natural ash	Synthetic ash
Na_2CO_3, %	99.9	99.8
NaCl, %	0.02–0.03	0.2
Na_2SO_4, %	0.02–0.04	0.02
Fe, ppm	7	15
water insolubles	0.00	0.00

process produces 60 lb/ft³ material directly. However, still higher bulk densities have appeared recently (1968). These can be prepared by special crystallization techniques (12) or by heat densification techniques.

The growth of the natural soda ash industry (13) is reflected in the tonnages produced, as shown in Table 5.

Table 5. Recent U.S. Soda Ash Production, in million tons

Year	Synthetic ash	Natural ash	Total
1952	4.40	0.32	4.72
1957	4.30	0.61	4.91
1962	4.61	0.98	5.59
1963	4.68	1.12	5.80
1964	4.95	1.28	6.23
1965	4.93	1.49	6.42
1966	5.09	1.74	6.83
1967	4.83	1.75	6.58

The natural ash figures include the production of the two operating Wyoming plants, as well as that from the saline deposits in California, which account for less than 350,000 tons. The increase in natural ash since 1952 is due entirely to Wyoming production. Synthetic ash production since 1952 has been nearly constant, and the demand for increased alkali has been met by new Wyoming natural ash capacity. The decline in soda ash production from the peak in 1967 was caused by the incursion of sodium hydroxide into the soda ash market. As the chloroalkali industry expands to supply the demand for chlorine in chlorinated organics, the excess of caustic co-product will put pressure on soda ash production. As a result, soda ash growth will probably be less than the national average for the next decade.

The price of soda ash has been $31.00/ton, freight-equalized, since 1956. Freight equalization means that the buyer only pays freight from the nearest soda ash plant; the seller absorbs the remaining freight charge. Competition from the more economical natural ash plants has stabilized the price. The basis for this competitive edge probably can be found in the high quality of the trona and the simpler chemical processing carried out in sophisticated modern chemical plants.

Initially, natural ash was marketed only west of the Mississippi River. Since 1958, improved distribution techniques have permitted natural ash to compete on the national and international level. Natural-ash producers have pioneered the uses of larger freight cars with capacities of 50, 80, 95, and 130 tons. The higher loadings have lowered the freight cost per ton of delivered soda ash. With a freight-equalized commodity this is an important consideration for the producer.

Compounds Related to Sodium Carbonate

Sodium carbonate forms various hydrates, and in addition there are sodium sesquicarbonate, $Na_2CO_3 \cdot NaHCO_3 \cdot 2H_2O$, and sodium bicarbonate. The phase relations of these compounds are shown in Figure 4, which shows the system Na_2CO_3–$NaHCO_3$–H_2O.

Sodium Carbonate Monohydrate and Decahydrate (15). The monohydrate is stable between 35.4 and 109°C, and the decahydrate below 32°C.

Sodium carbonate monohydrate is made by hydrating soda ash with a limited amount of water. More perfect crystals are made by recrystallizing soda ash from

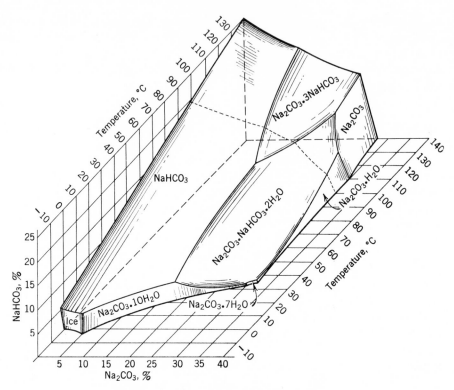

Fig. 4. Na_2CO_3–$NaHCO_3$–H_2O phase diagram.

solution in the stable temperature range. The decahydrate is prepared by carrying out the hydration below 30°C. The material is often cast in blocks. On additional heating above the transition temperature, the hydrate decomposes, liberating enough water to dissolve the crystal.

Sodium carbonate monohydrate is used in a variety of specialty applications. A photographic grade, meeting a higher purity specification, is sold. The price has been stable at 3.1¢/lb since 1957.

Sodium carbonate decahydrate was formerly an article of commerce, and well known in every household as "washing soda." With the development of modern detergents this market has disappeared, and the decahydrate is now manufactured only on a very small scale, if at all.

Sodium Sesquicarbonate, $Na_2CO_3 \cdot NaHCO_3 \cdot 2H_2O$. Sodium sesquicarbonate (density, 2.13 g/cm³) is a transparent, crystalline monoclinic compound which is more alkaline than sodium bicarbonate and less alkaline than sodium carbonate; as such it finds application in bath salts, as well as in detergent compositions. It is found in nature where the mineral is known as trona (see above).

Commercially the material is prepared by partial carbonation of soda ash solution, followed by crystallization, centrifugation, and drying. Alternatively, trona can be recrystallized directly (see under Sodium sesquicarbonate process). Production figures are not available as there are only two producers. The U.S. market is thought to be about 80,000 tons/yr. The cost is stable at $2.10/100 lb.

Sodium Bicarbonate (sodium hydrogen carbonate, sodium acid carbonate).   Sodium bicarbonate is a mildly alkaline substance.   It is produced as a finely divided, white, crystalline monoclinic compound which is stable under ambient conditions. At about 50°C it begins to decompose, the rate of decomposition increasing with temperature, as follows:

$$2 \ NaHCO_3 \rightarrow Na_2CO_3 + H_2O + CO_2$$

In solution it can be completely decomposed by boiling.   The density at 20°C is 2.217, heat capacity is 20.94 cal/(°C)(mole).

A crude form is produced as an intermediate in the Solvay process.   However, this material is heavily contaminated with ammonia and it is more economical to calcine it to soda ash, which is then recarbonated to bicarbonate (see Vol. 1, p. 734).   The commercial material is prepared by dissolving soda ash in stirred dissolvers.   Insoluble impurities are settled out, and the solution is cooled to about 40°C.   Carbonation of this solution with purified kiln gas is carried out in a tower similar to that used in the Solvay process:

$$Na_2CO_3 + H_2O + CO_2 \rightarrow 2 \ NaHCO_3$$

As the CO_2 is absorbed, a suspension of $NaHCO_3$ forms.   The slurry is filtered and the cake washed on the rotary drum filters.   The cake is then dried.   Care must be taken to prevent overheating which would cause calcining, thus increasing the alkalinity of the product.   The dried product is screened into six grades, depending on fineness. Sodium bicarbonate is usually sold at least 99.0% pure to meet the requirements of the *U.S. Pharmacopeia* (17th ed., 1965).

The production of $NaHCO_3$ (shown in tons, below) has increased significantly in the 1960s.

1960	157,000	1964	174,000
1962	167,000	1966	193,000

The material is used in foods (40%), chemicals (15%), pharmaceuticals (12%), fire extinguishers (10%), and a variety of other industries, such as rubber, plastics, washing products, and textile processing.   The largest growth area has been in commercial and household cake mixes.   In 1965 the price increased to 2.8¢/lb.

Bibliography

"Sodium Carbonates" in *ECT* 1st ed., Vol. 12, pp. 601–602, by J. A. Brink, Jr., Purdue University.

1. J. J. Fahey, "Saline Minerals of the Green River Formation," *U.S. Geological Survey Professional Paper 405*, 1962.
2. W. H. Bradley, *Second Symposium on Salt*, Northern Ohio Geological Society, Inc., Cleveland, Ohio, 1966.
3. W. G. Fischer, *Trans. Soc. Mining Engrs. AIME* **3**, 435–443 (1964).
4. R. F. Love, *Mining Eng.* **8**, 1101–1186 (1956).
5. W. G. Fischer, *Mining Eng.* **18**, 63–68 (1966).
6. U.S. Pat. 3,084,026 (Feb. 2, 1963), W. R. Frint and W. D. Smith (to FMC Corp.).   U.S. Pat. 3,026,096 (March 20, 1962), R. F. Love (to FMC Corp.).   U.S. Pat. 3,111,306 (Nov. 19, 1963), R. F. Love and W. Z. Wenneborg (to FMC Corp.).   U.S. Pat. 3,097,830 (Aug. 15, 1963), R. F. Love and T. S. Bernatis (to FMC Corp.).
7. H. A. Sommer, *Chem. Eng. Progr.* **56**, 76–79, 1960.

8. U.S. Pats. 2,639,217 (May 19, 1953), 2,704,239 (March 15, 1955), 2,780,520 (Feb. 5, 1957), 2,792,282 (May 14, 1957), 2,798,790 (July 9, 1957), R. D. Pike (to FMC Corp.). U.S. Pats. 2,954,282 (Sept. 27, 1960) and 3,072,466 (Jan. 8. 1963), W. C. Bauer and A. P. McCue, (to FMC Corp.). U.S. Pat. 2,989,369 (June 20, 1961), R. T. Osborne (to FMC Corp.). U.S. Pat. 3,037,-849 (June 5, 1962), W. R. Frint and W. C. Bauer (to FMC Corp.). U.S. Pat. 3,028,215 (April 3, 1962), W. R. Frint (to FMC Corp.). U.S. Pat. 3,084,026 (April 2, 1963), W. R. Frint and W. D. Smith (to FMC Corp.). U.S. Pat. 3,119,655 (Jan. 28, 1964), W. R. Frint and A. P. McCue (to FMC Corp.). U.S. Pat. 3,211,519 (Oct. 12, 1965), C. P. Roberts, H. A. Sommers, and N. J. Brunsvold (to Intermountain Research and Development Corp.). U.S. Pats. 3,189,-408 (June 15, 1965), 3,273,959 (Sept. 20, 1966), 3,336,104 (Aug. 15, 1967), W. S. Miller (to Intermountain Research and Development Corp.). U.S. Pat. 3,233,983 (Feb. 8, 1966), W. C. Bauer, A. P. McCue, and K. C. Rule (to FMC Corp.). U.S. Pat. 3,248,182 (April 26, 1966), J. F. Herink, and R. W. Waggener (to Intermountain Research and Development Corp.). U.S. Pat. 3,245,755 (April 12, 1966), H. J. Comer and A. B. Gancy (to Intermountain Research and Development Corp.). U.S. Pat. 3,309,171 (March 14, 1967), A. B. Gancy (to Intermountain Research and Development Corp.). U.S. Pat. 3,333,918 (Aug. 1, 1967), A. B. Gancy and P. M. DiBello (to FMC Corp.).

9. Anon., "New Soda Ash Plant," *Glass Ind.* **43**, 425 (1962).

10. U.S. Pat. 2,962,348 (Nov. 29, 1960), L. Seglin and H. S. Winnicki (to FMC Corp.). U.S. Pat. 2,970,037 (Jan. 31, 1961), N. A. Caldwell and W. C. Bauer (to FMC Corp.). U.S. Pat. 2,989,-369 (June 20, 1961), R. T. Osborne (to FMC Corp.). U.S. Pat. 3,028,215 (April 3, 1962), W. R. Frint (to FMC Corp.). U.S. Pat. 3,131,996 (May 5, 1964), L. Seglin and H. S. Winnicki (to Intermountain Research and Development Corp.). U.S. Pats. 3,189,408 (June 15, 1965), 3,264,057 (Aug. 2, 1966), W. S. Miller (to Intermountain Research and Development Corp.). U.S. Pat. 3,245,755 (May 12, 1966), H. J. Comer and A. B. Gancy (to Intermountain Research and Development Corp.). U.S. Pat. 3,244,476 (April 5, 1966), L. K. Smith (to Intermountain Research and Development Corp.). U.S. Pat. 3,273,958 (Sept. 20, 1966), G. D. Peverley (to Intermountain Research and Development Corp.). U.S. Pat 3,309,171 (March 14, 1967), A. B. Gancy (to Intermountain Research and Development Corp.). U.S. Pat. 3,335,105 (Aug. 15, 1967), E. V. Burnthall and J. J. Hirshfield (to Monsanto Co.).

11. U.S. Pat. 3,246,962 (April 19, 1966), W. S. Miller (to Intermountain Research and Development Corp.). U.S. Pat. 3,328,130 (June 27, 1967), A. B. Gancy (to FMC Corp.). U.S. Pat. 3,260,567 (July 12, 1966), H. D. Hellmers, J. V. Wiseman, and C. R. Beam (to Stauffer Chemical Co.). U.S. Pat. 2,770,524 (Nov. 13, 1956), M. Y. Seaton and R. D. Pike (to FMC Corp.).

12. U.S. Pat. 3,236,590 (Feb. 22, 1966), P. Sopchak and E. B. Port (to Allied Chemical Co.). U.S. Pat. 3,314,748 (April 18, 1967), C. J. Howard, P. Sopchak, and E. B. Port (to Allied Chemical Co.).

13. Current Industrial Reports, *Inorganic Chemicals and Gases Series M28A*, Bureau of the Census, Washington, D.C., 1967.

14. Properties of the sodium carbonates are compiled in *Gmelin's Handbuch der anorganischen Chemie*, 8th ed, *Natrium*, Ergänzungs-Band, Lieferung 3, 1966.

15. Stanford Research Institute, *Chemical Economics Handbook 1966–1968; American Standard Specification* PH4.227-1961, USA Standards Institute, New York.

Eric Rau
FMC Corporation

SODIUM HALIDES.   **Sodium Fluoride.**   See Vol. 9, p. 662.

Sodium Chloride

In this article the term salt refers to sodium chloride, NaCl, and aqueous salt solutions are termed brines. Salt supplies sodium and chloride ions, both of which are essential to animal life. It is one of the principal raw materials used in the chemical industry, being the source of almost all compounds containing sodium or chlorine.

PROPERTIES OF SALT

Sodium chloride is composed of 39.337% sodium and 60.663% chlorine by weight. The ionic crystal has a cubic close-packed lattice, with alternate positions occupied by sodium ions and chloride ions; the unit cell is 5.627 Å on edge. The lattice energy is 182 cal/mole.

Pure sodium chloride is colorless and, unlike glass, is transparent in the near- and mid-infrared regions also. The density is 2.165, hardness 2.5, refractive index n_D^{20} 1.544, specific heat 0.204 cal/(g)(°C), melting point 800.8°C, boiling point 1465°C, heat of fusion 123.59 cal/g. The critical humidity is 75.3% at 20°C.

The solubility of salt (expressed as g NaCl/100 g solvent at 25°C) is 1.40 in methanol, 0.065 in ethanol, 5.21 in formic acid, 7.15 in ethylene glycol, and 1.86 in monoethanolamine. At $-40°C$, 2.15 g of salt will dissolve in 100 g of liquid ammonia.

The solubility of salt in water is 35.7 g/100 g of water at 0°C, 39.8 g/100 g of water at 100°C. The solution is essentially neutral. Dissolution of salt in water is endothermic, integral heat of solution being $+898$ cal for one mole of salt in 1000 g of water at 25°C (1). At standard atmospheric pressure, saturated brine at its boiling point of 108.7°C (227.7°F) contains 28.41% sodium chloride. At 25°C (77°F) saturated brine contains 26.48% sodium chloride; the specific gravity (relative to water at 4°C) is 1.1978 (2), specific heat 0.784, vapor pressure 18 mm mercury.

The vapor pressure of a saturated salt solution is 13.2 mm Hg at 20°C, 69.5 at 50°C, 175.0 at 70°C, and 391.6 at 90°C.

An extensive tabulation of the physical properties of salt has been made by Kaufmann (3).

Figure 1 is the phase diagram for sodium chloride–water. The eutectic temperature is $-21.12°C$ ($-6.016°F$); the composition of the eutectic mixture is 23.31% salt and 76.69% water, or 37.68% $NaCl \cdot 2H_2O$ and 62.32% water. At low temperatures, brines more concentrated than 23.31% salt will deposit large, transparent crystals of monoclinic $NaCl \cdot 2H_2O$. These dihydrate crystals, although similar to ice in appearance, are birefringent.

OCCURRENCE

Salt is widely distributed throughout the world. It occurs in solution in seawater and other saline waters and in dry deposits as rock salt or playas.

Most of the world's salt is in the oceans, and seawater is an important source of salt. Table 1 shows the analysis of seawater. Except for such highly saline waters as the Great Salt Lake and the Dead Sea, naturally occurring inland saline waters are not important sources of salt.

Table 1. Composition of Seawater

Component	Wt %	Component	Wt %
sodium chloride	2.68	potassium chloride	0.07
magnesium chloride	0.32	sodium bromide	0.008
magnesium sulfate	0.22	water	96.582
calcium sulfate	0.12	total	100.00

A playa is a shallow basin in a desert plain. Leaching of the surrounding sediments, followed by evaporation, results in a deposit forming in the basin. Playas are not an important source of salt, but may be significant for other salines, such as sodium sulfate.

The bedded deposits are true sedimentary rocks; they are thus referred to as rock salt, which has the mineralogical name of halite. Rock salt is a very important source of salt. Bedded deposits were formed from evaporation of large inland seas which became separated from the ocean. Geologically, rock salt deposits are very old, dating back to Cambrian and perhaps pre-Cambrian periods.

In North America rock salt is found in tremendous quantity in four areas. The Silurian basin covers parts of Michigan, Ontario, Ohio, Pennsylvania, and New York.

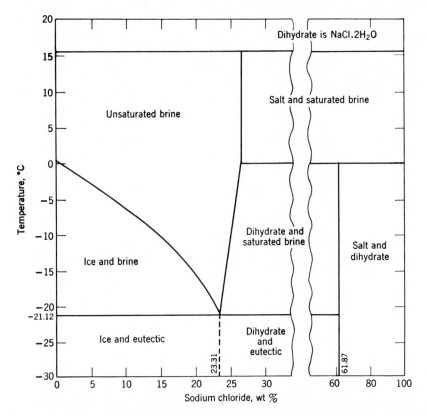

Fig. 1. The system sodium chloride–water.

Although most of this salt dates back to the Silurian period, there is also Devonian salt in the Michigan basin. The Permian basin covers parts of Kansas, Colorado, Oklahoma, New Mexico, and Texas. The Gulf Coast basin, from the pre-Jurassic period, covers parts of Mexico, Texas, Arkansas, Louisiana, Mississippi, and Alabama; it also extends out into the Gulf of Mexico. The Williston and Elk Point basins, covering parts of North and South Dakota, Montana, Saskatchewan, and Alberta, are Silurian-Devonian period salt.

The North American rock-salt deposits are among the most extensive in the world. However, there are very significant deposits in South America, England, Europe, and the Soviet Union (see maps, Figs. 2–4) (4).

Rock salt commonly occurs in layered strata of relatively pure salt separated by thin layers of calcium sulfate. The thickness of the salt strata generally is 20–100 ft or more. The deposits usually occur at depths of 500–4000 ft.

One of the most unusual and interesting types of rock-salt deposit is the salt dome. A salt dome is a large vertical column of salt. The domes which are commercially used for salt production have the top of the salt within a few hundred feet of the earth's surface. The depth of salt exceeds 10,000 ft. Some domes are estimated to have a

Fig. 2. Salt resources of North America (4). Courtesy Plenum Publishing Corporation.

volume of 20 cubic miles. Salt domes are believed to have been formed from bedded deposits by salt flowage. Halite is somewhat plastic, and the pressure of surrounding dense rock caused the bedded salt to flow and pierce the overlying rock through zones of weakness. Although salt domes occur in different parts of the world, they are most numerous around the Gulf of Mexico bordering Texas, Louisiana, Mississippi, and Alabama. There have been 329 proved domes located and characterized in this area (5). Deposits of sulfur and oil are commonly associated with salt domes.

The principal soluble impurity in naturally occurring rock salt is calcium sulfate, with small amounts of calcium chloride and magnesium chloride. The bedded rock-salt deposits generally contain about 2% calcium sulfate. Salt domes vary in calcium sulfate content from 1 to 10%.

Fig. 3. Salt resources of South America (4). Courtesy Plenum Publishing Corporation.

Fig. 4. Salt resources of the Eastern Hemisphere (4). Courtesy Plenum Publishing Corporation.

There is also much salt around the world occurring as sylvinite, which consists of mixed crystals of potassium chloride and sodium chloride. However, sylvinite is used principally as a source of potassium chloride; the associated salt is usually a waste product.

An interesting feature of some rock-salt deposits is the occurrence of pure, recrystallized salt, found in quantities from very small isolated patches to formations several tons in weight. This salt is extremely clear and free from defects; it is about 99.98% pure sodium chloride.

METHODS OF PRODUCTION

Salt is recovered by the following principal methods: (*1*) shaft mining, (*2*) solution mining, and (*3*) solar evaporation.

Shaft Mining. Salt is mined using methods very similar to those used in coal mining. A shaft is sunk to the rock-salt vein. Well-established techniques of undercutting, side shearing, drilling, blasting, loading, and transporting are used to remove the salt from the deposit for further processing. Processing of mined rock salt is primarily a materials-handling operation involving crushing, screening, bagging, and loading. In modern mines some of these operations may be carried out in the mine. In this way the less desirable fine salt produced by blasting and crushing can be left behind in the mine, thus avoiding the expense of hoisting it to the surface for disposal. Some fines are recovered by compaction to produce a product resembling natural rock salt. Rock salt is produced in grades designated Coarse (up to $\frac{3}{4}$ in.), Coarse Crushed (between $3\frac{1}{2}$ and 10 mesh), and Fine Crushed (passing a 10 mesh screen).

Rock salt is mined by the room-and-pillar method. As the salt is removed to form rooms, pillars are left to support the formation. In layered strata deposits the rooms are generally limited to 25 ft in height and 50–60 ft in lateral dimension.

In salt domes the limitation on room height is removed. Hence a special type of room-and-pillar mining referred to as quarrying may be used. This allows room height of up to 100 ft and lateral room size also of 100 ft.

Working conditions in a salt mine are excellent. The air is dry and the temperature moderate (about 60°F). The working areas are well lighted and the mine is ventilated with forced draft. Safety records in mines are excellent.

Solution Mining. Salt brine is obtained for further processing by pumping water into a rock-salt deposit, dissolving the salt, and bringing brine to the surface. Two principal techniques are used. One involves pumping water into and brine out of a single well. This is done by using a double pipe arrangement. Water is generally pumped into the well in the outer annular space between the pipes, and brine is removed via the inside pipe.

The second method can be used only in layered strata deposits. Two holes (500–1000 ft apart) are drilled into the deposit. The deposit is fractured between the two wells by use of high-pressure pumps in a process commonly called hydrofracing. Then water is pumped into one well and brine out of the other. If wells are properly arranged, one water-injection well can serve more than one brine-producing well.

Brine produced by solution mining is essentially saturated with sodium chloride. Its main impurity is calcium sulfate, which is almost always associated with salt deposits. As a result, the brine contains up to 0.5% calcium sulfate based on the weight of the brine. Smaller amounts of calcium and magnesium chlorides are usually present. It is not uncommon for minor amounts of hydrogen sulfide to be present.

Brine produced by solution mining serves as the raw material for salt produced by several different types of crystallizers or salt evaporators. Before discussing these a few comments on brine treatment are in order.

For ordinary grades of salt no brine treatment is required other than hydrogen sulfide removal, if necessary, and settling to remove any extraneous insolubles. Hydrogen sulfide is removed by aeration and chlorination. Special grades of salt for food and chemical use may require chemical pretreatment of brine, generally a treatment with lime or caustic soda and soda ash to remove the calcium and magnesium salts. The treatment is usually done on a batch basis, and the treated brine is allowed to settle to produce a sparkling clear brine. The principal impurity left in the brine by this type of treatment is sodium sulfate, which in most cases presents no problem in the final purity of the salt. However, if removal of sulfate is required, it can be accomplished by treatment with barium chloride.

Vacuum Pans. The multiple-effect vacuum-pan system is the most common and most important type of equipment used to evaporate water from brine to produce salt.

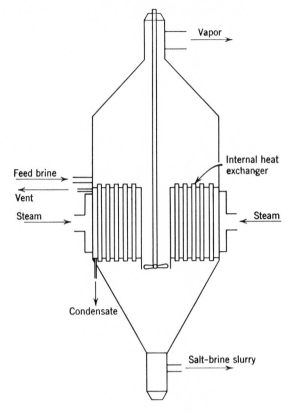

Fig. 5. Calandria evaporator.

Salt produced in this manner is called evaporated, or granulated, salt. It is generally in the form of well-formed cubes and in the size range between 20 and 70 mesh.

Vacuum pans are of two principal types, the Calandria (or internal heating-surface) type shown in Figure 5 and the forced-circulation (or external heat-exchanger) unit shown in Figure 6. A vacuum pan is nothing more than a vessel in which brine is boiled to evaporate water and crystallize salt. Provisions are made for removal and processing of the salt. The principal advantage of the multiple-effect system is heat economy. The vapors produced in one effect are reused to boil brine at a lower pressure in a following effect. Thus, in a triple-effect set of pans, 1 lb of steam can evaporate almost 3 lb of water.

Calandria pans generally are limited to operating at a steam pressure of 8 lb per square inch gage (psig) on the first effect. It has become fairly common practice to increase capacity by installing a forced-circulation evaporator operating at about 25 psig and providing vapor at 8 psig for the Calandria pans.

The older pans were cast iron vessels with copper heating tubes. Modern pan bodies are constructed of Monel with cupronickel or titanium tubes in the heaters. Vacuum pans are large vessels up to 25 ft in diameter and 60 ft in height.

A special problem in vacuum-pan operation has been scaling of heating surfaces with calcium sulfate because of the inverse solubility of calcium sulfate with temperature. This problem has been successfully controlled by maintaining a suspension of calcium sulfate seed crystals in the pans.

The salt is removed from the pans in a brine slurry. It is first washed counter-currently with fresh brine to hydraulically remove the calcium sulfate. The salt is then dewatered and dried on a top-feed rotary filter-dryer. The salt may also be dewatered in a centrifuge and dried in a rotary kiln dryer.

Some salt is produced in Oslo (or Krystal) type evaporators, which produce coarse crystals, usually quite spherical.

A special type of salt is produced in vacuum pans when a small amount of sodium ferrocyanide is added to the brine. This additive modifies the growth of the salt crystals, inhibiting the growth on the faces and promoting growth on the corners (6). This type of salt is called dendritic salt.

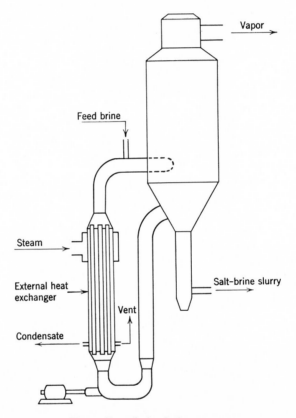

Fig. 6. Forced-circulation evaporator.

Grainers. The grainer process produces a special type of salt called "flake" salt. This process is very wasteful of heat and there are only a few grainer installations presently operating to satisfy the demand for this special type of salt.

A grainer is a long, narrow, shallow pan. Its dimensions are 100–200 ft in length, 12–20 ft in width, and about 2 ft deep. Heating coils in the grainer heat the brine, which is not agitated. Nucleation occurs at the surface and the growing crystal is supported by the surface tension of the brine. As its weight increases, the crystal gradually sinks and a hollow pyramid, or hopper crystal, is formed. These "hoppers" drop to the bottom and are removed by a raking mechanism. In the process of filtering and drying, the hoppers break up into the flakes which give this type of salt its name.

To overcome the disadvantages of internally heated grainers, a system with an external heater has been developed (7). In this process brine is recirculated through the grainer, and through an external heater and flasher. Brine is heated to 230°F, flashed to 220°F, and then fed to the grainer pan. In this process part of the water evaporated is removed in the flasher, relieving the grainer pan of part of the evaporation load.

There are two methods for synthetically producing salt with characteristics similar to flake salt. In one process, salt is fused and cast into molds. The cooled salt is crushed and screened. In another process, salt is compacted into a thin sheet which is crushed and screened.

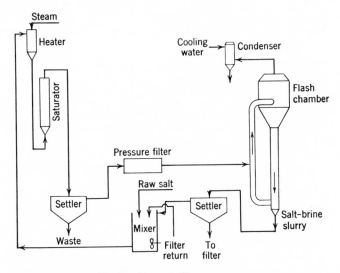

Fig. 7. Recrystallizer process.

Alberger Process. This process (8) produces a special type of salt which is a mixture of flake salt and fine cubic crystals. Brine is heated under pressure to 290°F and flashed down to atmospheric pressure, producing fine cubic crystals. The slurry is then fed to open circular evaporating pans, where flake salt is produced by surface evaporation. The salt is then mechanically raked out of the pans, centrifuged, and dried in rotary dryers.

Recrystallizer Process. This is a process developed by Richards and Hopper (9) primarily to convert solid salt to evaporated salt. A sketch is shown in Figure 7. Solid salt is introduced into the recirculating brine system. The slurry is heated by direct injection of live steam to dissolve the salt. The saturated brine is settled and filtered to remove all extraneous solids. The filtered brine is sent to a forced-circulation evaporator where water is flashed off under reduced pressure and salt is crystallized. One of the features of this process is that salt is crystallized during a cooling cycle. This prevents crystallization of calcium sulfate since its solubility is increasing during the flash cooling. The salt is dewatered and dried in conventional fashion.

Solar Evaporation. This is the third method of salt recovery, and historically the oldest. In the United States and Canada only about 5% of the total salt production comes from solar salt. San Francisco, Southern California, and the Great Salt Lake are the only producing areas. However, in other parts of the world, solar salt is of great importance.   Worldwide, solar salt accounts for close to 50% of the world's salt production.

Solar salt production is limited to those geographical areas that have the proper combination of meteorological conditions, land availability, and accessibility to markets.   Large and relatively level land areas, with reasonably impervious soil, are required.

Solar evaporation is basically a fractional crystallization process using the sun as a source of energy.   Seawater (or other natural brine) is brought to saturation in concentrating pond areas.   Further evaporation in crystallizing areas results in the crystallization of salt, which accumulates in a bed on the floor of the crystallizing pan.   The major brine constituents other than salt remain in solution and are discarded as bitterns.   The salt crop is recovered with special equipment in an operation called harvesting.   The harvested salt is washed and stockpiled.   It is then further processed in a plant by drying, crushing, and screening.

In some areas solar salt is converted to evaporated salt by redissolving it and processing the resultant brine in vacuum pans.

In addition to sodium chloride, the bitterns contain magnesium chloride, magnesium sulfate, potassium chloride, and magnesium bromide.   These can be processed in a chemical plant to recover additional values.   Magnesium compounds and bromine are being successfully recovered from bitterns.

SHAPE OF SALT CRYSTALS (CRYSTAL HABIT)

As indicated under the section on Properties of salt (p. 469), the lattice structure of sodium chloride is cubic close-packed lattice.   The shape (or habit) of salt crystals grown from aqueous solution is ordinarily that of a cube.   It is possible to alter the crystal habit of sodium chloride, but the crystal lattice is always cubic close-packed. Investigations of the crystal habit of salt are of theoretical and academic interest, and also of great practical importance.   Certain desirable physical properties can be obtained by altering the crystal habit.   Examples of this are lowering of the bulk density and increasing the rate of solubility.   Improved anticaking properties may also be obtained with habit-modified crystals.

Flake salt, produced by the grainer process, can perhaps be classified as the oldest type of crystal-habit modification.   This is produced by purely physical means and does not require chemical additives.   By restricting crystal growth at the surface of

Fig. 8.   Dendritic-type salt crystal produced by laboratory crystallization.

Fig. 9. Octahedral salt crystal.

brine which is not under agitation, so-called "hopper" crystals are produced. When these hoppers break up in handling, they produce salt consisting of rather flat flakes rather than cubes (see p. 476).

In the last fifteen years there has been considerable interest and work in connection with the use of chemical additives in brine during crystallization to modify the crystal habit of salt. Some truly remarkable results have been obtained. The effects of various additives have been quite well summarized in two papers by Phoenix (10,11).

The general mechanism by which chemical additives affect crystal habit is as follows: During crystallization from solution, the additive, which is dissolved in the solution, is adsorbed at the surface of the growing crystal lattice. Adsorption is selective at certain sites or on certain faces. Growth is retarded at sites of additive adsorption and accelerated at other sites. For example, sodium ferrocyanide, which produces dendritic salt, retards growth on the cube faces. Growth then occurs primarily on the edges and corners, producing a star-shaped crystal. An extreme example of a dendritic-type crystal produced by laboratory crystallization is shown in Figure 8.

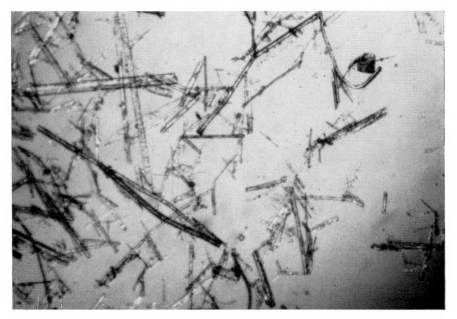

Fig. 10. Salt in form of very slender needles.

Since the additives function by adsorption, the resulting habit-modified salt crystals will contain some of the chemical additive.

One of the oldest known chemical-additive habit modifiers is urea, which will produce octahedral crystals. However, a very high percentage of urea, 10–20% by weight in the solution, is required.

There are a number of additives that function at very low concentrations in solution, from 1 to 100 ppm. The strongest class of habit-modifying chemicals are the complex metal ferrocyanides, such as sodium ferrocyanide. As indicated previously, they produce dendritic salt. Some carboxylic-type compounds produce octahedral salt as shown in Figure 9. Polyvinyl alcohol causes salt to grow as very slender needles as shown in Figure 10. These are the principal examples of strong effects on crystal habit at low concentration of the chemical additive.

Some chemical-additive habit modifiers are sensitive to pH and temperature, and therefore these must be considered in investigating this phenomenon.

There are also additives that cause growth of exceptionally well-formed, clear cubes with very sharp edges and corners. The clarity of the crystals is a result of the ability of the chemical additive to effect a considerable reduction in inclusions of mother liquor in the crystal. All crystals grown from aqueous solution trap mother liquor in the growing crystals. A high level of mother-liquor inclusions gives quite opaque crystals, and the clarity of the crystals increases as mother-liquor inclusions decrease. The best examples of this type of chemical additive are lead, cadmium, and manganese salts. These additives are also incorporated into the growing crystals.

ECONOMIC ASPECTS

The annual world production of salt in 1965 was 118 million tons. The U.S. production accounted for 35 million tons or almost 30% of the world total. There are fifty-eight companies operating ninety-seven plants in the United States. Table 2 (12) shows the salt production by states. Five states, Louisiana, Michigan, New York, Ohio, and Texas, account for 85% of the U.S. production.

Table 2. U.S. Salt Production by States, 1965

State	Short tons	% of total
California	1,638,000	4.7
Kansas	1,053,000	3.0
Louisiana	8,126,000	23.5
Michigan	4,171,000	12.0
New Mexico	60,000	0.2
New York	5,002,000	14.4
Ohio	5,026,000	14.5
Oklahoma	9,000	0.1
Texas	6,964,000	20.0
Utah	384,000	1.1
West Virginia	1,153,000	3.3
other states	1,097,000	3.2
total	34,687,000	100.0

Table 3 (12) shows the breakdown of production by the three basic methods: evaporated salt, rock salt, and brine. The largest percentage of salt is used as brine, which is the principal raw material for heavy chemicals.

Table 3. Salt Production by Basic Methods in the U.S. and Puerto Rico, 1965

Method of recovery	Production, short tons
evaporated	
bulk	
grainers	303,000
vacuum pans	2,547,000
solar	1,700,000
pressed blocks	375,000
total	4,925,000
rock	
bulk	9,742,000
pressed blocks	68,000
total	9,810,000
salt in brine	19,952,000
grand total	34,687,000

The total value of U.S. salt production in 1965 was 216 million dollars. The per capita consumption of salt was about 350 lb.

Since salt is one of the basic raw materials of the chemical industry, its consumption is historically closely correlated with the gross national product. As shown in Figure 11, salt production closely follows the total industrial production index (13).

Salt imported into the United States in 1965 totaled 2.4 million tons. Most of the imported salt is from Canada, but imports from Mexico and the West Indies are becoming more significant.

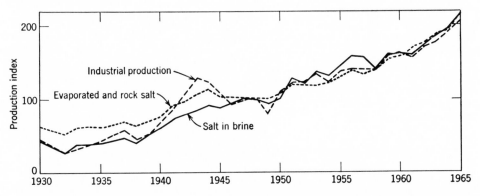

Fig. 11. Relationship of U.S. salt production and industrial production index, 1930–1965. Production index for 1947–1949 is taken as 100. From Federal Reserve Board index of industrial production.

Table 4. Salt Exports to and Production by Foreign Countries, 1965

Country	U.S. exports to, tons	Production by, tons
England	none	7,716,000
Germany (East)	none	2,200,000
Germany (West)	none	6,883,000
Japan	379,000	935,000
Russia	none	10,500,000
China	none	14,300,000

In 1965 the United States exported 700,000 tons of salt, mostly to Japan, Canada, and South America. Figures for the production of salt in the major producing foreign countries and the exports to these countries from the United States, in 1965, are given in Table 4.

USES

There are literally thousands of uses for salt, and it is possible to discuss only the major ones. Table 5 (12) shows the U.S. salt consumption by uses.

Table 5. Salt Consumption in the U.S. by Uses in 1965, thousands short tons

Use	Evaporated	Rock	Brine	Total
chlorine	W	W	12,136	14,257
soda ash	W	W	6,462	6,464
snow and ice control and stabilization	201	4,332	3	4,536
soap and detergents	25	9		34
other chemicals	326	701	1,144	2,171
textile and dyeing	W	141	W	242
meat packing, canning and casings	306	458		764
fishing	17	5		22
dairy	42	4		46
canning	177	37		214
baking	103	4		107
flour and cereal	59	10		69
other food processing	127	30		157
refrigeration	20	48		68
feed dealers and mixers	950	W	W	1,498
metals	56	89		145
ceramics and glass	4	9		13
rubber	W	W	53	86
oil	63	62	90	215
paper and pulp	W	137	W	196
water softening	W	287	W	540
grocery stores	595	387		987
miscellaneous				1,861
total				34,687

LEGEND: Withheld to avoid disclosing individual company confidential data.

Technologically, the most important reactions of salt are those in which it is used as a starting material for the production of other materials, many of which are used to produce still other chemicals. Salt is the raw material for almost all chemicals containing sodium or chlorine. The reactions shown in Table 6 (3) are the most important, chlorine, caustic soda, and soda ash being the largest consumers of salt (mostly as brine).

An increasingly important use of salt is for snow and ice removal, for which a 1970 consumption of 8 million tons is forecast. Another highway use of salt is for stabilization of secondary roads.

Salt is used in the meat, canning, baking, fishing, dairy, and other food-processing industries. Table salt is an important factor.

In the field of agriculture, salt provides the ideal carrier for supplying minerals and trace elements in the diet of animals. Salt is used in loose form or in pressed blocks.

A rapidly growing use of salt is for the regeneration of ion-exchange resins used to produce soft water.

The use of salt is also important in leather tanning (for prevention of bacterial decomposition in hides), in textile dyeing (for standardizing the strength of individual batches of dye and for setting the dye onto the fiber), in soapmaking (for separation of soap from water and glycerine), in pulp and paper manufacturing (as a precipitant for

Table 6. Chemicals Produced by Reactions Using NaCl as Raw Material

Process	Products
1. ammonia–soda (Solvay) process	Na_2CO_3, $CaCl_2$
$2NaCl + CaCO_3 \rightarrow Na_2CO_3 + CaCl_2$	
2. chlorine–caustic electrolytic cell	Cl_2, NaOH
$2NaCl + 2H_2O \rightarrow 2NaOH + H_2 + Cl_2$	
3. Downs sodium electrolytic cell	Cl_2, Na
$2NaCl \rightarrow 2Na + Cl_2$	
4. nitrosyl chloride process	Cl_2, $NaNO_3$
$3NaCl + 4HNO_3 \rightarrow Cl_2 + 3NaNO_3 + NOCl + 2H_2O$	
5. Mannheim furnace	Na_2SO_4, HCl
$2NaCl + H_2SO_4 \rightarrow Na_2SO_4 + 2HCl$	
6. Hargreaves process	Na_2SO_4, HCl
$4NaCl + 2SO_2 + O_2 + 2H_2O \rightarrow 2Na_2SO_4 + 4HCl$	
7. cyanamide electric furnace	$CaCl_2$, NaCN
$2NaCl + CaCN_2 + C \rightarrow CaCl_2 + 2NaCN$	
8. niter-cake retort	HCl, $NaHSO_4$
$NaCl + H_2SO_4 \rightarrow NaHSO_4 + HCl$	
9. chlorate electrolytic cell	$NaClO_3$
$NaCl + 3H_2O \rightarrow NaClO_3 + 3H_2$	

waterproofing compositions and for electrolytic generation of chlorine bleach), in metallurgy (for descaling and for fluxes and fused-salt baths), in ceramics (for surface vitrification of heated clays), in rubber manufacturing (for salting out rubber from latex), in refrigeration (either as salt-ice mixtures for direct cooling or in the form of brine pumped as a refrigerant), and in the petroleum industry (for inhibiting fermentation of starch in well-drilling mud and for preventing dissolution of rock-salt strata during the drilling operation).

Bibliography

"Salt" in *ECT* 1st ed., Vol. 12, pp. 67–82, by C. D. Looker, International Salt Company, Inc.

1. T. F. Young, in F. Daniels and R. A. Alberty, eds., *Physical Chemistry*, John Wiley & Sons, Inc., New York, 1955, p. 207.
2. *International Critical Tables of Numerical Data, Physics, Chemistry and Technology*, Vol. 3, McGraw-Hill Book Company, Inc., New York, 1928, p. 105.
3. D. W. Kaufmann, *Sodium Chloride*, Reinhold Publishing Corp., New York, 1960, pp. 587–626, 668–669.
4. S. J. Lefond, *Handbook of World Salt Resources*, in R. W. Fairbridge, ed., *Monographs in Geoscience*, Plenum Publishing Corporation, New York, 1968.
5. M. E. Hawkins and C. J. Jirik, "Salt Domes in Texas, Louisiana, Mississippi, Alabama and Offshore Tidelands," *U.S. Bur. Mines Inf. Circ. 8313* (1966).
6. U.S. Pat. 2,642,335 (1953), W. May and T. Scott (to Imperial Chemical Industries, Ltd.).
7. U.S. Pat. 2,660,236 (1953), W. H. Farnsworth (to Morton Salt Co.).
8. U.S. Pats. 351,082 (1886), 400,983 (1889), and 443,186 (1890), H. Williams, J. L. Alberger, and L. R. Alberger.
9. U.S. Pats. 2,555,340 (1951) and 2,876,182 (1959), C. M. Hopper and R. B. Richards (to International Salt Co.).
10. L. Phoenix, *Brit. Chem. Eng.* **11** (1), 34–38 (1966).
11. L. Phoenix, *School Sci. Rev.* **48** (164), 173–177 (1966).
12. William H. Kerns, ed., *Bureau of Mines Mineral Yearbook, 1965*, U.S. Department of Interior, Washington, D.C.
13. Arthur D. Little, Inc., *Chemical Industry Report M-50*, 1962, p. 13.

General References

D. W. Kaufmann, *Sodium Chloride*, Reinhold Publishing Corp., New York, 1960.
W. E. Ver Planck, *Salt in California*, Bulletin 175, State of California, Division of Mines, 1958.
H. Borchert and R. O. Muir, *Salt Deposits*, D. Van Nostrand Company, Inc., Princeton, N.J., 1964.
A. C. Bersticker, ed., *First Symposium on Salt*, Northern Ohio Geological Society, Cleveland, Ohio, 1963.
J. L. Rau, ed., *Second Symposium on Salt*, Vols. 1 and 2, Northern Ohio Geological Society, Cleveland, Ohio, 1965.
J. W. Mellor, *Comprehensive Treatise on Inorganic and Theoretical Chemistry*, Vol. II, Suppl. II, *The Alkali Metals*, John Wiley & Sons, Inc., New York, 1962, pp. 751–933.
G. L. Eskew, *Salt, The Fifth Element*, J. G. Ferguson & Associates, Chicago, Ill., 1948.
R. T. MacMillan, *Industrial Minerals and Rocks*, American Institute of Mining, Metallurgical and Petroleum Engineers, New York, 1960, pp. 715–721.
M. T. Halbouty, *Salt Domes—Gulf Region and Mexico*, Gulf Publishing Company, Houston, Tex., 1967.
S. J. Lefond, *Handbook of World Salt Resources*, in R. W. Fairbridge, ed., *Monographs in Geoscience*, Plenum Publishing Corporation, New York, 1968.
Richard B. Mattox, ed., *Saline Deposits*, Geological Society of America, Boulder, Colo., 1968. (Symposium based on papers from International Conference on Saline Deposits, Houston, Tex., 1962.)

Eugene J. Kuhajek and
Howard W. Fiedelman
Morton International, Inc.

Sodium bromide, NaBr, is a white (colorless) compound crystallizing in the cubic system. The lattice constant is 5.977 Å, specific gravity d_4^{25} is 3.200, and refractive index n_D^{25} is 1.641. Sodium bromide melts at 747°C, with a heat of fusion of 60.6 cal/g, and begins to vaporize at a somewhat higher temperature. The specific heat, C_p, is 0.119 cal/g at 25°C and 0.126 at 200°C. The compound has a feebly bitter, saline taste, is somewhat hygroscopic, and has a high solubility in water, as shown below. The solid phase in equilibrium with a saturated aqueous solution is anhydrous above 51°C and a dihydrate at lower temperatures. In alcohol at 25°C, the solubilities (g/100 g soln) are 14.8 in methanol and 3.97 in 95% ethanol.

Temperature, °C	0	20	30	50	100	140
g NaBr/100 g aq soln	44.5	47.6	49.6	53.8	54	56

The simplest way of obtaining pure sodium bromide is by the neutralization of sodium carbonate or hydroxide with hydrobromic acid, followed by evaporation and crystallization. Commercially the salt is obtained during the manufacture of sodium bromate, as in a variation of the seawater process for bromine (qv). After crystallization of bromate, the mother liquor is treated with a reducing agent such as ferrous iron; hydrated ferric oxide is filtered off and the solution is evaporated under conditions necessary to produce the desired crystalline form of the bromide. Processes for the direct formation of sodium bromide from bromine, sodium hydroxide or carbonate, and a reducing agent are also available (1–3).

Granular NF grade sodium bromide is shipped in 400-lb drums; the price in 1968 was quoted at 40¢/lb, in car lots or less, freight equalized.

The compound has varied uses, the major ones being in the formulation of a proprietary bleaching compound and in photography, both for the preparation of light-sensitive silver bromide emulsions and as a restrainer in developers. Pharmaceutically sodium bromide has been rather widely used as a mild sedative and depressant of the central nervous system. Production in the U.S. during 1967 was estimated to be over 2 million lb.

Bibliography

"Sodium Halides" treated in *ECT* 1st ed. under "Sodium Compounds," Vol. 12, pp. 603–605, by J. A. Brink, Jr., Purdue University.

1. U.S. Pat. 1,863,375 (June 14, 1932), C. W. Jones (to The Dow Chemical Company).
2. U.S. Pat. 1,916,457 (July 4, 1933), A. S. Behrman.
3. U.S. Pat. 2,269,733 (Jan. 13, 1942), E. P. Pearson (to American Potash and Chemical Company).

V. A. STENGER
The Dow Chemical Company

Sodium iodide, NaI, occurs as colorless, odorless crystals or as a white crystalline solid. It has a salty and slightly bitter taste. In moist air, it gradually absorbs up to about 5% water, which causes caking. It slowly becomes brown when exposed to air due to the liberation of iodine. Water solutions of sodium iodide are neutral or slightly alkaline to litmus and gradually become brown due to the formation of free iodine. Aqueous solutions can be made slightly alkaline (pH 8–9.5) to render them more stable.

Sodium iodide crystallizes in the cubic system; specific gravity d_4^{25} is 3.667 and refractive index n_D is 1.7745. Its melting point is 651°C and it boils at 1304°C. Its specific heat, C_p, in cal/g, is 0.083 at 0°C; 0.085 at 50°C; and 0.0072 at 150°C.

Sodium iodide is soluble in methanol, ethanol, acetone, glycerol, and several other organic solvents. Its solubility in water is as follows:

Temperature, °C	g NaI/100 g H₂O	Temperature, °C	g NaI/100 g H₂O
0	158.7	70	294
20	178.7	80	296
40	205.0	100	302
60	256.8	140	321

At temperatures below 65.6°C, sodium iodide is present in aqueous solutions as different hydrates containing varying amounts of water. When it is dissolved in water, heat is liberated due to the formation of the hydrates. At room temperature, sodium iodide crystallizes from water as $NaI.2H_2O$ in the form of colorless prismatic crystals.

Sodium iodide is prepared industrially by methods similar to those used for sodium bromide, but does not have large-scale industrial uses. Sodium iodide is used to some extent for the wet extraction of silver, in iodized table salt for the prevention of goiter, in animal feeds to prevent hoofrot, for photographic chemicals, and in the manufacture of organic chemicals. It has also been used in cloud seeding for artificial rainmaking. The price of USP sodium iodide is $2.98/lb in 25-lb drums (as of April 1969).

Sodium iodide USP XVII contains not less than 99% and not more than 101.5% NaI, calculated on the anhydrous basis. It is used interchangeably with potassium iodide as a therapeutic agent, except where sodium ion is contraindicated.

Intravenous sodium iodide solutions (with additives) have formerly been used for the treatment of thyroid, acute gouty arthritis, acute thyrotoxicosis, severe paroxysms of asthma, acute rheumatic fever, degenerative and rheumatoid arthritis, myalgias, and neuralgias. However, these solutions were omitted from the *National Formulary* XII, which indicates that their therapeutic value has not been satisfactorily demonstrated.

Veterinary uses include the treatment of horses, cattle, sheep, swine, and dogs for hyperplastic fibrous lesions, chronic bronchitis, botryomycosis, lymphangitis, goiter, and actinomycosis.

Bibliography

"Sodium Halides" treated in *ECT* 1st ed. under "Sodium Compounds," Vol. 12, pp. 603–604, by J. A. Brink, Jr., Purdue University.

F. N. ANDERSON
Mallinckrodt Chemical Works

SODIUM NITRATE, $NaNO_3$, occurs in nature, usually in deposits associated with sodium chloride, sodium sulfate, and other salts. Although natural sodium nitrate may be found in many parts of the world, by far the largest deposit is located in northern Chile; therefore, the material is also known in commerce as Chile saltpeter or Chile nitrate.

Sodium nitrate is a colorless solid, moderately hygroscopic, very soluble in water and in liquid ammonia. It crystallizes from water in the trigonal or rhombic system with a body-centered lattice containing two molecules of $NaNO_3$ per unit cell. For crystalline sodium nitrate specific gravity is 2.257 at 20°C; refractive index, n_D^{20} is 1.5874; heat of formation, $\Delta H_f^{298°}$ is $-111,540$ cal/mole; specific heat, 0.262 cal/g at 25°C (see Table 1); melting point, 306.3°C; and latent heat of fusion, -5355 cal/mole at 310°C.

Table 1. Specific Heat of Sodium Nitrate (1)

Temp, °C	Sp heat, cal/g	Temp, °C	Sp heat, cal/g
−50	0.224	100	0.294
0	0.249	200	0.330
25	0.262	250	0.359
50	0.270	300 (molten)	0.430

When dissolving in water, crystalline sodium nitrate has a heat of solution of −4889 cal/mole at 25°C. The solubility in water and the specific gravity of the saturated solution at various temperatures are shown in Table 2.

Table 2. Solubility of Sodium Nitrate in Water (1,1a,2)

Temp, °C	Wt % $NaNO_3$ in satd soln	Sp gr of satd soln, d_4^t
−18.1 (eutectic)	38.07	
−9.9	39.80	
0	42.23	1.3532
10	44.54	1.3683
20	46.80	1.3834
30	49.02	1.3986
40	51.20	1.4139
60	55.48	1.4447
80	59.67	1.4759
100	63.77	1.5074
110	65.80	1.5231
119 (bp)	67.62	1.5374
136	71.50	

When molten sodium nitrate is heated, it begins to decompose at 380°C. At 400–600°C, it gives off N_2 and O_2. NO appears at 700°C. The rate of decomposition increases with the temperature. From 775 to 865°C, small amounts of NO_2 and N_2O are also formed. The residue of the decomposition is Na_2O.

The Chile Nitrate

The natural sodium nitrate deposits of Chile were known from the early days of the Spanish occupation of the region. Later explorations revealed that these nitrate deposits occur in the northern part of the country, mostly along the eastern slopes of the coastal range of mountains and at elevations of 4000–7500 ft above sea level, and that they extend some 400 miles in the north-south direction and are 5–40 miles wide. They are 1–4 ft below an over-burden of sandy soil. The ore body varies in thickness from 0.5 to 14 ft. The ore beds are not continuous, and the composition is far from uniform. The composition varies considerably, especially from top to bottom, in the same ore body. The ore reserve is so immense that the total recoverable sodium nitrate has never been estimated, except for some selected areas no more than a few percent of the total area of the ore deposits.

The ores from the Chile nitrate deposits are of two grades: the high grade is called *caliche*, and the low grade is called *costra*. The costra generally occurs immediately below the caliche, with or without stratified demarcation. In the early days of mining, only the rich ore was taken by handpicking. Therefore the ore sent to the processing plant was mostly caliche which was reported to contain as much as 28–50% sodium nitrate. A typical sample of caliche in those days gave the following analysis:

Component	Percent	Component	Percent
$NaNO_3$	17.6	$CaSO_4$	5.5
NaCl	16.1	$MgSO_4$	3.9
Na_2SO_4	6.5	clay, sand, and insolubles	45.5
$NaIO_3$	0.11	undetermined, including	
$Na_2B_4O_7$	0.94	water	2.32
KNO_3	1.3	total	100.00
$KClO_4$	0.23		

When the primitive method of mining was used, even the costra showed a sodium nitrate content of 12–13%. As soon as the modern method of mining was introduced, using large power shovels, it was no longer practical to separate the caliche from the costra. Indeed, some of the barren earth was also scooped up along with the ore. Thus the average sodium nitrate content of the run-of-mine ore was only 8–9% and that of the ore going through the leaching plant was not higher than 8%. The situation remains unchanged to the present time.

Since there is only one grade of ore going through the processing plant, it is simply called caliche. The term costra is no longer used around the processing plant. The only distinction made is between the "coarse ore" and the "fines." The fines contain more sodium nitrate than the coarse ore. A typical sample of the fines at Pedro de Valdivia (1967–1968) shows the following analysis:

Component	Percent	Component	Percent
$NaNO_3$	9.25	Ca	2.31
NaCl	5.24	Mg	0.36
Na_2SO_4	15.31	H_2O	1.71
I_2	0.46	Clay, sand and others	
$Na_2B_4O_7$	0.69	(by difference)	64.02
K	0.63	total	100.00
$KClO_4$	0.02		

Commercial exploitation of the Chile nitrate deposits was first suggested by Thaddeus Haenke, a German, in 1809. The first shipment of the extracted sodium nitrate to Europe was made in 1830. From that time on until after the First World War, the Chile sodium nitrate constituted 70–80% of the world production of nitrogen compounds.

Manufacture

The manufacture of sodium nitrate from caliche involves the extraction of sodium nitrate from the ore with water and recovering it from the aqueous solution by crystallization. Following this general procedure small-scale operations were carried out as early as 1813, and continued for many years. Many operators entered the field, and the industry flourished in spite of the primitive methods used. Large-scale production started in 1876 when the Shanks process was put into operation.

The Shanks Process. Starting with a run-of-mine ore in pieces up to 10 in., a single-stage crushing reduces it to 1.5 to 2-in. pieces. The crushed ore is loaded into large steel vats, each holding about 75 tons, and equipped with steam-heating coils. Ten such vats are used in rotation, four of them for leaching in series. The operating cycle, including loading, leaching, washing, and unloading, takes about eight days. The leaching solution mostly consists of the mother liquor from the crystallizing step and contains about 450 g nitrate per liter. As it passes through one vat and then another, it builds up its nitrate content to a final concentration of about 700 g/l. This hot, rich liquor is then withdrawn to the preliminary cooling pan where the temperature drops to within a few degrees above the saturation temperature for $NaNO_3$. At this temperature some of the NaCl crystallizes out. The slimes are allowed to settle after adding a coagulant (eg, wheat flour). The clear liquor is run into the crystallizing pans for $NaNO_3$, where the temperature is allowed to drop to near the atmospheric temperature. After crystallization the mother liquor is withdrawn and pumped to the last stage of the leaching cycle. The crystals are piled up in a small area in the crystallizing pan to allow the mother liquor to drain away. Then the crystals are transferred to the drying floor where the remaining mother liquor dries up so that the final product is a crystalline material containing the following:

Component	Percent	Component	Percent
$NaNO_3$ (including up to 2% KNO_3)	95.5	other salts	1.00
NaCl	0.75	H_2O	2.3
Na_2SO_4	0.45	total	100.00

The Shanks process recovers about 60% of the sodium nitrate contained in the ore, and the tailings contain 5–8% nitrates. The fuel consumption is about 0.154 ton fuel per ton of $NaNO_3$ produced and shipped. At present, the Shanks process accounts for only about 1% of the total sodium nitrate produced in Chile.

The Guggenheim Process. It was well known even in the early days that the Shanks process was rather inefficient, both in extraction and in fuel consumption. With the aim of improving the efficiency, the Guggenheim brothers in the early 1920s developed the low-temperature leaching process, based on two important principles which they discovered, ie, (a) if the leaching of caliche is conducted at a sufficiently low temperature (eg, 40°C) only sodium nitrate is extracted, leaving behind most of the impurities such as sodium sulfate and sodium chloride in the slimes, and (b) if the leaching solution at the start contains certain "protective" salts, such as $CaSO_4$, $MgSO_4$, and K_2SO_4, the sparingly soluble double salt $NaNO_3 \cdot Na_2SO_4$ in the caliche is broken up and, therefore, more sodium nitrate may be extracted.

The Guggenheim brothers started their first large-scale operation at Maria Elena, Chile, in 1926, with a capacity of 520,000 metric tons of sodium nitrate per year followed by a larger plant at Pedro de Valdivia, which was completed in 1931 and rated at 750,000 metric tons per year.

According to the Guggenheim process (3,8) (Figs. 1 and 2) the run-of-mine ore, in sizes ranging from fragments to pieces weighing from 3 to 5 tons, is delivered by rail cars to the processing plant. There the ore is crushed by three stages of crushers to a size of ⅜–¾ inch. The crushed ore is screened to separate the undersize material, which normally amounts to about 20% of the total quantity of ore delivered to the

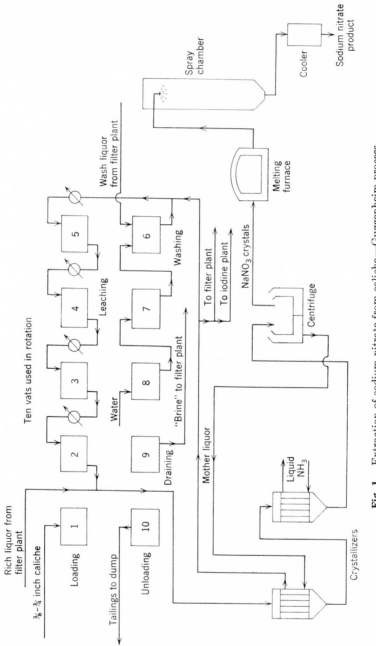

Fig. 1.   Extraction of sodium nitrate from caliche—Guggenheim process.

processing plant. The clean $\frac{3}{8}$–$\frac{3}{4}$ in. ore is treated in the leaching plant and the undersize material is ground to −20 mesh, which are the fines. The fines are treated in the filter plant.

The Leaching Plant (Fig. 1). The crushed and screened caliche is loaded by belt conveyors into one of ten large, open-air concrete vats. At Pedro de Valdivia these vats measure 110 × 160 ft by 20 ft deep and hold more than 10,000 tons of caliche each. Each vat is provided with bottom outlets for liquids, under a bed of broken stones covered with coco matting, to ensure the discharge of clear solutions and wash liquors. The vats are operated in rotation, namely, while one vat is being loaded, four vats filled with caliche are being leached in series, three vats containing leached caliche are being washed in series, one vat is being drained, and one vat is being unloaded.

The leaching solution is made up by combining the mother liquor from the crystallizing plant with the strong wash liquor from the washing cycle, and it normally has a nitrate content of 350 g/l as $NaNO_3$. The leaching solution is heated to a temperature of 40°C by heat exchange with hot water from the cooling systems of the Diesel power plant and the ammonia compressors for refrigeration. The warm leaching solution is pumped to the top of the vat which is at the last stage of the leaching cycle, percolates downward through the crushed caliche, and runs out through the bottom outlets. The dissolving of sodium nitrate from caliche has a cooling effect upon the leaching solution. In order to maintain a temperature of 40°C throughout the cycle, the underflow from one vat is reheated before it is pumped to the next vat. The leaching solution extracts sodium nitrate from the caliche as it advances through the four stages of the leaching cycle; the last stage is the vat containing the freshly loaded caliche. When it comes out of the latter vat, the leaching solution has built up its nitrate content to about 450 g/l, after a contact time of approx 40 hr; it is then sent to the crystallizing plant.

After leaching, the caliche residue in the vats (by now the bulk has shrunk appreciably) is washed by displacement in a cycle comprising three stages or vats. Fresh water is used for washing only at the last stage of the washing cycle, and even then it is used sparingly, or just enough to make up for the mechanical losses, losses through evaporation from open tanks, and for portions of solutions diverted for the recovery of by-products, such as iodine. The wash liquor from the last-stage washing is used in the second-stage washing; and that from the second-stage washing is used for the first-stage washing.

After washing the caliche residue is allowed to drain. The drainings, called "brine," are sent to the filter plant for use as washing liquor.

The operating schedule of the leaching plant is such that, with the ten vats used in rotation, every ten hours one vat is loaded while another is being unloaded. The unloading is done with 5-ton clam-shell grab buckets from a travelling gantry crane. The caliche residue, which contains 0.75–1.5% unrecovered nitrate, is taken by rail cars to the disposal area.

The Filter Plant (Fig. 2). The fines of caliche are produced during the crushing operation. If they were left with the crushed ore, they would interfere with the normal flow of liquids during leaching and washing operations. Therefore, they are removed by screening and treated separately in the filter plant. There the caliche fines are mixed with mother liquor containing about 350 g nitrate per liter which comes from the crystallizing plant, but is heated to 55–60°C. The mixing ratio is about two tons of fines to 1 m³ of mother liquor. The mixture is air-agitated to form a slurry and

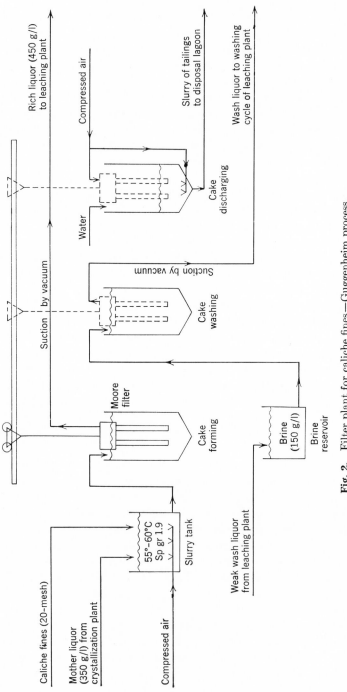

Fig. 2.   Filter plant for caliche fines—Guggenheim process.

filtered with Moore-type vacuum filters. These filters at the Chilean nitrate plants are very big units; each filter basket has forty canvas-covered filter leaves, each leaf is 9 ft wide by 7 ft from the header to the lower edge. The filter leaves are spaced 6 in. centers. A filter basket has about 6000 sq ft filter area, and when fully loaded with cake, weighs more than 45 tons.

The filtrate from the Moore filters contain about 450 g nitrate per liter. It is sent to the leaching plant where it is combined with the rich leaching liquor coming from the vat which is at the first stage (freshly charged caliche) of the leaching cycle. When the cake on the filter leaves has built up to about 1.5 in. in thickness, the filter basket is transferred by a 55-ton overhead travelling crane from the cake-forming tank to the washing tank, where the cake on the filter leaves is washed by displacement with brine taken from the leaching plant (see Figs. 1 and 2). The brine is maintained at a concentration of about 150 g nitrate per liter. This amount of nitrate and other salts in the brine are necessary to minimize the dissolution of unwanted salts from the cake. For the same reason fresh water is not used for washing the cake. If fresh water were used, it would cause holes to form in the cake, thereby impairing the washing efficiency. However, the omission of the fresh-water wash also has a disadvantage, namely, that the cake later discharged as tailings retains a somewhat higher percentage, of residual nitrate than the tailings from the leaching of the coarse ore. A part of this residual nitrate comes from the last amount of brine which vacuum drying fails to remove.

After washing, the filter basket is transferred from the washing tank to the drying tank (not shown in Fig. 2) where the washed cake is sucked dry by vacuum. Then the filter basket is transferred to the discharging tank, where the cake is pushed off the filter leaves by compressed air blown through the header. When the cake drops to the bottom of the tank, it is sluiced with water and pumped to the disposal lagoon.

The Crystallizing Plant. The rich liquor from the leaching plant and the filtrate from the filter plant are combined. The combined liquor contains about 450 g sodium nitrate per liter and has a temperature of about 40°C. It is sent to the crystallizers which comprise twenty vertical shell-and-tube units in series with the rich liquor inside the tubes.

At Maria Elena, each of the crystallizer units contains 500 tubes, 3 in. in diameter and 16 ft long. Mother liquor runs through fourteen of the twenty units on the shell side in countercurrent relationship with the rich liquor running through the inside of the tubes. Liquid ammonia runs through the shell side of the other six units. As sodium nitrate crystallizes out of the rich liquor, some crystals adhere to walls of the tubes. Mechanical scrapers are provided for occasional cleaning of the inside of the tubes. A similar but somewhat larger installation is used at Pedro de Valdivia.

For the first fourteen units, the coolant is the mother liquor from the centrifuges at a temperature of about 10° C. For the other six units the coolant is liquid ammonia. As the rich liquor passes through the series of these units, its temperature drops from the initial 40°C to a final reading below 10°C, and sodium nitrate crystals are formed in the liquor. In order to minimize the tendency of crystals to adhere to the tube walls, the rich liquor is sent through the tubes at a rapid rate. At the exits of the ammonia-cooled tubes, the liquor and crystals come out as a slurry with the size of the crystals about 48-mesh. This slurry is pumped to a bank of twenty-four centrifuges with baskets measuring 48 in. in diameter by 24 in. deep, each having a capacity of approx 0.5 ton every 7–8 min. After a light rinse with pure water, the crystals are discharged from the centrifuges. The discharged crystals are pure white and contain 3.0–3.5% moisture.

The Graining Plant. The sodium nitrate crystals from the centrifuges are charged into oil-fired reverberatory furnaces and melted. The molten sodium nitrate at 325°C is pumped to the top of the spray chamber more than 100 ft in height, and through ⅝-in. nozzles. The spray chamber at Pedro de Valdivia measures 100 × 250 ft by 115 ft high. The spray of molten sodium nitrate solidifies in the form of prills, up to ⅛ in. in diameter, before reaching the bottom of the spray chamber. From there the prills are conveyed on belts to the screens where the oversize and undersize materials are separated and returned to the melting furnaces.

The screened prills, 20 to 8 mesh, still quite hot (about 100°C), are sent through a bank of vertical shell-and-tube type coolers, each 6 ft diam by 10 ft high, with the prills flowing by gravity through the tubes, and cold mother liquor circulating around the tubes. By the time they come out of the coolers the prills have a temperature below 35°C. They are transported by belt conveyors to the rail cars which take them to the storage silos at the shipping port as the finished product which normally has the following composition:

Composition	Percent
$NaNO_3$	98.5
NaCl	0.85
Na_2SO_4	0.3
$KClO_4$	0.11
others, including moisture	0.24

The Guggenheim process recovers 85–88% of the $NaNO_3$ in the ore with a total fuel consumption of about 0.036 ton of fuel oil per ton of sodium nitrate produced. At present this process accounts for about 99% of the total sodium nitrate produced in Chile.

Linked with the Chilean nitrate operations, iodine is recovered from caliche by working over the mother liquor from the sodium nitrate crystallization step. In recent years Chilean iodine constitutes about 50% of the world iodine production.

Recently a process has been developed to recover potassium nitrate and other salts from caliche. This process (8) comprises a secondary leaching with plain water given to the caliche residue, concentrating the leaching solution thus obtained by solar evaporation, and crystallizing the potassium-rich salts by refrigeration. After that, other salts are recovered by natural crystallization.

Synthetic Processes. In the early days of fixation of atmospheric nitrogen, when the arc process was used in Norway to produce NO from air, the effluent from the arc furnaces was cooled to about 50°C, the NO was oxidized by the same air to NO_2, and the NO_2 was absorbed in an aqueous solution of soda ash which reacted with NO_2 to form both sodium nitrate and sodium nitrite in the solution:

$$Na_2CO_3 + 2 NO_2 \rightarrow NaNO_3 + NaNO_2 + CO_2$$

Then air was blown through the solution to oxidize the $NaNO_2$ to $NaNO_3$, after which the solution was concentrated by evaporation, and sodium nitrate was recovered by crystallization.

Later when nitric acid was manufactured from synthetic ammonia at relatively low cost, synthetic sodium nitrate was made from it either through the reaction between nitric acid and soda ash, or by direct absorption of nitrogen dioxide in an aqueous solution of sodium carbonate (see equation above). The sodium nitrate–nitrite solution is then heated with excess nitric acid to convert the nitrite to nitrate, and the NO thus produced is recycled to the nitric acid plant.

During the late 1930s when there appeared in the United States a need for a process of producing chlorine without the accompanying caustic soda, the so-called "nitrosyl chloride" was developed (4). According to this process sodium chloride and concentrated (63–67%) nitric acid are reacted to produce chlorine and sodium nitrate as coproducts, and nitrosyl chloride, NOCl, or dinitrogen tetroxide as by-products according to the following equations (5):

$$3 \text{ NaCl} + 4 \text{ HNO}_3 \rightarrow \text{Cl}_2 + 3 \text{ NaNO}_3 + 2 \text{ H}_2\text{O} + \text{NOCl}$$
$$2 \text{ NOCl} + \text{O}_2 \rightarrow \text{N}_2\text{O}_4 + \text{Cl}_2$$

During World War II and for several years thereafter, the nitrosyl chloride process was used commercially in the United States (see Vol. 1, pp. 677 and 703). However, this process was discontinued when it became no longer profitable in commercial operation.

Production and Consumption

The world production of sodium nitrate by the synthetic processes is very small compared to that of natural sodium nitrate. In Chile, which is the major producing country, the annual production of natural sodium nitrate reached a peak of 2,715,000 metric tons during 1916–1917, but production has been declining, especially since 1958, and in recent years it has decreased from 1,350,000 metric tons in 1959 to about 945,000 metric tons in 1966 (6). The decline is chiefly due to unfavorable competition with the synthetic nitrogen-containing products, such as ammonium nitrate and urea, which have become available in many countries and also in larger and larger quantities and at lower costs per unit of contained nitrogen.

The same situation exists in Egypt except on a much smaller scale. About 1940, Egypt was extracting sodium nitrate from 113,000 metric tons of ore (containing up to 7% $NaNO_3$) in the Qena district (7). The annual production decreased steadily; in recent years it declined from 6062 metric tons in 1962 to 4000 metric tons in 1966 (6).

In the United States the consumption of sodium nitrate as a fertilizer for direct application has been decreasing. In 1967, it was 200,685 short tons. The consumption of sodium nitrate in the preparation of mixed fertilizer is very small. For the manufacture of explosives, the latest statistics (1964) show a consumption of about 53,000 short tons per year. Other uses of sodium nitrate probably add up to 50,000 short tons per year. Thus, the current (1967) consumption of sodium nitrate in the United States may be estimated at about 310,000 short tons per year. Practically all of that amount is imported from Chile.

In Chile the consumption of sodium nitrate in recent years has been about 112,-000 metric tons per year (1966). With a production of about 945,000 metric tons, the surplus, which is exported to more than thirty countries, amounts to nearly 85% of the production.

Due to the tremendous build up of synthetic ammonia facilities all over the world in recent years, the position of sodium nitrate has fallen drastically. At present sodium nitrate accounts for less than 1% of the world production of nitrogen compounds, based on their nitrogen content.

In the United States, the current market price of domestic as well as imported sodium nitrate is \$44.00/short ton, bulk, carloads, fob works, and Atlantic or Gulf warehouses. This price has been unchanged since 1960.

Table 3. Typical Analyses of Technical-Grade Sodium Nitrate

Component	Chilean sodium nitrate[a]	Synthetic sodium nitrate[b]
$NaNO_3$	98.502 (by difference)	99.4–99.5 (assay)
water-insoluble matter	0.039	0.005
CaO	trace	0.005
MgO	0.167	0.001
Al_2O_3	trace	0.0004
Cu		0.00002
Mn		0.00003
$NaNO_2$	0	0.0012
NaCl	0.30	0.15
$Na_2B_4O_7$	0.046	
Na_2SO_4	0.299	0.30
KNO_3	0.223	
$KClO_4$		0.009
$KClO_4$ (including $KClO_3$)	0.038	
KIO_3 (including $KBrO_3$)	0.030	
Fe	trace	
SiO_2		0.003
H_2O	0.09	0.02

[a] Data furnished by Chilean Nitrate Sales Corp., New York, N.Y., December, 1968.
[b] Data furnished by Olin Mathieson Chemical Corp., December, 1968.

Table 4. Specification and Typical Analysis of USP Reagent-Grade Sodium Nitrate

Component	USP specification,[a] max	Typical analysis[b]
color	clear, colorless	clear, colorless
water-insoluble matter	0.005	0.005
Ca, Mg, R_2O_3 precipitates[c]	0.005	0.0003
K		0.0001
Cl	0.001	<0.001
heavy metals (Pb, etc)	0.0005	0.0001
Fe	0.0003	0.0001
PO_4	0.0005	0.0004
SO_4	0.003	<0.003
iodate and nitrite	0.001	see below
IO_3 (ACS specification)	0.0005	<0.0005
NO_2 (ACS specification)	0.001	<0.001

[a] *U.S. Pharmacopeia*, 17th ed., 1965, Mack Publishing Co., Easton, Pa., p. 1047. The ACS specification, 1968, for sodium nitrate is the same as that for the USP reagent, except for iodate and nitrite, as indicated.
[b] Mallinckrodt Chemical Works, St. Louis, Mo., December, 1968.
[c] R = Al, Fe, or both.

Standards and Specifications

Sodium nitrate as a commercial product is sold in two principal grades: the technical grade and the reagent grade. The technical grade may be subdivided into the domestic agricultural grade which includes the synthetic sodium nitrate, and the imported commercial grade which includes the Chilean nitrate. There is no official standard for the technical grade. Each producer or manufacturer generally sets up his own standards and adheres to them. These proprietary standards along with typical analyses of the products are usually available upon request. Examples of the analyses of the technical-grade sodium nitrate are shown in Table 3.

The reagent-grade sodium nitrate is officially specified in the *U.S. Pharmacopeia*, and by the American Chemical Society. These specifications are given in Table 4.

Toxicity

Although sodium nitrate was formerly used in medicine as a diuretic and for dysentery, large doses of it are toxic. However, when used in curing meat the sodium nitrate is almost completely converted to harmless sodium compounds at the end of the curing period. In the drinking water for chickens, the limit of tolerance is 300 ppm. When sodium nitrate exceeds 300 ppm it shows an adverse effect upon the growth rate of chickens (9).

Uses

By far the largest use of sodium nitrate is as a nitrogenous fertilizer. The next largest use is as a component of dynamite (see Vol. 8, p. 638). An appreciable quantity of concentrated nitric acid is still made by the classical method of reacting sodium nitrate with sulfuric acid. The other industrial uses of sodium nitrate are as raw material for potassium nitrate, in leather dressing, and in penicillin culture. In the molten state sodium nitrate mixed with sodium nitrite is used in the heat treatment of aluminum alloys.

Bibliography

"Sodium Nitrate" treated in *ECT* 1st ed. under "Sodium Compounds," Vol. 12, pp. 605–606, by J. A. Brink, Jr., Purdue University.

1. *International Critical Tables*, Vol. 3, McGraw-Hill Book Co., Inc., New York, 1928, p. 105.
1a. *Ibid.*, Vol. 5, 1929, pp. 100, 106.
2. A. Seidell, *Solubilities*, Vol. 2, 4th ed., Am. Chem. Soc., Washington, D.C., 1965, pp. 1066, 1069–1070.
3. E. S. Freed, *Anales Congr. Panam. Minas Geol., 1st Congr. Santiago des Chile* **5,** 2046–2055 (1942); *Chem. Abstr.* **45,** 6886h (1951).
4. Can. Pat. 363,800 (Feb. 2, 1937), U.S. Pats. 2,130,519 (Sept. 20, 1938), 2,138,016 (Nov. 29, 1938), 2,181,559 (Nov. 28, 1939), H. A. Beekhuis, Jr. (to Solvay Process Co.).
5. M. F. Fogler, "The Salt Process for Chlorine Manufacture," in J. S. Sconce, ed., *Chlorine, Its Manufacture, Properties and Uses*, Reinhold Publishing Corp., New York, 1962, pp. 235–249.
6. *Minerals Yearbook 1966*, Vols. 1–2, U.S. Dept. of Interior, Bureau of Mines, U.S. Govt. Printing Office, Washington, D.C., 1967, p. 986.
7. D. A. Pantony, in J. W. Mellor, ed., *Comprehensive Treatise on Inorganic and Theoretical Chemistry*, Vol. 2, Suppl. 2, John Wiley & Sons, Inc., New York, 1961, p. 1206.

8. H. L. Tower, Jr., and H. C. Brewer, "Natural Chilean Nitrate of Soda, Production and Use in Agriculture," in V. Sauchelli, ed., *Fertilizer Nitrogen—Its Chemistry and Technology*, Reinhold Publishing Corp., New York, 1964, p. 315–330.

9. A. W. Adams, R. J. Emerick, and C. W. Carlson, *Poultry Sci.* **45**(6), 1215–1222 (1966).

L. C. PAN

Chemical Construction Corporation

SODIUM NITRITE, $NaNO_2$, seldom occurs in nature. Synthetic sodium nitrite is a colorless or yellowish transparent solid, very hygroscopic, soluble in water and in liquid ammonia. It crystallizes from water in body-centered orthorhombic crystals with two molecules to each unit cell.

Sodium nitrite has a sp gr of 2.168 at 0°C; mp, 284°C; heat of formation, $\Delta H_f = -85,900$ cal/mole.

Crystalline sodium nitrite shows a transition point at 160–162°C, with a heat of transition of about 285 cal/mole. This transition point manifests itself in the physical properties with respect to changes in temperature, such as thermal expansion, electric conductivity, sp heat, and piezoelectric properties.

The specific heat of sodium nitrate increases with temperature, from about 0.235 cal/g at 60°C to about 0.277 cal/g at 200°C, with a steep peak value of about 0.548 cal/g at 161°C corresponding to the transition point (see Fig. 1).

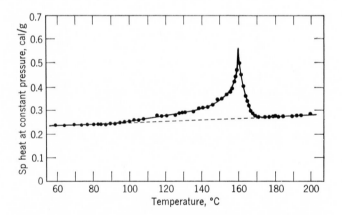

Fig. 1. Specific heat-temperature curve for sodium nitrite (1).

The thermal expansion of sodium nitrite crystal is anisotropic, being positive along axes a and b, but negative along axis c. All three linear thermal expansion curves show breaks at about 162°C, corresponding to the transition point (1).

Sodium nitrite is not oxidized by air at any appreciable rate at ambient temperature. When heated, it begins to decompose at 320°C, giving off N_2, O_2, and NO, leaving a residue of Na_2O.

When dissolved in water, sodium nitrite has a heat of solution of -3570 cal/mole. The solubility in water is shown in Table 1.

Manufacture

In the early days of nitrogen fixation, when nitric acid was made by oxidizing atmospheric nitrogen in the arc furnace in Norway, sodium nitrite was a by-product.

In the arc furnace, nitric oxide, NO, was formed through a direct combination of nitrogen and oxygen in the air. After cooling the gas to near the ambient temperature, the nitric oxide was further oxidized to form nitrogen dioxide, NO_2. The NO_2 was then absorbed in water to produce a 30% nitric acid by the well-known reaction

$$3\ NO_2 + H_2O \rightleftharpoons 2\ HNO_3 + NO$$

The residual gas containing both NO and NO_2 was scrubbed with a solution of soda ash. Both NO and NO_2 are absorbed and sodium nitrite was formed in the solution:

$$Na_2CO_3 + NO + NO_2 \rightarrow 2\ NaNO_2 + CO_2$$

Of the total nitrogen oxides produced in the arc furnace, about 83.3% was recovered as 30% nitric acid, about 14.7% recovered as sodium nitrite, and about 2% lost in the tail gas.

Table 1.   Solubility of Sodium Nitrite in Water (2)

Temp, °C	% NaNO₂ satd soln	Density of satd soln	Solid phase
−8.7	16.3		ice
−15.2	25.0		ice
−19.5	28.1		ice + $NaNO_2 \cdot \frac{1}{2}H_2O$ (eutectic)
−7.6	37.8		$NaNO_2 \cdot \frac{1}{2}H_2O$
−5.1	41.6		$NaNO_2 + NaNO_2 \cdot \frac{1}{2}H_2O$
0	41.65		$NaNO_2$
+11.9	43.72		$NaNO_2$
15.0	43.7	1.345	$NaNO_2$
20	45.8	1.358	$NaNO_2$
34.08	47.69		
48.77	50.56		$NaNO_2$
56.8	52.00	1.408	$NaNO_2$
64.7	54.07	1.422	$NaNO_2$
79.5	56.95	1.455	$NaNO_2$
99.9	61.5	1.514	$NaNO_2$
103	62.6		$NaNO_2$
108	68.7		$NaNO_2$

The scrubbing solution was used over and over again until nearly all of the sodium carbonate was converted to sodium nitrite. The solution was then treated with enough nitric acid to decompose the remaining sodium carbonate. It was concentrated by evaporation, and the sodium nitrite was recovered by crystallization.

The modern process of making sodium nitrite is very much like the one used in Norway fifty years ago except that the nitrogen oxides are prepared from synthetic ammonia by catalytic air oxidation, using the same kind of apparatus as for making nitric acid. But the departure starts from the oxidation of the nitric oxide. For making sodium nitrite, the supply of secondary air is carefully controlled to give a NO/NO₂ molar ratio such as to give minimum contamination by $NaNO_3$ in the product. The gas mixture is then treated with a saturated solution of sodium carbonate in an absorption column through which the sodium carbonate solution is circulated repeatedly until nearly all of the sodium carbonate is converted to sodium nitrite, care being taken that the pH value of the circulating solution does not go below 8.3, so as to minimize the formation of sodium bicarbonate.

When the conversion is complete, or very nearly so, the solution is withdrawn and treated with enough nitric acid to decompose the unconverted sodium carbonate. After that, the solution is concentrated by evaporation and cooled to crystallize the sodium nitrite. The small amount of sodium nitrate carried down with the nitrite is removed by recrystallization. However, if sodium bicarbonate should be present, it is more difficult to remove and often remains in the final product as an impurity.

The contamination of sodium nitrite by sodium bicarbonate can be completely avoided if the starting solution is prepared with sodium hydroxide instead of sodium carbonate. However, for economic reasons, this is not now done in the production of commercial grades of sodium nitrite. For producing sodium nitrite of higher purity, recrystallization is repeated until the desired purity is obtained. Three or four recrystallizations from water give a purity of 99.33%, and an additional recrystallization from 80% ethanol gives a purity of 99.7%.

Prices.   Sodium nitrite is currently made in the United States by some of the leading chemical manufacturers. The market prices (Jan. 12, 1968) of USP grade are bags, carloads works, \$9.65/100 lb, and drums, carloads, works, freight equalized, \$9.90/100 lb.

Standards and Specifications

Sodium nitrite as a commercial product is available in two principal grades: the USP grade and the reagent grade. Both grades are specified to contain 97.0% $NaNO_2$, minimum. These specifications and the typical analyses of the two grades are given in Tables 2 and 3, respectively.

Table 2.   USP Specification, Representative Commercial Standard, and Typical Analyses of Sodium Nitrite, %

Properties	USP[a] specification	Representative commercial standard[b]	Typical analyses[c] A	B
color	white, slightly yellow	white, slightly yellow	white, slightly yellow	
assay (dry basis)	97.0, min 101.0, max	97.0, min 100.5, max	98.4	99.30
water-insoluble matter				0.0002
$NaNO_3$				0.3
NaCl				0.02
Na_2CO_3				0.3
Na_2SO_4				0.003
As		0.0003 max	<0.0003	
heavy metals (Pb, etc)	0.002	0.001 max	<0.001	
Fe				0.00027
H_2O	1.0	0.250	0.03	0.08
solubility	1 g in 1.5 ml H_2O		passes USP test	

[a] *U. S. Pharmacopeia*, 17th ed., 1965, Mack Publishing Co., Easton, Pa., pp. 631–632.
[b] Mallinckrodt Chemical Works, St. Louis, Mo., December, 1968.
[c] Data from two manufacturers, respectively, December, 1968.

Table 3. Specification and Typical Analysis of USP Reagent-Grade Sodium Nitrite, %

Properties	USP reagent specification[a], max	Typical analysis[b]
color	white, or slightly yellow	
assay (dry basis)	97.0, min	99.8
water-insoluble matter	0.010	0.008
Ca	0.010	<0.010
K	0.005	<0.001
Cl	0.005	0.004
heavy metals (Pb, etc)	0.001	<0.0008
Fe	0.001	<0.001
SO$_4$	0.010	0.006

[a] *U.S. Pharmacopeia*, 17th ed., 1965, Mack Publishing Co., Easton, Pa., p. 1047. The ACS reagent specification, 1968, for sodium nitrite is the same as that for the USP reagent.

[b] Mallinckrodt Chemical Works, St. Louis, Mo., December, 1968.

Toxicity

Sodium nitrite is mildly toxic. For internal use as a vasodilator, a normal dose ranges from 15 to 60 mg. An overdose would cause flushing, headache, and gastric distress. Experiments with chickens show that the limit of tolerance is 100 ppm in the drinking water. If sodium nitrite is in the range 50–200 ppm in drinking water, it slows down the growth rate of chickens (2).

When sodium nitrite is properly used in curing meat, the microorganisms in the meat reduce it to nitrogen gas and harmless sodium compounds, so that at the end of the curing period, practically no residual nitrite is left in the meat, or the amount left is considerably lower than the tolerance limit, about 100 mg NaNO$_2$ per kg body weight per day (3).

Where the worker's bare skin is exposed to sodium nitrite solutions, the tolerance limit is 1.5% NaNO$_2$ in water. Stronger solutions, even those containing 2.0–2.5% NaNO$_2$, cause inflammation of the skin and pustular eruptions. The more severe cases involve insomnia, headache, rapid fatigue, and loss of appetite (4).

Uses

Sodium nitrite is used in the manufacture of diazo dyes, nitroso compounds, and other organic compounds. It is also used as a corrosion inhibitor, in medicine, in photography, in bleaching natural fibers, and in the dyeing and printing of textiles. It is used in fixing the color of meat and meat products. When mixed with sodium nitrate in the molten state, sodium nitrite is used in the heat treatment of light metals and alloys. The mixture of molten sodium nitrite and potassium nitrate is used as a heat-transfer medium (5).

Bibliography

"Sodium Nitrite" treated in *ECT* 1st ed. under "Sodium Compounds," Vol. 12, p. 606, by J. A. Brink, Jr., Purdue University.

1. S. Nomura, *J. Phys. Soc. Japan*, **16** (7), 1352–1357 (1961).
2. A. W. Adams, R. J. Emerick, and C. W. Carlson, *Poultry Sci.*, **45** (6), 1215–1222 (1966).

3. H. Druckrey, D. Steinhoff, H. Beuthner, H. Schneider, and P. Klaerner, *Arzneimittel-Forsch.* (in German) **13**, 320–323 (1963).

4. R. A. Nishchii, *Gigiena Truda i Profess. Zabolevaniya*, **4**(4), 50–52 (1960); *Chem Abstr.*, **54**, 23122f (1960).

5. W. S. Kirst, W. M. Nagle, and J. B. Castner, *Trans. Am. Inst. Chem. Engrs* **.36**, 371–394 (1940).

L. C. Pan
Chemical Construction Corporation

SODIUM SULFATES. Commercial forms of sodium sulfate are the anhydrous (Na_2SO_4), the decahydrate ($Na_2SO_4 \cdot 10H_2O$), and sodium hydrogen sulfate ($NaHSO_4$). Several other phases occur in the system Na_2SO_4–H_2SO_4. See Figure 1.

Properties

Some properties of the more important phases are given in Table 1. Figure 2 shows solubilities in the system Na_2SO_4–H_2O at various temperatures. Supersaturation of solutions is common and there are metastable extensions of the curves beyond the transition points. The solubility when the solution is simultaneously saturated with NaCl is also shown, because of the industrial importance of this condition. Figure 2 shows two isotherms of the system Na_2SO_4–H_2SO_4–H_2O. Figure 3 shows two isotherms of the system Na_2SO_4–$NaCl$–H_2O. The diagram in Figure 4 shows phase relations in the system Na_2SO_4–H_2SO_4.

Table 1. Properties of Sodium Sulfates

	Sodium sulfate		Sodium hydrogen sulfate
Properties	Anhydrous	Decahydrate	
formula	Na_2SO_4	$Na_2SO_4 \cdot 10H_2O$	$NaHSO_4$
specific gravity	2.698	1.464	2.742
heat of formation, kcal/g-mole	−333.5	−1033.9	−269.4
heat of solution, 18°C, cal evolved/g-mole	280	−18740	1740
heat of transition, 190–210°C, cal/g-mole	2587		
heat of fusion, 884°C, cal/g-mole	5670		
heat of dehydration, 50°C, cal/g-mole		59	

Na_2SO_4 has a significant vapor pressure, 0.015 mm Hg, at its melting point, 1620°F; at 2500°F, its vapor pressure is 1 mm Hg. When pure it can be volatilized, but common impurities (silica, alumina, iron oxide) lead to decomposition around 2000°F. Varying proportions of SO_2, SO_3, O_2, and Na_2O are formed. If carbon is present at about 1800°F, Na_2S or SO_2 is the main product, depending on the amount of air. A similar reduction with hydrogen can give—at about 1200°F, with one of the above catalysts—H_2S, Na_2S, or Na_2SO_3

The decahydrate melts incongruently near 90°F. Evaporation above this temperature gives the anhydrous crystals.

$NaHSO_4$ has a considerably lower melting point than Na_2SO_4 (Fig. 4). At higher temperatures (500–600°F) it forms the pyrosulfate:

$$2 \, NaHSO_4 \rightarrow Na_2S_2O_7 + H_2O$$

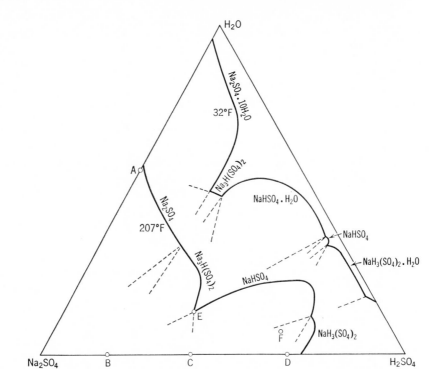

Fig. 1. Solubilities of Na$_2$SO$_4$–H$_2$SO$_4$ mixtures. LEGEND: A, Na$_2$SO$_4$.10H$_2$O; B, Na$_3$H(SO$_4$)$_2$; C, NaHSO$_4$; D, NaH$_3$(SO$_4$)$_2$; E, NaHSO$_4$.H$_2$O; F, NaH$_3$(SO$_4$)$_2$.H$_2$O.

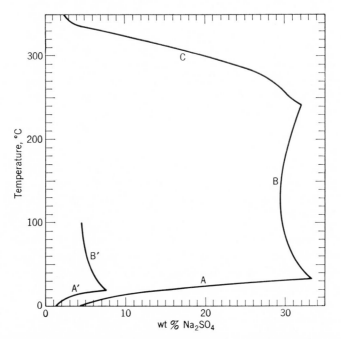

Fig. 2. Solubility of Na$_2$SO$_4$ (under pressure for the higher temperatures). LEGEND: A, solid phase: Glauber's salt, Na$_2$SO$_4$.10H$_2$O; B, solid phase: anhydrous rhombic Na$_2$SO$_4$; C, solid phase: anhydrous monoclinic Na$_2$SO$_4$; A′, B′, simultaneously saturated with NaCl.

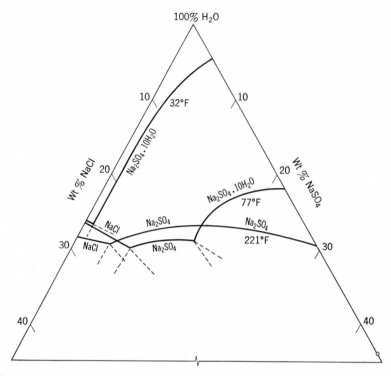

Fig. 3. System Na_2SO_4–$NaCl$–H_2O.

At still higher temperatures (ca 800°F) the pyrosulfate decomposes:

$$Na_2S_2O_7 \rightarrow Na_2SO_4 + SO_3$$

$NaHSO_4$ in solution has a moderate acidity corresponding to the dissociation constant of the second hydrogen ion of H_2SO_4.

Na_2SO_4 forms a large number of double salts with compounds frequently found in nature; an example is glauberite, Na_2SO_4–$CaSO_4$.

History

The history of the manufacture of sodium sulfate reflects many of the stages in the emergence of a chemical industry. Glauber, in the course of various preparations which were fundamental in the evolution of chemistry from alchemy, purified (and hydrated) the residue of the reaction:

$$H_2SO_4 + 2\ NaCl \rightarrow Na_2SO_4 + 2\ HCl\ (gas)$$

He also identified it as the same material he separated from the water of curative springs and promoted it widely to the physicians of the time as "Glauber's Miraculous Salt." (It is still in the medical books as a cathartic. The mineralogical name "mirabilite" recalls this earlier time.)

Just before the French Revolution Leblanc used the same reaction to make *salt cake* (impure Na_2SO_4); this was the beginning of the manufacture of an alkali from something other than ashes. In the early Leblanc plants the HCl was vented to the atmosphere in large quantities. Legal restriction of this venting was one of the first

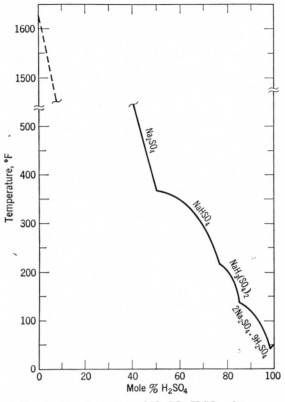

Fig. 4. Freezing points of Na₂SO₄–H₂SO₄ mixtures.

changes in the laissez-faire system of the early Industrial Revolution. Subsequently, uses for the HCl developed and increased to the point where the disposal of the co-product salt cake become a serious problem. This was accentuated by the decrease in salt cake consumption as the Solvay soda process displaced the Leblanc. Still later the demand for HCl from salt cake decreased because HCl became more readily available from electrolytic chlorine and hydrogen and from the chlorination of hydro-carbons. The resulting decrease in salt cake production was, perversely, accompanied by increasing demand from the developing sulfate paper process.

The fluctuations in the commercialization of salt cake were also affected by varia-tions in the nitric acid industry. Nitric acid was for a long time made by the reaction

$$H_2SO_4 + NaNO_3 \rightarrow NaHSO_4 + HNO_3 \text{ (gas)}$$

The product, *niter cake* (NaHSO₄), was used in the production of HCl by the Mannheim process (see Vol. 11, p. 311):

$$NaHSO_4 + NaCl \rightarrow Na_2SO_4 + HCl \text{ (gas)}$$

This was such an improvement, in terms of technique, that the process using H₂SO₄ became obsolete. Then ammonia displaced NaNO₃ as a source of nitric acid and cut the supply of niter cake. But in wartime the higher strength nitric acid conve-niently produced from NaNO₃ is in demand for nitrations and the supply of niter cake rises, resulting in an increase in Mannheim operations and, of course, increased supply of salt cake.

The periods of short supply promote production from other sources. The more viable supplies are, like true salt cake, by-products. Significant amounts of by-product Na_2SO_4 come from the manufacture of rayon, dichromate, and phenol, from the potash industry in Germany, and from the borax production at Searles Lake in California. Na_2SO_4 also comes from natural sources as the sole product; there is commercial production from brines in Texas and lake beds in Wyoming and Saskatchewan, and there are marginal deposits in many arid areas. There are still other sources: One plant uses the Hargreave process (see Vol. 11, p. 312):

$$4\ NaCl + 2\ SO_2 + O_2 + 2\ H_2O \rightarrow 2\ Na_2SO_4 + 4\ HCl\ (gas)$$

Recently the recovery of Na_2SO_4 from sulfate-paper waste was initiated (1). Processes such as the reactions between calcium sulfate and sodium carbonate (2) and between pyrites and salt (3) have been studied. Many schemes for recovering useful materials from ores and brines involve the coproduction of Na_2SO_4, for example, the proposed exploitation of Great Salt Lake brine.

When by-product sources dry up, sodium bisulfate is manufactured by heating Na_2SO_4 with H_2SO_4.

A consequence of the multiplicity of sources is an accumulation of names, as shown:

Sodium Sulfate. *Salt cake*, used generically, but may imply impurities; *Glauber's salt*, the decahydrate, implies purification; *sodium sulfate crystals*, same as Glauber's salt; *anhydrous*, implies manufacture from Glauber's salt; *sodium sulfate exsiccated*, implies pharmacological preparation; *thenardite* (Na_2SO_4), implies mineral origin; *mirabilite* (Glauber's salt), implies mineral origin; *rayon cake*, rayon by-product; *chrome cake*, green dichromate by-product; *phenol cake*, yellow phenol by-product; *kaiseroda*, German potash by-product; *crazy water crystals*, obtained from mineral springs (4); *synthetic salt cake*, a mixture of Na_2CO_3 and molten sulfur, a substitute usable in papermaking (5).

Sodium Bisulfate. *Niter cake*, used generically, implies impurities; *acid sulfate; sodium hydrogen sulfate*.

Supply and Demand

Another consequence of the multiplication of sources is, of course, a considerably increased availability. Figure 5 shows how demand has grown. The increase would

Table 2. Na_2SO_4 Production Capacity (U.S.A.—Active Producers—1968)

Product	Plants	Capacity, 1000 tons/year
by-product		
rayon	15	400
phenol	2	100
dichromate	4	100
other	15	150
subtotal	36	750
Mannheim (HCl coproduct)	6	150
Hargreave (HCl coproduct)	1	120
borax coproduct (brine)	2	450
natural	5	250
total	50	1720

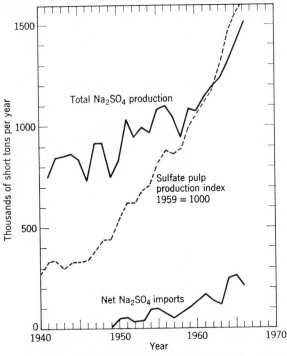

Fig. 5. Sodium sulfate production—U.S.A.

have been much greater if the most important consumer, the sulfate (kraft) paper industry (which has grown remarkably, as Figure 5 shows), had not been able to cut its unit consumption of salt cake to a fraction of its former usage.

By-product production can supply about half the market (Table 2) and production as a coproduct could supply most of the rest. However, coproduct production is responsive to effective demand and the price level is so low that freight costs make the supply location an important factor in the effectiveness of demand. This makes room in the market for considerable production from natural sources and imports (6).

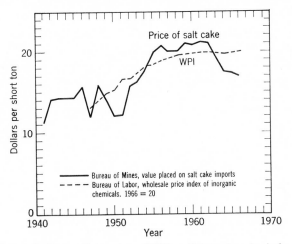

Fig. 6. Sodium sulfate price. (WPI = Wholesale price index.)

Figure 6 shows the moderating effect that the marginal production capacity has had on prices.

The importance of freight costs has reduced the proportion of sodium sulfate which is sold as Glauber's salt to less than 5%; 56% of its weight is the water of crystallization. For some purposes Glauber's salt is preferred because it dissolves easily, but usually its selection is a matter of habit.

Processing

Formerly Glauber's salt was the usual form of sodium sulfate because the easiest purification operation was recrystallization, taking advantage of the large temperature effect in the monohydrate region. (Impurities are precipitated with lime from the hot solution.) In Canadian lake-bed production (and reportedly in Russia) rainfall forms a saturated solution in the summer; the solution is pumped to ponds, and a crop of Glauber's salt is collected in the winter.

In producing anhydrous Na_2SO_4 in conventional evaporators, the reverse solubility curve leads to heavy scaling of the tubes. The addition of ethylene glycol has been extensively investigated (2). Glauber's salt crystals are sometimes dried with hot air in sufficient quantity to prevent a liquid phase. Evaporation of a solution with submerged combustion is an effective technique (8).

Glauber's salt tends to dry in storage, while the anhydrous is somewhat hygroscopic. The latter is sometimes "chemically dried" by adding some Na_2CO_3.

$NaHSO_4$ is normally manufactured by combining Na_2SO_4 and H_2SO_4 anhydrously.

$NaCl$ is a common component of Na_2SO_4 solutions and has a pronounced effect on Na_2SO_4 solubility, as shown in Figure 3. Additional components, of course, make the behavior more complex. The complexity frequently becomes extreme when compounds are present which form double salts with Na_2SO_4. This complexity is discussed in descriptions of Na_2SO_4 production from the brine of Searles Lake, California (9) and its recovery from by-product astrakhanite, $Na_2Mg(SO_4)_2.4H_2O$, and glauberite at the potash works in Germany (2). Notwithstanding its apparent attractiveness, the exploitation of the brine of Great Salt Lake has been delayed by the difficulties caused by the presence of double salts (10,11).

Uses

Table 3 gives the relative sizes of the Na_2SO_4 markets.

The kraft, or sulfate, paper process has advantages which, particularly with recently developed bleaching procedures, have led to its dominance of the paper industry. Sodium sulfide and hydroxide are the active agents, but salt cake is introduced into the recovery and recycle procedure as the most economical method of offsetting losses. It

Table 3. Sodium Sulfate Markets (6,12)

Use	%	Use	%
paper	70	dyeing	3
glass	10	sponge	1
detergents	10	others	6

was pointed out in Figure 5 that salt cake unit consumption has been markedly reduced over the years, but at present is still about 100 lb/ton of paper. A pulping-bleaching system has been announced that promises to cut salt cake consumption to a much lower figure (13).

In glass manufacture Na_2SO_4 is sometimes a cheap source of part of the Na_2O constituent. More commonly, it is used because it speeds the original melting of the charge and, when carbon is added, forms SO_2 which helps to remove other small gas bubbles ("fining"). It also improves the workability of high-silica glass. The SO_2 is, however, a pollution problem. The Na_2SO_4 attacks the furnace refractory, leading not only to extra maintenance, but also to discoloration of the glass by iron. The maintenance aspect is especially important in modern continuous glass furnaces.

Because of its vapor pressure, which is high for a salt, Na_2SO_4 is sometimes a problem in the vent gases from paper mills and glass factories. Airborne microcrystals of Na_2SO_4 have been suspected of contributing to Los Angeles smog (14) and have been found in the fumes from Vesuvius.

In detergents Na_2SO_4 is used as a "builder." These builders are not just a cheap diluent, but also improve detergency through their effect on the colloidal properties of the cleaning system.

In dyeing, Na_2SO_4 (Glauber's salt is liked) is used to "standardize" dyes; this is dilution to a standard potency. In the actual dyebath $NaHSO_4$ is used to adjust pH and (5–10%) Na_2SO_4 to "level" the color.

In viscose rayon manufacture Na_2SO_4 is an important constituent of the spinning bath, but is formed as the H_2SO_4 in the bath combines with the NaOH of the viscose solution. The separation necessary to maintain a constant bath composition gives the Na_2SO_4 production that is so important in the market.

Cellulose sponges are manufactured by incorporating particles of Glauber's salt into the viscose cellulose syrup. Heating sets the mix and further heating melts the Glauber's salt.

Cattle-feed supplement uses a surprising amount of Na_2SO_4 as a source of sulfur, essential in the formation of some proteins.

$NaHSO_4$ is commonly available as free-flowing crystals and in solution is quite acidic. Thus it can be considered as a cheap, easily handled, moderate-strength acid. Because of these characteristics, it is used as a cleaner for sanitary fixtures and automobile radiators, as a metal pickling agent, as a chemical catalyst, as a soil disinfectant, and with iron as a dye-reducing agent. The oxidizing properties of its H_2SO_4 component are used in the "carbonizing" of wool (removing carbonaceous impurities).

The low melting point of $NaHSO_4$ (Fig. 4) is one reason that it, rather than Na_2SO_4, is the nitric acid by-product. As a liquid the bisulfate is more easily handled under the temperature limitations of the manufacturing equipment and the decomposition of nitric acid. The low melting point and its acidic nature account for its use as a metallurgical flux. Molten $NaHSO_4$ dissolves Ti, V, and Zr.

Na_2SO_4, molten, as a vapor, or in solution, attacks most cements (apparently reacting with $Ca(OH)_2$). On the other hand, it is used in small amounts in some cements to control setting rates and to resist $MgCl_2$ (15).

In locations where Na_2SO_4 is much more available than NaCl, the former has been used to make Na_2CO_3 by a modification of the Solvay process and has been electrolyzed to H_2SO_4 and NaOH for rayon use.

Bibliography

"Sodium Sulfates" treated in *ECT* 1st ed. under "Sodium Compounds," Vol. 12, pp. 607–609, by J. A. Brink, Jr., Purdue University.

1. *Chem. Eng.* **72,** 74–76 (Aug. 16, 1965).
2. J. W. Mellor, *Comprehensive Treatise on Inorganic and Theoretical Chemistry*, Vol. 2, Suppl. 2, John Wiley & Sons, Inc., New York, 1962.
3. *Chem. Trade J.* **102,** 226 (1938).
4. George S. Brady, *Materials Handbook*, 9th ed., McGraw-Hill Book Co., Inc., New York, 1963, p. 746.
5. Emil R. Riegel, *Industrial Chemistry*, Reinhold Publishing Corp., New York, 1962, p. 75.
6. Weisman, *Chem. Eng. Progr.* **60** (11), 47–49 (Nov. 1964).
7. Alexander Findlay, *Phase Rule and Its Applications*, 9th ed., Dover Publications, Inc., New York, 1951, p. 239.
8. Weisman and Anderson, *Mining Eng.* **5,** 711 (1953).
9. Ryan, *Trans. AIME* **190,** 447 (1951).
10. Hadzeriga, *Trans. Soc. Mining Engrs. AIME* **227,** 169–174 (June 1964).
11. "Exploitation of Great Salt Lake," *Chem. Eng.* **75,** No. 13, 106–110 (June 17, 1968).
12. *Chemical Profiles*, Schnell Publishing, New York, 1965.
    A yearly publication of commercial data.
13. Anon., *Chem. Eng. News* **43,** 69 (March 8, 1965).
14. Cadle et al., *Arch. Ind. Hyg. Occupational Med.* **2,** 698–715 (1950).
15. U.S. Pats. 2,622, 989 (1952), Aram Keyishian; 2,673,810 (1954), N. C. Ludwig.

Joseph J. Jacobs
Jacobs Engineering Co.

SODIUM SULFIDES. Discussed here are sodium sulfide, Na_2S; corresponding sodium hydrosulfide, $NaHS$; and various polysulfides, Na_2S_x. Sodium sulfide and sodium hydrosulfide are very similar in their industrial uses.

Sodium Sulfide, Na_2S. In the pure form, this is a white crystalline powder. It has a density of 1.856 (1) and a melting point of 920°C. The solubility of sodium sulfide in water is shown in Figure 1.

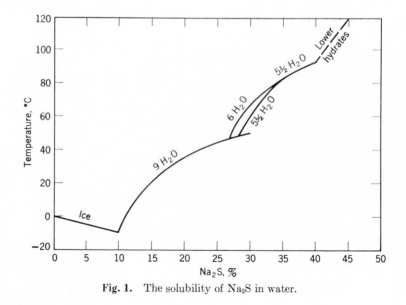

Fig. 1.   The solubility of Na_2S in water.

The heat of formation in the solid phase has been reported as 89.9 kcal/mole (2), 89.2 kcal/mole (3), down to 86.7 kcal/mole (4).

The first two references give a melting point of 1180–1200°C while the last reference gives 920°C.

The oldest method for the commercial production of sodium sulfide is the reduction of salt cake, Na_2SO_4, with powdered coal or other organic matter at 900–1000°C. The reactions are:

$$Na_2SO_4 + 4\,C \;\rightarrow\; Na_2S + 4\,CO$$
$$Na_2SO_4 + 4\,CO \;\rightarrow\; Na_2S + 4\,CO_2$$

This was the first step of the LeBlanc process for making sodium carbonate. It is not used at present, although at least one plant is still in standby condition in the United States.

A similar reduction of sodium sulfate to sodium sulfide takes place when sodium sulfate is added to the residual liquor, before furnacing, as makeup in the cycle of the sulfate or kraft process for making pulp (see Vol. 16, p. 702).

Sodium sulfide has been produced on an industrial scale at Leverkusen, Germany, by the reduction of salt cake with hydrogen. The reaction is carried out at about 600°C in a brick-lined rotating kiln, a catalyst consisting of finely divided ferric oxide being used. The advantages of this process over the old process are (a) continuous operation, (b) lower temperatures and less corrosive conditions, and (c) a product containing 95% sodium sulfide.

Production of sodium sulfide from hydrogen sulfide was commercialized in the late 1930s. Hydrogen, a by-product from electrolysis of salt brine, and sulfur were combined at an elevated temperature over a solid cobalt catalyst and then absorbed in caustic soda solution (5.7).

$$H_2 + S \;\rightarrow\; H_2S$$
$$H_2S + NaOH \;\rightarrow\; NaHS + H_2O$$

At this stage, heavy metal sulfides such as iron, nickel, copper, manganese, mercury, etc, are removed by filtration and the clear hydrosulfide solution may be concentrated in stainless steel equipment to 76% concentration. Above 70% concentration, solid hydrates, however, crystallize from the boiling solution.

By reacting hydrosulfide of proper concentration with flake caustic soda a sodium sulfide of 60–62% concentration is produced which is cast into drums or flaked.

$$NaHS + NaOH \;\rightarrow\; Na_2S + H_2O$$

Due to the high purity of the starting raw materials and the removal of heavy metals by filtration, a high-purity chemical grade of sodium sulfide is produced, suitable for use in dyes, rayon, photography, and leather unhairing.

An alternative route was developed as a by-product of carbon disulfide manufacture. In this process, methane or another low-molecular-weight hydrocarbong as is reacted with sulfur vapor over a solid alumina catalyst at 400–600°C to produce carbon disulfide and hydrogen sulfide (6).

$$CH_4 + 4\,S \;\rightarrow\; CS_2 + 2\,H_2S$$

The resulting gases are treated with cold caustic soda solution to produce dilute sodium hydrosulfide solution and liquid carbon disulfide.

In the preparation of viscose rayon, carbon disulfide is used to produce cellulose xanthate by reaction with soda cellulose. Sodium sulfide, or hydrosulfide, is used to desulfurize the crude viscose fiber. Thus, a viscose plant is often supplemented with a satellite plant making both carbon disulfide and sodium hydrosulfide.

Unfortunately, in the reaction of hydrocarbons with sulfur some thiols (mercaptans) are formed.

$$CH_4 + S \rightarrow \underset{\text{methanethiol}}{CH_3SH}$$

These thiols are very odorous and the resulting sulfide or hydrosulfide should not be used in leather unhairing or where a thiol odor would be objectionable in the end product.

Sodium sulfide is also produced commercially as a by-product in the manufacture of barium carbonate. Barium sulfate is roasted in a rotary kiln at 750–1000°C and the resulting product leached with water to give a barium sulfide solution. Further treatment with soda ash produces a commercial grade of barium carbonate (8), as follows:

$$BaSO_4 + 4C \rightarrow BaS + 4CO$$
$$BaS + Na_2CO_3 \rightarrow BaCO_3 + Na_2S$$

Three United States producers still concentrate and market a crude sodium sulfide product from such operations.

Two grades of sodium sulfide account for most of the marketed product. Flaked, fused, or chip forms range from 60 to 62% Na_2S with 39–37% water. They are yellow, pink, or red products, depending on the degree of purity. The yellow color results from polysulfide content and the red color from iron content. A crystal solid of 30–34% Na_2S with 69–65% water is sold mainly to the dye industry. Concentrated sodium sulfide containing 60–62% Na_2S is obtained by evaporating the liquor to 160°C or by reacting NaHS solution of proper concentration with flake caustic soda. Some aqueous solution is sold in drums and trailers but winter weather limits concentration to 15–18% Na_2S.

Current market prices for crystal solid are 4.5¢/lb as compared to 6.9¢/lb for flaked 60–62% material. As the price of sodium sulfide has increased due to increased costs of sulfur and processing labor, and since hydrosulfide has become available, the hydrosulfide has made inroads into the markets for sulfide in leather, dye, and viscose manufacture.

U.S. shipments of sodium sulfide as listed by the U.S. Bureau of Census were:

Year	Flakes calcd as 60–62%, tons	All grades calcd as 60–62%, total tons
1950		27,627
1955	26,871	35,296
1960	20,215	34,122
1965 est	18,500	46,300

Sodium sulfide is employed extensively in the leather industry for the removal of hair from hide before tanning. It is used as a reducing agent in the production of amino compounds, in the manufacture of sulfur dyes, and as a solvent for sulfur dyes. It is also used in engraving and lithography. Sodium sulfide can be used as the raw material for the preparation of sodium hydrosulfide and sodium polysulfides.

U.S. consumption by use is estimated:

Use	Percent	Use	Percent
leather unhairing	20	metals and minerals	12
colors and dyes	18	pulp and paper	
chemicals, misc	13	(makeup only)	5
rayon and film	13	export	19

Sodium Hydrosulfide, NaHS. This product is usually marketed under the trade name of "sodium sulfhydrate" to avoid confusion with sodium hydrosulfite, $Na_2S_2O_4$.

The anhydrous material, although not available commercially, is a white crystalline solid soluble in water and alcohol. Heating decomposes the product to monosulfide and hydrogen sulfide. Exposure to air results in rapid oxidation and if organic matter is present fire can result.

The heat of formation of the solid is 55.7 kcal; that of the liquid phase is 58.5–60.7 kcal.

The di- and trihydrates ($NaHS \cdot 2H_2O$ and $NaHS \cdot 3H_2O$) have been prepared at 0–18°C and lower hydrates are believed to exist at higher temperatures.

Two processes are used commercially to produce sodium hydrosulfide. In the first, high-purity hydrogen sulfide is produced by the reaction of hydrogen and sulfur and the resulting gas is absorbed in caustic soda solution. In the second, low-molecular-weight hydrocarbons are reacted with sulfur to produce carbon disulfide and hydrogen sulfide and the resulting gases are dissolved in caustic soda solutions. Both processes are described in greater details in the preceding section on sodium sulfide.

U.S. production of flake sodium hydrosulfide began in 1938, several years after production in Germany of dilute hydrosulfide solutions. The advent of commercial grades of suitable stainless steels for evaporation and flaking was the basic key to the development.

Sodium hydrosulfide has found a major use in the unhairing of hides before tanning. Its lime solutions are somewhat less alkaline than corresponding sodium sulfide lime solutions; thus, the swelling of the hide during treatment is less and the surface of the resulting leather is smoother. Also, if hair is recovered for sale, there is less breakdown of the hair fibers. At present, sodium hydrosulfide shares about half the leather industry uses with sodium sulfide.

Sulfur dyes shipped as leuco bases and thioindigo dyes are well established markets for sodium hydrosulfide.

The production of aliphatic thiols and, particularly, dodecanethiol (dodecyl mercaptan), by the conversion of aliphatic chlorides has consumed large amounts of sodium hydrosulfide.

$$RCl + NaHS \rightarrow NaCl + RSH$$

This market is decreasing as new direct routes to these thiols from olefins and alcohols reacted with hydrogen sulfide are becoming commercial.

Both sodium sulfide and sodium hydrosulfide are used in the flotation of copper ores with the sulfur group acting as the collection agent. In the separation of copper and nickel sulfides from complex Canadian mineral concentrates, the use of sodium hydrosulfide and sodium sulfide is of commercial importance in both the Orford and slow-cooling procedures.

The kraft wood pulping industry also uses some sodium hydrosulfide as a means of decreasing hydrolysis and increasing yields of pulp over the conventional sodium sulfide kraft route.

U.S. consumption by use is estimated:

Use	Percent	Use	Percent
chemicals misc	32	metals and minerals	12
colors and dyes	19	rayon and film	12
leather unhairing	16	export	9

Two grades of sodium hydrosulfide account for most of the market product. Flaked, chipped, or cast material, 72–75% NaHS and 27–24% water, is light yellow in color. It melts at about 140°F. Liquid grade is marketed, with 40–46% NaHS and 59–53% water content, depending on shipping temperatures. Flaked product sells at 5.9¢/lb, as compared with liquid at 3.3¢/lb.

U.S. shipments as reported by the U.S. Bureau of Census were:

Year	All grades calcd as 100% NaHS, total tons	Year	All grades calcd as 100% NaHS, total tons
1950	15,302	1960	20,431
1955	20,187	1965	24,900 est

Analysis of Na$_2$S and NaHS. A solution containing Na$_2$S and either NaHS or NaOH, according to the amount of sulfide present, can be completely analyzed by two titrations: (1) with acid, to the methyl red end point, and (2) with silver nitrate, on another sample, adding an excess along with ferric alum, and back-titrating with ammonium thiocyanate until a pink coloration is obtained.

One equivalent of Na neutralizes one equivalent of acid, whether sulfur is present or not:

$$NaOH + HCl \rightarrow NaCl + H_2O$$
$$Na_2S + 2\,HCl \rightarrow 2\,NaCl + H_2S$$
$$NaHS + HCl \rightarrow NaCl + H_2S$$

One equivalent of S reacts with two equivalents of silver nitrate, whether in the form of Na$_2$S or NaHS:

$$Na_2S + 2\,AgNO_3 \rightarrow Ag_2S + 2\,NaNO_3$$
$$NaHS + 2\,AgNO_3 \rightarrow Ag_2S + NaNO_3 + HNO_3$$

Thus, if only Na$_2$S is present, the acid used is equal to the silver nitrate; if only NaHS is present, the acid used is half the silver nitrate used. Mixtures of Na$_2$S and NaHS would fall between equal and half.

Sodium Polysulfides. Sodium monosulfide solutions dissolve sulfur, forming complex mixtures of polysulfides and hydrolysis products. The probable reactions are:

$$Na_2S + H_2O \rightarrow NaOH + NaHS$$
$$S_x + 6\,NaOH \rightarrow 2\,Na_2S_x + Na_2S_2O_3 + 3\,H_2O$$

Two homogeneous solid sodium polysulfides have been prepared (10) by the reaction of sodium hydrosulfide solutions with sulfur:

$$4\,NaHS + 3\,S_2 \rightarrow 2\,Na_2S_4 + 2\,H_2S$$
$$Na_2S_4 + 2\,Na \rightarrow 2\,Na_2S_2$$

The tetrasulfide is a dark yellow product with greenish tinge. On heating, it turns orange-red at 115–120°C and melts to a dark-red liquid at 258–267°C. The disulfide is a bright yellow crystalline solid which fuses to a dark-red liquid.

Sodium polysulfides are usually produced captively from purchased sodium sulfide and sulfur. A tetrasulfide solution containing 40–42% Na_2S_4 is, however, available for purchase.

The polysulfides are used as reducing agents for nitrocompounds, as ore flotation reagents, in the manufacture of sulfur dyes, in the preparation of metal sulfide finishes, and in the manufacture of polymers containing sulfur (see Vol. 16, p. 255). The ability of weak tetrasulfide solutions to resolubilize the proteins of dried hides has resulted in a material use for this purpose in the leather industry (8).

Bibliography

"Sodium Sulfides" in *ECT* 1st ed., Vol. 12, pp. 609–611, by J. A. Brink, Jr., Purdue University.

1. E. Rengade and J. Cousteau, *Compt. Rend.* (in French) **158**, 940 (1914).
2. K. A. Kraus and J. A. Redderhoff, *J. Am. Chem. Soc.* **56**, 79 (1934).
3. T. W. Bauer and R. M. Dorland, *Can. J. Technol.* **32**, 91 (1954).
4. N. A. Landiya, *Zh. Fiz. Khim.* (in Russian) **80**, 89 (1950).
5. U.S. Pat. 2,214,859 (1940), A. H. Maude and J. D. Sweeney (to Hooker Chem. Corp.).
6. D. R. Stull, *Ind. Eng. Chem.* **41** (9), 1968 (1949).
7. U.S. Pat. 2,252,867 (1941), J. S. Sconce and C. F. Berlinghoff (to Hooker Chem. Corp.).
8. *Mineral Facts and Problems 1965*, U.S. Bur. Mines, Washington, D.C., 1965, p. 93.
9. E. R. Theis and H. S. Zable, *Shoe and Leather Reporter* **235** (8), 17–25 (1945).
10. A. Rule and J. S. Thomas, *Trans. Chem. Soc.* **105**, 177 (1914).

J. S. Sconce
Hooker Chemical Corporation

SODIUM SULFITES.   See Sulfur Compounds.

SOIL CHEMISTRY OF PESTICIDES

The fate of chemicals in soils is a subject of current national interest due to its potential role in environmental pollution. Agricultural pesticides have been singled out for special consideration since large quantities are being dispersed on major agricultural soils. As a consequence, soils represent a vast reservoir receiving pesticides applied either intentionally or accidentally.

Pesticides are classified according to the target organism they control. The following five major classes generally recognized are *herbicides, insecticides, fungicides, nematicides,* and a small group composed of defoliants, desiccants, and growth regulators. In addition there are a limited number of chemicals used as miticides, rodenticides, repellents, and other pest control agents. The most reliable figures indicate that approx 119 million acres are sprayed for weed control (herbicides), 97 million acres are treated for insect control (insecticides), and about 25 million are treated for plant diseases (fungicides), for nematodes, or with defoliants, desiccants, or growth regulators (1). If one calculates that about 340 million acres of soil are under cultivation in the continental United States, then a large percentage of our most fertile soils are receiving one or more applications on a seasonal basis. See Fungicides; Insecticides; Weed killers; Poisons, economic; and Plant growth substances.

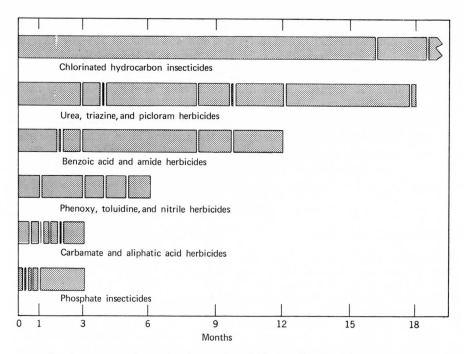

Fig. 1. Persistence of twelve major classes of pesticides in soils. Each bar represents one or more major class of pesticide; the open spaces represent individual pesticides in that major class; and the length of each bar represents the time required for a 75–100% loss of the pesticide as measured in months (2). Courtesy Charles C Thomas, Publisher, Fort Lauderdale, Fla.

Most research on pesticides in soils has centered on residual members of the first two classes of pesticides. The chlorinated hydrocarbon insecticides represent the most persistent class of pesticides. Under normal usage conditions, most polychlorinated insecticides remain in soil 2–5 years (Figs. 1 and 2). In contrast, many highly toxic phosphate esters decompose in a few months and consequently pose no residual problem (Fig. 2). The organic herbicides exhibit a wide spectrum of persistence, which may range from several days up to two years (Fig. 2).

One problem caused by residual pesticides in soils stems from the capacity of many plant species to absorb and translocate these materials into food and fiber products.

Table 1. Production and Sales of Pesticides in the United States in 1967 (4)

Type of pesticide	Quantity of pesticide, 1000 lb	Value, $1000	Unit value,[a] $
fungicides	120,413	56,333	0.37, 0.67
herbicides and plant hormones	287,582	429,980	1.55, 1.15
insecticides, rodenticides, soil conditioners, and fumigants	489,368	300,730	0.60, 0.64
total	897,363	787,043	0.92

[a]For cyclic and acyclic pesticides, respectively.

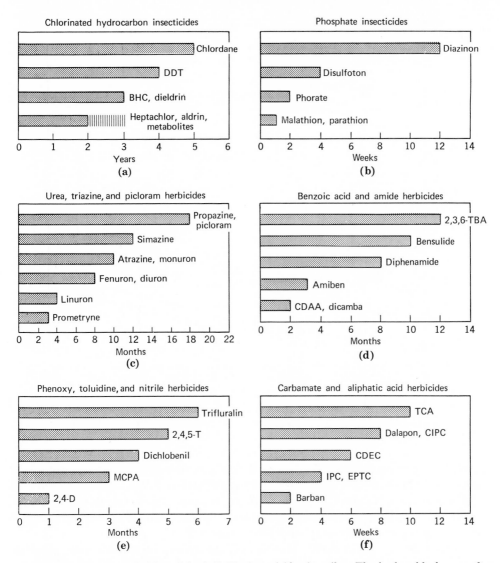

Fig. 2. Persistence of thirty-eight individual pesticides in soils. The broken black area after heptachlor and aldrin represents the additional insecticidal persistence caused by their respective metabolites, heptachlor epoxide and dieldrin (2). Courtesy Charles C Thomas, Publisher, Fort Lauderdale, Fla.

To keep abreast of the content of pesticides in soils and in other phases of the environment, extensive monitoring programs are conducted by the Government. Areas of high pesticide usage are monitored intensively to determine whether progressive accumulation is occurring. Market basket surveys, based on the diet of a 19-year-old male, are conducted periodically by the Food and Drug Administration. Surveys thus far indicate most samples contain residues well below established pesticide tolerances, and that only 3% of the total foods analyzed are above these established tolerances (3).

Residual pesticides in soils may present an additional problem from an agronomic and environmental standpoint. For example, residual herbicides have damaged crops

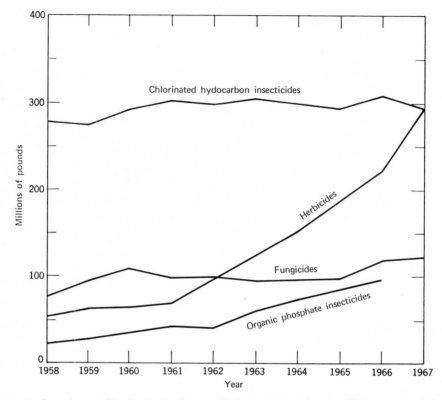

Fig. 3. Organic pesticide chemicals sold annually in the United States. Values are in millions of pounds of technical products. Values for organic phosphate insecticides in 1967 are not shown. Adapted from (4).

grown the following year. Residual insecticides have found their way into water, and consequently have affected marine life and their predators. As a further consequence, some reproductive failures have been reported in birds feeding on fish contaminated with the chlorinated hydrocarbon insecticides. The incidence of pesticides in wildlife is also being closely monitored in Government surveys.

Before considering in detail the chemical aspects of pesticides in soils, some information on the scope of the pesticide industry may be helpful. The total sales of pesticides have increased steadily over the past decade (Fig. 3). The total sales of chlorinated hydrocarbon insecticides have remained fairly stable during this period: In contrast, the herbicides have enjoyed considerable growth in total sales in this same period. Current trends indicate that herbicide and fungicide usage will remain fairly constant. The total production and sales of synthetic organic pesticides in the United States in 1967 are shown in Table 1 (see p. 516).

Chemistry of the Pesticides

Excellent reviews of the properties of selected pesticides may be found in the series by Metcalf (5) and in the text by Crafts (6). Any detailed consideration of the pesticides is difficult, since there are over 125 herbicides, 90 insecticides, and numerous other pest control agents presently being marketed. A list of the common and chemical names of the pesticides cited in the present text is found in Table 2.

Table 2. Chemical Designations of Pesticides Mentioned in Text

Common name	Type of pesticide[a]	Chemical name
aldrin	I	1,2,3,4,10,10-hexachloro-1,4,4a,5,8,8a-hexahydro-1,4-*endo-exo*-5,8-dimethanonaphthalene
amiben	H	3-amino-2,5-dichlorobenzoic acid
amitrole	H	3-amino-1,2,4-triazole
atrazine	H	2-chloro-4-ethylamino-6-isopropylamino-*s*-triazine
Banol[b]	I	6-chloro-3,4-xylyl *N*-methylcarbamate
barban	H	4-chloro-3-butynyl *m*-chlorocarbanilate
Baygon[b]	I	2-isopropoxyphenyl *N*-methylcarbamate
bensulide	H	*N*-(2-mercaptoethyl)benzenesulfonamide
γ-BHC	I	see lindane
cacodylic acid	H	dimethylarsinic acid
captan	F	*N*-trichloromethylmercapto-4-cyclohexene-1,2-dicarboximide
carbaryl	I	1-naphthyl *N*-methylcarbamate
CDAA	H	*N,N*-diallyl-2-chloroacetamide
CDEC	H	*S*-2-chloroallyl *N,N*-diethyldithiocarbamate
chlordane	I	1,2,4,5,6,7,8,8-octachloro-2,3,3a,4,7,7a-hexahydro-4,7-methanoindene (principal constituent)
chloroxuron	H	3-[*p*-(*p*-chlorophenoxy)phenyl]-1,1-dimethylurea
CIPC	H	isopropyl *m*-chlorocarbanilate
dalapon	H	2,2-dichloropropionic acid
2,4-D	H	2,4-dichlorophenoxyacetic acid
2,4-DB	H	4-(2,4-dichlorophenoxy)butyric acid
DDD	I	1,1-dichloro-2,2-bis(*p*-chlorophenyl)ethane
DDE	I	1,1-dichloro-2,2-bis(*p*-chlorophenyl)ethene
DDT:	I	mixture of following two:
p,p'-DDT		1,1,1-trichloro-2,2-bis(*p*-chlorophenyl)ethane
o,p'-DDT		1,1,1-trichloro-2-(*o*-chlorophenyl)-2-(*p*-chlorophenyl)ethane
diazinon	I	*O,O*-diethyl *O*-2-isopropyl-6-methyl-4-pyrimidinyl phosphorothioate
dicamba	H	3,6-dichloro-*o*-anisic acid
dichlobenil	H	2,6-dichlorobenzonitrile
dieldrin	I	1,2,3,4,10,10-hexachloro-6,7-epoxy-1,4,4a,5,6,-7,8,8a,-octahydro-1,4-*endo-exo*-5,8-dimethanonaphthalene
diphenamid	H	*N,N*-dimethyl-2,2-diphenylacetamide
diquat	H	6,7-dihydrodipyrido[1,2-*a:2'*,1'-*c*]-pyrazidinium salt
disyston	I	see disulfoton
disulfoton	I	*O,O*-ethyl *S*-2(ethylthio)ethyl phosphorodithioate
diuron	H	3-(3,4-dichlorophenyl)-1,1-dimethylurea
DNBP	H	4,6-dinitro-*o-sec*-butylphenol
DSMA	H	disodium methanearsonate
endrin		1,2,3,4,10,10-hexachloro-6,7-epoxy-1,4,4a,5,6,-7,8,8a-octahydro-1,4-*endo-endo*-5,8-dimethanonaphthalene

(continued)

Table 2 (continued)

Common name	Type of pesticide[a]	Chemical name
EPTC	H	S-ethyl N,N-dipropylthiocarbamate
fenac	H	2,3,6-trichlorophenylacetic acid
fenuron	H	1,1-dimethyl-3-phenylurea
ferbam	F	ferric dimethyldithiocarbamate
fluometuron	H	1,1-dimethyl-3-(α,α,α-trifluoro-m-tolyl)urea
heptachlor	I	1,4,5,6,7,8,8-heptachloro-3a,4,7,7a-tetrahydro-4,7-methanoindene
heptachlor epoxide	I	1,4,5,6,7,8,8-heptachloro-2,3-epoxy-2,3,3a,7a-tetrahydro-4,7-methanoindene
IPC	H	isopropyl carbanilate
isodrin	I	1,2,3,4,10,10-hexachloro-1,4,4a,5,8,8a-hexahydro-1,4-endo-endo-5,8-dimethanonaphthalene
lindane	I	γ-1,2,3,4,5,6-hexachlorocyclohexane
linuron	H	3-(3,4-dichlorophenyl)-1-methoxy-1-methylurea
malathion	I	S-[1,2-bis(ethoxycarbonyl)ethyl] O,O-dimethyl phosphorodithioate
Matacil[b]	I	4-dimethylamino-m-tolyl N-methylcarbamate
Mesurol[b]	I	4-(methylthio)-3,5-xylyl N-methylcarbamate
MCPA	H	4-chloro-2-methylphenoxyacetic acid
metobromuron	H	3-(p-bromophenyl)-1-methoxy-1-methylurea
monuron	H	3-(p-chlorophenyl)-1,1-dimethylurea
nabam	F	sodium ethylenebisdithiocarbamate
nitralin	H	4-(methylsulfonyl)-2,6-dinitro-N,N-dipropyl-aniline
paraoxon	I	O,O-diethyl O-p-nitrophenyl phosphate
paraquat	H	1,1'-dimethyl-4,4'-bipyridinium salt
parathion	I	O,O-diethyl O-p-nitrophenyl phosphorothioate
phorate	I	O,O-diethyl S-[(ethylthio)methyl] phosphorodithioate
picloram	H	4-amino-3,5,6-trichloropicolinic acid
prometryne	H	2,4-bis(isopropylamino)-6-methylthio-s-triazine
propanil	H	3',4'-dichloropropionanilide
propazine	H	2-chloro-4,6-bis(isopropylamino)-s-triazine
Semesan[c]	F	hydroxymercurichlorophenol
simazine	H	2-chloro-4,6-bis(ethylamino)-s-triazine
2,4,5-T	H	2,4,5-trichlorophenoxyacetic acid
2,3,6-TBA	H	2,3,6-trichlorobenzoic acid
TCA	H	trichloroacetic acid
trifluralin	H	α,α,α-trifluoro-2,6-dinitro-N,N-dipropyl-p-toluidine
vernolate	H	S-propyl N,N-dipropylthiocarbamate
Zectran[d]	I	4-dimethylamino-3,5-xylyl N-methylcarbamate

[a]NOTE: I, insecticide; H, herbicide; F, fungicide.
[b]Registered trademark of Farbenfabriken Bayer AG.
[c]Registered trademark of E. I. du Pont de Nemours & Co., Inc.
[d]Registered trademark of Dow Chemical Co.

Processes Acting on Pesticides in Soils

The processes acting on a pesticide in the soil environment can be roughly subdivided into three major areas: physical, biological, and chemical although some ambiguity exists about the specific processes to be listed under these major headings.

Under the physical processes may be listed photodecomposition, or alterations on the soil surface by ultraviolet radiation; volatilization, or movement in the vapor phase; leaching, or movement by capillary water into the soil profile; and physical adsorption onto various soil colloids. Under biological processes may be listed metabolism by soil microorganisms and root uptake, or absorption by the plant. Under chemical processes are included all reactions not mediated by the soil microorganisms, ie, those reactions catalyzed by various soil components and chemical adsorption. Finally, it must be realized that several of these processes are operating in concert on any particular pesticide and often they cannot be considered independently.

No accurate balance sheet has yet been devised for the contribution of each of these processes for a given pesticide in the soil. The persistence values given in Figures 1 and 2 indicate that some of these processes are extremely slow. The effective life of a pesticide in soil depends on the chemical properties of the molecule and the properties of the surrounding soil. At the soil surface, photodecomposition and volatilization are probably important; the remaining processes come into play after the molecule moves beneath the soil surface. Therefore, the time a molecule remains on the surface versus the time it remains in the soil proper is an important consideration as to its fate. Many pesticides are incorporated directly into the soil to prevent rapid losses due to volatilization and photodecomposition.

In the following sections, two of the better understood processes affecting pesticides will be discussed. Next, reactions dealing with the insecticides, herbicides, arsenical pesticides, and fungicides will be considered.

Adsorption. A variety of soil factors complicate prediction of a given pesticide's behavior. Furthermore, there are thousands of soil types in the United States, each differing in physical or chemical characteristics and subject to substantial differences in climate. These soil–climate parameters explain the greater effectiveness of a pesticide on a sandy soil compared to a neighboring clay loam and the greater persistence of certain herbicides in the cooler temperate regions than in semitropical areas. The complexity of soil factors is perhaps best seen in the adsorption of pesticides.

One of the most important physical or chemical processes governing pesticide behavior within soil is adsorption, ie, concentration at or exclusion from the solid surface. Adsorption directly or indirectly influences pesticide movement, photodecomposition, plant uptake, microbial and chemical decomposition, and volatilization. Compounds strongly adsorbed by soil components are not readily moved by water passing into and within the soil. When applied at the surface, such pesticides are more susceptible to photodegradation and volatilization. Organic cations such as paraquat and diquat are adsorbed so strongly that phytotoxicity is virtually eliminated in soils other than sands.

Adsorption of organic pesticides by soil colloids has been thoroughly reviewed by Bailey and White (7). Adsorption may arise from coulombic attraction, dipole interactions (van der Waals forces), or hydrogen bonding. Energy of adsorption is the summation of these forces: In general, van der Waals adsorption is weak and coulombic attraction strong.

The most significant soil factors governing adsorption behavior of a pesticide are the nature and amount of the soil components. Soil organic matter usually is the component most highly correlated with adsorption, loss of pesticide bioactivity, retention against leaching, and the like. Organic matter has a high adsorptive capacity for cationic pesticides because of its pH-dependent net negative charge, and for neutral molecules because of physical adsorption. In the latter category adsorption of chlorinated hydrocarbon insecticides, eg, aldrin, DDT, γ-BHC, increased with higher organic matter content and, to a lesser extent, clay content. Increased moisture content may decrease adsorption, enhancing bioactivity of certain insecticides. Adsorption and movement of neutral pesticides in soils have been treated as a partition-chromatographic process. Organic matter is considered the stationary phase: The "active fraction" of organic matter, or that portion which participates in the sorption process, can be determined experimentally. The adsorptive capacity of the soil organic matter is then measurable and designated as omega (Ω). The use of a distribution constant based on Ω is then a true constant, independent of soil type (8).

The second major soil component affecting adsorption is the mineral fraction. The crystalline layer silicate clays such as montmorillonite and vermiculite are of greatest importance because of their high cation exchange capacities (80–150 meq/100 g) and surface areas (600–800 m^2/g). In addition, kaolinite, halloysite, illite, chlorite, and interstratified variations of the clay minerals contribute further to adsorption capacity. See Clays.

Though often overlooked, oxides and hydroxides of iron and aluminum may contribute significantly to the soil chemistry of pesticides by development of a pH-dependent positive charge, coupled with high surface area. They are especially abundant in highly weathered soils such as those in tropical and semitropical regions of high rainfall. Thus, picloram is strongly adsorbed by hydrated metal oxides and a red lateritic soil, but poorly adsorbed by montmorillonite, kaolinite, attapulgite, and purified illite (9). Low pH and high organic matter also favor adsorption of picloram and other acidic herbicides, such as 2,4-D and 2,4,5-T.

Both adsorbent and adsorbate may be influenced by soil pH. At very low pH a variety of organic compounds are strongly adsorbed to montmorillonite, kaolinite, and illite (10). Anionic herbicides (2,4-D, 2,4,5-T, MCPA) are negatively adsorbed at pH greater than 6–7. Ion exchange resins and other polymers, often studied as model soil components, exhibit greatest adsorption of ureas and triazines at low pH.

Current research emphasis in pesticide adsorption is shifting from measurement of adsorption–desorption isotherms to elucidation of the adsorption mechanism. To this end, infrared spectroscopy appears to be the most promising technique.

Photodecomposition. Decomposition by light plays some part in the transformation of pesticides in the environment although the practical significance of this method of decomposition is difficult to assess quantitatively. Absorption of light by pesticides is a surface phenomenon which may occur on soil or leaf surfaces. One of the prime factors determining the readiness of a pesticide to decompose in sunlight is its absorption spectrum. Many pesticides are substituted aromatic compounds and have absorption maxima between 200 and 350 mμ, that is to say, in the near ultraviolet range. Sunlight is a poor source of such radiation since it contains negligible radiation of a wavelength less than 295 mμ. Consequently, solar energy is usually insufficient to effect direct fission of covalent bonds. However, many reactions do occur in aqueous solutions of pesticides receiving solar radiation although the precise mechanism by which energy transfer takes place requires further study. Additional information concerning the nature of sensitized processes and photolysis in the solid and adsorbed states is required. Contact of pesticides with trace metals and the proximity of naturally occurring complex organic compounds present in soil or leaf constituents provide favorable situations for energy transfer. In these circumstances the production of oxygenated or reduced derivatives may depend on the proximity of oxygen or hydrogen sources to the activated molecule.

The complexity of the natural environment has restricted photochemical studies primarily to the investigation of the products of photolysis in solution or as solid films. Often the study of photodecomposition has been undertaken to determine the loss of biological activity following irradiation. The rate of bioactivity loss reflects the rate of photodecomposition but affords little other chemical information.

Many organic pesticides are complex molecules and contain a number of functional groups. Photochemical reactions of individual groups are often predictable by reference to previously investigated models since even in a more complex molecular environment similar reactions may occur. However, the relative reactivity of functional groups becomes extremely difficult to predict. The replacement of a halogen atom by hydroxyl (or occasionally by hydrogen) in aqueous solution or by hydrogen in a hydrogen donor solvent, eg, methanol, is frequently observed when halogen atoms are bonded to an aromatic ring system. Photoreactivity of halogen atoms attached to an isolated double bond is observed in the cyclodiene insecticides. New carbon–carbon bonds are formed at the site of departure of the chlorine atom or reduction may occur in a hydrogen donor solvent at greater dilution.

Photooxidation usually transforms amines and phenols into dark-colored materials of high molecular weight. In aqueous solution halogenated phenoxyaliphatic acids generate polyhydroxyphenols photolytically by ether fission and replacement of halogen by hydroxyl. Since polyhydroxyphenols are extremely susceptible to oxidation at low pH, the resultant phenols readily polymerize and can only be isolated if their further oxidation is inhibited. It should be borne in mind that polyphenols (and many other classes of compounds generated by photolysis) are very reactive and can therefore be isolated from the reaction mixture only with difficulty. Another reaction of sufficient generality is the removal of alkyl or alkoxy groups attached to nitrogen atoms.

Several texts on organic photochemistry (11,12) are available and provide an excellent foundation for understanding the photochemistry of pesticides. However, predictions based on extrapolation from the photochemical behavior of a model system will be of limited value until broader knowledge of the effect of many complicating factors can be accumulated.

Insecticides

Three major classes of insecticides have been studied in soil: the *chlorinated hydrocarbons* (DDT, aldrin, dieldrin, endrin, heptachlor); the *organic phosphates* (malathion, parathion, diazinon); and the *methyl carbamates* (carbaryl, Banol, Baygon). Only the chlorinated hydrocarbons persist in soils (Fig. 1). Reported values for their rates of disappearance differ. Soils receiving high initial rates of application have been reported to contain 40–45% of the original material after 14 years (13). The low solubility of most of the chlorinated hydrocarbon insecticides probably contributes to their stability in soils. Other factors influencing their persistence are rate of application, moisture, pH, and microbial activity.

DDT. Total worldwide production of DDT since its introduction has been estimated at over 3.5 billion lb (4). Because of its extensive use in crop protection programs DDT is the pesticide most frequently found in soils. Due to its low solubility, DDT does not leach rapidly in soils. Because DDT is so extremely hydrophobic, it exhibits some interesting properties in water. DDT molecules in water tend to migrate to the surface. At this air–water interface, DDT evaporates with water molecules faster than would be predicted from its extremely low vapor pressure. The occurrence of DDT in untreated areas throughout the world may be a consequence of this ability to evaporate with water vapor. Two processes that alter this insecticide are microbial metabolism and photodecomposition.

The course of degradation of DDT (**1**) in soils is not fully established. Certain organisms possess the ability to dehydrohalogenate DDT to DDE (**2**): Resistant strains of insects are capable of effecting this conversion which is also brought about easily by base or catalytically by iron. Many microorganisms present in soil are capable of converting DDT to DDD (**3**) under anaerobic conditions. DDD is an important product of DDT degradation (14), but it has proved difficult to ascertain the route of further breakdown after initial conversion to DDD. The production of "polar material" which cannot be recovered from soils has been noted. The anaerobic breakdown of DDT by *Enterobacter aerogenes* microorganisms is reported to yield reduced dechlorinated compounds as well as oxidized derivatives and ultimately *p,p'*-dichlorobenzophenone (**4**) (15).

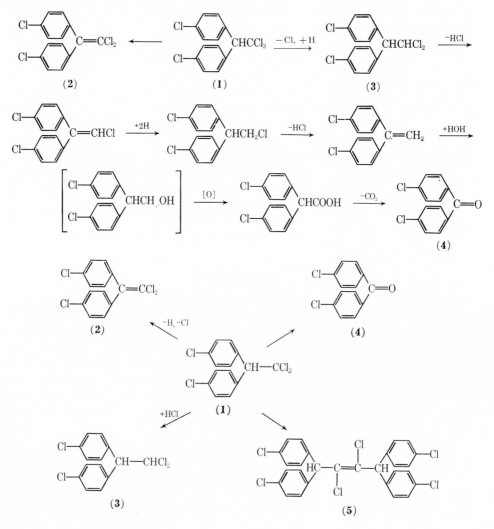

Irradiation of a solution of DDT in methanol or ethanol affords a mixture of compounds. A number of these have been isolated and characterized: DDD is formed by reductive dechlorination, DDE by dehydrochlorination, and *p,p'*-dichlorobenzophenone by oxidation. Also, 2,3-dichloro-1,1,4,4-tetrakis(*p*-chlorophenyl)-2-butene (**5**) has been isolated from solution (16). Solid DDT decomposes in sunlight and air in a similar manner but the rate of reaction is slower.

Cyclodienes. Aldrin (**6**) is oxidized to dieldrin (**7**) and heptachlor (**8**) to heptachlor epoxide (**9**) in soils (3). Both epoxides are insecticidal and prolong the biological activity (Fig. 2). Epoxidation is probably mediated by soil microorganisms.

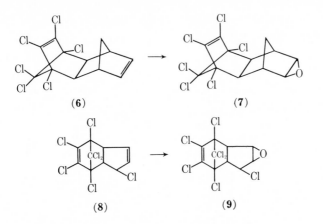

Dieldrin is degraded by a number of soil microorganisms. The major degradation products resulting from metabolism by *Pseudomonas* spp have been isolated and identified (17). The metabolic products were established for the microorganism and from the soil:

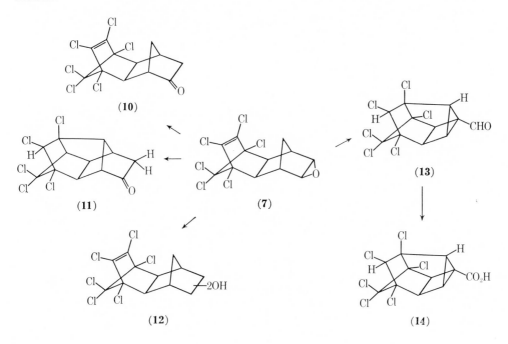

The major metabolites reported were aldrin, a ketone derived by rearrangement of the epoxide ring to a carbonyl function (**10**); a compound (**11**) formed by ring closure in (**10**); probably dihydroxydihydroaldrin (**12**); and, tentatively, an aldehyde (**13**) and an acid (**14**) formed by loss of carbon from the ring to which the epoxide function was formerly attached. *Enterobacter aerogenes* in a culture medium produces 6,7-*trans*-dihydroxydihydroaldrin, which is compound (**12**) with hydroxyl groups at the 6 and 7 positions in the trans orientation, aerobically from dieldrin (18).

The stereoisomeric chlorinated hydrocarbons, isodrin (**15**) and aldrin, and their corresponding epoxides, endrin (**16**) and dieldrin, undergo a number of reactions when irradiated with ultraviolet rays or natural sunlight (19–22). The yields and products, (**17**) to (**24**), vary with the wavelength of the light, the irradiation period, and the physical state of the irradiated material.

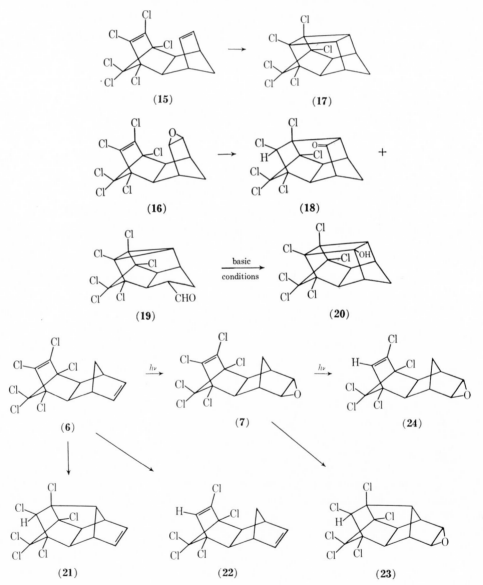

Isomerization occurs in the solid state to give structures in which an adjacent carbon atom has added to the halogenated double bond. In the process of photoisomerization of endrin, in addition to carbon–carbon bond formation, the epoxide ring rearranges to afford a ketone (**18**).

In dilute solution, one chlorine substituent from the carbon–carbon double bond of dieldrin or aldrin is replaced by a hydrogen atom. Photoexcitation is followed by hydrogen abstraction from the solvent.

Other photolysis products have been reported: For example, solid aldrin, on exposure to natural sunlight, yields dieldrin and the corresponding photolysis product of dieldrin (**23**) in addition to (**21**). Polymeric material forms the major portion of the photolysate.

Lindane (γ-hexachlorocyclohexane). Lindane (**25**) is less persistent in soil than DDT or the chlorinated cyclodiene insecticides. The degradation product of lindane in soils has been identified by cochromatography as γ-pentachlorocyclohexene (**26**). The evidence supports the view that this may be a microbial conversion (23).

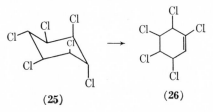

(25)   (26)

Carbamates. Several methyl carbamates are sold as broad-spectrum insecticides. Of these carbaryl (**27**) is the most extensively used. Unfortunately, very little published literature exists on the fate of these insecticides in soils. This scarcity of information probably relates to the short effective life of these compounds. Carbaryl, for example, has a half-life of about eight days in soils. Chemical hydrolysis is probably responsible for the rapid disappearance of carbaryl. Degradation generally involves an initial hydrolysis of the ester linkage. Most methyl carbamates are unstable in alkaline media and consequently localized areas of high pH in soils may facilitate hydrolysis. The products of hydrolysis may then be further degraded. Starting with carbaryl, the products of hydrolysis are 1-naphthol (**28**), methylamine, and carbon dioxide. Methyl isocyanate is a possible transient intermediate.

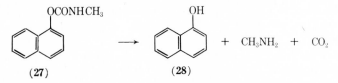

(27)   (28)

Since there is no direct evidence for methyl carbamate metabolism by soil microorganisms, one can only speculate as to probable sites of attack from a study of related systems. Possible points of metabolic attack include hydrolysis of the ester linkage, oxidation of the N-methyl group, ring substitution, and ring cleavage. Based largely on the rapidity with which carbaryl breaks down in soils, esterase activity is the favored mode of degradation. The other reactions are generally slower in most soils. Due to their lack of persistence, methyl carbamate insecticides are seldom, if ever, detected in the national soils-monitoring program. A number of carbamate insecticides decompose in sunlight, affording several products (24–26). Carbaryl, Baygon,

(29)

Banol, Matacil (**29**), Zectran (**30**), and Mesurol (**31**) are subject to photolysis. The major products from Mesurol are the sulfoxide (**32**) and the sulfone (**33**):

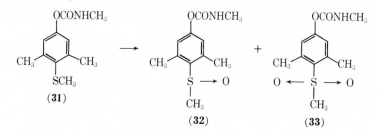

Matacil and Zectran undergo photooxidation. For example, the dimethylamino group of Zectran is oxidatively dealkylated to the amino (**34**), methylamino (**35**), formamido (**36**), and methylformamido (**37**) analogs. Matacil behaves in a similar manner. This reaction represents the major pathway of photodecomposition for these compounds.

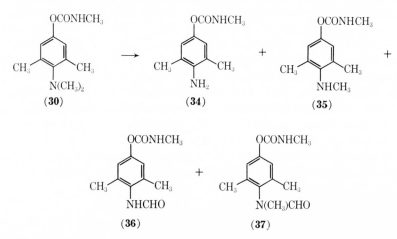

Phosphates.   Like the carbamates, the organic phosphates are cholinesterase inhibitors. Diazinon (**38**), parathion (**39**), and phorate are used to control soil-borne insects. The organophosphorus compounds are degraded fairly rapidly. The rate increases with soil moisture. Increase of soil pH favors hydrolysis. The products of hydrolysis of parathion are O,O-diethyl phosphorothioate (**40**) and p-nitrophenol (**41**). Hydrolysis of diazinon yields (**40**) and 6-hydroxy-2-isopropyl-4-methylpyrimidine (**42**):

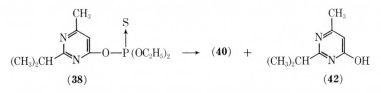

(**38**)   (**42**)

The process is catalyzed by adsorption and occurs at degradation rates up to 11% per day. Thus chemical hydrolysis may occur so rapidly as to preclude any extensive biological breakdown, especially at low pH values. Diazinon and related pesticides are also readily hydrolyzed in the presence of Cu^{2+} at pH 5–6.

Soil microorganisms have also been implicated in phosphate insecticide degradation. From a comparison of autoclaved and nonautoclaved soil, parathion breakdown was suggested to be influenced by the number and metabolic activity of soil microbes. Malathion was found to be rapidly metabolized by a soil fungus, *Trichoderma viride*, and a bacterium *Pseudomonas* sp isolated from soils receiving heavy applications of the insecticide (25a). *Pseudomonas fluorescens* and *Thiobacillus thiooxidans* metabolize phorate and other phosphorothioates.

It is still unclear as to the respective roles of soil microorganisms vs adsorption in the overall disappearance of organophosphate insecticides in soils. Several suspected microbial systems were reported to attack specific phosphate insecticides. Subsequently, the initial chemical hydrolysis of the phosphate linkage was shown to be followed by metabolism of the resultant products. Autoclaving not only reduces the microbial population, but also substantially alters the structure of many organic components in soils. Consequently, steam sterilization is not always a reliable indicator of microbial involvement, particularly if the initial reaction involves the participation of some labile organic compound in soils. For example, malathion and several other phosphate insecticides decomposed much faster in gamma-radiation-sterilized soils than in autoclaved soils. A heat-labile, water-soluble substance that accelerated malathion degradation has been extracted from several nonautoclaved and radiation-sterilized soils (25b). This substance was destroyed by heating soil suspensions for 10 min at 90°C, but remained stable at room temperatures. Thus, a third component, soil organic matter, appears to be important in phosphate degradation. The finding of a specific organic catalyst for this class of pesticides illustrates an important concept in the soil chemistry of pesticides, ie, the participation of purely organic reactions in soils not mediated by soil microorganisms. The inhomogeneity of soil organic matter, however, has made an understanding of such reactions difficult.

Oxidation of parathion increases the anticholinesterase activity of this insecticide. Thus paraoxon (**43**) is more toxic than the parent compound (26).

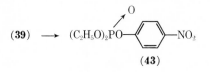

(**39**)   → $(C_2H_5O)_2PO$⎯⟨⟩⎯NO_2

(**43**)

Herbicides

From a research standpoint, the herbicides have been studied more extensively in soils than all other classes of pesticides. Many herbicides are active only when applied to soils. Secondly, and probably more importantly, residual herbicides can damage sensitive crops grown in rotation. As noted previously, about 125 herbicides are marketed commercially. Large numbers of these herbicides belong to a few chemical classes of compounds, each exhibiting similar properties in soils. The important chemical classes include the *phenoxyalkanoic acids* (2,4-D, 2,4,5-T, 2,4-DB, MCPA); the *s-triazines* (simazine, atrazine, propazine); the *phenylcarbamates* (IPC, CIPC, barban); the *chlorinated aliphatic acids* (dalapon, TCA); the *phenylureas* (fenuron, monuron, diuron); the *dinitrobenzenes* (DNBP, trifluralin, benefin); the *benzoic acids* (amiben, 2,3,6-TBA); the *dipyridyls* (paraquat, diquat); and the *thiocarbamates* (EPTC, vernolate). Within these nine classes are found the majority of the important herbicides. Certain herbicides, such as amitrole, are often considered as separate entities. A number of reviews cover the chemistry of herbicides in soils (28–30). Detailed discussions of reactions considered in the following sections will be found in these articles.

Phenoxyalkanoic Acids. The phenoxyalkanoic acids constitute the major single group of herbicides now used in the United States. Production of 2,4-D, 2,4,5-T, and their esters and salts accounted for 32% of the total herbicide production in 1967 (31). The phenoxy herbicides are related by the following common structure:

$$O(CH_2)_nCO_2R$$

(44)

Microbial metabolism is the principal mechanism of phenoxyalkanoic acid breakdown within soils. As indicated in Figure 4, loss of 2,4-D occurs more quickly than the

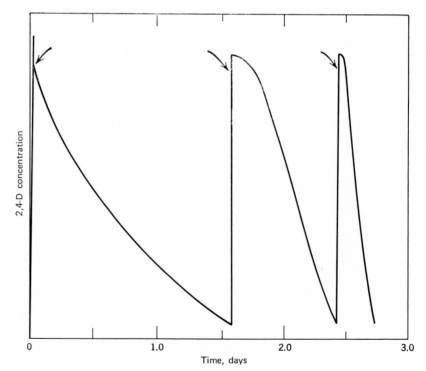

Fig. 4. Metabolism of 2,4-D by soil microorganisms. Degradation occurs more rapidly after each addition of 2,4-D (indicated by arrows.) Adapted from (32).

loss of either MCPA or 2,4,5-T, which is perhaps the most persistent phenoxy herbicide. Warm, moist, and well-aerated soil with ample organic matter favors the growth of microorganisms known to degrade the phenoxides; herbicide persistence can be expected to be fairly short in this environment. The rate of breakdown may also depend on the development of an adaptive population. Repeated increments of 2,4-D (Fig. 4) build up a microbial population which utilizes the herbicide as a carbon source; persistence, after each addition, becomes progressively shorter. An interesting corollary of this is the ability of MCPA-enriched soils to degrade other phenoxyacetic acids, sometimes faster than soils enriched in the test herbicides.

The two major routes of phenoxyalkanoic acid metabolism in soils appear to be (A) initial attack and removal of the aliphatic side chain, followed by alteration of the aromatic ring, and (B) direct hydroxylation of the benzene moiety, often with product accumulation.

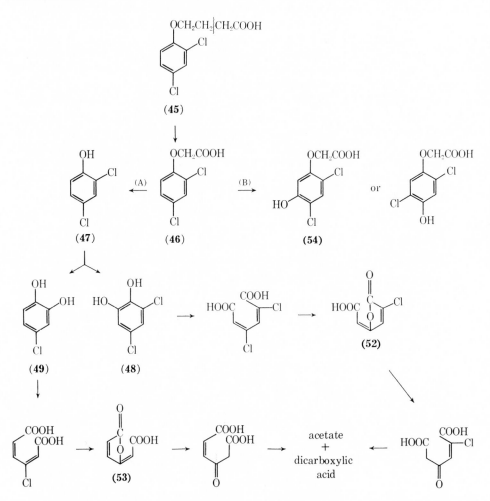

Pathway (A) may involve β-oxidation, ie, progressive cleavage of two-carbon fragments along the aliphatic chain. Thus, 2,4-DB (**45**) is converted in soil to its two-carbon analog, 2,4-D (**46**), perhaps via a crotonic acid intermediate. By another mechanism, a *Flavobacterium* sp cleaves the ether bond in a 2,4-dichlorophenoxyalkanoic acid directly, with formation of 2,4-dichlorophenol (**47**) and the fatty acid. The common metabolite in pathway (A) is the substituted phenol. Ring hydroxylation, a well-known mode of biological detoxication, apparently occurs next. In cultures and enzyme preparations of the soil-isolated bacterium *Arthrobacter* sp, 2,4-D is first converted to 2,4-dichlorophenol, then to 3,5-dichlorocatechol (**48**). By an analogous process, MCPA is cleaved to 4-chloro-2-methylphenol, then to an unidentified catechol. All steps require molecular oxygen. Other organisms may release chlorine during hydroxylation, affording 4-chlorocatechol (**49**) from 2,4-D. Cleavage of catechols may occur either adjacent to a hydroxyl, yielding a muconic semialdehyde (**50**), or between the hydroxyl, with formation of a muconic acid (**51**). Only muconic acids have thus far been isolated from cultures containing the phenoxy herbicides.

(**50**)   (**51**)

Further metabolism may proceed via lactone formation, eg (**52**) and (**53**) (observed with 2,4-D and MCPA), including loss of any carbon-4 halogen, and ultimate oxidation to carbon dioxide and, in chlorinated compounds, chloride.

Pathway (B), the second major route of phenoxyalkanoic acid metabolism, proceeds by hydroxylation of the aromatic ring. However, β-oxidation to a phenoxyacetic acid may occur initially. The fungus *Aspergillus niger* produces *ortho*- and *para*-hydroxylated phenoxyalkanoates from the unsubstituted acids; the same organism forms 5-OH-2,4-D (**54**) and 5-OH-MCPA as major products of 2,4-D and MCPA. The formation of 6-hydroxy intermediates by certain bacteria has been postulated; subsequent ether cleavage would yield catechols directly.

The relative importance in soils of the alternate metabolic pathways whereby phenoxies are degraded is unclear. Soil conditions which govern distribution of microbial populations may be the most influential factors.

The phenoxyalkanoic acids decompose in aqueous solution in sunlight. The major reactions occurring are the fission of the ether bond and sequential replacement of the halogen atoms by hydroxyl groups:

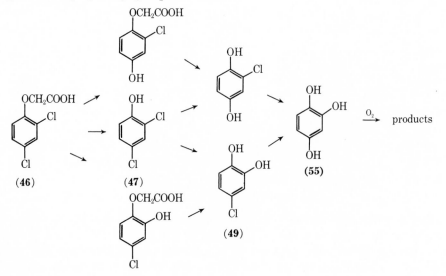

A trihydroxybenzene (**55**) is the ultimate photolysis product but this is susceptible to oxidation in air and can only be isolated (as the acetate) when an oxidation inhibitor such as sodium bisulfite is added to the reaction mixture. Oxidation of trihydroxyphenol by air gives dark-colored polymeric material resembling humic acid.

s-**Triazines.** The *s*-triazines are primarily used for weed control in corn. Structurally, herbicidal *s*-triazines are generally 2-substituted derivatives of the 4,6-bis-(alkylamino)-*s*-triazines (**56**), where X may be —Cl, —SCH₃, or —OCH₃, and R, R' are alkyl groups.

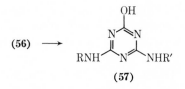

(**56**)

With a few exceptions, the *s*-triazine herbicides are considered to be immobile, nonvolatile, and unaltered in solution by sunlight. Simazine adsorbed on filter paper is inactivated by sunlight. Chemical and, to a lesser extent, biological reactions play an important role in altering these herbicides in soils. The principal degradation product is the corresponding 2-hydroxy-4,6-bis(alkylamino)-*s*-triazine (**57**). The dehalogenation reaction, in this case, is a chemical reaction facilitated by protonation at the surface of a clay colloid.

(**56**) ⟶

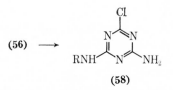

(**57**)

Certain soil fungi (*Aspergillus fumigatus, Rhizopus stolonifer,* and *Penicillium decumbens*) can dealkylate the side chain groups to produce the corresponding 2-chloro-4-amino-6-alkylamino-*s*-triazines (**58**).

(**56**) ⟶

(**58**)

Detailed radioactivity studies with alkyl-¹⁴C- and ring-¹⁴C-labeled *s*-triazine herbicides indicate that chemical reactions are primarily responsible for degrading the herbicidal 2-chloro-*s*-triazines in most soils.

Phenylureas. Phenylurea derivatives find wide application as herbicides, particularly in cotton growing. Most members of this family possess the 1,1-dimethyl-3-phenylurea moiety (**59**) as part of their structure, where X and Y may be various substituents, such as —H, —Cl, —CF₃, and —OC₆H₅. A few of the phenylureas are 1-methoxy 1-methyl substituted compounds.

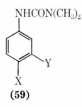

(59)

In soils, the phenylureas behave somewhat like the s-triazines, being relatively immobile and nonvolatile. Degradation occurs under conditions most conducive for microbial activity, ie, warm, moist soils with high organic matter content. Although the causative organisms are difficult to isolate, the following pathway has been proposed for the degradation of the phenylurea herbicides in soil:

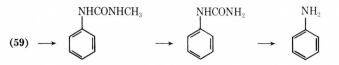

All of the corresponding products in the above pathway have been detected from the herbicides monuron, diuron, and chloroxuron. N-Dealkylation is a reaction common to many pesticides and is apparently mediated by mixed-function oxidase systems requiring molecular oxygen.

Urea herbicides readily undergo photolysis. Metabromuron (**60**), a representative urea herbicide, decomposes in aqueous solution on exposure to sunlight (33). The major product is 3-(p-hydroxyphenyl)-1-methoxy-1-methylurea (**61**). Present in lesser amounts are 3-(p-bromophenyl)-1-methylurea (**62**) and p-bromophenylurea (**63**). Substituted diphenyl derivatives may also be formed.

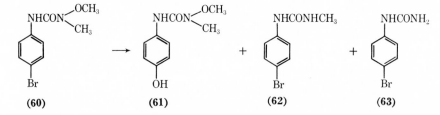

Chloroxuron decomposes on irradiation and degrades by sequential loss of N-methyl groups. Monuron, neburon, diuron, linuron, and fenuron are also degraded by sunlight.

Phenylcarbamates. The phenylcarbamate herbicides differ considerably from the methylcarbamate insecticides in soils. The herbicidal carbamates are lost from soils by volatilization and metabolism by soil microorganisms.

This group has as its primary structure a phenylcarbamic acid esterified with various alcohols (**64**).

(64)

Microorganisms (*Pseudomonas striata, Flavobacterium, Azobacterium*, and *Achromobacter*) metabolize these herbicides to an aniline, an alcohol, and carbon dioxide, as shown with CIPC (**65**).

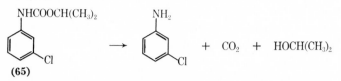

(**65**)

The acylanilides are also aniline-based herbicides closely resembling the phenyl-carbamates. An important member of this group is propanil (**66**), the principal herbicide used for weed control in rice. Soil microorganisms cleave propanil to yield 3,4-dichloroaniline and propionic acid. The dichloroaniline undergoes a condensation reaction to form the 3,3′, 4,4′-tetrachloroazobenzene (**67**).

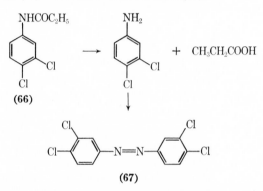

Azobenzenes have also arisen from several other chlorosubstituted anilines when incorporated in soils.

The carbamate herbicide IPC (**68**) photodecomposes by at least two pathways.

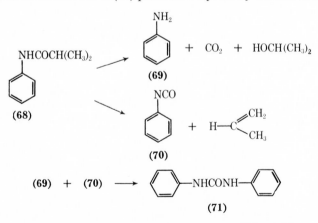

Reaction of the aniline (**69**) and phenyl isocyanate (**70**) yields *sym*-diphenylurea (**71**).

Chlorinated Alkyl and Aryl Acids. Two chlorinated aliphatic acids, TCA (**72**) and dalapon (**73**), are used extensively as herbicides.

CCl_3COOH CH_3CCl_2COOH

(**72**)   (**73**)

Microorganisms rapidly metabolize most members of this family of herbicides by replacing the halogen to form the corresponding hydroxy or keto acids. For example, dalapon yields pyruvic acid via enzymic hydrolysis by a system isolated from an *Arthrobacter* sp. Little is known about the metabolism of the chlorinated aromatic acids. Replacement of chlorine by the hydroxyl group commonly occurs when an aqueous solution of a chlorinated aromatic acid is exposed to sunlight. Reductive dehalogenation may also take place when chlorine is replaced by hydrogen; however, this reaction is more favored in hydrogen donor solvents such as cyclohexane.

Loss of chlorine from the ring is preferred in certain orientations: Amiben, 3-amino-2,5-dichlorobenzoic acid, loses the chlorine atom preferentially from the 2 position. A chlorine atom which is substituted meta to a carboxylic acid group is more resistant to photolysis than an ortho or para chlorine substituent. In addition, chlorinated phenylacetic acids also undergo reaction in the side chain and the probable sequence of reactions is indicated with fenac (**74**).

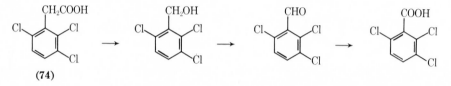

(**74**)

Amitrole. Amitrole gained national prominence in 1960 when residues of this herbicide were detected in cranberries. Metabolic studies with amitrole have been conducted in plants, where several adducts have been isolated and identified. The fate of amitrole (**75**) in soil is governed principally by the activity of soil microorganisms, adsorption on soil colloids, and chemical transformations. Free radicals, derived from microbial or chemical processes in soils, probably play an important role in amitrole degradation. A number of model free-radical-generating systems yield the following products:

$$\text{amitrole structure} \longrightarrow \text{NH}_2\text{CONH}_2 \ + \ \text{NH}_2\text{CN}$$

(**75**)

Similar systems are probably responsible for amitrole degradation in soils.

Amitrole degradation by ultraviolet irradiation affords the same products that are obtained by riboflavin-sensitized photolysis at the wavelengths of visible light. Urea and cyanamide can be obtained from the reaction mixture; the photolysis parallels the reaction of amitrole with hydroxyl radicals generated by Fenton's reagent (34).

Dinitroanilines. Trifluralin (**76**), nitralin, and bensulide are relatively new herbicides used in cotton and soybean cultivation. Photodecomposition, volatility, and soil microorganisms contribute to the disappearance of these herbicides. Degradation proceeds by sequential removal of the *N*-alkyl groups as shown with trifluralin:

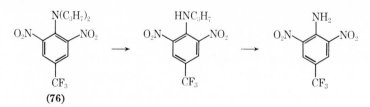

(**76**)

Under anaerobic field conditions, ie, in flooded soils, the nitro group in trifluralin is reduced to an amino group.

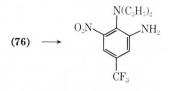

(76) $\longrightarrow$

Combinations of these two pathways occur in certain soils.

Dipyridyls. The organic cations, paraquat (**77**) and the closely related diquat (**78**), are desiccants and aquatic herbicides. In soils, they are tightly adsorbed by cation exchange to some soil particles and, consequently, inactivated almost immediately. In soil enrichment cultures, however, bacteria have been isolated which carry out the following series of reactions:

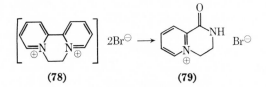

Similar degradation products of paraquat have been identified in photochemical studies. Diquat decomposes in sunlight and affords a tetrahydropyridopyrazidinium salt (**79**) as a major product.

(78)   (79)

Arsenical Pesticides

Inorganic arsenicals, such as arsenic trioxide, As_2O_3; arsenic pentoxide, As_2O_5; sodium arsenate, Na_2HAsO_4; sodium arsenite, nominally Na_3AsO_3; lead arsenate, $Pb_3(AsO_4)_2$; calcium arsenate, $Ca_3(AsO_4)_2$; and Paris green, $3Cu(AsO_2)_2 \cdot Cu(C_2H_3O_2)_2$, have been used in agriculture for many years as insecticides, herbicides, soil sterilants, and silvicides. Arsenic is ubiquitous in nature and occurs naturally in soils; the average content in soils collected from various countries is about 5 ppm. Quantities ranging from a trace to 14 ppm have been reported for most soils.

The continued use of arsenic pesticides in early pest control programs has increased the residual content in certain soils. For example, arsenic residues of 440 ppm have been reported in orchard soils with a history of lead arsenate applications. Beans exhibit toxic symptoms when grown on these soils (35). A more recent survey reports residues of up to 2500 ppm in soils treated with lead arsenate in the 1930s.

The inorganic arsenicals have largely been replaced by the less toxic organic arsenicals. Two important organic arsenicals in use today are DSMA, $CH_3AsO(ONa)_2$, and cacodylic acid, $(CH_3)_2AsO(OH)$. They are considerably less toxic than the inorganic arsenicals; LD_{50} equals 1800 and 830 mg/kg, respectively. DSMA is particularly effective against the perennial weed johnson grass and affords one of the most economical methods of control in areas of heavy infestation. Cacodylic acid is a contact herbicide which will defoliate or desiccate a large variety of plants.

Rice is particularly sensitive to arsenic residues in soils (36). One theory to explain the greater sensitivity of rice to arsenic residues maintains that under waterlogged conditions, soils are in a highly reduced condition and arsenate is reduced to the more toxic arsenite. The toxic trivalent form would seriously impair growth of rice. Another theory maintains that reduction of arsenic to arsine by certain soil fungi could explain the hypersensitivity of rice. The alkylarsines are foul-smelling gases, highly toxic to mammals. Trimethylarsine, $(CH_3)_3As$, is produced by certain strains of molds in the presence of arsenic trioxide or sodium cacodylate (37). It has been suggested that arsenic is lost from soils as an alkyl arsine.

Arsenate residues in soils exist in the following five forms: water-soluble, iron, aluminum, calcium, and nonextractable arsenate. The amount of any one form varies, depending on the amount of cation present. The water-soluble arsenate is the most toxic to plants. The iron and aluminum salts are extremely insoluble and consequently are relatively less phytotoxic.

Fungicides

Fungicides are used at low rates as seed protectants and disinfectants on a major portion of the total crop acreages. On more limited acreages, however, fairly high rates are used to control diseases on citrus, apples, and other deciduous fruits and, to a lesser extent, on other fruits and vegetables (1).

Most fungicides can be conveniently placed in the following classes of compounds: sulfur, copper, mercury, carbamate, imidazoline, quinone, and guanidine. Captan is an important fungicide not readily classified in the above system. Unfortunately, little published literature exists on the fate of many organic fungicides in soils. Several excellent references exist on fungicides (38,39) and their properties in soils (40).

Sulfur and Copper. The inorganic fungicides, including sulfur and Bordeaux mixture, $CuSO_4 + Ca(OH)_2$, are among the oldest known pesticides. Elemental sulfur was first recommended for the control of powdery mildews (*Ershiphaceae*) in 1835 (38). In soils, elemental sulfur is oxidized slowly by chemical means, but rapidly by microbiological reactions. Nonfilamentous, chemoautotrophic bacteria of the genus *Thiobacillus*, heterotrophic bacteria, fungi, and actinomycetes are the principal sulfur oxidizers in soil. The product of microbial oxidation is the sulfate ion, the form in which higher plants absorb practically all of their sulfur.

Copper, like arsenic, is a natural component in soils and ranges in concentration from 1 to 50 ppm (41). Organic soils tend to fix copper and hence it does not move from its site of application. In France, for the last sixty years, Bordeaux mixture has been applied annually to vineyard soils at a rate of about 2770 lb of copper sulfate per acre without phytotoxic effects. In the United States, 80 lb per acre of copper sulfate added over thirty-two years to some Long Island potato soils caused no plant injuries.

Mercury. Mercurous chloride, Hg_2Cl_2, and the organic mercurials, including methyl, ethyl, and phenyl mercury derivatives, are used as seed disinfectants. The action of mercurous and mercuric chloride applied to soils results from the release of mercury vapor. Soil factors which increase the reduction of mercury salts to metallic mercury include greater soil moisture and organic matter contents, pH, and temperature.

Metallic mercury and trace amounts of phenylmercury acetate (PMA) were detected in the air surrounding soil following PMA treatment (42). Ethyl mercury acetate treatment afforded approximately equal amounts of mercury vapor and the vapor of the ethylmercury compound. Methylmercury compounds gave methylmercury vapor with a trace quantity of mercury vapor. After 30–50 days a large portion of soil-applied organic mercurial compound was found to be unaltered.

Carbamates. Most commercially available carbamate fungicides are derivatives of dithiocarbamic acid, NH_2—CS_2—H. These derivatives may be classified into the following three groups: thiuram disulfides, R_2N—CS_2—CS_2—NR_2; metallic dithiocarbamates, R_2N—CS_2—metal; and ethylenebisdithiocarbamates, (CH_2—NH—CS_2)$_2$—metal.

The nonvolatile fungicides nabam (**80**) and ferbam (**81**) were reported to be inactivated nonbiologically in soils, whereas Semesan (**82**) was metabolized by soil microorganisms. Under similar conditions captan (**83**) was recovered unchanged after 150 days (43).

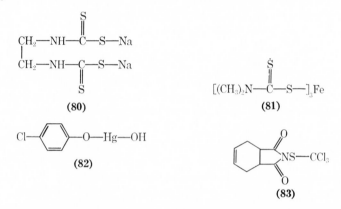

(**80**)   (**81**)

(**82**)

(**83**)

Nabam in soils produces a number of volatile fungitoxic materials, including carbon disulfide; ethylene diisothiocyanate, (CH_2—N=C=S)$_2$; and carbonyl sulfide, CSO (44). In addition, ethylenediamine, NH_2—CH_2—CH_2—NH_2; ethylene(thiocarbamoyl)disulfide; and ethylenebis(thiocarbamoyl)monosulfide have been reported as degradation products of ethylenebisdithiocarbamate fungicides (39).

Vapam (**84**) decomposes in soil to the methyl isothiocyanate and N,N'-dimethylthiourea. Decomposition is apparently a chemical process favored by increased soil temperature and decreased moisture content. At 40°C and 6% moisture, vapam degradation occurs after 1.5–2.5 hr (45).

$$CH_3—NH—\overset{\displaystyle S}{\overset{\|}{C}}—S—Na$$

(**84**)

Bibliography

"Soil Chemistry" in *ECT* 1st ed., Vol. 12, pp. 614–633, by E. R. Graham, University of Missouri.

1. Econ. Res. Ser., *Quantities of Pesticides Used by Farmers, USDA Agr. Econ. Rept. 131*, Washington, D.C. (1964).
2. P. C. Kearney, R. G. Nash, and A. R. Isensee, "Persistence of Pesticide Residues in Soils," in M. W. Miller and G. C. Berg, eds., *Chemical Fallout: Current Research on Persistent Pesticides*, Charles C Thomas, Springfield, Ill., in press.
3. R. E. Duggan, *Pesticide Monitoring J.* **2**, 2 (1968).

4. U.S. Tariff Commission, *United States Production and Sales of Pesticides and Related Products*, U.S. Govt. Printing Office, Washington, D.C., 1968.
5. R. L. Metcalf, ed., Vols. 1–6, *Advances in Pest Control Research*, Interscience Publishers, a division of John Wiley & Sons, Inc., New York, 1957–1965.
6. A. S. Crafts, *The Chemistry and Mode of Action of Herbicides*, Interscience Publishers, Inc., New York, 1961.
7. G. W. Bailey and J. L. White, *J. Agr. Food Chem.* **12**, 324–332 (1964).
8. S. M. Lambert, *J. Agr. Food Chem.* **16**, 340–343 (1968).
9. J. M. Hamaker, C. A. I. Goring, and C. R. Youngson, "Sorption and Leaching of 4-Amino-3,5,-6-trichloropicolinic Acid in Soils," in A. A. Rosen and H. F. Kraybill, eds., "Organic Pesticides in the Environment," *Advan. Chem. Ser.* **60**, 1966, Chap. 2.
10. M. J. Frissel, *Verslag Landbouwk. Onderzoek.* **67.3**, 1–54 (1961).
11. J. G. Calvert and J. N. Pitts, Jr., *Photochemistry*, John Wiley & Sons, Inc., New York, 1966.
12. N. J. Turro, *Molecular Photochemistry*, W. A. Benjamin, Inc., New York, 1965.
13. R. G. Nash and E. A. Woolson, *Science* **157**, 924–927 (1967).
14. F. A. Gunther and D. E. Ott, *Residue Reviews* **10**, 70–84 (1965).
15. G. Wedemeyer, *Appl. Microbiol.* **15**, 569–574 (1967).
16. E. Fleck, *J. Am. Chem. Soc.* **71**, 1034 (1949).
17. F. Matsumura, G. M. Boush, and A. Tai, *Nature* **219**, 965–967 (1968).
18. G. Wedemeyer, *Appl. Microbiol.* **16**, 661–662 (1968).
19. C. W. Bird, R. C. Cookson, and E. Crundwell, *J. Chem. Soc.* **1961**, 4809.
20. J. D. Rosen and W. F. Carey, *J. Agr. Food Chem.* **16**, 538 (1968).
21. J. D. Rosen, D. J. Sutherland, and G. R. Lipton, *Bull. Environ. Contam. Toxicol.* **1**, 133 (1966).
22. G. L. Henderson and D. G. Crosby, *J. Agr. Food Chem.* **15**, 888 (1967).
23. W. N. Yule, M. Chiba, and H. W. Morley, *J. Agr. Food Chem.* **15**, 1000 (1967).
24. A. M. Abdel-Wahab, R. J. Kuhr, and J. E. Casida, *J. Agr. Food Chem.* **14**, 290 (1966).
25. A. M. Abdel-Wahab and J. E. Casida, *J. Agr. Food Chem.* **15**, 479–487 (1967).
25a. F. Matsumura and G. M. Boush, *Science* **153**, 1278–1280 (1966).
25b. L. W. Getzin and I. Rosefield, *J. Agr. Food Chem.* **16**, 598–601 (1968).
26. D. G. Crosby, E. Leitis, and W. L. Winterlin, *J. Agr. Food Chem.* **13**, 204 (1965).
27. R. D. O'Brien, *Toxic Phosphorus Esters*, Academic Press, Inc., New York, 1961.
28. P. C. Kearney and D. D. Kaufman, eds., *Degradation of the Herbicides*, Marcel Dekker, Inc., New York, in press.
29. P. C. Kearney and C. S. Helling, *Residue Reviews* **25**, in press.
30. C. M. Menzie, *Metabolism of Pesticides, Special Scientific Report No. 96*, Washington, D.C., 1966.
31. *The Pesticide Review—1968*, Agricultural Stabilization and Conservation Service, U.S. Dept. of Agriculture, Washington, D.C., 1968.
32. J. S. Whiteside and M. Alexander, *Weeds* **8**, 204–213 (1960).
33. J. D. Rosen and R. F. Strusz, *J. Agr. Food Chem.* **16**, 568 (1968).
34. J. R. Plimmer, P. C. Kearney, D. D. Kaufman, and F. S. Guardia, *J. Agr. Food Chem.* **15**, 996 (1967).
35. R. Dickens and A. E. Hiltbold, *Weeds* **15**, 299–304 (1967).
36. E. A. Epps and M. B. Sturgis, *Soil. Sci. Soc. Am. Proc.* **4**, 215–218 (1939).
37. F. Challenger, *Chem. Ind.* **54**, 657 (1935).
38. E. G. Sharvelle, *The Nature and Uses of Modern Fungicides*, Burgess Publishing Co., Minneapolis, Minn., 1961.
39. A. L. Morehart and D. F. Crossman, *Studies on the Ethylenebisdithiocarbamate Fungicides*, *Delaware Expt. Sta. Bull. 357*, 1965, 26 pp.
40. C. A. I. Goring, *Ann. Rev. Phytopathology* **5**, 285 (1967).
41. F. A. Gilbert, "Copper in Nutrition," in A. G. Norman, ed., *Adv. Agr.* **40**, 147–177 (1952).
42. Y. Kimura and V. L. Miller, *J. Agr. Food Chem.* **12**, 253–257 (1964).
43. D. E. Munnecke, *Phytopathology* **48**, 581 (1958).
44. W. Moje, D. E. Munnecke, and L. T. Richardson, *Nature* **202**, 831 (1964).
45. N. J. Turner and M. E. Corden, *Phytopathology* **53**, 1388 (1963).

P. C. Kearney, J. R. Plimmer, and C. S. Helling
U.S. Department of Agriculture

SOLDERS AND BRAZING ALLOYS

Most of the metal articles in use today are assemblies of two or more parts. There are numerous methods of joining these parts together, and one of the most common is to solder or braze. Soldering and brazing are basically similar. The process may be defined as a method of joining metallic surfaces by flowing between them by capillary attraction alloys of lower melting point than the metals to be joined. The metal surfaces remain unmelted but are solidly united when the solder or brazing alloy solidifies. The temperature at which the joint is made is the chief feature which differentiates between soldering and brazing. Solders are alloys which melt below 800°F. The brazing alloys melt above 800°F.

The modern concept of soldering and brazing is to consider them both as welding processes. They differ from other welding processes in that the filler metal (solder or brazing alloy) is distributed throughout the joint by capillarity and in that the metal surfaces being joined are not melted. Thus the surfaces to be joined by soldering or brazing must be closely fitted in order to obtain the desired capillary attraction. In other welding processes the filler metal is either puddled into relatively wide gaps or the metal surfaces being joined are partially melted and bonded together by fusion, or a combination of puddling and fusion is used. See Welding.

Fundamentals of Soldering and Brazing

Certain fundamental principles must be recognized in order to form successful joints with solders or brazing alloys. If these are observed the actual making of the joint is relatively simple, and unskilled workmen may obtain a high proficiency after a short training period. The essential requirements for obtaining good joints may be divided into six steps: (*1*) design, (*2*) preparation of joint surfaces, (*3*) fluxing, (*4*) assembling and jigging, (*5*) heating, and (*6*) final cleaning.

Design.   There are two basic types of joint, butt and lap, and though these may appear in a variety of forms, all are essentially one or the other or a combination of the two. The area of a butt joint is necessarily limited to the cross section of the pieces being brazed, and the butt joint is not generally used except where lap joints cannot be accommodated by the shape of the parts. The most commonly used joint is the lap where the joint can be adjusted in length to give the desired strength. This is particularly true with soldered joints which do not have as high strength per square inch as brazed joints do. The use of lap joints also materially helps in the jigging of the assembly and often eliminates entirely the need for external jigs.

The strength of a soldered or brazed joint increases as the joint thickness increases. However, below 0.001 in. clearance in the joint, irregularities of the surfaces may cause blocks where metal-to-metal contact occurs, which will prevent the flow of the alloy and result in an improperly filled joint area. Consequently, clearances of 0.001–0.005 in. are normally recommended. If dissimilar metals with large differences in thermal expansion are being brazed, it may be necessary to use other clearances in order to have the proper clearances at the brazing temperature.

Preparation of Joint Surfaces.   Cleanliness is an important factor in soldering or brazing as grease, oxide, scale, and dirt of any kind will interfere with the formation of the bond. Either chemical or mechanical methods may be used in preparing the surface. Oil or grease is preferably removed by chemical means. Many reliable cleaning compounds are available, and the choice depends to a large extent on the nature of the oil or grease to be removed. Mechanical methods of removal of such substances are not recommended as they do not completely remove the film. Oxides and scales may be removed either by a suitable pickle or by mechanical means, such as filing, grinding, emerying, or sandblasting. Where a pickle is used, the particular pickle selected depends upon the type of base metal being cleaned. See Metal surface treatments.

Parts should not be allowed to stand for extended periods of time after cleaning before soldering or brazing, as some metals build up oxide films which are sufficient to interfere with the proper flow of the solder.

Fluxing. With few exceptions, a flux is required. Fluxes are used to prevent the oxidation of the filler metal and of the surfaces of the metals being joined during the heating. The flux will also dissolve oxides that may form during the heating operation. The flux should be fluid, chemically active, and free from excessive fuming at the temperature used for joining. Both joint surfaces and the solder metal should be covered with a thin layer of flux. Flux is applied so that the surfaces are thoroughly wetted; brushing is the preferred method although other methods, such as dipping or spraying, may be used.

Many fluxes have been developed. Both inorganic and organic fluxes are used for soldering. The common inorganic fluxes usually contain zinc chloride, ammonium chloride, hydrochloric acid, or hydrofluoric acid, either alone or in combination with each other. Of the organic fluxes, rosin is the best known and most widely used. However, other organic acids and organic halogen-containing compounds have been successfully used. Organic fluxes as a class are weaker than the inorganic ones; any residues left after soldering are in general much less corrosive, and in some cases need not be removed afterward.

The brazing fluxes normally have a sodium or potassium borate base with additions of boric acid, alkali metal fluorides, bifluorides, or other halides, depending upon the conditions of use. The flux should be designed to melt somewhat lower than the brazing alloy used and must be effective in removing the oxides of the particular base metal being brazed. It is possible to omit the use of fluxes in brazing if the brazing is conducted in a strongly reducing atmosphere which will prevent the formation of oxides on the surface both of the metals being joined and of the brazing alloy. A typical example is the copper brazing of steels in a hydrogen atmosphere.

Assembling and Jigging. After fluxing, the parts to be joined must be assembled. Where possible, it is advantageous to preplace the filler metal. Thin sheet or washers may be used between flat surfaces. On tubular members, rings made of rectangular strip or round wire are used. These rings may be inserted in grooves cut in the tubes or laid on projecting shoulders. It is preferable to place the alloy inside the joint in intimate contact with the parts but away from the source of heat. Otherwise, as the filler metal is usually of lighter gage than the parts being joined, the filler metal will heat more rapidly than the assembly and melt and fall off before the assembly is heated to the proper temperature.

Joints should be designed to be self-supporting as far as possible, but on some joints a jig is required to hold the parts in place. Jigging sometimes requires considerable ingenuity. The jig should be as simple and as light as possible, with the contact area between the jig and the assembly kept to a minimum.

Heating. The choice of the method of heating depends on such factors as the size and shape of the assembly and the quantities to be brazed. It is important that both members of the joint be heated uniformly and reach the brazing temperature as close to the same time as possible. In order to obtain good wetting and flow of the filler metal the joint surfaces must be heated slightly above the temperature at which the filler metal flows.

There are many methods of applying heat; the particular method used is not important provided it is capable of heating the joint surfaces to the proper temperature efficiently. In general, the strength of the joint is not affected by the heating method. With low-melting solders, heat is commonly applied by means of a soldering iron. The higher temperatures of the brazing alloys require other methods, such as various types of torches, furnaces, salt baths, high-frequency induction heating, or various means of heating by electrical resistance. In soft soldering, too, any of these methods may also be used where the size and quantities of assemblies warrant it.

Final Cleaning. After soldering or brazing, the final cleaning consists of removing residual flux, oxides which have formed on areas unprotected by flux, and excess filler metal which may have been added to the joint. Residual flux is removed because it may result in serious corrosion of the assembly if allowed to remain. Solution in hot water or suitable chemical baths is the usual procedure. Oxides are removed by appropriate pickling solutions depending upon the nature of the base metal. They may also be removed by mechanical means. Proper control of the amount of filler metal used will prevent the necessity of the removal of excess alloy. This is one of the advantages of soldering and brazing in contrast to other welding processes where large quantities of excess metal are generally used, the removal of which makes the final cleaning a significant factor in the cost of the joint. Excess filler metal when present is usually removed by mechanical means.

Solders

Solders, commonly referred to as soft solders, are alloys which melt below 800°F. Various tin–lead alloys are the most widely used, but many other combinations of metals melting below 800°F can be used. Antimony, for instance, may be added for the purpose of increasing the hardness of the tin–lead alloys. Silver is sometimes added to tin to raise the tensile strength, corrosion resistance, and electrical conductivity. Bismuth and indium are alloyed with lead and tin when very low melting temperatures are required. Alloys melting at 100°F or below may be made by the addition of mercury to the bismuth alloys. In Table 1 are listed some of the most commonly used solders.

The selection of a solder for a particular job depends on several factors. For fast soldering or furnace soldering a short melting range, such as the 60% tin alloy, ie Sn60, is in general desirable. Where a joint is to be wiped, as in soldering lead pipe, a long range is preferable and an alloy such as the 40% tin alloy, Sn40, would be selected. If strength at temperatures above room temperature is necessary, one of the higher-melting silver alloys would be chosen.

The use of solder may be dictated by the temperature that can be tolerated in assembling components. Using 50% tin at temperatures not exceeding 450°F, electrical joints are made in telephone equipment, radios, TV sets, etc, without destroying adjacent parts. Solder may also be used without destroying the hardness or spring properties of sheet metal. Solders are frequently used for sealing food containers, and for improving and maintaining electrical and heat conductivity in connections.

Soft solders are not satisfactory for joints subjected to any appreciable stress, and good design then demands reinforcement of the joint by interlocking seams, crimping,

Table 1. Chemical Composition Requirements of Solder,[a] wt %

Composition	Tin	Lead	Antimony	Bismuth, max	Silver	Copper, max	Iron, max	Zinc, max	Aluminum, max	Total of all others, max	Melting range, °F[b] Solidus	Liquidus
Sn70	69.5–71.5	remainder	0.20–0.50	0.25		0.08	0.02	0.005	0.005	0.080	360	380
Sn63	62.5–63.5	remainder	0.10–0.25	0.10–0.25		0.08	0.02	0.005	0.005	0.080	360	360
Sn62	61.5–62.5	remainder	0.20–0.50	0.25	1.75–2.25	0.08	0.02	0.005	0.005	0.080	350	372
Sn60	59.5–61.5	remainder	0.20–0.50	0.25		0.08	0.02	0.005	0.005	0.080	360	375
Sn50	49.5–51.5	remainder	0.20–0.50	0.25		0.08	0.02	0.005	0.005	0.080	360	420
Sn40	39.5–41.5	remainder	0.20–0.50	0.25		0.08	0.02	0.005	0.005	0.080	360	460
Sn35	34.5–36.5	remainder	1.60–2.00	0.25		0.08	0.02	0.005	0.005	0.080	360	475
Sn30	29.5–31.5	remainder	1.40–1.80	0.25		0.08	0.02	0.005	0.005	0.080	360	490
Sn20	19.5–21.5	remainder	0.80–1.20	0.25		0.08	0.02	0.005	0.005	0.080	360	530
Sn10	9.00–11.0	remainder	0.20, max	0.03	1.70–2.40	0.08		0.005	0.005	0.10	514	570
Sn5	4.5–5.5	remainder	0.50, max	0.25		0.08	0.02	0.005	0.005	0.080	518	594
Sb5[c]	94.0, min	0.20, max	4.00–6.00			0.08	0.08	0.030	0.030	0.030	450	464
Pb90[d]		remainder	11.00–13.00	0.25		0.08	0.02	0.005	0.005	0.080	476	478
Ag1.5	0.75–1.25	remainder	0.40, max	0.25	1.3–1.7	0.3	0.02	0.005	0.005	0.080	588	588
Ag2.5	0.25, max	remainder	0.40, max	0.25	2.30–2.70	0.30	0.02	0.005	0.005	0.030	580	580
Ag5.5	0.25, max	remainder	0.40, max	0.25	5.00–6.00	0.30	0.02	0.005	0.005	0.030	579	689

[a] From Federal Specification QQ-S-571c.
[b] Approximately, and for information only.
[c] Cadmium, max, 0.030.
[d] Arsenic, max, 0.600.

riveting, and other mechanical aids.   Strengths on the order of 3500–7000 psi are obtainable in tension.   The joints are relatively easy to break by shock or tearing forces. In tubular sleeve-type joints the strength of the joint can be controlled by adjusting the length of the sleeve.

Brazing Alloys

The brazing alloys melt above 800°F and were formerly called hard solders to distinguish them from the soft solders.   As any alloy which melts below the melting range of the metals being brazed and which will wet and flow on the surfaces to be joined may be used as a brazing alloy, it follows that the number of possible brazing alloys is practically unlimited.   Literally hundreds of alloys have been used for brazing, but in the tables below only those which have been used in considerable volume and which are readily available commercially are listed.   Even with this qualification the tables are by no means a complete listing of alloys used for brazing but are simply indicative of the range of typical brazing alloys.   The alloys given in the following tables were selected by a joint committee of the American Welding Society and the American Society for Testing and Materials.

The **aluminum–silicon alloys** (Table 2) are used for joining the following grades of aluminum and aluminum alloys: 2S, 3S, 4S, B50S, J51S, 53S, 61S, 62S, 63S, and cast alloys A612 and C612.   BA1Si-3, 4, and 5 are general-purpose alloys.   Alloys 3 and

Table 2.   Aluminum–Silicon Alloys

	AWS-ASTM classification			
	BAlSi-2	BAlSi-3	BAlSi-4	BAlSi-5
silicon, %	6.8–8.2	9.3–10.7	11.0–13.0	9.0–11.0
copper, %	0.25	3.3–4.7	0.30	0.30
iron, %	0.80	0.80	0.80	0.80
zinc, %	0.20	0.20	0.20	0.10
magnesium, %		0.15	0.10	0.05
manganese, %	0.10	0.15	0.15	0.05
chromium, %		0.15		
titanium, %				0.20
aluminum, %	remainder	remainder	remainder	remainder
solidus, °F	1070	970	1070	1070
liquidus, °F	1135	1085	1080	1095
brazing temperature range, °F	1110–1150	1060–1120	1080–1120	1090–1120

Table 3.   Copper–Phosphorus Alloys

	AWS-ASTM classification				
	BCuP-1	BCuP-2	BCuP-3	BCuP-4	BCuP-5
phosphorus, %	4.75–5.25	7.00–7.50	5.75–6.25	7.00–7.50	4.75–5.25
silver, %			4.75–5.25	5.75–6.25	14.50–15.50
copper, %	remainder	remainder	remainder	remainder	remainder
solidus, °F	1310	1310	1190	1190	1190
liquidus, °F	1650	1460	1485	1335	1475
brazing temperature range, °F	1450–1700	1350–1550	1300–1550	1300–1450	1300–1500

Table 4. Silver Brazing Alloys

AWS-ASTM classification	Composition, %						Solidus, °F	Liquidus, °F	Brazing temperature range, °F
	Silver	Copper	Zinc	Cadmium	Nickel	Tin			
BAg-1	44–46	14–16	14–18	23–25			1125	1145	1145–1400
BAg-1a	49–51	14.5–16.5	14.5–18.5	17–19			1160	1175	1175–1400
BAg-2	34–36	25–27	19–23	17–19			1125	1295	1295–1550
BAg-3	49–51	14.5–16.5	13.5–17.5	15–17	2.5–3.5		1170	1270	1270–1500
BAg-4	39–41	29–31	26–30		1.5–2.5		1240	1435	1435–1650
BAg-5	44–46	29–31	23–27				1250	1370	1370–1550
BAg-6	49–51	33–35	14–18				1270	1425	1425–1600
BAg-7	55–57	21–23	15–19			4.5–5.5	1145	1205	1205–1400
BAg-8	71–73	remainder					1435	1435	1435–1650
BAg-8a[a]	71–73	remainder					1410	1410	1410–1600
BAg-13	53–55	remainder	4.0–6.0		0.5–1.5		1325	1575	1575–1775
BAg-18[b]	59–61	remainder				9.5–10.5	1115	1325	1325–1550
BAg-19[c]	92–93	remainder					1435	1635	1610–1800

[a] Lithium, 0.15–0.3%.   [b] Phosphorus, 0.025%.   [c] Lithium, 0.15–0.3%.

5 are usually recommended for furnace or dip brazing processes, and alloy 4 is suggested for torch brazing. BA1Si-2 is supplied only as a coating on aluminum alloy sheet. It is essential to use fluxes with these alloys. After brazing, the flux must be removed to prevent corrosion. Most of the common fluxes used on aluminum alloys are soluble in boiling water.

The **copper–phosphorus alloys** (Table 3) are used primarily for joining copper and copper alloys, with some limited use on silver, tungsten, and molybdenum. As the phosphorus in these alloys will react with iron and nickel to form brittle phosphides at the interfaces of the joints, they should not be used on ferrous metals or on alloys containing more than 10% nickel. The alloys have self-fluxing properties when used on copper; however, a flux is recommended when they are used on all other metals, including the copper alloys. Joints made with these alloys on copper have excellent electrical and thermal properties. Corrosion resistance is generally equal to, or better than, that of the base metal joined, except in sulfurous atmospheres above room temperatures. In sulfurous atmospheres the joints disintegrate rapidly. This group of alloys is unique in that, unlike most brazing alloys, they are preferably used at temperatures well below the liquidus temperatures. The alloys containing over 6% phosphorus are difficult to fabricate, and the forms available are limited. When thin sheet or light-gage wires are required, the lower phosphorus content alloys should be selected.

Table 5. Alloys of Precious Metals

	AWS-ASTM classification			
	BAu-1	BAu-2	BAu-3	BAu-4
gold, %	37.0	79.5	34.5	81.5
copper, %	remainder	remainder	remainder	
nickel, %			2.5–3.5	remainder
other elements, total, %	0.15	0.15	0.15	0.15
solidus, °F	1815	1635	1785	1740
liquidus, °F	1860	1635	1885	1740
brazing temperature, range, °F	1860–2000	1635–1850	1885–1995	1740–1840

The **silver brazing alloys** (Table 4) are employed for joining all ferrous and nonferrous metals except aluminum, magnesium, and those metals which melt below the liquidus of the brazing alloys. They are widely used in the refrigeration and electrical equipment fields. They are also used in making automobiles, airplane parts, household goods, plumbing and heating fixtures, and silverware. The alloys having the lower silver contents are generally used in industrial applications, whereas those over 60% silver are mostly used in the arts, as in the fabrication of jewelry and silverware. Alloys 1, 2, and 7 are general-purpose alloys which can be used for a wide variety of applications. Alloys 3 and 4 are employed for joining carbide tool tips to tool shanks. They are also used extensively for brazing the chromium–nickel types of stainless steel. Alloys 5 and 6 are used particularly for brazing in the electrical industry. Also, along with alloy 7, they are used in the dairy and food industries, where cadmium alloys might be prohibited. Alloy 8 is used primarily in the assembling of electronic and vacuum tubes where a brazing alloy free from volatile constituents is required. Alloys 13, 18, and 19 are used chiefly for joining sterling silver articles.

Many other silver brazing alloys are available, and it is advisable to consult with the suppliers of these alloys for advice regarding the best alloy to use for a specific purpose.

The **alloys of precious metals** (Table 5). Brazing filler metals of the BAu classification are used for the brazing of iron, nickel, and cobalt-base metals where resistance to oxidation or corrosion is required. Because of their low rate of interaction with the base metal, they are commonly used on thin base metals. These filler metals are usually used with induction, furnace, or resistance heating in a reducing atmosphere or in a vacuum and with no flux. For other applications, a borax–boric acid flux is used. BAu-1, 2, and 3 brazing filler metals, when used for different joints in the same assembly, permit variation in brazing temperature so that step brazing can be used. BAu-4 brazing filler metal is used to braze a wide range of high-temperature iron and nickel-base alloys.

The **copper- and zinc-bearing alloys** (Table 6) are used for brazing various ferrous and nonferrous metals. Their relatively high melting ranges limit their use to materials

Table 6. Copper and Copper–Zinc Alloys

	AWS-ASTM classification				
	BCu-1	BCu-1a	BCu-2[a]	RBCuZn-A[b]	RBCuZn-D[b]
copper, %	99.90, min	99.0, min	86.5, min	57–61	46–50
zinc, %				remainder	remainder
tin, %				0.25–1.00	
iron, %				*	
manganese, %				*	
nickel, %					9.0–11.0
phosphorus, %	0.075				0.25
lead, %	0.02			0.05*	0.05*
aluminum, %	0.01			0.01*	0.01*
silicon, %				*	0.04–0.25
other elements, total %	0.10	0.30[c]	0.50[d]	0.50[e]	0.50[e]
solidus, °F	1980	1980	1980	1630	1690
liquidus, °F	1980	1980	1980	1650	1715
brazing temperature range, °F	2000–2100	2000–2100	2000–2100	1670–1750	1720–1800

[a] These chemical requirements pertain only to the copper oxide and do not include requirements for the organic vehicle in which the copper oxide is suspended.

[b] This AWS-ASTM classification is intended to be identical with the same classification that appears in the Specification for Copper and Copper-Alloy Welding Rods (AWS Designation A5.7, ASTM Designation B-259).

[c] Total other elements requirement pertains only to the metallic elements for this filler metal.

[d] Total other elements requirement pertains only to metallic elements for this filler metal. The following limitations are placed on the nonmetallic elements:

Constituent	%, max
chlorides	0.4
sulfates	0.1
oxygen	remainder
nitric acid–insoluble matter	0.3
acetone-soluble matter	0.5

[e] Total other elements, including the elements marked with an asterisk (*), shall not exceed the value specified.

which melt at correspondingly high temperatures. Copper, for instance, is used extensively in brazing ferrous metals, nickel and copper–nickel alloys. It is generally used in furnace brazing with a hydrogen or dissociated ammonia atmosphere and usually without flux. However, on metals that have constituents with refractory oxides (chromium, manganese, silicon, titanium, etc) a flux may be required. The zinc-bearing alloys usually require a flux. They may be applied by using torch, furnace, or induction heating processes. Where it is important for the brazing alloy to match the color of the steel or other white alloys it is customary to use one of the nickel-bearing alloys.

Bibliography

"Solders and Brazing Alloys" in *ECT* 1st ed., Vol. 12, pp. 634–640, by C. H. Chatfield, Handy & Harman.

1. R. M. MacIntosh, *Welding J. (N.Y.)* **31**, 881 (1952).
2. *Brazing Filler Metals*, AWS A5.8–62.
3. *Welding Handbook*, American Welding Society, New York, Sect. 1, 6th ed., 1968; Sect. 2–5, 5th ed., 1964–1967.
4. ASTM Standard Specification for Soft Solder Metals, B32–49.

C. H. Chatfield
Handy & Harman

SOLVENT RECOVERY

The term solvent recovery generally refers to a portion of a process in which a liquid is separated, purified, and returned to the process for reuse as a solvent. Some typical solvent-recovery processes are (*1*) the recovery of solvents vaporized in the drying of synthetic fibers and films, plastics and rubber products, smokeless powder, impregnated fabrics, adhesives, printing inks, paints, lacquers, enamels, and other organic coatings; (*2*) the recovery of solvents used in the solvent extraction of natural fats and oils, or in other solid–liquid extractions; (*3*) the recovery of solvents used in the solvent refining of mineral or vegetable oils, in other liquid–liquid extractions, in extractive and azeotropic distillations, or in gas-absorption processes; (*4*) the recovery of solvents used for degreasing fabricated parts, for drycleaning, or for other washing operations; (*5*) the recovery of solvents used as mediums for chemical reactions or for the precipitation and crystallization of solids.

If an organic liquid is separated and purified, but is not returned to the process for reuse as a solvent, the operation cannot strictly be referred to as solvent recovery. However, except for the use to which the liquid is put, such operations may resemble solvent-recovery systems in every respect. Typical of such closely related processes are (*1*) the recovery of natural gasoline and light hydrocarbons from natural and casinghead gas; (*2*) vapor recovery operations in petroleum refining; (*3*) the recovery of alcohol from fermentation gases; (*4*) the recovery of organic liquids from wood distillation and from coal tar distillation operations; (*5*) the recovery of products or of unused reagents from chemical syntheses.

The growth of solvent-recovery systems has followed closely the growth of processes which manufacture and use organic solvents. While condensation of alcohol from vapor-laden air has been practiced since ancient times, some 99% of today's solvent recovery systems were put into operation after 1930. Some of these systems were installed as integral parts of the processes using the solvents, while others were separate units installed either simultaneously with or some time after the installation of the main process. Many processes are still operating either without solvent recovery or with very inefficient systems. Despite the profitability of solvent-recovery units, some industries have regarded them as unnecessary complications. In a few cases state and local laws on atmospheric and stream pollution have made their installation mandatory.

Types of Recovery Systems

Solvent-recovery units may differ greatly from one another with respect to the type and arrangement of the equipment used. This is well illustrated by Figures 1–8, a

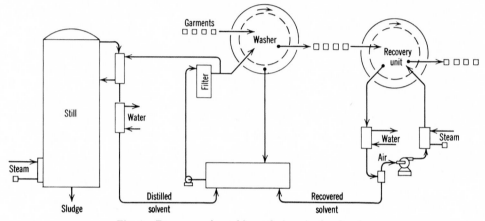

Fig. 1. Recovery of perchloroethylene in drycleaning.

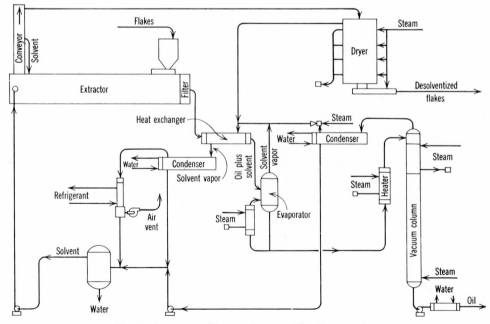

Fig. 2. Recovery of hexane in vegetable oil extraction.

series of flow diagrams adapted from actual installations or commercial designs. Adsorption, for example, plays an important part in Figure 5, absorption in Figure 4, crystallization in Figure 8, and liquid–liquid extraction in Figure 3. Figure 7 is exclusively a distillation process. The system in Figure 2 makes considerable use of vacuum

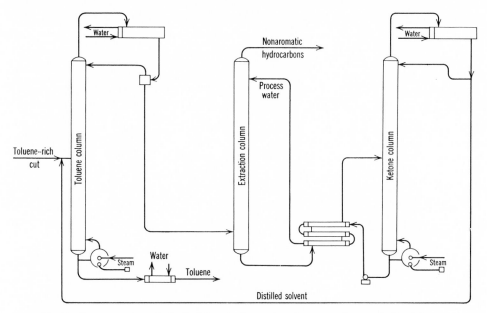

Fig. 3. Recovery of methyl ethyl ketone in azeotropic process for producing toluene.

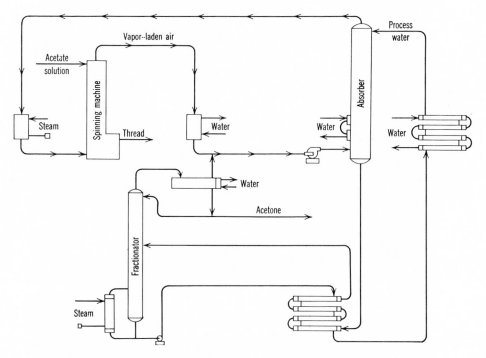

Fig. 4. Recovery of acetone from cellulose acetate spinning using water scrubbing.

while that in Figure 6 operates to a large extent under pressure.   Figure 1 shows a batch process, Figure 5 shows a semicontinuous process, and the rest show truly continuous processes.   Filtration, drying, refrigeration, decantation, and evaporation appear in varying degrees and modifications in the different applications.

Differences in design are often called for, not only where the applications are different, but also where the applications are similar or the same.   Thus Figures 1–8

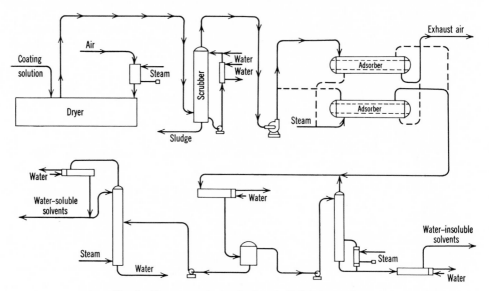

Fig. 5.   Recovery of mixed solvents in fabric coating.

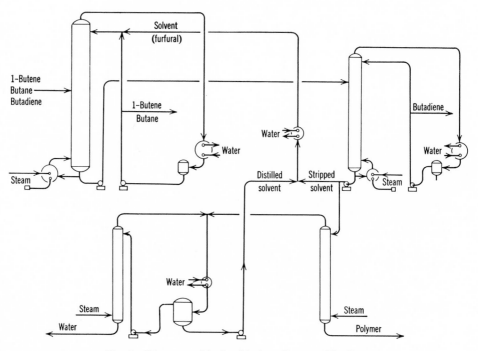

Fig. 6.   Recovery of furfural in butadiene purification.

are not standard designs for the industries in question, nor do they necessarily represent best practice for the particular application indicated. Figure 4, for example, shows a water absorption system for recovering acetone from cellulose acetate spinning. Such a system is economical only where a large supply of cold water is available for cooling. Where water temperatures are high, an adsorption system similar to Figure 5 might well be best for the same application.

The principal similarity which exists among solvent-recovery systems lies in the approach which must be taken in order to ensure a satisfactory design. The same techniques, such as absorption, adsorption, extraction, filtration, distillation, and condensation are available in all cases. The same factors, such as volatility, solubility,

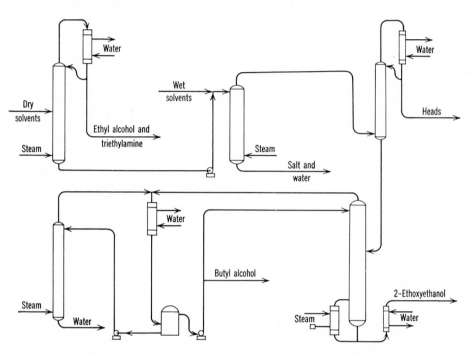

Fig. 7. Recovery of mixed solvents in antibiotic manufacture.

thermal stability, corrosion, purity requirements, capacity, steam and water conditions, safety, and economics must be taken into account. In general, each unit must be individually designed. Standardization is desirable only where all factors are substantially the same.

Solvent recovery units may be classified according to the method used to make the initial separation between the solvent and the product or the waste material. This separation may be made by any one of the following: (*1*) mechanical separation, such as filtering, settling, draining, decanting, centrifuging, or pressing; (*2*) extraction, using another liquid to wash out solvent or product; (*3*) evaporation; (*4*) fractional distillation; (*5*) drying the product in the absence of air or gas; (*6*) drying in the presence of air or gas followed by condensation, absorption, or adsorption.

Although the initial step in a solvent-recovery system may serve to classify it, subsequent steps may be of a different type. Thus in Figure 1 the mechanical separation of garments from solvent is followed by drying in the presence of air. In Figure 5 drying the product in air is followed by adsorption of solvent, evaporation, condensation, decantation, and distillation.

It may also be noted that some of the flow diagrams show more than one type of solvent-recovery system. Thus in Figure 6 the separation of the furfural solvent from butadiene and its separation from polymer may be considered different units. The same may be said for separating hexane from solvent–oil mixtures (*miscella*) and from

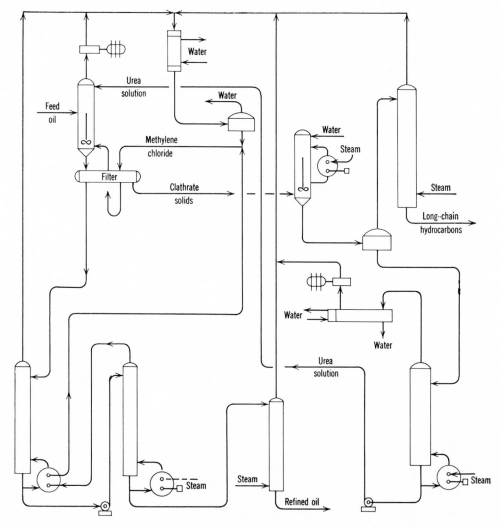

Fig. 8. Recovery of diluent and clathrating solution in solvent refining of oil (12,13).

spent flakes (*marc*) in Figure 2. In Figure 8 the recoveries of volatile methylene chloride and of nonvolatile urea solution are accomplished by entirely different techniques.

Mechanical Separation. Draining of liquids from solids is a common operation in solvent processes. The solids are usually retained either by stationary or by moving screens, perforated plates, baskets, belts, or chains. Agitation by shaking, tumbling, or rotation is sometimes used to promote separation. One example of draining is shown in Figure 2 where the conveyer which moves the extracted flakes from the extractor to the dryer allows solvent to drain back into the extractor. Another would be the draining of liquid from fabricated parts in solvent degreasing operations.

Filtration (qv) through screens or cloths is indicated where solids are present in smaller particle sizes. Batch, semicontinuous, or continuous filters using either pressure or vacuum are all available for separating solvents from solids. Because most solvents are volatile or valuable or flammable or noxious, closures on solvent filters should be pressuretight, or at least, fumeproof. Presses or open filters are usually avoided.

Continuous pressuretight filters have been used for years in the solvent refining of lubricating oils. The operation of the filter shown in Figure 8 is typical of such equipment. Here the solids are first filtered, then carried on a moving screen or drum to a section where they are washed with solvent, and then to sections where liquid is drawn out and the dry solids dumped into a screw conveyor. It is preferred to operate such filters under some vacuum so that any leakage in the rotary joints will be inward.

Equipment of this type is generally expensive and its use can be justified only where the throughput is relatively large. Batch filtration, on the other hand, may also be expensive because of the amount of operating labor required for removing the solids. An exception to this is the separation of dirt, fines, or impurities present only in small quantities. In such cases, disposable filter mediums are often used, and the filter is made sufficiently large that only occasional cleaning is required. Filtration is frequently complicated by the presence of polymer-forming, sticky, or very finely divided materials. Pretreatment with heat or chemicals, the addition of filter-aids, or of surface-active agents may be effective in solving these problems.

Settling and *decantation* may be used either for separating two immiscible liquids or for separating contained solids from liquid. Removal of liquid from the thickened solid is never complete, but in separating small quantities of sludge this may not be important.

Perforated basket centrifuges, centrifugal filters, and solid bowl centrifuges use centrifugal force to increase the efficiency of draining, filtering, and settling operations respectively. See Centrifugal separation. Examples may be found in the "extraction" step in drycleaning, in separating crystals from solvent solutions, and in the clarification of extracts. *Pressing* between rolls, inside membranes, or in screw expellers has also been employed for promoting separation of solvent from fibrous or flaky materials. *Magnetic* or *electrostatic separators* may also be used in appropriate cases.

The removal of dust, lint, or mist from air streams is often required to prevent the fouling of carbon adsorption beds. *Air filters* may be used except where the gases contain adhesive or varnish-forming materials. In the latter case, entrainment separators or slat-packed towers with water-washed surfaces are usually used (see Fig. 5). Such an arrangement may also serve to remove corrosive impurities from air.

Extraction (qv). Solvent and product are sometimes separated by washing with water or with another solvent (1,2). In Figure 3 the solvent is washed out of the nonaromatic hydrocarbon product with water. In other cases, for example penicillin concentration, the product is washed out of the solvent with an aqueous solution. Centrifugal contactors, mixer-settlers, and sieve-plate, baffled, or packed towers with or without agitation are some of the types of equipment available for *liquid–liquid extraction*. If the liquids are clean and of low viscosity, extractors of reasonable size will often give effective countercurrent contact equivalent to ten or more theoretical stages. However, if the liquids are viscous or turbid or if they tend to form emulsions, very low extraction efficiencies may be expected. Sometimes the solvent must be washed out of a solid product in which case various types of washers or *solid–liquid extractors* are used.

Extraction is sometimes accompanied by a chemical reaction between a component of the washing solution and the impurity (or product material) being extracted. In other cases the extraction step may be preceded by a chemical reaction step in which the impurity is converted into a more easily extractable compound. Chemical treatment may also be used to produce solid precipitates or immiscible liquid layers which can then be removed by mechanical separation. Chemical reaction techniques are particularly prominent in solvent recovery systems associated with the solvent extraction of metallic compounds from ores. Extraction with chemical reaction is performed in equipment of the same type as extraction without chemical reaction. However, the design calculations are somewhat more complex.

Evaporation (qv). Solvents may often be recovered by simple evaporation and condensation. A common example of this is found in drycleaning (see Fig. 1), where grease and dirt must be removed from the solvent. Package stills, complete with condenser, feed preheater, and semiautomatic controls are available for this purpose. These units are inexpensive and their use in industries other than drycleaning is often advantageous. Operation may be under vacuum, for high-boiling Stoddard solvent, or at atmospheric pressure, for lower-boiling chlorinated solvents. Feed may be either batch or continuous. Heating is usually with indirect steam, but provision for gas or electricity is made in some units. Direct steam may be added for final removal of solvent from the sludge.

The evaporator in Figure 2 is of the natural circulation type. The heater which follows is also an evaporator, namely a one-through type. The latter design is advantageous since the boiling point at the inlet is considerably lower than at the outlet. Other types of evaporators may, of course, be used. Multiple-effect evaporation is occasionally used as is its counterpart, vapor reuse distillation. The vaporization of methylene chloride in Figure 8 is double effect. Here condensing vapors from the second, high-pressure, column are used to supply heat to the reboiler of the first column.

When evaporation is used to separate a volatile solvent from a nonvolatile product, the product leaves saturated with solvent at the pressure in the evaporator. The introduction of direct steam into the boiling liquid will reduce the solvent partial pressure, but it is much more efficient to use steam stripping columns like the last one in Figure 6. Here the steam not only supplies heat and dilutes the vapor, but its condensate serves to wash the desolventized polymer out of the column. The vacuum column in Figure 2 is different in that condensation of steam and consequent emulsification must be avoided. Indirect heat is supplied to the top of the column to prevent solvent vaporization from lowering the temperature. This piece of equipment is in effect a falling-film evaporator with a steam purge.

Fractional Distillation. Solvents are commonly separated from products, from water, or from other solvents by the use of fractional distillation. The mixtures to be separated are usually nonideal, and are often azeotropic or partially miscible. Where more than one solvent is used, several different types of compounds may be present in one solution. The man-made mixtures resulting from the use of a variety of solvents are often much more complex than the mixtures of homologous structure found in nature or in reaction products. In Figure 7 for example, two alcohols, an amine, an alcohol ether, water, salt, and traces of hydrocarbons are all present in the feed.

Such complex mixtures may be separated into individual components, but a long series of distillation operations is often required. Additional components may be added to serve as entrainers in azeotropic or extractive steps (3,4). Fortunately a partial separation of mixed solvents is often sufficient to permit their reuse. Figures 5 and 7 would both require additional columns if complete separations were to be made. In Figure 7, a change in just one of the solvents used in the manufacturing process might necessitate a complete revision in the arrangement of the distillation train.

Methods for estimating multicomponent equilibria from binary data have been developed and designs of this type can now be calculated with assurance. Sieve-plate or bubble-cap columns are generally specified, but packed columns and other designs are also used. Operation is normally continuous except where very small quantities are to be handled. See Distillation.

Drying in the Absence of Air. Drying solids by vaporizing the solvent in the absence of circulating air or inert gas has many advantages. Explosion hazards may be reduced, mechanical circulation of air may be eliminated, and the problem of recovering the vaporized solvent is greatly simplified. On the other hand, heat transfer to the solid may be more difficult, and a higher temperature will be required for vaporization unless a reduced pressure is used.

Heat is usually supplied by surfaces heated with indirect steam or other mediums, although radiant lamps are occasionally used. The dryer in Figure 2 is of the rotary shelf type. Agitation and flow of solids is obtained by rotary rakes which move the marc inwardly and outwardly across successive steam-heated platens. Steam-jacketed screw conveyors would accomplish the same result in a somewhat different way. Vacuum drum dryers, cylinder dryers, rotary dryers, or other types of indirect dryers may also be used, provided the solid properties are suitable. Dryers which employ forced circulation of superheated solvent vapors through the solids give good heat transfer and eliminate contact of solids with moving parts or heated surfaces.

The solids discharged from these various dryers may be purged of solvent vapors with direct steam. If they are below 212°F condensation will occur, and where this can be tolerated, steam may be used as a source of heat as well as a diluent. Vacuum designs permit the use of lower temperatures, but solid discharge must be batchwise or through locks.

Drying with Air. Drying in the presence of air permits vaporization of solvent at lower temperatures than would be possible in the absence of air. In addition, hot circulated air gives good heat transfer and does not require contact of the product with hot surfaces. The importance of tight closure is reduced since additional air may be drawn into the dryer without serious consequence. Hot air may be the sole source of heat, or additional conducting or radiating surfaces may be provided inside the apparatus. If combustible solvents are present, a high rate of air circulation is normally used in order to stay well below the lower explosive limit. While flammable mixtures will still exist near the drying surface, the danger of explosion is greatly reduced. Operation may also be above the upper limit. The use of inert gas generators to remove oxygen from the air is good safety practice and can be justified especially where the air stream is recirculated.

Recovery of solvent from the air may be by adsorption, by absorption, or by condensation. Since recovery, particularly in the last case, is never complete, recirculation of air from the recovery system back to the dryer is often employed (see Fig. 1 and 4). Recirculation is not used where the return duct-work is expensive, where the exhaust air is relatively solvent-free, or where it tends to build up undesirable impurities (see Fig. 5). Even with recirculation, a small portion of air is generally discharged through a blower. The resulting suction draws air in through the dryer openings and prevents solvent vapors from contaminating the surrounding atmosphere. If dust is present in the surroundings, filtered air may be supplied at the dryer inlet and outlet. A similar arrangement may be used for inert gas.

Condensation. Vaporized solvents may be liquified either in surface condensers or in direct-contact condensers. Direct contact with water is largely restricted to solvents with very low water solubilities, since excessive losses in the decanted waste water would otherwise occur. Direct contact with cold solvent may be used in any case. Surface condensers are almost exclusively shell-and-tube. When vertical vapor-through-tube condensers are used, the condensed liquid and the vent gas leave at temperatures approaching those of the cooling water. With other types, separate vent condensers should be used or additional passes for vent gas provided inside the main condenser. Extended surface designs are advantageous for lean air streams where sensible heat is an appreciable proportion of the total. See Heat transfer.

The air or gas leaving a condenser contains solvent to the extent of its vapor pressure at the condensing temperature. The fourth column in Table 1 gives the volumetric concentration of solvent remaining in the air after condensation at 77°F. Comparison with the third column reveals that condensation from circulating air streams operating below the lower explosive limit would not be possible for most of the common flammable solvents. This restricts the use of condensation to high-boiling solvents, to nonflammable solvents, to systems using inert gas, or to systems where relatively small proportions of air are present.

Even in these cases, solvent loss may be high if an appreciable amount of air or gas is discharged to the atmosphere. Refrigeration of the vent gas to 32°F will reduce the concentration of solvent to about 20 or 30% of that obtained at 77°F (see Fig. 2). Compression of the gas before cooling and condensing has been much used by the petroleum industry in natural gasoline and vapor-recovery plants. In solvent recovery, however, compression has not found much favor, perhaps because of the somewhat corrosive nature of many solvent-air mixtures.

Absorption. Solvents may be recovered from air or gas streams more or less completely by scrubbing with a suitable liquid. Such operations constitute absorption (qv). It should be observed, however, that while much of the theory of absorption treats packed or continuous contact towers, most of the large absorbers in solvent-recovery plants are of the stagewise type. Bubble-cap, sieve-plate, and baffle-plate columns are used, as are banks of spray chambers arranged for countercurrent flow. Baffle-plate designs, spray designs, and randomly packed towers operating well below maximum capacity give low pressure drops and therefore tend to minimize the cost of power for circulating air. However, after considering all factors, sieve-plate or bubble-cap columns with moderate pressure drop designs are usually chosen.

Water is the principal scrubbing liquid used, the amount required depending largely on the type of solvent recovered. This is shown in the last column of Table 1, which gives the minimum number of moles of water theoretically needed for complete absorption of the compound from one mole of lean air at 77°F and atmospheric pressure. These values would be numerically the same as those in the previous column of Table 1 if the scrubbing liquid formed an ideal solution with the solvent, that is, one obeying Raoult's law. The ratio of the values in these two columns is the activity

Table 1. Recovery Characteristics of Some Typical Solvents

Solvent	Explosive limits in air,[a] atm		Vapor pressure at 77°F, atm	Minimum absorption requirement at 77°F, moles water/mole air
	upper	lower		
methanol	0.360	0.073	0.16	0.26
ethyl alcohol	0.190	0.043	0.075	0.33
n-propyl alcohol	0.135	0.021	0.026	0.37
n-butyl alcohol	0.112	0.014	0.009	0.44
acetone	0.128	0.026	0.29	2.1
methyl ethyl ketone	0.100	0.018	0.13	2.3
ethyl acetate	0.090	0.025	0.12	8
n-butyl acetate	0.076	0.017	0.018	15
ethyl ether	0.480	0.019	0.70	50
benzene	0.071	0.013	0.13	>100
toluene	0.071	0.012	0.037	>100
hexane	0.075	0.011	0.20	>100
decane	0.054	0.008	0.002	>100
carbon tetrachloride			0.14	>100
trichloroethylene			0.10	>100
perchloroethylene			0.025	>100

[a] From *National Fire Codes* (5).

coefficient of the compound in dilute aqueous solution. It is interesting to note that, in a homologous series of alcohols, the one with the highest vapor pressure is the most easily absorbed.

The temperature of absorption is also important in determining the quantity of scrubbing liquid required. With rich air streams the heat of absorption is sometimes removed by indirect cooling either inside the absorption column or externally between stages (see Fig. 4). Sometimes also the scrubbing liquid is refrigerated.

Adsorption (qv). The predominant method for removing solvent vapors from air streams is adsorption on activated carbon (see Vol. 4, p. 153) (6,7). As commonly practiced the air is fed alternately to one of two adsorbing vessels while the other is being fed with low-pressure steam (see Fig. 5).

The steaming operation causes the solvent to be vaporized, the latent heat being supplied by a portion of the steam which condenses into the bed. For some organic solvents this moisture interferes with subsequent adsorption, but for most it does not. If water can be tolerated, its action will be beneficial since its vaporization into the air stream helps keep the temperature down. In any case, if there is a net loss of heat around the cycle, the water content will rise to a point where it will stop adsorption. This water balance is often an important factor in the design of an adsorption unit; and heating, cooling, or special drying periods may have to be included in the cycle of operations.

While such a system has all the inherent disadvantages of intermittent processes, its advantages are for a great many applications unexcelled. Unlike water scrubbing, it may be applied to water-insoluble solvents. Unlike condensation, it may be made to reduce the solvent content of the air to as low a figure as is desired.

The theoretical stream requirement for carbon adsorption is usually less than for absorption. Heats of absorption are high, which means that the vapor pressure of solvent above activated carbon increases more rapidly with temperature than it does above liquid solutions. However, since the steaming operation in adsorption is somewhat inefficient, the actual steam requirement may show no advantage over a favorable water-scrubbing application. On the other hand, with mixed solvents and with those not ideally suited to absorption, water scrubbing may require excessive quantities of steam for reasons already noted. Low pressure drop may be obtained in adsorption systems by reducing the linear velocity of the air and the thickness of the bed. Beds are usually 1–3 ft thick with uniform pellets ranging from $\frac{1}{8}$ to $\frac{1}{16}$ in. in diameter. The beds are commonly supported inside horizontal cylinders so as to give a large flow cross section. Special devices must be used for distributing the air.

The success of carbon adsorption is dependent to a large extent upon proper control of the operating cycle. Where the rate of solvent recovery remains constant, automatic time-cycle controllers are usually used. Where flow varies widely, cut points must be determined by bed saturation. In large installations using many adsorbers, operations are usually staggered to eliminate the peaks in steam demand.

Some volatile compounds react on the surface of activated carbon to give undesirable products or to reduce the activity of adsorption. Entrained solids may foul the bed mechanically. Galvanic corrosion of metal parts may be accelerated by the electrical conductivity of the carbon. Sooner or later the pellets deteriorate and must be replaced. Most of the serious problems involved in adsorption processes have been solved by the manufacturers of activated carbon. Maintenance and operating labor has been minimized by sound engineering of process, equipment, and controls. Activated carbons resistant to poisoning and mechanical failure have been produced by careful control of the manufacturing process.

While carbon adsorption operations are usually conducted batchwise, continuous contacting is also feasible, especially on a large scale. Both moving-bed and fluidized-bed designs have been used for moving carbon particles from the adsorber to the stripper and back. A recent solvent-recovery installation uses a series of shallow fluidized beds to produce countercurrent contact between the solid and gas phases (8).

Adsorption may also be used in quite a different way for the recovery of solvents. Traces of high-molecular-weight compounds, undesirable because of color, odor, or other properties, may often be removed by treatment of the liquid with active carbons, clays, or other adsorbents. See Carbon (Activated carbon); Clays (Uses). These solids are first slurried with the solvent until adsorption is complete. They are then filtered from the purified liquid. The operation can be performed continuously, but it is usually done batchwise, on a small scale.

Automatic Control. Instrumentation has been an important factor in the development of satisfactory solvent-recovery units. Where these units are only auxiliary to the manufacturing operation, they should require as little personal attention as possible. The trend has been toward completely automatic control, which includes not only regulation during the operating period but also during the startup and shutdown periods. A number of fairly large installations require no manual labor other than the operation of a start-and-stop switch. Cycle control has put many sequenced batch operations on a par with continuous ones. A single piece of equipment may thus be used for a whole series of operations. One manufacturer, for example, uses a heated agitated vessel to solvent extract oil from flakes, to filter the marc out of the miscella, to vaporize solvent from the marc under vacuum, and to discharge the dried solids, with automatic control throughout the cycle.

Safety

Safety (qv) is a major factor in the design of most solvent-recovery processes. It may form the basis for choosing the particular solvent employed and it may motivate the installation of the recovery system. It may determine important operating conditions, or call for certain types of building designs, equipment, controls, or accessories. While safety is usually thought of in terms of flammable solvents, consideration must also be given to heat and mechanical hazards, and to the noxious properties of non-flammable solvents as well (9). See Industrial toxicology.

Accepted practice with regard to the handling of flammable solvents is contained in articles and codes of Underwriters Laboratories and of the National Fire Protection Association (5). These codes form a basis for municipal safety laws and for insurance inspection requirements. Subjects covered include the location, design, and ventilation of buildings; size, type, and construction of vessels; arrangement of piping, valves, pumps, and vents; distribution of alarm and extinguishing equipment; instruction of personnel; and many others. The codes for drycleaning and for the solvent extraction of fats and oils include rather detailed descriptions of the standard equipment items available to these industries. Such standardization is in the interest of safety especially where the installations are small and the operating personnel are lacking in scientific and engineering background. At the same time it is the intent of these codes to permit genuine improvements in design.

The use of most of the common flammable solvents creates conditions classified as Class I, Group D by the National Electrical Code (10). Motors and other electrical equipment in these locations should be explosionproof and specifically approved for this class of service. Sources of static electricity such as belt drives should be eliminated, and open flames such as welding torches, matches, or lighted tobacco should be prohibited during operation of the unit. Vents should be protected with flame arresters. Leakage of noxious or flammable vapors into operating rooms should be minimized and adequate ventilation provided to dissipate them. Pressure-relief systems should be used on equipment wherever there is a possibility of excessive internal pressure.

Air-solvent mixtures should be kept out of the explosive range wherever they are present in significant volume. Convenient automatic instruments are available for detecting the approach to this range both outside and inside equipment. It has been recommended that concentrations inside equipment be kept below one half of the lower explosive limit. When rules of this sort prove burdensome, it is sometimes possible under good management to operate with a narrower margin of safety. Careful control must be exercised in such cases and special precautions taken to guard against mishaps. Truly unsafe practice leads, sooner or later, to disaster.

Economics

Many processes employing large quantities of solvents would be economically inoperable were it not for the solvent-recovery systems associated with them. Efficient recovery makes possible the use of expensive solvents where inferior compounds might otherwise have to be used. A 99% recovery per pass may make a process economical where a 95% recovery would not.

Because the efficiency of the recovery unit can make or break a manufacturing process, design of the recovery system should be taken into account as early as possible in the development of the process. It may, for example, prove desirable to evaporate the solvent with steam rather than air since recovery in the latter case is more expensive and less efficient. Savings may also be effected if the process can use a different solvent—one which is nonflammable, less corrosive, or more easily recovered. Mixed solvents are generally more difficult to recover than single compounds, and individual solvents may vary greatly in their ease of recovery. Methanol, for instance, is easily dehydrated by straight fractional distillation. Ethyl alcohol and *n*-propyl alcohol form constant-boiling mixtures with water, and recovery in the anhydrous form necessitates the use of azeotropic entrainers. *n*-Butyl alcohol, on the other hand, is again easily dehydrated since decantation and stripping of the two layers may be used. In those cases where purification of the recovered solvent is difficult, it is sometimes possible for the manufacturing process to tolerate a lesser degree of purity. In others it may be advantageous to sell it or to use it in another process having less exacting requirements.

In 1968 the quoted price for most solvents other than methanol and the hydrocarbons was around 10¢/lb or higher. By comparison, costs of steam, water, and electricity for recovery are small, amounting to only a fraction of a cent per lb of solvent. Operating labor may be virtually eliminated by use of automatic control. Where a choice must be made between recovering solvent or not recovering it, almost the entire value of the solvent may be applied to returning the investment. Solvent recovery can be justified in eearly every case where the volume to be recovered is large.

With smaller throughput, however, fixed costs are proportionately higher and the investment per lb of recovered solvent may become too large for payout in a reasonable time. The size at which recovery can be justified varies with the type of system, the cost of the solvent, and the expected life of the process. Complete carbon adsorption systems have been installed to recover as little as 100,000 lb/yr. Simple stills for contaminated liquids may occasionally prove worthwhile for as little as 10,000 lb/yr.

For most large installations the use of solvent recovery is a foregone conclusion. In such cases utility cost per lb of recovered solvent and solvent loss per lb of recovered solvent are of major concern. Considerable increases in investment and in complexity of the system may be made in order to save small fractions of a cent in unit steam cost. In the recovery of acetic acid from cellulose acetate, for example, azeotropic distillation with a volatile entrainer was first used to reduce the steam required for straight fractional distillation of water from acid. This was followed by the use of less volatile entrainers, and then by liquid extraction with low-boiling solvents. Steam savings were realized in each successive process, and these were further improved by the use of multiple-effect and vapor-reuse techniques. It is now evident that extraction with higher boiling solvents gives still lower steam consumption.

Even with efficient recovery, some makeup solvent is always required. Designers of solvent-recovery equipment often claim that the solvent content of the various waste streams may be held to truly negligible values. While analyses of these streams usually corroborate their claims, inventory balances generally show losses to be much higher than those calculated. Only by a careful study of spillage, venting, gaging practice, chemical instability, and many other factors is it possible to bring these figures into line with each other.

Applications

Processes for the manufacture of synthetic fibers and sheets, impregnated fabrics, coated articles, and related products often use solvents as volatile vehicles for the deposition of the plastic material. While many of the newer resins are formed directly from the liquid by fusion or by chemical reaction, deposition from solvents continues to represent a large proportion of the total. In 1968 these industries in the United States recovered solvents to the extent of about 5 billion lb/yr. Recovery of acetone from cellulose acetate spinning was the largest operation in this group and accounted for a substantial proportion of the total. Usually in these applications the products are air dried and the solvent is recovered from the air by adsorption or absorption. Superheated steam has also been used for drying followed by simple condensation of the vapors. The recovery of solvents vaporized in painting operations is seldom practiced unless the operation is large and continuous. The automotive industry with its very extensive painting operations has long been reluctant to modify those operations so as to accommodate solvent recovery. However, under the influence of air-pollution legislation, acceptable solvent-recovery systems have appeared in recent years.

Solvent extraction of vegetable oils and other solid–liquid extraction processes in the United States use solvent recovery to the extent of 20 billion lb or more per year. Manufacture of oil from soybeans (qv) accounts for the largest part of this volume. Recovery is principally by evaporation from the miscella and drying of the marc using indirect heat or steam (11). Other oils are also extracted in quantity but the expressing process is sometimes favored for seeds of higher oil content. See Vol. 8, p. 797. The pharmaceutical industry also makes extensive use of solvents for the extraction of both natural and synthetic materials.

Solvent refining of lubricating oils and other solvent operations in the petroleum industry entail the recovery of solvents in quantities far exceeding all other applications. A single solvent-refining installation may circulate a billion or more lb of solvent per year (12). Extractive distillations or gas-treating operations can be of similar magnitudes. If steam stripping of absorber oils is classed as a solvent-recovery operation, the total volume of solvent recovered by this industry is truly immense. Liquid–liquid extraction is also being used extensively in the solvent extraction of nuclear intermediates and of other metallic compounds from ores (14). See also Vol. 14, p. 94. The organic streams in these metallurgical operations are ordinarily prepared for reuse by chemical treatment, additional extractions, and mechanical separations. However, evaporation and distillation are also used. Liquid–liquid extractions of appreciable size are also used in pharmaceutical manufacture. See Vol. 14, p. 695.

Solvent washing operations including drycleaning are small in size but large in number. In the United States about a billion lb of solvent are consumed each year in this way. Statistics are not available on the amount of redistillation practiced in this industry but a figure of 3–5 billion lb/yr seems reasonable. See Vol. 7, pp. 308, 316, 320. Improvements in aqueous detergents and the increasing popularity of washable fabrics represent serious threats to the future growth of drycleaning.

The use of solvents as mediums for performing and controlling chemical reactions is the fastest growing area for solvent recovery. About 30 billion lb/yr of solvent cyclohexane are recovered each year in the manufacture of high-density polyethylene alone (15). Recovery is mainly by mechanical separation and redistillation. Polypropylene manufacture and other polymerization processes also include large solvent-recovery operations. Recovery of acetic acid used as a solvent medium for the reaction of acetic anhydride with cellulose now amounts to about 3 billion lb/yr in the United States.

Bibliography

"Solvent Recovery" in *ECT* 1st ed., Vol. 12, pp. 641–654, by C. M. Cooper, Michigan State College.

1. R. E. Treybal, *Liquid Extraction*, 2nd ed., McGraw-Hill Book Co., Inc., New York, 1963.
2. R. E. Emmert and R. L. Pigford, "Gas Absorption and Solvent Extraction" in *Perry's Chemical Engineers' Handbook*, 4th ed., McGraw-Hill Book Co., Inc., New York, 1963, Section 14.
3. E. J. Hoffman, *Azeotropic and Extractive Distillation*, Interscience Publishers, a division of John Wiley & Sons, Inc., New York, 1964.
4. J. A. Gerster, "Distillation" in *Perry's Chemical Engineers' Handbook*, 4th ed., McGraw-Hill Book Co., Inc., New York, 1963, Section 13.
5. *National Fire Codes*, Vol. I, National Fire Protection Association, Boston, 1968–69.
6. N. R. Rowe, "Recovery of Organic Solvents from Polluted Air," *Air Pollution Control Assoc. Paper No. 63-33, Detroit, June, 1963.*
7. L. Scheflan and M. B. Jacobs, *The Handbook of Solvents*, D. Van Nostrand Co., Inc., Princeton, N.J., 1953, pp. 55–78.
8. Anon., *Paint Technol.* **29** (11), 38 (1965).
9. N. I. Sax, *Dangerous Properties of Industrial Materials*, Reinhold Publishing Corp., New York, 1963.
10. *National Fire Codes*, Vol. V, National Fire Protection Association, Boston, 1968–1969.
11. D. Swern, ed., *Bailey's Industrial Oil and Fat Products*, Interscience Publishers, a division of John Wiley & Sons, Inc., New York, 1964, pp. 704–711.
12. H. L. Hoffman et al., *Hydrocarbon Process. Petrol. Refiner* **45** (9), 220–239 (1966).
13. A. Hoppe, "Dewaxing with Urea," in J. J. McKetta, ed., *Advances in Petroleum Chemistry and Refining*, Vol. 8, Interscience Publishers, a division of John Wiley & Sons, Inc., New York, 1964, pp. 192–234.
14. W. D. Jamrack, *Rare Metal Extraction by Chemical Engineering Techniques*, The Macmillan Co., New York, 1963, pp. 125–191.
15. Phillips Petroleum Co., *Hydrocarbon Process. Petrol. Refiner* **46** (11), 222 (1967).

C. M. Cooper
Michigan State University

SOLVENTS, INDUSTRIAL

Industrial solvents may be defined as those liquid products of commercial importance that are capable of dissolving or dispersing other substances, such as polymeric materials, to form useful mixtures. In general, they may be considered as liquid processing agents which act upon solid substances in order to render the solids more commercially useful. The industrial solvent is then frequently discarded or reused to process other materials.

A large number of industries use industrial solvents in many areas of application. They are used in coatings, adhesives, textiles, pharmaceuticals, inks, photographic film, herbicides, and pesticides. Industrial solvents are used in drycleaning operations, metal degreasing and in a multitude of other operations such as lubricating-oil refining, secondary oil recovery, and as automotive and aviation fuel additives.

Solvents are selected for their particular properties from a wide range of chemicals and mixtures of chemicals, some of which have uses other than as solvents. Some physical properties of a number of common industrial solvents are given in Tables 6–8 near the end of this article.

The bulk of solvents are restricted to the broad classes of aliphatic, aromatic and chlorinated hydrocarbons, alcohols, esters, ketones, and glycol ethers. Table 1 contains the production history of some of the major industrial solvent groups as reported by the U.S. Tariff Commission. The production figures listed include all uses of these products, and not just the quantities used for solvent purposes. This makes estimation difficult, but it may be said that the total consumption of chemicals for industrial solvents usage was approximately 12 billion pounds per year in 1966. These 12 billion pounds were distributed in the following way: aliphatic hydrocarbons, 45%; aromatic hydrocarbons, 17%; chlorinated hydrocarbons, 13%; alcohols and esters, 10%; ketones, 8%; and all other categories, 7%.

Table 1. U.S. Industrial Solvent Production[a]

Solvent	Production, million lb			
	1950	1955	1960	1965
alcohols				
amyl alcohols	17	20[b]	25[b]	35[b]
butyl alcohols	324	475	623	827
ethyl alcohol (industrial)	1080	1440	1810	1980
isopropyl alcohol	866	925	1180	1538
methyl alcohol				
esters				
amyl acetates	12	8	8	9
butyl acetates	77	83	107	132
ethyl acetate	92	86	107	114
glycol ethers	110[b]	140[b]	170[b]	280[b]
ketones				
acetone	483	539	761	1124
methyl ethyl ketone	122[b]	195[b]	210[b]	318
chlorinated hydrocarbons				
carbon tetrachloride	217	287	373	594
chloroform	20	40	76	153
ethyl chloride	354	542	545	686
ethylene dichloride	305	510	1267	2456
methylene chloride	40	74	113	211
perchloroethylene	93[b]	178	209	429
trichloroethylene	215[b]	316	353	435
carbon disulfide	426	566	523	757
hydrocarbons (from petroleum)				
benzene	72	723	2267	5203
toluene	329	1038	1743	3810
xylenes	450	700	1976	2410

[a] As reported by U. S. Tariff Commission.   [b] Estimated.

Descriptions of the major solvent classes most commonly used by the major consuming industries are listed in Table 2.

Among the major solvent-consuming industries in 1965 were the coatings industry, 4 billion pounds; the drycleaning industry (qv), 2 billion pounds; and metal cleaning and degreasing, 1 billion pounds. (See Vol. 13, p. 285.) An example of the solvent disappearance by product type for the coatings industry is given in Table 3.

Although industrial solvents are used in many diverse applications, the term solvent is most frequently applied to those materials which are used to dissolve resinous materials, particularly in the field of organic coatings. This discussion is principally concerned with these applications.

Table 2. Some Applications of Industrial Solvents

Application	Solvents commonly used
adhesives	alcohols, esters, ketones, aliphatic hydrocarbons, aromatic hydrocarbons
coatings	alcohols, esters, ketones, aliphatic hydrocarbons, aromatic hydrocarbons, glycol ethers
textiles (manufacturing)	acetone, dimethylformamide, dimethylacetamide
drycleaning	perchloroethylene, aliphatic hydrocarbons
metal degreasing	trichloroethylene, aliphatic hydrocarbons
lubricating oil refining	methyl ethyl ketone, tetrahydrofuran, phenol
inks	alcohols, esters, ketones, aliphatic hydrocarbons, aromatic hydrocarbons, glycol ethers
fuel additives	chlorinated hydrocarbons, alcohols, glycol ethers, aromatic hydrocarbons
photographic film	acetone, methylene chloride, methanol, dimethylformamide
pharmaceuticals	alcohols, esters, ethers, ketones, aliphatic hydrocarbons, aromatic hydrocarbons

Table 3. Solvents Consumed in the Coating Industry in 1965[a]

Solvent	Consumption, million lb
hydrocarbons	
aliphatic	1500
aromatic	1000
other	85
total	2585
alcohols	400
esters	270
ketones	580
other	100
total	3935

[a] Industry estimates.

Theoretical Solubility Concepts

In the past, the solubility of macromolecules, such as those encountered in formulating industrial coatings, was determined by trial-and-error manipulations of end-use characteristics, such as viscosity and dilution ratios. These are still useful and will be discussed in a later section. In more and more initial screening, however, thermodynamic principles are used to determine the ability of an industrial solvent to dissolve a particular resin. Concepts such as the *solubility parameter* in particular have proved useful as tools in screening miscibility of solvent and resin. Other factors such as hydrogen bonding and dipole moment have helped correct anomalies encountered in thermodynamic treatment alone.

Thermodynamic Treatment of Solubility. The dissolution of a material is accompanied by a change in free energy. In order to have the process occur spontaneously the change in free energy, ΔG, must be negative.

$$\Delta G = \Delta H - T\Delta S$$

Generally speaking, the entropy change, ΔS, of a dissolution process will always be positive. To be able to predict whether a dissolution process will take place one must be able to evaluate the enthalpy term, ΔH. If it is negative or numerically smaller than the $T\Delta S$ term, dissolution will take place spontaneously. Prediction of the miscibility or solubility of substances will depend upon the numerical evaluation of the ΔH and ΔS terms. A number of methods have been advanced for determining the change in entropy of a system. These methods vary from the very simple to rather complex mathematical models. All have problems associated with them in that the simple systems are inadequate and the more sophisticated ones are too complex to handle by routine mathematics.

Solubility Parameter. The attempts to quantify the enthalpy term, ΔH, have been much more successful. The cohesive energy density, the potential energy of one cm³ of material, has been very useful in estimating the miscibility characteristics of materials. The more common term used is the square root of cohesive energy density, or solubility parameter. This concept has been used in solvents technology to predict whether a solvent and polymer will be miscible. For a number of years the expression "like dissolves like" has been used where "like" normally meant a substance of similar chemical composition. However, this expression was not always found to be true. In the solubility parameter concept, it is more apt to be true that "like dissolves like" if cohesive energy density is substituted for chemical composition.

Consider two materials, A and B. Before mixing, A contains a series of A—A bonds (interaction forces) and B, a series of B—B bonds. If A and B have like, or similar, cohesive energy densities, then each A—A and B—B bond may be randomly exchanged for two A—B bonds. If the cohesive energy densities are dissimilar, this will not happen and the materials will not be miscible. The new A—B bonds will be similar in energy content to the original A—A and B—B bonds for solutions where there is no change in volume on mixing and the heat of solution is zero or positive.

The cohesive energy density, as mentioned previously, is equal to the potential energy per cm³ of material, but opposite in sign. Thus, the solubility parameter, δ, is given by the following:

$$\delta^2 = \text{cohesive energy density (CED)} = -\frac{E}{V}$$

where E = the energy required to vaporize one mole; V = the molar volume.

If one transports all of the molecules of a substance from the condensed phase to the vapor phase, then all of the molecules are far enough apart for them no longer to attract one another and their potential energy is zero. The heat of vaporization (ΔH_v) is the energy required to vaporize one mole of material. During vaporization some volume change (work) also occurs. Therefore:

$$\text{CED} = \delta^2 = \frac{\Delta H_v - RT}{V}$$

If a compound can be vaporized, then the cohesive energy density and the solubility parameter, δ, may be calculated from experimental data.

The partial molal heat of mixing, ΔH_s, has been estimated by Hildebrand and Scatchard making the following assumptions:

1. The geometric-mean rule is valid. (This is a method of averaging the interaction of two quantities so that the mean value is equal to the square root of the product of the individual quantities. For example, the mean potential energy of the A—B bonds formed in the above discussion of miscibility can be calculated as follows:

$$E_{A-B} = (E_{A-A} E_{B-B})^{0.5}$$

A more complete discussion can be found in reference 4.)

2. The molar volumes of the solvent and solute are not significantly different.
3. Intermolecular interaction forces are central and additive.
4. No volume change occurs on mixing.
5. Mixing is random.

Then:

$$\Delta H_s = V_s (\delta_s - \delta_p)^2 v_p{}^2$$

where V_s = molar volume of the solvent; v_p = volume fraction of the polymer.

Interaction Parameter. Another criterion for solubility is the Flory-Huggins interaction parameter. This term, χ, may be obtained from the chemical potential of the system, $\Delta\mu$; the volume fraction of the polymer, v_p; and the ratio, m, of the molar volumes of polymer and solvent, as shown below.

$$\Delta\mu/RT = \ln (1 - v_p) + \left(1 - \frac{1}{m}\right)v_p + \chi v_p{}^2$$

The theoretical considerations of the Flory-Huggins proposition predict that χ must be equal to or less than some critical value, χ_c, as shown below.

$$\chi_c = 0.5 \left(1 + \frac{1}{m^{0.5}}\right)^2 \qquad \chi \to 0.5 \text{ when } \frac{1}{m} \to 0$$

The value of χ has also been shown to be dependent upon the solubility parameters of the components.

$$\chi = \chi_{\Delta s} + v_s(\delta_p - \delta_s)^2/RT$$

However, the values of $\chi_{\Delta s}$ cannot be predicted accurately and are found to be temperature and concentration dependent.

Correction Factors for Solubility Parameter. Sheehan and Bisio (1) have shown the Flory-Huggins interaction parameter, χ, to be useful in predicting solubility on the basis of homologous series of solvents. However, in the case of solvent blends this has not been investigated. Several authors have used solubility parameters to predict dissolution. Burrell (2) reduced this concept to practice for the coatings chemist. The solubility parameter was insufficient in many cases to explain the solubility phenomena found. Therefore, Burrell added a hydrogen bonding classification which permitted the mapping of the solubility areas as a function of solubility parameter and hydrogen bonding. However, the hydrogen bonding classification was expressed only in the most general terms, ie, strong, medium, and weak. Lieberman (3) attempted to quantify hydrogen bonding, based upon empirical results, on a scale ranging from 0.3 for weak, 1.0 for moderate, to 1.7 for a strong hydrogen bonding. This method, when used for mapping solubilities, improved the predictive aspects of this technique. However, a great many cases remained unexplained even with this semiquantitative treatment of hydrogen bonding. Several authors have gone on to use other constants in conjunction with solubility parameter to explain and predict solubility relationships. Gardon (4) and Crowley, Teague, and Lowe (5) have tried to introduce some measure of polarity of the molecule. Gardon introduced fractional polarity as an additional type of solubility parameter. This *fractional polarity*, p, may be calculated from known physical constants (ionization constant, dielectric constant, and polarizability) and is equal to the fraction of total interactions which are due to dipole–dipole interactions. He has shown that the fraction of interactions due to dispersion forces, d, and induction forces, i, may in turn be calculated from the fractional polarity.

$$p + i + d = 1$$

The use of polar and nonpolar solubility parameters (6) has been advocated where inductive interactions have been neglected. This treatment also requires that the geometric-mean rule be valid for determining the heat of mixing.

Walker (7) has shown that an interaction parameter may be used to correct for deviations from the geometric-mean rule. Gardon (4) has shown that it is possible to calculate this constant from the fractional polarity values of the solvent and solute. Gardon has also shown that a good solvent matches the fractional polarity and solubility parameter of the solute (polymer).

Hydrogen Bonding. Crowley, Teague, and Lowe attempted to incorporate hydrogen bonding into a workable solvent selection system. Gardon recognized the value of assigning some qualitative value to hydrogen bonding. Hansen (8) has deduced a system using a hydrogen-bonding solubility-parameter contribution term, in addition to a solubility parameter for dispersion forces and dipole–dipole interactions. The approximations of hydrogen bonding by most of the investigators were either qualitative or semiquantitative but all failed to take into account the type of hydrogen bonding. Small (9) proposed that hydrogen bonding could be described by two parameters: a donating capacity, D, and an accepting capacity, A. He then proposed the following as a measure of the heat of mixing due to hydrogen bonding, H_{HB}:

$$H_{HB} = v_1v_2(A_1 - A_2)(D_1 - D_2)$$

where v_1 and v_2 are the volume fractions of the components.

Although we do not have at this time any measure of these donating or accepting capabilities, it is interesting to assess the equation qualitatively to see what happens when various types of solvent are mixed. If a donor–acceptor solvent, eg, an alcohol, is mixed with a nonhydrogen-bonding solvent, eg, heptane, then A_1 and D_1 are both greater than zero, also A_2 and D_2 are zero; hence ΔH_{HB} is positive, ie, mixing is endothermic, and the materials tend to be immiscible considering only the heat of mixing. If A_2 and/or D_2 are greater than zero and greater than A_1 or D_1, eg a mixture of an alcohol and a ketone, then ΔH_{HB} can become negative, thus indicating the materials would be miscible, provided all other energy changes are favorable.

There is no doubt that all of these systems provide varying degrees of effectiveness in selecting solvents for polymers. However, in the case of solvent blends it becomes necessary to estimate the solubility parameters of the blend.   In the case of the solubility parameter, δ, it has been shown that the solubility parameter of the blend may be calculated by volume-fraction weighting the solubility parameter of each component as follows:

$$\delta_{\text{blend}} = v_1\delta_1 + v_2\delta_2 + \ldots + v_n\delta_n$$

Most authors have assumed that if the solubility parameter itself can be volume-fraction weighted, then the other parameters may be weighted in the same manner.

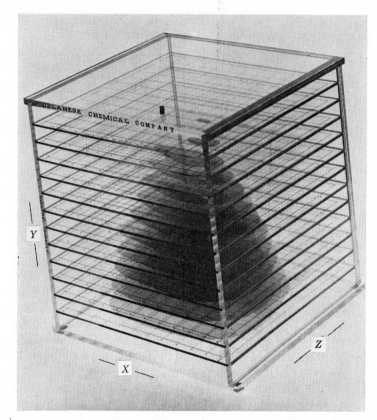

Fig. 1. Three-dimensional solubility model for cellulose nitrate showing solubility parameter on the x-axis, hydrogen bonding on the y-axis, and dipole moment on the z-axis.

Visual Presentation of Solution Behavior.   Crowley, Teague, and Lowe and Hansen give methods for estimating solubility by a three-dimensional representation. Crowley et al. have reduced the three dimensions to two by the use of contour maps. The same effect has been achieved using triangular diagrams by Teas (10).   These modifications help in visualizing and plotting out solvents and mixtures of solvents. Hunt and Katz (11) designed a clear plastic model of the three-dimensional solubility pattern for cellulose nitrate and other resins by plotting solubility parameter on the x-axis, hydrogen bonding on the y-axis, and dipole moment on the z-axis, as shown in Figure 1.

The methods of Burrell, Lieberman, Crowley et al., Gardon, and Hansen can be used to design solvent blends, once sufficient information is available regarding the polymer and its solubility. The normal procedure has been to "construct" a solubility "map" of the solute in terms of solvents and simple solvent blends and plot the individual points as either soluble or insoluble. Then an attempt is made to define an area which includes all or most of the soluble points, realizing that there may be exceptions. The problem arises as to the concentration at which the solubility data are obtained. The point having most significance will be the concentration at which the

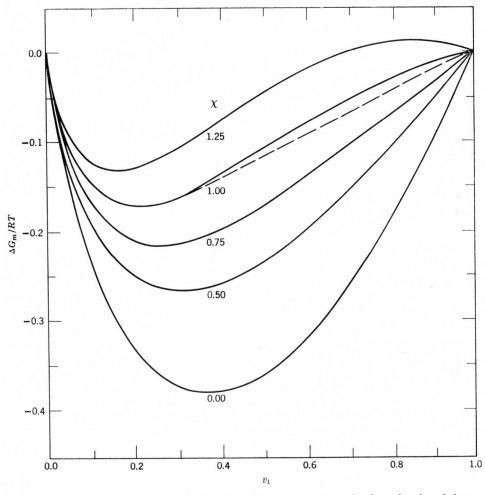

Fig. 2. Variation in free energy as a function of the χ parameter and volume fraction of the solvent, v_1.

material will be used. Many times, however, such a point is difficult to define because it may vary with the application. The definition first used many years ago—a good solvent for a material will dissolve the material in all proportions—can be used as a basis if we assume that the material that dissolves at 1–5% solids also dissolves at 95–99% solids (albeit with more difficulty). For polymers and resins it has been known that if a resin dissolves at very low solids (1%) it will normally dissolve also at higher concentrations. This type of behavior has been shown theoretically by the Flory-Huggins treatment of the partial free energy of mixing as follows:

$$\Delta G_m/RT = \ln v_1 - \left(1 - \frac{1}{m}\right) v_2 + \chi v_2{}^2$$

If $\Delta G_m/RT$ is plotted against v_1 for a system where the molar volume of the polymer, V_2, is 25 times the molar volume of the solvent, V_1, the result is the graph shown in Figure 2. Where the χ curves become convex upward, two liquid phases will result. Thus, at higher χ values, which are poor solvents, one expects solubility at only one end of the curves (ie, low v_1 values). However, as χ decreases (low χ values indicate good solvents) the chance of solubility at higher v_1 values increases; χ has a limiting value of 0.5 for a polymer of high molecular weight. Thus, to approach the ideal concept of solubility one should make the maps at very low concentrations. However, the shape of solubility maps usually does not change dramatically in the 1–20% region and, in the case of polymers and resins having relatively low molecular weight, it is possible to map at higher concentrations, which more closely approach working solids levels.

Once a map has been established for the polymer or resin, the next step is to select the area of the map in which to design a solvent blend. A glance at the map, whether it be three-dimensional or two-dimensional, will usually indicate which areas are the most attractive from a cost standpoint. Most solvents for coatings, adhesives, and other applications are mixtures of active solvents, cosolvents (latent solvents), and nonsolvents for the particular resin or resins being dissolved. In general, the cosolvents and nonsolvents are used for purposes of cost reduction.

After the general areas of the map have been selected, the individual solvents that will be needed to make the blend are selected on the basis of empirical knowledge. Thus, combining empirical knowledge with the theoretical principles of physical chemistry should enable the formulator to develop a good starting-point formulation, one that could be modified to meet the demands of the particular application involved.

Empirical Methods of Evaluating Industrial Solvents

Before the development of the thermodynamic and kinetic approach to solvent selection, much useful information had been developed regarding the use of solvents in industry (12–14). Most of this information was of a practical nature and involved the techniques of formulation rather than fundamental theory.

Since the use of cellulose nitrate lacquer coatings parallels the development of the industrial solvent industry, much information about solution coatings has been gained from working with cellulose nitrate. In recent years other film-forming polymers have been developed to meet the specific needs of industry. There has been a tendency, therefore, to apply principles of solvent technology, which had been developed from working with cellulose nitrate, to solutions of the newer coating resins.

Cellulose nitrate, in order to be used as a coating material, is dissolved in a mixture of solvents. The mixture is called the solvent system and is composed of liquids that have varying degrees of solvent power for the polymer. They are broadly classed as *active solvents*, *latent solvents* (*cosolvents*), and *diluents*. The liquids described as active solvents actually dissolve the polymer or, more precisely, put it in a dispersed usable form. They are usually polar substances having functional groups containing oxygen.

Aliphatic esters of acetic acid, ketones, and glycol ethers are the active solvents most commonly employed. Latent solvents are alcohols and do not dissolve the polymer by themselves. However, when present with the active solvents, they add to the solvating effect. Diluents are used to modify and lower the cost of the solvent system and are usually aliphatic or aromatic hydrocarbons. It is important to note that although hydrocarbons are diluents for cellulose nitrate, vinyl resins, and other polymers, they are active solvents for a broad range of products, including alkyd resins, which are used to modify cellulose nitrate lacquers. Therefore, their function in solvent systems is frequently more complex than just cost reduction.

Practical Tests for Solvents

The tests concerned with the evaluation of industrial solvent strength and effectiveness in solution coatings are relatively simple to perform and, in general, are not related to theoretical considerations.

VISCOSITY

This is not a measure of solvent strength in the thermodynamic sense but, since it describes the resistance to flow (or fluidity) of a resin solution, it gives information on how the solution can be handled and applied. Knowing the viscosity also makes it possible to predict some of the initial flow properties of a coating after application. Table 8 lists the viscosities of some common industrial solvents along with other lacquer solvent properties.

There are any number of methods of measuring viscosity. With clear solutions, capillary-tube viscometers may be used. ASTM D-2515 (15a) describes the viscosity measurement with Cannon-Fenske viscosity tubes. Another method of determining viscosity of clear solutions is the Gardner-Holdt bubble viscometer. This is commonly used to measure the viscosity of oils, varnishes, and resin solutions. Effluent-type viscometers include the Ford viscosity cups, which are described in ASTM D-1200 (15b), the Zahn viscosity cups, and others. Rotational types include the Stormer [ASTM D-562 (15c)] and the Brookfield viscometers.

DILUTION RATIO

In the preparation of a thinner or balanced mixture of solvents, cosolvents, and diluents, it is desirable to know the extent of dilution possible. The dilution ratio of cellulose nitrate solvent systems is used to determine the amount of relatively cheap hydrocarbons that can be added to the more expensive oxygenated active solvent.

The dilution ratio is the volume ratio of diluent to solvent in the particular blend that just fails to completely dissolve cellulose nitrate at a concentration of 8 g/100 ml of the solvent blend. This test is usually conducted with the specific procedure outlined in ASTM D-1720 (15d). (See Table 8 for a listing of the dilution ratios of some solvents.)

OTHER TESTS

Viscosity behavior and dilution ratio measurement can be used to predict much of the behavior of industrial solvents and mixtures for a particular resin or resin system. Other tests, however, are helpful in obtaining information on the properties of solvents and solvent mixtures. Some of the more widely used tests are listed below.

Solvent Power Tests. *Kauri-butanol value* is intended to indicate the relative solvent power of hydrocarbon solvents (or diluents in the case of cellulose nitrate and other resins). The kauri-butanol value of a hydrocarbon solvent is the volume in milliliters at 25°C of the solvent required to produce a defined degree of turbidity when added to 20 g of a standard solution of kauri (see Vol. 17, pp. 385–386) in normal butyl alcohol. The test is usually run in accordance with ASTM D-1133 (15c). Values usually range from approximately 30 for paraffinic hydrocarbons to 105 for toluene.

The kauri-butanol test is useful in determining the relative solvent power of commercial hydrocarbon solvents. However, due to the compositional variations in these commercial products, only practical testing with the given resin system will indicate the viscosity-reduction power of the solvent.

Aniline Point. The aniline point is defined as the minimum mutual solution temperature of equal volumes of aniline and an aliphatic-type hydrocarbon; the mixed aniline point is the minimum mutual solution temperature of aniline and equal parts of an aromatic-type hydrocarbon and heptane.

This test provides a determination of solvent power in terms of miscibility temperature in the presence of aniline. High aniline point numbers indicate the presence of saturated hydrocarbons; low numbers indicate unsaturated and aromatic hydrocarbons. Performance of the test is described in ASTM D-1012 (15f).

Heptane Number of Hydrocarbon Solvents. This test is intended for determining the relative solvent power of high-solvency hydrocarbons in the presence of certain resins not soluble in heptane. The heptane number is described as the ratio of the volume of *n*-heptane required to produce a certain degree of turbidity in a solution of resin in the test solvent and in a solution of the same resin in 2° toluene (that is, commercial toluene boiling within a 2 deg range; see Toluene). The procedure for this test is described in ASTM D-1132 (15g).

Heptane Miscibility of Lacquer Solvents. This test is used to determine the miscibility of *n*-heptane and lacquer solvents. It may also be used to detect qualitatively the presence of moisture in esters and ketones. ASTM D-1476 (15h) describes the procedure for titrating heptane into the sample and determining the presence and amount of turbidity.

Physical Tests. In addition to solvent power tests much useful information on the performance of solvents and solvent systems can be obtained from physical tests designed to indicate specific performance properties.

Distillation Range. The distillation range of a solvent provides an empirical set of data which imparts much useful information peculiar to a solvent or mixture and the apparatus used. The test is widely used in quality control, but is also valuable as a qualitative analytical tool.

Distillation range procedures usually report initial boiling point, the percent distilled at various intermediate temperatures, and the dry point. ASTM methods D-86, D-235, and D-1078 (15i) describe procedures for distillation range determinations on various liquids.

Flash Point Determinations. Since all solvents are volatile and most are flammable, safety factors are extremely critical. The flash point of a solvent is the lowest temperature at which it will flash under conditions of the test. The following two methods have been developed by ASTM for flash point determination of industrial solvents: Tag open-cup apparatus (D-1310) in which the solvent vapors are allowed to diffuse in the ambient air during the test and the Tag closed-cup tester (D-56) in which the solvent vapors flash within a confined area (15j). Of the two methods the closed-cup tester gives greatest precision and also lower values.

Other ASTM tests (15k) which are useful in the determination of specific data are the following: copper corrosion tests (D-849 and D-1616), nonvolatile matter in volatile solvents tests (D-1353), color of clear liquids tests (D-1209), specific gravity tests (D-891).

Empirical Formulating Techniques

In order to formulate a solvent system for any given polymer or resin, it must be determined which solvents are active, which will perform as latent solvents (cosolvents), and which solvents will act as diluents for the system. In choosing the diluents, it must be determined which are relatively better by using data such as kauri-butanol value or aniline cloud point. With information of this nature a basis for the formulation of a solvent mixture for a particular polymer or resin can be considered.

The next things to be considered in the stepwise formulation are the application and application techniques which will be used. Up to this point the discussion has been primarily concerned with the properties of industrial solvents involved in the dissolu-

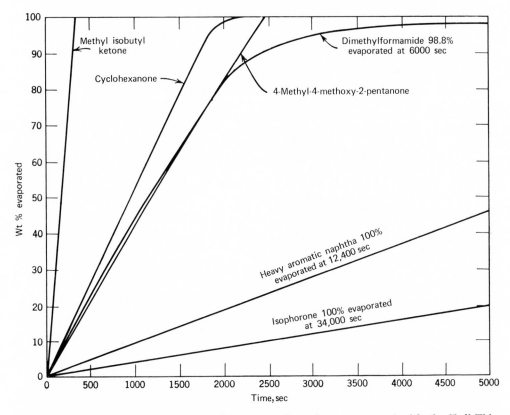

Fig. 3. Evaporation rate curves of some slow evaporating solvents measured with the Shell Thin Film Evaporometer.

tion of a polymer or resin, eg, with solubility factors. In the preparation of cellulose nitrate and other resin-based solution coatings systems, other physical properties of the solvents which influence the removal of the solvents from the coatings during and after application must be considered.

Evaporation Rate. The evaporation rate of the solvents influences many of the coating properties and is extremely important (16). The volatility of solvents and solvent mixtures influences such solution coating properties as sprayability, flow or leveling, bubbling and pinholing tendencies, print resistance, blush resistance, and overspray melt-in characteristics.

Measurement of the evaporation rate of solvents and solvent mixtures must be carefully controlled. There are a number of procedures which may be followed; one of these is the measurement of evaporation rate in the Shell Thin Film Evaporometer (17–18). Here the rate of evaporation of the solvent from filter paper is measured at 0% humidity with an air flow of 21 liters/min. A graph plotting the evaporation rates of several important industrial solvents is shown in Figure 3. Evaporation rates are also listed in Table 8.

Blush Resistance (20). Blush resistance has been mentioned in relation to flow. Blushing in nitrocellulose lacquers is precipitation of resin due to condensation of moisture as the temperature is lowered by rapidly evaporating solvents.

COATING PROPERTIES

In formulating a coating, the solvent mixture must be determined by the method used for application and the final use of the material. For example, if the lacquer is to be applied by brushing, the evaporation rate of the solvent mixture must be slow enough so that the viscosity does not build up too rapidly and cause streaking. For application by spraying, a certain amount of the solvent should be lost in the spray cone as the material leaves the spray gun. This helps to atomize the coating particles and increase the viscosity, thus controlling film thickness.

Cost is always a consideration when formulating industrial products. Not only must a solvent mixture be balanced to provide proper performance, but also the mixture must be formulated to reflect the economic demands of the particular end use. Thus, there are always cost–performance compromises.

Toxicity (19) and safety aspects must be considered for each formula and for the application involved. Solvents and solvent vapors are flammable and usually toxic; therefore, proper control of manufacturing and application conditions must be considered by the formulator.

Preparation and Testing of a Cellulose Nitrate Lacquer

By utilizing the procedures previously discussed, a formulation for a cellulose nitrate lacquer can be derived if the requirements of the end use and the conditions of application are known. Usually a cellulose nitrate lacquer will contain from 20 to 30% solids which include, in addition to the nitrocellulose, alkyd resins, hard resins (such as modified rosin products), and plasticizers which act as very low volatility solvents.

The liquid portion, or solvent mixture, consists of a balance of active solvent, latent solvent (cosolvent), and diluent. In addition to the proper balance of the solvent types, the solvent strength as measured by viscosity reduction and evaporation characteristics must be determined.

A typical cellulose nitrate solvent mixture would contain the following:

Components	Wt %
active solvents	
fast evaporating	12
medium evaporating	20
slow evaporating	5
total	37
latent solvent (cosolvent)	13
diluent (aromatic	
hydrocarbons)	50

Active Solvents. In the fast evaporating category the most commonly used active solvents for cellulose nitrate lacquers are acetone, methyl ether ketone, ethyl acetate, and isopropyl acetate. Medium evaporating active solvents for cellulose nitrate are n-propyl acetate, methyl isobutyl ketone, isobutyl acetate, and n-butyl acetate. Slow evaporating or retarder solvents are amyl and hexyl acetates, ethyl amyl ketone, cyclohexanone, and ethers of ethylene glycol and their esters. Ethylene glycol monoethers are known under a number of trademarks as shown in Table 4. Vinyl resins usually require a ketone for maximum solubility with essentially the same evaporation rate restrictions as required for cellulose nitrate lacquers.

Table 4. Some Proprietary Names for Ethylene Glycol Ethers

Company	2-Methoxyethanol	2-Ethoxyethanol	2-n-Butoxyethanol
Celanese	Glycocel EM	Glycocel EE	Glycocel EB
Shell	methyl Oxitol	Oxitol	butyl Oxitol
Union Carbide	methyl Cellosolve	Cellosolve	butyl Cellosolve
Jefferson	Jeffersol EM	Jeffersol EE	Jeffersol EB
Dow	Dowanol EM	Dowanol EE	Dowanol EB
Olin Mathieson	Poly-Solv EM	Poly-Solv EE	Poly-Solv EB
	2-(2-Methoxyethoxy) ethanol	2-(2-Ethoxyethoxy) ethanol	2-(2-(n-Butoxyethoxy) ethanol
Celanese	Glycocel DM	Glycocel DE	Glycocel DB
Shell	methyl Dioxitol	Dioxitol	butyl Dioxitol
Union Carbide	methyl Carbitol	Carbitol	butyl Carbitol
Jefferson	Jeffersol DM	Jeffersol DE	Jeffersol DB
Dow	Dowanol DM	Dowanol DE	Dowanol DB
Olin Mathieson	Poly-Solv DM	Poly-Solv DE	Poly-Solv DB

Latent Solvents. Ethyl alcohol, isopropyl alcohol, isobutyl alcohol, and n-butyl alcohol represent the most widely used latent solvents. Occasionally higher boiling alcohols such as hexyl or octyl alcohols are used. In general, these slow evaporating alcohols are used to modify evaporation rate although resin solubility and water miscibility may be mitigating factors.

Diluents. Toluene, xylene (usually mixed isomers), and special aliphatic hydrocarbon lacquer diluent comprise the bulk of the diluents used in cellulose nitrate lacquers. Aromatic hydrocarbons are the more efficient diluents and in fact are almost mandatory for vinyl resins and most acrylic resins. However, beginning in the 1960s air pollution regulations in certain areas restricted aromatic hydrocarbons usage and thus have imposed a severe strain on formulating practices for many resin systems.

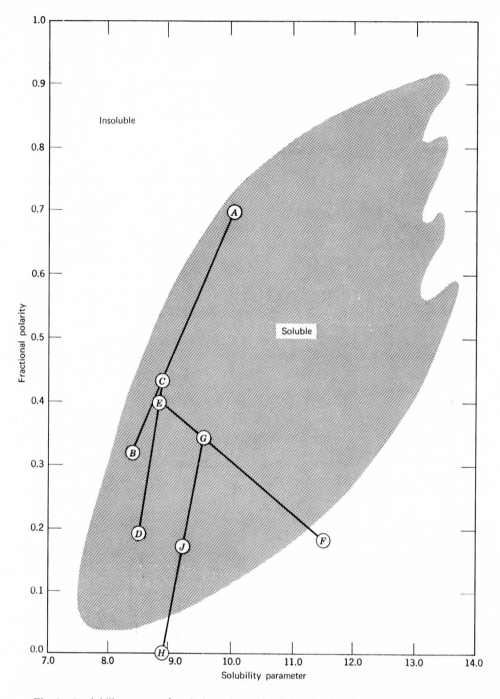

Fig. 4. A solubility map used to design solvent blends. *A*–low boiling active solvent; *B*–medium boiling active solvent; *C*–30/70 ratio of low to medium boiling solvents; *D*–high boiling active solvent; *E*–13/87 ratio high to low and medium boiling active solvents; *F*–latent solvent; *G*–30/10 ratio of active to latent solvent; *H*–aromatic hydrocarbon, *J*–50% hydrocarbon–50% oxygenated solvents.

Formulation Using Theoretical Considerations

Once theoretical principles are understood and empirical knowledge has been accumulated, the two can be put together to formulate a solvent mixture for a particular polymer or resin. Theoretical principles are used to construct a map as shown in Figure 4. Once a map has been constructed and an area of the map selected for design of a solvent system, empirical knowledge of other similar systems is used to set up constraints or limitations on the design. In the case of a cellulose nitrate lacquer system, some of these constraints would be as follows:

1. Active solvent content should be approximately three times the latent solvent content.

2. Hydrocarbon content should be regulated by the cost of the formula; usually the content is from 40 to 60%.

3. High boiling active solvent content should be approximately 10% of the total active and latent solvents, and high boiling diluent, if any, should not exceed three times the high boiling, ie, slow evaporating, active solvent.

4. The low boiling active solvents should not exceed 20% of combined active and latent solvents to ensure proper flow and blush resistance.

The specimen formulation discussed in the preceding section meets all the constraining requirements stated above. It then becomes a simple task to plot out solvents from each category on a map.

It should be restated and emphasized that in all of the calculations that have been discussed here the assumption is made that the properties of the individual solvents in a blend can be volume-fraction weighted to give that property of the blend as follows:

$$\delta_{\text{blend}} = v_1\delta_1 + v_2\delta_2 + \ldots + v_n\delta_n$$

Another useful application of solution theory and the mapping techniques is to design a new solvent blend to match the properties of an old solvent blend. The solubility parameters are calculated by volume using fraction weighting. The point is plotted on the solubility map. Again, the Gardon fractional polarity and solubility parameter will be used as examples for plotting the solubility parameters. Then, knowing certain empirical rules and the composition of the original, a new blend may be formulated to meet the constants of the old by setting up constraints such as those listed below:

1. The relative amounts and types of low boiling solvent which may be used.

2. The concentration of high boilers.

3. The active-to-latent ratio.

4. The total amount of hydrocarbon to be used.

Attempts are then made to reach the control point by choosing the correct solvents and/or compromising the constraints as little as possible.

The exact method of designing solvent blends using a two-dimensional map and Gardon's fractional polarity (Table 5) is as follows:

1. Locate the solubility parameter and fractional polarity point where the new solvent blend should be, as shown in Figure 4 at Point J.

2. Choose the low and medium boiling solvent. Then locate the parameters of the low (acetone) and medium boiling (methyl isobutyl ketone) solvents and draw a line connecting these two points (A and B). Assume that the constraints have been

set up so that the ratio of low to medium boiling solvent is 30/70. Now the line between the low and medium solvents is divided according to this ratio by the lever principle; ie, the line section opposite the medium boiling solvent represents its concentration.

Table 5. Constants for Some Common Industrial Solvents[a]

Solvent	Solubility parameter	Fractional polarity
alcohols		
methyl alcohol	14.5	0.388
ethyl alcohol, 95%	13.2	0.296
n-propyl alcohol	11.9	0.152
isopropyl alcohol	11.5	0.178
n-butyl alcohol	11.4	0.096
sec-butyl alcohol	10.8	0.123
isobutyl alcohol	10.7	0.111
4-methyl 2-pentanol[b]	10.0	0.066
esters		
methyl acetate	9.6	0.182
ethyl acetate	9.1	0.167
n-propyl acetate	8.8	0.129
isopropyl acetate	8.6	0.100
n-butyl acetate	8.6	0.120
s-butyl acetate	8.2	0.082
isobutyl acetate	8.3	0.097
2-ethoxyethyl acetate	8.7	0.073
2-methoxyethyl acetate	9.2	0.095
2-*n*-butoxyethyl acetate	8.2	0.060
amyl acetate	8.5	0.067
"methyl amyl" acetate[b]	8.2	0.050
ethers and glycol ethers		
tetrahydrofuran	9.9	0.075
2-methoxyethanol	10.8	0.126
2-ethoxyethanol	9.9	0.086
2-*n*-butoxyethanol	8.9	0.048
hydrocarbons		
n-hexane	7.3	0
cyclohexane	8.2	0
super VM & P naphtha	7.6	0
toluene	8.9	0.001
xylene	8.8	0.001
ketones		
acetone	10.0	0.695
methyl ethyl ketone (MEK)	9.3	0.510
methyl isobutyl ketone (MIBK)	8.4	0.315
ethyl amyl ketone (EAK)	8.2	0.223
4-methyl-4-methoxy-2-pentanone	8.2	0.190
cyclohexanone	9.9	0.380
isophorone	9.0	0.191
nitroparaffins		
nitromethane	12.6	0.780
nitroethane	11.1	0.710
1-nitropropane	10.2	0.710
2-nitropropane	9.9	0.720

[a] *Solvent Notes*, Shell Chemical Company IC:67-64-SN.
[b] The expression "methyl amyl alcohol" is used commercially for 4-methyl-2-pentanol.

3. This point (C) on the line now can be used to represent the blend of low and medium boiling solvents. The second assumption is that a desirable ratio of medium and low boiling active to high boiling active will be 9/1. Now locate the position of the high boiling solvent (4-methyl-4-methoxy-2-pentanone) and construct a line segment between its point (D) and the point representing the mixture of low and medium boiling solvents. The line is divided according to the lever principle to represent the concentration of the mixture and the high boiling solvent. This point (E) now represents the solubility parameters of the blend of active solvents.

4. A ratio of active to latent solvent of 3 to 1 gives maximum viscosity reduction. Using this ratio, construct another line segment to join the point of the active solvents with the alcohol solvent (isopropyl alcohol) (Point F). This segment is divided in a 3/1 ratio (25%) according to the lever principle to locate Point G. This completes the oxygenated portion of the solvent blend.

5. To find the final composition, a line segment is constructed from the total oxygenated point to the point representing the hydrocarbons (Point H). Dividing this line in half locates the solvent blend on the map having 50% hydrocarbon solvent as shown in Figure 4 (Point J).

In this example the restrictions were rigid and the solvents were selected without due regard for specific performance requirements. Other solvents could have been used to impart specific properties to the solvent blend. Similarly, cost was not considered and again proper selection of solvents would help to minimize the cost of the solvent blend. A similar procedure can be used to design solvent blends which may be used to replace a second blend. In this instance the solubility parameter and fractional polarity are calculated and noted on the graph. The solvents are then selected so that the parameters of the combinations of the solvents approach the parameters of the given blend.

Air Pollution Regulations (21)

The atmosphere of industrial areas is becoming more polluted each year as a result of the waste products of man's activities. Considerable concern has been shown and work has been done regarding the sources of pollution. The problem of air pollution is receiving considerable national publicity. The Federal Government has shown its concern in the Air Quality Act of 1967. Action has been taken to combat several types of pollution. For example, all new automobiles have air pollution devices on them to control the engine emissions. In certain geographical areas there is local legislation controlling the emission of materials into the air. Los Angeles was the first major metropolitan area to enact legislation which places limitations upon the emission of solvent vapors into the atmosphere (Rule 66). The San Francisco Bay Area also has air pollution regulations (Regulation 3) in effect which limit the types and amounts of solvent vapors which may be emitted into the air. Similarly, Orange County, located south of Los Angeles, has adopted the Los Angeles solvent emission regulation, Rule 66.

Rule 66 and Regulation 3 both limit the type and amount of solvents which may be emitted, but they do so differently. Rule 66 limits the emission of the following three classes of compounds:

1. Olefins (including cycloolefins)—limited to 5% by vol of the solvent blend.

2. Aromatic hydrocarbons having eight or more carbon atoms (except ethylbenzene)—limited to 8% by vol of the solvent blend.

3. Toluene, ethylbenzene, trichloroethylene, and ketones having a branched hydrocarbon structure—limited to 20% by vol of the solvent blend.

The aggregate sum of these compounds in a solvent blend is limited to 20% by vol or the solvent will be considered to be photochemically reactive and its emission into the air must be controlled. There are other aspects of this rule which consider the drying and/or curing process and the effluents produced in these steps.

Regulation 3 of the San Francisco Bay Area regulates the emission of solvent vapor from surface coatings, restricting certain solvents, and also controls the effluents of ovens used for curing and drying coatings. The solvent restrictions are based upon defining coating as industrial or nonindustrial. Under both categories, aromatic, olefinic, and aldehydic compounds are restricted unless the effluents are controlled. Aromatic compounds which are monosubstituted can be used up to 20% by vol of the blend in both industrial and nonindustrial coatings. However, polysubstituted aromatic compounds may be used up to 20% by vol in industrial and 8% by vol in nonindustrial coatings. Up to 20% by vol olefinic compounds may be present in industrial coatings, but only 8% by vol are allowed in nonindustrial coatings. Aldehydes follow the same restrictions as olefins. The aggregate sum of these compounds in solvent blends is limited to a maximum of 20% by vol. Branched chain ketones and trichloroethylene are not controlled by Regulation 3.

Table 6. Physical Properties of Some Common Industrial Solvents

Solvents	Specific gravity, 25/25°C	Boiling point, 760 mm Hg, °C	Flash point, ±5°F (Tag open cup)	Freezing point, °C	Vapor pressure, 20°C, mm Hg	Refractive index, n_D^{20}	Surface tension, 20°C, dyne/cm
active solvents							
fast evaporating (relative evaporation rate >3.0)							
acetone	0.7879	56.13	15	− 94.9	185.95	1.3590	23.32
ethyl acetate (85–88% wt)	0.8814	77.1	40	− 83.5	74.4	1.3725	23.9
ethyl acetate (95–98% wt)	0.8913	77.1	56	− 83.5	74.4	1.3725	23.9
ethyl acetate (99% wt)	0.8966	77.1	56	− 82.4	74	1.3719	23.9
isopropyl acetate	0.8661	88.7	60	− 73.1	43.2	1.3770	21.2
methyl acetate	0.9304	57.1	20	− 98.1		1.3594	
methyl ethyl ketone	0.8023	79.59	20	− 86.3	70.21	1.3788	24.6
methyl isopropyl ketone	0.8031	93.94		− 92		1.3862	
tetrahydrofuran	0.8853	66.0	6	−108.5	142	1.4073	26.4
medium evaporating (relative evaporation rate = 0.8–3.0)							
n-butyl acetate	0.8720	126.1	100	− 73.5	7.8	1.3947	24.0
sec-butyl acetate	0.8569	112.2	85	− 98.9	16.2	1.3887	22.8
diethyl ketone	0.8121	101.5	55	− 42		1.3905	
isobutyl acetate	0.8648	117.3	90	− 97.1	12.5	1.3907	23.3
mesityl oxide[a]	0.8520	129.8	98	− 52.9	7.3	1.44575	22.9
methyl alcohol	0.7890	64.5	62	− 97.8	97.3	1.329	22.6
methyl isobutyl ketone	0.7985	116.2	73	− 80.2	14.96	1.3957	23.64
methyl *n*-propyl ketone	0.8047	102.3	72	− 77.5	26.9	1.3902	23.6
nitroethane	1.0439	114.0	106	− 90	15.6	1.3916	31.3
nitromethane	1.0440	101.2	112	− 29	27.8	1.3818	37.0
1-nitropropane	0.9987	131.6	120	− 108	7.5	1.4015	30.0
2-nitropropane	0.9871	120.3	103	− 93	12.9	1.3941	30.0
n-propyl acetate	0.8762	101.6	65	− 92.5	23.0	1.3844	23.9

Table 6 (continued)

Solvents	Specific gravity, 25/25°C	Boiling point, 760 mm Hg, °C	Flash point, ±5°F (Tag open cup)	Freezing point, °C	Vapor pressure, 20°C, mm Hg	Refractive index, n_D^{20}	Surface tension, 20°C, dyne/cm
slow evaporating (relative evaporation rate < 0.8)							
primary amyl acetate	0.8734	146.0	106	−100	3.8	1.405	28.5
amyl acetate (from fusel oil)	0.8658	146.0	93	−100	5.2	1.401	24.3
amyl acetate (from pentane)	0.8619	146.0	105	−100	5.2	1.401	24.3
2-(2-n-butoxyethoxy)ethanol	0.9560	230.6	240	− 68.1	0.01	1.430	30.0
2-(2-n-butoxyethoxy)ethyl acetate	0.9767	246	240	− 32.2	<0.01		
2-n-butoxyethyl acetate	0.9400	191.6	190	− 64.6	0.25	1.4200	30.3
butyl lactate	0.9772	188	168	− 43	0.4	1.4216	27.8
2-n-butoxyethanol	0.8992	171.1	165	− 75	0.76	1.418	27.3
2-(2-ethoxyethoxy)ethanol	1.1004	195.0	205	− 90	0.13	1.425	31.8
2-ethoxyethyl acetate	0.9703	156.2	150	− 61.7	1.7	1.4030	28.2
cyclohexanone	0.9456	156.7	129	− 47	7	1.4507	27.7
diacetone alcohol[b]	0.9375	183.8	36[c]	− 44	0.81	1.4234	28.9
diisobutyl ketone	0.8055	169.3	120	− 41.5	1.4	1.4320	22.5
dimethylformamide	0.9376	153	153	− 61	2.7	1.4269	35.2
ethyl amyl ketone	0.8176	160.5	135	− 57.9	2.0	1.4124	24.6
ethyl butyl ketone	0.8163	147.6	115	− 39	3.8	1.4085	
2-ethylhexyl acetate	0.8698	199	190	− 80	0.4	1.4103	
ethyl lactate	1.0290	154.5	130	− 25	1.8	1.4118	29.9
hexyl acetate	0.8709	169.2	138		0.9		
isobutyl isobutyrate	0.8522	147.3	120	− 81		1.3999	
isophorone[d]	0.9194	215.2	205	− 8.1	0.18	1.4775	32.3
methyl amyl acetate	0.8539	146.3	110	− 63.8	1.25	1.4008	22.6
methyl n-amyl ketone	0.8140	150.5	120	− 35	2.6	1.4110	
methyl isoamyl ketone	0.8123	145.4	115	− 74.21	1.52	1.4069	28.5
2-(2-methoxyethoxy)ethanol	1.0237	193.6	200	− 85	0.18	1.424	34.8
2-methoxyethanol	0.9633	124.6	115	− 85.1	6.0	1.4023	30.6
2-methoxyethyl acetate	0.9632	145.1	140	− 65.1	2.0	1.4025	30.2
2-ethoxyethanol	0.9284	135.6	130	−100	3.7	1.4080	27.9
4-methoxy-4-methyl-2-pentanol	0.8918	167	145 <− 50		1.5	1.4204	27
4-methoxy-4-methyl-2-pentanone	0.9061	160	141	− 35.45	2.2	1.4181	26
latent solvents							
amyl alcohol	0.8141	133.1	11	− 90	2.9	1.4014	23.8
tert-amyl alcohol	0.8072	102.2	20	− 8.4		1.4048	
n-butyl alcohol	0.8082	117.7	115	− 89.0	4.3	1.3993	24.6
sec-butyl alcohol	0.8052	99.5	80	−114.7	12.5	1.3069	23.0
tert-butyl alcohol	0.7817	82.4	60	25.66	42	1.3841	20.7
cyclohexanol	0.9460	161.1	154	25.15	15[f]	1.4656	35.1
2-ethylhexanol	0.8312	183.5	185	− 76	0.05	1.4300	
isobutyl alcohol	0.8006	108.3	100	−108	9.0	1.3953	22.8
isopropyl alcohol	0.7832	82.33	60	− 88.43	32.8	1.3772	21.35
ethyl alcohol 95%	0.8085		70		[e]		
ethyl alcohol (anhydrous)	0.7967		70				
methyl alcohol	0.7890	64.5	62	− 97.8	97.3	1.329	22.6
4-methyl-2-pentanol	0.8050	131.8	131	− 90	4.99	1.4110	22.8
n-propyl alcohol	0.8032	97.15	90	−127	14.5	1.385	23.8

(continued)

Table 6 (*continued*)

Solvents	Specific gravity, 25/25°C	Boiling point, 760 mm Hg, °C	Flash point, ±5°F (Tag open cup)	Freezing point, °C	Vapor pressure, 20°C, mm Hg	Refractive index, n_D^{20}	Surface tension, 20°C, dyne/cm
		°F	*Tag closed cup,* °F	°F	*at* 68°F	$n_D^{68°F}$	
diluents							
benzene	0.878	175–176	10		42	72.0	1.5008
toluene	0.866	230–231	41	−139		23.0	1.4968
xylene (mixed isomers)	0.865	281–284	81			5.9	1.4976
aliphatic lacquer naphtha (typical product)	0.721	197–218	20			32.0	1.42
mineral spirits (typical product)	0.752	324–398	108			1.3	1.45

^{a} $(CH_3)_2C{=}CHCOCH_3$.
^{b} $(CH_3)_2C(OH)CH_2COCH_3$.
^{c} Extrapolated.

^{d} $COCH{=}C(CH_3)CH_2C(CH_3)_2CH_2$.
^{e} 1.7 psi at 100°F.
^{f} At 70°F.

Table 7. Water Miscibility Properties of Some Common Industrial Solvents

Solvents	Volume coefficient of expansion per °C, at 20°C	Solubility, 20°C, % wt		Azeotrope with water	
		Compound in water	Water in compound	Boiling point, °C	% wt of compound
active solvents					
fast evaporating (relative evaporation rate > 3.0)					
acetone	0.00143	complete	complete	nonazeotrope	
ethyl acetate (85–88% wt)	0.00134	8.7	3.3	70.4	93.0
ethyl acetate (95–98% wt)	0.00134	8.7	3.3	70.4	93.0
ethyl acetate (99% wt)	0.00134	5.54	3.4	70.4	94
isopropyl acetate	0.00134	2.9	1.8	76.6	89.4
methyl acetate		24.5	8.2	56.4	96.5
methyl ethyl ketone	0.00131	27.1	12.5	73.4	88.7
methyl isopropyl ketone		6.53	2.39	79	87
tetrahydrofuran		complete	complete	64	94.7
medium evaporating (relative evaporation rate = 0.8–3.0)					
n-butyl acetate	0.00117	0.68	1.2	90.5	72.0
sec-butyl acetate	0.00118	0.8	3.6	87.0	77.5
diethyl ketone		3.4	2.6	82.9	14
isobutyl acetate	0.00119	0.63	1.02	87.5	80.5
mesityl oxide^a	0.00106	3.17	3.1	91.8	68
methyl alcohol	0.00119	complete	complete	nonazeotrope	
methyl isobutyl ketone	0.00115	2.04	2.41	87.9	75.7
methyl *n*-propyl ketone	0.0012	4.3	3.3	83.8	80.4
nitroethane	0.00112	4.5	0.9	87.1	73.6
nitromethane	0.00115	9.5	2.2	83.6	77.1
1-nitropropane	0.00101	1.4	0.5	91.2	64.5
2-nitropropane	0.00104	1.7	0.6	88.4	73.1

Table 7 (*continued*)

Solvents	Volume coefficient of expansion per °C, at 20°C	Solubility, 20°C, % wt Compound in water	Solubility, 20°C, % wt Water in compound	Azeotrope with water Boiling point, °C	Azeotrope with water % wt of compound
n-propyl acetate	0.00126	2.3	2.6	82.2	87.5
slow evaporating (relative evaporation < 0.8)					
primary amyl acetate	0.00119	0.20	0.90	92.95	67
amyl acetate (from fusel oil)	0.00104	0.17	1.15	92.95	67
amyl acetate (from pentane)	0.00110	0.17	1.15	95.95	67
2-(2-n-butoxyethoxy)ethanol	0.00088	complete	complete	nonazeotrope	
2-(2-n-butoxyethoxy)ethyl acetate		6.5	3.7	99.8	8
2-butoxyethyl acetate	0.00104	1.1	1.6	98.8	71.9
butyl lactate	0.00099	4.0	14.5		
2-butoxyethanol	0.00092	complete	complete	98.8	20.8
2-(2-ethoxyethoxy)ethanol	0.00082	complete	complete		
2-ethoxyethyl acetate	0.00112	22.9	6.5	97.5	45.5
cyclohexane	0.00094	2.3	8.0		
diacetone alcohol[b]	0.00094	complete	complete	98.8	12.7
diisobutyl ketone	0.00102	<0.05	0.75	97.0	48.1
dimethyl formamide		complete	complete	nonazeotrope	
ethyl amyl ketone	0.00125	0.26	0.90		
ethyl butyl ketone	0.00106	1.43	0.78	94.6	57.8
2-ethylhexyl acetate		0.03	0.55	99	26.5
ethyl lactate	0.00110	complete	complete		
hexyl lactate		0.2	0.60	97.4	39
isobutyl isobutyrate				95.5	60.6
isophorone[c]	0.00085	1.2	4.3	99.5	16.1
methyl amyl acetate	0.00110	0.13	0.58	94.8	63.6
methyl n-amyl ketone	0.00104	0.43	1.5	95.2	54.6
methyl isoamyl ketone	0.00107	0.55	1.4	93.0	25
2-(2-methoxyethoxy)ethanol	0.00086	complete	complete	nonazeotrope	
2-methoxyethanol	0.00095	complete	complete	99.9	15.3
2-methoxyethyl acetate	0.00109	complete	complete	97.1	48.2
2-ethoxyethanol	0.00097	complete	complete	99.4	28.8
4-methoxy-4-methyl-2-pentanol	0.00084	complete	complete	98.6	66.8
4-methoxy-4-methyl-2-pentanone	0.00090	31	9.5	97.6	61.4
latent solvents					
amyl alcohol	0.00092	1.7	9.2	92.95	63.8
tert-amyl alcohol	0.00133			87.35	72.5
n-butyl alcohol	0.00090	7.7	20.1	93.0	55.5
sec-butyl alcohol	0.00101	22.5	60.0	87.45	72.65
tert-butyl alcohol	0.00133	complete	complete	79.9	88.24
cyclohexanol	0.00077	3.6	11	97.8	20.0
2-ethylhexanol	0.00088	0.07	2.6	99.1	20
isobutyl alcohol	0.00096	10.0	15.0	90.0	67
isopropyl alcohol	0.00104	complete	complete	80.16	87.70
ethyl alcohol 95%	0.0011				
ethyl alcohol (anhydrous)	0.0011				
methyl alcohol	0.00119	complete	complete	nonazeotrope	
4-methyl-2-pentanol	0.00103	1.64	6.35	94.3	55.6
n-propyl alcohol	0.00096	complete	complete	87.7	71.7

[a] $(CH_3)_2C = CHCOCH_3$.

[b] $(CH_3)_2 C(OH) CH_2COCH_3$.

[c] $COCH = C(CH_3)CH_2C(CH_3)_2CH_2$.

Table 8. Lacquer Solvent Properties of Some Common Industrial Solvents

Solvent	Purity,[a] % wt min	Viscosities, cP Cellulose nitrate solution[b]	Neat,[a] 25°C	Blush resistance (% relative humidity 80°F)	Dilution ratio Toluene	Dilution ratio Aliphatic naphtha	Distillation range,[a] 760 mm Hg, °C	Evaporation rates Relative, n-BuOAc=1.0	Shell Thin Film Evaporometer to 90% evaporation, sec
active solvents									
fast evaporating (relative evaporation rate > 3.0)									
acetone	99.5	10	0.34	<20	4.4	0.8	1° incl. 56.1	6.0	75
ethyl acetate (85–88% wt)	85	18	0.47	35	3.3	1.3	70–80	4.1	110
ethyl acetate (95–98% wt)	95	19	0.46	44	3.1	1.1	73–80	4.2	108
ethyl acetate (99% wt)	99	20	0.46		3.4	1.1	76–79	4.5	100
isopropyl acetate	95–97	27	0.52	62	2.8	1.3	85–90	3.6	125
methyl acetate		16	0.42	<35	2.9	0.9	56.7–58.9	4.9	93
methyl ethyl ketone	99.5	15	0.41	36	4.3	0.9	1.5° incl. 79.6	4.0	112
methyl isopropyl ketone		19	0.48		3.8	0.9		4.0	138
tetrahydrofuran	99.5	21	0.50	50	2.9	1.1	65–67(95%)	5.0	90
medium evaporating (relative evaporation rate = 0.8–3.0)									
n-butyl acetate (99%)	99	44	0.70		2.7	1.3		1.1	419
n-butyl acetate	90–92	35	0.71	82	2.7	1.4	118–128	1.0	452
sec-butyl acetate	90	33	0.65	76	2.6	1.3	104–125	1.9	241
diethyl ketone		20	0.47	76	3.0	0.7	97–106	2.5	179
isobutyl acetate	96	37	0.68	78	2.2	1.1	114–118	1.5	303
mesityl oxide[c]	97	24	0.62	83	4.0	1.1	123–132	0.8	555
methyl alcohol	99.85	19	0.56		2.2	0.5	1° incl. 64.5	2.0	220
methyl isobutyl ketone	99.5	30	0.55	78	3.6	1.0	114–117	1.6	277
methyl n-propyl ketone	95	20	0.50	70	4.0	1.1	97–106	1.6	185
nitroethane	90	40	0.68	74	1.4	0.4	112–116(90%)	1.2	390
nitromethane	95	36	0.61	71	1.2	imm[f]	100–103(90%)	1.4	328
1-nitropropane	94	72	0.81	85	1.2	0.4	129–133(90%)	0.8	600
2-nitropropane	94	63	0.75	82	1.2	0.4	119–122(90%)	1.1	405
n-propyl acetate	90–92	26	0.59	65	3.2	1.5	98–102	2.3	197
slow evaporating (relative evaporation < 0.8)									
primary amyl acetate	95	55	0.83	92	2.3	1.4	135–150	0.4	1,105
amyl acetate (from fusel oil)	85–88	39	0.83	88	2.5	1.7	100–150	0.7	680
amyl acetate (from pentane)	85–88	52	0.86	91	2.2	1.2	126–155	0.6	770
2-(2-n-butoxyethoxy)ethanol	96	215	5.3	85	3.9	1.9	220–235	<0.01	
2-(2-n-butoxyethoxy)ethyl acetate	95		3.1		1.8	0.9	235–250	<0.01	
2-n-butoxyethyl acetate	99	102	1.7	96	1.8	1.2	188–192	0.03	13,250
butyl lactate	97	128	3.2	89			145–230	−0.03	13,600
2-n-butoxyethanol	99	107	2.9	96	3.3	1.8	166–173	0.06	8,125

Table 8 (*continued*)

Solvent	Purity,[a] % wt min	Viscosities, cP Cellulose nitrate solution[b]	Neat,[a] 25°C	Blush resistance (% relative humidity 80°F)	Dilution ratio Toluene	Aliphatic naphtha	Distillation range,[a] 760 mm Hg, °C	Evaporation rates Relative, n-BuOAc=1.0	Shell Thin Film Evaporometer to 90% evaporation, sec
2-(2-ethoxyethoxy)ethanol		209	7.2	<50	1.9	imm[f]	185–205	<0.01	64,000
2-ethoxyethyl acetate	99	60	1.2		2.4	0.9		0.2	2,500
2-ethoxyethyl acetate	95	57	1.2	91	2.5	0.9	145–165	0.2	2,825
cyclohexane	99.3	74	2.0	92	5.8	1.3	153–160.8	0.3	1,720
diacetone alcohol[d]	99	137	2.9	82	2.3	0.6		0.1	4,320
diisobutyl ketone	95	126	0.95	95	1.5	0.8	163–173	0.2	2,470
dimethyl formamide	99	14	0.82		7.7	0.2	2°incl. 153	0.2	2,400
ethyl amyl ketone	97.5	58	0.80	94	2.2	0.9	156–162	0.2	2,025
ethyl butyl ketone	97.0	49	0.70	94	2.6	0.8	143–151	0.5	1,020
2-ethylhexyl acetate	95	140	1.4	94	1.3	0.9	192–205	0.03	
ethyl lactate	98	85	2.4	82	5.3	0.8	119–176	0.2	2,475
hexyl lactate	95–98	78	1.0		1.8	1.3	165–169	0.2	2,410
isobutyl isobutyrate	98	87	9.83		1.3	0.8	144–151	0.5	980
2-isobutoxyethanol								0.1	3,450
isophorone[e]	98	97	2.3	97	6.2		205–220	0.03	27,600
methyl amyl acetate	95	85	0.87	92	1.7	1.0	140–150	0.5	900
methyl n-amyl ketone	95	42	0.77	93	3.9	1.2	147–154	0.4	1,250
methyl isoamyl ketone	98	40	0.73	89	3.8	1.1	140–148	0.4	1,035
2-(2-methoxyethoxy)ethanol		122	3.8	57	2.3	imm[f]	188–198	<0.01	
2-methoxyethanol	99	50	1.6	45	3.4	0.2	123.5–125.5	0.2	2,825
2-methoxyethyl acetate	99	51	1.6	85	4.0	imm[f]	132–152	0.3	884
2-ethoxyethanol	99	59	1.9	67	4.9	1.1	132.5–136	0.4	1,260
4-methoxy-4-methyl-2-pentanol	99	100	2.0	93	4.7	1.3	165–170	0.2	3,000
4-methoxy-4-methyl-2-pentanone	98.5	60	1.2	91	3.1	0.9	157–162	0.2	2,175
latent solvents									
amyl alcohol	98.0		3.7				125.5–137	0.3	
tert-amyl alcohol	98		3.5				100–103.5	1.1	430
n-butyl alcohol	99		2.6				116–118	0.5	1,006
sec-butyl alcohol	99		2.9				98–101	0.9	400
tert-butyl alcohol	99		4.4				81.5–83	1.1	430
cyclohexanol	99						160–162.4	<0.1	
2-ethylhexanol	99.9		7.7				182–186	0.01	
isobutyl alcohol	99		3.4				2° incl. 107.9	0.7	635
isopropyl alcohol	99.7		2.4				1° incl. 82.33	1.6	290
ethyl alcohol 95%	95						73–80	1.6	290
ethyl alcohol (anhydrous)	99.9		1.3					1.9	
methyl alcohol	99.85	19	0.56		2.2	0.5	1° incl. 64.5	2.0	220
4-methyl-2-pentanol	98		3.8				130–133	0.3	1,785
n-propyl alcohol			2.0				2° incl. 97.15	1.0	450

[a] Commercial product.
[b] Standardized conditions.
[c] $(CH_3)_2C{=}CHCOCH_3$.
[d] $(CH_3)_2C(OH)CH_2COCH_3$.
[e] $COCH{=}C(CH_3)CH_2C(CH_3)_2CH_2$.
[f] Immiscible.

Bibliography

"Solvents, Industrial," in *ECT* 1st ed., Vol. 12, pp. 654–686, by Arthur K. Doolittle, Carbide and Carbon Chemicals Company, A Division of Union Carbide and Carbon Corporation.

1. C. J. Sheehan and A. L. Bisio, *Rubber Chem. Tech.* **39** (1), 149 (1966).
2. H. Burrell, *Offic. Dig., Federation Paint and Varnish Prod. Clubs* **27**, 748 (1955).
3. E. P. Lieberman, *Offic. Dig., Federation Soc. Paint Technol.* **34**, 30 (1962).
4. J. L. Gardon, *J. Paint Technol.* **38**, 43 (1966).
5. J. D. Crowley, G. S. Teague, Jr., and J. W. Lowe, Jr., *J. Paint Technol.* **38**, 269 (1966).
6. R. F. Blanks and J. M. Pravsnitz, *Ind. Eng. Chem. Fundamentals* **3**, 1 (1964).
7. E. E. Walker, *J. Appl. Chem.* **2**, 470 (1952).
8. C. M. Hansen, *J. Paint Technol.* **39**, 104 (1967).
9. P. A. Small, *J. Appl. Chem.* **3**, 71 (1953).
10. J. P. Teas, *J. Paint Technol.* **40**, 19 (1968).
11. E. Hunt and R. Katz, *Bulletin No. 1022-68*, Celanese Chemical Co., New York, 1968.
12. N. G. Baker and J. W. Wyart, *Modern Plastics Encyclopedia*, Vol. 34, McGraw-Hill Publishing Co., Inc., 1956, p. 362.
13. A. K. Doolittle, *Technology of Solvents and Plasticizers*, John Wiley & Sons, Inc., New York, 1954.
14. A. Mellon, *Industrial Solvents*, Reinhold Publishing Corp., New York, 1950.
15. Refs. 15a–k from *ASTM Standards*, American Society for Testing and Materials, Philadelphia.
15a. *ASTM D 2515, Specifications for Kinematic Glass Viscometers* (1966).
15b. *ASTM D 1200, Test for Viscosity of Paints, Varnishes, and Lacquers by Ford Viscosity Cup* (1958).
15c. *ASTM D 562, Test for Consistency of Paints Using the Stormer Viscometer* (1955).
15d. *ASTM D 1720, Test for Dilution Ratio in Cellulose Nitrate Solutions for Active Solvents, Hydrocarbon Diluents, and Cellulose Nitrates* (1962).
15e. *ASTM D 1133, Test for Kauri-Butanol Values of Hydrocarbon Solvents* (1961).
15f. *ASTM D 1012, Test for Aniline Point and Mixed Aniline Point of Hydrocarbon Solvents* (1962).
15g. *ASTM D 1132, Method of Test for Heptane Number of Hydrocarbon Solvents* (1953).
15h. *ASTM D 1476, Test for Heptane Miscibility of Lacquer Solvents* (1968).
15i. *ASTM D 86, Test for Distillation of Petroleum Products* (1967); *ASTM D 235, Specifications for Petroleum Spirits (Mineral Spirits)* (1961); *ASTM D 1678, Test for Distillation Range of Volatile Organic Liquids* (1967).
15j. *ASTM D 1310, Test for Flash Point of Volatile Flammable Materials by Tag Open-Cup Apparatus* (1967); *ASTM D 56, Test for Flash Point by Tag Closed Tester* (1964).
15k. *ASTM D 849, Test for Copper Corrosion of Industrial Aromatic Hydrocarbons* (1966); *ASTM D 1616, Test for Copper Corrosion by Mineral Spirits* (1960); *ASTM D 1353, Test for Nonvolatile Matter in Volatile Solvents for Use in Paint, Varnish, Lacquer, and Related Products* (1964); *ASTM D 1209, Test for Color of Clear Liquids* (1962); *ASTM D 891, Test for Specific Gravity of Industrial Aromatic Hydrocarbons and Related Materials* (1959).
16. J. P. McGuigan, *Paint and Varnish Production* **46** (12), 31 (1956).
17. *Offic. Dig., Federation Paint and Varnish Prod. Clubs* **28**, 1060 (1956).
18. *Offic. Dig., Federation Paint and Varnish Prod. Clubs*, **30**, 1203 (1958).
19. E. Holstein, *Chem. Zentr.* **2**, 826 (1947).
20. *Test Methods and Technique of the Surface Coating Industry*, 2nd ed., Shell Chemical Co., 1967.
21. G. C. Esposito, *J. Paint Technol.* **40** (520), 214 (1968); A. C. Stern, *Air Pollution*, Vol. 1 of *Air Pollution and Its Effects*, Academic Press, Inc., New York, 1968; C. H. Parker, *Soc. Plastics Engrs. J.* **23** (12), 26 (1967); L. R. Fontaine, *Paint Varn. Prod.* **58** (1), 49 (1968); A. P. Altshuller, *Anal. Chem.* **39** (5), 10 R (1967); E. C. Larson and H. E. Sipple, *J. Paint Technol.* **39** (508), 258 (1967); L. W. Ross, *Chem. Eng.* **74** (15), 191 (1967).

JOHN W. WYART
Celanese Chemical Company
MARK F. DANTE
Shell Chemical Company

SORBIC ACID

Sorbic acid (*trans,trans*-2,4-hexadienoic acid), CH_3—CH=CHCH=CHCOOH, is a white crystalline solid. It is a naturally occurring product which was first obtained from the oil of the rowanberry (sorbapple or mountain ash berry) in 1859 by treatment with alkali or mineral acid.

Sorbic acid and its water-soluble potassium salt (collectively referred to as sorbates) are of major commercial significance as preservatives for foods and, to a lesser extent, for drugs and cosmetics. Following the initial recommendations of Gooding (1) in 1945, the sorbates have been adopted in a wide range of consumer products where the inhibition of yeast, mold, and certain bacterial growth is essential to the safe and economical marketing of the products. The use of the sorbates parallels, and in many food categories, dominates the applications historically served by other organic carboxylate acids and salts, such as sodium and calcium propionate, sodium benzoate, and sodium diacetate.

Properties and Reactions

The solubility of sorbic acid in water increases from 0.15% at 20°C to 3.8% at 100°C, hence water is a convenient medium for purification by recrystallization. The comparative solubilities of sorbic acid and potassium sorbate are shown in Table 1.

Table 1. Solubilities of Sorbic Acid and Potassium Sorbate at 20°C, g/100 g soln

Solvent	Sorbic acid	Potassium sorbate
acetic acid, glacial	11.5	
acetone	9.2	0.10
benzene	2.3	< 0.01
carbon tetrachloride	1.3	< 0.01
cyclohexane	0.28	
ethanol, anhydrous	12.9	2.0
20%	0.29	54.6
ethyl ether	5.0	0.1
glycerol	0.31	0.2
methanol	12.9	16
cottonseed oil	1.0	0.01
propylene glycol	5.5	24
sodium chloride, 15%	0.038	15
water	0.15	58.2

The preferred form of the preservative for inclusion in foods normally depends upon the method of addition, ie, the more soluble salt form is selected for spray, dip, or solution applications and the acid for dusting and dry-blending.

Other physical properties of sorbic acid and potassium sorbate are given in Table 2.

Sorbic acid is a doubly unsaturated aliphatic acid. The conjugated unsaturation and carboxylic groups define the nature of its reactivity. As an acid, sorbic acid forms salts readily by reaction with alkalis. Esters, amides, and the acid chloride are formed in the conventional manner (2,3).

The addition reactions of sorbic acid and of its carboxyl derivatives are complex because of the different modes of addition to the unsaturated positions. Partial hydrogenation (reduction) and bromination, for example, can occur at different

Table 2. Physical Properties of Sorbic Acid and Potassium Sorbate

Property	Sorbic acid	Potassium sorbate
boiling point, °C		
760 mm	decomposes	
50 mm	143	
10 mm	119[a]	
melting point, °C	134.5	decomposes over 270°C
density (g/ml), 20°C		1.360
vapor pressure,[a] mm Hg		
20°C	<0.01	
120°C	10	
140°C	43	
flash point,[b] °C	126	
ionization constant at 25°C	1.73×10^{-5}	

[a] Solid–vapor equilibrium.   [b] Cleveland open-cup tester, ASTM D-92.

positions in the molecule, depending on the reaction condition and catalysts. Sorbic acid undergoes the Diels-Alder reaction with many dienophiles (styrene, maleic anhydride, acrylates, etc) (4,5). In many cases, the products are complex mixtures owing to the different modes of addition, shifting of double bonds, and other rearrangements and isomerizations.

Sorbic acid polymerizes readily when catalyzed by free radicals. Copolymers with other unsaturated monomers, including butadienes, vinyls, and acrylics, have been studied. No commercial uses of significant volume have been developed for sorbic acid polymers, primarily because of the relatively high cost of the sorbic acid.

Oxidizing agents attack sorbic acid and its salts and esters at the olefinic bonds. Autoxidation results in formation of peroxides, followed by degradation and polymerization. Of the various oxidizing agents, only ozone attacks both double bonds. Peracetic acid gives a 4,5-dihydroxy acid, which yields fumaric acid upon further oxidation.

Manufacture

Sorbic acid is produced commercially by two different processes, the oxidation of 2,4-hexadienal, and the reaction of ketene and crotonaldehyde, through a polymeric ester.

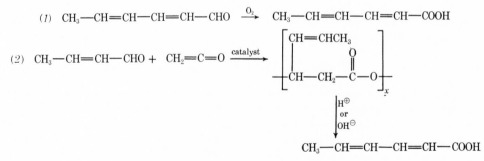

Oxidation of Hexadienal. 2,4-Hexadienal is obtained by the condensation of three molecules of acetaldehyde. This synthesis, and the synthesis by the condensation of acetaldehyde and crotonaldehyde, have been well known for many years, but the yields were low, and large amounts of the branched isomer (2-vinyl-2-butenal) and higher condensation products were formed and could be separated only with difficulty. The present commercial process results in good yields of 2,4-hexadienal with very little formation of the branched isomer (6,7).

The oxidation of 2,4-hexadienal is effected with air as the oxidizing agent by using specially developed equipment and procedures. Conventional methods of oxidizing aldehydes are not satisfactory in the case of hexadienal because of peroxidation of the ethylenic bonds and polymerization. In the commercial process the oxidation is carried out continuously in a solvent, and in the presence of an oxidation catalyst, under precisely controlled conditions in a manner such that the aldehyde is converted to sorbic acid rapidly and completely.

Ketene–Crotonaldehyde Route. One of the first commercial methods (8) for making sorbic acid was the reaction of ketene and crotonaldehyde in the presence of a Lewis acid catalyst, preferably boron trifluoride (9,10). This reaction yielded a polymeric product, identified as poly(hexeno-β-lactone):

$$(CH_3—CH=CH—CH—CH_2—CO—O)_n$$

The polymeric lactone was converted to sorbic acid by boiling with an aqueous solution of hydrochloric acid.

A more recent modification of the basic process employs as catalysts carboxylic salts of bivalent transition metals (eg, zinc isovalerate) in the ketene–crotonaldehyde reaction (11). As with acid catalysts, a polymeric intermediate is obtained; using more modern analytical techniques, the polymer has been identified as a polyester of 3-hydroxy-4-hexenoic acid (12):

$$H \left[O—CH—CH_2—CO_2 \atop \overset{\displaystyle CH=CH—CH_3}{|} \right]_n H$$

Many foreign patents have been issued for processes using the ketene–crotonaldehyde route to sorbic acid; most of the syntheses use zinc salts as catalysts.

The polyester obtained from this reaction can be isomerized into sorbic acid using several different types of catalysts and techniques. Patents have been issued on processes using alkali metals (11), alkalis (13), strong inorganic acids (10,14), phosphoric acid (15), or p-toluenesulfonic acid (16). A wide variety of yields are obtained, depending upon the catalyst used in the depolymerization–isomerization step as well as in the reaction step.

Purification and Specifications

Sorbic acid and its salts obtained by the previously described processes must be refined to a high degree of purity for use as a fungistatic agent in foods, the principal commercial use for these products. Purification can be achieved by recrystallization of the acid from water or mixed solvents. Another method of purification is by codistillation under vacuum with an organic solvent having the same general distillation range (17). Food-grade sorbate salts are prepared from the purified acid. Sorbic acid and potassium sorbate are now defined by Food Chemicals Specifications (18) having the quality requirements shown in Table 3.

Sorbic acid is routinely assayed in foods using a spectrophotometric method described by Alderton and Lewis (19). In foods where interfering substances absorb in the 260-mμ range, Ciaccio (20) selectively oxidizes the sorbic acid after determination of the optical density and computes the sorbic content by difference. Where a spectrophotometer is not available, the bromine titrimetric method of Spanyar and Sandor

Table 3. *Food Chemicals Codex* Specifications for Sorbic Acid and Potassium Sorbate

Specification	Sorbic acid	Potassium sorbate
melting point, °C	133–137	
water, wt %, max	0.5	1.0
purity by titration, wt %	99–101	98–102
heavy metals, ppm, max	10	10
ash, %, max	0.2	
arsenic, ppm, max	3	3

(21) may be used or acidimetry (22) when other acids are not present. The thiobarbituric acid (TBA) method of Schmidt (23) is also used in the quantitative determination of sorbic acid. There are also several qualitative methods for detecting sorbates. An excellent review on this entire subject may be found in an article by Schuller and Veen (24).

Use of Sorbic Acid and Its Salts

The major commercial use of sorbic acid and its alkali salts is as a fungistatic agent in foods. The use of sorbic acid for this application was patented initially in 1945 (1) and has been the subject of additional patents in many different food areas (25–31). Extensive studies related to its effectiveness in various foods, its toxicity, metabolism of fungistatic action, fate in foods, methods of application, and its analytical methodology have been undertaken. An excellent, although dated, bibliography of these studies may be found in an article by Melnick (32) and in a more recent bulletin put out by Chas. Pfizer & Co., Inc. (33).

The effectiveness of sorbic acid as a fungistatic agent is attributed to its α,β-unsaturated character and is undoubtedly enhanced by its fatty acid structure. In normal saturated fatty acid oxidation, essential to fungal metabolism, dehydrogenation occurs at the α,β position, forming an unsaturated fatty acid (β-oxidation pathway). The dehydrogenase enzyme system required for this reaction is inhibited by an excess of unsaturated fatty acids (eg, sorbic acid), the initial product of the β-oxidation pathway. As these products accumulate, they inhibit the dehydrogenase enzyme system, thereby significantly depressing fatty acid metabolism. This stops the growth of the microorganisms, but does not necessarily exert a lethal effect on them. In high mold populations, sorbic acid is not able to inhibit the highly active enzyme system and serves as a metabolite for molds (34), or is degraded to a harmless product (35).

Sorbic acid inhibits the growth of most fungi and a few of the bacteria normally associated with food spoilage. Its activity, as previously stated, is entirely static with respect to fungi and selected bacteria. Its use in a liver infusion media has been reported as a means of selective growth of catalase-negative lactic acid bacteria and *Clostridia* sp, where it inhibited the growth of catalase-positive actinomycetes, bacteria, molds, and yeasts in acidic media (pH 5.0–5.5) in the absence of phosphate salts (36).

The antimicrobial activity of sorbic acid is enhanced as the pH decreases. Bandelin (37) has shown that as the pH decreases from 9.0 to 3.0 the minimum concentration of sorbic acid required to inhibit the growth of four molds decreases from more than 0.2 to 0.005%. Other workers have also confirmed the interrelationship of low pH and the effectiveness of sorbic acid as a preservative. Beneke and Fabian (38) found 0.05% sorbic acid an effective antimycotic in tomato juice at pH 4.4, and at a 0.075% level in strawberry puree at a pH of about 4.0. Bell and co-workers (39) in examining the activity of sorbic acid for use in pickling applications used over 60 species of fungi, over 30 species of yeast, and 6 species of the lactobacilli. They found 0.1% sorbic acid inactive at pH 7.0, but quite active against the yeasts and fungi at pH 4.5. Below pH 3.5, even the lactic acid bacteria were inhibited.

Food in which sorbates have been demonstrated to have commercially effective activity include baked goods, cheese, confectionery (cake frostings and icings), chocolate coatings, dried fruits, fish products, fruit butters, fruit juices and fresh fruit salads, jellies (artificially sweetened), margarines, nonalcoholic beverages, pastry fillings, pet foods, pickled foods, poultry, prepared salads, salad dressings, sauces, sausage casings, dry sausage, syrups, and wines. They are also effective in some pharmaceutical preparations and in cosmetics. Other nonfood applications in which sorbic acid is used as a preservative include tobacco and silk-screen inks. Sorbic acid is generally more effective than other commercially used chemical food preservatives, such as benzoic and propionic acid, and as a consequence lesser amounts are required. This is a distinct advantage in bland foods where the taste and odor contributions of the preservative to the food are of critical concern. Like benzoic and propionic acids, sorbic acid requires an acidic pH for effectiveness, but functions at higher pH values than either benzoic or propionic acid. The concentration of sorbic acid used in foods varies from about 0.02 to about 0.3% by weight of the food.

The toxicity of sorbic acid is extremely low, about one third that of benzoic acid. Feeding studies have established that it is metabolized as a fatty acid ultimately into carbon dioxide and water in the same manner (ie, β-oxidation) as other unsaturated fatty acids normally found in foods. Comprehensive pharmacological data have established the safety of sorbic acid used in food packaging materials which are in intimate contact with the food. Studies which have shown that sorbic acid can migrate (40) from a packaging material into a foodstuff have been the basis for the utilization of sorbic acid-coated films to protect cheese.

On the basis of expert opinion that sorbic acid is safe for its intended use as a food preservative, the U.S. Food and Drug Administration regards it as GRAS (generally recognized as safe), Food Additives Regulation §121.101. It may be used without limitation in all foods not covered by Federal Standards of Identity, provided the use conforms to good manufacturing practice. Foods subject to Federal Standards of Identity in which the use of sorbic acid has been included in the Standards are shown in Table 4. In Table 5, a listing of uses for sorbates in products not covered by Standards is presented. The starred (*) foods mentioned in the following sections may be found in Table 4 and the daggered (†) foods in Table 5.

Bakery Products. At the present time, sorbic acid is limited to nonyeast-raised bakery products because of its inhibitory effect on yeast growth. The use of a post-baking spray of sorbic acid applied to yeast-raised products, such as English muffins,† has been used as a means of circumventing its effect on yeast. Sorbic acid, which is four times as effective as sodium propionate or sodium benzoate at a 0.2% level, is currently

Table 4. Foods Covered by Standards of Identity Which Include the Use of Sorbates

Foods covered by Standards of Identity	Food Additives Regulation or Food Standards	Sorbic acid or potassium sorbate
Cheese, processed cheese, cheese spreads		
cheddar, curd, colby, granular, swiss, gruyère, brick, muenster, edam, gouda, monterey, monterey jack, high-moisture jack, provolone, caciocavallo, siciliano parmesan, low-moisture mozzarella, low-moisture scamorze, low-moisture part-skim mozzarella, low-moisture part-skim scamorze, romano, asiago fresh, asiago medium, asiago old; and other hard, semisoft, semisoft part-skim, spiced, part-skim spiced, and hard grating cheeses not otherwise specifically defined by names or Standards of Identity	§19.500–19.680	up to 0.3% (either or both)
pasteurized process; pasteurized process with fruits, vegetables or meats; pasteurized process pimento; pasteurized blended; pasteurized blended with fruits, vegetables or meats; pasteurized process cheese food, pasteurized process cheese food with fruits, vegetables or meats	§19.750–19.770	up to 0.2% (either or both)
pasteurized process cheese spread; pasteurized cheese spread; pasteurized process cheese spread with fruits, vegetables, or meats; pasteurized cheese spread with fruits, vegetables, or meats; cold-pack cheese	§19.775–19.785	up to 0.2% (sorbic acid only)
cold-pack cheese food; cold-pack cheese food with fruits, vegetables, or meats	§19.787–19.788	up to 0.2% (sorbic acid only)
Jellies		
fruit jellies, preserves, jams	§29.2, 29.3	no
Jellies, artificially sweetened		
artificially sweetened fruit jellies, artificially sweetened fruit preserves	§29.4, 29.5	up to 0.1% (either or both)
Lemonade, colored lemonade, limeade		
	§27.99, 27.100, 27.131	no limit (potassium sorbate only)
Margarine, liquid margarine		
	§45.1, 45.2 Consumer and Marketing Service, USDA	up to 0.1% (potassium sorbate only)
Orange juice with preservative, concentrated orange juice with preservatives		
	§27.113, 27.115	up to 0.2% (sorbic acid only)

Table 4 (*continued*)

Orange-juice drink, orangeade, orange drink

§27.120–27.122   no limit (sorbic acid only)

Sausage, dry

Consumer and Marketing Service, USDA   2.5% in aqueous dip (potassium sorbate only)

Soda water, carbonated, plain, sweetened and/or flavored; club sodas, colas, tonics, etc

§31.1   no limit

Table 5. Use of Sorbates in Nonstandardized Foods

Product	Reference	Product	Reference
apple cider	(42,50,51)	fruit salads	(42,53)
apple juice	(52,53)	grape juice	(66)
bananas, slices	(53)	icing	(74)
cakes	(55,56)	maraschino cherries	(67)
carrots, pre-peeled	(57)	margarine, imitation diet	(68)
celery	(41,58)	mushrooms, brined in oil	(68)
chappaties	(59)	pancake batter	(68)
cherries	(44)	peach slices	(42)
chicken, smoked	(45)	pet-food patties	(69)
citrus salad	(43)	pickles	(70)
cucumbers	(61)	prunes	(71)
English muffins	(54)	strawberries	(38,44,53)
figs	(62)	tangarine, sherbet base	(72)
fish, smoked and salted	(63–65)	tomato juice	(38)
fruit-pie fillings	(55)	wine	(73)

used to protect cakes†, fruit-pie fillings†, cake frosting and icings, and the toasted fruit-filled tart products. The level of sorbate used varies from 0.075% (acidic fruit fillings) to 0.125% in "neutral" cakes (chocolate, cheese) to as much as 0.3% in devil's food cake.

Dairy Products. One of the principal uses of sorbic acid on foods today is in the protection of packaged cuts and slices of processed cheese. The quantities of sorbate that may be added to various cheeses covered by Standards of Identity are summarized in Table 4. The sorbate is added in one of five general methods: dip, spray, direct, dust, or as a coating on the wrapper film. The quantity and manner of application of sorbate required for protection varies for the different varieties. Dips and sprays use potassium sorbate solutions of 20–40% concentration.

Sorbates, while proven effective in extending the shelf life of cottage (60) and cream cheeses, are not named as ingredients in Federal Standards of Identity for these products and may not be used in interstate commerce. The users should consult state regulations for use of sorbates in intrastate commerce.

Potassium sorbate is the only form permitted by the Federal Standards of Identity for incorporation in margarine*. Used at a concentration of 0.1%, sorbate effectively inhibits the growth of spoilage organisms in salted, unsalted, and low-calorie, imitation margarine. The potassium sorbate may be blended into the fat emulsion, sprayed on the surface of the finished margarine, or incorporated into the wrapper film.

Fruit and Vegetable Products. There is limited use of sorbates with some fermented vegetable products, such as pickles†, where sorbic acid reduces surface yeast scum formation in brining tanks. Hall (41) has reported the use of potassium sorbate to control the discoloration of the butts of prepackaged celery†. After studying fruit products, Robinson et al. (42) found sorbic acid to be an effective preservative with peach slices†, apple cider†, and fruit salad†. Rushing and Senn (43), working with citrus salads†, and Salunke et al. (44), testing strawberries† and cherries†, also found sorbic acid useful as a preservative.

A considerable amount of work has been done in studying the effectiveness of sorbates in fruit juice† preservation. The shelf life of apple juice or cider† has been extended significantly with sorbic acid and it is also used to prevent fermentation in grape juice† stored in holding tanks. Other juices that have been preserved with sorbates include tomato†, orange*, and lemonade*.

Dips or sprays of potassium sorbate solutions are routinely used to preserve such dried fruit products as prunes†, figs†, apricots, and mixed dried fruits.

Various convenience foods which are kept under refrigeration, such as potato salad, cole slaw, macaroni salad, and gelatin (especially with fruit added), demonstrate marked shelf-life improvement with the addition of sorbates. The preservative may be added either in the cream dressing or in the hot water (gelatin).

Beverages, Beverage Syrups, and Syrups. Sorbates are used, often in conjunction with benzoates, to protect and to extend the shelf life of noncarbonated beverages (especially those containing fruit) and in various fountain syrups. Chocolate syrup, which is prepared at relatively high pH levels, requires sorbate protection. Recently, a trend toward the use of sorbates with maple-flavored syrups has been established.

Wines. Sorbate is added to various red and white table wines† in conjunction with sulfur dioxide to effectively inhibit yeast fermentation and increase product life. In practice, as little as 0.05% potassium sorbate plus 10 ppm SO_2 provides the desired protection.

Low-Calorie Foods. Sorbic acid or its potassium salt has been found to be an excellent preservative in low-calorie foods where the normal high sugar content, which acts as a preservative, has been lowered. Removal of fat and substitution of water also increases product susceptibility to microbial attack. Examples of this new generation of foodstuffs include imitation jams, jellies, and preserves*, fruit-flavored syrups, chocolate and maple syrups, soda*, margarine*, salad dressings, and candies.

Meat, Fish, Poultry, and Pet Food. Pet-food patties† of the soft-moist variety generally contain ∼25% moisture. To permit long-term storage of these products, about 0.3% sorbate is added to the meat, poultry, or fish emulsion, in conjunction with propylene glycol. This combination provides the antimycotic stability necessary for this product.

Potassium sorbate is permitted, under present Meat and Poultry Regulations, as an additive only in dry sausage*. Here a 2½% potassium sorbate solution is used as a dip for the casing either before or after stuffing.

Sorbates have been used to protect salted and smoked fish†. They are generally applied as 10% aqueous sprays or used at a 5% concentration in a dip solution. There is also a reported use of sorbate for protecting smoked chicken† (45). Users are advised to check appropriate Federal, State, or local regulations prior to use of sorbates in meat, poultry, and fish products.

Miscellaneous. Sorbates have been used for many other products, generally at a concentration between 0.025 and 0.10%. Improvement in keeping quality was found in such diverse products as Chinese egg roll dough, cucumbers, maraschino cherries, pancake batter, etc (see Table 5).

Sorbic acid may be applied to foods in a variety of ways, including direct incorporation, as a spray, as a powder dusting, and via an organic carrier such as ethanol, propylene glycol, or vegetable oil. The potassium salt, or to a very limited extent the sodium salt, of sorbic acid is used principally because of its high water solubility. However, for fungistatic activity, the pH of the foodstuff must be below 6.5. On an equivalent weight basis, the potassium salt has 74% of the activity of sorbic acid. Therefore, higher concentrations are required to obtain the antimycotic activity comparable to that of sorbic acid.

The nonfood uses of sorbic acid which are of significance include cosmetics, tobacco, and latex-based emulsions such as silk-screen inks. In cosmetic formulations, sorbic acid, unlike the p-hydroxybenzoate esters, is not inactivated by the commonly used nonionic emulsifier systems, and formulations with excellent physical and biological stability have been prepared (46,47). A comprehensive survey of cosmetic preparations by Lück (48) covers a wide range of applications for sorbic acid and presents convincing bibliographic material which indicates that sorbic acid and its salts can be used without pharmacological and dermatological contraindications for preserving cosmetic emulsions.

Sorbic acid is used domestically to prevent mold growth during the aging of tobacco, and, in Japan, to destroy molds upon which beetles feed, thereby eliminating a tobacco beetle problem (49). Inks which contain significant amounts of latexes in their formulations also are protected from mold attack by sorbic acid.

Bibliography

"Sorbic Acid" in *ECT* 1st ed., Vol. 6, pp. 272–274, by J. A. Field, Union Carbide and Carbon Corp.; Suppl. 1, pp. 840–849, by A. E. Montagna, Union Carbide Chemicals Company.

1. U.S. Pat. 2,379,294 (June 26, 1945), C. M. Gooding (to Best Foods, Inc.).
2. Cronk, D. H., Zopf, L. C., and Jones, J. W., *J. Am. Pharm. Assoc. Sci. Ed.* **38**, 455–457 (1959).
3. U.S. Pat. 3,056,830 (May 7, 1962), S. Koopal, U. Verstrijden, W. Pesch, and J. M. Deumens (to Stamicarbon N.V.).
4. Alder, K., Decker, K. H., and Lienau, R., *Ann.* **570**, 214–230 (1950).
5. Deno, N. C., and Johnston, J. D., *J. Am. Chem. Soc.* **74**, 3233–3236 (1952).
6. Astle, M. J., *The Chemistry of Petrochemicals*, Reinhold Publishing Corp., N.Y., 1956, p. 240.
7. Anon., *Chem. Week* **77**, 73 (Aug. 13, 1955).
8. Anon., *Chem. Week* **77**, 73–76 (Aug. 13, 1955).
9. Hagemeyer, H. J., Jr., *Ind. Eng. Chem.* **41**, 765–770 (1949).
10. U.S. Pat. 2,484,067 (Oct. 11, 1949), A. B. Boese, Jr. (to Union Carbide Corp.).
11. U.S. Pat. 3,021,365 (Feb. 13, 1962), H. Fernholz and E. Mundlos (to Farbwerke Hoechst).
12. Polyanskii, N. G., Chernysheva, D. A., and Rubtsova, N. D., *Zh. Prikl. Khim.* **39**, 1211–1213 (1966).
13. Fr. Pat. 1,241,776 (Aug. 16, 1960), Société des Usines Chimiques Rhône-Poulenc.
14. Fr. Pat. 1,309,051 (Oct. 1, 1962), Deutsches Hydrierwerk Rodleben.
15. Brit. Pat. 919,187 (Feb. 20, 1963), H. P. Crocker and J. W. Hamlin.
16. Coldwell, J. R., *Official Gazette U.S. Pat. Office* **673**, 873 (1953).
17. U.S. Pat. 2,936,267 (Nov. 14, 1956), H. Fernholz, E. Mundlos, and O. Probst (to Farbwerke Hoechst).

18. *Food Chemicals Codex*, 1st ed., Publication No. 1406, National Academy of Science–National Research Council, Washington, D.C., 1966.
19. Alderton, G., and Lewis, J. C., *Food Res.* **23**, 338–344 (1958).
20. Ciaccio, L. L., *Food Technol.* **20**, 73–75 (1966).
21. Spanyar, P., and Sandor, A., *Z. Lebensm.-Untersuch.-Forsch.* **108**, 402–405 (1958).
22. Mourel, A., and Touye, M., *Ann. Fals. Expert. Chim.* **55**, 297–308 (1962).
23. Schmidt, H., *Deut. Lebensm.-Rundschau* **58**, 1–4 (1962).
24. Schuller, P. L., and Veen, E., *J.O.A.C.* **50**, 1127–1145 (1967).
25. U.S. Pat. 2,858,225 (Oct. 23, 1958), C. M. Gooding, D. Melnick, and H. W. Vahlteich (to Best Foods, Inc.).
26. U.S. Pat. 2,932,574 (April 12, 1960), R. C. Bour.
27. U.S. Pat. 2,933,399 (April 19, 1960), J. T. R. Nickerson and L. D. Starr (to Dirigo Sales Corp.).
28. U.S. Pat. 2,974,046 (March 7, 1961), G. A. Perry and R. L. Lawrence (to Corn Products Co.).
29. U.S. Pat. 2,997,394 (Aug. 22, 1961), D. Melnick, H. W. Vahlteich, and R. T. Bohn (to Corn Products Co.).
30. U.S. Pat. 3,021,219 (Feb. 13, 1962), D. Melnick (to Corn Products Co.).
31. U.S. Pat. 3,202,514 (Aug. 24, 1965), H. M. Burgess and R. W. Mellentin (to General Foods Corp.).
32. Melnick, D., Vahlteich, H. W., and Hackett, A., *Food Res.* **21**, 133–146 (1956).
33. *Food Preservatives*, Chas. Pfizer & Co., Inc., New York, 1966.
34. Deuel, H. J., Calbert, C. E., Anisfeld, L., McKeehan, H., and Blunden, H. D., *Food Res.* **19**, 13–19 (1954).
35. Marth, E. H., Capp, C. M., Hosenzahl, L., Jackson, H. W., and Hussong, R. V., *J. Dairy Sci.* **49**, 1197–1205 (1967).
36. Emard, L. O., and Vaugh, R. H., *J. Bacteriol.* **63**, 487–498 (1952).
37. Bandelin, F. J., *J. Am. Pharm. Assoc., Sci. Ed.* **47**, 691–694 (1958).
38. Beneke, E. S., and Fabian, F. W., *Food Technol.* **9**, 486–488 (1955).
39. Bell, T. A., Etchells, J. L., and Borg, A. F., *J. Bacteriol.* **77**, 573–580 (1959).
40. Lehman, A. J., and Patterson, W. I., *Mod. Packaging* **28**, 115 (1955).
41. Hall, C. B., *Proc. Fla. State Hort. Soc.* **72**, 280–284 (1959).
42. Robinson, J. R., and Hills, C. H., *Food Technol.* **13**, 251–253 (1959).
43. Rushing, N. B., and Senn, V. J., *Food Technol.* **16**, 77–79 (1962).
44. Salunke, D. K., Cooper, D. M., Dhaliwal, A. S., and Riveis, A. L., *Food Technol.* **16**, 119–123 (1962).
45. Falcon, P. R., and Olaivar, S. F., report to Chas. Pfizer & Co., Inc., from the Meat Processing Laboratory, Department of Animal Husbandry, College of Agriculture, University of the Philippines, 1957.
46. Charles, R. D., and Carter, P. J., *J. Soc. Cosmetic Chemists* **10**, 383–394 (1959).
47. Tice, L. F., and Barr, M., *J. Soc. Cosmetic Chemists* **9**, 171–180 (1958).
48. Lück, E., *Soap, Perfumery Cosmetics* **37**, 981–984 (1964).
49. Anon., *Japan. Chem. Weekly* **7**, 4 (Nov. 10, 1966).
50. Harrington, W. O., and Hills, C. H., *Food Technol.* **20**, 1360–1362 (1966).
51. *Ibid.* **22**, 1451–1454 (1968).
52. Ferguson, W. E., and Powrie, W. D., *Appl. Microbiol.* **5**, 41–43 (1957).
53. U.S. Pat. 2,992,114 (July 11, 1961), E. A. Weaver (to U.S. Government).
54. DeSa, C., *Baker's Dig.* **40**, 50–52 (1966).
55. Bradshaw, W., *Baker's Dig.* **32**, 58–61 (1958).
56. Pomeranz, Y., and Adler, L., *Bull. Res. Council Israel Sec. C* **6**, 220–226 (1958).
57. Francis, F. J., *Pre-Pack-Age* **9**, 8 (1965).
58. Hall, C. B., *Proc. Fla. State Hort. Soc.* **81**, 354–357 (1962).
59. Rao, G. K., Malathi, M. A., and Vijayaraghavan, P. K., *Food Technol.* **20**, 1070–1073 (1966).
60. Bradley, R. L., Harmon, L. G., and Stine, C. M., *J. Milk Food Technol.* **25**, 318–323 (1962).
61. Heiligman, F., *Am. Vegetable Grower* **5**, 28 (Jan. 1957).
62. Harrison, N., Unpublished data, California Fig Growers and Packers, Inc., Fresno, Calif. (1959).
63. Thompson, M. H., *Com. Fisheries Rev.* **24**, 5–11 (1962).

64. Versamin, S. V., Macalincag, N., and Legaspi, A. S., *Indo-Pacific Fisheries Council Proc.* **9,** 98–101 (1962).

65. Amano, K., Shibasaki, I., Yokoseki, M., and Kawabata, T., *Food Technol.* **22,** 881–885 (1968).

66. Pederson, C. S., Albany, M. N., and Christensen, M. D., *Appl. Microbiol.* **9,** 162–167 (1961).

67. Bowen, J. F., *1955 Rep. Can. Comm. Fruit Vegetable Preserv.*, p. 11.

68. Moline, S. W., unpublished data, Union Carbide Corp., Tarrytown, N.Y., 1968.

69. Spiegel, L. S., *Petfood Industry* **10,** 8–9 (1968).

70. Etchells, J. L., Borg, A. F., and Bell, T. A., *Appl. Microbiol* **16,** 1029–1035 (1968).

71. Bolin, H. R., and Boyle, F. P., *J. Sci. Food Agr.* **18,** 289–291 (1967).

72. Patrick, R., and Atkins, C. D., *Proc. Fla. State Hort. Soc.* **67,** 194–196 (1954).

73. O'Rourke, C. E., and Weaver, E. A., *Wines and Vines* **43,** 28–30 (1962).

74. U.S. Pat. 3,276,881 (Oct. 4, 1966), J. A. Troller (to Proctor & Gamble).

S. W. Moline, C. E. Colwell,
and J. E. Simeral
Union Carbide Corporation

SORBITE.   See Steel.

SORBITOL, $CH_2OH(CHOH)_3CH_2OH$.   See Alcohols, polyhydric.

SORGHUMS.   See Wheat and other cereal grains.

SOYBEANS

The soybean, *Glycine max* (L.) Merrill, also known as soya bean, soja bean, Chinese pea, and Manchurian bean, is a native of eastern Asia. It is grown rather extensively in various parts of the world, particularly in the temperate zones. In the Far East, it is an important source of edible protein. In the United States, soybeans have been used primarily as a source of food fat and animal feed. Commercially, no single variety of beans dominates the market, because the soybean is markedly affected by the length of day. Agronomic research has developed a number of varieties well suited to the different parts of the Mississippi Valley where more than 80% of U.S. soybeans are grown. Since most of these varieties were unknown before 1955, further improvement should be expected. Present varieties have an oil content 2–4% higher than the beans grown in 1930. Soybean breeders of the U.S. Department of Agriculture (USDA) and their cooperators in many state experiment stations have been primarily responsible for this change. Leading varieties recommended in 1968 for the major growing areas were the following: Amsoy, Clark 63, Corsoy, Hark, Harosoy 63, and Wayne for the Midwest; Bragg, Hill, and Lee for the South; and Chippewa 64, Hark, Merit, and Portage for Minnesota and Canada (1,2).

This typical legume seed is attached to the plant in short hairy pods containing two to three seeds. Seeds are separated from the pods in the field by combines. Size, shape, and color of the bean varieties are quite different, ranging from small, round beans to large, oblong, rather flat seeds and including yellow, brown, green, and reddish hues, as well as black. As shown in Figure 1 for the Lincoln soybean, formerly grown widely in Illinois, Iowa, and Indiana, the hilum or seed scar, *h*, is linear-elliptical. The chalaza, *c*, is at one end of the hilum where the seed coat joins the body of the ovule. The micropyle, *m*, is the minute opening at the other end of the hilum where the primary root of the germinating seed emerges. The outline of the hypocotyl, *hy*, can be seen beneath the seed coat. The seed consists primarily of hull and embryo, but it has a very rudimentary endosperm.   In Figure 2, the major parts of the bean are seen in cross section. The hull consists of an outer layer of palisade cells, *p ep;* a secondary layer of hourglass cells, *s ep,* and smaller compressed or partially compressed layers of parenchyma, *par;* aleurone cells (filled with dense protein), *al;* and compressed endosperm cells, *com.*

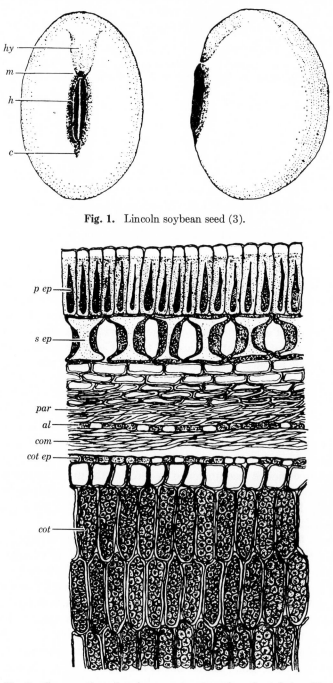

Fig. 1.   Lincoln soybean seed (3).

Fig. 2.   Cross section of soybean coat and portion of cotyledon (3).

The embryo constitutes the major part of the seed with the cotyledon epidermis *cot ep*, and two cotyledons, *cot*, the hypocotyl, *hy*, and the plumule. The hourglass cells are unusually large in soybean seeds, varying from 30 to 70 μ in length and from 16 to 36 μ in width. The elongated palisadelike cells of the cotyledons are filled with protein and oil (3).

Soybeans are usually grown in rows 21–42 in. apart. The length of the growing season, the growth characteristics of the variety, and the fertility level determine the optimum width of the row. In the Northern states, rows from 21 to 30 in. wide give the best yields but in the South, wider rows and later planting give higher yields. Planting is often delayed up to 30 days beyond the optimum dates and narrow rows are favored. May is the optimum planting time in the North but 10–15 days later is preferred in the Southern states. Planting is risky after June 30 in the North and after July 5–15 in the South. Fields inoculated with *Rhizopium japonium*, a nitrogen-fixing bacterium, require little nitrogen fertilizer because the plant is symbiotic with the microorganisms. The plant furnishes carbohydrate to the bacteria in nodules of the roots, and the bacteria convert nitrogen of the air to nitrates for use by the plant. Thus, in one year the soybean may add 16 lb of nitrogen per acre per crop, exclusive of the nitrogen removed by the crop. Soybeans do remove considerable amounts of mineral per acre when they are harvested for beans and the straw is returned to the soil. The amounts are as follows: 11 lb of phosphorus, 33 lb of potassium, 5 lb of calcium, and 6 lb of magnesium, based on a yield of 29 bu per acre (2,4).

Composition. Commercial soybeans usually contain approx 8% hull or seed coat, 90% cotyledons, and 2% hypocotyl and plumule. Values for the proximate composition of whole beans, cotyledons, hull, hypocotyl, and meals are given in Table 1 (5,6).

Table 1. Approximate Composition of Soybeans and Derived Meals[a], %

Assayed	Protein (N × 6.25)	Fat	Carbohydrate	Ash
whole bean	40	21	34	4.9
cotyledon	43	23	29	5.0
hull	8.8	1.0	86	4.3
hypocotyl[b]	41	11	43	4.4
meal (7)				
extruded	41 min	3.5 min	7.0 max[c]	
extracted	44 min	0.5 min	7.0 max[c]	
dehulled	49 min[d]	0.5 min	3.0 max[c]	

[a] Moisturefree basis.

[b] Hypocotyl and pumule are sometimes incorrectly referred to as embryo.

[c] Maximum fiber.

[d] Minimum of 49% protein established in 1968.

Although the soybean contains mainly oil and protein, it does have an appreciable amount of carbohydrates, such as polysaccharides (20%), stachyose (3.8%), raffinose (1.1%), and sucrose (5.0%); there are also phosphatides (2–5%) (see Lecithin); sterols (see steroids) (including sitosterol and stigmasterol); tocopherols (see vitamin E under Vitamins); and ash. The inorganic constituents of whole soybeans are all listed in Table 2 (8).

Oil and protein contents vary with variety, fertility, and weather conditions; the best-characterized, globulinlike protein, often called glycinin, is a mixture of proteins that have sedimentation constants of 2, 7, 11, and 15 S (Svedberg units) (9). Inorganic

Table 2. Inorganic Constituents of Soybeans

Constituent	Average, %	Constituent	Average, %
ash	5.0[a]	chlorine	0.024
potassium	1.67[a]	iodine	0.000054[a]
sodium	0.34	iron	0.0097
calcium	0.28[a]	copper	0.0012
magnesium	0.22	manganese	0.0028
phosphorus	0.66[a]	zinc	0.0022
sulfur	0.41	aluminum	0.0007

[a] Calculated on a dry-matter basis; all others on air-dry basis.

constituents also vary, depending primarily on fertility and weather conditions. Soybeans also contain small amounts of enzymes, including urease and lipoxidase, and inhibitors, such as hemaglutinin and antitrypsins. All are inactivated by the moist heat used in processing (10).

Standards and Trading Rules. Because soybeans are classified as cereal grains, trading is regulated under the U.S. Grain Standards Act. This act is administered by the USDA in conformance with the *Handbook of Official Grain Standards of the United States*. Soybeans are classified according to color, and yellow soybeans are the major commercial class. Grades are determined by test weight, moisture content, percentages of splits, damaged kernels, and foreign material. Table 3 shows requirements for numerical and sample grades of soybeans (11). Futures in soybeans, oil, and meal are conducted by the Chicago Board of Trade to permit hedging against any major price change. Decatur, Ill., is the base point in pricing soybeans.

Table 3. Requirements of Numerical and Sample Grades of Soybeans

Requirements	Grade			
	No. 1	No. 2	No. 3	No. 4
test wt, lb/bu,[a] min	56	54	52	49
moisture, %	13	14	16	18
limits, %, max				
splits	10	20	30	40
damaged kernels	2	3	5	8
foreign material	1	2	3	5
colored[b] beans	1	2	5	10

[a] The volume of a bushel is 8 gal (U.S.). The legal weight of a bushel is 60 lb for sale purposes. However, soybeans of the various grades must not fall below the min wt shown for the various grades.

[b] Not yellow or green.

NOTE: *Sample grade*—soybeans which do not meet the requirements of grades 1–4, inclusive; or which are musty, sour, or heating; or which have an objectionable odor.

Handling and Storage

Soybeans are unique among grains grown in the United States because 80–90% of all beans harvested are processed or exported for processing to separate oil from meal. As a consequence, large amounts of soybeans must be stored just after harvest to permit an orderly processing of the crop. All the large processors have substantial storage capacity to maintain ample supplies. During normal marketing, the crop is harvested in September or October and distributed to the processors mainly through country elevators. As a result of comparatively low prices between October and December, storage facilities both on and off the farm have expanded considerably and permit a more orderly marketing of the crop throughout the year.

Commercial storage bins are concrete silos having diameters of 20–40 ft and heights above 150 ft. Usually, the bins are placed in double or triple rows so that considerable storage capacity is gained from the interstitial bins. Many processing mills have storage capacities running up to several million bushels. Deterioration of soybeans in storage is not a major concern throughout most of the processing industry, because the beans are usually dry enough to keep in raintight bins. Proper moisture content of the beans is essential for successful storage. Soybeans with 12% or lower moisture can usually be held satisfactorily for two years or more with no significant change in grade. Seasonal migration of moisture has been noted in stored soybeans, so that transfer from one bin to another to facilitate mixing is a common commercial practice (12). Beans of 13–15% moisture have to be stored for shorter periods, particularly during cool weather. Beans with higher moisture are usually dried to permit safe storage. High-moisture content promotes mold growth which results in moldy odor that may reduce beans to sample grade. Continued mold growth causes beans to heat, which results in charred or damaged beans. Table 4 shows the relation of the

Table 4. Effect of Moisture Content on Respiration, Acid Value of Oil, Germination, and Mold Growth of Soybeans Stored at 38° C for 11 Days

Moisture, initial, %	Respiratory rate,[a] mg CO_2/100 g dry matter	Acid value of oil	Germination, %	Visual condition
11.8	0.5	1.0	85	moldfree
13.0	0.9	1.1	74	moldfree
13.9	0.9	1.3	60	moldfree
15.1	0.9	1.5	43	moldfree
16.0	5.4	1.8	15	moldfree
18.3	73.3	6.9	0	moldy

[a] On the eleventh day, during a 24-hr. period.

moisture content of stored beans to respiration and other criteria at 38°C (13). Long-term storage of soybeans can lower nutritive value more than similar storage of corn or wheat. The whole bean is largely living germ whereas only a small part of the corn or wheat kernel is germ. Soybean meal of low moisture content stores readily for three years with little loss in nutritive value (14).

Processing

Because soybeans are relatively easy to store and have a high bulk density (45 lb/ft³), they are often processed relatively far from the growing areas. In the United States, however, almost all beans are processed close to where they are grown for marketing reasons. Solvent extraction is the major processing method for soybeans, but some continuous screw-pressing and extruder-cooker operations are used.

In 1932 there were no major solvent extraction plants for soybeans in the United States, but England, Germany, and the Low Countries had a number of such plants, both batch and continuous. Shortly thereafter, two major German plants were installed in the United States. One was a Hansa-Mühle, and the other a Hildebrandt

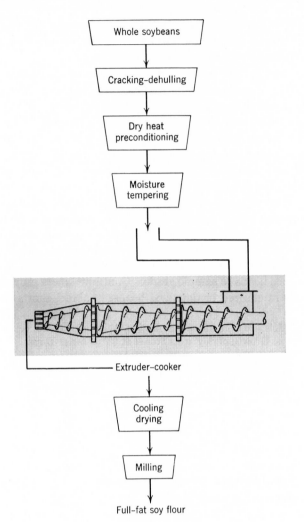

Fig. 3. Schematic diagram of operations with an extruder-cooker (16).

extractor. Since then, American capacity to extract soybeans has increased enormously. Screw-press operations expanded during World War II, but extraction operations increased rapidly after 1946. In 1949 the two processes were approximately equally important, but the more efficient removal of oil from soybean flakes by extraction has made this process the more economical one as long as oil prices remain substantially above those of meal. More than 95% of beans processed in the United States are solvent extracted and the total capacity in 1968 was estimated at 750 million bu (15).

Although use of solvent extraction has grown in both the United States and Europe, continuous screw presses still operate for certain products and in developing countries. One recent use of the extruder cooker has been to make full-fat flour from soybeans or pet foods from a combination of soybeans and cereal grains (16). Flowsheets for both solvent-extractor and extruder-cooker operations are shown in Figures 3 and 4, respectively. Key notations for Figure 4 are listed in Table 5.

Preparation. Soybeans are similarly prepared for these processing methods until the beans have passed through the cracking rolls. Sound beans are permitted to flow into a feeding hopper that regulates the flow of the beans into the plant. A magnetic separator removes foreign iron and steel objects. After weighing, the beans go through cleaners which may be either a simple scalping shoe or a more complex combination of multiple screening and aspiration. Screens remove heavy, coarse, and fine trash while aspiration separates light trash and hulls. After cleaning, the beans are cracked. Cracking rolls may be single or double strand and 2–3 pairs high. Their actual arrangement and number depend upon the size of the plant and the floor space available (17).

The beans are dehulled in the manufacture of 49% meal and soy flour or when it is desired to increase the capacity of an extraction plant by approx 5 or 6%. The hulls may be drawn off between the first and second pairs of cracking rolls by air suction, and then passed over a screen to recover any meats that adhere. Hulls represent approx 8% of the soybean by wt of which dehulling removes 60–80%. The hulls are ground, fed back into the defatted meal stream and toasted along with the meal in extraction plants. Hull can be processed separately into soybean mill feed (13% protein), or mill run (11% protein) (10).

For continuous screw pressing, the moisture content of cracked beans is reduced to about 3%. Cracked beans are dried by dropping onto hot pipes; the dried beans are conditioned to compensate for any hardening of the bean (case-hardening). The temperature of the beans entering the press varies, but is usually held to 270–280° F (17).

For solvent extraction, cracked beans are conditioned to a moisture content of 10–11% at about 165°F. After conditioning, the beans are flaked on rolls 20–32 in. in diameter and 42 in. long. The larger the diameter the greater the capacity; a 20-in. roll flakes about 100–125 tons per day. The thickness of the flakes varies from about 0.008 to 0.012 in. Since flakes are somewhat fragile, they are usually transported in mass-flow conveyors to avoid formation of fines. The flakes generally have about 10% moisture and a temperature of about 140°F when they enter the extractor (18,19).

Screw-Press and Extruder-Cooker Operations. These systems are similar in their use of a continuous screw but differ in design. The screw press, but not the extruder cooker, has openings that permit oil to escape and be collected separately. Oil is reabsorbed in the meal before it leaves an extruder-cooker. In both, pressures increase as the cracked beans feed through the screws and as the cell structures are broken to release oil. Initial sections in the press may have bars as much as 0.02 in. apart, while bars in the last section may be 0.005–0.01 in. apart (17,20,21). Both machines have choke mechanisms to increase pressure. An extruder-cooker may have sections separated by perforated plates to create back pressure and a tapered or nose-cone section. Both press and extruder operations are comparatively rapid. For example, only 4 min are required for preconditioning, mixing, cooking, and extruding cracked beans. Moisture contents of the entering and exiting materials, however, are not the same. During press operations usually about a 3% moisture content is maintained, but this is raised to 12% before marketing the meal. In extruder operations, moisture is raised and kept at about 20% before and during cooking, and afterward the extruded product is dried.

Most continuous screw presses are cooled either by flowing cooled oil over the barrel or circulating cold water through the barrel in a passage designed for this purpose. The oil flows from the press through a screening tank and a plate-and-frame filter press to remove foots and meal particles. It is then pumped to storage or to tank

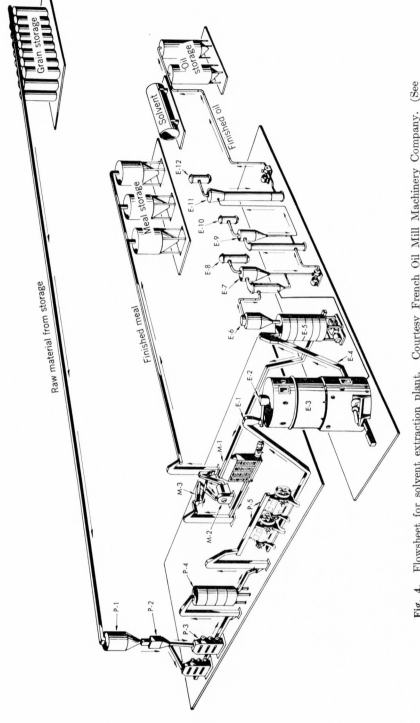

Fig. 4. Flowsheet for solvent extraction plant. Courtesy French Oil Mill Machinery Company. (See Table 5 for key notations.)

Table 5. Key Notations for Figure 4

Preparation	Extraction and oil handling	Meal handling
P-1, surge bin	E-1 and -2, flake conveyor	E-4, spent-flake elevator
P-2, scale	E-3, extractor	E-5, desolventizer-toaster
P-3, cracking roll	E-7 and -8, first-stage oil stripper and condenser	E-6, vapor scrubber
P-4, conditioner	E-9 and -10, second-stage oil stripper and condenser	M-1, louvered meal cooler
P-5, flaking rolls	E-11 and E-12, final oil stripper and condenser	M-2, meal grinder
		M-3, meal screen

cars for shipment. Under optimum conditions, oil content of the resultant meal is reduced to 3.5–4% but may be as high as 5–8%. Most presses of this type process about 22–25 tons of soybeans per day. Steam consumption per ton of soybeans varies from 550 to 900 lb; power consumption can be from 80 to 100 kW and the yield of crude oils is approx 9.6 lb/bu, or 320 lb/ton (17,20,21).

Solvent Extraction. Tempered soybean flakes are usually extracted with petroleum hydrocarbons, hexane, or heptane. Outside temperatures generally determine which solvent is used. Solvent usually flows countercurrent to flakes in special closed systems, such as stationary or horizontal basket extractors (see Extraction). Solvent is removed in a desolventizer-toaster by live steam (22). The steam evaporates the solvent, condenses to increase the moisture content to above 20%, and cooks or toasts the flakes. Solvent is removed from the miscella by use of preheaters, rising film evaporators, and stripping columns (see Solvent recovery). Flakes are used to prepare meal and protein products. The oil is degummed by hydration and centrifugation to give crude degummed oil and lecithin (qv). Power consumption per ton of soybeans processed generally ranges from 25 to 35 kW, steam consumption from 700 to 1500 lb, and requirements for cooling water (60°F) from 1600 to 2000 gal. The yield of crude oil per ton of beans averages 343–380 lb and depends on the efficiency of flaking and on the oil and moisture content of the beans (18,19,21).

Soybean Products

Oil (see also Fats and fatty oils). Crude oil coming either from stripping columns in the extraction process or from filters in the plants equipped with the continuous screw presses can be degummed to remove the phosphatides or treated directly by alkali refining. Crude or degummed oil is refined with sodium hydroxide or sodium carbonate to remove free fatty acids and phosphatides. The refined oil is either bleached and deodorized to give a salad oil or bleached, hydrogenated, and deodorized to give shortenings (qv) and margarine oils (see Fats and fatty oils; Margarine).

More soybean oil products are consumed in food fats and oils than any other visible fat. More than 4.3 billion lb were used in the year ending October 1967: about 1.69 billion lb for shortening, 1.27 billion lb for margarine, and 1.3 billion lb for salad and cooking oils (23). Consumption in 1968 is expected to increase about 5%.

About 0.5 billion lb were used for nonfood products: 100 million lb each in paint-varnish and resins–plastics and the remainder for foots for conversion into fatty acids or to feeds.

Soybean oil or its fatty acids can be used in alkyd resins (qv), in the preparation of polyamide plastics (qv), and for epoxy plasticizers (see Plasticizers).

Sterols (see Steroids) present in soybeans are isolated from deodorizer distillates and can be used in the preparation of certain steroidal hormones (see also Hormones) (24).

The flavor of soybean oil is more sensitive to the presence of trace metals than is the flavor of many other vegetable oils. Even 0.01 ppm of copper or 0.03 ppm of iron accelerates the appearance of undesirable flavors. The flavors are described as rancid, grassy, painty, and fishy. Reportedly, linolenic acid is the major precursor of these flavors, and oils containing more than about 4% of this acid develop the flavors readily in the presence of trace amounts of copper and iron. Through applied research at the U.S. Department of Agriculture's Northern Regional Research Laboratory and from industrial developmental studies, we have learned how appearance of these off-flavors in many edible products can be delayed substantially. Citric acid is now added to almost all soybean oil products at levels of 0.005% to inactivate metals and precautions are taken to avoid unnecessary exposure to air (25,26). Some edible-oil refiners hydrogenate and then winterize soybean oil to lower the linolenic acid content to about 3%. Winterizing consists of gradually cooling the oil to a desired temperature for a considerable time and filtering the oil to remove solidified fats. See Vol. 7, p. 401. Winterization decreases the saturated fatty acid content so that the hydrogenated oil does not solidify in the refrigerator. This comparatively new salad and cooking oil is called hydrogenated-winterized soybean oil (26,27).

A typical fatty acid analysis for unhydrogenated soybean oil is the following (%): palmitic, 10.8; stearic, 4.2; oleic, 28.9; linoleic, 50.2; and linolenic, 6.8; and for hydrogenated-winterized oil as follows: saturated acids, 27.5; oleic-like, 44.6; linoleic-like, 38.9; and linolenic-like, 2.2.

Crude soybean oil is usually traded under Rule 102 of the National Soybean Processors Association, which defines the grade and quality of crude and crude degummed oils. Under this rule the buyer receives a rebate for any refining loss in excess of 5% and pays a premium for any refining loss less than 5%. Loss and unsaponifiables shall not exceed 7.5 and 1.5%, respectively. The rebates and penalties on loss are at the rate of 1% of the contract price for each percent over or under 5, and the maximum premium is 4.5%. Moisture or volatile matter higher than 0.5% is not permitted. Additional discounts are based on the refined, bleached color, with a special standard for green crude soybean oil. Discounts are also in effect when a tank-car shipment of oil contains settlings or solid residues, usually phosphatides (7).

Meal and Meal Products. Soybeans are processed for animal feeds because (a) the separated oil is a valuable source of edible and industrial products; (b) the amount of oil in the meal should be reduced; and (c) protein feed quality can be substantially increased (28). Feeding unprocessed soybeans to swine gives "soft" pork, that is, pork having fat of low melting point. Heating approximately doubles the relative protein efficiency for feed and destroys certain growth inhibitors in the meal (10). In screw-press operations, heating is accomplished during tempering for 10–15 min at 240–280°F and during pressing for 2–3 min at 280–300°F. In the extruder-cooker operation, the temperature is raised from 80 to 200°F during 3 min of preconditioning and from 200 to 240 to 280°F for about 1 min in the cooker. In solvent extraction, the flakes are toasted in the desolventizer-toaster by steaming the flakes to remove hexane and adjusting the moisture with continued heating at 220–235°F for 30–45 min. Toasted flakes are also prepared by adding moisture and heating under 15 lb steam pressure for about 15 min. The products are ground to obtain meal. About 13.4 million tons was produced in the

Table 6. Amino Acid Composition of Soybean Meal from Hawkeye Beans[a]

Amino acid	g amino acid/ 16 g N	Amino acid	g amino acid/ 16 g N
arginine	8.4	methionine	1.6
histidine	2.6	cystine	1.6
lysine	6.9	leucine	7.7
tyrosine	3.9	isoleucine	5.1
tryptophane	1.3	valine	5.4
phenylalanine	5.0	glycine	4.5
threonine	4.3	glutamic acid	21.0

[a]Protein (N $\times$ 6.25) = 61.4%.

United States in 1967 of which 10.7 million was used in feeds and 2.7 million exported (2 million to Western Europe).   Table 6 shows the amino acid composition of meal prepared from Hawkeye beans (29).   Meal is traded under Rules 1 through 18 of the National Soybean Processors Association (see Table 1 for data on some compositional limits).

Soybean flakes are also the source of a number of industrial soybean protein products.   Powdered soybean flakes are used by the plywood-glue industry for adhesives (qv) in water-resistant plywood (qv), and a more finely divided soy flour goes into paper-coating adhesives, particularly in wallpaper.   *Soybean protein* (isolated from untoasted flakes by extracting with dilute alkali and precipitating with acid at pH 4.2) finds use in special adhesives, such as those needed in the manufacture of high-gloss, machine-coated papers suitable for the reproduction of fine halftone engraving; in emulsion paints, such as resin–oil combinations and synthetic rubber emulsions; in fire foam stabilizers; and in a variety of miscellaneous applications.

Soy Flour and Related Products.   Several kinds of soy flours are available, full-fat, low-fat, refatted, and defatted.   Defatted soy flour is made by steaming and then grinding flakes obtained from the solvent extraction of oil.   Refatted flour has specified amounts of oil or fat added to defatted flour.   Low-fat flour is made by treating cracked beans with steam and processing through a continuous screw press.   Full-fat flour is prepared by steaming dehulled beans, cracking them, and then grinding (30).   An alternative method for full-fat flour is to use an extruder cooker (16).   Nearly all varieties of soy flour are prepared from dehulled beans.

For defatted soy flour, soybeans are cleaned, cracked, dehulled, tempered, flaked, and extracted.   The resulting flakes can be treated in numerous ways, depending on the protein solubility desired.   The standard desolventizer-toaster reduces the protein dispersible index (PDI) from about 90 to 8–20%.   Steam-jacketed paddle conveyors called Schneckens usually lower the PDI to 65–70%.   Flours with a wide range of PDI are made in a desolventizer-deodorizer-toaster system.   Flakes are treated continuously in a rotating drum where part of the effluent vapors are superheated and recirculated.   Deodorization and debittering are achieved with steam in a deodorizer section.   Further treatment with steam can toast the product to give PDI's from 70% for the initially deodorized product to 10% for the final toasted flakes.   PDI's for flour from the extruder-cooker range from 13 to 21.   Whatever the prior treatment the flakes, are ground in a hammer mill to pass through a 100-mesh U.S. standard screen.   Soy grits of larger particle size are available and are described in terms of other U.S. standard screens: coarse, Nos. 10 to 20; medium, Nos. 20 to 40; fine, Nos. 40 to 80.   Flours for human food are ground in equipment not used for the production of animal feeds, and under sanitary conditions as required by the Food and Drug Administration.

The nutritional value of soybean protein products recommends their addition to other foods, but it is usually their functional value that furnishes an economic basis in the United States (30). Addition of 0.5% untoasted soybean flours, rich in lipoxidase, bleaches the color bodies in white bread. Soybean flours chemically treated with hydrogen peroxide and calcium chloride give excellent loaf volume and other characteristics when used in white bread to replace more costly additives. Full-fat soy flour has found considerable use in the manufacture of commercial premixes for cake doughnuts where the soy flour reduces the fat penetration during frying (31). Full-fat soy flour is often an ingredient used in sweet rolls. Soy flour and grits serve the meat industry as binders and emulsifiers in sausage, meat loaves, and similar products. Other outlets include pet foods and milk replacements. See also Bakery products.

One combination of 25% defatted soy flour, 65% partially gelatinized corn meal, and 5% nonfat dry milk, known as CSM (Corn, Soy, Milk), has been distributed to more than 100 countries under the Food for Peace program (32). Flakes and flour have also found use in prepared breakfast foods and in the brewing of beer, where they improve the media for yeast growth and impart greater foam stability to the finished

Table 7. Composition of Soy Flours and Protein Concentrates, %

Constituent	Defatted flour	Full-fat flour	Protein concentrate	Protein isolate
protein	50.5	41.0	71	98.4
fat	1.5	20.5	0.3	
fiber	3.2	2.8	3.4	0.2
ash	5.8	5.3	4.8	2.7
carbohydrate	34.0	25.2		

product (33). Special soybean albumins prepared by enzymic hydrolysis of the protein to give lower molecular-weight fractions are aerating agents for confections, such as creams, nougats, divinity, and marshmallows, as well as for the icings to decorate cakes (34).

Two other soybean proteins are closely related to defatted soy flour. One product is made from flakes by extracting with water or alcohol at the isoelectric point of pH 4.2; it is called protein concentrate and contains about 70% protein. The other is isolated protein described briefly above (see p. 609). Table 7 lists the composition of four of the soybean protein food products (30,35).

An estimated 550 million lb of soy flour was marketed in 1967. About one-half of this amount went into pet foods and the rest into foods for humans. The concentrate and isolate find use in such comminuted meat products as sausage, luncheon loaves, and related products and in bread, cereals, and dietary products and simulated dairy products. Specially textured products made from soy flour or isolate are also widely used in meatlike products that provide protein and serve as a carrier for meatlike flavors. Flour or isolate are extruded by special but different techniques that give fibrous materials that are specially flavored to simulate beef, ham, chicken, and other meats (30,36).

Soy Sauce and Other Food Specialties. According to historical records in the book of Chau Lai, the Chinese have used soybean products for more than 3000 yr. Consequently, a wide variety of foods have been developed which contain soybeans as a principal ingredient (37). Soy sauce, one of the older Chinese products, has become an important condiment in the United States, not only for use by itself but in special sauces that often contain from 10 to 30% of it. The variety of ways of preparing soy sauces can be divided into the following two main classes: (a) fermentation or enzymic hydrolysis of the protein to give amino acids and low-molecular-weight polypeptides (38) and (b) acid hydrolysis.

Although the fermentation procedure has numerous modifications, it usually consists of a brine fermentation in which molds, yeasts, and lactic acid bacteria are present. Soybeans are washed, cooked, and combined with ground parched wheat. Cultures of mold, yeast, and lactic acid bacteria are added to this soybean–wheat mixture and allowed to ferment for 4 or 5 days. Salt is added to the soybean culture and the entire mixture placed in a deep vat. After 30–90 days, the mash is strained and pressed to obtain the soy sauce. In acid hydrolysis, a mixture of ground soybean flakes and wheat is hydrolyzed by refluxing with hydrochloric acid until a maximum amount of amino acids is obtained. The ground flakes may be leached before the hydrolysis with acid to remove carbohydrate materials that produce an excess of humin. The acid solution is neutralized with 50% alkali and, before bottling, is aged preferably in hardwood storage tanks. In the Orient, soybeans have also been used as a source of monosodium glutamate, one of the characteristic constituents of soy sauce.

Soybean milk can be prepared from thoroughly washed and soaked soybeans ground in a stone or other suitable mill. This slurry is boiled to reduce the bitter and beany flavor, and then the solid residue is removed by filtration or centrifugation. The milk is prepared from this solution by the addition of sugar, salt, and additional fat if necessary. In the Far East, it is sold much like soft drinks in the United States (39).

Other soybean foods include *tofu*, or soybean curd, made by precipitating the protein from soybean milk (37); *miso*, a fermented mixture of soybeans and rice or barley (40); *natto*, a product prepared with *Bacillus subtilis* and similar to cheese (37); and *tempeh*, a lightly fermented solid containing a mold, *Rhizopus oligosporus* (41).

Sprouted soybeans are prepared by soaking the soybeans overnight and permitting them to sprout in covered tubs or crocks which have perforated bottoms. These sprouts are often used as food; they are used in the same manner as sprouts from mung beans. The sprouting seeds are watered thoroughly every 4 hr for approx 5 days. Then they are packed and sold as bean sprouts.

Green vegetable varieties of soybeans are grown and harvested in the United States for the manufacture of food specialties and for combination with corn as succotash, which is marketed both canned and frozen.

Production and Export

The principal soybean-producing states and countries and their estimated annual production over a number of years are given in Table 8 (1,42,43). International trade in soybeans, oil, and meal has grown considerably in the past twenty-five years. Before 1941, Manchuria was the major world producer and exported large quantities to Europe. Because of unsettled conditions in China and Manchuria since World War II, the United States has supplied a large part of the soybeans imported to Europe, Japan,

Table 8. U.S. and World Production of Soybeans

State or country	Yield per acre, bu, av			Production, millions of bu, av		
	1945–1949	1960–1964	1967	1945–1949	1960–1964	1967
Arkansas	17.6	19.8	23.0	5	83	92
Illinois	22.0	27.5	31.0	77	159	184
Indiana	20.4	27	24.5	30	73	70
Iowa	16.7	28.1	27.0	28	150	146
Minnesota	15.7	21.3	19.5	12	80	70
Mississippi	4.6	20.4	23.5	1.5	43	50
Missouri	14.9	22.6	22.0	14	85	74
Ohio	19.6	24.7	22.5	19	42	50
United States	19.6	24.0	24.5	209	660	973
China (mainland)	16.9	13.4	12.6	190	278	255
Brazil	19.0	15.1	19.5	0.5	11	25
Canada		27.0	27.9		6	8
Indonesia	9.7	9.2	9.9	6	14	14
Japan	12.1	19.3	20.0	7	12	7
USSR		6.4	10.1		12	22
total	17.1	18.3	19.6	551	1015	1333

and other countries. The growth of U.S. soybean production and export between 1940 and 1968 has been phenomenal. Production has increased in steps, as shown below.

Year	Annual production, million bu	Year	Annual production, million bu
1939	50	1955–1959	500
1940–1945	200	1960–1964	700
1950–1954	300	1965–1968	900–1000

Table 9 shows that U.S. exports also grew rapidly after 1950, particularly with the impetus given by the government-industry sponsored promotion carried out by the

Table 9. Exports of Soybeans and Soybean Products

Year[a]	Soybeans, million bu	Oil, million lb	Meal, 1000 tons
1950	28	490	181
1955	68	556	400
1960	134	721	590
1965	250	948	2656
1966	262	1105	2705

[a] Beginning October.

Soybean Council of America since 1955. For 1968, preliminary estimates cite production as 1079 million bu. Processing of the 1967 crop rose to 576 million bu with 267 million bu of soybeans exported. Oil usage rose to 5 billion lb, meal rose to 10.8 million tons, while exports of these were 1 billion lb and 2.9 million tons, respectively (44).

Bibliography

"Soybeans" in *ECT* 1st ed., Vol. 12, pp. 689–701, by J. C. Cowan, U.S. Dept. of Agriculture.

1. *Soybean Blue Book*, American Soybean Association, Hudson, Ia., 1968.
2. R. W. Judd, *Soybean Crops Improvement Council*, National Soybean Processors Association, Chicago, Ill., 1966.
3. L. F. Williams, "Structure and Genetic Characteristics of the Soybean," in K. Markley, ed., *Soybean and Soybean Products*, Vol. I, Interscience Publishers, Inc., New York, 1951, pp. 111–134.
4. J. L. Cartter and E. E. Hartwig, in A. G. Norman, ed., *Management of Soybeans, The Soybean*, Academic Press, Inc., 1963, pp. 162–221.
5. S. Kawamura, *Tech. Bull. Fac. Agr. Kagawa Univ.* **15** (2), 117–131 (1967).
6. L. H. Bailey, R. G. Copen, and J. A. LeClerc, *Cereal Chem.* **12**, 441–472 (1935).
7. *Yearbook and Trading Rules* 1967–1968, National Soybean Processors Association, Chicago, Ill., 1967.
8. W. J. Morse, "Chemical Composition of Soybean Seed," in reference 3, pp. 135–156.
9. W. J. Wolf and A. K. Smith, *Food Technol.* **15** (5), 12–13, 16, 18, 21, 23, 31, 33 (1961).
10. I. E. Leiner, "Effect of Heat on Plant Proteins in Processed Plant Proteins," in A. M. Altschul, ed., *Processed Plant Protein Foodstuffs*, Academic Press, Inc., New York, 1958, pp. 79–130.
11. *Official Grain Standards of the United States*, USDA, Consumer and Marketing Service, Washington, D.C., 1966.
12. L. E. Holman and D. G. Carter, "Soybean Storage in Farm Type Bins," *Illinois Univ. Agr. Expt. Sta. Bull. 553*, 1952.
13. M. Milner and W. F. Geddes, *Cereal Chem.* **23**, 225–247 (1946).
14. K. A. Kuiken, "Effect of Other Processing Factors on Vegetable Protein Meals" in reference 10, pp. 131–152.
15. "Fats and Oil Situation," *U.S. Dept. Agr. Econ. Res. Serv.* (issued 5 times a year) *FOS 240* (Nov. 1967).
16. G. C. Mustakas, E. L. Griffin, and V. E. Sohns, "Full-Fat Soybean Flours by Continuous Extrusion Cooking," in "World Protein Sources," *Advan. Chem. Ser.* **57**, 101–108 (1966).
17. L. F. Langhurst, "Mechanical Processing of Soybeans," in reference 3, pp. 503–540.
18. L. F. Langhurst, "Solvent Extraction Processes," in reference 3, pp. 541–590.
19. R. P. Hutchins, *J. Am. Oil Chemists' Soc.* **33**, 457–462 (1956).
20. J. W. Dunning, *J. Am. Oil Chemists' Soc.* **33**, 463–470 (1956).
21. F. A. Norris, "Extraction of Fats and Oils," in Daniel Swern, ed., *Bailey's Industrial Oil and Fat Products*, 3rd ed., Interscience Publishers, a div. of John Wiley & Sons, Inc., New York, 1964, pp. 637–718.
22. U.S. Pat. 2,585,793 (Feb. 12, 1952), N. F. Kruse (to Central Soya Co.).
23. Reference 15, *FOS 241* (Jan. 1968).
24. A. Poulos, J. W. Greiner, and G. A. Fevig, *Ind. Eng. Chem.* **53**, 949–962 (1961).
25. J. C. Cowan, "Progress in Technology of Soybeans," in R. T. Holman, W. O. Lundberg, and T. Malkin, eds., *Progress in Chemistry of Fats and Lipids*, Vol. 5, Pergamon Press Inc., New York, 1958, pp. 53–90.
26. J. C. Cowan, *Soybean Dig.* **25** (8), 16–17 (1965).
27. *Ibid.*, **26** (12), 48–53 (1966).
28. W. W. Cravens and E. Sipos, "Soybean Oil Meal," in reference 10, pp. 353–397.
29. J. J. Rackis, R. L. Anderson, H. A. Sasame, A. K. Smith, and C. H. VanEtten, *J. Agr. Food Chem.* **9**, 409–412 (1961).
30. F. E. Horan, "Defatted and Full-Fat Soy Flours by Conventional Processes," in "Soybean Protein Foods," *U.S. Dept. Agr. ARS 71–35*, 129–141 (May 1967).
31. R. M. Bohn, *Bakers' Helper* **82**, 40, 51 (Sept. 23, 1944).
32. F. R. Senti, M. J. Copley, and J. W. Pence, *Cereal Sci. Today* **12**, 426–430, 441 (1967).
33. A. S. Wahl, *Handbook of the Brewing Industry*, Wahl Institute, Chicago, Ill., 1944, pp. 515–529.
34. C. Carilli, *Candy Ind.* **6** (11), 27 (1947).
35. E. W. Meyer, "Soy Protein Concentrates and Isolates," in "Soybean Protein Foods," in reference 30, pp. 142–155.
36. W. H. Thulin and S. Kuramoto, *Food Technol.* **21**, 168–171 (1967).

37. A. K. Smith, *Cereal Sci. Today* **8** (6), 196–200, 210 (1963).

38. L. B. Lockwood, *Soybean Dig.* **7** (12), 10 (1947).

39. H. W. Miller, *Soybean Dig.* **25** (8), 19–21 (1965).

40. C. W. Hesseltine, "Fermented Products—Miso, Sufu, and Tempeh," in "Soybean Protein Foods," in reference 30, pp. 170–179.

41. C. W. Hesseltine, M. Smith, B. Bradle, and K. S. Djien, *Develop. Ind. Microbiol.* **4**, 275–287 (1963).

42. "World Agricultural Production and Trade," *U.S. Dept. Agr. Foreign Agr. Serv.* (March 1968).

43. "U.S. Fats and Oils Statistics, 1909–1965," *U.S. Dept. Agr. Econ. Res. Serv.* (Aug. 1966).

44. Reference 15, *FOS 244* (Sept. 1968).

J. C. Cowan
U.S. Dept. of Agriculture

SPANDEX AND OTHER ELASTOMERIC FIBERS

An elastomeric fiber is characterized by ready extensibility to elongations of several hundred percent and ability to recover rapidly and nearly completely from stretch. At room temperature it is soft in comparison to "hard" fibers such as cotton or nylon. The generic name "spandex" designates a "fiber...comprised of at least 85% of a segmented polyurethane" (1). Practically, this has come to mean a polyurethan which is elastomeric because it has urethan or urethan–urea "hard segments" connecting polyether or polyester "soft segments" (2). "Hard segments" are high melting (150°C and above), and one of their functions is to act as essentially unextendable crosslinks. "Soft segments" melt at 50°C or lower and are the extensible portion of the chain.

Spandex is a result of combining isocyanate chemistry and fiber technology. An elastomeric polyurethan fiber was first described by Dr. Ervin Windemuth of Farbenfabriken Bayer (3). Spandex fibers, however, were invented independently at both Uniroyal, Inc. (formerly U.S. Rubber Co.) and E. I. du Pont de Nemours & Co., Inc., (Du Pont) and were introduced nearly simultaneously in the late 1950s as commercial products.

"Elastic" Fiber Types

In popular terminology and in the textile trade an "elastic" material is one with high stretch; hence, steel wire and ordinary nylon filament are not considered "elastic fibers" even though they show true elastic behavior within their limits. Fibers can be classed conveniently with respect to their reaction (strain) to tensile loading. Figure 1 shows the strains induced by increasing loads on various fibers. Those fibers which have several hundred percent extensibility are the ones currently of interest for elastic fabric.

Hard Fibers. Nylon and other hard fibers usually show only a few percent elongation.

Elastic Hard Fibers. Polypropylene is an example of a hard fiber which can be obtained by special processes in a state such that it will show 80–90% recovery from elongations on the order of 50%. This state is attained by control of the orientation and crystallinity (4). Figure 1 shows the stress behavior of such a fiber cycled over modest elongations. The retraction or unloading curve shows that considerably less work is obtained from polypropylene when it retracts than was expended in stretching

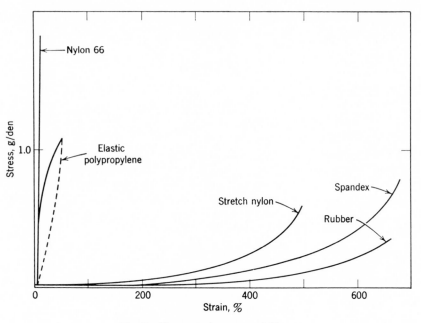

Fig. 1. Stress-strain curves of fibers.

the fiber. The rate of retraction of this polypropylene is fairly rapid. However, it has such a high modulus (loading required for a given deformation) that practical-sized fibers in fabric may not stretch without application of what would be considered excessive force. The potential of this class of fibers is largely unexplored.

Stretch Yarns. Stretch nylon (see Vol. 16, p. 60) is made by physically deforming filament-yarn fibers so that they act as a mechanical spring. Figure 1 shows the stress-strain extension curve for a false-twist-type yarn from 2-ply 70-den filament yarn. Such yarns retract relatively slowly and with low power, and the retraction curve (not shown) lies very much below the extension curve. Other methods of texturizing lead to yarns having stretches in the 100–200% range.

Fabrics made from these lofted, bulked, or false-twisted yarns have a good hand and some springiness, but they lack the retractive power of elasticized fabrics with an elastomeric fiber component. These textured yarns are used extensively in knit goods such as shirts and socks.

Elastomeric Fibers. In the trade these fibers are usually referred to as yarn or thread. Natural-rubber thread was essentially the only elastomeric thread before the advent of spandex. It is made in two ways, and the products are called *latex thread* and *cut thread* (see p. 629). Neoprene latex was used commercially to make an elastomeric thread during wartime shortages of natural-rubber latex. Neoprene costs more, however, and presents certain processing problems, so now natural rubber is the only latex used. Other common synthetic rubbers need carbon black to develop good tensile properties and thus are not acceptable as textile materials.

Also, it has been demonstrated that when suitable chemical blocks are put together (5), other classes of polymers, such as polyamides (6), polyesters (Eastman Kodak Co.), and polyacrylates (Rhee Industries Division, Rohm and Haas Co.), can give elastomeric fibers. The polyamide has remained a laboratory fiber, but the polyester fiber was developed in the 1960s and sampled to the trade, although it was not offered commercially (7). The polyacrylate fiber was announced late in 1968 (8).

Properties

The properties of spandex fibers can vary widely. The urethan groups, —NH-COO—, normally constitute only about 5% of the weight of the spandex (see Urethan polymers). The remainder is not specified by the definition of spandex. The variations in properties among the various brands of spandex arise from the different soft segments, diisocyanates, and chain extenders used. Other factors influencing properties are differences in reactant ratios and the processes discussed below under Manufacture. Also, there may be differences in the values of the physical properties when these values are determined on different-sized yarns of one brand of spandex (9).

Spandex is a continuous-filament fiber. A yarn of given size may be made as a monofilament or as a coalesced multifilament. Figure 2 shows how this mono–multifilament factor affects the cross-sectional appearances of representative spandexes. Overall appearance and some handling characteristics depend on whether the yarn is a multifilament and how well the individual filaments adhere. The size of a spandex yarn is usually given in *denier*, the weight in grams of 9000 m (a unit widely

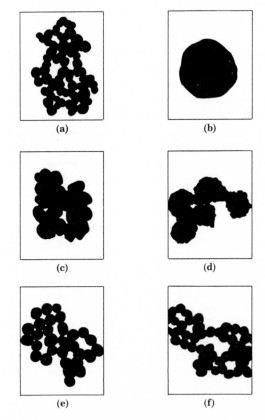

Fig. 2. Cross sections of various spandexes: (**a**) Lycra (Du Pont); (**b**) Vyrene (Uniroyal); (**c**) Glospan (Globe Rubber); (**d**) Numa (American Cyanamid); (**e**) Espa (Toyobo); (**f**) Dorlastan (Bayer).

used in the textile field). However, rubber thread and some monofil spandex yarns are sized by *gage* (gauge), the number of diameters or ends in one inch. Gage can be converted to denier when density and cross-sectional shape are known. For round cross section, denier $= 455 \times 10^4 \times$ sp gr/gage^2.

PHYSICAL PROPERTIES

Some of the commonly determined physical properties of several spandexes and of Hevea latex thread are given in Table 1. In comparison with Hevea latex thread the spandexes have higher tenacities and moduli. Therefore, the same size spandex yarn will give greater power to an elasticized garment, and a finer spandex yarn will give equal power. Spandexes have a toughness which allows knitting of bare spandex which is not protected by a hard-fiber covering. In addition, spandex can be made in much finer sizes than latex. These three characteristics can be utilized to make sheerer garments. All of these features have led to wide acceptance of spandex.

Testing should be done by precise techniques under textile standard conditions of 20°C (68°F) and 65% humidity and not under rubber testing conditions. The mechanical properties of some spandex yarns are quite sensitive to variations in humidity and temperature. Spandex filament pulls out from the edge of a clamp so that the linear amount of fiber being pulled changes during the test and invalidates

Table 1. Physical Properties of Elastomeric Fibers[a]

Properties	Lycra[b]	Vyrene[c]	Glospan[d]	Natural-rubber latex thread
den	460	450	560	490
density, g/cm³	1.15	1.32	1.27	1.10
moisture regain,[e] %	0.8	1.0	1.1	0.6
tenacity, g/den	0.94	0.69	0.56	0.26
breaking elongation, %	580	660	620	530
stress, 50% elongation, g/den	0.036	0.020	0.034	0.010
stress, 200% elongation, g/den	0.12	0.040	0.096	0.026
toughness,[f] J/g	149	98	123	32
elastic recovery,[g] %, from				
100% elongation	98	100	98	100
200% elongation	95	99	96	99
400% elongation	90	97	92	98
set,[h] %, from				
100% elongation	2	0	2	0
200% elongation	10	2	8	2
400% elongation	40	12	32	8

    [a] Adapted from data in reference 10 on measurements made at 20°C and 65% rh. Stress values calculated on original material cross section.

    [b] E. I. du Pont de Nemours & Co., Inc.

    [c] Uniroyal, Inc.

    [d] Globe Rubber Works, Inc.

    [e] Moisture pickup under standard conditions, based on dry-fiber weight.

    [f] An index based on the area under the stress-strain curve. The stress-strain curve is probably that of the sample pulled to its breaking elongation on a first extension.

    [g] The values for elastic recovery (10) were presumably calculated as one hundred times the ratio (elongated length − length of recovered sample) to (elongated length − original sample length).

    [h] Percent set calculated as (100 − % elastic recovery) × % elongation/100. Extension rate, 1000%/min. Hold, under strain, 10 sec. Recovery time, without tension, 1 min.

elongations (strains) determined as jaw-separation distances. Actual slippage may also occur. The true stress-strain relation can be determined by putting marks ("bench marks") on the yarn and noting the stresses causing these bench marks to separate by measured distances. These are usually multiples of the original distance between the marks. The test is run to the breaking elongation. It is also desirable to determine the stress-strain relationship on cycling the yarn between 0% and some upper elongation such as the breaking elongation less 100%. This procedure can be used to evaluate most of the properties which are important in designing fabric that will give the desired power and comfort in an elasticized garment.

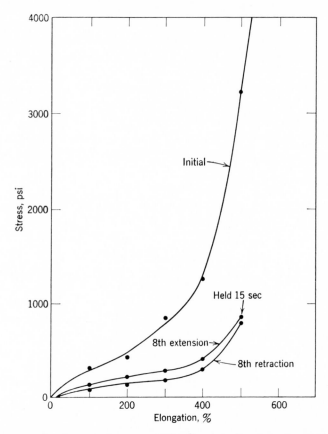

Fig. 3. Vyrene spandex stress-strain curves (12). Courtesy American Association of Textile Chemists and Colorists.

Cycling should be continued until there is no significant change in properties between successive cycles. Five to eight cycles are usually adequate. Ordinarily certain characteristics of the stress-strain cycle are noted instead of reproducing the complete curves as has been done in Figures 3 and 4.

The eighth-cycle extension curve represents the force necessary to extend the elastomer in active service. As such it can be a measure of the restraint on body movement that the elastomeric yarn would have in service. The 200 or 300% modulus is often used as the measure. In rubber technology a 200% modulus is the load per unit area of original cross section which gives a 200% elongation.

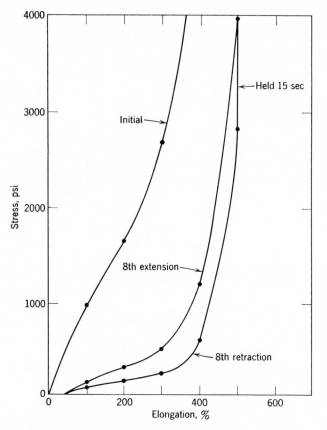

Fig. 4. High-set spandex stress-strain curves (12). Courtesy American Association of Textile Chemists and Colorists.

The *restoring force* or "power" of the yarn is given by the retraction curve. Although here again the 200 or 300% modulus is often used, a more useful point would be the midrange of the extensions at which the yarn will actually be employed. The average of the extension and retraction moduli can be used; this value is called a Schwartz number. Schwartz numbers are most appropriately used for elastomeric yarns which have a low hysteresis, such as natural-rubber latex thread.

Hysteresis is the difference between the work required to extend the yarn and the work performed by the yarn in retracting. In Figures 3 and 4 hysteresis is given by the area within the loop, ie the difference between the work performed in stretching the fiber and that regained on retraction. A low hysteresis is desirable. The biggest hysteretic loss is in the first cycle, and the biggest change in properties is noted between the first and second cycles.

Stress decay is the decrease in force exerted by a yarn held at a fixed elongation. There is a logarithmic dependence of stress on time; this means that most of the stress decay takes place in a few seconds and that the decay taking place after a few minutes is insignificant for fabric uses.

Set is the increase in length of a yarn sample after it is cycled and allowed to relax. Set is expressed as a percentage of the original sample length. It arises because spandex is not a perfect elastomer under conditions of use and does not immediately

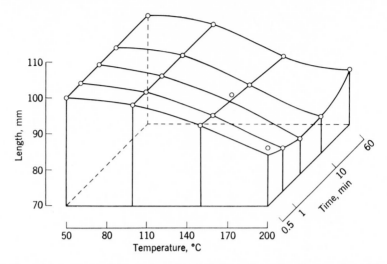

Fig. 5. Length of samples of Lycra type 124, 140 den, after being heat-treated without a load. Lycra shrinkage shown as a function of time and temperature of treatment. Original Lycra sample length, 100 mm.

retract to its original length on release from strain. Set decreases directly with the length of time elapsed between release from strain and measurement of the set length. A 1-min recovery time is often used, but set tests are not standardized. Set depends on inherent properties of the elastomer, such as chemical composition and crosslink density, and on the extent, duration, and rate of strain.

The physical properties discussed above arise in part from time-dependent molecular interactions, and the properties are not independent of one another (11). Low set, low hysteresis, and low stress relaxation tend to go together. Figure 3 (12) shows stress-strain curves for Vyrene (Uniroyal), a low-set spandex. This sample of Vyrene had a tensile strength in excess of 10,000 psi at about 700% elongation, which is outside the limits of Figure 3. The first pull curve may represent the effort necessary to get into a spandex garment relative to the power of the garment. The power is given by the 8th retraction curve. This curve lies close to the 8th extension curve, so that Vyrene has a low hysteresis. It also shows a very low stress decay. After cycling eight times with 15-sec holds at 500% elongation, the yarn shows a 15% set 1 min after release from strain. In hot water further retraction takes place to essentially 0% set. Natural-rubber latex yarn behaves similarly but has a lower modulus level. This behavior derives from the covalently crosslinked nature of the elastomer.

The stress-strain behavior displayed by Vyrene has the following features desirable in a general-purpose elastomeric thread: good working modulus, which determines power in a fabric; low hysteresis (related to garment comfort at a desired power level); low slope, which means leveled power in the working range of covered threads; low set and negligible stress relaxation, leading to easy design of fabric and power retention in use.

Experimental threads have been made (12) having anywhere from 0 to 100% set. Figure 4 shows stress-strain curves for an experimental high-set spandex. This particular one has some features similar to early-production Lycra (Du Pont) spandex. It has a set of 45% after eight cycles and in hot water retracts further to a set of 15%. Lower sets are obtained at lower cycling elongations. This yarn has a fairly high

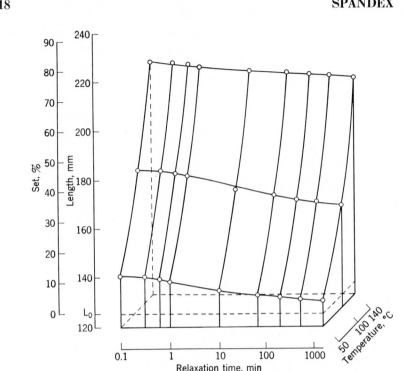

Fig. 6. Permanent set and sample length of Lycra type 125 after being heat-treated at a fixed strain. Set shown as a function of temperature of treatment and of relaxation time following release from strain. Fixed elongation, 100%; original sample length, 125 mm; time of heat treatment, 60 min; conditioning time in standard atmosphere before release from strain, 15 min.

hysteresis and a pronounced stress decay. Such elastomers are susceptible to heat setting and may also shrink when unstretched and exposed to heat. These properties derive from the thermoplastic nature of the polymer, which gets most of its effective crosslinks from sources other than primary valence bonds.

Figure 5 shows the shrinkage of Lycra type 124 (13). The shrinkage of the free-hanging, unweighted threads is dependent on both temperature and time. It is most noticeable at 200°C that, following an initial shrinkage, in time the yarn begins to flow under its own weight.

Heat setting is accomplished by holding a yarn or fabric extended and heating until the material does not return to its initial length when released. The extent of heat setting increases with time and temperature. Figure 6 shows the effect of temperature on setting Lycra type 125 during 1 hr at 100% elongation (13). Figure 6 also shows the decrease in permanent set with time of relaxation. With Lycra type 124, less time or lower temperature will lead to the same extent of heat setting. Commercially, Lycra fabrics are stabilized at 180–200°C with times up to 1.5 min (14).

The problems in fabric design and manufacture brought about by high-set spandex can be overcome, and the heat settability confers advantages such as high fabric yield, ability to finish a fabric to a desired width, and ability to knit bare spandex to give a stable fabric with fair power. These advantages are enhanced if initially the spandex has a very high modulus.

The modulus values for rubber are usually based on the original cross section of the sample. This method is not completely satisfactory when applied to an elastomeric filament that may have as much as 50% set. When the fiber has been heat-set and is virtually a new fiber, the original data become less meaningful. To provide fabric designers and elastic-yarn makers with meaningful information, it has been suggested that data be normalized to the denier (size) actually existing under the applied stress (15,16).

Also, Figures 3 and 4 illustrate another deficiency of conventional physical-property comparisons among spandexes. The spandex of Figure 3 has a higher breaking elongation and a higher maximum cycling elongation than that of Figure 4. For commercial applications, the Figure 3 spandex is covered and used at a higher extension, so that listing 200% moduli does not give the best information. Yarn and fabric men understand the problem and they design to the point of maximum modulus that will still allow adequate stretch beyond this point (12,17,18).

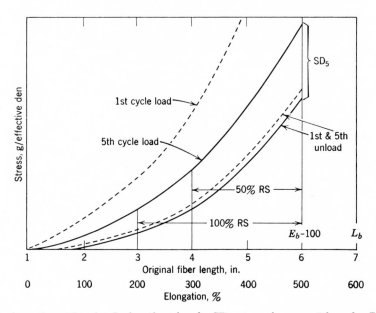

Fig. 7. E_b, elongation at break; L_b, length at break; SD_5, stress-decay on 5th cycle; RS, residual stretch.

Effective presentations of these concepts as applied to bare spandex have been made, and these schematics (15,18) have been adapted as Figure 7. Using the breaking elongation minus 100% as the design reference point is convenient and will allow simple cycling of most spandexes. The maximum cyclable elongation may be somewhat higher, but the stretch near the breaking elongation where the modulus curve rises rapidly is not really available in donning and doffing garments. In selecting a modulus design point it is necessary not only to have adequate remaining stretch but to remember that the flatness of the stress-strain curve in the use range is an indicator of comfort in the garment. The fabric construction imposes constraint on the stretch and is often the limiting factor. It is possible at a fixed residual stretch value to get a comparison of the power of yarns and fibers of different deniers as well as breaking elongations.

CHEMICAL PROPERTIES

Some of the advantages of spandexes over Hevea thread are due to the chemical composition of the spandex. Rubber is an unsaturated hydrocarbon and is attacked by oxygen and ozone, particularly in the presence of light, but these have minimal effects on spandex. The polar nature of spandex makes it dyeable and drycleanable. However, the urethan linkages, and especially the ester linkages, if present, are susceptible to hydrolytic attack, which is not a problem with Hevea thread.

The tendency of white spandex foundation garments to develop a gray cast on repeated laundering is also a drawback. Spandexes may be discolored by light, by hypochlorite bleach, and by certain atmospheric fumes, such as the nitrogen oxides (17). These discolorations are due in part to the reactions which are possible with the aromatic ureas and urethans derived from the diisocyanate. Spandexes vary in their color stabilities, and most brands have been improved in recent years. The improvement may be due to more desirable reagents or to better control of the reactions. Use of an aliphatic isocyanate would eliminate much of the color instability.

Table 2 shows the action of various solvents on Hevea latex thread and on Vyrene spandex (12). The polar nature of the spandex and the unsaturated hydrocarbon of the Hevea explain the differences. The polyester-based Vyrene degrades at the boil in dilute alkali.

Table 2. Percentage Linear Swelling[a] of Vyrene Spandex and of Hevea Latex Thread (12)[b]

	Vyrene		Hevea latex	
Solvent	0.5 hr	2.0 hr	0.5 hr	2.0 hr
heptane	0	0	35	35
Skellysolve[c] B	0	0	35	40
benzene	25	25	45	45
toluene	15	15	45	50
carbon tetrachloride	10	10	50	60
chloroform	70	80	45	60
acetone	30	35	5	5
acetic acid, glacial	50	50	5	5
acetic anhydride	40	40	5	5
50% sulfuric acid[d]	0	0	0	0
96% sulfuric acid[d]	∞	∞	55	90
40% sodium hydroxide[d]	0	0	0	0
zinc chloride satd	0	0	0	0
95% phenol[d]	85	90	5	5
dimethylformamide	70	75	0	5

[a] Thread immersed in solvent at room temperature for specified times and increase in length measured.

[b] Courtesy of the American Association of Textile Chemists and Colorists.

[c] Registered trademark of Skelly Oil Co. Skellysolve B is a petroleum distillate, essentially n-hexane, bp 60–68°C.

[d] Solutions are given in weight percent.

Lycra is not noticeably dissolved (after 5 min at the boil) by acetone, acetonitrile, carbon tetrachloride, xylene, monochlorobenzene, or 5% sodium hydroxide solution. Similar insolubility is noted at 93°C with glacial acetic acid, benzyl alcohol, cyclohexanone, dioxane, and pyridine. Lycra is soluble at 93°C in dimethylformamide and in boiling cyclohexanone (19).

Hypochlorite bleaches tend to discolor or degrade spandexes and should be avoided. Sodium perborate is generally an acceptable bleach.

Manufacture

General Chemistry of Polyurethans. The isocyanate group, —NCO, will react with a compound, H—A, containing an active hydrogen

$$
\begin{array}{ccc}
& \overset{\displaystyle O}{\underset{\displaystyle \|}{}} & \overset{\displaystyle O}{\underset{\displaystyle \|}{}} \\
\text{R—N=C} & \rightarrow & \text{R—N—C} \\
\text{H—A} & & \text{H} \quad \text{A}
\end{array}
$$

If the active hydrogen is from an alcohol, the product, RNHCOOR′, is a urethan; an amine, HNR′R″, gives RNHCONR′R″, a substituted urea.

Urethan polymers (qv) can be made simply by reacting a diisocyanate with a dihydroxy compound.

Spandex. The preparative reactions and procedures depend on the fiber-spinning process to be used. In general, conventional polyurethan ingredients are used. Extraordinarily rigid control must be maintained in raw-material specifications, in weights of reactants used, and in reaction technique, to ensure processability and uniform fiber.

A linear, hydroxyl-capped soft segment is chosen and is either a polyadipate,

$$\text{H(OROCOCH}_2\text{CH}_2\text{CH}_2\text{CH}_2\text{CO)}_n\text{OROH}$$
from glycol, HOROH

a polycaprolactone,

$$\text{H(OCH}_2\text{CH}_2\text{CH}_2\text{CH}_2\text{CH}_2\text{CO)}_n\text{OROH}$$
with HOROH starter

or a polytetramethylene glycol (PTMG),

$$\text{H(OCH}_2\text{CH}_2\text{CH}_2\text{CH)}_n\text{OH}$$

This soft segment is reacted with a diisocyanate, usually toluene diisocyanate (TDI),

or methylenebis(4-phenylisocyanate) (MDI),

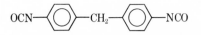

to give an isocyanate-terminated prepolymer. This prepolymer is extended or crosslinked to a high-molecular-weight elastomer with a glycol or diamine.

In the schematic of Figure 8 a urethan group is formed from every isocyanate reaction with hydroxyl, and a urea group from the reaction with amine. These high-melting moieties constitute the hard segments and have structures such as those bracketed

$$(\text{OCONHC}_6\text{H}_4\text{CH}_2\text{C}_6\text{H}_4\text{NHCO[NHCH}_2\text{CH}_2\text{NHCONHC}_6\text{H}_4\text{CH}_2\text{C}_6\text{H}_4\text{NHCO]}_9\text{O}\text{———})_n$$

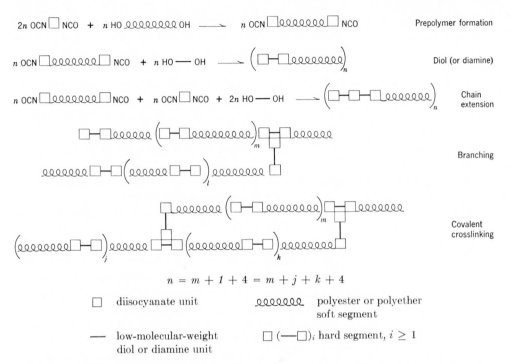

$$n = m + 1 + 4 = m + j + k + 4$$

☐   diisocyanate unit   ℓℓℓℓℓℓℓ   polyester or polyether
                                         soft segment

—   low-molecular-weight   ☐ (—☐)$_i$ hard segment, $i \geq 1$
    diol or diamine unit

Fig. 8. Schematic of polyurethan formation showing end groups only for first three sets of reactants and prepolymer product. Products only are shown from the branching and crosslinking
reactions of the second set of reactants.

when methylenebis(4-phenylisocyanate) and ethylenediamine, $H_2NCH_2CH_2NH_2$, are
used. The modulus of the polyurethan will increase if the weight fraction of these
groupings is increased. One way of doing this is shown in the second chain-extension
reaction in Figure 8. In that case g in the formula above would have an average value
of 2. The average number of repeat units in the hard segments could have any value,
eg 1.5 or 3.2.

Branching (or gelation) and crosslinking can occur by reaction of an isocyanate
and group with a urethan or urea grouping. Using one of the repeat units in the
formula above, a terminal isocyanate on another chain could react with the substituted urea to form a branch through a biuret grouping.

$$-NHCH_2CH_2NCONHC_6H_4CH_2C_6H_4NHCOO——$$
$$OCNHC_6H_4CH_2C_6H_4NHCOO——$$

Repetition of this reaction on branched molecules will lead to crosslinking.

The branching reaction can be troublesome during processing reactions, as it
increases viscosity and leads to gel; it may be desirable in the fiber as a source of
covalent crosslinks. Control over the branching reaction is exercised through the
temperature and time of reaction, the concentration of the reactants, and the use of
selective catalysts. Covalent crosslinks can also be introduced by using a triol or
polyisocyanate, and this procedure has been recommended (20–22). An appreciable
quantity of such an agent will lead to processing difficulties.

Other materials are used in spandex manufacture. If a solvent is used it is most
likely to be N-dimethylformamide. Protectants such as ultraviolet absorbers (qv),

antioxidants (qv), and antifume agents may be used. Finally, there are fiber agents such as titanium dioxide delusterant and the finish lubricant. The nature of these protectants depends on the chemical groupings in the particular polyurethan, and producers have generally not made this information available. The protectants may not give complete protection and may also have a limited life due, for example, to removal by laundering. Elimination of the particular grouping causing the trouble may be the only permanent solution; this can sometimes be done by substitution of reagents. Use of an aliphatic diisocyanate in place of an aromatic diisocyanate leads to substituted urethans and urea which either are not attacked or have reaction products that are not colored.

Fiber-Spinning Processes. The procedure for combining the raw materials in preparation for spinning is dependent on the spinning method to be used. The term spinning includes the extrusion of a polymer through a small orifice, any operation on the extrudate necessary to form a filament line, and the winding up of the filaments. Spandex fiber might be made by solution spinning, reaction spinning, melt spinning, and intergradations of these three systems. In solution spinning, a high-molecular-weight polymer is dissolved in a solvent or is initially formed in the solvent. The solution is metered by a pump through the orifices of a spinneret plate, and the solvent is diffused out to form the filaments. In reaction spinning, a liquid prepolymer of low molecular weight is extruded and contacted with a chain-extending or crosslinking agent. Polymerization to high molecular weight occurs as the filament is being shaped and pulled to the takeup drum. In melt spinning, a polymer of molecular weight high enough to form a fiber is melted in an extruder, pumped through a spinneret, and cooled to form the filaments.

Continuous gradation between any two of these systems is possible. For example, a solution of a high-molecular-weight polymer with reactive ends could be extruded and a minor amount of further reaction used to crosslink it.

For any of the above systems, if the spinneret extrudes into a gaseous chamber, it is "dry" spinning; if into a liquid, it is "wet" spinning. The gas or liquid serves to diffuse out solvent, diffuse in reactant, or take out heat, respectively, in the three systems. In solution spinning, provision must be made for recovery of the solvent.

Dry spinning can be conducted at speeds up to 3000 ft/min. In wet spinning, speeds may be down to one-tenth this amount due to effects of the viscosity of the medium.

The modulus level and tenacity of a synthetic hard fiber such as nylon is largely determined by the degree of orientation brought about by drawing. Drawing is the process of pulling down the as-spun fiber diameter. Spandex fibers are generally not subjected to a drawing operation. Some orientation may take place during spinning, however, and this can affect physical properties. Heat setting of a stretched spandex yarn can involve both orientation and plastic flow. Orientation of spandex lowers the elongation, raises the modulus, and tends to increase heat shrinkage.

Solution Spinning of Spandex. Dry spinning of polyurethan solutions has produced the biggest share of spandex. Wet spinning is also used. The polyurethan is best prepared in solution, because dissolving a solid polyurethan is difficult and preparation in solution offers opportunities for controlling the viscosity. Lycra spandex is based on polytetramethylene glycol (PTMG) and was probably made initially in the following way (23,24):

$$\text{PTMG (92, 0.19)} + \text{2,4-TDI (8, 0.09)} \xrightarrow[80°\text{C}]{\text{2-3 hr}} \text{PTMG dimer (100, 0.10)}$$

$$\text{dimer (100, 0.10)} + \text{MDI (25, 0.20)} \xrightarrow[80°\text{C}]{\text{1 hr}} \text{prepolymer (125, 0.10)}$$

$$\text{prepolymer (125, 0.10)} + \text{DMF (75)} + \text{H}_2\text{NNH}_2.\text{H}_2\text{O (2.5, 0.10)} + \text{DMF (425)}$$
$$\xrightarrow{\text{2-3 min}} \text{solution (20\% solids)}$$

$$\text{solution} + \text{TiO}_2 + \text{protectants} \to \text{fiber by dry spinning}$$

The first figure in the parentheses indicates the parts by weight; the second is the number of chemical equivalents.

The polytetramethylene glycol is first coupled with 2,4-toluene diisocyanate to form a diol of about twice the molecular weight of the original polytetramethylene glycol. This dimer diol is then capped with diphenylmethane diisocyanate, forming a reactive prepolymer. Dimethylformamide solutions of the prepolymer and of the hydrazine are brought together with vigorous mixing. Hydrazine reacts rapidly, and only a few minutes are required for the chemical reaction.

In the solution spinning of fibers, it is the practice to filter the polymer solution intensively to remove dirt, gel, and lint which would plug spinnerets. Since these polyurethan solutions may increase in viscosity on standing, there is a problem of how to handle them before spinning. The first two steps can be carried out in conventional closed reactors. The hydrazine reaction is carried out in a high-shear mixer. Delusterant and any protectants are added in the mixer. For factory production a continuous polymerization and preparation system might be best. Then, by controlling input rates into properly sized equipment, residence times can be controlled and solution storage avoided (25).

The compounded solution is pumped through a spinneret into a heated flue where the dimethylformamide solvent evaporates from the filaments. The individual filaments, while still in a sticky state, are twisted together at a point below the spinneret to give a coalesced bundle which subsequently acts somewhat like a yarn or monofil. The photomicrograph of a Lycra-spandex cross section in Figure 2 shows that the individual filaments are indeed rather loosely aggregated. The dumbbell shape of the individual filaments is also observed in some other fibers dry-spun from solution.

A spin finish is applied to the spandex before it is wound up on a package. The spin finish prevents the spandex from sticking to itself on the package and acts as a lubricant in subsequent operations.

Many variations in materials and procedure are possible. These variations will lead to elastomeric fibers differing in physical properties from the spandex given by the procedure above.

Lycra type 124 has been the standard Lycra spandex through the 1960s. It is generally safe to assume that any reported work has been on type 124 unless specified otherwise.

Lycra type 125 was introduced in 1964 and offers improved chlorine resistance as compared to type 124. It is appreciably lower in modulus and requires more vigorous conditions for heat setting.

Lycra type 126 was released late in 1967. Type 126 has somewhat improved whiteness retention after exposure to atmospheric fumes and body oils, as compared to type 124, and is much more resistant to hypochlorite discoloration. Its other chemical properties are generally similar to those of type 124.   Type 126 has slightly lower modulus and power characteristics.   It is more easily heat-set than type 124.

Reaction Spinning of Spandex.   For successful reaction spinning it is necessary that sufficient tensile strength be developed from a liquid prepolymer to drag the filament through a setting bath and onto a takeup drum in a fraction of a second. Therefore, a chemical system must be chosen such that the components react extremely rapidly to form high-molecular-weight polymers, and the chain-extender component must be able to diffuse rapidly into the prepolymer component.   In practice this has meant a prepolymer from an aromatic isocyanate and a low-molecular-weight diamine as the chain extender.   The bulk of the spandex not made by solution spinning has been made by reaction spinning.   (Reaction spinning is a specialized form of inter-facial polymerization (26).)

Vyrene spandex is based on a polyester and was probably made initially in the following way:

$$\text{polyester (100, 0.1)} + \text{MDI (25, 0.2)} \xrightarrow[100°C]{1 \text{ hr}} \text{prepolymer (125, 0.1)}$$

$$\text{prepolymer (125, 0.1)} + \text{TiO}_2 + \text{additives} \rightarrow \text{compounded prepolymer}$$

$$\text{compounded prepolymer} + \text{excess aqueous diamine} \rightarrow \text{fiber by wet spinning}$$

A poly(ethylene–propylene adipate) of low melting point is one polyester that has been used.   Since the cooled prepolymer is stable it may be stored before extrusion. The prepolymer is made and compounded most conveniently in a stirred, closed reactor.

The prepolymer is extruded into an aqueous bath containing the diamine.   This chemical reaction formally resembles the final step in the preparation of the poly-urethan for solution spinning.   However, control of the stoichiometry is more complex and is based on a different set of principles.   Too little diamine reaction leads to a weak thread line which may cause a thread break during spinning or a deformed fiber on the drum.   Too much diamine reaction leads to a spandex with inferior proper-ties.   Diamine reaction is controlled by fiber residence time, diamine concentration, temperature, and various additives which help to regulate the diffusion rate (27). Additional curing of the raw fiber in warm water may lead to superior physical proper-ties (28).   Some type of postspinning treatment is usually necessary.   Vyrene is a dense monofil, as shown by its cross section, but a coalesced multifilament can be made by the reaction spinning system.

Here again many variations in materials and procedure are possible.   With the proclivity of isocyanates to undergo all possible reactions, it is not surprising that this process can be quite sensitive to small changes.

Melt Spinning of Spandex.   A linear, thermoplastic polyurethan is required for melt spinning.   This is a necessary but not a sufficient requirement.   The reactions of isocyanates with alcohols and amines to form urethans and ureas are reversible. High temperatures are necessary to reduce the melt viscosity to a spinnable range. At high temperatures under shearing conditions considerable structural change may take place.   Much ingenuity is required to devise a polyurethan that will melt smoothly, suffer insignificant degradation during its residence in the extruder, and process easily through the fiber machinery to give a spandex of the desired physical properties.

One formulation (29) calls for a two-step process starting with polytetramethylene glycol (PTMG) of molecular weight 2000:

PTMG (100, 0.1) + H$_2$O (0.15, 0.017) + MDI (35.6, 0.285) + wax (0.25) $\xrightarrow[70\text{–}100\text{C}^\circ]{}$ prepolymer

prepolymer (136, 0.168) + HOCH$_2$CH$_2$CH$_2$CH$_2$OH (14.7, 0.164) $\xrightarrow[110^\circ\text{C}]{2\ \text{hr}}$ polyurethan

For a large batch the prepolymer and 1,4-butanediol extender are mixed in an internal mixer and poured onto pans or a belt to finish the reaction. The wax tends to act as a release agent and may reduce the stickiness of the filaments. After standing for one week at room temperature the batch is melt-extruded to give a spandex of 13,500 psi tensile strength and 550% breaking elongation. When the ratio of equivalents of butanediol to equivalents of prepolymer diisocyanate changes to 1.01, 0.95, and 0.93, the breaking elongation changes to 600, 530, and 475%, respectively.

The outline given here does not justify the assumption that this process would operate satisfactorily in a factory. Only extensive work would assure this, because such factors as uniformity and filament-handling characteristics are so important. Also, when there is an excess of isocyanate over hydroxyl ions, the isocyanate can react with urethan to form chain branches. If this reaction can be brought about in the extruded thread, it will give covalent crosslinks. If the reaction occurs during storage or extrusion, the polymer may become unprocessable. Other formulations for melt-spinnable spandex have been described (30,31).

Melt spinning would seem to have much in common with other thermoplastic-extrusion techniques. While melt spinning appears simple and straightforward, the difficulties are such that there has been no known successful commercialization.

Natural-Rubber Latex Thread. Hevea latex thread is made by extruding a concentrated aqueous dispersion of high-molecular-weight polymer into a coagulating bath. The latex (see Rubber, natural) comes from certain plantations which are able to collect and concentrate the latex into a dirtfree, mechanically stable, and biologically sterile material. The latex is shipped in this form. At the rubber factory it is compounded with stabilizers, rubber-curing agents and protectants, and pigments. These compounding ingredients are ball-milled to finely dispersed, high-quality dispersions before being stirred into the latex with a low-shear mixer.

The compounded latex particles are precured by heating at about 40°C for several hours, but this heating must be carefully controlled. Precuring leads to better wet strength on coagulation. The latex is strained, homogenized, and deaerated. Because latex may coagulate and foul metering pumps, it is usually gravity-fed through glass nozzles into an acetic acid coagulating bath. The thread is washed and then dried and cured in a hot-air oven while supported by a traveling belt. The thread is dusted with talc and not treated with a wet finish as is usual for spandex and other fibers. For maximum properties the thread on spools or beams may be postcured for several hours in an oven at 75–80°C. This technology is widely known. Detailed processing directions and formulations for thread for various purposes are available (32–34).

Cut Thread. A considerable amount of natural rubber and some spandex are made into thread by this process. The starting materials are natural-rubber smoked sheets or a millable gum polyurethan (35,36). Curatives, protectants, and pigments are milled in and the stock is calendered into a continuous sheet of the desired thickness. From the calender it is taken up on a roll, along with a liner to keep the layers separated. It is cured by heating with exclusion of oxygen by some means, such as wrapping or submerging. The cured sheet is slit to the desired thread width, normally with a square cross section for textile applications.

Dyeing and Finishing. Spandex fibers are dyeable with a wide range of dyestuffs. Since spandex is always used with a hard fiber, such as cotton, rayon, or nylon, there is the problem of the rate and extent of dyeing between the two fibers to get a good color match. Covered yarns (see p. 631) present less of a problem, because much of the spandex is not exposed. In scouring, dyeing, and finishing operations it is important that temperatures, times, and reagent concentrations be kept as low as is feasible in order to prevent damage to the spandex. Because the spandexes are structurally different, the detailed procedures that have been developed for dyeing and finishing may differ considerably among the various brands of spandex (12,14,37).

In general the dyes that are useful for nylon and wool will dye spandex. Both acid and premetalized dyes are suitable for most spandexes, have a good dyeing rate, and give a good buildup of color. Lightfastness and washfastness are satisfactory. Selected chrome dyes and disperse dyes will give excellent to poor results, depending on the type of spandex.

In finishing fabrics, allowances must be made for the heat-shrinking and heat-setting characteristics discussed above. These characteristics are used advantageously in many cases (14).

Economic Aspects

By the 1950s natural-rubber thread was a mature product with sales growth tied to population and the general economy. Spandex offered advantages in some areas where natural-rubber thread was already established. Spandex expanded these areas beyond the limits attainable with natural-rubber thread but at the same time took

Table 3. Spandex Producers and Brand Names

Producers	Brand names
United States	
E. I. du Pont de Nemours & Co., Inc.	Lycra
Uniroyal, Inc.	Vyrene
Globe Rubber Works, Inc.	Glospan
American Cyanamid Co.	Numa
Carr-Fulflex Inc.	Duraspan
International Stretch Products	Interspan
Union Carbide Corp.	Unel
Europe	
Elastomeric	Spanzelle
(Courtaulds-Firestone) (England)	
Bayer (Germany)	Dorlastan
AKU (Netherlands)	Enkaswing
Kölnische (Germany)	Lastralene, I-Faden
UCB (Belgium)	Sarlane
Pirelli (Italy)	Vairin
Fillattice (Italy)	
Rhodiaceta (France)	
Japan	
Toyobo	Espa
Fuji	Fujibo
Nisshin	Mobilon
Teijin Houdry	Neoron
Toyo Products	Opelon

away some of the market for natural-rubber thread. Spandex has had less than the predicted success in opening up new areas, as in outerwear clothing.

In the Western Hemisphere spandex production will be about 10 million lb/yr by 1970. The production of Hevea latex thread has been estimated at 14 million lb/yr in the United States and is showing little annual change. Natural-rubber cut-thread production is at least 5 million lb/yr.

West European production of spandex is estimated to be less than 3 million lb/yr. Lycra plants are operated by Du Pont at Dordrecht in Holland and at Maydown in Northern Ireland. These Lycra plants are in addition to other European manufacturers of spandex listed in Table 3. Hence, capacity is probably much above production. Japanese production of synthetic fibers increased sharply in the 1960s but the volume of spandex production is unknown. Capacity is reported to be in excess of 20 million lb/yr.

Producers and Brand Names. Table 3 lists American, West-European, and Japanese spandex producers together with brand names; some of these companies, however, may not be in actual commercial production (even in cases where brand names are given). Also, several companies have withdrawn from the business and are not listed here. The availability of spandex raw materials probably accounts for the large number of producers.

Prices. The selling prices of spandex yarns have undoubtedly attracted some manufacturers. The following were typical 1969 prices:

Price, $/lb	15	11.50	7.35	5.75	4.10	3.50	3.10
Denier	40	70	140	420	840	1120	2240

These prices can be understood in view of the following considerations: The spandex is difficult to handle, especially in the fine sizes; raw materials are moderately expensive and conversion costs are high; quality-control costs are also high. Profits from spandex have been a disappointment, especially to low-volume producers.

Typical natural-rubber latex-thread prices in 1969 were as follows:

Price, $/lb	2.30	1.90	1.80	1.55	1.30	1.27	1.12	1.05
Gage	110	100	90	75	60	50	40	30
Denier	375	450	560	800	1250	1800	2850	5050

Despite the higher strength of spandex, latex thread is priced competitively on a strength basis in the sizes that are efficiently produced.

Uses

Spandex is used both bare and covered with a hard-fiber wrapping. Latex thread is used almost exclusively as a covered yarn. In covering, the elastomeric fiber is elongated and wrapped with a hard fiber in such a way that release from strain will enable the elastomer to retract only part way before it is restrained by the hard-fiber cover. Thus the elastomer in a covered yarn will begin its work cycle at a considerable distance out on its stress-strain curve. This confers power advantages (12).

A balanced, stable yarn, such as Lastex (Uniroyal) covered thread, is obtained by stretching the elastomer and spirally wrapping with two yarns, one in the right-hand and the other in the left-hand direction. This, however, is a slow, expensive operation; a cheaper process consists of combining the spandex with a staple yarn in one of the normal textile-mill spinning processes for making yarn from staple. A roving, which is a soft strand of hard fibers partially processed to yarn, is drafted on a spinning frame and combined with an elongated spandex yarn in the front drafting rolls. When this combination is taken up on the spinning tube the product is called a core-spun yarn. The elastomer in core-spun yarn is in an extended state and is woven into fabric while under strain. The fabric is allowed to relax the desired amount and is stabilized by heat-setting the spandex. For some knitting applications the spandex may be heat-set in yarn form. The toughness of spandex helps in the core-spinning process, and the heat settability is important in using the core-spun yarns.

Foundation garments account for nearly 75% of the spandex used. The bulk of this is in powernet (Raschel knit), in which bare spandex may be employed. Some warp-stretch leno-weave fabric goes into foundation garments as well as into some circular knit in the less expensive garments. Support (medical) hosiery, swimwear, and sock tops are other major uses for spandex. While foundation garments may run 20–40% spandex and swimwear up to 10%, many products contain as little as 2–5% spandex. Spandex is employed in very few types of outerwear clothing, probably due to the huge increase in use of texturized nylon.

Latex thread has the same general applications as spandex but now (1969) tends to be used also in the heavier fabrics, in braids, etc. Cut thread is used in heavy-duty-fabric applications and in nontextile uses, such as for golf balls.

Bibliography

1. *Rules and Regulations under the Textile Fiber Products Identification Act* (U.S. Public Law 85-897), U.S. Federal Trade Commission, Washington, D.C., effective March 3, 1960.
2. E. M. Hicks, Jr., A. J. Ultee, and J. Drougas, *Science* **147**, 373 (1965).
3. Ger. Pat. 826,641 (Jan. 3, 1952), E. Windemuth (to Bayer Farbenfabriken); U.S. Pat. 2,650,212 (Aug. 25, 1953), E. Windemuth (to Bayer).
4. Fr. Pat. 1,327,329 (May 4, 1963), A. J. Herrman (to E. I. du Pont de Nemours & Co., Inc.); U.S. Pat. 3,256,258 (June 14, 1966), A. J. Herrman (to Du Pont).
5. W. H. Charch and J. C. Shivers, *Textile Res. J.* **29**, 536 (1959).
6. E. L. Wittbecker, R. C. Houtz, and W. W. Watkins, *Ind. Eng. Chem.* **40**, 875 (1948).
7. Experimental polyester fiber T-1700, Eastman Kodak Co., Rochester, N.Y.; A. A. Nishimura and H. Komagata, *J. Macromol. Sci. A* **1**, 617 (1967).
8. Anon., *Chem. Eng. News* **46**, 23 (Dec. 9, 1968). (The "XE" fiber discussed in this article was preceded by another acrylate fiber named Orofil, manufactured by Rhee Industries Division, Rohm and Haas Co., Warren, R.I.)
9. W. Wegener and B. Wulfhorst, *Chemiefasern* **17**, 736 (1967).
10. R. Meredith and I. A. Fyfe, *Textile Inst. Ind.* **2**, 154 (1964).
11. The influence of structure on properties, and the nature of the bonds conferring strength to polyurethans, are important theoretical and practical questions. For a summary see:
    a. J. H. Saunders and K. C. Frisch, "Polyurethanes—Chemistry and Technology," in *High Polymers*, Vol. 16, Part 1, John Wiley & Sons, Inc., New York, 1962, pp. 261–343.
    For leading references to later work see:
    b. D. Puett, *J. Polymer Sci. A-2* **5**, 839 (1967).
    c. H. S. Yanai, *J. Polymer Sci. C* **23**, 205 (1968).
12. R. A. Gregg, F. G. King, and M. W. Chappell, *Am. Dyestuff Reptr.* **53**, 334 (1964).
13. W. Wegener and B. Wulfhorst, *Chemiefasern* **17**, 830 (1967).
14. *Dyeing and Finishing of Core-Spun Yarns and Fabrics Containing Lycra*, Lycra Bulletin L-43, Textile Fibers Dept., E. I. du Pont de Nemours & Co., Inc., Wilmington, Del., Aug. 1966.
15. S. M. Ibrahim and A. J. Ultee, in *Encyclopedia of Polymer Science and Technology*, Vol. 6, John Wiley & Sons, Inc., New York, 1967, p. 573.
16. W. Kirk, *Am. Dyestuff Reptr.* **52**, 725 (1963).
17. A. F. Smith, *Am. Dyestuff Reptr.* **54**, 196 (1965).

18. R. J. Elia and J. Drougas, *Man-Made Textiles* **42** (491), 30–33 (1965); R. J. Elia and J. Drougas, *Chemiefasern* **15**, 876 (1965).

19. *Physical and Chemical Properties of Lycra*, Lycra Bulletin L-53, Textile Fibers Dept., E. I. du Pont de Nemours & Co., Inc., Wilmington, Del., June 1967.

20. Ital. Pat. 733,216 (March 15, 1967) (to Fillattice).

21. J. W. Britain and N. R. Nardo, *American Chemical Society Polymer Division Preprints*, pp. 1536–1540, Sept. 1968.

22. U.S. Pat. 3,354,251 (Nov. 21, 1967), W. Thoma and H. Rinke (to Bayer).

23. U.S. Pat. 2,957,852 (Oct. 25, 1960), P. E. Frankenburg and A. H. Frazer (to Du Pont).

24. U.S. Pat. 2,999,839 (Sept. 12, 1961), H. C. Arvidson and N. Blake (to Du Pont).

25. U.S. Pat. 3,111,368 (Nov. 19, 1963), J. E. Romano (to Du Pont).

26. P. W. Morgan, "Condensation Polymers: By Interfacial and Solution Methods," Vol. 10 of H. Mark and E. H. Immergut, eds., *Polymer Reviews*, Interscience Publishers, a division of John Wiley & Sons, Inc., New York, 1965, pp. 54–61.

27. U.S. Pat. 3,111,369 (Nov. 19, 1963), R. A. Gregg and C. V. Tallman (to U.S. Rubber Co.).

28. U.S. Pat. 2,953,839 (Sept. 27, 1960), R. C. Kohrn, D. G. Slovin, and F. L. Bliven (to U.S. Rubber).

29. Neth. Appl. 6,600,989 (July 28, 1966) (to United Elastic). Brit. Pat. 1,064,229 (April 5, 1967) (to United Elastic).

30. U.S. Pat. 3,357,954 (Dec. 12, 1967), D. Kirkaldy (to British Nylon Spinners).

31. Japan. Pat. 7426/68 (March 21, 1968) (to Nissin Spinning); Plasdoc 03273Q.

32. G. G. Winspear, *The Vanderbilt Latex Handbook*, R. T. Vanderbilt Co., Inc., New York, 1954, pp. 190–195.

33. R. J. Noble, *Latex in Industry*, 2nd ed., Palmerton Publishing Co., New York, 1953, pp. 582–591.

34. M. Mancinelli in G. Génin and B. Morisson, ed., *Encyclopédie Technologique de l'Industrie du Caoutchouc*, Dunod, Paris, 1953, pp. 451–483.

35. N. D. Ghatge and V. B. Phadke, *Rubber Age* **100**, 60 (1968).

36. *Vibrathane 5003*, Form 740-B26, Chemical Division, Uniroyal, Inc., Naugatuck, Conn.

37. *Ciba Review*, 1963/1962, Ciba Ltd., Basle, Switzerland, pp. 35–40.

ROBERT A. GREGG
Uniroyal, Inc.

SPEARMINT OIL. See Vol. 14, p. 212.

SPECIFIC GRAVITY. See Density and specific gravity.

SPERMACETI; SPERM OIL. See Waxes.

SPHALERITE, ZnS. See Zinc.

SPICES. See Flavors and spices.

SPIEGELEISEN. See Vol. 12, p. 897.

SPODUMENE, $LiAlS_2O_6$. See Vol. 12, p. 530.

SPORINITE. See Coal.

SPRAYS

A spray is a dispersion of liquid in a gas, involving the dynamic generation of droplets. Sprays lie between the extremes of quiescent fogs and liquid cascades, but can comprise droplets of widely varying size, from submicron up to several hundred microns (micrometers) in diameter. Usually, the droplets are dispersed at a rather high velocity by an atomizing device. Liquid atomizers have four basic functions:

1. Creation of small droplets to provide the large surface area required for evaporation, combustion, and reactions in many chemical processes.
2. Metering, or the control of liquid throughput.
3. Distribution of liquid in a specified pattern.
4. Generation of high velocity, momentum, or penetration.

At least one of these functions is involved in every spraying process, and selection of the optimum atomizer depends on the requirements of a given application.

Mechanics of Atomization

Sprays may be produced in various ways. Perhaps the simplest situation is the disintegration of a laminar jet issuing from a circular orifice. In his classic study (1), Lord Rayleigh postulated the growth of small disturbances that produce breakup when the amplitude of the disturbance reaches half the diameter of the jet. His theory predicts the formation of drops having a diameter nearly 1.9 times that of the jet. Observation of actual jets shows close agreement with this theory, but also reveals the creation of satellite droplets as the stream necks down and separates.

Rayleigh's analysis takes into account surface tension and inertial forces, but neglects viscosity. Actually, all three liquid properties affect breakup. Hence, the dimensionless Reynolds and Weber numbers are useful when certain atomization parameters are correlated. (See also Dimensional analysis.)

$$\text{Reynolds number, } N_{Re} = 7746 \, LV\rho_l/\mu_l \tag{1}$$

$$\text{Weber number, } N_{We} = 2360 \, LV^2\rho_l/\sigma \tag{2}$$

These numbers help define distinct regimes of flow through plain orifices. At low velocities and Reynolds numbers, large droplets drip or dribble from the orifice. As velocity increases, a jet forms and Rayleigh breakup occurs. At higher velocities, the jet displays a sinuous twisting motion, resulting from the influence of the ambient air. Finally, aerodynamic forces become sufficiently large to cause thorough atomization. At several hundred pounds per square inch of liquid pressure, a small orifice is capable of producing a narrow spray comprised of fine droplets.

Cone Sprays. Many applications, however, require a wide conical or flat pattern to provide adequate coverage or space for gas–liquid mixing. Of the several types of atomizers designed for conical spray patterns, a centrifugal pressure nozzle is the most popular. It converts the energy of pressurized liquid into a high-velocity swirling film that collapses into ligaments and droplets outside the nozzle. Because of the complex breakup mechanism, droplets of widely different size are formed. A sequence of high-speed photographs (Fig. 1) illustrates several stages of film disintegration as liquid pressure increases. Initially, a small "bulb" below the orifice condenses into a narrow twisting film having sufficient centrifugal force to fling out ulterior droplets and interspersed satellites in a uniform cyclic manner. The central stream collapses into

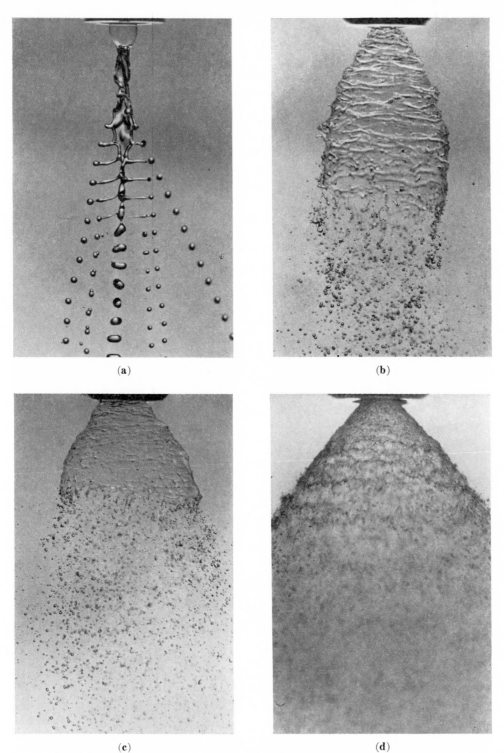

(a)   (b)

(c)   (d)

Fig. 1. High-speed photographs showing progressive development of hollow-cone spray with increase in nozzle pressure. Courtesy A. E. Dickson, Delavan Manufacturing Co.

correspondingly larger drops that exhibit axial oscillation between a compressed and elongated state. Photograph 1b shows a "tulip" formation that occurs as increasing pressure extends and opens the bulbous film. Breakup at the leading edge produces coarse droplets. With a further pressure increase, a well-defined conical film persists for some distance beneath the nozzle. Regularly spaced waves caused by ambient gas are rapidly propagated to the edge of the cone, where flapping of the thin liquid sheet produces disintegration. Liquid sprayed into a vacuum atomizes in a somewhat different way, namely through turbulence and tiny perforations that quickly expand into large holes, resulting in ligaments and droplets. The perforations may be due to penetration of the sheet by droplets already formed, or possibly by high-frequency pulsations (2). The final photograph illustrates a high-pressure spray where breakup occurs near the orifice.

Fan Sprays. The atomization mechanism for flat sheets is not unlike that described for swirling conical films. Ambient gas usually produces waves whose increasing amplitude promotes breakup of the liquid fan that is simultaneously spreading out and becoming thinner. In a vacuum, growth and merging of perforations is again a controlling phenomenon.

Pneumatic Atomization. In plain orifices, centrifugal-pressure atomizers, and fan-spray nozzles, unstable jets and sheets are created through hydraulic energy. Another important source of atomizing energy is pressurized air, steam, or gas that may be mixed with liquid inside a nozzle or applied externally. Gas can also be utilized to generate sonic, ultrasonic, or shock waves that may improve the efficiency of certain spray processes. Air used for atomization, or to augment breakup in pressure nozzles, acts in a vigorous manner that might be described as rippling, ruffling, or shattering of the liquid. Disintegration can be thorough, but the degree of atomization is very sensitive to nozzle design, particularly the way in which the gas and liquid interact. Pneumatic devices are usually required for droplets in the aerosol range (smaller than about 30μ; see also Aerosols).

Other Mechanisms. Liquid breakup may be achieved by other mechanisms, such as centrifugal force in spinning discs and in rotating cups or nozzles. Liquid is flung out as individual droplets, as a film, or as ligaments that disintegrate into droplets.

Impact or impingement of a liquid jet on a solid surface or another jet utilizes velocity energy to produce a spray. Vibrating plates and transducers have also been used. Transducers at ultrasonic frequencies create a liquid film cavitation that can generate a fog. (See also Ultrasonics.)

There has been substantial development work on electrical and electrostatic atomizers. An electrical charge may be applied to the liquid or the atomizer, or may be induced on droplets already discharged from a nozzle. An electric field helps overcome surface tension, and is capable of improving the regularity of the breakup mechanism.

Representation of Droplet Size

Distribution Functions. Liquid jet or film instability, wave formation, aerodynamic and ambient effects, ligament collapse, and droplet collisions and coalescence all combine to create an exceedingly complex breakup mechanism. This accounts for the wide spectrum of droplet sizes produced by most atomizers. It also precludes

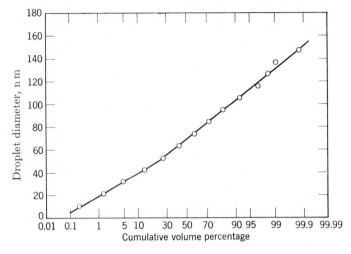

Fig. 2. Droplet size distribution curve.

any rigorous theoretical procedure for predicting or representing droplet size distributions. Investigators usually resort to empirical methods in which statistical equations or curves are fitted to experimental data. Most of these relationships show droplet diameter (or size range) as a function of frequency or percentage of the total spray. A normal Gaussian distribution generally is unsatisfactory. Most actual curves are skewed and may exhibit more than one peak when the number of droplets is plotted against droplet size. By substituting surface area or volume of the droplets on the ordinate scale, the distribution curve changes contour and shifts to the right.

One convenient technique is to plot the data on probability paper as shown in Figure 2. The droplet diameter is plotted on the ordinate, though sometimes the square root or the logarithm of the diameter will give a straighter line. The abscissa is the cumulative percentage of one of four values: droplet number, length, surface area, or volume. The slope indicates the uniformity or "spread" of droplet sizes, and can be expressed as the standard deviation. The standard deviation can be obtained by reading the difference between the diameters corresponding to the cumulative 50 and 84.13% points in Figure 2.

Other distribution functions have been proposed for spray droplets. These include the Rosin-Rammler (3) and Nukiyama-Tanasawa (4) equations, and more recent expressions developed by Kim (5) and others. Most of these functions have a limitation. Theoretically, they place no restriction on the size of the largest droplets that may exist in the spray. In reality, there is a maximum stable droplet size that Mugele (6) has termed a "physically significant quantity." Supplementary studies by Evans (7), Tresh (8), and Golovkov (9) have derived distribution functions that specify a maximum droplet diameter. Such functions, therefore, take into account this parameter as well as a mean diameter and the spread (or standard deviation).

Characteristic Diameters. Droplet size is frequently denoted only by a mean or median diameter, but there are at least a dozen from which to choose. Some of the more popular mean diameters are defined as follows (for the parameters used, see under Nomenclature, p. 652):

Arithmetic Mean—simple weighted average based on the diameters of all the individual droplets in the spray

$$D_L = \frac{\sum\limits_{s=1}^{s=k} (N_s D_s)}{\sum\limits_{s=1}^{s=k} N_s} \tag{3}$$

Surface Mean—diameter of a droplet whose surface area, if multiplied by the total number of droplets, equals the surface of all particles in the spray

$$D_A = \left[\frac{\sum\limits_{s=1}^{s=k} (N_s D_s^2)}{\sum\limits_{s=1}^{s=k} N_s} \right]^{1/2} \tag{4}$$

Volume Mean—diameter of a droplet whose volume, if multiplied by the number of droplets, equals the total volume of the sample

$$D_V = \left[\frac{\sum\limits_{s=1}^{s=k} (N_s D_s^3)}{\sum\limits_{s=1}^{s=k} N_s} \right]^{1/3} \tag{5}$$

Sauter Mean—diameter of a droplet whose ratio of volume to surface area is equal to that of the entire spray

$$D_{VA} = \frac{\sum\limits_{s=1}^{s=k} (N_s D_s^3)}{\sum\limits_{s=1}^{s=k} (N_s D_s^2)} \tag{6}$$

A median droplet diameter divides the spray into two equal portions by number, length, surface area, or volume. Of the four, the median diameter based on number would be the smallest. On a surface or volume basis, the larger droplets are weighted more heavily. Median diameters may be determined from cumulative distribution curves of the type shown in Figure 2. In this example, the volume median diameter is 68 μ. In Table 1, this is compared with the numerical values of other median and mean diameters for the same spray.

Table 1. Mean and Median Droplet Diameters for Simplex Nozzle Operated with 0.72 gal/hr Water at 100 psig

Diameter	Microns	Diameter	Microns
arithmetic mean	23	number median	14
surface area mean	32	length median	42
volume mean	39	surface area median	56
Sauter mean	59	volume median	68

The spread in these values underscores the need for careful selection and stipulation of the diameter to be used. One must decide which is the most suitable for a particular application. Some diameters are easier to visualize and comprehend. Others may appear in equations that have been derived. Occasionally it is convenient to use a certain diameter because of the droplet measurement technique employed. Finally, a given diameter may be selected to emphasize a certain aspect of the distribution, eg, the number of small droplets or the total surface area in the spray. Because the latter is important in many chemical processes involving mass or heat transfer to liquid droplets, the Sauter mean (volume/surface) diameter is widely used in applications involving combustion reactions, evaporation, and drying. The mass median is also popular, and typically is about 20 or 25% larger than the Sauter mean diameter. The ratio between these (or any other two values) is a measure of the spread in the droplet size distribution. If the spray consisted of uniform droplets, all diameters obviously would be identical. Prediction of droplet size will be included in the subsequent discussion of performance characteristics for specific atomizer types.

Measurement of Droplet Size

The published literature reveals literally dozens of techniques for measuring droplet size. This attests to the importance of information on the droplet size for the many scientific disciplines and industries that are concerned with liquid sprays. It also indicates the difficulty in obtaining reliable data on droplet size, and the fact that no completely satisfactory method has yet been developed. According to DeCorso (10), the "ideal" technique should (a) not interfere with the spray pattern or breakup mechanism, (b) permit a rapid means of sampling, (c) provide a rapid means of counting the samples obtained, (d) have good size discrimination over the whole range being measured, (e) permit variations in the atomized liquid and in the ambient gas properties, and (f) permit determination of both the spatial and temporal droplet size distributions.

No single technique fulfills all these criteria, and the capabilities and limitations must be recognized. One may classify the experimental methods into several broad categories. The first includes all techniques in which individual liquid droplets are collected for subsequent observation or counting. In some instances, the droplets are preserved long enough for analysis; in others, they create stains or impressions on sampling cards or coated slides. The next classification also includes collection methods, but those in which droplets are frozen or cooled and sized as solid particles.

The third category includes all methods where droplets are sorted on the basis of inertial or velocity differences. Depending on its size, a droplet may impact or fail to impact on a solid surface, or may follow a different trajectory. This kinetic behavior within a spray may be used to differentiate between droplet size ranges.

One of the principal objections to all of the preceding methods is that the measuring apparatus interferes with the spray, and may affect or incorrectly interpret the true droplet size distribution. This objection is overcome by high-speed photographic techniques which give stopped-motion images of the droplets; these photographs are recorded for subsequent counting or analysis. These techniques, on the other hand, are not capable of giving the temporal distribution of droplet sizes as produced by the atomizer. This is true because the large droplets maintain a higher velocity after leaving the atomizer than do the smaller droplets. Hence, the spacing between large droplets is greater, and they are not as likely to appear within the instantaneous photographic field. For this reason, it is necessary to convert the apparent spatial distribution to the true temporal distribution by multiplying the number of droplets of any given size by the velocity for that size.

Finally, there are a number of methods that could be classified as optical: those based on light diffraction, or absorption, or the recently developed systems which involve rapid scanning and laser holography. Summaries of the state of the art have been prepared by Pearson and Martin (11), Putnam et al. (12), Tate and Olson (13), and Matthews et al. (14).

Description of Atomizer Types

The various types of atomizers are described below, giving for each the design features, and the characteristics of the spray produced. This section is largely based on

R. W. Tate's table in "Sprays and Spraying for Process Use—Part I," *Chemical Engineering* **72,** July 19, 1965, pp. 159–160. (Courtesy McGraw-Hill, Inc.)

CENTRIFUGAL PRESSURE NOZZLES

Simplex. A circular orifice outlet is preceded by a swirl chamber with one or more tangential inlets. A slotted distributor may also be used. The spray has a hollow conical pattern with spray angles generally between 30 and 120°. Droplet size is moderate; finest atomization occurs at low capacities, high pressures, and wide spray angles. Capacities extend up to thousands of gallons per hour. For a given nozzle, the discharge varies approximately with the square root of the operating pressure.

Solid Cone. The design is similar to that of the simplex nozzle but with a special core or axial jet to fill in the center of the conical pattern. Solid (full-cone) nozzles are available in extremely high capacities, but they also range down to 1 gal/hr or lower. Atomization at low capacities is similar to that of the corresponding hollow-cone nozzles, but coarser droplets occur as the tangential flow component is diminished. Droplets at the center of the pattern are usually larger than those near the edge.

Square Spray. This has a swirl chamber construction with a special orifice outlet configuration to accent the corners of the spray pattern. It is a relatively solid pattern, with somewhat coarser droplets than most hollow-cone types. A multiple-nozzle arrangement is recommended where uniform coverage of large areas is required.

Bypass (Spill). This is a simplex construction, but with a return flow line at the rear, side, or front of the swirl chamber, and a valve to control the quantity of liquid removed from the chamber. Virtually infinite turndown ratios are possible since nearly all the liquid can be bypassed and returned to supply. The supply pressures are normally held constant, with the flow rate modulated by adjusting the bypass pressure. This construction provides a hollow-cone pattern, with a slight increase in the spray angle as the flow is reduced. Maximum discharge rates are at least 200 gal/hr.

Duplex. A circular orifice is combined with two sets of distributor slots, each having a separate liquid supply. The pattern and the droplet size are similar to those of the simplex nozzle. However, a greater flow range is possible by programming the liquid through the two separate distributor systems. The spray angles are widest near minimum discharge, but become narrower as the flow is increased.

Dual Orifice (Duple). There are two concentric orifice–distributor systems (one within the other), each having a separate liquid supply. External or integral flow-divider valves are required. Even larger flow ranges are possible (turndown ratios as high as 50:1). Low capacities are achieved with an inner (primary) orifice and a distributor, with transition to a combined primary-secondary operation, giving much larger flow rates. A relatively constant spray angle and degree of atomization are maintained throughout most of the operating range.

FAN–SPRAY NOZZLES

Elliptical or Oval Orifice. The orifice is formed by the intersection of a V groove with a hemispherical cavity communicating with a cylindrical liquid inlet. It produces a liquid sheet parallel to the major diameter of the orifice. It is the most popular type of fan-spray nozzle, producing a narrow elliptical pattern with tapered edges which provide uniform distribution when overlapped. Extremely small carbide orifices (1 gal/hr at 500 psi) are possible for high-pressure coating operations. Excellent atomization and patterns are obtained with viscous materials. At the other extreme, orifices exceeding 0.5 in. permit several thousand gallons-per-hour flow at low pressures. This orifice can be designed for a wide range of spray angles, from approx 110° down to a straight stream.

Rectangular Orifice. A liquid sheet is produced by various types of rectangular or slotted orifices. The orifice may be formed at the end of a converging tube, or may be cut perpendicular to the surface of a cylindrical tube to produce a curved slot. Although not as popular as the elliptical type, some commercial nozzles are designed with rectangular or slit-type orifices. The sheet width and thickness are controlled by the orifice dimensions and the approach passage. There is little available information on the pattern or the atomization quality.

Deflector. A liquid discharges through a plain circular orifice and impinges on a curved deflector plate. Although sometimes referred to as a flooding nozzle, this type produces relatively coarse droplets, particularly at low pressures. Wide spray angles are possible, with flow rates ranging from about 10 to several thousand gallons per hour. Because the nozzle passages are relatively large, plugging is minimized.

Impinging Jet. Two or more liquid jets collide outside the nozzle, producing a liquid sheet which is perpendicular to the plane of the jets. A circular liquid sheet is formed by the impingement of fully opposed concentric jets. The principal advantage of this atomizer is the isolation of different liquids until they impinge outside the nozzle. High stream velocities and wide impingement angles are necessary to approach the spray quality obtainable with other types. A symmetric flat pattern and good atomization are possible only if extreme care is exercised to align the jets. Depending on the operating conditions, mean droplet sizes from 100 to 1000 μ have been reported. Bimodal droplet size distributions are typical.

TWO–FLUID ATOMIZERS

Internal Mixing. Gas and liquid mix within the nozzle before discharging through the outlet orifice. Fluids are sometimes supplied through tangential slots to encourage turbulence and thorough mixing. The liquid is usually metered externally, since the flow is affected by interaction with the gas. This atomizer is capable of extremely fine atomization, especially at high air/liquid ratios. Since pneumatic energy is inefficiently utilized, power consumption is excessive at large capacities. However, particles in the aerosol range are obtainable with sufficient gas flow and pressure. Spray angles tend to be narrow (30–60°), and are not as well defined as in other atomizers.

External Mixing. High-velocity gas impinges on a liquid at, or outside, the orifice. Pneumatic energy, however, is still utilized for liquid breakup. Back pressures are avoided because there is no internal communication between gas and air, and the device may be used as a metering nozzle. This type is somewhat less efficient than the internal-mixing two-fluid nozzle, and higher air/liquid ratios are usually required. Large flow rates are uneconomical because of high air consumption. (Steam or other gases may also be used.) High-viscosity liquids can be atomized effectively. Low-flow nebulizers produce submicron droplets.

Syphon (**Aspirating**). This is a pneumatic atomizer in which the liquid is aspirated by gas and syphoned through a height of several inches. For a given nozzle, the flow rate and droplet size are extremely sensitive to air pressure and syphon height (or gravity head). The device is most effective in the 0.1–3.0-gal/hr range. The spray angles are narrow.

Sonic (**Gas Generator**). Intense sonic radiation is generated by Hartmann whistles or other gas generators focused on liquid sheets or streams to implement breakup. Sonic or ultrasonic compressions and rarefactions are claimed to improve breakup. The sonic and pneumatic effects are difficult to isolate from each other. There is little information on atomization efficiency and spray quality.

ROTARY ATOMIZERS

Spinning Disc. A liquid is introduced at the center of a high-speed rotating disc, several inches in diameter. The discs may be smooth plates, bowls, or saucers with curved, sharp edges. Many, however, are designed with straight or curved vanes or slots to guide the liquid to the periphery. Some installations involve multiple-tier designs or concentric sets of vanes. A 360° spray pattern with improved atomization develops as the peripheral speed increases and the flow rate is reduced. At low flows, droplets form near the edge of the disc; at higher feed rates, liquid filaments or sheets develop and break up because of instability. Nearly uniform atomization is possible with small discs operated at low capacities and extremely high speeds. At higher flow rates (up to several thousand gallons per hour), the droplet-size spectrum is rather broad, similar to that of many nozzles. Discs are usually installed in a cylindrical or conical chamber where an umbrella-like spray is produced by downward gas currents.

Rotary Cup. This is similar to the disc, but usually smaller in diameter, and is shaped like an elongated bowl or cup. It is sometimes operated with an air blast around the periphery. There are various methods of introducing feed. Liquid fed at one end of the cup progresses as a smooth, swirling film, to the opposite end, where a 360° sheet perpendicular to the cup axis is released. Depending on the design, the rotational speed, and the flow rate, the liquid film breaks down into ligaments and droplets of different sizes at various distances from the cup edge.

Spinning Nozzle. This atomizer is distinguished from the above-mentioned rotating devices because of the peripheral orifices, which form liquid jets through centrifugal action. Jet breakup is sometimes aided by hydraulic pressures in these rotary nozzles or "slingers." Various models are available for diverse applications, but are seldom used as industrial atomizers.

OTHER TYPES

Plain Orifice. This consists of a nozzle having a plain circular orifice that produces a straight stream. This is the simplest possible nozzle. It is often specified where high impact or momentum is required. Atomization is virtually nil, except at high pressures; however, fine droplets are produced at several thousand pounds per square inch because of jet instability and the relative velocity of ambient gas.

Movable Poppet. A conical liquid sheet is formed by an annular gap between a cylindrical orifice and a conical poppet that moves axially under force of liquid pressure. As the poppet (restrained by a spring) is pushed further out, the annular discharge area enlarges, magnifying the effect of the pressure on the flow. The liquid pattern is determined entirely by the orifice–poppet configuration, and good spray quality is difficult to achieve unless the parts are precisely aligned. Poppet vibration can also be a problem. The practical spray angle range is 45–120°, and the angle remains fairly constant over a wide operating range.

Vibrative. An electrically activated vibrating reed flicks droplets from a liquid reservoir. In another device, the liquid flowing across the surface of a vibrating bar is atomized at zones of maximum amplitude. Good efficiency is claimed at resonant frequencies. Ideally, vibrative atomizers are capable of generating very uniform droplets; this has been demonstrated with reeds oscillating at a fixed frequency. With vibrating bars, capillary waves are formed which break free from the liquid film, forming individual droplets in the 100–1000-μ range. The particle size can be changed by varying the vibrational frequency.

Ultrasonic (Transducer). This atomizer is similar to the above in principle. The liquid is fed through or over a transducer and horn excited at ultrasonic frequencies to provide the small wavelengths necessary for fine atomization. The system requires a signal generator, a power supply, and an amplifier. This device is relatively recent, and further development is indicated before a completely satisfactory spray can be achieved. Nevertheless, the design principle is well suited for low flow rates that are difficult to achieve with certain other types of atomizers. These transducer devices should not be confused with sonic or ultrasonic atomizers utilizing gas generators.

Electrostatic. A liquid film or jet is subjected to an intense electric field that overcomes surface tension forces, producing discrete droplets. Recent research has been done on capillary tubes and conical discs, directly charged at high voltage. In other systems, a charge is induced on droplets by electrodes outside a conventional nozzle. Droplet size is a function of the physical and the electrical properties of the liquid, the electrical potential, the flow rate, and the construction of the atomizer. One practical problem is that of a suitable power supply; it should be sufficiently rugged, safe, and inexpensive for industrial applications.

Discussion of Types

CENTRIFUGAL PRESSURE NOZZLES

The centrifugal pressure nozzle is one of the most important types. Figure 3 illustrates two such nozzles that have been used extensively for spraying turbine fuel and heating oil. A simplex version is shown schematically in Figure 4. The tangential

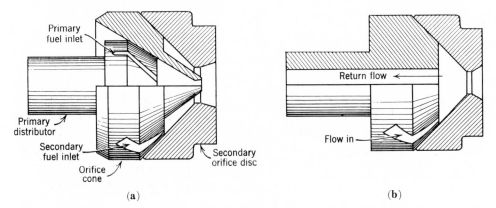

(a)   (b)

Fig. 3. Centrifugal pressure nozzles. (**a**) Dual-orifice fuel injector. (**b**) Bypass or spill nozzle.

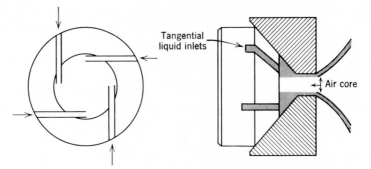

Fig. 4. Elements of simplex pressure nozzle, including slotted distributor, swirl chamber, and orifice.

inlets and rotating liquid create an air core extending from the rear of the swirl chamber down through the center of the orifice. Since the orifice does not run full, the *discharge coefficient* may be as low as 0.1 or 0.2, depending on the tangential flow component. The *discharge coefficient, K*, is defined as follows:

$$K = \frac{0.0335 Q_l \; \rho_l{}^{0.5}}{(\Delta P)^{0.5}(d_o)^2} \tag{7}$$

Hydrodynamic theory (15), assuming formation of a free vortex, leads to additional equations which relate the discharge coefficient to the ratio of the air core and orifice diameters:

$$K = \sqrt{a^3/(2 - a)} \tag{8}$$

$$a = 1 - (d_c/d_o)^2 \tag{9}$$

The average axial velocity component of the liquid film in the orifice is also a function of d_c and d_o, as follows:

$$V_a = 0.409 Q_l/(d_o{}^2 - d_c{}^2) \tag{10}$$

Hence, if the nozzle flow rate, discharge coefficient, and orifice diameter are known, the film thickness and axial velocity may be computed from the preceding equations. Assuming constant angular momentum (free vortex), the tangential velocity at the orifice may be estimated from the following expression that applies to nozzles having flat swirl chambers:

$$V_t = 0.642 Q_l R/A d_o \tag{11}$$

Some of these parameters have been combined in a dimensionless group (16) that correlates well with the discharge coefficient, as illustrated in Figure 5. Spray angle may also be shown as a function of K (Fig. 6). To summarize, a high V_t/V_a ratio in a swirl atomizer is characterized by a large air core, small discharge coefficient, wide spray angle, and good breakup. In fact, several empirical equations for mean droplet size include this ratio of tangential to axial velocity. Nelson and Stevens (17), for example, have proposed the following expression for mass median diameter (note that this also involves the Reynolds and Weber numbers that reflect the liquid viscosity and surface tension forces that must be overcome in producing droplets):

$$\frac{D_{V_{50}}}{d_o} = f\left[N_{Re}\left(\frac{N_{We}}{N_{Re}}\right)^{0.55}\left(\frac{V_t}{V_a}\right)^{1.2} \right] \tag{12}$$

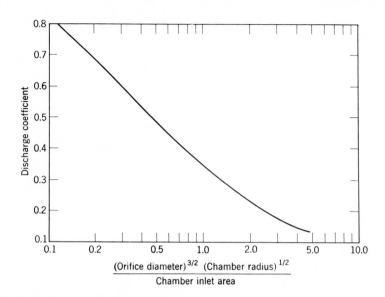

Fig. 5. Relationship between discharge coefficient and dimensionless group of design parameters for simplex nozzle having flat swirl chamber with one tangential inlet.

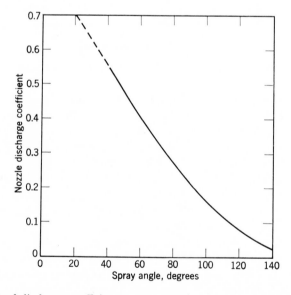

Fig. 6. Effect of discharge coefficient on spray angle of typical hollow-cone nozzle. Wider angles are associated with relatively large tangential velocities and air cores, resulting in lower capacities. Courtesy McGraw-Hill Book Co., Inc.

In their study of large-scale pressure nozzles, Kim and Saunders (18) also related the mass median diameter to V_a and V_t:

$$D_{V_{50}} = \frac{7670 d_o{}^{0.33}}{(V_{a_o})^{0.11}(V_t)^{0.40}}$$

(13)

By dimensional analysis, Fraser et al. (19) postulated the following:

$$D \; \propto \; \left(\frac{K'\sigma}{\Delta P\theta}\right)^{\frac{1}{3}}\left(\frac{\rho_l}{\rho_a}\right)^{\frac{1}{6}} \tag{14}$$

Though not stated explicitly, the liquid velocity components affect the flow number and spray angle terms in this equation. The literature contains numerous other droplet-size correlations for centrifugal pressure nozzles. Some of these pertain to specific atomizers and narrow ranges of operating conditions. Others are more general and include parameters for liquid properties and ambient conditions.

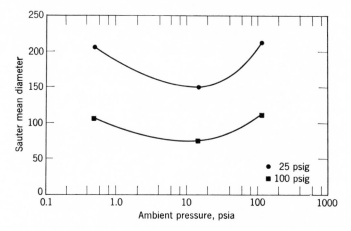

Fig. 7. Variation in mean droplet diameter with ambient pressure for two nozzle pressures (DeCorso).

Liquid Properties. Both flow and droplet size are affected by liquid properties, principally density, viscosity, and surface tension. In theory, volumetric flow through a pressure nozzle varies inversely with the square root of the liquid density. However, since it is seldom possible to change the density without affecting some other liquid property, this relationship must be interpreted cautiously. Smaller droplets usually occur with denser liquids, but surface tension has the opposite effect; since it must be overcome in creating droplets, liquids having a high surface tension are more difficult to atomize. Some data indicate that droplet size is proportional to about the one-third power of the surface tension.

In many respects, viscosity is the most important liquid property. It can vary over an extremely wide range, and it affects not only the flow rate and the droplet size but also the spray pattern. An increase in viscosity generally produces a narrower pattern and angle, and at very high viscosities the spray may collapse and approach a straight stream. The effect of viscosity on flow is complex and depends on the Reynolds number. In hollow-cone nozzles, a moderate increase in viscosity can actually augment flow. This is explained by the reduction of the air core as internal friction damps the tangential flow component, resulting in a larger discharge coefficient. At high viscosities, however, the flow rate usually decreases with an increase in viscosity. The exact effect must be determined experimentally for the specific nozzle design and operating conditions. When viscous forces are large, less energy is available for breakup, and coarser droplets result. As a rule of thumb, droplet size may be assumed to be proportional to the one-fourth power of viscosity for pressure nozzles.

Ambient Conditions. The ambient pressure and density also affect droplet size. Figure 7, based on DeCorso's (20) data and substantiated by Neya and Sato (21), shows minimum droplet size at atmospheric ambient pressure. At higher or lower pressures (assuming constant nozzle ΔP), there is a tendency toward coarser atomization. When a liquid is sprayed into a partial vacuum, there is less aerodynamic shearing, which would normally contribute to breakup. A dense environment, on the other hand, permits more gas to be induced against the spray sheath because of the flow paths shown in Figure 8. Hence, the spray is concentrated within a narrower zone, encouraging coalescence and larger droplets.

Spray Patterns. Patterns are also affected by nozzle ΔP. Spray cones may "pull in" as the liquid pressure increases and more ambient gas is induced. This results in narrower spray angles a few inches from the nozzle, but does not substantially change the angle close to the orifice. Theoretically, the latter depends only on the nozzle dimensions and the flow coefficient.

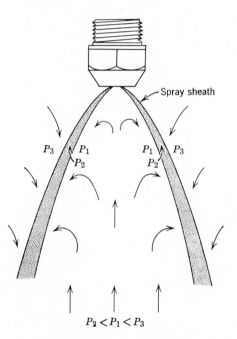

Fig. 8. Probable air flow in region of hollow-cone spray sheath (DeCorso and Kemeny).

Spray patterns are important in most applications, and may be analyzed in several ways (22). Spray symmetry about the nozzle axis can be measured using a circular, sectored vessel containing at least six equal compartments, as diagrammed in Figure 9. A quantitative "patternation index" may be calculated as shown, or one may use the minimum/maximum sector ratio.

Distribution of liquid along a diameter beneath the orifice may be established with a straight row of vertical tubes. The open-ended tubes collect liquid in proportion to the spray concentration, and provide a profile or histogram. This not only reveals irregularities, but also indicates how hollow the pattern is. Many factors can cause poor spray patternation. These include (a) improper configuration of the nozzle, (b) poor alignment between the nozzle orifice and the distributor or swirl chamber,

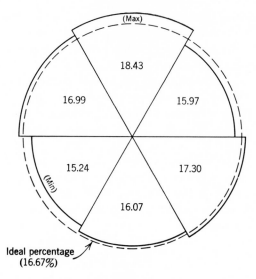

Fig. 9. Diagram of typical sector patternation data, showing calculation of index and minimum/maximum ratio, as follows:

Sector number	Volume collected (percentage of total)	Difference between actual volume, percentage and ideal (16.67%)
1	18.43	1.76
2	15.97	0.70
3	17.30	0.63
4	16.07	0.60
5	15.24	1.43
6	16.99	0.32

patternation index = 5.44

minimum/maximum ratio = 15.24/18.43 = 82.8%.

(c) surface roughness, tool marks, or burrs in sensitive metering areas, (d) plugged or contaminated metering passages, (e) insufficient pressure to produce a fully developed spray, (f) extremely high liquid viscosity, and (g) air turbulence generated by high spray velocity.

FAN–SPRAY NOZZLES

Two of the more common types are illustrated in Figure 10. Because no air core is created, flow coefficients for fan-spray nozzles usually exceed those of centrifugal pressure atomizers. For equivalent flow and pressure, some investigators have reported larger droplets for fan-spray nozzles, but other data indicate nearly identical droplet size for the two types. Coarse atomization is more likely with deflector (flooding) nozzles.. Fraser's equation for estimating the Sauter mean diameter of elliptical-orifice fan-spray nozzles closely resembles his previous equation 14, as follows:

$$D_{VA} = 181(K'\sigma/\Delta P\theta)^{1/3} \tag{15}$$

Dombrowski and Hooper (23) have reported the effect of ambient pressure. As it increases, the droplet size for flat spray nozzles passes through a minimum. Hence, the behavior is analogous to that observed for swirl atomizers.

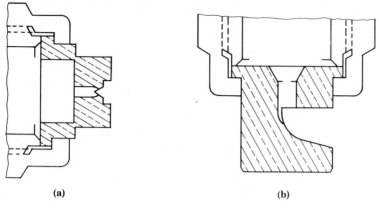

(a)   (b)

Fig. 10. Fan-spray nozzles. (**a**) Elliptical orifice formed by intersection of V groove and hemispherical cavity. (**b**) Deflector or flooding nozzle in which liquid from a plain orifice impinges on a curved deflector, producing a flat spray.

Pressure Jets. A limiting case of both centrifugal and fan-spray nozzles is the straight stream. It is occasionally utilized at low pressures when large drops are required for prilling, simulation of rainfall, of dribbling of agricultural chemicals. Diesel injectors also produce straight jets, but in a higher-pressure range where aerodynamic shear provides fine atomization.

TWO–FLUID ATOMIZERS

Compared with most other atomizers, two-fluid nozzles consume considerable power and are usually uneconomic where large capacities are needed. For small flow rates, they are very effective in producing fine droplets and in handling viscous ma-

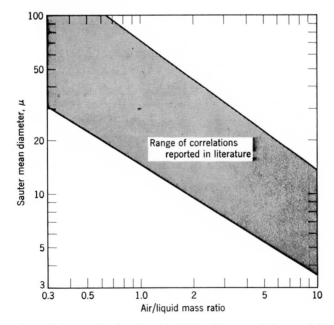

Fig. 11. General trend of mean droplet size with air/liquid mass ratio in two-fluid nozzles (28).

terials. Since liquid pressures are usually low, the passages can be kept relatively large, minimizing contamination and plugging. With internal-mixing and syphon types, liquid flow is affected by the gas pressure and volume. Hence, metering is normally done with an external orifice, valve, or pump.

As with other atomizers, two-fluid nozzles produce finer droplets when the energy input per unit quantity of liquid is increased. This is shown in Figure 11, where mean droplet size is plotted against the air/liquid mass ratio. Though there is a distinct trend, the broad range shown in the diagram is indicative of performance variations reported by several investigators. This does not necessarily signify unreliable data or differences in the methods of measuring droplet size. The degree of atomization is very sensitive to nozzle design, particularly the manner in which the gas and liquid interact. As one might expect, internal-mixing types are usually more efficient and require less gas for the same droplet size. On the other hand, external-mixing nozzles are capable of extremely fine atomization even though the air/liquid ratio is relatively large. Nebulizers are an example of the latter type. There is an almost endless variety

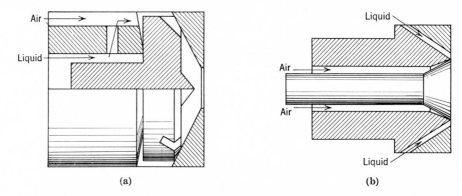

Fig. 12. Two-fluid atomizers. (**a**) Internal-mixing type. (**b**) External-mixing type.

in the construction of pneumatic atomizers, nebulizers, and aerosol generators. Figure 12 depicts two representative nozzles. In certain devices, gas impinges on a central liquid stream, whereas in others gas is introduced through the center of the atomizer.

Thorough mixing of gas and liquid prior to discharge is a characteristic feature of many such atomizers. Because of the vigorous interaction of the two phases, their respective inlet pressures must be nearly equal to avoid throttling or backup of either stream. Liquid pressure and metering dimensions therefore do not firmly establish flow rates in internal-mixing nozzles. Discharge rates and spray patterns are definitely affected by the air flow.

As shown in Figure 11, most droplet-size correlations for two-fluid nozzles involve the air/liquid mass ratio. A term for gas velocity also appears in most equations. Kim and Marshall (5) referred to an "air dynamic force" that was defined as $V_{rel}{}^2\rho_a$ in their empirical correlations.

The Nukiyama-Tanasawa equation includes relative velocity in addition to the air/liquid ratio:

$$D_{VA} = \frac{1919}{V_{rel}} \left(\frac{\sigma}{\rho_l}\right)^{0.5} + 75\left(\frac{\mu_l}{\sqrt{\sigma\rho_l}}\right)^{0.45}\left(\frac{1000Q_l}{Q_a}\right)^{1.5} \tag{16}$$

Gretzinger and Marshall (24) utilized the air mass velocity in the following relations. The first applies to a converging pneumatic nozzle, the second to a pneumatic impinging nozzle:

$$D_{V_{50}} = 2600 \left[\left(\frac{W_l}{W_a} \right) \left(\frac{\mu_a}{G_a L} \right) \right]^{-0.40} \tag{17}$$

$$D_{V_{50}} = 122 \left(\frac{W_l}{W_a} \right)^{0.60} \left(\frac{\mu_a}{G_a L} \right)^{0.15} \tag{18}$$

Other equations appear in the literature, but all droplet-size correlations for two-fluid atomizers are valid only for a particular type of device and a rather limited range of operating conditions. Some droplet-size data have been reported for atomizers designed with sonic or ultrasonic generators (whistles), and there is no clear evidence that gas utilized in this manner is more efficient from the standpoint of liquid breakup than in conventional pneumatic nozzles.

ROTARY ATOMIZERS

Centrifugal force was mentioned earlier as a means of atomizing liquids. Of the several types of rotary devices, the spinning disc is probably best known. Operated at speeds up to more than 10,000 rpm, a single disc can handle capacities as high as several thousand gallons per hour. Material fed under gravity or low pressure to the center of the disc is accelerated toward the edge across a smooth surface or through vanes or slots. Disc diameters range from a few inches up to several feet. This type of atomizer is particularly suitable for thick slurries or suspensions that easily clog or erode nozzle passages. Another advantage is flexible operation, because feed rate and disc speed can be varied independently. Droplet size can be reduced by increasing disc speed or lowering feed rate. Equations for estimating droplet size have been developed by Friedman et al. (25), Adler and Marshall (26), Herring and Marshall (27), and others.

Rotary cups use the same principle as discs but are shaped as narrow cylinders or bowls with liquid fed in at one end. A swirling liquid film is confined within the cup until reaching the opposite end where breakup occurs at a sharp edge. Annular air is sometimes used to improve atomization. Spinning nozzles are rotary devices in which liquid is forced through peripheral orifices, sometimes with auxiliary hydraulic pressure. Some discs are designed with radial orifices to improve droplet size uniformity.

Chemical Applications of Sprays

A remarkable number of processes involving production of chemicals and metals, and utilization of chemicals, fuels, and foodstuffs require sprays (28). Table 2 lists some examples. Though a small component in most systems, the atomizer must be chosen carefully. The following factors enter into proper selection, and might be regarded as a check list when specifying spray equipment: (a) the nature of the process, including characteristics of any sprayed products; (b) properties of the liquid to be atomized—temperature, density, viscosity, and surface tension; percent solids in suspensions, slurries, and pastes; (c) total flow rate; (d) required droplet size distribution or mean droplet diameter; (e) liquid or gas pressures available for nozzles, or power required for rotary atomizers; (f) ambient gas temperature, pressure, and flow patterns;

Table 2. Spray Applications

(a) production or processing

    spray drying (dairy products, coffee and tea, starch, pharmaceuticals, soaps and detergents, pigments, etc)

    spray cooling

    spray reactions (absorption, roasting, etc)

    atomized suspension technique (effluents, waste liquors, etc)

    powdered metals

(b) treatment

    evaporation and aeration

    cooling (spray ponds, towers, reactors, etc)

    humidification and misting

    air and gas washing and scrubbing

    industrial washing and cleaning

(c) coating

    surface treatment

    spray painting (pneumatic, airless, and electrostatic)

    flame spraying

    insulation, fibers, and undercoating materials

    multicomponent resins (urethans, epoxies, polyesters, etc)

    particle coating and encapsulation

(d) combustion

    oil burners (furnaces and heaters, industrial and marine boilers)

    diesel fuel injection

    gas turbines (aircraft, marine, automotive, etc)

    rocket fuel injection

(e) miscellaneous

    medicinal sprays

    dispersion of chemical agents

    agricultural spraying (insecticides, herbicides, fertilizer solutions, etc)

    foam and fog suppression

(g) conditions that may contribute to atomizer wear or corrosion; (h) size and shape of vessel, enclosure, or combustor containing spray; or area to be coated or treated; (i) economics of the spray operation, taking into account long-term atomizer performance and operating expenses; and (j) analysis of all pertinent information and selection of atomizer type, spray pattern, number of atomizers, flow per atomizer, and other operating conditions.

Nomenclature

a = function of orifice and air core dimensions

A = swirl chamber inlet area, in.^{2}

d_c = air core diameter, in.

d_o = orifice diameter, in.

D = droplet diameter, μ

D_A = surface mean droplet diameter, μ

D_L = arithmetic mean droplet diameter, μ

D_s = droplet diameter for a given size class, s

D_V = volume mean droplet diameter, μ

D_{VA} = Sauter mean droplet diameter, μ

$D_{V_{50}}$ = volume median droplet diameter, μ

G_a = mass velocity of air at nozzle outlet

k = limit denoting largest size class sampled

K = nozzle discharge coefficient

K' = nozzle flow number
L = characteristic length or wetted periphery, in.
N_s = number of droplets sampled in a single size class
N_{Re} = Reynolds number
N_{We} = Weber number
Q_a = volumetric flow rate of air
Q_l = volumetric flow rate of liquid, gal/min
R = radius to center of swirl chamber inlet, in.
s = number of droplet size class
V = liquid velocity, ft/sec
V_a = axial velocity of liquid film at orifice, ft/sec
V_{ao} = superficial axial velocity of liquid at orifice, ft/sec
V_t = tangential liquid velocity at orifice, ft/sec
V_{rel} = relative air–liquid velocity, ft/sec
W_a = mass flow rate of air
W_l = mass flow rate of liquid
ΔP = pressure drop across nozzle, psig
θ = sine of half spray angle
θ' = fan-spray angle, rad
μ_a = air viscosity
μ_l = liquid viscosity, cP
ρ_a = air or gas density, g/cm^3
ρ_l = liquid density, g/cm^3
σ = liquid surface tension, dyn/cm

Bibliography

"Sprays" in *ECT* 1st ed., Vol. 12, pp. 703–721, by W. E. Meyer and W. E. Ranz, The Pennsylvania State University.

1. J. W. S. Rayleigh, *Proc. London Math. Soc.* **10**, 4–13 (1878).
2. R. P. Fraser, P. Eisenklam, N. Dombrowski, and D. Hasson, *A.I.Ch.E.J.* **8**, 672–680 (1962).
3. P. Rosin and E. Rammler, *J. Inst. Fuel* **7**, 29–36 (1933).
4. S. Nukiyama and Y. Tanasawa, *Trans. Soc. Mech. Engrs. (Japan)* **4, 5, 6** (1940).
5. K. Y. Kim and W. R. Marshall, "Drop-Size Distributions from Pneumatic Atomizers," *Papers 58th Annual Meeting, Am. Inst. Chem. Engrs., 1965.*
6. R. A. Mugele, *A.I.Ch.E.J.* **6**, 3–8 (1960).
7. R. A. Mugele and H. D. Evans, *Ind. Eng. Chem.* **43**, 1317–1324 (1951).
8. G. Tresh, *Questions in Rocket Technology*, **4** (1955).
9. L. G. Golovkov, *Inzh.-Fiz. Zh. Akad. Nauk Belorussk. SSR* **7**, 55–61 (1964).
10. S. M. DeCorso, *Papers API Research Conference on Distillate Fuel Combustion*, Chicago, Ill. June 18–19, CP63-64.
11. J. E. Pearson and G. E. Martin, *An Evaluation of Raindrop Sizing and Counting Techniques*, Illinois State Water Survey and University of Illinois, Urbana, Ill., 1957.
12. A. A. Putnam et al., *Injection and Combustion of Liquid Fuels*, Battelle Memorial Institute, WADC Tech. Rept. 56–344, 1957.
13. R. W. Tate and E. O. Olson, *Techniques for Measuring Droplet Size in Sprays*, Delavan Manufacturing Co., West Des Moines, Iowa, 1964.
14. B. J. Matthews, R. F. Wuerker, and D. T. Harrje, "Small Droplet Measuring Technique," *TRW Systems*, AFRPL-TR-67-295, 1968.
15. W. R. Marshall, "Atomization and Spray Drying," *Chem. Eng. Progr. Monograph Ser.* **50** (2), 15–22 (1954).
16. M. Doumas and R. Laster, *Chem. Eng. Progr.* **49**, 518–526 (1953).
17. P. A. Nelson and W. F. Stevens, *A.I.Ch.E.J.* **7**, 80–86 (1961).
18. K. Y. Kim and E. Saunders, "Drop-Size Distributions from Large-Scale Pressure Nozzles," *Papers 2nd Joint Meeting, AIChE-IIQPR, Tampa, Fla., May 19–22, 1968.* (IIQPR is the Instituto de Ingineros Quimicos de Puerto Rico).

19. R. P. Fraser, P. Eisenklam, and N. Dombrowski, *Brit. Chem. Eng.* **2** (Aug.–Nov. 1957).

20. S. M. DeCorso, *Trans. ASME, Ser. A* (*J. Eng. Power*), 10–18 (January 1960).

21. K. Neya and S. Sato, *Papers 27 Ship Res. Inst.* (*Japan*), Feb. 1968.

22. R. W. Tate, *Ind. Eng. Chem.* **52**, 49A–55A (1960).

23. N. Dombrowski and P. C. Hooper, *Chem. Eng. Science* **17**, 291–305 (1962).

24. J. Gretzinger and W. R. Marshall, *A.I.Ch.E.J.* **7**, 312–318 (1961).

25. S. J. Friedman, F. A. Gluckert, and W. R. Marshall, *Chem. Eng. Progr.* **48**, 181–191 (1952).

26. C. R. Adler and W. R. Marshall, *Chem. Eng. Progr.* **47**, 515–522, 601–608 (1951).

27. W. M. Herring and W. R. Marshall, *A.I.Ch.E.J.* **1**, 200–209 (1955).

28. R. W. Tate, *Chem. Eng.* **72** (15), 157–162 (1965); (16), 111–116 (1965).

R. W. TATE
Delavan Manufacturing Company

SPUTTERING.   See Vol. 9, p. 200;   Vol. 13, p. 279.

STAINS, INDUSTRIAL

In this article a stain will be defined as a solution or dispersion of colorants in a vehicle designed primarily to be applied to the surface of articles to impart color effects, rather than to form a protective coating. Thus they differ from paints and other coatings. However, because stains are useful media for the simultaneous application of many other types of materials as well as the colorants, the distinction between staining, coating, and dyeing is not always sharp. See also Coatings, industrial; Dyes and dye intermediates; Dyes (application); Paints.

Industrial stains are applied by many methods to a wide variety of materials. Although their principal function is to change the color of surfaces, they are frequently formulated to serve also as cleaners, glazes, impregnants, inks, polishes, primers, waterproofers, and for many other purposes. Stains are used by handicraft and native-industry workers on a wide assortment of products. They are used commercially as architectural finishes, for concrete, paper products (suit boxes), plastics, textiles, feathers, films, and numerous wood products, and also for branding and other identification and signal systems. No single type of stain could be expected to be suitable for all these various applications, and in practice stains are usually expressly formulated for specific uses. Consequently stains vary widely in composition.

There is no general agreement about the exact mechanisms of staining. Undoubtedly, the fixation of coloring agents is the result of different forces in differing applications, and with dyes or pigments of varying chemical nature and physical properties. Actual chemical combination with surface materials may occur, and probably does occur between some dyes and previously applied mordants. In other cases the coloring effect may be due to adsorption, to mechanical admixture or entrapment, or to dipole attraction and absorption. In stains containing resinous or amphoteric protein binders (such as casein or glue) there may be reactions between the dye and the binder. If the dye or pigment is inert, the binder may just hold the coloring agent glued to the surface to be colored.

Major Types

Although many proprietary stains are on the market, the larger users of stains often develop stains with application and fastness properties to fill their own specifications. Antique and hobby shop craftsmen also prepare numerous specialty stains designed to serve their own unique needs. Most of the stains used in industry can be classified, for discussion, under four major groups: nongrain-raising, oil, spirit, and water stains.

Nongrain-Raising Stains. These are the most recently developed wood stains, and into their formulation, now thoroughly covered by current patents, may go selected mixtures of the various solvents. Their name is undoubtedly derived from the fact that they show a minimum tendency to raise the wood grain. Because of this feature, their use eliminates much of the labor and production time formerly required to sand the wood to its original smoothness. Essentially, these stains are solutions of the acid dyes or selected spirit-soluble dyes, or both, in nonaqueous vehicles. The stains are composed 0.5–6% of dyes, 5–10% of dye solvent 20–50% of alcohols (usually methanol) and the remainder of medium-boiling hydrocarbons (especially toluene), or other liquids nonmiscible with water. The dye solvent is usually a mixture of medium- to high-boiling or practically nonvolatile liquids, and these are the last fractions to evaporate, thereby maintaining the dye in solution long enough to stain the wood. If too great a proportion of these liquids is used, they may first penetrate into the wood, then spew, or more often, slowly sweat or exude to the surface, and loosen any top-coating films. The diethyl ether of ethylene glycol, and methyl and ethyl lactate, are typical of the better ingredients used as dye solvents. Others are ethylene glycol, diethylene glycol, and the monomethyl, monoethyl, and isopropyl ethers of ethylene glycol and propylene glycol. Acetone and other ketones also have been used for this purpose.

These stains yield bright, transparent, light-resistant effects. They can be so formulated as to be nontoxic and to have very little odor. Their use is growing for all types of high-quality wood-staining applications.

Oil Stains. *Penetrating oil stains* are essentially 1–3% solutions of oil-soluble dyes in aromatic hydrocarbons (such as toluene or coal-tar naphtha), containing 5–10% of resins, drying oils, or varnish. Part or all of the aromatic hydrocarbon can be replaced with the aliphatic types (petroleum fractions) for certain formulations, depending on the solubility characteristics of the dyes present. Because of the antioxidant effect of the dyes these stains will dry very slowly if too much drying oil is incorporated. Many of the oil-soluble dyes required for these stains will tend to migrate through or bleed into almost any top coating, although a first coating of shellac will help greatly to seal the top coating and minimize their migration. Some of these dyes also tend to sublime at low temperatures and, accordingly, stains containing them should be used with caution on the inside of furniture drawers or other places where the subliming dyes might stain articles. Here, again, sealing coats of shellac help to minimize this effect. These stains can be formulated to yield bright, transparent color effects and to penetrate well into surfaces. As the colors obtained are generally fugitive to light, these stains are used only on interior work and mostly on inexpensive articles and furniture and in wood refinishing applications. When large proportions of varnish are incorporated, they are called *penetrating varnish stains*. Usually oil stains do not raise wood grain.

Nonpenetrating oil stains are dispersions of insoluble pigments in dilute varnishes or drying oils. They are usually opaque, or at best translucent. Accordingly, they are used only when nonbleeding effects and extreme fastness to light are needed, or when an opaque, uniform color effect is desired, as on furniture and articles made of both light- and dark-colored materials. In these stains, the extent to which the wood grain is obscured depends on the formulation and method of application. Nonpenetrating oil stains can be formulated with materials that dry and penetrate slowly so that brush or swab marks can be readily wiped away. For this reason they are sometimes called *wiping stains*. If large proportions of varnish are present, these stains are often called *nonpenetrating varnish stains*. The preliminary sponging and sanding treatments of the wood required when water stains are used are unnecessary with these oil stains, as they show little tendency to raise the wood grain. When weatherfast pigments are used, these stains are suitable for outdoor applications. However, they are chiefly employed on interior woodwork and for refinishing furniture. They are widely used for both wood and concrete floors; for the latter application the stains are sometimes colored with mixtures of both soluble dyes and insoluble pigments. Certain carefully prepared pigment–oil dispersions, often combined with basic dyes, basic dye bases, or azine dye bases in oleic acid, are widely used as typewriter ribbon inks and for carbon papers.

Spirit Stains. Spirit stains are generally 0.5–12% solutions of dyes in alcohols. Very frequently they also contain shellac (qv) and other alcohol-soluble resins or various chemical mordants. They have less grain-raising effect on wood than the water stains, but they do raise wood grain more than the nongrain-raising and oil stains. The spirit stains are characterized by quick and deep penetration, and by rapid drying; the latter feature makes them difficult to apply evenly to large areas, except with machines (calender staining). The better grades of these stains are colored with the faster-to-light alcohol-soluble, metalized azo dyes (qv), usually incorporated with lacquers (*lacquer stains*) or dissolved in glycol ether–alcohol mixtures for staining wood. Basic dyes are used when tinctorially powerful and bright color effects are desired, despite their poor fastness to light and water. Their tendency to bleed into water can be reduced somewhat by using the basic dye bases instead of the water-soluble basic dye salts, and it can be greatly reduced by using basic dye–mordant (tannin) combinations. Large quantities of these dye–mordant complexes are used in the calender staining of paperboard. When applied without binders, the basic dyes tend to crock (rub off), although this tendency is less when they are applied to materials containing natural mordants (for example, kraft paper). Ten to twenty percent solutions of the basic dyes or basic dye–mordant complexes, frequently also containing 4% of shellac, are widely used for high-speed and offset printing inks, commonly called "aniline inks" or "flexographic inks." The same dyes in alcohol-toluene–o-dichlorobenzene solutions are useful leather stains (shoe stains, brush dyeing). Many of the water-soluble acid dyes and a few direct dyes can be incorporated in spirit stains, particularly if first dissolved in a suitable glycol ether. The certified grades of acid dyes are particularly recommended for stains for toys and for children's art supplies. Some of the oil-soluble dyes also can be incorporated in spirit stains, particularly with alcohol–acetone–toluene solvents, and these stains are occasionally useful for special refinishing applications. All the dyes used in spirit stains tend to bleed into top coatings, particularly into lacquers. Except for those containing oil-soluble dyes, the spirit stains can be used to finish the insides of cabinets and drawers and to impart color to a wide variety of materials. They are useful in certain branding, marking, stencil, and spirit duplicator inks, although with spirit duplicator inks the solvent is applied to the copy sheet.

Water Stains. Water stains are 1–3% solutions of water-soluble dyes. Although almost any water-soluble colorant may be used, the majority of industrial stains are prepared from a very limited number of dyes because of cost, solubility, and other factors. These stains are sometimes formulated to contain binders, sizes, wetting agents, and many other types of materials. The acid dyes are used for high-grade furniture and interior woodwork as they give the faster-to-light effects, although their use entails many sanding operations because the water raises wood grain. Occasionally solutions of leuco vat dyes are used; then care should be taken to wash off the residual chemicals. Basic dyes are used on short-lived objects and where their brilliant hues add sales appeal, as on fruit crates, baskets, etc, particularly where cost limitations prevent the use of the basic dye–mordant spirit stains. Probably the most important water-soluble dye of natural origin used in water stains is sap brown, a solubilized peat. Ten percent solutions of this dye yield khaki to walnut color effects of good fastness to light on wood; it has been widely used in combination with a copper sulfate mordant and chlorophenolic preservatives for staining crates for military supplies. Inorganic dyes, such as the permanganates used by nineteenth-century craftsmen, are still used occasionally. Generally, the soluble colorants used in water stains have little tendency to bleed into oleoresinous top coatings, or into lacquers formulated with a minimum of alcohols and glycol ethers present. They are economically important because of their good resistance to light, their low cost, and the cheapness of their water vehicle. They can be applied by practically every staining process, although brushing, dipping, infusion, and impregnation are the methods most commonly used. They are particularly useful where their tendency to raise the grain of wood, and their relatively slow evaporation or drying rate are unimportant, for example, on the backs of furniture, on rough-finish shipping crates, and as ruling, drawing, and writing inks.

Stable *pigment dispersions in water* have become commercially available during recent years and are gaining wide use in stains and other finishes. There are two principal types of these dispersions: One is readily compatible with most soluble binders, latexes, and resin emulsions; and the second type is adversely affected by alcoholic additions, although still compatible with many other materials. They are suitable for aqueous wiping stains and polishes when resistance to light and water is desired.

Ingredients

A few stains are merely solutions or dispersions of colorants in alcohols, hydrocarbons, water, or similar liquids. However, no less than fourteen other types of ingredients are used by professional formulators: adhesives, antifreeze agents, antioxidants, buffers, catalysts, dispersants, fillers, foam controllers, mordants, preservatives and toxic agents, stabilizers, surfactants, thinners, and viscosity controllers.

COLORANTS

Some of the colorants used by the ancient artisans in staining and dyeing are in use today, although many of them are now made synthetically. Asphaltum, indigo, logwood, and ultramarine blue are typical. However, except perhaps in localized native arts, most of the natural colorants formerly used have been displaced by synthetic agents. Although nearly any dye or pigment could be used in one or another type of stain, professional colorists now usually limit their choice to those given in Tables 1–3. (The dye names used are mostly those adopted by the American Association of Textile Chemists and Colorists (1) for their annual *Year Book*. For dyes listed in the *Colour Index* (2), the CI number is given. See also Colors for foods, drugs, and cosmetics.)

Table 1. Water-Soluble Dyes

Acid dyes	CI no.	Basic dyes	CI no.
Technical grade		Basic dyes	
Azo Rubine	14720	Certified (for toys)	
Brilliant Crocein M	27290	D&C Red No. 19	45170
Orange II	15510	Technical grade	
Orange G	16230	Fuchsine	42510
Tartrazine	10140	Rhodamine B	45170
Metanil Yellow	13065	Rhodamine 6G	45160
Naphthol Green B	10020	Chrysoidine G	11320
Naphthol Blue Black	17000	Auramine	41000
Nigrosine, water-soluble	50420	Malachite Green	42000
Certified (for toys)		Methylene Blue	52015
FD&C Red No. 1	16155	Victoria Blue B	44045
D&C Orange No. 4	15510	Methyl Violet B	42535
FD&C Yellow No. 5	19140	Bismark Brown G	21000
FD&C Green No. 1	42085	Soluble inorganic and organic natural dyes	
FD&C Blue No. 1		or coloring agents	
FD&C Violet No. 1	42640	acids (concentrated)	
D&C Brown No. 1	20170	ammonia (for fuming staining)	
D&C Black No. 1	20470	dichromates and chromates	
		caustic alkalis (for caramelization)	
		gallotannic acids and tannins	
		lead salts (sulfided after application)	
		sap brown (solubilized peats)	
		silver nitrate (for blacks)	

Table 2. Ester-, Hydrocarbon-, and Oil-Soluble Dyes

Dyes	CI no.	Dyes	CI no.
Technical grade		Certified	
Sudan II (Scarlet)	12140	D&C Red No. 18	
Sudan I (Orange)	12055	D&C Red No. 17	26100
Amino Azo Toluol	37210	FD&C Red No. 32	
Oil Yellow	11020	FD&C Orange No. 2	
Alizarine Cyanine Green Base	61565	D&C Yellow No. 11	47000
Alizarine Irisol Base	60725	D&C Green No. 6	61565
Induline Base	50400	D&C Violet No. 2	60725
Nigrosine Base	50415B		
Dye Base–oleic acid complexes			

Alcohol(Spirit)-Soluble Dyes. Most of the synthetic organic dyes listed in Table 1 can be used also in alcoholic stains, either directly or after first being dissolved in glycol ethers.

Certain metalized azo dyes are soluble in alcohols, typical examples being the Calcofast Spirit Red B, Calcofast Spirit Orange R, Calcofast Spirit Yellow 2R, Calcofast Spirit Brown GN, and Calcofast Spirit Black RB dyes.

There are on the market mixtures of certain basic dyes and mordants (usually tannins) which are soluble in alcohol or in alcohol–water mixtures. When applied and dried, the dye and mordants interact to produce water-resistant, colored effects. They were originally developed to color straw hats which would not dribble dye if

Table 3. Insoluble Colorants (Pigments (qv))

Technical grade	Ochers	
Alizarine Red Lake	Burnt Sienna	
Rhodamine Toners	Burnt Umber	
Lithol Maroon Toners	Iron Oxides	
Eosine Lakes	Carbon Blacks	
Lithol Red Toners		
Benzidine Orange Toners	Certified	*CI no.*
Benzidine Yellow Toners	D&C Red No. 7	15850
Malachite Green Toners	D&C Red No. 9	15585
Chrome Greens	D&C Red No. 11	15630
Hydrated Chromium Oxide	D&C Red No. 12	15630
Phthalocyanine Green	D&C Red No. 21	45380A
Peacock Blues	D&C Red No. 30	73360
Iron Blues	D&C Red No. 34	15880
Phthalocyanine Blues	D&C Red No. 35	12120
Ultramarine Blues	D&C Orange No. 17	12075
Alkali Blue Toners	D&C Yellow No. 7	45350
Victoria Blue Toners	D&C Blue No. 6	73000
Methyl Violet Toners	D&C Blue No. 9	

caught in a rainstorm. They are very widely used for staining paperboard containers (suit boxes) and as the "aniline inks" or "flexographic inks."

Two types of dyes of the azine group are alcohol-soluble, namely, the induline spirit-soluble, and the nigrosine spirit-soluble, useful for shoe and leather stains, and stencil and marking inks.

Glycol-, Glycol Ether-Soluble Dyes. Most of the synthetic, organic, acid, and basic dyes listed in Table 1 are also soluble in glycols, glycol ethers, and glycerin. These liquids are often used in the nongrain-raising wood stains and in cold-temperature stains.

SOLVENTS (qv)

The clear, fluid stains, being merely dyes dissolved in a single solvent, may have simple formulas. More frequently, however, rather complex mixtures of solvents are used, sometimes for their synergistic effects, sometimes to get a wider range of evaporation temperatures and rates, and occasionally to bring into one liquid mixture materials soluble in different solvents. Stain liquids are often referred to as "low, medium, or high boilers," depending upon their boiling points. They often serve more than one function in a stain. The solvents used in stains can be classified conveniently according to the following:

Acetic, cresylic, linoleic, and occasionally nitric *acids* are used.

Of the *alcohols*, generally methanol, ethyl alcohol, isopropyl alcohol, and 1-butanol are used as solvents, blending aids, antifoaming, antiblushing and antifreezing agents, and preservatives. They are the principal liquids used in spirit stains, shellac inks, and varnish stains made with spirit-soluble resins, and they are useful in lacquer stains.

Waxy, aliphatic *amides* are used occasionally in specialty stains; and certain sulfonamides, notably *N*-ethyl-*p*-toluenesulfonamide, are useful in lacquer stains as high-boiling, powerful solvents and plasticizers having low vapor pressure.

Several types of *amines* are used in the formulation of miscellaneous stains: aliphatic amines and hydroxyamines (amino alcohols)—diamylamine and the ethanolamines and isopropanol amines, which are particularly useful in emulsions; cyclic aliphatic amines—morpholine; aromatic amines—aniline, N-(2-hydroxyethyl)aniline (2-anilinoethanol), which must be used with proper health precautions; miscellaneous amines—including 2-amino-2-ethyl-1,3-propanediol, tri(hydroxymethyl)aminomethane (2-amino-2-(hydroxymethyl)-1,3-propanediol), and urethan.

The natural *esters* most commonly used in stains are the drying oils (qv). These are usually triglycerides of long-chain, unsaturated, fatty acids. They dry, or polymerize, by oxidation to form films, and this property distinguishes them from the nondrying oils and the ester plasticizers. They serve not only as solvents, but also as binders, softeners, and pore sealers. The drying oils dissolve the ester-soluble dyes, but the dyes have a strong antioxidant effect and greatly retard the drying of the oil. Fish, linseed, soybean, and tung oils are typical drying oils.

A large number of synthetic esters are commercially available. Typical of the esters useful in stains are ethyl acetate, *n*-butyl acetate, ethyl lactate, di-*n*-butylphthalate, and diethylene glycol ricinoleate. They serve as solvents for resins and ester-soluble dyes, as antiblushing agents, and as film modifiers. Esters are essential ingredients of lacquer stains.

Ethers are excellent solvents for oils, resins, and waxes and also are good blending agents for solvent mixtures. The ester-oil-and spirit-soluble dyes tend to dissolve in ethers, as well as in ether and toluene and ether and alcohol mixtures. Chemically the ethers used in stains can be classified into four groups: unsubstituted ethers, R—O—R, of which isopropyl ether is an example; hydroxy ethers, R—O—ROH, widely used in stains, particularly the glycol ethers, such as ethylene glycol monomethyl ether; chlorinated ethers, ClR—O—RCl, such as 2,2-dichloroethyl ether (bis(2-chloroethyl) ether); cyclic ethers, R——R, which contain a characteristic three-membered ring,

$$\overset{\displaystyle R\text{———}R}{\underset{O}{\bigvee}}$$

typified by propylene oxide. Dioxane may also be classed with the cyclic ethers.

The *furans* (furfural and other furan compounds) are unsaturated cyclic compounds characterized by a ring of four carbon atoms and one oxygen atom. Furfuryl alcohol and tetrahydrofurfuryl alcohol are derivatives which are useful in some stains. The tendency of furfuryl alcohol to darken on exposure to light and to resinify in the presence of acids has been used to advantage in stains for laboratory benches (4). Tetrahydrofurfuryl alcohol has solubility properties approaching those of a mixture of methanol and toluene. These furans are used only in specialty stains.

The *glycols* are useful humectants, antifreeze agents, softeners, and plasticizers for water-soluble binders. They dissolve many water-soluble dyes and are useful blending agents for nongrain-raising wood stains.

Many *hydrocarbons* and substituted hydrocarbons are useful in stains. They serve as solvents for dyes, oils, resins, and waxes. Some of them are also useful thinners and viscosity modifiers.

Dipentene, pine oils, and the turpentines are examples of the alicyclic hydrocarbon–terpineol mixtures useful as resin solvents and blending agents in stains. Their pronounced characteristic odors and their allergic effects on some persons limit their uses primarily to varnish stains and specialty formulations.

Straight- and branched-chain paraffins and isoparaffins are very useful liquids in stains, particularly gasolines, heavy mineral spirits, kerosine, petroleum ether, Stoddard solvent, and V.M. & P. naphtha (see Petroleum (products)). The solid types of these hydrocarbons are also occasionally useful; they include asphaltums, gilsonite, pitch, tar, and waxes. The viscosities, boiling ranges, and flash points of these compounds cover a wide range. Some of them contain chemically unsaturated fractions which may tend to polymerize and form resinous products on aging. Aliphatic hydrocarbons are useful as solvents for resins and as thinners. They dissolve only the oil-soluble dyes, and those only to a rather limited extent, and some pigments and vat dyes tend to bleed into certain of these liquids. In most cases they are combined in use with toluene and similar aromatic hydrocarbons. The aromatic types of petroleum naphthas are technical-grade blends of naphthenes, toluene, xylenes, and C_9, C_{10} hydrocarbons derived from mineral-oil processing rather than from coal tars.

Aromatic hydrocarbons of the benzene and hydrogenated naphthalene series are excellent solvents for the hydrocarbon-soluble dyes, coal-tar pitches, tars, oils, certain plastics, some resins, and many waxes. A number of acetate dyes and certain azine and vat dyes tend to bleed into these solvents also. They are effective as evaporating and antiblushing aids because they form azeotropic mixtures and moisture barriers on surfaces, and they are useful thinners in many types of stains. The solvents form a layer of vapor above the surface, thus preventing the deposition of moisture on the stained surface as the stain dries. Benzene, coal-tar naphtha, toluene, xylenes, tetra- and decahydronaphthalenes are the aromatic hydrocarbons most frequently used in stain work.

Certain of both the aliphatic and the aromatic *halogenated hydrocarbons* are used in stains as solvents for oil-soluble dyes, resins, and waxes. Formulators of specialty stains also take advantage of the fungicidal action and nonflammability of these liquids, and their particularly good adaptability for polish stains. Typical examples of these liquids are: aliphatic (carbon tetrachloride, chloroform, di- and trichloroethylene) and aromatic (o-dichlorobenzene, chlorinated diphenyls, and chlorinated naphthalenes).

The aliphatic *nitro hydrocarbons* are solvents for hydrocarbon-soluble dyes and for some resins. They have been found useful in certain dipping stains for plastics. The aromatic nitro hydrocarbons are equally good solvents, but their toxicity tends to limit their use, which is legally forbidden for shoe stains in many localities. Examples are: aliphatic (1-nitropropane, 2-nitropropane), and aromatic (nitrobenzene).

Ketones are colorless, often sharply odorous liquids that are excellent solvents or swelling agents for most resins and good blending agents for solvent mixtures. They dissolve oil-soluble dyes and certain spirit-soluble dyes and tend to increase the solvent power of alcohols and hydrocarbons for resins and dyes. The more volatile types tend to chill surfaces below the dewpoint and thereby induce "blushing" due to occluded moisture, particularly with lacquer stains. They are flammable liquids. Ketones tend to dissolve the polyvinyl polymers. Acetone, diacetone (diacetone alcohol), diisobutyl ketone, methyl ethyl ketone, and methyl isobutyl ketone are typical.

Nitriles dissolve oil-soluble dyes. Those having boiling points in the range 200–360°C are sometimes used as plasticizers, wetting agents, and solvents or resins. Typical examples are the high-molecular-weight nitriles of the straight-chain fatty acids, such as caprinitrile (decanenitrile), $CH_3(CH_2)_8CN$, and myristonitrile (tetradecanenitrile), $CH_3(CH_2)_{12}CN$.

Certain *salts* formed from organic bases reacted with acids are used in stains as emulsification aids and as mutual solvents for dyes, oils, and waxes. Such soaps are excellent aids in introducing water-soluble dyes into oil- and wax-base specialty stains.

Some ammonium salts of resin acids act in a closely similar manner as pigment and resin dispersants and as binders. Salts that have been found particularly useful in emulsion stains are ethanolamine oleate and ammonia–borax–shellac complexes. Nigrosine stearates, Victoria Blue oleates, and similar dispersions of dye bases in fatty acids might well be classified in this group, although their principal function is as colorants rather than as solvents.

Several liquid *sulfur compounds* are occasionally useful in specialty stains. Usually they are malodorous. One of the more useful compounds is thiodiethylene glycol (2,-2'-dihydroxydiethyl sulfide), which is practically colorless, nonvolatile, hygroscopic, neutral, and water-soluble. It is a solvent for acid, basic, direct, sulfur, and vat dyes and therefore has been used in screen printing and stencil inks. 2-Mercaptoethanol (thioethylene glycol) has similar properties. Carbon disulfide and ethyl mercaptan (ethanethiol) are low-boiling-point, highly flammable sulfides possessing good solvent power for many elastomeric polymers and the oil-soluble dyes. They are, however, used more often for quick-setting rubber cements than in stains. Generally these liquids present health and fire hazards.

Soft or distilled *water* is one of the most useful ingredients for stains. It dissolves acid, acid mordant, basic, direct, and developed dyes, and, with the aid of sodium sulfide, sodium hydrosulfite, and alkalis, will dissolve the sulfur and vat dyes. Many carbohydrate and protein binders are soluble in water. It is the most readily available and lowest-cost stain liquid. However, it has some important adverse features for staining work, including its tendency to raise the grain and to be repelled by the resinous areas of wood, its relatively slow evaporation rate, high freezing point, and a tendency to favor the growth of bacteria, fungi, and molds.

OTHER INGREDIENTS

Adhesives (qv). These are the binders used to hold the colorants and other ingredients to surfaces and/or to help fill the pores or to size the surfaces. The many products used for these purposes can be classified into three major groups: water-soluble, emulsion-dispersible, and organo-liquid-soluble materials.

1. Water-Soluble Adhesives. *Carbohydrates:* alginates, dextrins, gums, methylcellulose, starches. *Plastics:* polyethylene glycols, polyvinyl alcohol, urea–aldehyde polymers. *Proteins:* albumins, caseinates, gelatin glues. *Salts:* sodium carboxymethylcellulose, sodium silicates. *Soaps:* rosin sizes, shellac–borax products, sodium oleates, palmitates, and stearates.

2. Emulsion-Dispersible Adhesives. *Oils:* drying oils. *Resins:* latexes, and organo- or water-soluble. *Waxes.*

3. Adhesives Soluble in Organic Liquids. *Asphalts:* gilsonite, pitches, tars. *Cellulose derivatives:* acetates, ethers, nitrates. *Oils:* drying oils. *Plastics and resins:* natural—dammar, Manila, rosin, shellac; synthetic—coumarone–indene, vinyl polymers. *Varnishes:* oleoresinous polymers. *Waxes:* animal, mineral, synthetic, vegetable.

Antifreeze Agents. Proprietary stains shipped, stored, or used under freezing conditions usually are formulated to contain liquids of low freezing points, such as glycerin or glycols. As large proportions of these agents in a stain usually leave the surfaces wet and tend to exude from pores, they are generally rinsed from the surface after application of the stain.

Antioxidants. Antioxidants are occasionally incorporated in specialty stains to inhibit oxidation reactions, which might cause gelation, odor development, or resinification. They are usually organic complexes. Sodium hydrosulfite, $Na_2S_2O_4$, is used both as a reducing agent and as an antioxidant with leuco-vat-dye stains.

Buffers. These are pH control agents, such as soluble borates and phosphates, added to stains to maintain a desired pH.

Catalysts. Catalysts are added to chemically reactive stains, usually just before use, in order to control reactions. Examples are formaldehyde, acids, and other hardeners added to caseinates and urea–aldehyde polymers, and the organic peroxides added to polyesters.

Dispersants. These are agents used to disperse and retain in suspension insoluble ingredients of stains. They frequently also act as "anticaking" agents. Both soluble and insoluble dispersants are used, examples being ammonium caseinates, cellulose ethers, and colloidal clays.

Fillers. Fillers are insoluble ingredients which are added to stains for the purpose of filling holes and pores in surfaces to which the stains are applied. Ground chalk, heavy-metal soaps, silica, and talc are examples.

Foam Controllers or Antifoaming Agents. These are added to some stains to hasten the escape of trapped air bubbles when labile stains are shaken and applied to surfaces. The air may be trapped within a stain itself or in the pores of the surface being colored and, unless it is rather quickly eliminated, bubble-spots and unevenly colored effects may result. Alcoholic, fatty, and silicone additives are typical products used as antifoaming aids.

Mordants. Mordants are chemical reagents selected to bind the colorants to surfaces and to react with and modify the properties of the colorants. Usually mordants are applied to the surfaces and permitted to dry before the stains are used. However, when both the mordants and the dyes are soluble in the stain vehicle, they can sometimes be premixed before application. Alum, chromium fluoride, ferric chloride, lead acetate, tartar emetic (potassium antimony(III) tartrate), and tannic acid are typical mordants. The use of mordants seems to be declining in present-day staining, particularly where the processing entails two steps.

Preservatives and Toxic Agents. Some specialty stains, in addition to their coloring function, are designed to serve also for the application of preservatives and antimildew, antirot, insecticidal (antitermitic), and other toxic agents. Stains prepared with carbohydrate and protein binders also require preservatives to prevent their fermentation or putrefaction. The creosotes added to shingle stains, and the chlorophenols sometimes added to ammunition-crate stains, are typical preservatives, and DDT is an example of an insecticide.

Stabilizers. Stains usually undergo changes during prolonged storage. Their "shelf-life" is often greatly affected by: the presence or absence of buffers and preservatives; evaporation losses; the settling out or deposition of suspensoids; crystal growth of pigments; degradation of dyes and resins; reaction with the containers (corrosion); caramelization; oxidation; polymerization; putrefaction; resinification; interactions between various ingredients within a stain; and probably other effects. Some of these factors are controlled by the solvents and other ingredients; for example, alcohol present primarily as a solvent may also prevent a dye–mordant reaction or at least maintain the reaction product in solution; or again it might inhibit the growth of molds, etc. However, certain stabilizers are added to control specific reactions. For example, soluble chromates reduce container corrosion and prevent dye destruction by hydrogen or acetylene released by corrosive reactions; cadmium soaps and tribasic lead compounds retard the degradation of certain vinyl polymers; and amino phenols delay the oxidation resinification of gasolines and similar ingredients.

Surface-Active Agents (see Surfactants). These substances are used to reduce the interfacial tension between a stain and the surfaces to which it may be applied. They aid the wetting of resinous areas of wood, polished (waxy) areas, mixed materials, and grimy, dirty surfaces. There are three types: anionic, nonionic, and cationic. The first two types are generally compatible with acid dyes, but the cationic types usually may be used only with the basic dyes. A large selection of these agents is available, but as many of them are sold admixed and under nondescriptive sales names, careful trials should be made before incorporating into a stain any surfactants of unknown composition. Surfactants must be used with special caution in stains used to produce design effects (inks, prints, etc) because these agents may induce feathering and affect the penetration of the stain, with resultant loss of design definition or sharpness.

Thinners. Thinners are liquids added to reduce the concentration of stains, often being added just before the application of the stain to a surface. Reduction of stain concentration may be required for several reasons, including the lessening of its tinctorial power, increased fluidity, and lower costs. Thinners are seldom single liquids; rather, they generally must be carefully formulated and added with caution or the solubility of other ingredients may be adversely affected, emulsions may become unstable, and the evaporation rates may be changed. Usually they are carefully balanced mixtures of solvents and nonsolvents, often blends of low-, medium-, and high-boiling liquids. Even when water is used as a thinner, its purity, temperature, pH, rate of addition, and the degree and type of stirring may be critical.

Viscosity Controllers. Often stains having controlled consistency, fluidity, plasticity, and viscosity have to be prepared. These features are affected by many ingredients; the ratio of solids in solution or dispersion; the type of solids; the composition and proportions of the liquids; the temperature; the presence or absence of electrolytes; the wettability, particle size, oil absorbency, porosity, and surface area of pigments and other insoluble materials present; and probably many other factors. The compounding process used may also be important; for example, the consistency of an emulsion may vary when processed on a three-roll mill, in a ball mill, or through a colloid mill. Some resins give more viscous solutions in one solvent than in others. Certain binders, notably gums, methylcellulose, and starches, may vary greatly in the consistency of their solutions with temperature. The 2% of gum arabic in marking stains, the 4% of shellac in spirit stains, and the 5% or more of varnish in oil stains are examples of fluidity and viscosity control as well as of binder action.

Compounding

There is still a large degree of art in the preparation of the necessary solutions or dispersions or both, but the following may be helpful.

Equipment and Containers. The equipment employed should be resistant to the abrasive and corrosive action of the materials.

Bimetallic equipment systems should be avoided. For example, copper kettles with iron fittings may set up electrolytic reactions; tinned iron wire holders for application daubers, if used in bottled stains, tend to liberate acetylene and atomic hydrogen, which destroy many coloring agents; and for the same reasons terneplate cans should not be used as containers for many types of stains.   Metallic salt contaminants from rust and tank or container corrosion often tend to precipitate and modify the color of colorants; this is particularly noticeable when mixed dyes are present.

Precautions should be taken to minimize fire and health hazards.   These precautions include explosionproof electrical equipment, forced ventilation and fume-exhausting systems.

Factors Influencing Solution Preparation.   Some important factors that affect the efficient and economical preparation of solutions are as follows:

The Colloidal State of Materials.   Many high-molecular-weight materials, particularly dyes, when in the colloidal state tend to form curds, emulsions, gels, gummy masses, and sticky pastes; these agglomerations are almost impractical to work with. The use of warm solvents and the addition of the materials in controlled amount, rate, and manner will minimize the formation of such masses.

Temperature Control.   The temperature of both the solvents and the materials affects greatly the degree and ease of solubility of most products.   Usually high temperatures have a favorable effect, but with a few substances, notably methylcellulose, the solubility tends to decrease as the temperature is raised.   The use of cold solvents, such as those stored outdoors in winter, may lead to great processing trouble because of the formation of colloidal, gummy pastes.   Often materials that dissolve poorly in cold solvents may tend to rush into solution when temperatures from 60°C to boiling are used.   On occasion, if the temperature of a "stock solution" is permitted to drop, some of the ingredients may grain out and deposit.

Physical Structure of Materials.   The crystalline, amorphous, or resinous nature of materials affects their solubility, particularly the speed and ease of solution.   Although crystals have relatively small surface areas open to the attack of solvents, the liquids usually can flow around and through them much more readily than in the case of finely divided amorphous materials.   If solvents are poured over fine powders, a slime may form on the top of the material and delay further solvent action; consequently it is often better to scatter such materials on the surface of the solvents. Resinous masses should be separately dissolved in warm liquids or in refluxing apparatus.

Particle Size.   As with structure, the size of the material particles affects the speed and ease of solubility.   Usually very large chunks and floury powders require processing different from material of rather uniform intermediate size ranges.

Adhering and Occluded Impurities.   The presence of air, gases, moisture, antidusting agents, grease, electrolytes, excess intermediates, and other organophilic or hydrophilic materials can affect the ease and completeness of solution.

Solvent Mixtures.   The many types of solvent mixtures employed influence the solubility.   Usually the solubility of a material in a mixture of its good solvents will approach the average for each liquid; occasionally, however, synergistic effects are met.

Good Plus Poor Solvents (Thinners).   In many cases the solubility of a material in a mixture of a good and a poor solvent is not the expected average of its solubility in each liquid used alone, although materials vary greatly in this respect.   For example, one oil-soluble dye, which gives an 8% solution in toluene and a 2% solution in V.M. & P. naphtha, gives a 7% solution in a 50-50 mixture of these two liquids; whereas another, which also gives an 8% solution in toluene but only a 0.2% solution in V.M. & P. naphtha, gives only a 1% solution in the 50-50 mixture of these liquids.

Poor Solvents. Usually the degree of solubility of a material in two poor solvents approaches the expected average of its solubility in either liquid alone. However, sometimes unexpected synergistic results are obtained; for example, Nigrosine Base, which gives 2% solutions in either alcohol or toluene, will give a 20% solution in a 50-50 mixture of these two liquids.

Immiscible Solvents. Formulations requiring the use of immiscible liquids usually include either blending agents or emulsifiers. For example, a mixture of water and toluene can be blended by the addition of acetone or glycol ethers, or emulsified with ethanolamine oleate. Usually materials soluble in one type of liquid are insoluble in another, but a compatible mixture may result when suitable blending agents are added. It is usually best to dissolve each ingredient in its proper solvent before blending or emulsifying the immiscible fractions.

Solutions as Solvents. The presence of one or more materials in a solution generally affects its solvent power for other substances. For example, the presence of salts and tannins in water will tend to reduce greatly its solvency for many dyes. In contrast, alcoholic solutions of resins sometimes are better solvents for certain dyes than alcohol used alone. The presence of acids and of alkalis in water often has a marked effect on its solvent power for a number of materials. Therefore, it is frequently better engineering practice first to dissolve each type of ingredient separately and then to mix these solutions under properly controlled conditions.

Dispersions. To make dispersions, each particle of the insoluble materials must be isolated and suspended and its surface wetted. Powdered materials have very large surface areas, depending on the particle size and porosity of the material. For example, 1 g of an iron blue pigment may have a surface area of 100 m^2. Usually these surfaces hold occluded gases, plus adhering moisture and air, while often anti-dusting agents, humectants, oils, and grime are present; these barrier substances must be displaced by the liquids in which the dispersion is made. This usually requires that a large amount of mechanical work be done on the system. Many types of machines and processing techniques may be used. See Emulsions.

Basis of Stain Selection

Industrial users of stains frequently must employ formulations specifically designed to meet their own engineering requirements and end-use specifications. However, for many applications a review of the job requirements often indicates which of the four principal types of stains may be the one to choose. The data in Table 4 and the following discussion of the outstanding features of each of these types of stain may serve as the basis for selection.

Nongrain-raising stains are primarily designed to be used for staining wood products. They are generally high in cost, but this feature is often balanced by the saving of labor for sanding operations. They may contain the same dyes as any one or all of the other three groups, as they can be formulated to dissolve water-, spirit-, and oil-soluble dyes to a large degree. To some extent they combine the better features of all the other stains.

Oil-soluble stains are moderate in cost, considering that they have nonaqueous vehicles. They are an older, special group of nongrain-raising stains. Their use avoids some sanding operations, and they also can be readily incorporated in varnishes or lacquers to fill, prime, and stain in one operation. The penetrating types contain dyes which are only moderately resistant to light and which tend greatly to delay the drying of drying oils and varnishes. The nonpenetrating types contain pigments of

Table 4. Type of Stain

Characteristics	Nongrain-raising	Oil	Spirit	Water
solvent	mixed, nonaqueous	hydrocarbons	alcohol	water
thinner	mixtures	V.M. & P. naphtha	various	water
toxicity of liquids	varies widely	considerable	varies widely	slight
binder	resins	varnish	shellac	rosin size
drying rate	moderately fast	slow	fast	slow
effect on wood grain	slight	slight	moderate	raises
light resistance	good	moderate[a]	varies	good
bleeding resistance				
alcohols	bleed	moderate[a]	bleed	bleed
lacquers	bleed	bleed[a]	bleed	moderate
oils	good	bleed[a]	good	good
shellac solutions	bleed	moderate[a]	bleed	bleed
varnishes	very good	bleed[a]	good	very good
water	bleed	good[a]	moderate	bleed

[a] Nonpenetrating oil stains containing pigments have "very good" resistance to both light and bleeding.

good resistance to light and bleeding. They can be applied as wiping stains on large surfaces because of their slow drying rates.

Spirit-soluble stains are the third highest in cost. They cut through old finishes well, dry quickly, and can be so formulated as to be nonbleeding in water. They are used on shipping containers and baskets, inside rough-finished surfaces and drawers, and on toys. However, their principal applications are in other fields, notably in paper and leather staining and high-speed press inks.

Water stains are the lowest in cost; however, when they are used on wood, this advantage is largely counterbalanced by the labor cost of the sanding operations concomitant to their use, because of their marked grain-raising action. They have good-to-moderate resistance to light and only a slight tendency to bleed into varnish and lacquer top coatings.

Representative Formulas

Formula 1. Wood Stains

(Dissolve in water or in nongrain-raising formulas)

Dye	Mahogany	Maple	Golden oak	Dark oak	Walnut
Orange G	1.0[a]	3.75			
Brilliant Crocein	2.5	0.90	0.05	0.22	1.15
Metanil Yellow			1.94	0.32	0.90
Naphthol Blue Black	0.5	0.05	0.01	0.16	0.45

[a] Ounces of dye per gallon.

Formula 2. Spirit Stain,[a] Flexographic Ink

Constituent	Amount
Calcofast Spirit Red B, g	10
refined shellac (5 lb/cut), ml	25
alcohol, ml	75

[a] In Formulas 2–9 the amounts for all coloring agents and other solids are given in parts by weight and all solvents and nonsolid additives in parts by volume.

Formula 3. Penetrating Oil Stain (Mahogany)

Constituent	Amount
Oil Red	1.26
Sudan I	0.14
Alizarine Cyanine Green Base	0.60
toluene	63.00
V.M. & P. naphtha	25–10.00
varnish	10–25.00

Formula 4. Nonpenetrating Oil Stain (Cedar)

Constituent	Amount
Golden Ocher	9.0
Toluidine toner	1.0
boiled linseed oil	89.2
drier (concentrated)	0.2

Formula 5. Stain for Lacquer Coatings

Constituent	Amount
Chrysoidine	0.7
methanol	84.3
water	15.0

Formula 6. Crate Stain

Constituent	Amount
Sap Brown	5
pentachlorophenate	2
copper sulfate	2
ammonia	3
water	88

Formula 7. End-Grain Sealer

Constituent	Amount
Metanil Yellow	0.5
shellac[a]	10.0
borax[a]	2.5
water	87.0

[a] Dissolved together at boil in part of the water.

Formula 8. Laundry Marking Ink

Constituent	Amount
Nigrosine Base	9
cresylic acid	66
phenol	25

Formula 9. Gloss Black Spirit Stains

Constituent	Amount
Nigrosine spirit-soluble	2
methanol	50
shellac (5 lb/cut)	50

Application Methods

At least seven general application methods are used in staining surfaces, and numerous modifications of these processes are used to get special coloring effects. These methods are often coupled with forced-drying (baking) procedures and the use of specialty stains designed to save labor, as, for example, the use of nongrain-raising stains to eliminate the need for many sanding operations in wood staining. Notable advances have also been made by using high-speed presses, padders, and calenders. Consequently, production in certain lines has been so speeded that it is not uncommon to have articles built, sanded, stained, coated, and shipped within the same day. These procedures have required the development of specialty stains uniquely adapted to them.

Many of the application methods used with stains have been discussed in other articles. For brushing, spraying, dip application, padding, tumbling, calender staining, and knife coating, see Coated fabrics; Coatings (industrial); Dyes (application). See also Paper. For intaglio printing, screen printing, and offset printing, see Dyes (application), Vol. 7, p. 505; Printing Processes. The "aniline inks" often used in offset printing are generally basic dye–mordant or acid dye–basic dye complexes dissolved in alcohol, sometimes with 4% shellac. The larger number of graphic printing inks, however, are varnish or lacquer stains. Usually extremely fine and uniform colorant dispersions are needed for screen printing. In intaglio printing, careful control of the viscosity of the stain is generally necessary. Important special methods of stain application are discussed below.

Stainers have at their command a very wide variety of stains that enable them to produce color effects on surfaces rather quickly, easily, safely, and at minimum labor costs. Successful application, however, requires skill and artistry because of the differences in the self-color, structure, absorbency, and other properties of surfaces, and the application characteristics of the various types of stains. Frequently the ability to match colors and a knowledge of color harmony and designing are also required. Technology has improved the composition and application methods for stains, but their use still remains an art.

Impregnation. Frequently articles to be stained are first exposed to vacuum for $\frac{1}{2}$ to 2 hr or longer to remove air and moisture from capillaries and cells; a stain is then drawn or pumped into the chamber and allowed to remain in contact, often under pressure overnight, until the desired depth of penetration is obtained. Impregnation is, therefore a special dip-staining process. It is often used to color pencil slats, logs (railroad ties), walking canes, musical instrument stock, and densified (colorant–resin impregnated) wood. Often antirot agents and other toxic materials are incorporated in impregnation stains. See also Wood.

Lacquer Coating Stains. These stains may be part of the lacquer, or they may be applied to the surface after the lacquer dries.

Spattering. Spattering is a special spraying process in which the air–stain dispersion is nonuniform, so that the stain is deposited in relatively large drops scattered irregularly over the surface. Very coarse sprays from a gun are used, although experienced operators can produce these effects by merely drawing a stick across a stiff brush wet with the stain. It is a method for obtaining irregularly spotted effects over uniformly colored grounds. Fast-drying stains are used in order to minimize any tendency for the scattered stain drops to spread, run, or streak.

Spatter Prints. Spatter prints are obtained by masking portions of the ground color with removable stencils before applying the spatter coating. The silhouettes obtained when the stencils are removed can then be further decorated. Sometimes the spattering is done with several stains of differing color, but, unless done with a knowledge of color harmony and considerable physical skill, the effect may not be attractive.

Flowing. Surfaces often can be colored by simply pouring on a liquid stain and letting the excess, unabsorbed stain drain off before drying. It is a convenient means of applying stains to test strips. It is the reverse of the dipping process, but it leaves the top surfaces of the object in the same draining condition as when removed from a dipping bath. It is useful for limiting the staining to but one surface or portion thereof in contrast to the overall staining obtained in regular dipping baths. It is most adaptable to coloring flat and convex surfaces. Usually the lower portions of the draining surfaces will appear more strongly colored than the upper portions when this process is used, because these portions receive more stain.

Infusion. This staining process is used for freshly cut flowers and logs. When clear, fluid stains are introduced into the capillaries and sap systems of flowers or logs, the stain is diffused throughout the plant or log. The butts of recently cut logs are submerged in a stain containing dyes and wood preservatives until infusion carries the stain through the plant system. The logs may then be sawed into planks and kiln-dried. Similarly, when freshly cut flowers are placed with their stems in a stain, usually a solution of a dye in water, the plants tend slowly to absorb it. Probably the most common application of this process is the production of the green-colored carnations (originally white) so popular for St. Patrick's day bouquets.

Fuming. This is the process of developing colored effects on surfaces by exposing the area to reactive gases. It was used even in ancient times for special wood color effects, particularly for fuming oak, by exposing the wood to smoke or ammonia fumes. Probably the latest modern adaptation of this process is the treatment of fabrics and other materials with dispersions of esters of leuco vat dyes, and then developing the color effects by "acid aging" with acetic or formic acid fumes.

Graining. Graining is done by master varnishers, who apply varnish stains in transparent films of uneven thickness over a light, opaque ground color to simulate the grain effect of wood; special tools are used for this purpose. For a more lightfast, but similar, effect a dispersion of insoluble pigments in drying oils (nonpenetrating oil stains) is first applied; graining tools or an artist's brush is used, and, when this application has dried thoroughly, an uncolored or colored transparent gloss varnish lacquer or other coating is applied. It is essentially a hand printing process.

Stippling. Stippling is also an effect obtained by deliberately uneven film applications. An opaque ground color is applied and dried, then a second coating or stain is applied, colored to harmonize or contrast with the ground color. This second coating is formulated with a vehicle that is slow to pick up or penetrate the ground coating and that also does not dry too quickly to permit stippling. The stippling is done either by rolling a special tool over the second coat or by patting it with a crushed or crumpled sheet stock.

Imbibition Printing. This is the contact process of transferring a stain from one gelatin film (photographic positive) to another (photographic color print). The stains used are usually dilute dye solutions in 2% acetic acid solution. A separate film is used to transfer each colorant. This process yields the brightest-colored photographic prints yet obtained. Not all water-soluble dyes will transfer under the processing conditions, and the hues of the dyes used must be selected for the particular effect desired; for example, a greenish-yellow dye is used if bright green effects predominate, and a reddish-yellow dye is preferable if attractive brown color effects are desired.

Transfers and Decalcomanias. These products produce many stainlike effects, even though they are not strictly classifiable as stains. They are usually print effects on thin sheet stocks or film, produced with stains composed of insoluble colorants and adhesives. When wet with suitable liquids and pressed against a surface, the colorants transfer and are glued to the new surface. The process is different in mechanism but gives much the same effect as imbibition printing.

Wiping. This is the process of applying "wiping stains" to a surface with a swab or mop, or the removal of excess stain by such means. This process is much used for staining and filling floors and similar large flat areas. Usually an excess of stain is applied and allowed to remain for 20 min or more to penetrate; then the excess stain is wiped off or absorbed. Solutions of oil-soluble dyes or pigment dispersions in drying oils are used as "oil stains." Sometimes these are thinned with hydrocarbons ("penetrating stains"), or they contain resins and waxes ("wax effect stains").

Filling. Filling is the application of a wiping stain having a relatively high content of insoluble colorants, and fillers or extenders. Although they produce colored effects, their principal function is to fill cracks, dents, pores, and scratches in surfaces. These filler stains generally are marketed with puttylike consistencies, and they are usually thinned out with boiled linseed oil, turpentine, or varnish before application.

Stain Polishing. This is the application of wiping stains of high wax content. With these stains the coloring effect is usually subordinate to that of the wax finish. Often only enough colorant is used to tint the wax, except in the case of the "scratch-eliminator" crayons, which are colored to match the principal wood colors. Polish stains are usually emulsions, and after application they may be buffed to improve the glossy appearance.

Bibliography

"Stains, Industrial," in *ECT* 1st ed., Vol. 12, pp. 722–740 by William H. Peacock, American Cyanamid Company.

1. American Association of Textile Chemists and Colorists, *1953 Technical Manual and Year Book*.
2. *Colour Index*, 2nd ed. (1956) and Suppl. (1963), Soc. Dyers Colourists, Bradford, England, and AATCC, U.S.A.
3. W. H. Peacock, "The Formulation and Uses of Stains" in Mattiello, *Protective and Decorative Coatings*, John Wiley & Sons, Inc., New York, Vol. 3, p. 769.

WILLIAM H. PEACOCK
American Cyanamid Company

STARCH

Starch has been known for several thousand years. The Romans called it *amylum*, a word which appears to have been derived from the Greek *amylon*. Starch was probably first separated from wheat flour or from other cereals known to the ancient world. In more recent times it has been produced from potatoes in Europe and Japan, from manihot (cassava or tapioca) roots and rice in the Orient, and from corn in the Americas.

Starch is the reserve carbohydrate of plants and therefore is found widely distributed in nature. The many botanical varieties and species yield starches which exhibit differences both in physical properties and chemical compositions. Those starches that are obtained from grains such as corn (maize) and sorghum, from roots and tubers such as tapioca, arrowroot, or potato, and from the pith of the stems of certain palms such as sago are of principal industrial importance. See also Wheat and other cereal grains.

Starch is a high-polymeric carbohydrate (see also Carbohydrates) composed of glucopyranose units joined together by α-glucosidic linkages. The approximate molecular formula is $(C_6H_{10}O_5)_n$ where n varies from a few hundred to over one million. Starch occurs in the form of white granules, usually made up of both a linear polymer (amylose) and a branched polymer (amylopectin). The granules are spherocrystals in which the two types of polymers are positioned radially. While much of the material is in an amorphous condition, there is sufficient crystallinity within the granules to make them insoluble in cold water and comparatively resistant to hydrolysis by enzymes.

Properties

PHYSICAL PROPERTIES

Starch granules from cereal grains vary between 3 and 30 μ with respect to the average size of their largest diameter, and those from roots and tubers between 10 and 100 μ; palm starches are medium large in size, having a diameter of about 50 μ. Most native granules are birefringent and show a characteristic cross-shaped shadow when viewed under polarized light. Granular starches give x-ray diffraction patterns which have been designated as A, B, and C types. Ordinary corn starch gives the A type; high-amylose corn starch and potato starch show the B type; sago and tapioca give a C-type x-ray pattern. High-amylose starches also show x-ray diffraction lines of the V or helical structure. Several reviews of the x-ray analysis of starches have been written (1–4).

Starch granules gelatinize in water when the temperature is raised into the 60–70°C range. As the temperature is raised further the granules swell progressively to form a paste or sol, and the shorter linear molecules dissolve. With gelatinization there is a loss of birefringence and a disintegration of the granule into molecules and starch granule fragments. The paste or sol may form a gel upon cooling, depending on the variety and concentration of the starch present. The best definition of gelatinization temperature is that point at which the granule loses birefringence when viewed under a polarizing microscope. Although an individual granule gelatinizes quite sharply, not all of the granules in a sample gelatinize at the same temperature, but rather over an 8–10°C range. Each starch has a characteristic gelatinization range. Schoch and Maywald (5) have given a detailed description of the method for measuring gelatinization temperatures, together with a list of such temperatures for various

Table 1. Gelatinization Ranges

Starch source	Temperatures, °C
wheat	58–64
potato	59–68
corn	62–72
sorghum	68–78
rice	68–78
high-amylose corn	67–>100

starches. In Table 1 gelatinization temperatures of some representative starches are given.

The temperature of gelatinization in water is altered by the addition of certain chemicals. Caustic alkalis, urea, and some amines lower the gelatinization temperature, and, if present in proper concentration, are solvents for starch even at room temperature. Formamide and dimethyl sulfoxide are examples of solvents which dissolve the starch granules at room temperature. Salts, such as sodium sulfate, repress gelatinization, probably by competing for the water present; they are added during some derivatization reactions to prevent swelling of the granules. Mullen and Pacsu (6) found that the heat of gelatinization varies from 5700 gal per glucose unit for the very small rice starch granule to 9080 cal per glucose unit for the relatively large potato starch granule. The value for corn starch is 7100 cal per glucose unit. (Gelatinization is a net endothermic process involving hydration of the starch molecules, separation of the starch molecules, and the rupture of some hydrogen bonds between glucose units.)

The organization of the granules may be disrupted by mechanical means, such as extensive grinding of the starch in the dry state. After rupture along certain lines of cleavage, the granule tends to gelatinize even in cold water. In this disrupted state the starch is more susceptible to the action of enzymes. Some granules are more fragile than others; for example, granules of potato starch are more easily disrupted than those of rice starch.

The most important colloidal characteristics of starch in aqueous dispersion or solution are clarity, color, rheology, gel strength, adhesive strength, and film-forming properties. Frequently the manufacturer sells various starch products according to specifications for these properties, which are graded on arbitrary scales. Some of the tests used in industry to measure these properties have been described (7,8).

Starch is an adsorbent for water. On exposure to moist air it assumes an equilibrium moisture content. The amount of water sorbed depends upon the temperature and relative humidity, and varies with the botanical origin of the starch. Under normal atmospheric conditions most starches contain 10–17% moisture. Like cellulose they give sigmoid sorption isotherms (see Vol. 4, p. 600), and adsorption-desorption cycles show a hysteresis effect; higher moisture content is reached when starch is equilibrated from a moist rather than from a dry state (9). The water contents of corn, tapioca, and potato starches in equilibrium with saturated vapor have been determined as 39.9, 42.9, and 50.9 g/100 g starch, respectively (9). By an indirect method, Leach has found that corn and potato starches will sorb, respectively, 42.8 and 56.7 g of water per 100 g of dry starch (10). Hydration of the dry starch granule causes reversible swelling, with an increase in diameter up to 9.1% for corn starch and 28.4% for tapioca starch.

Table 2. Physical Properties of Starches

Starch source	Heat of hydration, cal/g	Refractive index[a]	Density[b] (pycnometer), g/cm³	Density[c] (xylene displacement), g/cm³	Average granule diameter,[d] μ	Surface area[d] (from diameter), m²/g	Surface area[e] (by N₂ adsorption), m²/g
corn	25[a]	1.5222	1.490	1.517	13.9	0.288	0.70
wheat	25[f]	1.5245	1.500	1.542			
potato	28[f]	1.5135		1.511	41.3	0.0969	0.11
rice	26[g]	1.5219			5.25	0.767	

[a] Reference 11.	[c] Reference 13.	[e] Reference 15. [g] Reference 17.
[b] Reference 12.	[d] Reference 14.	[f] Reference 16.

Varying moisture content as well as methods of isolation and drying have marked effects on the physical properties of starch. Consequently, there are wide variations in some of the physical constants reported in the literature. In Table 2 are given representative values, believed to be the best available.

The specific heat of starch varies with the moisture content; an average value is 0.33 cal/g (11). The heat of combustion has been found to be between 4183 and 4228 cal/g (11). For cereal starches the specific rotation is $[\alpha]_D^{25} = +203°$ on a dry basis (18). It has been observed that both the amylose and amylopectin fractions of starch have a specific rotation of $+200°$ in water, but that the rotation falls to $+162°$ and $+163°$, respectively, in $1M$ sodium hydroxide solution (19). Both components show plain optical rotatory dispersion curves.

The infrared spectra of corn and potato starches and some of their derivatives have been published (20). For amylose the infrared spectrum has been analyzed and most of the absorption bands have been assigned (21).

CHEMICAL PROPERTIES

Most varieties of starch contain two types of polymers which differ in molecular weight and in chemical structure. The linear polymer, amylose, is comprised of long chains of D-glucose units joined by α-1,4-glucosidic bonds (see Fig. 1). The branched polymer, amylopectin, has, in addition to the normal chain of glucose units joined by α-1,4-linkages, side chains joined to the main chain by α-1,6-glucosidic bonds. The side chains may in turn have other side chains, resulting in a bush form of molecule (see Fig. 2). End-group analysis (methylation followed by hydrolysis) shows that 4% of the glucose units of amylopectin are at the end of chains. Thus, there is on the

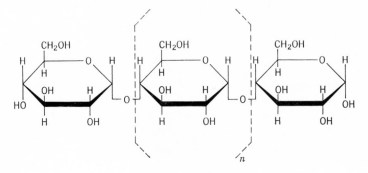

Fig. 1. Amylose molecule.

average a branch at one of every twenty-five glucose units. For both kinds of polymers there is only one hemiacetal reducing end per molecule.

The linear polymer and the longer branches of the nonlinear polymer show a pronounced tendency to orient and associate with each other. This property is characteristic of many threadlike molecules which contain a large number of hydroxyl or other hydrogen-bonding groups distributed along the chain length. Such attraction leads to highly associated areas within the starch granule.

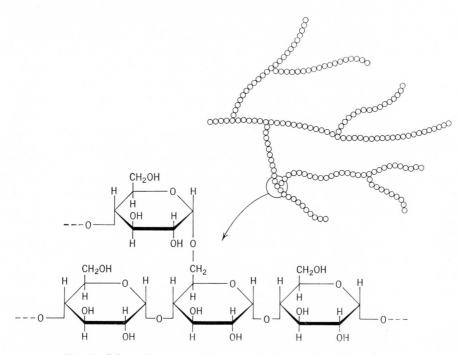

Fig. 2. Schematic representation of part of an amylopectin molecule.

Pastes or sols of starches, which contain the linear component (amylose), tend to form a gel or precipitate upon cooling. This phenomenon is called retrogradation and results from the association of the linear molecules. A three-dimensional gel network forms in more concentrated pastes and a white crystalline precipitate forms in dilute pastes. Pastes from starches which contain only the branched molecules (amylopectin) form weak gels at high starch concentration, and do not form precipitates in dilute solution. When gel formation occurs, it is caused by the association of the outer branched segments of the amylopectin molecules.

In structure amylopectin resembles glycogen, the reserve polysaccharide of animals, but it is not as highly branched. The starch of sweet corn, sometimes called phytoglycogen, is intermediate between amylopectin and glycogen in degree of branching (22). Most starches contain from 15 to 30% amylose; a few, such as those from waxy maize and waxy sorghum, show no amylose by the normal methods of detection. Some starches have been isolated with a much higher amylose percentage; a variety of wrinkled pea contains starch with over 60% amylose (23). Recently geneticists have developed new strains of corn with as much as 85% amylose. Some high-amylose corn is being grown for commercial starch production.

Both amylose and amylopectin exist in a broad range of molecular size, the amylopectin fractions generally being of higher molecular weight. The usual methods for determining molecular weight of polymers (see Vol. 16, p. 249) have been used with starches. End-group analysis or osmotic pressure values are used to calculate average molecular weights; light-scattering methods are used to determine weight-average molecular weight. In all cases great care must be employed to ensure that the molecular weight is not altered by the process used to dissolve the polymer. A summary of molecular weight data determined prior to 1955 has been prepared (24). Recent determinations have shown that both polymers are larger than was previously reported. The sizes depend on the source of the starch. The weight-average molecular weights, by light scattering, for amylose from corn and potato starches are 0.31×10^6 (25) and 1.9×10^6 (26), respectively; those for amylopectin from corn and potato are 1500×10^6 (27) and 315×10^6 (28), respectively.

An important property of starch, from an industrial standpoint, is the ease of hydrolysis of the bonds between glucose units by acids or enzymes. Acids may be used to hydrolyze (depolymerize) starch in either its native granule form or in gelatinized form, whereas enzymes (amylases) hydrolyze starch efficiently only in the swollen granule or paste state. Enzymes suitable for hydrolysis of starch are obtained from a variety of sources, such as bacteria, fungi, vegetables, and animals. The most common amylases fall into three broad classifications, depending on the nature of the hydrolysis which they promote. These are the α-amylases, β-amylases, and glucoamylases.

Like acids, α-amylases cause a more or less random cleavage of the starch molecule by hydrolyzing the α-D-$(1 \rightarrow 4)$ glucosidic bonds. Characteristic of this reaction is the rapid decrease in the viscosity of the starch dispersion with the very slow production of reducing sugars. Microbial α-amylases are used commercially to produce low-viscosity sizes, adhesives, and syrups from native starches. They are also used to remove starch warp sizes from textiles. The presence of α-amylases in the saliva and pancreatic juice of animals is necessary for digestion of the starch in their diet. In plants the α-amylase is generally associated with β-amylase. Such a mixture in malt amylase is of great value in the brewing, distilling, and baking industries for the conversion of starch into fermentable sugars.

Although pure β-amylase is too expensive to be used industrially, it is of considerable interest to research workers because of its ability to split the disaccharide maltose directly from the starch molecules. Hydrolysis is accomplished by the stepwise removal of maltose units from the nonreducing ends of the amylose and amylopectin. Amylose molecules are almost quantitatively hydrolyzed to maltose in this manner. Amylopectin molecules are hydrolyzed only to branch points in the molecule because the β-amylase cannot bypass the 1–6 glucosidic linkages present at these points. The residue which remains (β-amylase limit dextrin) is of comparatively high molecular weight and still contains the 1–6 glucosidic bonds which were present in the original starch molecule.

A third type of amylase, called glucoamylase, splits both kinds of starch molecules directly to the monosaccharide, D-glucose (dextrose). In both cases hydrolysis proceeds by the stepwise removal of glucose from nonreducing ends of the molecular chains. When an α-D-$(1 \rightarrow 6)$ linkage is encountered at a branch point in amylopectin, it is hydrolyzed at a much slower rate. An enzyme preparation, containing primarily glucoamylase activity, produced by a selected culture of *Aspergillus niger*, is used in the commercial production of dextrose (qv) (29). Pazur has reviewed the chemistry involved in the action of various enzymes on starch (30).

All starches are hydrolyzed by acid to D-glucose. In the past this reaction has been the commercial method for the production of dextrose and starch syrups (mixtures consisting of dextrose, maltose, and higher oligosaccharides). Today, enzymic methods are replacing all or part of the acid process because the economics are more favorable. In contrast with enzymes, acid penetrates the ungelatinized starch granule, causing hydrolysis at temperatures below those causing gelatinization of the starch. This fact is used in the manufacture of acid-modified (thin-boiling) starches (31). These are granular products which can be heated in water to give pastes of lower viscosity at a given concentration than those obtained from the native starch.

A number of side reactions may accompany the acid hydrolysis of starch. Glucose may recombine (reversion) to give various di- and polysaccharides or it may decompose into products such as 5-hydroxymethylfurfural and levulinic acid (32). Although alkaline solutions of starch are more stable than acidic ones, prolonged contact with alkali, particularly in the presence of oxygen, also leads to depolymerization of the molecule (33).

The alcohol groups in starch may be oxidized to form aldehyde, ketone, and carboxyl groups. The course of oxidation varies with the oxidant and conditions employed. The oxidation of starch with alkaline hypochlorite solution is one of the oldest industrial starch reactions (see below under Uses) (34). Incorrectly called chlorination, this reaction produces carboxyl groups along the starch molecule, as well as a small number of carbonyl groups. Hypochlorite oxidation also reduces the length of the molecules and increases their water solubility, particularly in dilute alkaline solution. Other oxidants, such as periodate, attack the adjacent secondary hydroxyl groups, converting them into aldehydes with rupture of the bond between carbons 2 and 3. The resulting commercial product is known as dialdehyde starch.

The hydroxyl groups in starch undergo the normal esterification and etherification reactions of alcohols. These reactions are discussed below under the preparation of starch derivatives (p. 685). A number of vinyl monomers have been used to form graft copolymers with starch. These grafts are usually attached to the starch through radicals generated at the starch hydroxyls. None of the graft copolymers appears to have found practical use. The alcohol groups in starch react with aldehydes under acidic conditions, by a condensation reaction in which crosslinks are very likely formed between adjacent starch molecules. The resultant product is nondispersible in water. Other bifunctional reagents, such as acrolein, epichlorohydrin, and phosphorus oxychloride, react to give similar derivatives. If the degree of crosslinking is kept to a very low level (one crosslink per several hundred glucose units), the products will gelatinize to give pastes of increased viscosity and resistance to shear and to acid thinning (35).

Starch, or more particularly the amylose fraction of starch, reacts characteristically with iodine to form a blue-colored helical inclusion complex. This iodine test is used in food analysis as a test for unconverted starch.

The aldehyde group in the starch molecule is reducible. Catalytic hydrogenation, particularly in the presence of a small amount of acid, causes hydrogenolysis to form the polyhydric alcohol, sorbitol (see Alcohols, polyhydric) (32).

Manufacture

The raw material for most starch manufacture in the United States is dent corn, a type of *Zea mays*. The whole grain normally contains 15–20% moisture and about 70% dry-basis starch. The balance consists of protein, oil, fiber, minerals, and low-molecular-weight water-soluble constituents. If a corn kernel is cut in half, lengthwise, it appears much like the drawing in Figure 3. The corn grain is comprised of four regions: the outer covering is known as the hull or pericarp; the germ, containing most of the oil, is located toward the tip end of the grain; the horny endosperm, a mixture of gluten—the substance containing most of the corn protein—and starch, is found bulging in toward the center of the kernel; the floury endosperm is the white starchy part extending from the top of the kernel down around the germ. The starch is separated from the other components in the process called wet milling.

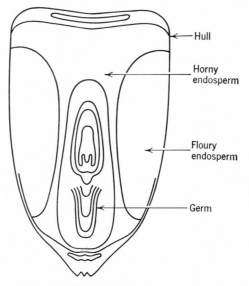

Fig. 3. Schematic drawing of longitudinal bisection of a corn kernel.   Courtesy Corn Industries Research Foundation.

PRODUCTION OF UNMODIFIED CORN STARCH BY WET MILLING

The starch located in the floury endosperm consists of large, round granules associated with a relatively small amount of protein. Separation of these granules in the milling process offers no serious problem. Smaller, polygonally shaped granules are tightly held in a water-insoluble protein matrix in the horny endosperm region. The hydration and disintegration of the protein in order to loosen the starch, the separation of the starch from the finely dispersed protein, and the accomplishment of these ends without damaging the more fragile granules of the floury region constitute the chief problems in milling. An excellent description of the modern practices has been given by S. A. Watson (36). This wet-milling process separates the four main parts of corn—germ, hull, gluten, and starch—in that order (see Fig. 4).

Shelled grain is prepared for milling in cleaners where air currents blow out light chaff, and screens and magnets remove heavier pieces of foreign material. The cleaned corn is softened by soaking (steeping) for 30–50 hr in warm (50°C) water

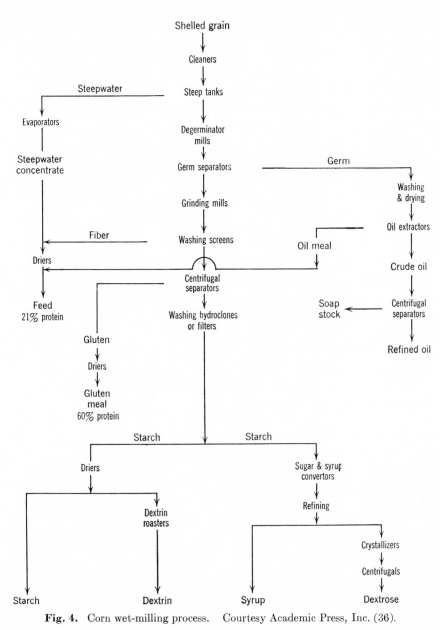

Fig. 4. Corn wet-milling process.   Courtesy Academic Press, Inc. (36).

acidified with sulfur dioxide to a pH of 3 to 4.   The dilute sulfurous acid controls bacterial fermentation and aids in the disintegration of the protein matrix so that starch and other components can be separated more easily.   During steeping, the water content of the grain increases to 45%.

The softened kernels are separated from the steepwater and then coarsely ground with water from degerminating or attrition mills.   These mills tear the kernels apart, freeing the germ and loosening the hull.   Care must be taken to minimize breaking the rubbery germ, for if oil is liberated from the germ at this step, it is absorbed by the gluten and is not recovered.   The lighter germ floats to the surface where it is easily

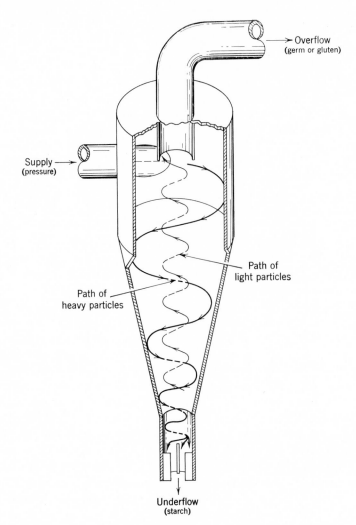

Fig. 5. Cutaway diagram of Hydroclone separator.   Courtesy Dorr-Oliver Inc., Stamford, Connecticut.

removed from the other particles. Separation was formerly accomplished in flotation troughs, but most modern plants use hydroclone separations (Fig. 5) with the germ passing out in the overflow (37). The remaining mixture of starch, gluten, and hulls passes out in the underflow.

The starch-containing mixture is next finely ground in steel mills of special design. An attrition mill with special impact ring (38,39), or an impact-type mill known as the Entoleter (40), may be used. In the latter, slurry dropped onto the rotating horizontal disc is spun with great force against both rotating and stationary pins. The coarser fiber particles are then removed by a screening operation. This is accomplished by passing the slurry over sieves made of metal or nylon fabric and supported on vibrating or rotating frames, or by pumping the slurry over static screens of special design (41).

The mixture of starch and gluten which passes through the sieves as a slurry must still be separated; in most starch factories continuous centrifuges are used to accomplish this separation. These machines, operating on the principle of a cream separator, eject the heavier starch granules at the periphery of the centrifuge bowl while the lighter gluten particles flow out at the center (43).

After separation from the gluten, the starch is filtered and washed or passed through washing hydroclones as in Figure 5 (44). At this point it may be dried and packaged for market, or converted to specialty starches, dextrins, syrups, or dextrose. Drying is accomplished first by dewatering on a drum filter or basket centrifuge. Then it may be dried on a moving belt that carries the starch through chambers of warm circulating air (45). More rapid drying is provided by a flash dryer where the filter cake is injected into a stream of heated air. Several flash dryer arrangements have been described by Baunack (46). The new continuous processes developed for starch factories lend themselves to control by instrumentation. These operations in closed equipment permit maintenance of the high level of sanitation required for food processing.

Water is used according to countercurrent principle in the wet milling and steeping of corn. The only fresh water entering the system contacts the starch in the last hydroclone washing stage, just before drying or conversion. The filtrate from the first washing is used to slurry the starch for the next-to-last washing step. Water works its way back through the washing and milling steps, increasing the solubles content until it is used for the steeping operation. In the process it is diluted and reconcentrated until its solids level is 0.10–0.20% before being used for steeping.

The by-products of the refining process are of economic importance. The steepwater (see Fig. 4) which contains proteins, minerals, and carbohydrates is used as a nutrient for the molds which produce penicillin and other antibiotics. The steepwater is normally mixed with hulls and oil meal and dried to give corn gluten feed.

Corn oil is extracted from the germ by mechanical and solvent processes. The oil is refined for use as a cooking or salad dressing oil. The gluten is dried and ground into meal for use as an ingredient of high-protein poultry feed. Although commercial yield figures are not available for the wet-milling process, Watson (36) has estimated yields, based on the recalculation of laboratory results (see Table 3).

The manufacture of starch from milo is almost identical to the wet-milling process for corn. Manufacture of potato starch, which has been important in Europe for many years, is growing in the United States. Modern potato starch plants use rasp or

Table 3. Yield of Products from Corn Grain After Wet Milling

Products	Yield, % dry basis
Intermediates	
starch	68.5
gluten	5.8
germ	7.3
solubles	7.6
fiber	9.5
End products	
starch	68.5
feed	25.9
oil	4.3

hammer mills to disintegrate the potatoes in water containing sulfur dioxide. Centrifugal sieves separate fibrous material, while centrifugal separators are used to wash and concentrate the starch. Dewatering is effected by vacuum filters and flash or rotary dryers.

Starch products are merchandised in the dry state in several physical forms: *pearl*, which is roughly ground starch as received directly from the dryers; *powder*, which is made by grinding and passing the starch through fine sieves; *lump*, which is flash-dried starch made up of aggregates of 25–100 granules; and *pregelatinized products*, which are precooked and dried by the manufacturer.

PRODUCTION OF MODIFIED STARCHES

Before the final dewatering operation, the starch slurry may be modified with chemical reagents at temperatures below the gelatinization point. The most important products are the thin-boiling starches, which are made by a partial hydrolysis with acid, and the oxidized starches, which are made by treating the starch with hypochlorite. In making thin-boiling starches, the starch is suspended in about $0.1N$ sulfuric acid at 50°C for 6–24 hr, depending on the extent of modification or fluidity desired. The action is stopped by the addition of sodium carbonate, and the product is filtered, washed, and dried. The effects of variations in the procedure have been reviewed (31).

Manufacture of oxidized starches consists essentially of the addition of predetermined quantities of sodium hypochlorite to the aqueous starch slurry. Alkali is added to maintain the pH at 8–10 throughout the reaction, and cooling is used to maintain the temperature in the desired range, usually 21–38°C. The amount of hypochlorite added is usually equivalent to between 0.5 and 6.0% available chlorine, based on starch, and is determined by the fluidity grade of starch to be made. The more reagent added, the less will be the viscosity of the starch when gelatinized. Following a reaction period of 5–24 hr, the slurry is neutralized and any free chlorine present is destroyed with sodium bisulfite. The starch is washed on continuous vacuum filters or centrifugal devices to remove soluble by-products before it is collected on vacuum filters and dried. Production and uses of oxidized starches have been reviewed (34).

Dextrins are made by heating, with or without the addition of chemical reagents. The resultant *pyrodextrins*, or *torrefaction dextrins*, are classified into three groups, depending on the amount of modification. The *British gums* are prepared by heating starch with agitation for 10–20 hr at 170–195°C. The products have a buff to brown color. Sometimes alkaline materials, such as sodium bicarbonate or ammonia, are added before pyrolysis. *White dextrins* are prepared by spraying a powdered starch with acid, usually dilute hydrochloric acid, before it is heated at 95–120°C for 3–8 hr (47,48). The use of less acid and more strenuous conditions (150–180°C for 6–18 hr) produces the *yellow* or *canary dextrins*.

SPECIFICATIONS

Specifications of starch and starch products relate to purity and the extent of modification, if any, of the high polymer. Common impurities are ash, protein, lipids, as well as cold-water extractives remaining in the starch. Excessive moisture may also be included in the list. Thus, for unmodified corn starch maximal limits may be: moisture, 12%; ash, 0.1%; protein, 0.4%; lipids (total of ether-extractable material as well as adsorbed fatty acids), 0.90%; and cold-water extractives, 0.2%. Modified starch products such as dextrins are often sold at lower moisture contents of

5–10%. The amount of water-soluble material may increase to very high values as starch is modified. Thus, a dextrin may be almost completely water soluble; this solubility test may be used to determine the extent of the reaction, and specifications set accordingly.

Pure starch is white, and off-colors are the result of extraneous materials such as ether-extractives and gluten. Since the color of starch is frequently improved by bleaching procedures, independent specifications may be set up, based on the degree of whiteness in reference to some standard such as magnesium oxide. Methods for making this comparison, as well as the other specification tests, have been described by Smith (8).

Because most starch applications involve the use of cooked pastes, the consistency of such pastes is of great importance. A number of different procedures have been devised based on rotational devices and flow-through orifices. Unfortunately, starch manufacturers do not all use the same methods of testing. The most commonly used methods have been described (8), and of these the Scott test for hot-paste consistency is worthy of note. This test is performed by mixing a suitable amount of starch with 280 ml of water in a metal beaker and then immersing the beaker in boiling water. After this mixture has been stirred and heated under specified conditions, it is transferred to a Scott viscosity cup. The number of seconds required for the delivery of the first 100 ml of paste is taken as the Scott viscosity. A sample weight is taken that will give a cooked paste delivering 100 ml in 40–80 sec.

Unmodified corn starch should have a minimum Scott test of 40 sec/100 ml at a concentration of 12 g/280 ml. Modified starches, such as acid-hydrolyzed and oxidized, have lesser Scott values. These viscometric tests are used by the manufacturer to control the extent of modification. Modified starches are generally classified according to fluidity number, an inverse measure of viscosity (49). It is determined on an arbitrary scale for commercial starches of from 10 to 90, the lower the viscosity the higher the fluidity. Unmodified corn starch, gelatinized at a concentration of 5 g in 100 ml of 1% sodium hydroxide solution at 25°C, has a fluidity of one; water on this arbitrary scale has a fluidity of 100.

General Economics

In the U.S. corn is the largest grain crop, and corn starch is the principal industrial starch. Annual world production of corn for 1967 was 9.3 billion bushels, of which the U.S. produced 4.7 billion bushels. (There is approximately 70 lb of corn per bushel.) Of the total annual U.S. corn production, wet millers grind about 5% to produce approximately 2.6 billion lb of starch to be sold as such and nearly 4.1 billion additional

Table 4. Annual U.S. Shipments of Products from the Corn-Wet Milling Industry, million lb (52)

Year	Starch (all types)	Derived from starch			Corn by-products		
		Corn syrup	Corn sugar	Corn sugar molasses (hydrol)[a]	Corn oil	Corn gluten feed and meal	Steepwater (50% solids)
1960	2,128	1,990	870	273	281	2,188	53
1962	2,341	2,356	927	276	303	2,438	46
1964	2,495	2,799	1,049	351	367	2,699	68
1966	2,756	2,947	1,081	270	351	2,912	94

[a] See Vol. 13, p. 624.

pounds to make products such as dextrins, syrups, and dextrose (see also Dextrose and starch syrups).

The price of unmodified corn starch averaged 6¢/lb in bulk during 1954–1959 (50). However, severe competition within the wet-milling industry resulted in price cuts, and in 1968 fob prices for pearl starch were quoted as low as 4.15¢/lb in bulk and 4.45¢/lb in 100-lb bags (51). The prices for pregelatinized, acid-modified, and oxidized starches usually average 1–2¢/lb more than unmodified starch. Annual shipments of corn starch and related products are given in Table 4.

Potato starch is manufactured in Europe, Japan, and some sections of America. It is estimated that 125–150 million lb of potato starch and a similar amount of wheat starch are manufactured in the United States each year. Tapioca starch is manufactured principally in Thailand and Brazil; approximately 300 million lb are imported by the United States annually.

Uses

About 60% of the corn starch produced in the U.S., roughly 4 billion lb each year, is used to make a variety of sugar products by hydrolysis with acids and enzymes. The principal products are corn syrup solids, glucose syrup, and the refined sugar, D-glucose, more often referred to as dextrose (qv).

In addition to this captive use, another 2.6 billion lb of starch is shipped to other users. Approximately half of the starch shipped is unmodified starch, and the balance is modified starch and starch derivatives. The largest customers for these products are the paper and related industries that consume between 1 and 1.5 billion lb of starch products each year. The next largest markets for starches are the textile sizing and food industries which require 350–400 million lb per year each. Other consumers utilize starch as a binder for pills, for sand core foundry molds, for wallboard and ceiling tiles, for briquets, and for explosives (see Vol. 8, p. 601). Starch is also used as a laundry size, as a flocculant in the mining industry, and in the manufacture of adhesives.

Unmodified corn starch is used primarily in the food industries for the preparation of pies, puddings, salad dressings, and confections. A substantial amount is also sold to manufacturers who modify the starch into intermediate products by means of enzymes. The brewing trade converts starch into fermentable sugars by means of malt enzymes. The paper and textile industries liquefy starch with α-amylases and use it in the preparation of various sizes and adhesives.

Pregelatinized starch products are employed for such varied uses as the sizing of paper pulp at the beaters, the preparation of adhesives used in the manufacture of corrugated paperboard (see Paper) and the preparation of instant food products such as puddings. They also prevent the loss of water from the drilling muds used in the drilling of oil wells (see Drilling fluids).

Modified Starches. Thin-boiling starches, obtained by the acid modification of granular starch, are used primarily by the textile industry. The lower-fluidity grades are used to size yarn warps before the weaving operation. The higher-fluidity grades are used in finishing various woven fabrics and as laundry starches. In addition, certain thin-boiling starches are confectioners' starches for gumdrops, fruit slices, and jelly beans. Fluidity grades of 40 to 60 are commonly used for this purpose.

Oxidized starches, prepared by treatment of granular starch with alkaline hypochlorite, are noted for giving clear stable pastes which resist gelling. They are used primarily by the paper industry. Lower-fluidity oxidized starches are used as textile warp sizes and in textile finishes.

Dextrins and British gums are used in a great variety of adhesive applications (48). Because their pastes give lower viscosities than those from raw starches, they can be used at higher concentrations, giving films which dry rapidly with fast tack. They are used for envelope and labeling adhesives; as adhesives for postage stamps, gummed tape, and cardboard boxes; and in many of the other binding and sizing applications given above under Unmodified corn starch.

Source of Organic Chemicals. Starch and its conversion products could provide an almost inexhaustible source of raw materials for the manufacture of organic chemicals. However, with current petroleum prices, starch is at an economic disadvantage for the production of compounds that are essentially hydrocarbons. This is due to the large weight loss sustained when it is necessary to reduce the high ratio of hydroxyl groups to carbon atoms present in the starch monomer unit, glucose. Starch is on a more equal footing as a source of hydroxylated compounds. In more recent years sorbitol (see Alcohols, polyhydric), gluconic acid, glucoheptonic acid, and methyl glucoside have been prepared.

Derivatives

The D-glucose units in starch contain, on the average, one primary and two secondary alcohol groups. Derivatives, mainly ethers and esters, are formed by reaction at the hydroxyl groups. In most commercially available starch derivatives only a small number of hydroxyl groups are substituted. The degree of substitution (DS) is the average number of substituents per glucose unit. Thus, an ester with a DS of 1.0 has, on the average, one substituent for each glucose unit; maximum possible DS is 3.0. Many derivatives in which the DS is less than one are water soluble and resemble the natural gums in colloidal properties. The introduction of a relatively small number of substituents, on the order of one for every twenty-five glucose units, may profoundly alter the colloidal properties of the starch when it is dispersed in water. Of these properties, increased clarity of the aqueous sol, decreased tendency to form a gel, and improved film-forming ability are of the greatest industrial importance. Highly derivatized starch ethers and esters, those with a DS approaching the range of 2 to 3, are relatively insoluble in water, but are soluble in many organic solvents; they are often thermoplastic. A voluminous patent literature exists on the art of starch derivatization, the basic patents of which have been summarized (53). See also Cellulose derivatives, Vol. 4, p. 616.

Industrially, the more important starch derivatives are those in which the degree of substitution is of a relatively low order (less than 0.1) and the product is in a cold-water-insoluble, granular state. These are made with reagents capable of acting on starch in an aqueous slurry or in a semidry state. It is common practice to add a derivatizing agent to starch slurried in water containing an alkaline catalyst and a salt, usually sodium chloride or sodium sulfate, to inhibit swelling of the granules. The slurry is stirred at some temperature below the gelatinization point until reaction is complete. An alternative method consists of heating starch containing 5–20% moisture with a reagent at temperatures as high as 150°C to give low to intermediate DS products which retain the granular structure. The cost of chemical reagents for making products of higher DS and the cost of using nonaqueous media have restricted the use of the highly substituted derivatives in markets served by competitive products.

STARCH ACETATE (54)

One of the first commercial derivatives of starch to be marketed was a low-DS acetate sold under the trade name Feculose (55). Beginning in 1905, this product was manufactured in England by a semidry process in which starch containing about 5% moisture was heated with glacial acetic acid at 90–120°C for several hours. Although the starch molecules were partially depolymerized, the product could be washed in cold water. It was used as a substitute for gelatin and natural gums in paper and textile sizing and as a confectionery thickener.

The current practice in the United States is to manufacture low-DS acetates (up to 0.2 DS) by an aqueous slurry reaction. To the starch suspended in water are added simultaneously acetic anhydride and sufficient 3% sodium hydroxide solution to maintain the pH in the 8.0 to 8.4 range (56,57). An alternative acetylating agent is vinyl acetate (58). The products have lower gelatinization temperatures than the parent starch and give clear, stable sols with little tendency to form gels. It is believed that in both esterification and etherification of starch the introduction of a relatively small number of substituent groups along the starch molecules prevents these molecules from orienting and associating into aggregates. Association abnormally increases the viscosity of starch sols with age, involves gelation effects, or produces turbidity. Lowering of the gelatinization temperature is of particular value with high-amylose starches, which are so highly associated that they do not gelatinize on cooking in boiling water.

Like acetates of lower-molecular-weight alcohols, starch acetates are unstable at high pH or low pH and tend to hydrolyze to regenerate the parent starch. Specifications usually prescribe a certain percent acetyl. This is determined from the amount of alkali consumed in the hydrolysis of the ester (57).

Starch acetates are being used by the food, paper, and textile industries. At the present time, FDA regulations permit up to 2.5% acetyl content in starches used in foods (59). Derivatives with 0.5–2.5% acetyl are used as food thickeners because they give clear sols which do not change in viscosity and texture when stored for prolonged periods of time, even if at low temperatures. To improve their viscosity stability under conditions of high temperature, high shear, and low pH, the acetates are often crosslinked with bifunctional reagents such as epichlorohydrin or acrolein. Producers of baby foods and fruit and cream pie fillings are among the users of such starches. In the paper industry, the major use of starch acetates is in surface sizing. Here they give improved printability and lower surface porosity with better abrasion and solvent resistance. The textile industry uses starch acetates in the warp sizing of synthetic fiber blends and polyester–cotton blends where it protects the fibers from the abrasion of the weaving process. Acetates prepared from high-amylose starch are also used to size glass fibers. Since films prepared from high-amylose starch acetates are both water soluble and edible, they have enjoyed some use for packaging materials where the wrapper is to be dissolved in water or eaten.

STARCH PHOSPHATES (60)

Potato starch is a naturally occurring phosphate derivative containing 0.06–0.10% phosphorus present as dihydrogen orthophosphate esters. One type of commercial starch phosphate, containing from 0.35 to 2.5% bound phosphorus, is prepared by heating a dry mixture of starch and sodium tripolyphosphate (61,62) or an orthophosphate (63–65). In a typical reaction, a solution of the phosphate is sprayed onto

$$\text{starch—OH} + \text{Na}_5\text{P}_3\text{O}_{10} \rightarrow \text{starch—OPO}_3\text{Na}_2 + \text{Na}_3\text{HP}_2\text{O}_7$$
$$\text{starch—OH} + \text{NaH}_2\text{PO}_4 \rightarrow \text{starch—OPO}_3\text{HNa} + \text{H}_2\text{O}$$

starch with good mixing. The mixture is dried to 10% moisture before it is heated at 120–140°C for an hour. Variations in time, temperature, and pH are used to give products of varying fluidities. The inorganic salts may be left in the product or removed by washing.

Starch phosphates are anionic polyelectrolytes. At DS levels as low as 0.01 the starch phosphates give pastes with increased viscosity and clarity over that of the parent starch. As with other polyelectrolytes, salts reduce the paste viscosity. The products are used mainly as thickeners in the food industry. Because phosphation of the starch to a low degree of substitution improves the freeze-thaw stability of starch pastes, starch phosphates are particularly useful as thickeners in frozen foods and pie fillings.

Another class of starch phosphates is obtained when starch is treated with sodium trimetaphosphate (66) or phosphorus oxychloride (67). These reagents crosslink the starch molecules, giving distarch esters. Such cross-bonded derivatives are used

$$2 \text{ starch—OH} + \text{Na}_3\text{P}_3\text{O}_9 \rightarrow (\text{starch—O})_2\text{PO}_2\text{Na} + \text{Na}_2\text{H}_2\text{P}_2\text{O}_7$$

where stability to shear and acid thinning are important in food starches. FDA approval for starch phosphate formed by the reaction of starch with sodium tripolyphosphate plus sodium trimetaphosphate permits up to 0.4% phosphorus in the derivative (59).

HYDROXYALKYL STARCH ETHERS (68)

Since 1950 hydroxyethyl starch of a low degree of substitution (0.05–0.1 DS) has been prepared commercially. Annual rate of production exceeds 100 million lb/yr.

The low-DS hydroxyethyl starch sells for 8–9¢/lb and the hydroxypropyl derivative sells for about 13¢/lb. In the wet process of manufacture (69,70) a 40–45% slurry of starch in water is made alkaline (pH 11–12) by the addition of an alkali metal or alkaline earth metal hydroxide; a salt is added to prevent gelatinization. After the addition of the required amount of ethylene oxide or propylene oxide, the mixture is stirred in a closed vessel for 24–48 hr at temperatures below 50°C. The slurry is acidified to about pH 6 before the solid is collected and washed with water. The maximum practical degree of substitution by this method is about 0.1, since greater substitution causes the granules to swell so much that they cannot be filtered and washed readily.

Hydroxyethyl starch can also be prepared by the reaction of air-dried starch with ethylene oxide gas in the presence of a catalyst (71,72). Although the product obtained from the reaction of ethylene oxide with starch is called hydroxyethyl starch, some polyoxyethyl groups are formed as well, particularly at higher degrees of substitution. Their formation is indicated by the following equations.

$$\text{starch—OH} + \text{H}_2\text{C} \overset{\text{O}}{\overbrace{\quad\quad}} \text{CH}_2 \rightarrow \text{starch—OCH}_2\text{CH}_2\text{OH}$$

$$\text{starch—OCH}_2\text{CH}_2\text{OH} + n\,\text{H}_2\text{C} \overset{\text{O}}{\overbrace{\quad\quad}} \text{CH}_2 \rightarrow \text{starch—O(CH}_2\text{CH}_2\text{O})_n\text{CH}_2\text{CH}_2\text{OH}$$

Like starch acetate, hydroxyalkyl starches show several improved properties over unmodified starch. They have lower gelatinization temperatures and faster granule swelling and dispersion on cooking in water. Their pastes show better clarity and cohesiveness with less tendency to gel on cooling and aging. In addition to these properties, which they share with starch acetate, they are more stable to cleavage by acids and alkalis since they are ethers rather than esters. Because of this they can be acid-modified without losing the substituent groups, and they can be used in alkaline media.

Hydroxyethyl starches are widely used in the paper industry for coating and sizing where they impart strength, stiffness, and surface smoothness. They are used as adhesives for clay coatings on paper where the good viscosity stability of their pastes gives desirable flow properties. A combination of hydroxyethyl starch and glyoxal gives improved water-resistance properties to paper clay coatings (73). The derivatives are also used as textile warp sizes. Although hydroxyethyl starches are not approved for food use, FDA regulations permit the use of hydroxypropyl starches as food additives (59). These hydroxypropyl derivatives are being used in pie fillings and salad dressings.

CATIONIC STARCHES (74)

Cationic starches are a class of specialty derivatives which have attained commercial importance since the early 1960s. The products now available fall into two types, tertiary aminoalkyl ethers and quaternary ammonium alkyl ethers. The tertiary amine derivatives are manufactured by the reaction of an alkaline starch slurry with 2-dimethylaminoethyl chloride (75).

$$\text{starch—OH} + \text{ClCH}_2\text{CH}_2\text{N(CH}_3)_2 + \text{NaOH} \rightarrow \text{starch—OCH}_2\text{CH}_2\text{N(CH}_3)_2 + \text{NaCl} + \text{H}_2\text{O}$$

These tertiary amine derivatives must be treated with acid to convert them to the cationic tertiary ammonium salts. Production of a quaternary ammonium starch ether is accomplished by the reaction of an alkaline starch slurry with N-(2,3-epoxy-propyl)-trimethylammonium chloride (76). Both products are prepared by heating

$$\text{starch—OH} + \text{H}_2\overset{\text{O}}{\overset{\diagup\diagdown}{\text{C}}}\!\!-\!\!-\text{CHCH}_2\overset{+}{\text{N}}(\text{CH}_3)_3 + \text{Cl}^- \rightarrow \text{starch—OCH}_2\text{CHOHCH}_2\overset{+}{\text{N}}(\text{CH}_3)_3 + \text{Cl}^-$$

the reactants at 40–50°C in a slurry at pH 11–12 with salt added to prevent gelatinization. The mixture is acidified to about pH 6 before the solid is isolated by filtration.

Commercial cationic products have a DS from 0.02 to 0.05. The presence of tertiary amine or quaternary ammonium groups lowers the gelatinization temperature in proportion to the degree of substitution. The hot paste viscosity of the tertiary amine derivatives is higher than that of the parent starch but not as high as that for the quaternary ammonium derivatives. Both derivatives give pastes with reduced paste retrogradation tendency. This is due to the forces of repulsion between the cationic groups. For quaternary ammonium derivatives, cold water swelling begins at about 0.07 DS in contrast to a DS of 0.2–0.3 required for cold water swelling of hydroxyethyl starch. These products show affinity for negatively charged substrates such as cellulose, some synthetic fibers, and aqueous suspensions of minerals.

Cationic starches are used principally as internal binders in the manufacture of paper. They are added to the paper furnish before the sheet is formed. Since a cationic starch is three to four times as effective as underivatized starch in improving paper strength, it can be used at correspondingly lower levels (74). Cationic starch binders have the added advantage that they aid in the retention of the mineral fillers used in the manufacture of paper. A second use of cationic starch in the paper industry is as an emulsifying agent for water-repellent sizes. The sizing agent, emulsified in water with gelatinized cationic starch, is added to the cellulose fibers before the paper sheet is formed. A third application for cationic starches in paper manufacture involves their use as paper-coating binders. Acid-thinned or dextrinized cationic starches can be made compatible with paper-coating colors, and in the presence of insolubilizers such as glyoxal they impart wet-rub resistance to the coatings (77).

Production figures for cationic starches are not available. It is estimated that annual production exceeds 25 million lb of products selling in the 10–20¢/lb price range.

Bibliography

"Starch" in *ECT* 1st ed., Vol. 12, pp. 764–778, by R. W. Kerr, Corn Products Refining Company.

1. D. French, "Physical Properties of Starch," in R. W. Kerr, ed., *Chemistry and Industry of Starch*, 2nd ed., Academic Press, Inc., New York, 1950, Chap. 7.
2. H. F. Zobel, "X-ray Analysis of Starch Granules," in R. L. Whistler, ed., *Methods in Carbohydrate Chemistry*, Vol. 4, Academic Press, Inc., New York, 1964, Chap. 29.
3. R. H. Marchessault and A. Sarko, *Advan. Carbohydrate Chem.* **22** (**1967**), 421.
4. B. Zaslow, "Crystalline Nature of Starch," in R. L. Whistler and E. F. Paschall, eds., *Starch: Chemistry and Technology*, Vol. 1, Academic Press, Inc., New York, 1965, Chap. 11.
5. T. J. Schoch and E. C. Maywald, "Industrial Microscopy of Starches," in R. L. Whistler and E. F. Paschall, eds., *Starch: Chemistry and Technology*, Vol. 2, Academic Press, Inc., New York, 1967, Chap. 26.
6. J. W. Mullen and E. Pacsu, *Ind. Eng. Chem.* **34**, 807 (1942).
7. R. W. Kerr, *Chemistry and Industry of Starch*, 2nd ed., Academic Press, Inc., New York, 1950, Chaps. 6 and 24.
8. R. J. Smith, "Characterization and Analysis of Starches," in R. W. Whistler and E. F. Paschall, eds., *Starch: Chemistry and Technology*, Vol. 2, Academic Press, Inc., New York, 1967, Chap. 25.
9. N. N. Hellman, T. F. Boesch, and E. H. Melvin, *J. Am. Chem. Soc.* **74**, 348 (1952).
10. H. W. Leach, "Gelatinization of Starch," in R. L. Whistler and E. F. Paschall, eds., *Starch: Chemistry and Technology*, Vol. 1, Academic Press, Inc., New York, 1965, Chap. 12.
11. M. Samec, *Kolloidchemie der Stärke*, Steinkopff, Leipzig, 1927.
12. R. J. Smith, "Determination of Absolute Density," in R. L. Whistler, ed., *Methods in Carbohydrate Chemistry*, Vol. 4, Academic Press, Inc., New York, 1964, Chap. 27.
13. H. W. Leach and T. J. Schoch, *Cereal Chem.* **38**, 40 (1961).
14. E. Hanssen, E. Dodt, and E. G. Niemann, *Kolloid-Z.* **130**, 19 (1953).
15. N. N. Hellman and E. H. Melvin, *J. Am. Chem. Soc.* **72**, 5186 (1950).
16. F. Schierbaum and K. Taeufel, *Staerke* **14**, 233 (1962).
17. W. G. Schrenk, A. C. Andrews, and H. H. King, *Ind. Eng. Chem.* **39**, 113 (1947).
18. R. J. Dimler, "Determination of Optical Rotation," in R. L. Whistler, ed., *Methods in Carbohydrate Chemistry*, Vol. 4, Academic Press, Inc., New York, 1964, Chap. 32.
19. W. B. Neely, *J. Org. Chem.* **26**, 3015 (1961).
20. J. R. van der Bij and W. F. Vogel, *Staerke* **14**, 113 (1962).
21. H. G. Higgins, C. M. Stewart, and K. J. Harrington, *J. Polymer Sci.* **51**, 59 (1961).
22. I. A. Wolff, P. R. Watson, and C. E. Rist, *J. Am. Chem. Soc.* **75**, 4897 (1953).
23. A. L. Potter, V. Silvera, R. M. McCready, and H. S. Owens, *J. Am. Chem. Soc.* **75**, 1335 (1953).
24. C. T. Greenwood, *Advan. Carbohydrate Chem.* **11** (**1956**), 335.
25. E. M. Montgomery, K. R. Sexson, and F. R. Senti, *Staerke* **13**, 215 (1961).
26. P. J. Killion and J. F. Foster, *J. Polymer Sci.* **46**, 65 (1960).
27. F. R. Senti, "High-Amylose Corn Starch: Its Production, Properties, and Uses," in R. L. Whistler and E. F. Paschall, eds., *Starch: Chemistry and Technology*, Vol. 2, Academic Press, Inc., New York, 1967, Chap. 21.
28. S. R. Erlander and R. Tobin, *Makromol. Chem.* **111**, 212 (1968).
29. U. S. Pat. 3,012,944 (Dec. 12, 1961), F. C. Armbruster (to Corn Products Co.).

30. J. H. Pazur, "Enzymes in Synthesis and Hydrolysis of Starch," in R. L. Whistler and E. F. Paschall, eds., *Starch: Chemistry and Technology*, Vol. 1, Academic Press, Inc., New York, 1965, Chap. 7.

31. P. Shildneck and C. E. Smith, "Production and Uses of Acid-Modified Starch," in R. L. Whistler and E. F. Paschall, eds., *Starch: Chemistry and Technology*, Vol. 2, Academic Press, Inc., New York, 1967, Chap. 9.

32. J. N. BeMiller, "Acid Hydrolysis and Other Lytic Reactions of Starch," in R. L. Whistler and E. F. Paschall, eds., *Starch: Chemistry and Technology*, Vol. 1, Academic Press, Inc., New York, 1965, Chap. 20.

33. J. N. BeMiller, "Alkaline Degradation of Starch," in R. L. Whistler and E. F. Paschall, eds., *Starch: Chemistry and Technology*, Vol. 1, Academic Press, Inc., New York, 1965, Chap. 21.

34. B. L. Scallet and E. A. Sowell, "Production and Use of Hypochlorite-Oxidized Starches," in R. L. Whistler and E. F. Paschall, eds., *Starch: Chemistry and Technology*, Vol. 2, Academic Press, Inc., New York, 1967, Chap. 10.

35. C. H. Hullinger, "Production and Use of Cross-Linked Starch," in R. L. Whistler and E. F. Paschall, eds., *Starch: Chemistry and Technology*, Vol. 2, Academic Press, Inc., New York, 1967, Chap. 19.

36. S. A. Watson, "Manufacture of Corn and Milo Starches," in R. L. Whistler and E. F. Paschall, eds., *Starch: Chemistry and Technology*, Vol. 2, Academic Press, Inc., New York, 1967, Chap. 1.

37. U.S. Pat. 2,913,112 (Nov. 17, 1959), P. L. Stavenger and D. E. Wuth (to Dorr-Oliver, Inc.).

38. U.S. Pat. 3,040,996 (June 26, 1962), M. E. Ginaven (to Bauer Brothers Co.).

39. U.S. Pat. 3,118,624 (Jan. 21, 1964), R. R. Dill and M. E. Ginaven (to Bauer Brothers Co.).

40. U.S. Pat. 3,029,169 (April 10, 1962), D. W. Dowie and H. D. Martin (to Corn Products Co.).

41. U.S. Pat. 2,995,246 (Aug. 8, 1961), M. L. E. Van Tittelboom (to Corn Products Co.).

42. R. W. Kerr, *Chemistry and Industry of Starch*, 2nd ed., Academic Press, Inc., New York, 1950, Chap. 2.

43. U.S. Pat. 2,973,896 (March 7, 1961), A. Peltzer, Sr. (to Dorr-Oliver, Inc.).

44. U.S. Pat. 2,778,752 (Jan. 22, 1957), H. J. Vegter (to Stamicarbon N.V.).

45. U.S. Pat. 2,338,619 (Jan. 4, 1944), S. Bogaty (to Proctor and Schwartz, Inc.).

46. F. Baunack, *Staerke* **15**, 299 (1963).

47. D. Horton, "Pyrolysis of Starch," in R. L. Whistler and E. F. Paschall, eds., *Starch: Chemistry and Technology*, Vol. 1, Academic Press, Inc., New York, 1965, Chap. 18.

48. R. B. Evans and O. B. Wurzburg, "Production and Use of Starch Dextrins," in R. L. Whistler and E. F. Paschall, eds., *Starch: Chemistry and Technology*, Vol. 2, Academic Press, Inc., New York, 1967, Chap. 11.

49. W. G. Bechtel, *J. Colloid Sci.* **4**, 265 (1949).

50. *Starch*, U.S. Tariff Comm. Rept., March 1960.

51. *Chem. Week* **102** (25), 92 (1968).

52. *The Corn Refining Industry*, Corn Refiners' Association, Inc., Washington, 1967, p. 48.

53. H. J. Roberts, "Starch Derivatives," in R. L. Whistler and E. F. Paschall, eds., *Starch: Chemistry and Technology*, Vol. 2, Academic Press, Inc., New York, 1967, Chap. 13.

54. L. H. Kruger and M. W. Rutenberg, "Production and Uses of Starch Acetates," in R. L. Whistler and E. F. Paschall, eds., *Starch: Chemistry and Technology*, Vol. 2, Academic Press, Inc., New York, 1967, Chap. 15.

55. J. Traquair, *J. Soc. Chem. Ind.* **28**, 288 (1909).

56. U.S. Pat. 2,461,139 (Feb. 8, 1949), C. G. Caldwell (to National Starch Products, Inc.).

57. O. B. Wurzburg, "Acetylation," in R. L. Whistler, ed., *Methods in Carbohydrate Chemistry*, Vol. 4, Academic Press, Inc., New York, 1964, Chap. 64.

58. U.S. Pat. 2,928,828 (March 15, 1960), C. E. Smith and J. V. Tuschhoff (to A. E. Staley Manufacturing Co.).

59. *Code of Federal Regulations*, Title 21, Food and Drugs, Chapter I, Part 121, Subpart D, "Food Additives Permitted for Human Consumption," Section 121.1031, "Food Starch-Modified," U.S. Govt. Printing Off., Washington, D.C., revised Jan. 1, 1966.

60. R. M. Hamilton and E. F. Paschall, "Preparation and Uses of Starch Phosphates," in R. L. Whistler and E. F. Paschall, eds., *Starch: Chemistry and Technology*, Vol. 2, Academic Press, Inc., New York, 1967, Chap. 14.

61. U.S. Pat. 2,884,413 (April 28, 1959), R. W. Kerr and F. C. Cleveland, Jr. (to Corn Products Co.).

62. E. F. Paschall, "Phosphation with Inorganic Phosphate Salts," in R. L. Whistler, ed., *Methods in Carbohydrate Chemistry*, Vol. 4, Academic Press, Inc., New York, 1964, Chap. 67.

63. U.S. Pat. 2,865,762 (Dec. 23, 1958), H. Neukom (to International Minerals and Chemical Corp.).

64. U.S. Pat. 2,884,412 (April 28, 1959), H. Neukom (to International Minerals and Chemical Corp.).

65. U.S. Pat. 2,961,440 (Nov. 22, 1960), R. W. Kerr and F. C. Cleveland, Jr. (to Corn Products Co.).

66. U.S. Pat. 2,801,242 (July 30, 1957), R. W. Kerr and F. C. Cleveland, Jr. (to Corn Products Co.).

67. U.S. Pat. 2,935,510 (May 3, 1960), O. B. Wurzburg (to National Starch and Chemical Corp.).

68. E. T. Hjermstad, "Production and Uses of Hydroxyethylstarch," in R. L. Whistler and E. F. Paschall, eds., *Starch: Chemistry and Technology*, Vol. 2, Academic Press, Inc., New York, 1967, Chap. 17.

69. U.S. Pat. 2,516,633 (July 25, 1950), C. C. Kesler and E. T. Hjermstad (to Penick and Ford, Ltd., Inc.).

70. U.S. Pat. 2,801,241 (July 30, 1957), K. C. Hobbs (to Corn Products Co.).

71. U.S. Pat. 2,516,632 (July 25, 1950), C. C. Kesler and E. T. Hjermstad (to Penick and Ford, Ltd., Inc.).

72. U.S. Pat. 2,516,634 (July 25, 1950), C. C. Kesler and E. T. Hjermstad (to Penick and Ford, Ltd., Inc.).

73. G. W. Buttrick and N. R. Eldred, *Tappi* **45**, 890 (1962).

74. E. F. Paschall, "Production and Uses of Cationic Starches," in R. L. Whistler and E. F. Paschall, eds., *Starch: Chemistry and Technology*, Vol. 2, Academic Press, Inc., New York, 1967, Chap. 16.

75. U.S. Pat. 2,813,093 (Nov. 12, 1957), C. G. Caldwell and O. B. Wurzburg (to National Starch Products Inc.).

76. U.S. Pat. 2,876,217 (March 3, 1959), E. F. Paschall (to Corn Products Co.).

77. E. D. Mazzarella and L. J. Hickey, *Tappi* **49**, 526 (1966).

General References

R. L. Whistler and E. F. Paschall, eds., *Starch: Chemistry and Technology*, Vol. 1, Academic Press, Inc., New York, 1965.

R. L. Whistler and E. F. Paschall, eds., *Starch: Chemistry and Technology*, Vol. 2, Academic Press, Inc., New York, 1967.

R. L. Whistler, ed., *Methods in Carbohydrate Chemistry*, Vol. 4, Starch, Academic Press, Inc., New York, 1964.

J. Honeyman, *Recent Advances in the Chemistry of Cellulose and Starch*, Heywood and Company Ltd., London, 1959.

R. W. Kerr, ed., *Chemistry and Industry of Starch*, 2nd ed., Academic Press, Inc., New York, 1950.

J. A. Radley, ed., *Starch and Its Derivatives*, 4th ed., Chapman and Hall, Ltd., London, 1968.

J. Seidemann, *Staerke-Atlas*, Paul Parey, Berlin, 1966.

R. P. Walton, ed., *A Comprehensive Survey of Starch Chemistry*, The Chemical Catalog Co., Inc., New York, 1928.

C. T. Greenwood, "The Thermal Degradation of Starch," *Advan. Carbohydrate Chem.* **22** (**1967**), 483–515.

D. J. Manners, "Enzymatic Synthesis and Degradation of Starch and Glycogen," *Advan. Carbohydrate Chem.* **17** (**1962**), 371–430.

J. Muetgeert, "The Fractionation of Starch," *Advan. Carbohydrate Chem.* **16** (**1961**), 299–333.

G. V. Caesar, "Starch Nitrate," *Advan. Carbohydrate Chem.* **13** (**1958**), 331–345.

C. T. Greenwood, "The Physical Chemistry of Starch," *Advan. Carbohydrate Chem.* **11**(**1956**), 336–385.

STANLEY M. PARMERTER
Corn Products Company

STARCH NITRATE. See Vol. 8, p. 601.

STEAM

After water, steam is the most common and important fluid used in chemical technology. It is used in the generation of power, for the distribution of heat under controlled conditions of temperature, and as a reacting medium. Steam is also widely used as a blanketing or smothering material in fire protection and fire fighting, as an inert agent in some systems, as a distillation aid, and as a cleaning agent. The range of applications of steam extend from pressures of a few inches of water to several thousand pounds per square inch and corresponding saturated temperatures. The superheating of steam has been considered at temperatures as high as 2000°F. The thermodynamic and physical properties of steam over the range of 0.1 to 15,000 psia are well-established; the chemical properties of steam and of substances in steam are very poorly covered in comparison. Steam may be generated from water in a variety of devices, depending upon the pressure and temperature desired. At subcritical pressures and temperatures, the boilers used to generate steam range from simple fire-tubed units to water-tubed natural or controlled circulation drum types, to once-through types. The sources of heat can come from the combustion of natural gas, coal, fuel oil, or waste products, from gaseous or liquid process streams (the temperature of which must be reduced), and more recently from nuclear fission reactions. The steam so generated may be superheated to varying degrees by using the exhaust gases from the combustion process taking place in the furnace of the steam generator, the combustion of fuel in a separate furnace, or the waste heat in gaseous or liquid process streams. See also Power generation; Water.

Properties of Steam

Physical Properties. The wide use of steam for power generation and for the distribution of heat has led to extensive study of the thermodynamics and transport properties of steam. A concerted effort was begun in 1921 by the American Society of Mechanical Engineers to provide reliable and consistent tables of these properties. This work resulted finally in the publication of the 1967 ASME Steam Tables (1). These tables present the thermodynamic properties of steam at saturation from 32°F to 705°F, the critical point. They present also the specific volume, enthalpy, and entropy of superheated steam and compressed water for temperatures ranging from

Table 1. Properties of Steam

Pressure, psia	Temp, °F	Spec vol, ft³/lb	Enthalpy, Btu/lb	Entropy, Btu/lb × °F
saturated				
14.7	212	26.80	1151	1.757
30	250	13.82	1164	1.699
165	366	2.752	1196	1.562
300	417	1.540	1203	1.510
700	503	0.656	1202	1.430
1000	545	0.448	1193	1.391
1800	621	0.219	1152	1.308
2600	674	0.121	1082	1.222
supercritical				
3500	1000	0.207	1422	1.471
4400	1000	0.131	1365	1.400

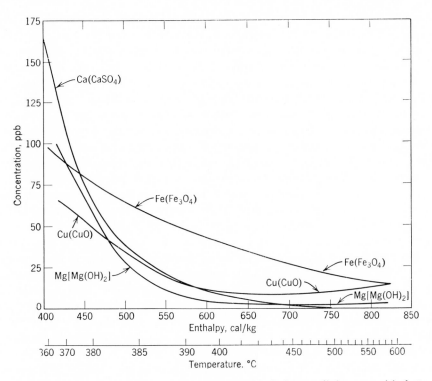

Fig. 1. Solubility of some compounds (expressed as ppb of the metal) in supercritical steam vs enthalpy at 225 atm (3300 psia) (4).   Courtesy Combustion Publishing Co., Inc.

32 to 1500°F and from pressures of 0.12 to 15,500 psia. Isobaric heat capacities are also given for the temperature range 32–1500°F and for pressures of 1–15,000 psia. Values for viscosity, thermal conductivity, and Prandtl numbers are likewise given over similar ranges. A brief summary of important properties is given in Table 1.

Although the cataloguing of the physical properties of steam is very complete and adequate for current technology, a similar cataloguing of the chemical properties of steam as a solvent and of the associated physical and chemical properties of substances dissolved in high-temperature steam are not nearly as well documented. Such information as does exist has been acquired for specific purposes. A good review of the current knowledge of high-temperature, aqueous solutions, including steam, is given by Cobble (2).   That work which is available has largely been the result of efforts to obtain solutions to specific problems in two areas: geochemical processes and the generation of power using high-pressure, high-temperature steam. For example, Morey and Hesselgesser (3) developed data on the solubility of quartz and other substances in superheated steam at high pressures from the geochemical point of view.

The importance of the solvent characteristics of high-temperature, high-pressure steam arises in large part from problems with deposit formation in steam turbines in large power plants. Substances dissolved in the steam may result either through volatilization from the boiler water or by carryover of droplets of boiler water into the steam or, in the case of supercritical steam generators, they may have been present in the feedwater to the steam generator. Whatever the source, they experience reduced solubility as the temperature and pressure of the steam are dropped by passage through the steam turbine. The steam thus becomes supersaturated with respect to dissolved substances which deposit on the blades of the turbine. Styrikovich (4) in the U.S.S.R. has contributed much information on the solubility of substances in high-temperature steam used for power generation purposes. Figure 1 by Styrikovich and Martynova shows the solubility of a number of substances in supercritical steam over a range of temperatures. Hoppe (5) presents analyses showing the selectivity of deposition that is generally encountered in turbines. Additional data on the solubility of copper and its oxide in supercritical steam is given by Pocock and Stewart (6). This latter work was occasioned by the discovery of deposits of pure copper and copper oxide in supercritical steam turbines. In this instance the copper and copper compounds entered the supercritical steam generator in the feedwater in concentrations greater than the maximum solubilities encountered in the high-pressure stages of the turbine. Typical solubilities of copper oxide were found to be 15 parts per billion (expressed as Cu) at 4500 psig and 1150°F, but only 3 parts per billion at 3200 psig and 1050°F.

Styrikovich proposed, and others have generally confirmed, that the solubilities of most salts in high-temperature and high-pressure steam are a function of the density of the fluid. Styrikovich also concluded that most of the salts present in steam generation are dissolved in the steam as nondissociated molecules and, hence, that the solubility of any of these compounds practically does not depend (within the concentration range of importance for steam turbine units) upon the availability of other compounds in the steam. These conditions result primarily from the fact that low-pressure steam is a rather low polar solvent in which even the strongest electrolytes do not dissociate. Even with increasing pressure and a slight increase in the steam polar property, a strongly dissociated salt such as sodium chloride behaves in

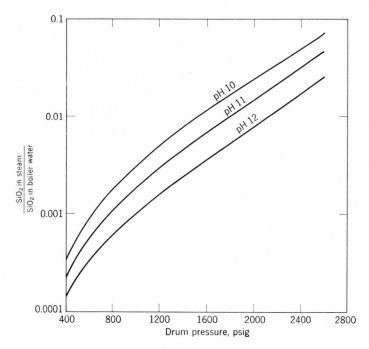

Fig. 2. Ratio of silica in steam/silica in boiler water versus boiler drum pressure at selected boiler water pH.

steam like a weak electrolyte (dissociation constant equals 5×10^{-7} mole/liter). Less strongly dissociated salts such as sodium sulfate are present in the high-pressure steam entirely in the form of neutral molecules within the whole concentration range of practical importance.

In the subcritical region, where steam is generated from boiling solutions of water, the purity of the steam is dependent not only upon the efficiency of the mechanical separation of water from steam but also on the volatility of salts dissolved in the water at the temperature and pressure at which generation takes place. The distribution ratio (the concentration of the salt in steam divided by its concentration in boiler water) for a salt is a function of its dissociation constant in water and of the ratio of the density of steam to the density of water. For the weaker electrolytes such as silica, which are completely un-ionized in boiler water at elevated temperature and pressure, the distribution ratio is a function only of the density ratio. A graphical presentation of the distribution ratio for silica is shown in Figure 2 as given in the ASTM Manual (7) based upon the data of Coulter, Pirsh, and Wagner (8). Styrikovich (9,10) has also published volatility data for a number of salts as have Ulmer and Klein (11), Straub (12), and Rubright (13). Later work (10) has shown that some of the early volatility data (except that for silica) was in error in not taking into account the degree of dissociation of the salts at the temperature in question.

In addition to volatile transport, salts can enter the steam in the entrained droplets of boiler water. The concentration of such salts in the steam is thus a function of their concentration in the boiler water and the percentage of entrainment where the latter is a function of separator efficiency. As the saturated steam is superheated, the entrained water evaporates and the salts dissolve in the steam to the limit of their solubility.

Most salts experience increasing solubility in the steam as the temperature is raised. It is thus possible through mechanical entrainment to have much greater concentrations dissolved in the steam than those that result from volatility of the salts in the boiler at boiler pressure and temperature. Sodium sulfate, however, is an example of a compound whose solubility at first decreases before beginning to increase as the temperature increases; as a result, deposits of sodium sulfate in superheaters are often found concentrated at a point 50–70°F higher than the saturation temperature with no deposits either before or after this temperature zone.

Silica is sufficiently volatile at pressures greater than 400 psi so that normal concentrations of silica in the boiler water will result in sufficient silica in the steam to exceed its solubility at the temperature and pressure existing in the exhaust end of condensing steam turbines.

Sampling. The deposition of salts from superheated steam as the temperature is reduced also presents problems in the sampling of the superheated steam to determine the degree of contamination. Cobb and Coulter (14) were the first to report on a detailed examination of this problem of deposition in the sampling line and sample coil as the temperature of superheated steam is reduced prior to the formation of saturation steam within the coil. Very significant quantities of the salts dissolved in steam can deposit in the sampling system itself, resulting in lower concentrations in the final condensed sample and thus, erroneously low estimates of contamination.

The sampling of saturated steam also poses certain difficulties since the sample invariably contains small amounts of moisture in the form of very fine droplets. Studies by Lawlor and Clark (15) and Goldstein and Simmons (16) pointed up the nonhomogeneity of saturated steam over the cross section of a pipe under flow conditions and the necessity of employing special care in the location of the sampling nozzle to avoid obtaining nonrepresentative samples of the flowing steam. Earlier work by Miskimen(17) as well as Jackson's report on steam sampling in Russia (18) underscored the fact that droplets of moisture in saturated steam tend to flow in a boundary layer along the walls of pipe and are especially concentrated on the outside radius of bends in the pipe. A complete treatment and recommended practice for sampling both saturated and superheated steam is given in ASTM D-1066-67T (19).

Part of the early difficulty in establishing the accuracy of sampling methods was the lack of sensitive methods of analysis. Most of the salts in steam generators are sodium salts. Coulter (20) and Rice (21,22) have reported on the application of the flame-photometer for the analysis of sodium and have demonstrated that its sensitivity allows practical determination of at least one part per billion of sodium in steam. Such accurate, sensitive measurement of sodium in steam led directly to the necessity to develop more sophisticated sampling techniques.

The need to accurately measure the amount of substances dissolved in high-temperature, high-pressure steam is not limited to problems of deposit formation in steam power turbines. Large synthetic ammonia plants, which react steam, air, and methane at high pressures to produce ammonia, encounter severe problems at portions of the cycle where the high-temperature gas contacts silica refractory lined vessels. Sufficient silica dissolves in the high-temperature steam–gas mixture to cause serious deposition problems later on in catalyst beds where the temperature of the gas is reduced.

Steam Generation

The simplicity of developing a large quantity of energy by merely pumping a small volume of water to the desired pressure level and then expanding the fluid volume by heating is an important feature of the steam cycle for power generation and accounts for the wide use of steam in industry (959×10^9 gal/yr makeup) and the choice of steam cycles for electric power generation (23). The limits of steam production are fixed in practice by the construction materials able to withstand the pressures generated at the temperatures employed. Steam generators have been built for and operated at pressures in excess of 4500 psia and at temperatures in excess of 1200°F although not necessarily concurrently.

Steam below the critical pressure is normally generated in boilers though it may also be generated in evaporators. In the former case the steam is generated for its power or heating value; in the latter case it is generated to produce, through its condensation, a pure water from an impure source. Some subcritical steam generation is performed in once-through units where 100% of the feedwater to the unit is transformed into steam in a single passage through the generator. Some very small subcritical steam generators are of the flash type where the water is simply dropped on the heated surface and completely converted to steam.

FUEL–FIRED BOILERS

Boilers are of many types. They may be classified by their physical design, such as stationary or movable; by types of energy source, such as fossil fuel or nuclear; by types of fossil fuel, such as oil, coal, or gas; by types of heating surface, such as fire-tubed or water-tubed; and, if water-tubed, by whether they are natural or controlled circulation or once-through. At one time the most common types of low-pressure boilers were undoubtedly domestic home boilers, most of which operate at pressures well under 15 psig. These are simple water-filled or water-shielded devices of sectional construction in which coal, oil, or gas is burned. These systems normally have very low heating output and are so simple that they require very little attention. With the advent of hot-air heating in homes and electric radiant heating, most of such small steam boilers are now found only in smaller apartment houses and office buildings.

Process steam generating boilers, as well as central heating boilers, normally operate at higher pressures and are more nearly continuous in operation or more uniformly loaded than home boilers. The conventional range of pressures for such boilers is between 15 and 150 psig. The old kettle or fire-tubed type of boiler used for process steam generation has gradually been displaced in industry to the extent that it represents only a small fraction of the steam generating devices used to date. Most of the fire-tubed boilers that are currently in service are of the small package type, completely instrumented and controlled for unattended operation, with capacities up to 50,000 lb/hr available in standard designs. Such units are primarily used in heating service in apartment, office, and industrial buildings. However, more and more building heating systems are employing high-temperature, high-pressure water as a replacement for steam (24). The demise of fire-tubed boilers in larger sizes for process steam generation is a result of the fact that they have very large volumes of water compared to their heating surfaces and this, in the case of mechanical failure resulting in tube burnout, can lead to explosive release of a large quantity of steam from the boiler water.

Most modern boilers for process steam generation and large central heating are, therefore, of the water tubular type in which the water is circulated through tubes which are exposed to radiant heating or convection gas heating to provide the heat necessary to transform the water into steam. Such boilers are practically all of the thermosyphon circulating type. These boilers operate on a recirculating principle; water from an upper steam–water disengaging drum is carried down to the lower end of banks of water-filled tubes in which steam is generated as the mixture rises to the steam-separating drum under the influence of the heat absorbed in the furnace of the boiler. Such natural circulation boilers represent the greatest number of water-tubed boilers in service and are available in a great many different varieties, depending on fuel to be used, size, and pressure.

Steam generators used for power generation in central power stations can be designed for either subcritical or supercritical pressures; selection is based on the economic evaluation of unit capacity and fuel type and cost. In general, units up to about 600,000 kW in size will tend to be subcritical; units in larger capacities will be supercritical.

Subcritical power station steam generators are either the once-through type or the drum type with recirculation provided either by the natural density difference between heated riser tubes and unheated downcomers (natural circulation unit) or by mechanical pumps (controlled circulation unit). There is very little difference in first cost, operating cost, or reliability between the natural and the controlled circulation system; thus, selection remains a matter of individual preference.

Some subcritical once-through steam generators have been marketed. These units are very similar to supercritical pressure steam generators in that feedwater pumped to the steam generator passes through it and is converted completely to steam at the exit at the desired pressure and temperature. Such units have all the control problems associated with supercritical steam generators, and, moreover, retain the problems of boiling heat transfer of subcritical boilers in general.

A tabulation of new order commitments for U.S. central station units during a recent two-year period shows the following distribution of circulation systems:

Type of steam generator	*Number of units*	*Total capacity,* MW
subcritical		
once-through	1	600
natural circulation	50	11,300
controlled circulation	18	8,400
total, subcritical	*69*	*20,300*
supercritical		
once-through	38	24,700

In all of the drum-type boilers with either natural or controlled circulation, means must be provided within the drum to separate the steam formed in the generating tubes from the remaining boiler water. The required efficiency of this separation depends to a great extent on the intended use of the steam and whether it is to be superheated or not. Where the steam is to be used saturated, as in heating installations without long distribution lines, steam containing 0.25–0.5% moisture can be tolerated and still have enough separation within the drum to get stable control of the drum water level and to prevent slugging of steam traps and development of steam hammer in the steam line. Where the steam is to be superheated, which is the more usual case, and is to be used for heating or in process, it is necessary to have sufficient separation of water within the drum so that the steam entering the superheater contains no more than 1 ppm of dissolved salts. Amounts of salts in excess of this concentration are likely to cause formation of deposit on the steam side in the superheater tubes, resulting in excessive elevation of temperature and failure of the tubes. Where the superheated steam is to be used primarily in steam turbines, the quality of the steam produced is even more important. In this latter case the amount of salts entering the superheater in the saturated steam should not exceed 0.1 ppm in order to avoid excessively rapid formation of deposits on the blades in the steam turbine.

There is thus a severe demand upon the efficiency of the steam-separating devices employed within the drum; this has resulted in a wide range of designs for such

Table 2. American Boiler Manufacturers Association Allowable Boiler Water Concentrations (25)

Pressure at outlet of steam generating unit, psig	Total solids, ppm	Total alkalinity, ppm	Suspended solids, ppm
0– 300	3500	700	300
301– 450	3000	600	250
451– 600	2500	500	150
601– 750	2000	400	100
751– 900	1500	300	60
901–1000	1250	250	40
1001–1500	1000	200	20
1501–2000	750	150	10
2001 and higher	500	100	5

Table 3. Quality Requirements of Water at Point of Use for Steam Generation and Cooling in Heat Exchangers[a] (26)

Characteristic	Boiler feedwater				Cooling water			
	Industrial				Once through		Makeup for recirculation	
	Low pressure, 0–150 psig	Intermediate pressure, 150–700 psig	High pressure, 700–1500 psig	Electric utilities, 1500–5000 psig	Fresh	Brackish[b]	Fresh	Brackish[b]
silica	30	10	0.7	0.01	50	25	50	25
aluminum	5	0.1	0.01	0.01	c	c	0.1	0.1
iron	1	0.3	0.05	0.01	c	c	0.5	0.5
manganese	0.3	0.1	0.01	e	c	c	0.5	0.02
calcium	c	d	d	e	200	420	50	420
magnesium	c	d	d	e	c	c	c	c
ammonia	0.1	0.1	0.1	0.7	c	c	c	c
bicarbonate	170	120	48	e	600	140	24	140
sulfate	c	c	c	c	680	2,700	200	2,700
chloride	c	c	c	e	600	19,000	500	19,000
dissolved solids	700	500	200	0.5	1,000	35,000	500	35,000
copper	0.5	0.05	0.05	0.01	c	c	c	c
zinc	c	d	d	e	c	c	c	c
hardness ($CaCO_3$)	20	d	d	d	850	6,250	130	6,250
alkalinity ($CaCO_3$)	140	100	40	d	500	115	20	115
pH, units	8.0–10.0	8.2–10.0	8.2–9.0	8.8–9.2	5.0–8.3	6.0–8.3	c	c
organics:								
methylene blue active substances	1	1	0.5	d	c	c	1	1
carbon tetrachloride extract	1	1	0.5	d	f	f	1	2
chemical oxygen demand	5	5	0.5	d	75	75	75	75
dissolved oxygen	2.5	0.007	0.007	0.007	c	c	c	c
temperature, °F	c	c	c	d	c	c	c	c
suspended solids	10	5	d	d	5,000	2,500	100	100

NOTE: Application of the above values should be based on references 27 and 28.

[a] Unless otherwise indicated, units are mg/liter and values shown should normally not be exceeded. No one water will have all the maximum values shown.

[b] More than 1000 mg/liter of dissolved solids by definition of 1963 census of manufacturers.

[c] Accepted as received (if meeting total solids or other limiting values); has never been a problem at concentrations encountered.

[d] Zero, not detectable by test.   [e] Controlled by treatment for other constituents.   [f] No floating oil.

separating devices. In the simplest case, only saturated steam with no superheat, a simple perforated pipe in the steam space in the top of the drum may suffice. Where maximum efficiency of separation must be achieved, several separation devices are employed in sequence: first a centrifugal-type separator, followed by one or more stages of impingement-baffled-type separators.

The continuing effort to increase the thermal efficiency of fossil-fuel steam power generating plants has led to the development of steam at pressures above the critical point. In such plants the feedwater to the steam generator is raised to the desired pressure for the system which must be above the critical pressure of water, 3206 psia; it is then passed once through the unit to emerge at the desired temperature, for example, 1000°F (24a). In the process of passage through the steam generator there is no boiling in the usual sense since there is never any phase change. The density of the fluid simply decreases continually as the heat is added and the temperature raised. The supercritical steam, after it emerges from the steam generator, passes through the high-pressure turbine from which it emerges typically at a pressure of 750 psia and a temperature of 600°F. This high-pressure turbine exhaust steam is then returned to the steam generator where additional heat is added to raise the temperature to 1000°F. From the reheater the steam returns to a low-pressure turbine, exiting from it into the surface condenser where it is condensed and the water is returned to the steam generator. The water fed to such supercritical steam generators must be of exceptionally high quality; generally it should contain less than 50 parts per billion of dissolved or suspended matter. All such dissolved or suspended matter entering the steam generator must either deposit within it or become dissolved within the high-temperature supercritical fluid and be carried into the turbine where deposition may then occur. In drum-type subcritical boilers, discussed previously, the change in phase from water to steam allows most of the impurities entering in the feedwater to the steam generator to be retained within the boiler as a recirculating fluid. Table 2 shows the recommended limits for the dissolved and suspended matter in the boiler water in subcritical drum-type boilers.

Table 3 gives the quality requirements for water of various steam generators. The requirements in this table all apply to a quality of water prior to the addition of substances used for internal conditioning.

NUCLEAR GENERATORS

The steam generators discussed above are fired by fossil fuels or else use waste heat from some process.

In recent years energy from nuclear fission reactions has become important in the production of steam for large electric power generation installations. Some 50% of the new power generation capacity purchased in 1967, for example, uses energy supplied by nuclear fuels. Nuclear steam supply systems are of many types; the following three are currently the most important.

Pressurized water reactors (PWR) circulate primary high-pressure water at 2000 psi through the reactor vessel containing the nuclear fuel (29). This primary water is not used directly, but is used to generate steam in a secondary cycle. It emerges from the reactor vessel typically at 600°F and passes to the steam generator which may be an inverted U-tube heat exchanger with the high-temperature primary water circulating through the inside of the inverted U-tubes. On the shell side of the U-tubes in the steam generator, water is boiled and saturated steam is generated typically at pressures of 750–900 psi. The saturated steam then goes to a condensing steam turbine. Water is returned from the condenser and pumped to the shell side of the steam generator. This secondary cycle is similar to that of conventional steam generators in the nature of the engineering problems encountered. Unless leaks occur between the primary water and the secondary water, the secondary cycle is free from any radioactivity.

The *boiling water reactor* (BWR) differs from the PWR previously described in that it has only one fluid circuit instead of two (30). In the BWR the water fed to the reactor vessel is turned into steam in the reactor vessel and taken directly to the turbine–condenser unit. Intense radiation within the reactor causes radiolytic action with substances in the water and the water itself, generating a steam that contains high amounts of oxygen and other impurities compared to steam generated in conventional cycles or in the secondary cycle of the PWR. Intense radiation in the reactor also poses special problems in the allowable additives to the feedwater to the reactor. Any carry-over of boiler water from within the reactor into the steam to the turbine can cause transport of highly radioactive material with subsequent deposition in the turbine and other parts of the steam cycle. Therefore, great care must be used in the design of the steam–water separation facilities in the reactor as well as in the control of the dissolved matter in the reactor water.

In the *high-temperature gas-cooled reactor* (HTGR) (31) the nuclear fuel in the reactor heats a recirculating stream of gas which is usually helium or carbon dioxide; the gas stream is then used to heat the tubes in the steam generator. In this system the water passes through the inside of the tubes in the steam generator which is of the subcritical once-through type. Because the pressure in the steam generator on the water side is so very much higher (2400 psi) than the external gas pressure, there is no possibility of any radioactive contamination of the water or the steam generated from it. The steam generating cycle is thus similar in many ways to that of conventional fossil-fuel-fired steam generators in both engineering and water treatment problems. The nature of the design of the nuclear reactor in the HTGR allows for the production of very much higher steam temperatures (1000°F) including the ability to reheat to 1000°F and thus the efficiency of the steam cycle in the generation of electric power is much greater than in either the PWR or the BWR.

A much-talked-about variation in nuclear power plant design has been the coupling of such power plants with large multieffect, multistage flash evaporators for the production of potable water from seawater. In such plants the steam from the nuclear steam generator passes into the turbine but instead of exhausting into a normal surface condenser the steam that exhausts from the turbine is used to heat seawater. The seawater in turn flows through the various stages of a flash evaporator, producing steam in each stage; this steam is used to heat the cold seawater in a countercurrent fashion. All steam condensed from the evaporator in excess of that required to be returned to the nuclear steam generator is thus potable product water.

PACKAGE UNITS

In recent years steam generators known as package units or shop-assembled units have become a large part of the total number of steam generators under 100,000 lb/hr in single boilers installed. These units normally have capacities of from a few thousand lb/hr to as high as 225,000 lb/hr in a single boiler. Such units are completely assembled by the manufacturer and are mounted on bases which support the entire unit except for the stack and the few auxiliaries. These units have their own forced-air blowers, oil- or gas-burning equipment, and controls for pressure, feedwater flow, and drum level. Such package units cost much less per pound of steam capacity than the corresponding size of field-erected boiler because of the savings in erection cost at the jobsite and the duplication of design in fabrication. The dimensions of package units or shop-assembled units are determined in part by the dimensions of railroad flatcars and tunnel clearances since shipment of the larger units are by rail. These dimensional restrictions apply primarily to the vertical cross section of the boiler and hence such units are very long compared to their height and width. The very high heat transfer rates and the small-diameter steam drums employed in such units pose special problems in terms of water treatment and design of steam separation facilities. For a given pressure, package units generally require feedwater of higher purity and better control of feedwater treatment than corresponding field-erected units.

COMBINED POWER GENERATION AND PROCESS STEAM

The rise in cost of fuel has led many industries that have a demand for process steam to install combination power generation and process steam producing power plants. Such plants generally require a power plant of minimum capital cost and high depreciation, as compared to a large central-station power generation facility. Thus, there is a growing use of combination steam and gas turbine plants which bring an increase in the power generation per mass unit of processed steam compared with the direct fuel-fired steam generator furnishing steam to a back-pressure or topping turbine generator. In such gas turbine–steam generator installations, a gas turbine which drives a generator exhausts into a specially designed steam generator which is usually subcritical and of the drum type. (Additional firing in the furnace of the steam generator with oil or gas may be employed to supplement the heat in the turbine exhaust, depending on the relative requirements for steam versus electricity; the greater the requirement for steam versus electricity, the greater the supplemental firing employed.) The steam from the steam generator then passes to a back-pressure steam turbine which drives an additional electrical generator. In both cycles described the steam leaving the steam turbine then goes to process where it is condensed in heating process fluids or is used directly in process reactions (32).

BOILER FUELS

Natural gas may be burned in boilers on a practically comparable basis with oil. In gas-producing areas or in areas of the country served by long gas-transmission lines, gas may be less costly than either coal or oil. Control of gas firing is much the easiest since there is little or no fuel handling equipment required other than pressure and flow control valves. Oil is next in ease of handling since it need only be pumped and mechanically atomized or pumped and steam-atomized. The steam-atomizing oil-burning installation can handle relatively dirty or mixed-base oils without too much difficulty due to clogging. Very high viscosity oils and tars may be handled without difficulty using high-temperature steam for heating.

Coal-burning boilers may be of the stoker-fired or pulverized-fuel types. Coal fired on a chain grate stoker may be automatic but it is less responsive to variations in firing demand than pulverized-coal-burning or gas- or oil-burning installations. A considerable amount of equipment and attention is necessary for the coal-burning installation to ensure that the coal is properly processed and, if powdered coal is burned, that it is properly ground before being fed to the boilers. In addition coal-burning installations require a means for collecting the ash and properly disposing of it. Because of the generally higher cost of coal compared to the other fuels and the higher cost of the coal-handling and ash-handling equipment, very few installations are made currently of stoker-fired, coal-burning boilers. Pulverized-coal-burning boilers of very large size constitute almost all of the coal-fired units being installed.

Waste incineration is being used more and more as a source of heat for steam power generation. Organic sludges from biological treatment processes, either in industrial waste systems or from municipal sewage treatment plants, are incinerated and the heat is recovered by the generation of steam for power. The problem of trash disposal in large metropolitan areas is also leading to the use of such combustible waste materials for steam generation.

The choice of fuel for steam generation frequently is determined by location and price; it is also being determined more and more by the effect that the fuel has on the nature of the stack gases and their effect, in turn, on the surrounding air environment. Air pollution control regulations are forcing close attention to be paid to the sulfur content as well as the particulate matter content of the stack gases. High-sulfur fuel oils as well as high-sulfur coals require either preliminary processing to reduce the sulfur content or elaborate apparatus for the removal of sulfur from the furnace exhaust (see Sulfur). Elaborate mechanical and electrostatic filters are necessary on the exhaust stack from pulverized-coal-fired furnaces in order that the stack gas will meet air pollution control standards for particulate matter.

Where large installations are involved, especially power plants and public utilities generating upwards of 1,000,000 lb/hr of steam, coal-burning installations are the most economical, particularly when located close to the coal mines. As the cost of transmitting electric power over long lines has become less in comparison with the cost of hauling coal to the power plant, very large steam power plants, in excess of 4,000,000 lb/hr, are being located at the mine mouth in the coal-producing area. In such installations the disposal of the ash presents a real engineering problem. In some installations the ash is returned to the mined-out open coal pits or strips; in other installations it is slurried and pumped back into worked-out sections of deep coal mines.

STEAM ACCUMULATORS

Some plants in the process industries require steam at a very high rate for a short period of time and then at a low rate for a considerable length of time: For example, in a brewery there may be frequent cyclic demands for a tremendous amount of heat to quickly sterilize a large fermentor. Under these conditions it would be quite uneconomic to install boiler capacity of adequate size to generate steam at the high peak-flow requirement. The problem can be solved by the use of accumulators. These are merely insulated high-pressure reservoirs containing water into which steam is charged at high pressure during times of low steam demand. At the time of peak withdrawal from the system the rated output of the boiler, augmented by the flow of flash steam from the accumulator, is released to the low-pressure flow line. Pressure on the system is allowed to drop as the demand is met so that the final flow from the accumulator is at the least pressure required for process operation.

Steam for Power

In general, steam is used to produce power in the following two ways: (*1*) A steam turbine is connected to a generator of electric power for transmission and use and (*2*) a steam turbine is connected to rotating mechanical machinery, such as pumps and gas compressors. Steam turbines are very efficient at high-load ratings and depending upon the steam balance in a plant, they are normally considered as drive units if over 50 hp is required. Where many small loads are to be handled separately in a plant, it may be preferable to generate electric power by passing the steam through a back-pressure turbine connected to an electric generator; the generated electricity in turn may be fed into the motors throughout the plant. Steam turbines operate very effectively at high speeds (3,000–10,000 rpm) and thus lend themselves well to large horsepower, high-speed drives for gas compressors, multistage high-pressure pumps, such as boiler feedpumps, and other high-speed rotating equipment. In such installations the steam may be fed to the turbine and extracted at various stages of its expansion corresponding to the desired process operating pressures. This is done in order to obtain a more economical and efficient utilization of the maximum mechanical energy above the temperature and pressure necessary for process use. Where multiple steam turbine drives are employed in the plant, one or more of them are usually the compound extraction–condensing type which, by shifting the percentage of steam flow to extraction or to condensing, can make changes in the ratio of process steam to electric power and thus allow changes to take place in the steam balance of the plant without wasting steam to the atmosphere.

Steam may be used directly to move and pump fluids by means of ejectors or eductors. These devices depend on the velocity of steam flowing through a nozzle to induce the flow of other fluids. Steam in these instances moves fluids without the use of any mechanical moving parts. Efficiency will not be very high if the only desired effect of the steam is to move the fluid, such as air or a noncondensable gas. However, if it is also desired to heat the fluid so that the entire heating value of the steam is utilized as well as the energy of the steam, the overall efficiency may be higher than for any other type of pumping. One of the most common uses of steam ejectors is the production of suction or vacuum.

Steam is a very useful medium for educting air or other noncondensable mediums from a process vessel or fractionating system. Probably the biggest single use for multistage steam-jet ejectors is in evacuating noncondensable gases and air from steam condensers. In such multistage ejectors, in order to reduce the volume of gas educted at each stage, the steam used in one stage is condensed before the noncondensable gas is admitted to the next successive stage. The final stage normally discharges into a barometric condenser or directly into the atmosphere.

Steam Heating

For all practical purposes steam may be considered as a single component material and consequently it has a definite pressure for each fixed boiling or condensing temperature which it is desired to maintain. Therefore, the control of the desired temperature for any process-heating requirement may be fixed by choosing the steam pressure at which the steam is to operate. This is true if the system is assumed to be operating at saturation conditions. It is customary for steam to be generated under slightly superheated conditions if the steam generator is to be located at a considerable distance from the various users. However, superheat normally has only an insignificant function in effecting the temperature of heating and is customarily disregarded by engineers if the heating operation involves condensing steam in a heating unit.

Once the temperature for heating has been fixed, the pressure of the steam-heating medium is likewise fixed. This is both an advantage and a disadvantage. When only moderate temperatures are required, the pressure involved is of little consequence; but when higher temperatures are needed, the higher corresponding pressure becomes most important in the design of equipment. The steam pressure rises quite rapidly with temperature and becomes of major concern for heating conditions at temperatures above 350°F. The use of steam for heating is normally limited to pressures under 300 psig. The cost of the heat-transfer equipment becomes very great for sizable heating units as higher pressures are required. The matter of closures and design of pressure parts becomes decidedly important if temperatures are to exceed 400°F. An example of the effect of pressure on cost is illustrated in Table 4.

Table 4.   Relative Cost of 1000-ft² All-Steel Steam Heaters[a]

Steam pressure, psig	Steam temperature, °F	% of 150 lb design cost
150	366	100
300	422	117
600	488	130

[a] Process fluid at 50 psig on shell side.

Evaporators. Steam-heating systems have often been installed in a cascade system, as in multiple-effect evaporators (see Evaporation). This arrangement makes possible the recovery of heat at several successive levels merely by reducing the pressure at each of the stages. Condensing all the steam vaporized in one stage by heating and vaporizing the material present in the succeeding stage at lower operating pressure produces good economy of heat. This system of heating operates best in the low-pressure range because at higher pressures the equilibrium temperature changes more slowly with the pressure.

Control (see also Instrumentation). When a given temperature of operation is desired and close temperature control is required in order to prevent overheating of material being processed or to assure a high heating density, steam is the medium normally used. A pressure regulator controlling the steam pressure to a heating unit will maintain temperatures usually within five degrees of design conditions on the process side. It is possible, of course, for greater temperature variations to exist on the process side, particularly if the material being heated is not at its boiling point. Under this condition, material adjacent to the heating tubes or heating surfaces may be much hotter than that in the main body of fluid, unless there is agitation or circulation of the heated material. Nevertheless, the steam-heating medium will assure that the temperature of the process fluid, even against the heated surface, cannot greatly exceed that of the selected temperature as long as a careful pressure regulation at the desired level is maintained.

There are a number of means for controlling application of heating steam to processes. Where variations in the load on the process side are possible and it is still desired to limit maximum temperature, the use of pressure controls is probably the most practical. It will assure that the temperature of the heating surface, T_s, cannot exceed the temperature corresponding to the saturation temperature of the steam at the selected pressure, P. Within the limits of the heater and the availability of the steam, the temperature level, T, and the heat supplied will correspond automatically to that of the process demand. Where the process heat load results from a boiling operation, the heat output or duty obtainable will be very high, for the fact that the steam is condensing on one wall of the heating surface and the fluid being processed is boiling on the other surface leads to very high overall heat-transfer rates. Examples of practical commercial heating on the order of 500 Btu per hr per ft² per °F difference between the steam temperature and the boiling liquid temperature have been experienced in heating applications of this sort. In the petroleum industry, where much boiling of materials like gasoline, benzene, and toluene takes place by exposure to steam-heated reboilers, transfer coefficients of 150–300 have been found. To be sure, the surfaces may become fouled or contaminated by deposits resulting from cracking or polymerization which may reduce these values. Despite these conditions, the use of steam heating prevents overheating and exposure to excessive decomposition which might take place by use of other heating mediums.

Control of heat application at temperatures corresponding to subatmospheric pressure is more difficult because of the inability of the condensate produced to be discharged under its own pressure. A condensate pump to raise the pressure of the condensate to superatmospheric pressure is usually the most satisfactory method. Sometimes the condensate pumping is achieved by a barometric leg, but this necessitates a corresponding physical elevation of the equipment. Supply of the steam may be controlled by temperature, pressure, or rate of flow.

In some steam-heating systems the very close relations of temperature and pressure of the heating medium are a disadvantage. When mixtures of very narrow-boiling-range components are being heated in, say, the kettle of the reboiler connected to a distillation tower, the properties of steam may be a serious handicap to the control of the system. If the materials being fractionated have very close boiling characteristics, the use of temperature or pressure is not a satisfactory means for control. In these cases requiring very closely controlled heat input, it is more customary to control the rate of steam admission to the system by a flow regulator. In this manner the actual Btu input to the system is controlled to the desired uniformity. Such a flow regulator may be "reset" by a temperature regulator if sufficient accuracy can be obtained at some intermediate point in the system for resetting the flow. Otherwise, a constant refluxing of the fractionating system may not be obtained. In this case, a rate-of-flow controller is used as primary steam admission control, but this controller may be further "reset" upward or downward to maintain a desired temperature at a given point by a temperature controller. The condensate may be self-discharged or pumped, depending on the pressure of operation.

Limitations. The use of steam heating has practical limitations due to cost of the heating apparatus and of the steam generating facilities for high temperatures and pressures. It may be practically stated that the use of steam for process heating is limited to about 350°F, because, beyond this, small differences in temperature are accompanied by large changes in pressure. When temperatures in excess of 350–400°F are required, other heating mediums are usually preferred. An example of such a medium is Dowtherm, having much higher boiling temperatures for greatly reduced pressures of operation. Other mediums also used are the molten salts, mercury vapor, molten sodium, etc. See Heat-transfer media.

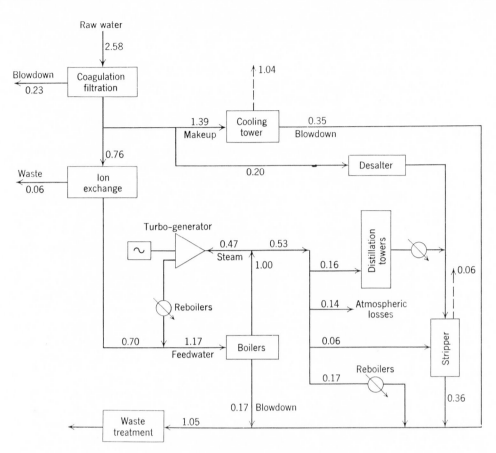

Fig. 3. Refinery steam–water balance.

Steam Extraction. Steam may be generated in a boiler at a processing plant location at a pressure in excess of 300 psi, but for most of these cases the higher pressure is utilized for the generation of power. In such applications, steam may be generated at pressures of 600 psi and then expanded through mechanical-drive turbines or through turbines of electric generators in order to produce electric power. Steam for process heating may be extracted from such turbines at pressures ranging from a few pounds above atmospheric to as high as 200 psig. In some instances, combinations of this sort will result in production costs for electricity which are much cheaper than the cost of generating power alone because of the high heat recovery obtained in using the extracted steam for process purposes. A power plant inevitably must condense the steam passed through its turbines, and this can be accomplished only by discarding into the condensers approximately 1000 Btu for each pound of steam passed through the turbogenerator. Under these conditions, the useful heat taken from the steam represents only some 20–30% maximum of the available heat which was put in at the boilers (although heat recovery approaching 40% has been reported). But when a large part of the 1000 Btu per pound can be used in the process, it is obvious that much greater overall economy is obtained. The complexity of such installations is illustrated in Figure 3, which shows a typical steam–water balance for an integrated petroleum refinery.

Steam Generation in Heat-Recovery Systems

Although most steam is raised as a direct consequence of the combustion of a fuel, there is much steam which is generated as a by-product to other principal objectives. These may be roughly classified into the following four categories:

1. Removal of heat from vessels in which exothermic chemical reactions are to proceed at essentially isothermal temperature conditions (eg, oxidation of naphthalene or o-xylene to phthalic anhydride).

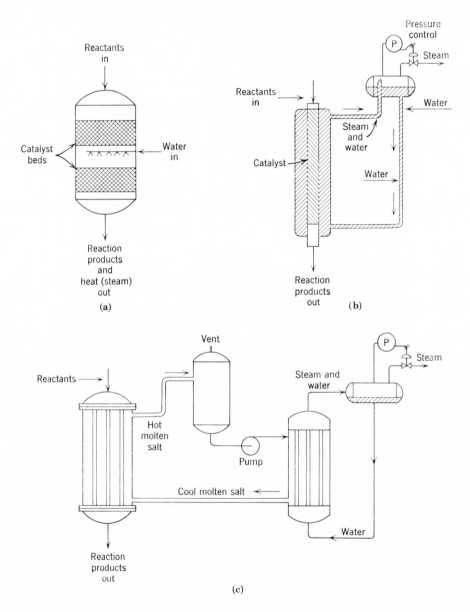

Fig. 4. Heat recovery systems using steam: (**a**) direct quenching with water; (**b**) circulation of water and steam; (**c**) generation of steam by molten salt.

2. Cooling of process streams and/or removal of latent heat of condensation at temperature levels capable of generating steam (eg, heat removal from secondary reformer and shift converter effluents in ammonia synthesis–gas production).

3. Combustion of burnable materials which are subjected to oxidation processes in order to convert them into gases, and in which the combustion gases thus produced are capable of generating steam (eg, carbon removal from catalysts, incineration of waste products, and sulfur oxidation to sulfur dioxide).

4. Combustion of fuel to produce elevated temperatures primarily for physical or chemical processes in which the by-product flue gases thus produced are capable of generating steam (eg, drying, evaporation, calcining, smelting, and primary reforming of methane–steam gas mixture).

The generation of steam as a means of controlling the temperature at which an exothermic reaction takes place is of considerable interest in the chemical industry. The reaction may require careful temperature control in order to avoid production of undesired by-product materials or, perhaps, in order to avoid short life or physical breakdown of the catalyst. Systems of this sort operating in the temperature ranges of 200–400°F are frequently held in careful balance by the use of steam generation. Figure 4 shows three ways of heat recovery. The reaction may be controlled by direct removal of heat in the reaction mass (Fig. 4a), or by indirect control such as circulation of the cooling fluid (Fig. 4b), or by circulation of an intermediate indirect cooling medium (Fig. 4c) from which steam is generated.

In some instances, the catalyst chambers or reaction vessels are filled with tubes which may contain the catalyst on the inside or the outside of the tube. Where relatively low temperatures are involved, so that the pressure in the steam generator is correspondingly low, reaction may take place in the tubes of a tubular reaction vessel with water and steam circulating outside the tubes in the shell of the vessel, such as a large vertical heat exchanger. The steam generated by the circulating water will be taken off at an upper steam drum and the unvaporized water recirculated. Such a system is illustrated in Figure 4b. In this instance, the circulation is maintained by the thermosyphon characteristics of the system.

When the temperature of the operation is high, which may result in generation of steam at high pressure, the catalytic reaction may take place on the shell side of the heating unit, in which case the steam is generated in the tube side at higher pressure. Under these conditions, provided the process side operates at low pressure, steam is also generated, but the cost of the apparatus will be lower because the pressure is controlled inside the smaller surfaces of the tubular vessel. The degree of temperature control necessary on the reaction side may govern the arrangement of the equipment. When no more than very small temperature changes may be permitted in the reaction mass, small tubes or small spaces between tubes will be required in order to prevent excessive temperature rise in the reaction. There are cases of reaction rates and heat release so high that small tubes of 1–2 in. diameter may be required in order to prevent the rise of temperature in the middle or center of the catalyst mass from exceeding what may be a safe temperature at the wall of the reaction tank or tube.

A good example of high-pressure steam generation as a by-product of the heat of reaction of a chemical process is shown in the diagram of a large synthetic ammonia plant (Fig. 5) where steam is generated on the inside of bayonet-type tubes inserted into the reaction vessel. Steam at a pressure of 1700 lb is generated from the waste heat unit and constitutes the entire source of steam required to generate the necessary

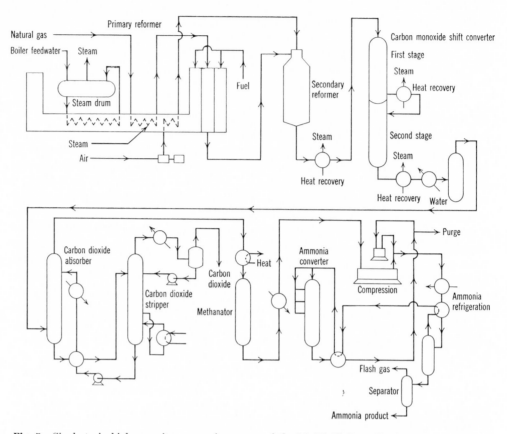

Fig. 5. Single-train high-capacity ammonia process of the M. W. Kellogg Co. featuring centrifugal compressors (33).

mechanical power through a topping turbine driving a compressor. The exhaust steam is used in the reaction process as well as for other drives and for heating service. In this instance, the requirement for bayonet-type generating tubes brings the requirement of very careful control of the purity of the boiler water circulating within those tubes. Modern ethylene plants are likewise large generators of steam from waste heat from the reaction stream from the ethylene furnaces (see Ethylene).

Another example of heat recovery by generation of steam is that which occurs in some catalytic cracking operations utilizing the fluid technique. Here the cracking catalyst may be passed through or be in contact with the tubes of a steam evaporator which takes heat from the main mass or reaction to control the temperature.

In this type of reaction temperature control, it is always important to observe that the hydrostatic head on the circulating medium may involve an appreciable temperature difference between the top and bottom of the reaction vessel. If a reaction takes place at temperatures of only 150–220°F, it would not be advisable to use a tall vertical reactor containing 15–20 ft of water, since this static head will increase the pressure at the base of the vessel by a pressure of about 8 psi which will raise the temperature at boiling and prevent careful temperature control at the base of the reaction vessel: a temperature difference of approximately 20–50°F is entirely possible from this cause. If the reaction will tolerate this much temperature spread, the designer will not be concerned; but, if a careful temperature control is required, then the vessel height must be shortened since the temperature will not be closely regulated otherwise. As the control temperature approaches 300°F, the effect of static pressure on the boiling temperature has less significance, and it becomes more practical to lengthen the reaction vessel.

The use of steam applications of this type also has another advantage. Often the reaction systems must first be brought to reaction temperature to initiate the reaction. With the use of steam-generating system, it is possible at start-up to remove the condensate or hot water from the system and admit steam at the operating pressure. Under these conditions, the system will come up to operating temperature through the application of steam supplied from external sources. However, as soon as reaction has started, the temperature becomes self-sustaining, the system will reverse, and steam will begin to be generated.

The steel industry has long practiced heat recovery from its open-hearth furnace operations. The exhaust gas exiting from the furnace first passes through the brick checker work used to preheat the incoming combustion air and then passes to waste-heat boilers where the temperature of the exhaust gas is further reduced in the generation of steam. Such steam generators resemble the design of the convective section of conventional fuel-fired boilers and are usually natural circulation drum types. The exhaust gas from the steam generator then passes to one or more stages of mechanical and/or electrical filters for removal of the particulate iron oxide generated in the oxygen-enriched open-hearth furnace.

Where basic oxygen furnaces are used, the cupola or hood into which the furnace discharges when blowing may be cooled by the generation of steam within tubes lining the inside of the cupola. Continuous casting machines forming a continuous billet of steel from a basic oxygen furnace also require the removal of large amounts of heat and some use steam generation for this purpose.

Applications of this type differ from steam boilers in that they are not direct-fired. Nevertheless, many of the features required by state and local codes for the generation of steam must be considered in the design of the apparatus. For instance, if the system is subject to building excessive pressures because of run-away reactions as the temperature rises, then safety features to ensure a secondary source of feedwater, to provide adequate overpressure relief, etc., may be very necessary. In addition all of the usual features for ensuring proper measurement of water levels and feedwater supply to the system are necessary. Where, however, the system cannot get greatly out of balance because of a limited temperature for the reaction, the process steam generator need not be as stringently provided with safety features as for a direct-fired boiler.

Process Steam

In many chemical plant processes, steam is used directly as a reactant in the process. In others, although it does not actually participate in the chemical reactions, steam is added as a diluent gas or as a means of quenching or controlling reaction rate. It can also be added as an aid to distillation or can be used as a stripping medium in the separation of products. Probably the widest use of steam in chemical reactions is the gas reform process in which steam and methane are reacted over a nickel catalyst to form carbon monoxide and hydrogen; then this gas mixture is reacted in turn with additional steam over an iron oxide catalyst to form carbon dioxide and hydrogen.

Removal of carbon dioxide by various absorption processes produces a stream of relatively pure hydrogen for use in further reactions. One of the most important current uses of this process is in the production of synthetic ammonia where the gas reform process is used to produce the hydrogen which in turn is reacted with nitrogen from the air at high pressure and temperature over a suitable catalyst to produce ammonia. In this synthetic ammonia process approximately 0.75 lb of water as steam are required in the reaction to produce 1 lb of ammonia. A very large synthetic ammonia plant (shown in Fig. 5) uses a single-train process with steam-turbine-driven centrifugal compressors; the exhaust steam is used for the foregoing gas reforming reaction. The high-pressure steam thus generated from waste heat is the heart of the energy system for the process which in turn is the key to the process economics.

General Economics

Many small chemical plants require only a few thousand pounds of steam per hour. In such instances, the steam generator may be of the once-through, flash-boiler type. When larger quantities of steam must be generated, or, when a great proportion of the boiler feedwater must be makeup water, as is the case when the steam is used for direct process injection, the use of package boilers is indicated. Such units are sold on very competitive bases. These package boilers may be considered as almost automatic, requiring very little operating attention, inasmuch as they are equipped with practically fully automatic controls.

In the larger chemical plants, which require steam in quantities above 100,000 lb per hour and under special pressure and temperature conditions, the selection of a boiler of individual design is justified. In these cases, the boiler may also be designed to generate steam at higher pressure in order to meet the power demands of the plant, particularly if it is in a remote area. If power can be purchased from the local utility companies without excessive charges, then generation of power is of questionable justification. However, where large quantities of steam are required for process needs, and power demands are in reasonable balance with steam demands, the combination of steam generation for power and process use is to be considered. Power normally so generated will be attained through the use of turbogenerators, and in these cases the turbines will probably be designed to extract steam at the desired process operating level.

The selection of the process operating level will depend to a large extent on the process requirements as well as on the economics of distribution of steam from the generating point to the point of use. Naturally, the power obtained from the steam will be greater as the process extraction pressure is reduced. There will be a balance, however, between this pressure and the economical pressure for heating. One must take into consideration the effect of reducing the steam pressure on the size of the process heating units. The smaller the demand, the lower the pressure may be, assuming that the pressure level always corresponds to a temperature high enough to meet the process demand.

In the case of a larger process heating load, however, it must be remembered that in general the temperature difference between the process-fluid heating side and the steam heating side must be kept as large as possible or the cost of the equipment or apparatus will become uneconomical. Suppose, for instance, that process heating must be at a temperature level of approximately 250°F. Such heating might be carried out in tubular heat exchangers using steam at 50 psig, which corresponds to a temperature of 298°F and produces a differential temperature of nearly 50°F. The surface of the heat exchanger transmitting this heat may be very large, say 1000 ft², if the temperature differential is only 50°F. Let us assume, however, that the extraction pressure of the turbine was increased to 100 psig. At this pressure, the temperature for use in the process unit would be on the order of 335°F. This will produce a temperature differential on the heating surface of 85°F in comparison to the 50°F temperature difference with 50-lb steam. In comparison, the heating surface will be reduced to about 600 ft², or by the ratio of 50 to 85, and represent a saving in surface of 40%. Since the piping systems to transport the steam will be of the same pressure rating and unit cost, there is an advantage in using the higher pressure level since smaller sizes will be required for the distribution of the steam, and considerable savings in the heat-transfer apparatus will also result. There are special instances in heat-exchanger design, however, where close temperature approaches between steam and process are beneficial. This is particularly true where the maintenance of isothermal process conditions is important.

Economically, the reduction of pressure must be justified on the basis of balancing power demand with steam demand and the equipment cost with the power generating cost. No specific formula is available to apply to all of these cases, but it will be evident that a review of the conditions which dominate the selection will permit a reasonably easy decision as to the approximate pressures to be set. The exact selection of the pressure may not be quite as easy, considering that many other factors may come into play before a final analysis can be reached.

The economy of using steam "twice," as is sometimes said, has many obvious advantages. If the power and steam demand are in good balance, the quantity of steam to be generated for power is the same in units of weight per unit of time, and only the total heat input per pound increases with power generation. This is small, however, if one compares the total heat content of the steam for process, and of the steam for power and process. Assume process steam is to be extracted at 150 psig and negligible superheat. Its total heat content is 1196 Btu/lb. Now suppose that in order to generate power, steam is required at 585 psig and 650°F, which corresponds to a total heat of 1280 Btu/lb. The total added heat per pound is only 85 Btu or about 7%. The effect of this on the cost of the boiler plant is small.

The cost of the turbogenerator is all added to the cost of the steam plant, so that the cost of the former and the operating labor are chargeable to the power generated. As far as the cost of prime energy for power is concerned, all that is frequently charged against the power generator is the amortization charges for the extra cost of the boiler due to the increased design pressure and the cost of the fuel represented by the 85 Btu/lb of steam. Such economies produce very cheap power.

Considering the systems for distribution of steam, it should be noted that the industry has developed piping standards which should be kept in mind as pressures are selected. For instance, piping standards are set at pressures of 150 psig, 300 psig, 400 psig, 600 psig, etc. These pressures are such that steam at corresponding saturation (or higher above 150 psig) temperatures may be used. It would not be economical generally to consider steam at 175 psig, particularly if the distribution system were at all long and complicated, since this pressure requires the use of 300-lb piping facilities. Most process systems will probably come within the pressure range of the 150 lb standard and, in practically all cases, the 300 lb standard will be adequate. In a few cases, the higher pressure ranges mentioned may be required.   For power generation, pressures will extend to very high levels and designers should resort to the tables of standards available.

Bibliography

"Steam" in *ECT* 1st ed., Vol. 12, pp. 778–793, by H. N. La Croix, Foster Wheeler Corporation.

1. *Thermodynamic and Transport Properties of Steam*, American Society of Mechanical Engineers, New York, 1967.
2. J. W. Cobble, "High Temperature Aqueous Solution," *Science* **152**, 1479–1484 (1966).
3. G. W. Morey and J. M. Hesselgesser, "Solubility of Quartz and Some Other Substances in Superheated Steam at High Pressures," *Trans. ASME, Ser. A: J. Eng. Power* **73**, 865–875 (1951).
4. M. A. Styrikovich and O. I. Martynova, "Some Physico-Chemical Problems of Steam Generators at Large Power Plants," *Combustion* **39**, 20–26 (July, 1967).
5. P. J. Hoppe, "Turbine Blade Deposits," *Power Engrg.* **31**, 56–57 (Sept. 1967).
6. F. J. Pocock and J. F. Stewart, "The Solubility of Copper and Its Oxides in Supercritical Steam," *ASME Paper No. 61-WA-140*, New York (1961).
7. "Percentage of Silica in Steam Versus Boiler Drum Pressure of Selected Boiler Water pH," *Manual on Industrial Water and Industrial Waste Water*, 2nd ed., ASTM Spec. Tech. Publ. No. 148-L, American Society for Testing and Materials, Philadelphia, Pa., 1967, p. 963.
8. E. F. Coulter, E. A. Pirsh, and E. J. Wagner, Jr., "Selective Silica Carryover in Steam," *Trans. ASME Ser. A: J. Eng. Power* **78**, 869–873 (1956).
9. M. A. Styrikovich, "Investigation of the Carryover of Salts in Steam and of the Hydrodynamics of the Steam–Water Mixture by Beams of Radioactive Isotopes," *Bulletin on the Geneva Conference for the Peacetime Uses of Atomic Energy*.
10. M. A. Styrikovich, O. I. Martynova, and F. S. Belova, "Some Features of the Carryover of Sodium Chloride from Boiling Water into Steam," *Teploenergetika* **12** (9), 86–89 (1965).
11. R. C. Ulmer and H. A. Klein, "Impurities in Steam from High Pressure Boilers," *ASTM Proc.* **61**, 1396–1423 (1961).
12. F. G. Straub, "Solubility of Salts in Steam of High Pressure," *Proc. of the 3rd Annual Water Conference*, Engineers' Society of Western Pennsylvania, 1942, pp. 31–42.
13. M. M. Rubright, "The Stoichiometry of the Vaporous Carry-over of Sodium Chloride from High-Pressure Boiler Water," *ASTM Proc.* **61**, 1370–1382 (1961).
14. R. V. Cobb and E. F. Coulter, "The Prevention of Errors in Steam Purity Measurement Caused by Deposition of Impurities in Sampling Lines," *ASTM Proc.* **61**, 1386–1395 (1961).
15. M. Lawlor and C. Clark, An Experimental Investigation of Some of the Factors Which Influence the Accuracy of Steam Sampling, *ASME Paper No. 61-WA-266*, New York (1961).
16. P. Goldstein and F. B. Simmons, "An Experimental Investigation of Factors Which Influence the Accuracy of Steam Sampling–Series II," *Proc. Am. Power Conf.* **26**, 720–726 (1962).
17. T. A. Miskimen, "Results of Steams Sampling Nozzle Tests on Evaporator Vapor," *ASME Paper No. 59-A-301* (1959).
18. J. Jackson, "Steam Sampling in Russia," *Power Engrg.*, **64**, 627 (Nov. 1960).
19. *Tentative Method of Sampling Steam, ASTM Designation D1066-67T*, American Society for Testing and Materials, Philadelphia, Pa., 1967.
20. E. F. Coulter and T. M. Campbell, Jr., "Steam Purity Determination by Tracer Technique," *Symposium on Steam Quality, ASTM Special Technical Publication No. 192*, American Society for Testing and Materials, Philadelphia, Pa., 1956.
21. J. K. Rice, "Steam Quality Measurements by Flame Photometer," *Proceedings of the 17th Annual Water Conference*, Engineers' Society of Western Pennsylvania, 1956.
22. J. K. Rice, "Measuring Steam Quality: Part I," *Power* **106**, 75 (Sept. 1962).
23. P. H. Cootner and G. O. Löf, *Water Demand for Steam Electric Generation*, Resources for the Future, Inc., Washington, D.C., 1965, Table I, p. 13.
24. W. Diskant and R. E. Hinkle, "High-Temperature Water Shows Many Advantages Over Steam for Large Scale Heating Systems," *Power Eng.* **70**, 48–51 (June 1966).
24a. P. L. Kenny, "Once-Through Boiler Control," *Power Eng.* **72**, 36–39 (Jan. 1968).

25. G. R. Fryling, ed., *Combustion Engineering*, rev. ed., Combustion Engineering Inc., New York, 1967, Tables 8–11.

26. *Report of the Committee on Water Quality Criteria*, Federal Water Pollution Control Administration, Supt. of Documents, U.S. Government Printing Office, Washington, D.C., 1968, Table V-5.

27. *Book of ASTM Standards*, Part 23, American Society for Testing and Materials, Philadelphia, Pa., 1968.

28. *Standard Methods for the Examination of Water and Wastewater*, 12th ed., American Public Health Association, New York, 1965.

29. H. W. Dierman, H. L. Russo, and W. R. Thompson, "Overall Plant Design–Symposium on Indian Point Nuclear Generating Station Unit No. 2," *Proc. Am. Power Conf.* **29**, 206–218 (1967).

30. J. R. Parrish, G. M. Rox, and F. G. Baily, "Nuclear Power Plant of TVA at Brown's Ferry–Background and Description," *Proc. Am. Power Conf.* **29**, 102–115 (1967).

31. A. L. Habush and R. F. Walker, "The Fort Saint Vrain HTGR," *Proc. Am. Power Conf.* **29**, 126–134 (1967).

32. R. E. Cabert, "Combined Steam and Gas Turbine Plant Producing Electricity and Process Steam Simultaneously," *Combustion* **36**, 36–41 (Aug. 1964).

33. "Kellogg's Single Train Large Ammonia Plants Achieve Lowest Costs," *Chemical Engineering* **74** (24), 112–117 (1967).

J. K. Rice
Cyrus Wm. Rice and Company

STEARIC ACID, $CH_3(CH_2)_{16}COOH$. See Fatty acids.

STEATITE. See Talc.

STEEL

Steel is the generic name for a group of ferrous metals (composed principally of iron) which, because of their abundance, durability, versatility, and low cost, are the most useful metallic materials known to man. Steel, in the form of bars, plates, sheets, structural shapes, wire, pipe and tubing, forgings, and castings, is used in the construction of buildings, bridges, railroads, aircraft, ships, automobiles, tools, cutlery, machinery, furniture, household appliances, and many other things upon which our convenience, comfort, and safety depend. Steel is an essential material for spacecraft and their supporting facilities, and is found in practically every kind of matériel needed for the national defense.

The abundance of steel is indicated by the fact that, in a typical year, over 500 million tons of raw steel are produced throughout the world.

The durability and versatility of steel are shown by the wide range of mechanical and physical properties possessed by different kinds of steel. By the proper choice of carbon content and addition of alloying elements, and by suitable heat treatment, steel can be made so relatively soft and ductile that it can be cold drawn into complex shapes like automobile bodies or the deep, one-piece tubs for domestic washing machines. Conversely, steel can be made extremely hard to resist wear, or tough enough to withstand enormous loads and shock without deforming or breaking. In addition, some steels are made to resist corrosion by the atmosphere, or by a wide variety of chemicals, or by heat.

The usefulness of steel is enhanced by the fact that it is one of the cheapest of all metals: its cost ranges from about $8\frac{1}{2}$¢ per lb for the commoner grades to several dollars per lb for special steels such as some of the tool steels.

This article will describe both early methods of steelmaking and modern methods, along with the composition and properties of different modern kinds of steel. As a beginning, it should be pointed out that all of the commercial modern steels fall into one of three categories: carbon steels, alloy steels, or stainless steels. Tool steels, both carbon and alloy types, are discussed elsewhere in this encyclopedia, as are the heat-resistant alloys not included among the stainless steels. See High-temperature alloys; Tool materials.

Evolution of Steelmaking. It has been known for many centuries that iron ore, embedded in burning charcoal, can be reduced to metallic iron. Iron was being made by this method at least as early as 1200 BC, when ironmaking was being practiced generally in the ancient world. It is not known when the first metal resembling modern carbon steel was made deliberately. Some authorities believe that steel was being made in what is now India at least as early as 1000 BC. Remains of swords with steel blades have been found in Luristan, a western province of Iran (formerly Persia) at sites dated at about 800 BC.

The first man-made iron closely resembled modern wrought iron, in that it consisted almost entirely of pure iron. Wrought iron is relatively soft, malleable, ductile, and readily hammer-welded when heated to a sufficiently high temperature. To the ancients, it was a very useful metal for many purposes, including agricultural implements and many kinds of tools.

Most steel contains more than 98% of iron. However, it also contains carbon which, if present in sufficient amounts (up to about 2%), gives steel a property unmatched by any of the metals available to ancient man. This property is the ability of steel to become extremely hard if cooled very quickly (quenched) from a high enough temperature, as by immersing it in water or some other liquid. The hardness of steel and its ability to take and hold a sharp cutting edge make it an extremely valuable metal for weapons, tools, cutlery, surgical instruments, razors, and other special forms.

It was not until the eighteenth century that carbon was even recognized as a chemical element, and it is quite certain that no early metallurgist was aware of the true reason for the unique properties of steel as compared with those of wrought iron. There are a number of ways in which carbon can be alloyed with iron to make steel, and all of the methods to be described have been used at various times in many localities for perhaps three thousand years or more.

One of these ways is to pack bars of low-carbon wrought iron in airtight containers along with charcoal or other carbonaceous material. By heating the containers to a red heat and holding them at that temperature for several days, the wrought iron will absorb carbon from the charcoal; this method became known as the cementation process, described below. Another way in which carbon could alloy with iron would be if the iron made in primitive furnaces, during and after its reduction, absorbed carbon from the charcoal fuel. There is evidence that the Romans and others recognized this and built and operated furnaces that produced a steel-like metal instead of wrought iron. In neither of the two foregoing cases did either the iron or the steel become molten.

In very ancient times in India, a steel called "wootz" was made by placing very pure iron ore and wood or other carbonaceous material in a tightly sealed pot or crucible and then heating the pot and its contents to a very high temperature for a considerable time. At high temperatures, some of the carbon in the crucible reduced the iron ore to metallic iron which absorbed any excess carbon. The resulting iron–carbon alloy was an excellent grade of steel. In a somewhat similar way, pieces of low-carbon wrought iron were placed in a pot along with some form of carbon and melted to make a fine steel. A variation of this method, in which bars that had been carburized by the cementation process were melted in a sealed pot to make steel of the best quality, became known as the crucible process (see below).

Prior to the invention of the Bessemer process for steelmaking in 1856, the cementation and crucible processes were the only ones of any considerable industrial importance. Although both of these processes were known to and practiced by the ancients, their practice seems to have been abandoned in Europe prior to the Middle Ages. The cementation process was revived in Belgium around 1600, while the crucible process was rediscovered in England by Benjamin Huntsman in 1742. Both processes were practiced in secret for some time after their revival, and little is known of their early history. The following brief descriptions will, therefore, be confined to practices followed after the processes had become well developed and had come into general use.

Cementation Process. This highly developed process, which flourished in England during the eighteenth and nineteenth centuries, continued to be used to a limited extent into the early part of the twentieth century.

The process depended on the fact that when a low-carbon ferrous metal such as wrought iron was heated to a red heat in contact with carbonaceous material such as charcoal the metal absorbed carbon which, up to the saturation point of about 1.70%, varied in amount according to the time the metal was in contact with the carbon and the temperature at which the process was conducted. For carrying on the process, a type of muffle furnace or pot furnace was used and the iron and charcoal were packed in alternate layers.

In the softer grades (average carbon content about 0.50%), the center portion of each bar remained unaltered. In the harder grades (average carbon content as high as 1.50%) the outside of a bar might have a carbon content of 1.50–2.00%, with a center containing 0.85–1.10%. Steels made by this method were called cement steels.

Crucible Process. Huntsman, a clockmaker, desired a more uniform steel for springs than could be made from inhomogeneous cement steel. He originated the idea of melting cement steel in crucibles, in order to make the steel homogeneous.

The crucible process gave steels that were not only homogeneous throughout but were free from occluded slag originating in the wrought iron used to make cement steel. Crucible steel was so superior to cement steel for many purposes that the crucible process quickly became the leader for the production of the finest steels—a position it held for nearly two hundred years. One drawback of the crucible process was that each crucible held only 80–120 lb of steel.

Advent of Modern Steelmaking Methods. The steelmaking processes discussed above were all destined eventually to be supplanted by entirely new methods. The first of the new techniques was the pneumatic or Bessemer process (1856). Closely following the invention of the pneumatic process was the development of the regenerative-type furnace that, now known as the open-hearth furnace, became adapted to steelmaking and evolved into the principal means for producing steel throughout the world. The electric furnace is a relative newcomer to the field of steelmaking and is gradually finding more and more application in the quantity production of quality steels.

The most recently developed steelmaking method is a pneumatic process that involves blowing high-purity oxygen onto the surface of a bath of molten pig iron contained in a suitable vessel; this method is known in the United States as the basic oxygen steelmaking process.

Chemical Principles of Steelmaking. Pig iron and iron and steel scrap are the sources of the element iron for steelmaking in basic oxygen furnaces and in open-hearth furnaces; electric furnaces rely on iron and steel scrap. In the basic oxygen and open-hearth furnaces, the pig iron is used in the molten state as obtained from the blast furnace; in this molten form, pig iron is referred to as hot metal.

Pig iron consists of the element iron combined with numerous other chemical elements, the most abundant of which are carbon, manganese, phosphorus, sulfur, and silicon. Depending upon the composition of the raw materials used in the blast furnace—principally iron ore (beneficiated or otherwise), coke, and limestone—and the manner in which the furnace is operated, pig iron may contain 3.0–4.5% of carbon, 0.15–2.5% or more of manganese, as much as 0.2% of sulfur, 0.025–2.5% of phosphorus, and 0.5–4.0% of silicon. In refining pig iron to convert it into steel, all five of these elements must either be removed almost entirely or at least reduced drastically in amount. The same is true of these and any other unwanted percentages of elements that may enter a steelmaking process in the scrap.

Modern steelmaking processes are divided into two general classes from the chemical standpoint: acid processes and basic processes. Carbon, manganese, and silicon can be removed with relative ease by any of the processes, acid or basic. The removal of phosphorus and sulfur requires special conditions that can be met only by the basic processes, wherein lime is added to the chemical system to form a basic slag that is capable of forming compounds with phosphorus and sulfur during refining operations, thereby removing them from the metal. Because of the chemical nature of the slags, each of the processes must be carried out in equipment lined with refractories of the proper chemical composition; otherwise the slags would react with and be neutralized by the lining material and thereby destroy the lining rapidly. Thus, the basic processes are carried out in vessels or furnaces lined with basic refractories such as dolomite or magnesite, while the acid processes are carried out in equipment lined with acid refractories such as silica brick, sintered silica sand, or ganister.

The chemical principle of oxidation is employed to convert a molten bath of pig iron and scrap, or scrap alone, into steel. Each steelmaking process has been devised primarily to provide some means by which controlled amounts of oxygen can be supplied to the molten metal undergoing refining. The oxygen combines with the unwanted elements (with the exception of sulfur) and, unavoidably, with some of the iron, to form oxides which either leave the bath as gases or enter the slag. The mechanism by which sulfur is removed does not involve direct reaction with oxygen but depends instead on whether the slag is sufficiently basic and high enough temperatures are attained. As the purification of the pig iron proceeds, due to the removal of carbon, the melting point of the bath is raised, and sufficient heat must be supplied from some source to keep the bath molten.

In general, steels that have similar chemical compositions have similar mechanical and physical properties, no matter by which process they are made.

Table 1. Raw-Steel Production in the United States (1), 1000 net (short) tons

Year	Open-hearth	Bessemer	Basic oxygen	Electric	Total
1967	70,690	see note[a]	41,434	15,089	127,213
1966	85,025	278	33,928	14,870	134,101
1965	94,193	586	22,879	13,804	131,462
1964	98,098	858	15,442	12,678	127,076
1963	88,834	963	8,544	10,920	109,261
1962	82,957	805	5,553	9,013	98,328
1961	84,502	881	3,967	8,664	98,014
1960	86,368	1,189	3,346	8,379	99,282
1959	81,669	1,380	1,864	8,533	93,446
1958	75,880	1,396	1,323	6,656	85,255
1957	101,658	2,475	611	7,971	112,715
1956	102,841	3,228	506	8,641	115,216
1955	105,359	3,320	307	8,050	117,036
1954	80,328	2,548		5,436	88,312
1953	100,474	3,856		7,280	111,610
1952	82,846	3,524		6,798	93,168
1951	93,167	4,891		7,142	105,200
1950	86,262	4,535		6,039	96,836
1949	70,249	3,946		3,783	77,978
1948	79,340	4,243		5,057	88,640

[a] Included with open-hearth.

A large percentage of the steel made in the United States for a considerable period was produced by the basic open-hearth process. Some acid open-hearth furnaces have been and are being used for the production of steel castings and specialty steels. Most of the electric furnaces for making steel for ingots are of the basic type; acid electric furnaces are confined to steel foundries for producing steel for castings. The basic oxygen process is challenging the basic open-hearth process for the position of the leading steelmaking method in the United States. Table 1 shows the annual production of steel by the various processes in the United States over a period of years. It will be observed that the Bessemer process is no longer a factor in raw-steel production here, while use of the basic oxygen steelmaking process has increased steadily since 1955, when it was first used commercially in the United States.

There has been a continuation of interest in processes for making iron and steel by direct methods from ore, without first reducing the ore in the blast furnace to make pig iron and then purifying the pig iron in a second step, as in conventional steelmaking. None of these processes, generally referred to as direct-reduction processes (see p. 803), has yet attained general acceptance, although some have been successful in certain localities where a combination of favorable conditions makes them practical.

Bessemer Processes

The original pneumatic steelmaking process, developed independently by William Kelly of Eddyville, Kentucky, and Henry Bessemer of England, involved blowing air through a bath of molten pig iron contained in a bottom-blown vessel lined with acid (siliceous) refractories. The process was the first to provide a large-scale method whereby pig iron could rapidly and cheaply be refined and converted into liquid steel. Bessemer's American patent was issued in 1856. Although Kelly did not apply for a patent until 1857, he was able to prove that he had worked on the idea as early as 1847. Thus, both men held rights to the process in the United States, and this led to considerable litigation and delay. Lacking financial means, Kelly was unable to perfect his invention and Bessemer, in the face of great difficulties and many failures, developed the process to a high degree of perfection and it came to be known as the acid Bessemer process or, more simply, the Bessemer process.

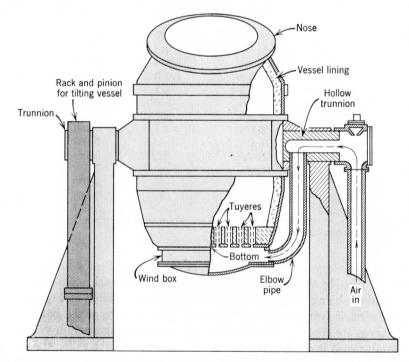

Fig. 1. Principle of the Bessemer converter. The air blast enters the wind box beneath the vessel through the pipe indicated by the arrow and passes into the vessel through holes in tuyeres set in the bottom of the converter.

The fundamental principle proposed by Bessemer and Kelly was that the oxidation of the major impurities (silicon, manganese, and carbon) was preferential and occurred before the major oxidation of iron. Further, they discovered that sufficient heat was generated in the vessel by the chemical oxidation of the above elements in most types of pig iron to produce liquid steel without the need for an external source of heat. Because the process converted pig iron to steel, the vessel in which the operation was carried out came to be known as a converter. The principle of the bottom-blown converter is shown in Figure 1.

The Bessemer process produced the majority of the world's steel from 1870 until 1910. The success of the process was dependent upon the quality of pig iron available. At first, Bessemer produced satisfactory steel in a converter lined with siliceous (acid) refractories by refining pig iron that, smelted from Swedish ores, was low in phosphorus, high in manganese, and contained enough silicon to meet the thermal requirements of the process. However, when applied to irons which were higher in phosphorus and low in silicon and manganese, the process did not produce satisfactory

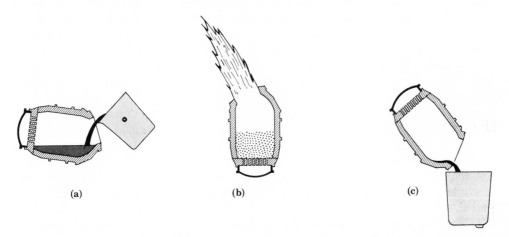

Fig. 2. Cross sections showing positions assumed by the Bessemer converter when (**a**) pouring molten pig iron into the vessel, (**b**) blowing compressed air through the molten metal, and (**c**) pouring the refined metal (steel) into the ladle, whence it is poured into ingot molds (2).

steel. In order to save his process in the face of opposition among steelmakers, Bessemer built a steel works at Sheffield in England and began to operate in 1860. Even when low-phosphorus Swedish pig iron was used, the steels first produced there contained much more than the admissible amounts of oxygen, which made the steel "wild" in the molds. Sulfur from the coke used as fuel in melting the pig iron in cupolas contributed to the "hot shortness" of the steel. These objections were overcome by the addition of manganese in the form of spiegeleisen (an iron–manganese alloy) to the steel after blowing was completed. The beneficial effects of manganese were disclosed in a patent by R. Mushet in 1856. The carbon and manganese in the spiegeleisen partially deoxidized the steel, while part of the manganese combined chemically with some of the sulfur to form compounds that either floated out of the steel into the slag, or were comparatively harmless if they remained in the steel.

As already stated, the success of the acid Bessemer process depended upon the quality of pig iron available, which in turn required reliable supplies of iron ore and metallurgical coke of relatively high purity. At the time of the invention of the process, large quantities of suitable ores were available in England, continental Europe, and the United States. With the gradual depletion of high-quality ores abroad (particularly low-phosphorus ores) and the rapid expansion of the use of the bottom-blown basic pneumatic process (also known as the Thomas, Thomas-Gilchrist, and basic Bessemer process), and the basic open-hearth and basic oxygen steelmaking processes over the years, acid Bessemer steel production has essentially ceased in the United Kingdom and on the continent of Europe.

In the United States, the Mesabi Range provided a source of relatively high-grade ore for making pig iron for the Bessemer process for many years. In spite of this, for economic and metallurgical reasons, the acid Bessemer process declined from a major to a minor steelmaking process in the United States and has now virtually been abandoned.

The early use of acid Bessemer steel in this country involved production of a considerable quantity of rail steel, and for many years (from its introduction in 1864 until 1908) the acid Bessemer was the principal steelmaking process in the United States. The acid Bessemer process was used in more recent times, principally in the manufacture of steel for butt-welded pipe, seamless pipe, free-machining bars, flat-rolled products, wire, steel castings, and blown metal for the duplex process.

Sequence of Operations. A schematic diagram of a Bessemer converter, giving the names of its principal parts, is shown in Figure 1. Figure 2 shows the positions assumed by the converter during various stages of its operation.

With the vessel in charging position (Fig. 2a), scrap was dumped into the converter (to act as a coolant, if required). Roll scale or iron ore could be added to hasten the blowing operation. Then molten pig iron was poured into the converter. In the horizontal position shown, the metal contained in the "belly" of the converter did not come into contact with the tuyeres. The air blast was then turned on and the converter was turned to a vertical position where it remained throughout the blowing period.

The Bessemer blow was considered as divided into three stages: the first period, the second period, and the afterblow.

The first period, or silicon blow, as it was commonly called, began as the blast was turned on and the converter was turned up. During this period of the blow, a short, transparent flame extended from the mouth of the converter. As blowing continued, the flame started to lengthen after about 4 min and the second period or carbon blow began.

The long, brilliant flame characteristic of the carbon blow continued until the elimination of carbon approached completion, when there was a definite change in the appearance of the flame. The flame gradually shortened in length and seemed to fan out. As viewed through the colored glasses worn by the operator (called the blower), streaks of red appeared in the flame at the mouth of the converter, and then almost instantaneously the whole flame changed from the usual golden yellow to a reddish-appearing color. This change, which always occurred at the same level of carbon content in the metal from blow to blow, was designated as the end point. Blowing of some grades of steel stopped promptly at the end point; these were said to be young-blown heats. Other grades of steel required blowing for as long as 15 or 20 sec after the end point; the time interval of blowing after the end point was termed the after-blow, and heats blown in this manner were said to be full-blown.

Molten pig iron having the following range of composition was desirable: silicon, 1.10–1.50%; manganese, 0.40–0.70%; phosphorus, 0.090% max; sulfur, 0.030% max. Carbon content of the iron ranged from 4.00 to 4.50%, but was not considered critical within this range.

A typical charge for a 25-ton converter (a common size) would consist of 55,000 lb of molten pig iron (hot metal) and 7,000 lb of scrap. With this charge, the blowing time would vary from 11 to 15 min. For small, 10-ton converters, the time would average 9–11 min.

After the blow was terminated, the converter was turned down and the blast was turned off. A ladle was positioned under the mouth of the converter and the blown metal was poured into it, retaining as much slag in the converter as possible. Deoxidizers and recarburizers were added to the metal as it poured into the ladle.

Chemistry of the Process. Although the acid Bessemer process, for economic and metallurgical reasons, has fallen into disuse, a discussion of the oxidation-reduction reactions involved in it will serve as a useful introduction to the chemical principles involved in all steelmaking processes.

At the start of the blow, oxygen from the air blast and some of the iron combined to form ferrous oxide (FeO), which reacted with manganese and silicon:

$$2\,FeO + Si \rightarrow SiO_2 + 2\,Fe$$
$$FeO + Mn \rightarrow MnO + Fe$$

The products of these three reactions combined to form the slag:

$$FeO + SiO_2 \rightarrow FeO.SiO_2$$
$$MnO + SiO_2 \rightarrow MnO.SiO_2$$

The iron and manganese silicates in the slag were not of fixed composition, but could contain more or less ferrous oxide than the ideal compositions given above, depending upon chemical conditions in the system.

Carbon in the metal could be oxidized either by oxygen in the air blast to form carbon monoxide or by iron oxide in the metal to form carbon dioxide. If the concentration of silicon and manganese was high enough, both of these elements could reduce carbon monoxide:

$$2\,CO + Si \rightarrow SiO_2 + 2\,C$$
$$CO + Mn \rightarrow MnO + C$$

After the manganese and silicon had been largely removed, carbon would react with the iron oxide in the metal to form carbon monoxide:

$$FeO + C \rightarrow Fe + CO$$
$$FeO + Fe_3C \rightarrow 4\,Fe + CO$$

It was the carbon monoxide from these two reactions, burning at the mouth of the converter, that produced the long, brilliant flame characteristic of the carbon blow.

All of the above reactions were exothermic except the last two involving the oxidation of carbon and iron carbide by ferrous oxide. In the acid Bessemer process, the oxidation of silicon provided most of the heat required.

Phosphorus and sulfur were not oxidized in the acid process. Weight is lost from from the bath by the elimination of carbon, manganese, and silicon, by mechanical ejection of material from the bath by the blast, and by retention of iron (in the form of iron oxide) in the slag. Assuming that this weight loss amounts to 10% of the weight of the charge, then for iron containing 0.030% sulfur and 0.075% phosphorus, the metal at the end of the blow would contain about 0.033% sulfur and 0.083% phosphorus. Some nitrogen from the air blast was absorbed by the molten metal, resulting in a final nitrogen content of the steel of perhaps 0.015%.

At the end of the blowing period, the metal in the converter consisted of molten iron containing very little carbon, manganese, or silicon, but in an overoxidized condition due to its content of iron oxide resulting from the blowing process. Overoxidized steel effervesces wildly in the molds and produces unsound, unsatisfactory ingots. The chemical composition of the blown metal was adjusted by the addition of deoxidizers and recarburizers that reduced the oxygen content of the metal to the desired level and raised the carbon, manganese, and silicon contents to the specified range. The additions most commonly made were ferromanganese (about 75% Mn), or various combinations of that and spiegeleisen (10–23% Mn, see Vol. 12, p. 897), ferrosilicon, anthracite coal, and pig iron, as well as aluminum when necessary. Anthracite coal and pig iron provided sources of carbon and were used principally as recarburizers. The manganese content of ferromanganese and spiegeleisen served as a deoxidizer and also reacted with some of the sulfur in the steel to form relatively harmless manganese sulfide. Spiegeleisen, because of its high carbon content, also could serve as a recarburizer. Ferrosilicon and aluminum are both deoxidizers.

After the additions had had time to mix and react with the steel, the molten metal was poured from the converter into a bottom-pour ladle from which it was teemed (poured) into ingot molds. After the steel had solidified in the molds to form ingots, the molds were stripped from the ingots which were then sent to the soaking pits to be heated for rolling.

Basic Bessemer (Thomas) Process. The basic Bessemer process, known as the Thomas process in Europe, was patented in 1879 by Sidney G. Thomas in England. It was never used in the United States. The process uses equipment generally similar to that of the acid Bessemer process, except that the converter is lined with a basic refractory material instead of siliceous (acid) refractories. The basic lining permits the use of a basic flux (lime) as a slag-forming ingredient in the process, which makes it possible to refine pig irons made from the high-phosphorus iron ores common to many sections of Europe. The chief use of the Thomas process is in the countries of the European Coal and Steel Community, where about 40% of the steel produced was still being made by this method in 1966 (3).

The major chemical differences between the bottom-blown acid and basic Bessemer processes lies in the chemical reactions involving the removal of phosphorus, and to some extent sulfur, from the iron. The effective removal of these elements depends on slag–metal reactions which are absent in the acid Bessemer process. Oxidation of carbon, manganese, and silicon occurs in essentially the same manner for both processes.

Removal of both phosphorus and sulfur in the basic process depends upon the concentration of lime in the slag; however, removal of phosphorus is favored by a high content of iron oxide in the slag and oxygen in the metal, while sulfur removal is favored by the reverse of these conditions. Thus, only a small amount of sulfur is removed in the basic process unless slags with a high lime content are formed. Further, because of the nature of the dephosphorization reaction, it occurs largely after the removal of the majority of the carbon, in the period known as the afterblow that begins at the end point (drop of the carbon flame as in the acid process) and may continue from 3 to 5 min, depending upon circumstances.

A blast-furnace iron for the Thomas process may contain 0.2–0.4% silicon, 0.6–1.0% manganese, 1.5–2.0% phosphorus, and 0.03–0.05% sulfur. The phosphoric acid anhydride (P_2O_5) content of the final slag produced in bottom-blowing iron of the above composition in a basic converter, using 300 lb of lime per ton of steel, is about 16–18%, with a slag volume of about 20–22%. Slags of this composition make desirable fertilizers and they are processed and sold for this purpose, thus aiding the economics of the process. See Vol. 9, p. 109.

Open-Hearth Processes

The success of the Bessemer process, coupled with the ever-increasing demand for steel, attracted many inventors to the study of new and improved methods of steel-making. The only method destined to first become a rival of, and then to outstrip, the Bessemer process was developed through the invention of the regenerative process by Karl Wilhelm Siemens, a German-born naturalized British citizen. The regenerative principle involves using what would otherwise be waste heat from a furnace to heat separate chambers filled with brickwork, one at each end of the furnace. These chambers are called regenerators. After the regenerator at one end of the furnace is heated sufficiently, the air to be used for combustion of fuel in the furnace passes through the regenerator on its way to the combustion chamber and is preheated to a high temperature. When gaseous fuels of low heating value are to be burned, they too may be preheated, in which case provision is made for preheating the gas and air separately. Gaseous fuels of high heating value and liquid fuels such as fuel oils and pitch–tar mixtures, do not require preheating. Combustion of preheated air and fuel produces flames having very high temperatures, capable of heating a furnace sufficiently to melt steel and keep it molten during refining operations.

The waste gas from the furnace leaves through the regenerator at the other end of the furnace, heating it to a high temperature. After the regenerator that has been used for heating has cooled somewhat, the furnace is reversed; that is, the direction of flow of fuel and air are reversed so that the gases to be preheated now enter the furnace through the hot regenerator and the hot waste gases leave the furnace through the partially cooled regenerator to restore the heat that it has lost and prepare it for its heating role after the next reversal.

Siemens devised a furnace consisting of a shallow, rectangular covered hearth, on which was placed a charge of solid pig iron or pig iron and scrap. Fuel gas (producer gas in the early furnaces) and air were preheated in regenerators and burned in the space above the hearth between the charge and the roof. The charge was heated by radiation from the flame and from the hot roof, until all had melted. Iron ore was fed to the bath to provide oxygen for the purifying reactions. The elements that were oxidized both by the iron ore and by excess air in the furnace atmosphere were carbon, silicon, and manganese, all three of which could be reduced to as low a limit as in the Bessemer process.

Siemens, like Bessemer, was forced to build his own steel works to prove that his process was practical. At first, this plant produced steel of good quality simply by remelting such scrap as old rails, plates, and so on. In the meantime, Siemens was developing the idea that steel could be made from pig iron by oxidizing the carbon content of the latter with iron ore and, by 1868, proved that this method, which came to be known as the pig and ore process, was practical. The pig and scrap process was originated by Emile and Pierre Martin in France who, by substituting scrap for some of the ore in Siemens' pig and ore process, found it possible to dilute the charge with steel scrap to such an extent that less oxidation was necessary. It was thus that the process known in English-speaking countries as the Siemens or open-hearth process became known as the Siemens-Martin process on the Continent.

The hearth of Siemens' early furnaces was built of acid refractories consisting of a layer of burned-in silica sand over siliceous firebrick, essentially as in the acid open-hearth furnaces of today. Later, to permit the charging of limestone to form a basic slag for the removal of phosphorus, steelmakers built hearths of magnesite brick covered with a layer of burned dolomite or magnesite; such furnaces were designated as basic furnaces and the process carried out in them was called the basic open-hearth process.

Early Open-Hearth Furnaces in the United States. As early as 1868, a small open-hearth furnace was built at Trenton, New Jersey, but satisfactory steel at a reasonable cost did not result and the furnace was abandoned. Later, at Boston, Massachusetts, a successful furnace was designed and operated, beginning in 1870. Following this success, similar furnaces were built at Nashua, New Hampshire, and in Pittsburgh, Pennsylvania, the latter by the Singer, Nimick and Company, in 1871. The Otis Iron and Steel Company constructed two 7-ton furnaces at their Lakeside plant in Cleveland, Ohio, in 1874. Two 15-ton furnaces were added to that plant in 1878, two more of the same size in 1881, and two more in 1887. All of these furnaces had acid linings, using a sand bottom for the hearths.

A furnace with a basic bottom, rammed from Austrian magnesite, produced basic steel at the Otis plant in January, 1886. The longer refining time inherent in the basic process due to slag-making reactions and the additional time required for removal of phosphorus made the production rate on the basic furnace seem so low compared to that normally achieved with an acid bottom that the basic bottom was torn out after four months and replaced by an acid bottom. Following the Otis installation, these companies also installed open-hearth furnaces: The Cleveland Rolling Mills, The Pennsylvania Steel Company, the Schoenberger Works, and Carnegie, Phipps and Company. It was in the last-named plant that the commercial production of steel by the basic open-hearth process was achieved first, the initial heat being tapped March 28, 1888. By the close of 1890, there were sixteen basic furnaces operating at that plant.

The economic advantage of the basic open-hearth process lay in its ability to use the pig iron and scrap of higher phosphorus and sulfur contents that were abundant and available at lower cost than the raw materials for the acid process, and it soon became the dominant steelmaking method.

From 1890 to 1900, magnesite for basic bottoms began to be imported regularly, and the manufacture of silica refractories for open-hearth furnace roofs was begun in American plants. For these reasons, as well as the economic reasons mentioned above, the construction of basic furnaces expanded rapidly and, by 1900, furnaces larger than 50 tons were being planned. It may be noted that silica (acid) bricks that were highly refractory could perform satisfactorily in the roof of a basic open-hearth furnace because they were not in direct contact with the basic slag.

While the Bessemer process could produce steel possibly at a lower cost above the cost of materials, it was restricted to ores of limited phosphorus content and its use of scrap was also limited. The basic open-hearth was not subject to these restrictions so that annual production of basic open-hearth steel increased rapidly and, by 1908, surpassed the total tonnage produced annually by the Bessemer process, which decreased rather steadily thereafter.

Some of the advantages of the basic open-hearth process are: (*1*) By the use of iron ore as an oxidizing agent and by the external application of heat, the temperature of the bath is made independent of the purifying reactions and the elimination of impurities can be made to take place gradually, so that both temperature and composition of the bath are under better control than in the Bessemer process. (*2*) For the same reasons, a greater variety of raw materials can be used (particularly scrap, not greatly consumable in the Bessemer converter) and a greater variety of products may be made by the basic open-hearth process than by the Bessemer process. (*3*) There is an increased yield of finished steel from a given quantity of pig iron as compared to the Bessemer process because less iron is lost than in the Bessemer, and in addition there is the iron from the iron content of the ore used for oxidation. (*4*) The basic open-hearth furnace has the ability to eliminate phosphorus from the bath.

The basic open-hearth furnace permits the economical use of iron of any phosphorus content up to 1.00%. This was of great importance in the United States, because it facilitated the use of the immense iron-ore deposits which were available, but which had phosphorus contents too high for making steel by the acid Bessemer or acid open-hearth processes, and too low for the basic Bessemer or Thomas process.

It may be mentioned that a method called the duplex process was used to a considerable extent in the United States in former years. In this method, pig iron was partially purified by blowing in an acid Bessemer converter, after which the blown metal was transferred to a basic open-hearth furnace for finishing. The rapid removal of most of the carbon, manganese, and silicon in the converter greatly lessened the amount of oxidation required in the basic open-hearth furnace in which phosphorus could be reduced to the desired level. Steel could be made faster by the duplex process than by the basic open-hearth alone.

Basic open-hearth furnaces range in capacity from 100 to 600 tons in this country; even larger furnaces are used in some other countries. Most of the more recently built open-hearths have capacities of 300–450 tons. The capacity of a furnace represents the amount of steel normally made in the furnace at one time; these individual batches of steel are referred to as "heats." The making of a heat of steel in the basic open-hearth furnace requires an average of 10 hr. The process can be speeded up by blowing gaseous oxygen into or onto the molten bath to hasten the oxidation of carbon.

In the United States in 1967, slightly over 55% of all of the raw steel made was produced in basic open-hearth furnaces; less than 0.2% was made in acid open-hearth furnaces. The preponderance in favor of the basic open-hearth process has been based on the ability of this process to remove phosphorus and some sulfur, as well as carbon, silicon, and manganese; while the acid open-hearth process (like the other acid processes) is limited to the removal of carbon, silicon, and manganese and must use carefully selected raw materials that contain less than the specified amounts of phosphorus and sulfur permissible in the finished steel.

Open-Hearth Furnace. Figure 3 is a schematic cut-away drawing of a modern open-hearth furnace. Figure 4a is a general view of a row of open-hearth furnaces from the charging floor. Figure 4b shows the tapping or pit side of a row of furnaces. The pit-side floor is about 20 ft below the charging floor.

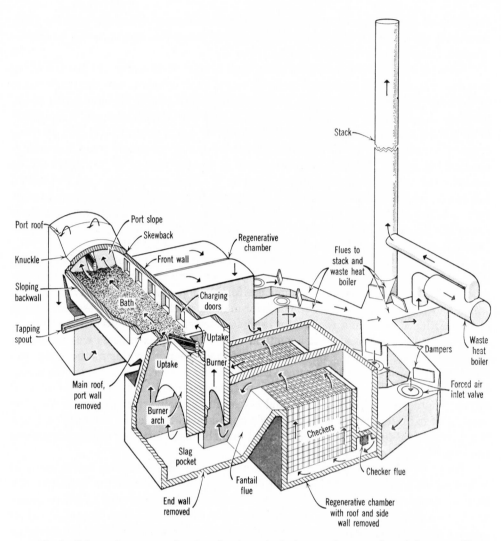

Fig. 3. Schematic cut-away drawing showing principal parts of an open-hearth furnace. Heavy curved arrows indicate direction of flow of air, flame, and waste gases when a liquid fuel is fired through a burner in the trench at the right end of the furnace. Direction of arrows reverses when the furnace is "reversed" and fired from the left end (2).

The hearth of the furnace forms a shallow, rectangular basin. In acid furnaces, it is built up by "burning-in" layers of silica sand covering the silica-brick subhearth. In basic furnaces, the subhearth is built of basic brick covered by a layer of rammed basic material and finished by "burning-in" a top layer of magnesite.

Modern basic open-hearth furnaces have their front walls, end walls, and sloping back walls built of basic refractories. Formerly, these walls, like the roof, were constructed of silica brick in both basic and acid furnaces.

Silica brick were employed for building the roof of both acid and basic furnaces for many years. The roof consisted of a series of free arches that supported each other sideways while the skew-backs, braced by structural steel work, took the thrust of the arches. Recently, basic refractories have been adopted for building the roofs of basic furnaces, especially those furnaces in which gaseous oxygen is used to speed up the steelmaking operation, as will be discussed later (see p. 741).

Heat for the furnace is supplied by burning liquid fuels (fuel oil, tar–pitch mixtures) or gaseous fuels (coke-oven gas, natural gas).

(a)

(b)

Fig. 4. (a) General view of the charging floor of an open-hearth steelmaking plant, showing the fronts of eight of the eleven furnaces in the plant. The charging machine is visible in the far left rear. The five doors on each furnace can be raised as required for charging the furnaces and working the heat. (b) General view of the rear or tapping side of an open-hearth furnace, showing a heat being tapped into a ladle supported in a stand at the plant ground level. Slag overflowing the ladle is loaded by high-lifts into dump trucks for removal after it has cooled and solidified. The men at the upper left are standing at the charging-floor level.

Fig. 5. View overlooking the charging machine in an open-hearth shop. A box locked to the end of the machine's "peel" is about to be thrust through the opened door of the furnace.

Open-hearth furnaces may have five to seven doors in the front wall through which access may be had to the hearth. A track runs in front of the furnace on which operate the charging buggies that carry charging boxes loaded with scrap, limestone, iron ore, or other materials used in the process. Also on the charging floor in front of the furnace is a very wide-gage track on which runs the charging machine that is designed to pick up charging boxes, one by one, thrust them through an open door of the furnace, and turn them over to dump their contents on the hearth, after which the boxes are righted, withdrawn from the furnace, and replaced on the charging buggies (Fig. 5).

At the back of the furnace, the taphole which is kept plugged during the steel-making operation connects the hearth with the tapping spout. A ladle is positioned beneath the spout to receive the finished steel when the plug is removed.

Basic Open-Hearth Steelmaking. In making up the charge for a basic open-hearth furnace, the proportions of solid pig iron, molten pig iron, and iron and steel scrap are selected so that when the solid materials have all been melted and the molten pig iron has been added, the carbon content of the liquid bath will be 0.30–0.50% above the carbon content desired in the finished steel.

The solid parts of the charge are placed in the furnace and heated for a sufficient time before charging molten pig iron. The limestone is charged first and any iron ore that is to be charged is spread over the limestone. The solid steel scrap is then charged. Any solid pig iron is charged immediately after the scrap.

The quantity of limestone for the greater part of American practice ranges from 5 to 8% of the total metallic charge. If burned lime is used instead of limestone, an equivalent fluxing effect will be obtained with 3–4% of lime. The weight of CaO added by these fluxes is proportioned on the basis of the weight of silicon, phosphorus, and sulfur in the total charge; silica in the limestone and ore; sulfur in the fuel; and so on.

The amount of iron ore charged varies from 0 to 25% of the total metallic charge, the high limit being required when unusally large proportions of molten pig iron are used. With charges of above 45–50% of molten pig iron, general practice is to charge ore with the initial charge and then to feed ore to the completely melted charge if needed.

Since the removal of unwanted elements from the bath involves their oxidation to the desired degree, it is desirable to summarize the sources from which oxygen is available for the process (assuming that no gaseous oxygen is used in ways to be described below). These sources are (1) oxides formed on the scrap during melting; (2) oxidizing oxides in slags at different stages; (3) carbon dioxide resulting from calcination of limestone; (4) excess oxygen from air supplied for combustion of the fuel; and (5) iron oxides in ore, roll scale, and so on that may be charged with the initial charge or fed after the charge is completely melted.

Many modern open-hearth furnaces are equipped with water-cooled "lances" that can be raised and lowered vertically through openings in the roof of the furnace to permit gaseous oxygen to be blown onto the molten bath to hasten oxidation reactions. Gaseous oxygen has also been used during the latter stages of refining to hasten the oxidation of carbon: A steel-pipe lance is inserted through a door opening so that its end is immersed beneath the surface of the molten metal, and gaseous oxygen is blown through the pipe into the molten bath.

After the molten pig iron has been added to the furnace, important reactions take place. Silicon and manganese are the first elements to be oxidized, forming SiO_2 and MnO that become part of the slag. When silicon and manganese have been substantially removed, oxidation of carbon begins at an accelerated pace. Carbon is oxidized to carbon monoxide gas which, in escaping, agitates the bath. Eventually, phosphorus is oxidized to P_2O_5 and becomes part of the slag. Sulfur is transferred to the slag and held there as CaS.

When a high percentage of molten pig iron is used, the evolving CO gas causes foaming of the slag, which can run from the furnace through openings provided for the purpose; this method of operation is called flush practice. Run-off slags remove from the furnace considerable phosphorus and silicon (as oxides) and also sulfur (as sulfides).

The period during which evolved carbon monoxide resulting from the oxidation of carbon causes turbulence in the bath is called the ore boil; more properly, it may be called the iron oxide boil since oxygen comes from other sources than iron ore, as mentioned earlier.

As the carbon content of the bath decreases and its temperature rises, the ore boil subsides and the calcination of limestone evolves CO_2 that causes a violent bubbling of the bath. This period is known as the lime boil. The calcined lime rises to the top of the bath and replaces iron and manganese in the phosphates, sulfates, and silicates present and becomes part of the slag.

After the ore boil and lime boil have subsided, the working period or refining period begins. The end of the melting period is generally taken as about the time when all the lime has risen from the bottom through a substantially melted charge.

The aims of the working period are (*1*) to lower the phosphorus and sulfur contents to levels safely below the maximum level specified; (*2*) to eliminate carbon as rapidly as possible and still allow time for proper conditioning of slag and attainment of proper temperature; and (*3*) to bring the heat to a condition ready for final deoxidation in the furnace or for tapping, with the slag having the proper viscosity and chemical composition and with the desired carbon and oxygen levels in the bath and the proper final bath temperature for the composition and grade of steel being produced. The slag must contain large quantities of oxidizing agents during the working period, but must be strongly basic at the end of the period: the way in which these ends are achieved depends upon whether the grade of steel being made is to be killed, semi-killed, or rimmed (see below under Ingots, p. 752), and also on the carbon content wanted in the finished steel.

Based upon using ore practice (no gaseous oxygen), a basic open-hearth furnace of 200–225 tons capacity, fired with a liquid fuel such as tar or oil, the time consumed during the various stages of a heat are as follows:

Stage	Time, hr
melt down (simultaneous with charging)	2.5
hot metal addition	0.5
ore boil	3.0
lime boil	1.5
working period	2.5
total heat time	10.0

In oxygen roof-lance practice, the flow of oxygen is started as soon as hot metal has been added, and the ore boil, lime boil, and working period tend to merge into one. The increased rates of reaction due to the increased availability of oxygen and higher temperatures attainable with oxygen practice reduce the overall heat time to about 8 hr, charge-to-tap, compared to the 10 hr for an ore-practice heat, for a similar furnace with a comparable charge making a similar grade of steel.

The finishing temperature of a heat of basic open-hearth steel will be in the neighborhood of 2900°F, varying according to the composition and grade of steel.

When the heat is ready to be tapped, the tapping hole at the back of the furnace is opened and the furnace is emptied of its molten contents, which are directed into a steel ladle through the tapping spout. Because the highest level of the tapping hole is at the lowest point in the hearth and slopes downward to meet the tapping spout, the greater portion of the steel flows out of the furnace before slag appears in the spout; this relatively late appearance of slag permits additions of recarburizing, deoxidizing, and alloying materials to the spout and, principally, to the ladle. Some slag is kept in the ladle to serve as a covering for the liquid steel: the excess overflows the ladle through a slag spout.

Acid Open-Hearth Steelmaking. In acid open-hearth practice, the initial charge consists normally of cold pig iron, or cold pig iron and scrap. No ore can be added with the charge as in the basic open-hearth process, for the iron oxide, being a base, would combine with the acid lining and rapidly destroy the bottom and banks. For the same reason the melting of scrap alone would be bad practice as its oxidation products would have a similar detrimental effect. Hence, the use of hot metal (molten pig iron) to supply the whole of the pig iron charge is impracticable, for it would necessarily have to be added after the scrap was hot and had been considerably oxidized. If the scrap were not hot enough, it would chill (and perhaps even solidify) the molten pig iron; also, start of the oxidation of the impurities in the pig iron would be delayed unless oxides from oxidation of the scrap were present. As noted above, the presence of such oxides would destroy the refractory lining of the hearth.

The proportion of scrap to pig iron may vary over wide limits. As previously pointed out, Siemens originally used no scrap, and ore was added to the pig iron after melting to hasten oxidation. Later, the Martins used scrap with only enough pig iron to make the melt have the carbon content desired in the finished steel. The modern method, in which a charge of pig iron and scrap is melted, then "ored down" if the carbon content of the melt is too high, or "pigged up" to increase the carbon content if it is too low, may be looked upon as a combination of the two early methods.

Care must be exercised to assure that the average sulfur and phosphorus contents of the charge are somewhat below those desired in the finished steel. Silicon, carbon, and manganese are oxidized quite readily and require less consideration in the selection of materials.

As soon as the furnace has been charged the fuel, which has usually been partly or wholly turned off during charging, is turned on full to melt down the charge as quickly as possible. From 4-5 hr are required to melt the charge. The bath after melting is completed should contain about 0.20–0.40% more carbon than is required in the finished steel.

If the charge was made up largely of a low-silicon pig iron and the heat was given the proper attention during melting, practically all of the silicon and manganese will have been oxidized and neutralized, forming the slag. The fluidity of the slag, as determined by tests, can be used to establish the need for additions to the slag to make it more or less oxidizing with respect to the bath. If the carbon content of the bath is relatively high, iron ore may be added to react with and eliminate carbon. If the carbon content is too low, pig iron may be added to increase it. By frequent sampling and adjustment of the carbon content of the bath, the carbon content and temperature are brought to the point where the heat can be tapped.

In the acid open-hearth process, additions are made to the heat both in the furnace and in the ladle. In making high-carbon heats, it is usual to have the heat ready for tapping when the carbon content has fallen to the desired level. In making medium- and low-carbon heats, the carbon content may be reduced to 0.10–0.12% in the furnace, and the carbon content restored to the desired level by adding recarburizers to the steel in the ladle. Additions of alloying elements that are unoxidizable may be made in the furnace. In addition to anthracite for recarburizing, ladle additions may include ferromanganese, ferrovanadium, ferrosilicon, ferrotitanium, and aluminum.

The tapping temperature of properly made acid open-hearth steel is around 3000°F. Heats are tapped by the methods described for the basic open-hearth process.

Electric-Furnace Steelmaking

The electric-arc furnace is the principal electric steelmaking furnace. The carbon arc was discovered by Sir Humphry Davy in 1800, but it had no practical application in steelmaking until Sir William Siemens of open-hearth fame constructed, operated, and patented furnaces operating on both direct-arc and indirect-arc principles in 1878. At that early date, the availability of electric power was limited and its cost high. Also, carbon electrodes of the quality to carry sufficient current for steel melting had not been developed.

In indirect-arc heating, the arcs are made between electrodes supported above the metal in the furnace, which thus is heated solely by radiation from the arc. In direct-arc heating, the current must flow through the metal bath so that the heat developed by the electrical resistance of the metal, though relatively small in amount, is added to that radiated from the arcs. The path of the current in a direct-arc furnace is through one electrode and thence through the arc between the foot of the electrode and the bath, then through the bath and up through an arc between the bath and an adjacent electrode, completing the circuit through this second electrode.

The first successful direct-arc steelmaking furnace, patented by Heroult in France, was placed in operation in 1899, and the first shipment of electric steel was a carload of bars from Heroult's plant at La Praz to the firm of Schneider and Company at Creusot, France, on December 28, 1900. The Heroult patent covered single-phase or multi-phase furnaces with the arcs in series through the metal bath. This type of furnace, utilizing three-phase alternating-current power, has been the most successful in the production of steel.

The first direct-arc furnace in the United States was a single-phase two-electrode rectangular furnace of four tons' capacity at the Halcomb Steel Company, Syracuse, New York, which made its first heat on April 5, 1906. Two years later, a similar but smaller furnace was installed at the Firth-Sterling Steel Company in McKeesport, Pennsylvania. In 1909, a 15-ton three-phase furnace was installed in the South Works of the Illinois Steel Company, in Chicago, Illinois: at that time, this was the largest electric steelmaking furnace in the world and was the first round instead of rectangular furnace; it operated on 25-cycle power at 2200 V and tapped the first heat on May 10, 1909.

The foregoing furnaces all were for making steel for ingots. The first electric furnace for the production of steel for commercial castings was that of the Treadwell Engineering Company, Easton, Pennsylvania. It was a single-phase two-electrode furnace with a capacity of two tons and was operated first in August, 1911.

In recent years, the direct-arc principle has been applied to vacuum consumable-electrode furnaces, see p. 740.

Induction Furnace. Another type of electric melting furnace is the high-frequency coreless induction furnace, now used in the production of complex, high-quality alloys such as tool steels. It is used also for remelting scrap from fine steels produced in arc furnaces, melting chrome–nickel alloys and high-manganese scrap, and, more recently, has been applied to vacuum steelmaking processes.

The induction furnace had its inception abroad and was first patented by Ferranti in Italy in 1877: this was a low-frequency furnace. It had no commercial application until Kjellin installed and operated one in Sweden. The first large installation of this type was made in 1914 at the plant of the American Iron and Steel Company in Lebanon, Pennsylvania, which was not successful. Some other low-frequency furnaces have operated successfully, especially in making stainless steel.

The first high-frequency coreless induction furnaces were built and installed by the Ajax Electrothermic Corporation, who also initiated the original researches by E. F. Northrup leading to the development of the furnace. For this reason, the furnace is often referred to as the Ajax-Northrup furnace.

The first high-frequency coreless induction furnaces for the production of steel on a commercial scale were installed in Sheffield, England, and began regular production of steel in October, 1921. The first commercial steel furnaces of this type in the United States were installed by the Heppenstall Forge and Knife Company in Pittsburgh, Pennsylvania, and were producing steel regularly in November, 1928.

Commercial use of the high-frequency furnace for ordinary melting is not extensive in the steel industry.

Electric-Arc Furnace Steelmaking. Electric-arc steelmaking furnaces until relatively recently were considered chiefly for the production of alloy steels. However, during the middle 1960s, something over 60% of all electric-furnace production was carbon steel. Total steel production in electric furnaces nearly doubled between 1960 and 1966 (about 15 million tons in 1966 compared with 8.5 million tons av between 1959 and 1961, inclusive). Electric-arc furnaces possess the advantages of low investment cost, and the ability to (*1*) produce steels of a wide range of compositions (carbon, alloy, and stainless), (*2*) make heats smaller than the full capacity of the furnace, (*3*) take advantage of changing costs of scrap and pig iron, and (*4*) produce quality steels without a source of hot metal.

Electric-arc furnaces may be lined with either acid or basic refractories. Technical and economic obstacles to the use of select scrap (low in phosphorus and sulfur) and the increasing utilization of alloy steels have greatly decreased the use of acid-lined furnaces. Almost all furnaces used for ingot-steel production and a large percentage of foundry furnaces for making steel for castings are now basic-lined.

In the acid process, because of the selected materials in the charge, the use of a single siliceous oxidizing slag predominates. Thus, under such oxidizing conditions, the making of alloy steels is complicated by the fact that alloying elements such as chromium and manganese are rapidly oxidized and lost to the slag. Oxidizable elements can be added to the furnace only after the heat has been deoxidized, just before tapping, or in the ladle after the steel is tapped. Large additions to the ladle are undesirable because of their chilling effect and because the additions cannot mix readily with the molten steel. Alloying elements that do not oxidize readily (eg, copper, nickel, and molybdenum) may be added in the furnace at any time.

In the basic process, a two-slag procedure generally is used: the basic oxidizing slag that first forms is removed from the furnace and replaced by a reducing slag. Removal of the oxidizing slag removes a large proportion of the phosphorus from the furnace. The reducing slag in the basic process makes possible a high degree of refinement of the bath, minimizes loss of alloying elements by oxidation, and removes objectionable impurities such as sulfur to a high degree. The reducing slag in the basic process also decreases the oxygen content of the bath to a low value; consequently, relatively few deoxidation products are formed when the final deoxidizers are added, because less of the latter are needed.

Figure 6 indicates typical refractories used in (left) an acid lining and (right) a basic lining of electric-arc steelmaking furnaces. Figure 7 shows the schematic arrangement of the electrodes for a three-phase furnace, their supporting arms, and the electrical power leads.

Basic Electric-Arc Process. With the power turned off, the solid scrap and other components of the charge are placed in the furnace. Alloying materials that are not easily oxidized can be and usually are charged in the furnace prior to melting down the charge. It is desirable to melt down with excess carbon in the bath so that some carbon can be worked out by ore additions or oxygen injection. If the metallic charge is too low in carbon, a recarburizer in the form of coke or scrap electrodes is charged with the scrap to allow for a carbon content at melt-down that will be 0.15–0.25% higher than the carbon content of the finished steel.

Although iron ore or other forms of iron oxide may be used to lower the carbon content, the use of gaseous oxygen injected into the molten bath is more common.

After charging has been completed, the arcs are struck and the charge is melted as quickly as possible. Since the arcs melt the portion of the charge directly beneath each electrode, the electrodes "bore" through the solid charge with the melted metal forming a pool on the hearth. From the time this pool forms, the charge is heated from

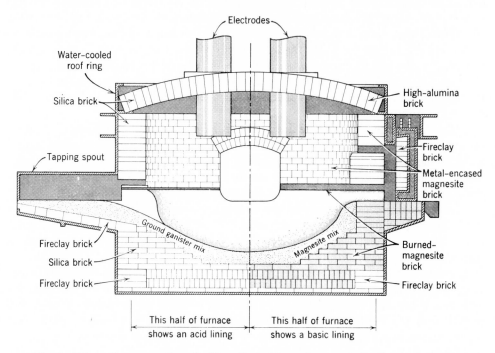

Fig. 6. Schematic cross section of a Heroult electric-arc furnace, indicating typical refractories employed in (left) an acid lining and (right) a basic lining. Although only two electrodes are shown, furnaces of this type have three electrodes and operate on three-phase current.

the bottom up by radiation from the pool, by heat from the arcs, and by the resistance offered to the current by the scrap. This continues until the charge is completely melted.

From the time the molten metal begins to form until the entire charge is in solution, oxidation of phosphorus, silicon, manganese, carbon, and other elements occurs in varying degrees. Oxygen for these and other oxidizing reactions is obtained from (*1*) oxygen gas injected into the bath, (*2*) oxygen in the furnace atmosphere, (*3*) calcination of limestone (if used), (*4*) oxides of alloying elements added in the furnace, and (*5*) iron ore or other iron oxides (if charged or added later). As oxidation progresses, the temperature of the bath is raised to promote carbon removal and to increase the fluidity of the bath so that inclusions may rise through the molten metal to its surface and into the slag. The reaction of carbon with oxygen forms carbon monoxide gas that bubbles out of the bath, giving rise to the phenomenon known as the boil.

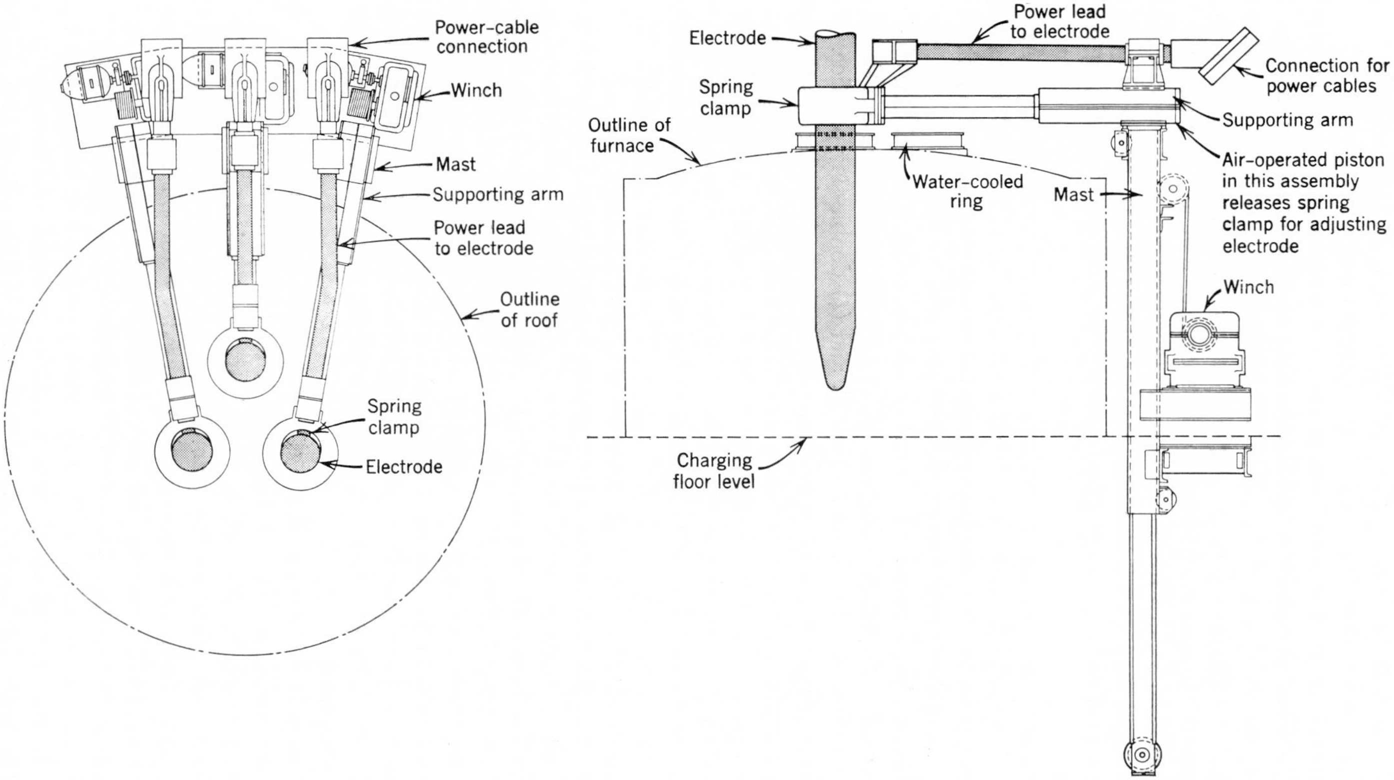

Fig. 7. Schematic arrangement of the electrodes, their supporting masts, and the electrical power leads for an electric-arc steelmaking furnace (2).

The reactions taking place in the basic electric-arc furnace during the oxidation period are similar to those in the basic open-hearth, except that the electric furnace can heat the bath to higher temperatures and there is no continuous supply of oxygen to the bath such as results from excess oxygen in the open-hearth flame.

Electric-furnace steel is sometimes made by a single-slag process in which the slag is first oxidized as described and then made reducing by adding the proper materials during the refining period. The usual practice is to use a double-slag method in which the first oxidizing slag is completely removed and replaced by a reducing slag. The materials used in building up the second or reducing slag are burnt lime, fluorspar, and silica sand, with powdered coke to supply carbon for forming calcium carbide. For making low-carbon steels (under 0.12% carbon), a lime–silica, a lime–alumina, or a modified slag of the calcium-carbide-bearing type, containing less coke, may be used.

The steel is not kept under the second slag any longer than necessary. As soon as chemical analyses establish that the chemical composition of the bath is correct, the steel is poured from the furnace (tapped) by tilting the furnace to allow the molten steel to run through the furnace spout into a waiting ladle.

Acid Electric-Arc Process. Four major variations of the acid electric-furnace practice are used: (1) partial oxidation, (2) complete oxidation (with a single slag), (3) complete oxidation with silicon reduction, and (4) double-slag practice. Partial oxidation practice is used chiefly to produce steel for low-priced castings that do not require any acceptance tests other than superficial surface inspection, because it is the cheapest method. The double-slag process is employed where it is desired to have positive control of the oxidizing power of the finishing slag. Silicon in the slag can be reduced to enter the metal in acid-electric practice, and this procedure is employed in Europe but not generally in the United States. The great majority of all American steel foundries employ the complete-oxidation process with a single slag.

With the exception of the necessity for using scrap having a low content of phosphorus and sulfur (which cannot be removed in the acid process), charging and melting procedures in the acid process are similar to those in the basic electric-arc process. As soon as the charge has melted down, the slag formed by the oxidation of silicon, manganese, and iron in the scrap is tested to make certain that its iron oxide (FeO) content is sufficiently high. The carbon content of the metal is determined at the same time, and, as in the basic process, should be higher than the carbon content desired in the finished steel. The iron oxide content of the slag is adjusted by adding silica sand or iron ore, as required.

After the bath is covered with the proper oxidizing slag and the carbon content of the metal is high enough, the temperature of the bath is increased to bring on the "boil." The boil is caused by the reaction of carbon with oxygen in the steel and promotes the manufacture of "clean" steel, since the hotter steel, being more fluid, and the agitation caused by carbon monoxide bubbling out of the bath both promote the rise of solid oxidized products to the slag, thereby reducing the number of nonmetallic inclusions that make steel "dirty." The amounts of carbon and oxygen in the bath should be sufficient to maintain the boil for at least 10 min, during which time the carbon content of the metal is falling. When analysis shows that the carbon content has reached the proper level, silicon and manganese in the form of ferroalloys are added to the bath to "kill" (deoxidize) the steel and prevent further lowering of the carbon content. The heat should be tapped as soon as these additions have melted completely and diffused through the bath.

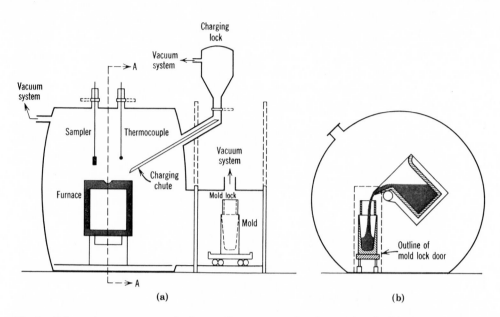

Fig. 8. Schematic arrangement of a furnace in a vacuum chamber equipped with charging and mold locks for vacuum induction melting (2). (**a**) Front cross section; (**b**) section AA during pouring.

The foregoing applies to the manufacture of plain-carbon steel. If alloy steel is made, copper, nickel, and molybdenum can be added at any time without loss by oxidation. Chromium, being easily oxidized, is added as ferrochromium after the steel has been deoxidized. Alloys such as aluminum, titanium, zirconium, vanadium, and boron are added in the ladle.

Induction Furnace Melting of Steel. The high-frequency induction furnace used for melting steel consists of a refractory crucible surrounded by a water-cooled copper coil through which alternating current flows. The rapidly changing magnetic field of the coil at high flux density generates heavy secondary currents in the solid metal of the charge. Resistance of the metal to flow of the induced current generates heat that melts the charge.

In most steel plants using induction furnaces, the melting procedure is essentially a "dead-melt" process: that is to say, the solid constituents of the charge melt quietly and mix with each other. Little if any refining is attempted in ordinary induction melting, so there are no chemical reactions whose gaseous products agitate the molten bath. The charge is selected to produce the composition desired in the finished steel with a minimum of further additions except, possibly, small amounts of ferroalloys as final deoxidizers. Commercial use of the high-frequency induction furnace for ordinary melting is not extensive in the steel industry. It is employed in the production of complex high-quality alloys such as alloy tool steels, and also for remelting scrap from fine steels produced in arc furnaces, as well as for melting chrome–nickel alloys and high-manganese scrap. More recently, it has been applied to the vacuum steelmaking processes described below.

Vacuum and Atmosphere Melting. This method employs a coreless high-frequency induction furnace of the type described above, enclosed in a container or tank which can be either evacuated or filled with a gaseous atmosphere of any desired composition or pressure. Provision is made for making additions to the melt, and for

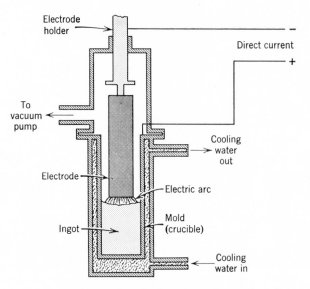

Fig. 9. Schematic representation of the principle of design and operation of a consumable-electrode furnace for melting steels in a vacuum (2).

tilting the furnace to pour its contents into an ingot mold also enclosed in the tank or container, without disturbing the vacuum or atmosphere in the tank (Fig. 8).

While vacuum melting often has been employed simply as a remelting operation for very pure materials or for making electrodes for the vacuum consumable-electrode furnace described below, it is more generally useful in those applications where some refining is accomplished. Oxygen, nitrogen, and hydrogen can be removed from the molten metal in vacuum melting, as well as carbon when alloys of very low carbon content are being produced.

Consumable-Electrode Melting. This is a refining process used to produce special-quality alloy and stainless steels, originally made by one of the conventional steelmaking processes, by casting or forging the steel into an electrode that is remelted and cast into an ingot in a vacuum (Fig. 9). Some of the special steels include bearing steels, heat-resistant alloys, ultrahigh-strength missile and aircraft steels, and rotor steels.

A consumable-electrode furnace consists of two sections: a tank above ground level that encloses the electrode, and a water-cooled copper mold below ground level. After the furnace has been evacuated, power is turned on and an arc is struck between the electrode and a starting block that is placed in the mold before operation begins. Heat from the arc progressively melts the end of the electrode. Melted metal is deposited in a shallow pool of molten metal on the top surface of the ingot being built up in the mold. Rate of descent of the electrode is automatically controlled to maintain the arc. The remelting operation removes gases (hydrogen, oxygen, and nitrogen) from the steel, improves its cleanliness, produces an ingot that exhibits practically no center porosity or segregation, improves hot workability of the steel, and improves the mechanical properties of the steel at both room and elevated temperatures.

Electroslag Remelting. In this process, which has as its objectives the same general purposes as consumable-electrode melting, a conventional air-melted ingot serves as a consumable electrode. No vacuum is employed. Melting takes place under a layer of slag that removes unwanted impurities. Grain structure and orientation are governed by controlled cooling during soldification.

Oxygen Steelmaking Processes

In the commonest form of the oxygen steelmaking processes, a jet of gaseous oxygen of 99.5% purity is blown at high velocity onto the surface of a bath of molten pig iron in a basic-lined, barrel-shaped furnace by a vertical water-cooled retractable pipe or lance inserted through the mouth of the vessel (Fig. 10). Steelmaking in this manner is called the basic oxygen process in the U.S.A. (sometimes abbreviated to BOP).

Blowing with oxygen was investigated by R. Durrer and C. V. Schwarz in Germany and by Durrer and H. Hellbrüge in Switzerland some years before the first commercial steelmaking plants to use the method began operation in Linz and Donawitz in Austria in 1952–1953. These latter operations were designed to employ pig iron produced from local ores that were high in manganese and low in phosphorus: such iron is not suitable for either the acid Bessemer or basic Thomas process. From these beginnings, the process spread rapidly all over the world. The original process was generally referred to as the L-D process; the numerous variations developed in Europe to accommodate the use of high-phosphorus pig irons have other names.

The Basic Oxygen Process. The basic oxygen process can be modified to adapt it to making steel from blast-furnace metal of medium- and high-phosphorus contents. It is particularly attractive where it is desirable to employ a steelmaking process that uses large percentages of "hot metal" (molten pig iron from the blast furnace) as the principal source of metallic iron; eg, in areas where supplies of iron and steel scrap are inadequate for the open-hearth or electric-furnace processes.

It has been estimated that about half of the world's steel will be produced by variations of the basic oxygen process by the early 1970s, when it is anticipated that world capacity for making steel by this method will be over 300 million tons annually.

The most common arrangement for oxygen steelmaking in the United States is a cylindrical basic-lined furnace with a dished bottom and truncated-cone-shaped top section wherein the mouth of the vessel is located. The furnace is mounted in a trunnion ring so that it can be tilted backward or forward as desired. Because of the limitations regarding sulfur and phosphorus in the raw materials of any acid steelmaking process, only a basic process has been considered for oxygen steelmaking.

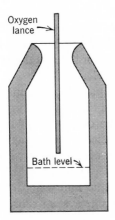

Fig. 10. Schematic cut-away sketch of a basic oxygen steelmaking furnace, with oxygen lance inserted through the mouth of the furnace (2).

Fig. 11. Pouring molten pig iron into a basic oxygen steelmaking furnace prior to the commencement of the production of a "heat" of steel. The furnace has been tilted to receive the molten metal. Another furnace, in upright position, is visible at the left of this view.

With the furnace tilted toward the charging floor (which is on a platform above general ground level), solid scrap is dumped by a charging machine into the mouth of the vessel. Scrap can form up to 30% of the charge unless it is preheated, when up to 40% may be used. The self-propelled charging machine then moves away from the furnace and an overhead crane carries a transfer ladle of hot metal to the furnace and pours the molten pig iron on top of the scrap (Fig. 11).

The furnace is immediately returned to the upright position, the lance is lowered into the furnace to the desired height above the bath, and the flow of oxygen is started (Fig. 12). Striking the surface of the liquid bath, the oxygen immediately starts reactions leading to the formation of iron oxide, part of which disperses rapidly through the bath. Carbon monoxide generated by the reaction of iron oxide with carbon is evolved, giving rise to a violent circulation that accelerates refining.

Slag-forming fluxes—chiefly burnt lime, fluorspar, and mill scale (iron oxides)—are added in controlled amounts from an overhead storage system shortly before or

Fig. 12. View of a basic oxygen steelmaking furnace during the early stages of making a heat of steel. The furnace is in upright position. Oxygen is being blown into the furnace through a water-cooled "lance" that extends vertically into the furnace: the lance cannot be seen here because of the hot gases leaving the mouth of the furnace, except where it extends through the hood near the top of the picture.

after the oxygen jet is started. These materials, which produce a slag of the proper basicity and fluidity, are added through a chute built into the side of a water-cooled hood positioned over the mouth of the furnace. This hood collects the gases and the dense reddish-brown fume emitted by the furnace during blowing and conducts them to a cleaning system where the solids are removed from the effluent gas before it is discharged to the atmosphere. Where there are no contaminants in the recovered solids that would create problems, the solids can be added to the mix fed to sintering machines used to agglomerate fine ore, blast-furnace dust, and so on. Otherwise, the solids are disposed of by dumping.

The use of pure oxygen for refining does not change the fundamental chemical reactions involved in steelmaking although the order and speed of the reactions differ from other processes. The oxidizing reactions take place extremely rapidly, so that a 150-ton heat, for example, can be blown in about 20 min. The extremely high temperatures created where the oxygen contacts the bath are in part responsible for the rapid refining which takes place.

The mechanics of carbon elimination are similar in the basic oxygen and the open-hearth processes and involve oxidation of carbon to carbon monoxide and carbon dioxide. The chemical reactions and end results are the same in both cases. Figure 13 shows how the reactions progress.

The general reaction in basic open-hearth practice, whereby silicon is oxidized to silica and transferred to the slag, applies also to the basic oxygen process. Oxidation of silicon is important mainly because of its thermal effects. Only a trace of silicon remains in the steel at the end of the refining period.

The residual manganese content of the blown metal before ladle additions generally is higher than in open-hearth practice and is closely related to the amount of manganese in the basic oxygen furnace charge.

A high fluidity of slag and excellent slag-metal contact provide for efficient removal of phosphorus from the metal into the slag, even before the carbon has been reduced to the desired point.

Efficiency of sulfur elimination is as good as or better than that in the basic open hearth, due to more vigorous bath action, higher operating temperatures, and the fact that there is no fuel that can be a source of sulfur.

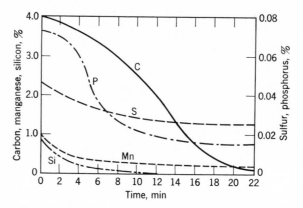

Fig. 13. Progress of refining in the basic oxygen steelmaking process (2).

Because the basic oxygen process uses a refining agent containing practically no nitrogen, the steel produced has an exceptionally low nitrogen content. Residual oxygen levels in basic oxygen steels are comparable to those obtained in normal open-hearth practice for steels of the same carbon content.

Residual alloying elements such as copper, nickel, or tin are usually considered undesirable in many steels. The main source of these unwanted elements is purchased scrap. The generally high consumption of hot metal in the basic oxygen process results in a low residual alloy content because less purchased scrap need be used.

The basic oxygen process requires no external source of heat from fuel. In fact, a major problem in the basic oxygen process is one of limiting temperature rather than increasing it.

When the blow is completed, the lance is withdrawn and the furnace is tilted to a horizontal position. A temperature reading is taken with an immersion-type thermocouple and a sample of steel is withdrawn for chemical analysis. If the steel is too hot, the furnace is returned to the vertical position and scrap or limestone is added as a coolant through the chute in the hood. If the steel is too cold, the lance is again lowered and oxygen is blown for a short period.

When the temperature and composition are satisfactory, the furnace is tilted toward its taphole side and the steel is tapped into a waiting ladle; alloying additions are added to the steel in the ladle through a chute.

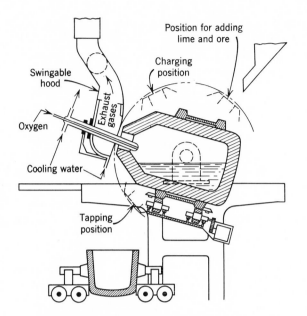

Fig. 14. Kaldo vessel in the blowing position (2).

After the steel has been tapped, the furnace is tilted toward its opposite side to invert it and dump the slag remaining in it into a slag pot. From this inverted position, the furnace is turned to charging position and is ready to receive its charge for the next heat.

Kaldo Process. The designation Kaldo process is an abbreviation of the Stora-Kaldo process, the name of an oxygen steelmaking process developed in Sweden. In this process, oxygen is introduced at an angle to the surface of the bath contained in a tilted, rotating vessel. The first plant in the United States to employ the process began operation in 1962, with two vessels each of 150-ton heat size.

The Kaldo furnace is tilted at about 15 to 20° from the horizontal while operating and, in this position, can be rotated around its longitudinal axis at speeds up to 30 rpm. The single opening at the mouth of the furnace serves for charging, making additions, slag removal, introduction of the oxygen lance, and discharging the refined metal, and as an outlet for exhaust of waste gases.

Sequence of operations is as follows: (*1*) the vessel is tilted backward (Fig. 14) until the mouth of the vessel is beneath the charging chute and the necessary additions of scrap, lime, and iron ore are made; (*2*) the vessel is tilted down to approximately its operating position and hot metal is poured into it; (*3*) the vessel is tilted to its operating position and the water-cooled waste-gas hood and oxygen lance are swung into position with the lance extending into the vessel; and (*4*) oxygen blowing and rotation of the vessel are begun and continued until the refining is carried to the desired end point. Commercial oxygen of 95% purity is used at about 45 lb/in.^{2} pressure. The rate of oxygen input and the speed of vessel rotation can be regulated separately to control mechanical agitation of the slag and metal and relative rates of elimination of carbon and phosphorus.

Rotation of the vessel exerts a stirring action that promotes thermal and chemical uniformity in the molten bath. Also, the refractory lining above the bath becomes

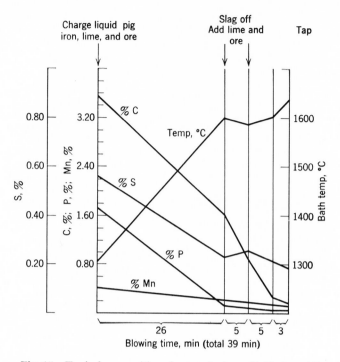

Fig. 15. Typical composition changes during a Kaldo heat (2).

appreciably hotter than the bath due to its exposure to the superhot gases from the chemical reactions. As it rotates, the lining of the vessel is continuously passing under the bath, giving up its excess heat and continually exposing fresh refractory surfaces to the gases above the bath.

As in other basic steelmaking processes, carbon is oxidized to carbon monoxide, silicon is oxidized to silica that is taken up by the basic slag, manganese oxide that is formed becomes part of the slag, and the P_2O_5 resulting from oxidation of phosphorus combines with the lime of the slag. Most of the carbon monoxide evolved by the oxidation of carbon is burned to carbon dioxide inside the vessel, contributing considerable heat to the process. Figure 15 illustrates the changes in composition with time during the blowing of a high-phosphorus hot metal, using the double-slag practice that is employed when blowing medium- or high-phosphorus charges. Iron ore or scrap can be used as a coolant, and up to 40% scrap can be consumed by the process when refining medium-phosphorus hot metal typified by the "basic iron" used in steelmaking in the United States.

Rotor Process. Another basic oxygen steelmaking process, called the rotor process, was developed in Oberhausen, Germany. The rotor furnace, sometimes called the Oberhausen rotary furnace, employs the same rotary principle as the Kaldo furnace, except that the speed of rotation is much slower, being only about ½ to 2 rpm. Also, the rotor furnace has the appearance of a rotary kiln (almost a horizontal cylinder) rather than the barrel-like shape of a Kaldo furnace. The furnace can be used for the direct production of steel, or to prerefine high-phosphorus hot metal (molten pig iron) for use in other steelmaking processes. Such furnaces have been installed in Germany, South Africa, and the United Kingdom.

The rotor furnace is mounted in a cradle so that its longitudinal axis can be tipped toward either end. The cradle also carries the supporting rollers that permit the furnace to rotate about its longitudinal axis. The furnace is charged and tapped at opposite ends. The working lining is of tar–dolomite brick, backed with magnesite brick.

Two oxygen lances are provided. One injects high-purity oxygen into the metal bath in which it is immersed, while the other blows low-purity (as low as 45%) oxygen into the space above the bath to burn carbon monoxide evolved by the bath reactions to carbon dioxide (thereby generating considerable additional heat for the process).

Reactions in this process are generally similar to those of the other basic oxygen processes.

Tonnage Oxygen for Steelmaking. Relatively high-cost oxygen produced by the fractional distillation of liquid air was used prior to 1940 in the steel industry for scarfing, cutting, and welding. It was purchased in cylinders of comparatively small capacity. Most of this oxygen was of the high-purity (99.5%) grade.

The development of plants for producing oxygen of lower purity was accelerated in Germany during World War II. Shortages of fuel oil led to the use of oxygen in hydrogenation plants for making the required synthesis gas. Oxygen for this process did not have to be of the high-purity grade. Due to the great demand for oxygen, the low-purity oxygen plants were of greater size than earlier plants and, accordingly, were less expensive to build and operate per unit of product.

During this same period, American manufacturers were developing portable, high-purity gaseous oxygen plants for the armed services and for field hospitals. From this combined experience, reliable low-cost oxygen plants became available after the war. The steel, chemical, coal, petroleum, and other industries then had available dependable large-volume supplies of oxygen at a cost conducive to its much wider use than had been economically feasible until then.

Gaseous oxygen of the desired purity is produced by using the proper process for the fractional distillation of liquefied atmospheric air, carried out at very low temperatures and elevated pressures. The design and mode of operation of oxygen plants depends upon the purity of the product that is desired, and on whether or not other products (eg, argon) are simultaneously recovered.

Because of the large amounts of oxygen required in steelmaking, the larger mills usually have an "on-site" plant for making enough oxygen of the desired purity to meet their needs. Smaller plants may obtain supplies of liquid oxygen by railroad tank car or tanker trucks. The oxygen is stored as a liquid, and is gasified and distributed to the points of use in the plant as required.

Duplex Processes

Technically, the term "duplex process" refers to any steelmaking process that involves two separate stages of refining in two different furnaces. Various combinations of acid Bessemer converters, basic open-hearth furnaces, and electric furnaces have been used; however, such processes are little used at the present time.

In the United States, the term duplex process was restricted by custom to mean the use of an acid Bessemer converter to partially refine hot metal by removing the silicon, manganese, and most of the carbon, after which the blown metal was transferred to a basic open-hearth furnace where the phosphorus and the remainder of the carbon were removed to the desired degree.

Determination of Chemical Composition

Chemical composition of a given steel generally is specified by the customer within rather narrow limits for each element (other than residual elements). The steelmaker needs to know the chemical composition of finished steel to make sure that specifications have been met. Just as important to the steelmaker is a knowledge of the chemical composition of the steel at various stages during its refining in the steelmaking furnace. Carbon content of the steel at any stage of the process is one piece of knowledge that dictates further procedures in refining.

In early days of steelmaking, practiced melters could estimate the carbon content fairly closely by examining the fracture of a broken sample of the steel that had been taken molten from the furnace and poured into a mold, where it solidified as a small bar-shaped piece. This empirical method was not good enough as specifications became more rigid and steelmaking processes became more rapid. Considerable effort was devoted to the development of rapid laboratory analytical methods for the determination of content, especially of carbon, manganese, sulfur, silicon, and phosphorus. Eventually instruments were devised that could be used near the furnaces to determine the carbon content of steel in relatively short times, as a guide to the melter during the refining operation.

Analytical methods for determining other elements—manganese, silicon, phosphorus, sulfur, for example—still required that samples of the steel be analyzed in a chemical laboratory, sometimes located at a considerable distance from the furnaces.

At the present time, the spectrograph is used mostly for the very rapid determination of the chemical composition of steel. Samples are sent to the laboratory by pneumatic tube or other fast means, the samples are analyzed, and the results are transmitted to the furnace area by teletype. Ten, twelve, or more single elements can be determined quickly and accurately by this method.

Scrap for Steelmaking

Scrap consists of the by-products of steel fabrication and worn-out, broken, or discarded items containing iron or steel. It is one of the two principal sources of the metal iron for steelmaking; the other principal source is iron from the blast furnace,

Table 2. Consumption of Scrap and Hot Metal and Pig Iron by Steelmaking Processes and Blast Furnaces in the United States,[a] 1967

| | Consumption, 1000 net tons | |
Process	Scrap	Hot metal and pig iron
open-hearth furnaces	32,298	46,266
basic oxygen steelmaking	13,955	33,607
electric furnaces	13,351	279
blast furnaces	4,280	

[a] Data from American Iron and Steel Institute.

either molten as it comes from the furnace (hot metal) or in solid pig form. Scrap is of great practical value. Every ton of scrap consumed in steelmaking is estimated to displace and conserve for future use $3\frac{1}{2}$ to 4 tons of natural resources including iron ore, coal, and limestone. On the average, the steel industry consumes about one-fifth more pig iron (mostly as hot metal) than scrap. According to the American Iron and Steel Institute, the steel industry consumes an average of about 55 million tons of iron and steel scrap in producing 100 million tons of raw steel.

In discussing the various steelmaking processes, it was pointed out that they differ in their abilities to consume scrap. The basic oxygen steelmaking process uses 25–30% (up to 40% with preheating), and the Kaldo process about 40%. The open-hearth processes may utilize 35–60%. The electric-arc furnace usually is charged almost entirely with cold scrap. Table 2 summarizes the consumption of scrap by the leading steelmaking processes and the blast furnaces in the United States in the production of about 127 million tons of steel in 1967. The consumption of hot metal and pig iron by the same steelmaking processes is also shown in the table.

Types and Sources of Scrap. Scrap iron and steel may be classified as originating from two sources: *home scrap* produced as unsalable products unavoidably resulting in the course of steelmaking and finishing operations, and *purchased scrap.*

Home scrap (also called *revert scrap*) includes such items as pit scrap; ingots too short to roll; rejected ingots; ingot crops; crop ends from blooms and billets; shear cuttings from trimming flat-rolled products to specified size; products irrecoverably damaged in handling and finishing; ends cut from bars, pipe, and tubing to bring them to standard or exact ordered length; turnings from machining operations; and so on. Bloom crops constitute the largest single item of home scrap.

In general, about 30 million tons of home scrap would result from the manufacture of 100 million tons of raw steel and the processing of this steel into finished products. Since, as stated earlier, 55 million tons of scrap are required to produce 100 million tons of raw steel, 25 million tons of purchased scrap would have to be used to supplement the 30 million tons of home scrap. *Purchased scrap* is divided into two general classifications: *dormant scrap* (sometimes called *country scrap*) and *prompt industrial scrap.*

Dormant scrap comprises obsolete, worn out, or broken products of consuming industries. Typical examples of dormant scrap are: discarded steel furniture, washing machines, stoves and other outdated consumer goods; beams, angles, channels, girders, railings, grilles, pipe, etc, arising from the demolition of buildings; useless farm machinery; broken or damaged industrial machinery; old ships; railroad rails and rolling stock that have outlived their usefulness; wrecked automobiles. This type of scrap, because of its miscellaneous nature, requires careful sorting and classification to prevent the contamination of steel in the furnace with unwanted chemical elements that may be present in some of the scrap. It should also be of such physical size as to facilitate handling and charging into the furnaces. The need for proper classification and preparation of dormant scrap is emphasized by the existence of over seventy different specifications covering various grades of scrap for use in blast furnaces, acid and basic open-hearth furnaces, electric furnaces, the basic oxygen steelmaking process, gray-iron foundries, and elsewhere. In addition, the Association of American Railroads has forty-five specifications applying to scrap of railroad origin.

Junked automobiles represent a large tonnage pool of steel scrap. Formerly, after stripping, entire bodies were squeezed into compact blocks in huge hydraulic presses. However, the expense of getting them to a collection center and stripping them of copper, lead, chromium, nickel, and other unwanted metals and combustibles gradually reduced the profitability of junk cars to scrap collectors. However, in recent times and partly for esthetic reasons, a concerted effort has been made to empty the auto "graveyards" and get rid of abandoned cars in the countryside, on streets, and in vacant lots. One answer to the problem that is being tried with some success is to feed the bodies of automobiles (after removal of engines, transmissions, rear axles, etc, that are recovered separately) into huge machines called "shredders" that cut the body into small pieces. The shredded material is then passed through magnetic-separating equipment that discards practically all nonferrous material to produce a high-quality steel scrap. In 1967, about fifty shredder or fragmentation plants were in use or being installed. Other methods have been proposed or are being used or investigated. One recently developed device can crush an engine block into sortable chunks in 42 sec.

Prompt industrial scrap is generated by consumers of steel in making their products. It may consist of the unwanted portions of plate or sheet that has been cut or sheared to the desired final size and shape, trimmings resulting from stamping and pressing operations, machine turnings, rejected products scrapped during manufacture, short ends, flash from forgings, and other types of scrap. Prompt industrial scrap can usually be identified easily as to source and composition, provided the proper plans for segregation are in effect in the consumer's plant, the scrap dealer's yard, and the steel plant.

Chemical Composition of Scrap. Certain chemical elements are desirable constituents of scrap for steelmaking, especially when used in electric furnaces. In general, however, scrap for all of the steelmaking processes should be free from unknown and unwanted elements referred to as "tramp alloys." The increasing use of alloy steels aggravates the tramp alloy problem, since more and more purchased scrap may be expected to include unidentified alloy steels.

The segregation of home scrap according to its chemical composition is relatively simple. Purchased scrap, especially dormant scrap, presents some problems because a large percentage of it is of unknown origin and composition. It is impractical to chemically analyze each piece of the huge amounts of dormant scrap consumed every year, but the chemical analysis of selected samples from individual lots is sometimes employed in the classification of scrap. Spectrographic analysis is sometimes employed because it is faster than chemical analysis; however, both are relatively time-consuming and expensive and both require careful selection and preparation of samples. Some less costly but less accurate tests are commonly used: these include magnetic tests, spark tests, spot tests, and pellet tests.

When the chemical composition of scrap is known, the scrap can be a valuable source of alloying elements needed in the production of alloy steels. Full advantage is taken of this source in the production of alloy steels in the electric furnace. In the open-hearth furnace, however, most production consists of carbon and low-alloy steels and, in general, alloying elements in scrap are a source of trouble.

Tin, copper, nickel, and other elements in scrap will alloy readily with steel and, in many cases, render it unfit for its intended use. Relatively small amounts of these metals can contaminate an entire heat of steel. Tin and copper in certain ranges of composition cause brittleness and bad surface conditions. Nickel and tin not only contaminate heats into which they may be unintentionally introduced, but may leave a residue in the furnace that is absorbed by subsequent heats with resultant contamination. Lead is extremely harmful to furnace bottoms and refractories and, if present in sufficient quantities, may cause furnaces to break out by penetrating joints or cracks in the bottom to form channels that may be followed by molten steel.

Addition Agents

Steelmaking involves the deliberate addition of various chemical elements to the molten metal to effect several desirable ends. These ends may be deoxidation of the molten metal to the desired degree, control of grain size, improvement of the mechanical and physical properties and corrosion resistance of the steel, increase of the response to heat treatment, or attainment of other specific effects. Originally, the chemical element to be incorporated into the steel was added to the bath in the form of an alloy that consisted principally of iron but was rich in the desired element. Such alloys, because of their high iron content, became known as ferroalloys, and most of the available types were produced in the iron blast furnace. Eventually the production of alloys for steelmaking purposes began to be carried out in electric-reduction and other types of furnaces as well, and a number of alloys now produced contain very little iron. For this reason, the term addition agent is preferred to describe any of the materials added to molten steel for altering its composition or properties; under this definition, the ferroalloys form a special class of addition agents.

The more common addition agents definitely in the ferroalloy class include alloys of iron with aluminum, boron, calcium, chromium, niobium, manganese, molydenum, nitrogen, phosphorus, selenium, silicon, tantalum, titanium, tungsten, vanadium, and zirconium. It may be noted that metallurgists still employ the name "columbium" (symbol Cb) for niobium. This is partly due to its use in specifications that are not amenable to rapid change (see Table 6, for example). However, the name of this element has been formally declared to be niobium by IUPAC (in 1949), is used by chemists generally, and will be used in this encyclopedia. Some of these chemical elements and others are available in addition agents that are not ferroalloys, as well as in almost pure form; these include relatively pure metals such as aluminum, calcium, cobalt, copper, manganese and nickel; oxides of molybdenum, nickel, and tungsten; carbon, nitrogen and sulfur in various forms; and alloys consisting principally of combinations of two or more of the foregoing elements. Some rare-earth alloys also are used for special purposes, but to a minor extent. See Vol. 17, pp. 160, 165.

Addition agents may be added with the charge in the steelmaking furnace, in the molten bath near the end of the finishing period, in the ladle, or in the molds. Timing of the alloy additions is dependent upon the effect of the addition on the temperature of the molten metal, ease with which specific addition agents go into solution, susceptibility of a particular addition agent to oxidation, and formation and elimination of reaction products.

The economical manufacture of alloy steels requires consideration of the relative affinity of the alloying elements for oxygen as compared with the affinity of iron for oxygen. For example, copper, molybdenum, or nickel may be added with the charge or during the working of the heat and are fully recovered. Chromium and manganese, because they are easily oxidized, should be added late in the heat and all or part of these two may be added in the ladle. Easily oxidized materials such as aluminum, boron, titanium, vanadium, and zirconium normally are added in the ladle in order to minimize oxidation losses.

It is often necessary to preheat the additions to avoid undue chilling of the bath. When large additions are made entirely to the bath, time must be allowed for the molten steel to be reheated to the desired temperature before tapping. Additions may be split between the furnace and the ladle, and in cases where excessive chilling of the metal in the ladle is to be avoided, the lower alloy recovery in the furnace must be accepted. To offset the chilling tendency of large additions and to minimize or eliminate the necessity for preheating, some addition agents such as ferromanganese and ferrochromium can be obtained mixed with chemical reagents to provide exothermic reactions that permit these agents to be added to the bath without undue chilling of the steel.

Ingots

The finished steel, from whatever type of furnace—basic oxygen furnace, open-hearth furnace, or electric furnace—is tapped into ladles. Most ladles are capable of holding the entire amount of steel produced as a heat in one furnace. Some of the slag which runs from the furnace after most of the steel has been tapped is allowed to float on the surface of the steel in the ladle and form a protective blanket. Excess slag overflows the ladle through a slag spout and is either collected in slag pots or allowed to run onto the floor adjacent to the ladle stand, from which it is removed, when solidified, by high lifts or other mechanical means.

A ladle consists of an open-topped steel shell, lined with refractory brick, with an off-center opening in its bottom equipped with a nozzle (Fig. 16). A stopper-rod assembly enables the pourer to open or close the opening to control flow of steel through the nozzle. The ladle is carried by an overhead crane to a pouring platform where the steel is teemed (poured) into a series of molds of the desired dimensions. The steel solidifies in each of the molds to form a casting called an *ingot*.

Until recently, the ingot was the first solid form taken by all steel as the first step in the sequence of rolling and other operations that are required to make finished steel products. Most of the steel produced still is cast into ingots. After removal from the mold, a process called stripping, the ingot is placed with other ingots in a pit-type furnace called a soaking pit where it is heated to the proper temperature for hot working. Hot working for most ingots consists of rolling them into semifinished products called *blooms*, *slabs*, and *billets* on primary rolling mills. The semifinished products form the starting material for further hot rolling on secondary and finishing mills. Some blooms, slabs, and billets are now produced by continuous casting, a process that will be described later (p. 759).

The size and shape of an ingot depends upon the product to be made and the type of equipment available for the hot-working operations. For example, ingots

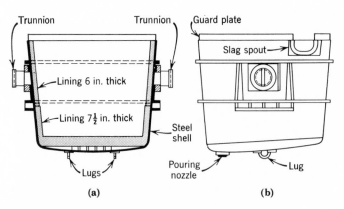

Fig. 16. (**a**) Vertical section of a steel ladle through the trunnions; (**b**) side view of the same ladle (2).

for rolling slabs from which flat-rolled products such as plates and sheets are made range in weight from 10 to 40 tons, with many of them in the 20-ton range. Some forging ingots will weigh 300 tons.

Ingot molds are made of cast iron. Their dimensions determine the size and shape of the ingots cast in them. Their cross sections may be square, rectangular, or

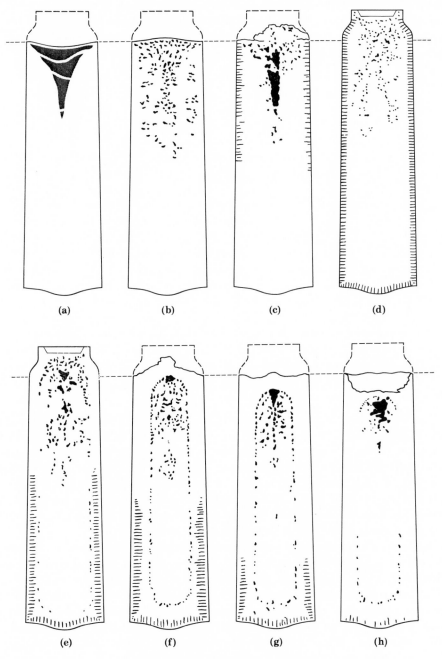

(a)　　　　　(b)　　　　　(c)　　　　　(d)

(e)　　　　　(f)　　　　　(g)　　　　　(h)

Fig. 17.　Series of ingot structures.

round. The mold cavity is tapered from top to bottom to facilitate the stripping of the ingot from the mold.

As a mold is being filled with molten steel, the metal next to the mold walls and mold stool (a cast base on which the mold rests) is chilled by contact with the relatively cold surfaces and solidifies in these regions to form a shell or skin. Early during solidification, the ingot skin contracts and forms an air gap between itself and the mold wall: this gap reduces the rate at which heat can be transferred to the mold and thence to the atmosphere. Also, as solidification proceeds, the thermal gradients become less steep. For these reasons, the thickness of the ingot skin (frozen zone) increases rapidly at first but slows down greatly as solidification proceeds.

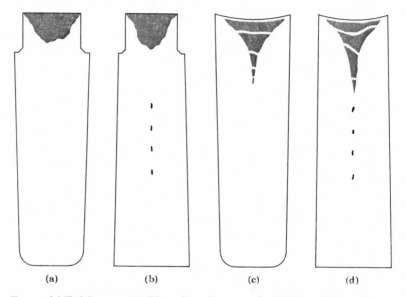

(a)   (b)   (c)   (d)

Fig. 18. Types of killed ingots. (**a**) Big-end-up, hot-topped; (**b**) big-end-down, hot-topped; (**c**) big-end-up, not hot-topped; (**d**) big-end-down, not hot-topped.

The solubility of gases in molten steel decreases with decreasing temperatures, especially when steel changes from the liquid phase to the solid phase. During the solidification of ingots, the gases are liberated in amounts dependent upon the amount of gases originally present in the molten steel. Oxygen is the chief gas that is involved. In the form of FeO, it reacts with carbon in the steel and produces carbon monoxide that is evolved from the steel. The addition of deoxidizing agents to the liquid steel decreases the amount of dissolved oxygen, and the degree of deoxidation establishes four types of steel—killed, semikilled, capped, and rimmed.

It is important to note that the chemical equilibrium between carbon and oxygen in the steel changes with decreasing temperatures, so that the two elements react continuously as the temperature continues to fall, in the direction toward a new equilibrium. Molten steel does not solidify at one definite temperature but over a temperature range, so that the gases evolved from still liquid portions may be trapped at solid–liquid interfaces of the remaining liquid with previously solidified metal to produce blowholes. Figure 17 shows diagrammatically eight typical conditions in commercial ingots, cast in identical bottle-top molds, in relation to the degree of gas evolution. The dotted line indicates the height to which steel originally was poured in each ingot mold. Figure 17a represents a fully killed ingot that evolved no gas because it was completely deoxidized. Its top is slightly concave, and directly below the top is an intermittently bridged shrinkage cavity that is commonly called pipe. Actually, fully killed steels are almost always poured in big-end-up molds, equipped with refractory hot tops, exothermic inserts, or some other means for maintaining the steel at the top of the ingot molten long enough for the pipe to be confined to a relatively small part of the top of the ingot that can be discarded later with a minimum of waste, as shown in Figure 18.

Figure 17b shows a typical semikilled ingot in which only a small amount of gas was evolved. Nevertheless, the resulting blowholes were sufficient in volume to compensate fully for the shrinkage during solidification. Ferrostatic pressure (hydraulic pressure exerted by liquid steel due to gravity) prevented the formation of blowholes in the lower half of the ingot. The pressure caused by the trapped gases in the blowholes was sufficient to bulge the surface of the ingot to produce a domed top.

Fig. 17e represents a typical capped ingot. It evolved so much gas that the resulting strong upward currents along the sides in the upper half of the ingot swept away the gas bubbles that otherwise would have formed blowholes. Even in the lower half of the ingot, the blowholes could not form until the gas evolution had moderated somewhat. The result was that a thick solid skin formed first that was then followed by the zone containing the blowholes. The increase in the apparent volume of the ingot was sufficient to cause the steel to rise to the cap at the top of the ingot mold.

Figures 17f–h show rimmed ingots. In the ingot in Figure 17f the evolution of gas, while greater than in the ingot in Figure 17e, was insufficient to prevent the honeycomb blowholes from exceeding in volume the amount required to offset solidification shrinkage, and the top surface of the ingot rose slightly as it froze in from the sides of the mold.

Figure 17g represents a typical rimmed ingot in which gas evolution was so strong that the formation of blowholes was confined to only the lower quarter of the ingot. The apparent increase in volume due to blowholes offset the shrinkage that occurred during solidification. As a result, the top of the ingot did not rise or fall appreciably during solidification.

Figure 17h illustrates a violently rimming ingot, typical of low-metalloid steel. Honeycomb blowholes could not form and the top surface of the ingot fell markedly during solidification.

From the foregoing, it is seen that in all except killed steels the evolution of gas produces cavities of roughly cylindrical shape (skin or honeycomb blowholes) or spherical shape (located deeper in the ingot). Blowholes serve a useful purpose in diminishing or preventing the formation of pipe and increasing the amount of usable steel in an ingot. Except for the blowholes located within several inches of the top of the ingot, blowholes tend to have interiors free of an oxide coating and clean enough to weld easily and to become completely closed during rolling. If the blowholes extend to the surface of an ingot, or lie at such a shallow depth beneath the surface as to become exposed by scaling of the ingot surface during heating for rolling, they can become oxidized and will not weld, giving rise to seams in the rolled product. Properly made ingots have gas evolution so controlled that there will be a skin of adequate thickness over those blowholes closest to the surface.

Segregation. Segregation may be explained in simplified terms as follows: The metal that solidifies rapidly close to the mold wall (the chill zone) has about the same chemical composition as the liquid metal entering the mold. As the rate of solidification decreases, the mechanism of solidification is such that crystals of purer metal solidify first; that is to say, the first crystals to form adjacent to the chill zone as the skin grows in thickness contain less carbon, manganese, phosphorus, sulfur, and other elements than the liquid steel from which they formed, and the remaining liquid is enriched by these elements that are continually being rejected in the crystallization process. Thus, the last material to solidify contains the largest amount in total of the rejected elements. Those locations where the content of an element is greater than the average are said to exhibit positive segregation; when the content is less than the average, it is termed negative segregation.

Some elements tend to segregate more than others. Sulfur segregates to the greatest degree. The following elements also segregate, but to a lesser degree, and in descending order: phosphorus, carbon, silicon, and manganese. The tendency for elements to segregate is increased by increasing time for solidification, so that large ingots tend to show more severe segregation than smaller ones.

Turbulence due to gas evolution during solidification tends to increase segregation. Therefore, killed steels are less segregated than semikilled, and the semikilled less segregated than capped or rimmed steels. In a rimmed ingot, the first part of the steel to freeze and form the skin is low in carbon, phosphorus, and sulfur; that is, it exhibits negative segregation. The core of the ingot, or the final portion to freeze, exhibits positive segregation. The boundary between the rim and core zones of a rimmed ingot is very sharp, and these zones are so different with respect to chemical composition that they resemble different steels.

The thick skin of relatively clean metal on rimmed-steel ingots makes them desirable for rolling products where the surface of the finished products is most important. The higher range of carbon content of most rimmed steel is $0.12–0.15\%$; the lower range is $0.06–0.10\%$.

Capped steel has a thin rimmed zone that is relatively free from blowholes, and a core zone that is less segregated than that of a rimmed ingot of the same volume. Capped steel is used to advantage when the carbon content is above 0.15%. Steel of this type is used for sheet, strip, skelp, tin plate, wire, and bars. (Skelp is a hot-rolled flat strip used in making butt-weld pipe.)

Semikilled steel finds wide application in structural shapes, plates, and merchant bars. Its carbon content ranges from 0.15 to 0.30%, as required for a given product.

Killed steel generally is used when a homogeneous structure is required in the finished steel. Alloy steels, forging steels, and steels for carburizing are of this type, when the essential desired quality is soundness. In general, all steels with more than 0.30% carbon are killed steels.

Vacuum Degassing of Steel for Ingots. Gases absorbed by liquid steel from the atmosphere and from raw materials used in steelmaking can cause embrittlement, flaking, voids, inclusions, and other undesirable and even harmful phenomena in the steel after it has solidified. Hydrogen, in particular, has been recognized for a considerable time to be the cause of flaking and embrittlement. Oxygen and nitrogen combine with various addition agents and alloying elements to form oxide, cyanonitride, or nitride compounds that remain in the steel as inclusions that can be removed only by some remelting process. The vacuum melting processes (see p. 739)

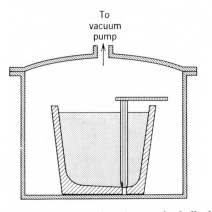

Fig. 19. Schematic arrangement of equipment for ladle degassing (2).

provide means for eliminating gases and inclusions from relatively small quantities of molten steel. Vacuum consumable-electrode melting (see p. 740) is another means.

Several methods have been developed since about 1950 for degassing large quantities (up to 300 tons) of liquid steel produced in conventional steelmaking furnaces: these may be classified as ladle degassing, stream degassing, and recirculation degassing.

In ladle degassing (Fig. 19) the ladle of steel to be degassed is placed in a gastight tank that has an outlet to a vacuum pump. Evacuation of the space within the tank causes gases to escape from the steel with an accompanying boiling action. Hoppers in the tank top permit making additions to the ladle. An inert gas such as argon or helium may be injected into the steel in the ladle to agitate it and promote the boiling effect, or induction stirring may be used for the same purpose. When degassing is complete, the tank is purged with an inert gas, its internal pressure is raised to atmospheric, and the ladle is removed from the tank. The degassed steel is teemed in the conventional manner.

Stream degassing is accomplished by placing an empty ladle (or mold) in a tank. A bottom-pour ladle containing the molten steel to be degassed is set upon the evacuated tank; the bottom of the ladle and the top of the tank are equipped with mating seals to prevent entrance of air. When the stopper rod of the tapping ladle is raised, molten metal flows through the nozzle, melts a metal diaphragm that seals the opening to the tank, and passes into the ladle (or mold) in the vacuum tank. As the stream of molten metal enters the evacuated space, it breaks up into tiny droplets, exposing an enormous surface to the degassing influence of the vacuum. After purging the tank, its internal pressure is raised to atmospheric, and the ladle of degassed steel is removed and the steel teemed in the usual manner. Figure 20 illustrates the principle of stream degassing.

In a variation of the foregoing method, the vacuum equipment is set up adjacent to an electric-arc furnace on the tapping side. The ladle to receive the degassed metal is equipped with a gastight cover with openings for making additions from a hopper, for exhausting the space within the ladle, and for admitting molten steel. A stopper-equipped intermediate container for molten metal called a tundish is sealed to the top of the ladle cover. After the ladle is evacuated, steel is poured directly from the electric furnace into the tundish and from thence, by raising the tundish stopper, into the evacuated space in the ladle through the opening provided in the ladle cover.

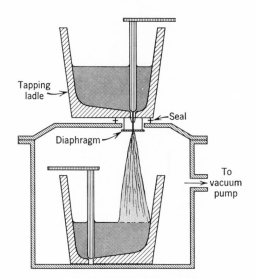

Fig. 20. Schematic arrangement of equipment for stream degassing (2).

In one of the recirculation degassing processes (Fig. 21), a vacuum vessel with a downwardly projecting tube is lowered until the end of the tube is immersed in the liquid steel. Vacuum pumps then lower the pressure in the upper chamber of the vessel to about 1 mm Hg, and atmospheric pressure causes liquid steel to rise into the chamber. As the steel enters the evacuated space, there is a violent evolution of gas that exposes a large surface area of the steel (in the form of droplets) to the vacuum. Raising the vessel without removing the tube from the liquid steel permits the degassed steel to partially flow back into the ladle. By repeating this operation for the required number of cycles, the entire contents of the ladle can be degassed.

In the second recirculation process to be described here, a vacuum chamber suspended over the ladle has two projecting tubes that extend into the liquid steel. After the chamber is evacuated, argon gas is injected into the steel in one of the tubes and, in effect, decreases the density of the column of liquid metal in that tube and

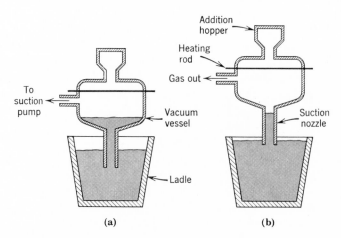

Fig. 21. Principle of operation of one of the recirculation degassing processes (2). (**a**) Vessel lowered; (**b**) vessel raised.

causes a "pumping" action resulting from the imbalance between the metal in that tube and the denser column of liquid steel in the other tube. The liquid steel rises into the evacuated chamber through the tube into which the argon is injected, absorbed gases are evolved from the metal with a boiling action, and the degassed metal returns to the ladle by way of the other tube. Circulation of the metal from the ladle into the evacuated chamber is continued until the desired degree of degassing is achieved.

There are numerous variations of vacuum-degassing methods.

Continuous Casting

Formerly, all steel for hot working was cast into ingots by the methods described above. Most steel is still handled this way. After the steel cools in the molds, the ingot is taken from the mold and transferred to a heating furnace called a soaking pit where its temperature is raised and equalized to prepare the steel for rolling on the primary rolling mills. The products of the primary mills are the semifinished products

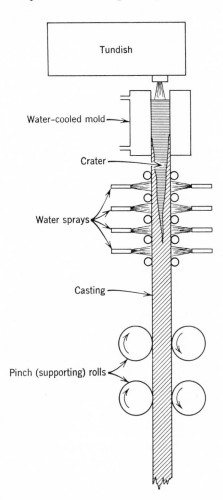

Fig. 22. Schematic representation of the progress of cooling of steel during continuous casting.

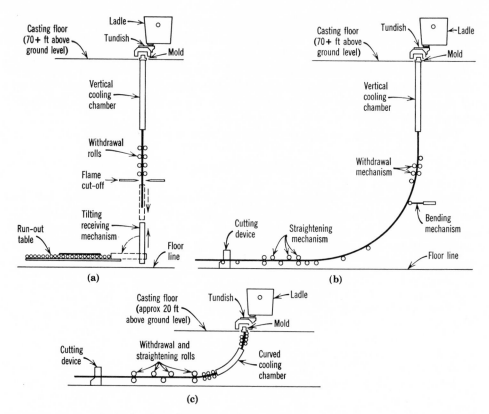

Fig. 23. Three methods that have been successfully applied to the continuous casting of steel (2).

called blooms, slabs, and billets. This series of operations is both time-consuming and expensive and results as well in some loss of steel.

The possibility of casting molten steel continuously into useful shapes equivalent to conventional semifinished shapes and thus eliminating the ingot and primary-mill stages of rolled-steel production led to a long series of attempts by many investigators, using a variety of designs of machines.

The high melting point of steel and its high specific heat and low thermal conductivity made most of the attempts abortive or only partially successful in the case of ferrous metals, although the continuous-casting principle proved practicable for nonferrous metals. Success in the nonferrous field spurred continuing study of the problem of applying continuous casting to steel and, eventually, the problem was solved.

The first continuous-casting machine for steel that operated on any consistent scale in the United States was developed in the late 1930s and early 1940s. Relatively little new continuous-casting equipment was added in this country until about 1960. Between 1960 and 1968, thirty-five continuous-casting machines were installed in the United States, and numerous additional machines were planned. Steelmakers in other countries have adopted continuous casting on a large scale.

Although the continuous casting of steel appears deceptively simple in principle, many difficulties are inherent in the process. Figure 22 illustrates schematically one of the problems. When molten steel comes into contact with the walls of the water-cooled mold, a thin solid "skin" forms. However, due to the physical characteristics of steel mentioned above, and also because thermal contraction causes the skin to separate from the mold wall shortly after solidification, the rate of heat abstraction from the casting is so slow that molten steel persists within the interior of the section for some distance below the bottom of the mold. The thickness of the skin increases due to the action of the water sprays as the casting moves downward and, eventually, the whole section is solid.

The mass of the solid steel casting is supported as it descends by driven pinch rolls that also control the speed of descent by controlling the rate of withdrawal of the casting from the mold. Any tendency for the casting to adhere to the mold wall may cause the skin to rupture due to the tensile forces exerted by the pinch rolls. The use of molds that move up and down for predetermined distances at controlled rates during casting has practically eliminated the sticking problem.

The continuous cast section issuing from the withdrawal or supporting rolls may be disposed of in several ways, some of which are illustrated in Figure 23.

A number of other designs of continuous-casting machines are in use. They are being used successfully in the production of steel shapes corresponding to all the semi-finished sections, and for the production of stainless, alloy, and carbon steels.

Bottom-Pressure Casting

Another method developed in recent years for producing semifinished steel shapes directly from molten steel, bypassing the ingot and primary rolling stages with the same advantages outlined above for continuous casting, is the bottom-pressure casting method, illustrated in Figure 24. In this method, a ladle filled with

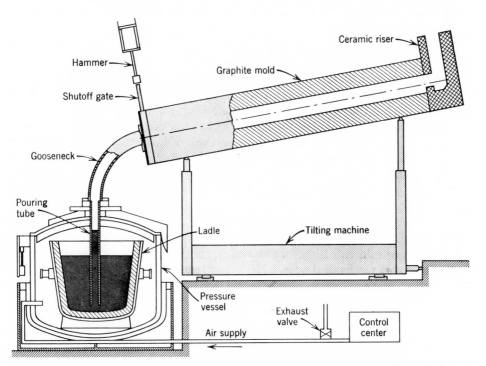

Fig. 24. Principle of operation of the bottom-pressure casting method as applied to slabs (2).

molten steel is placed in a pressure vessel. The pressure vessel is covered with a lid in which has been inserted a pouring tube that dips down into the molten steel in the ladle, almost to its bottom. A gooseneck tube connects the pouring tube to the mold. The mold is supported in an inclined position, with the gooseneck attached to its lower end. When air pressure is applied to the vessel, molten metal is forced upward through the pouring tube and gooseneck into the mold. Metal rises in the mold until it reaches the upper end where there is a riser that fills with molten metal to feed the casting as it solidifies to prevent formation of a pipe. When metal appears at the proper level in the riser, a gate at the lower end of the mold is closed to isolate the mold from the gooseneck; then, after a short interval, the pressure in the vessel is released to drain the metal in the gooseneck back into the ladle. After the casting has solidified, the mold is removed and prepared for the next casting. The method is said to increase the amount of usable product obtained from a given amount of steel and to produce such shapes as slabs and billets with improved surfaces that require little conditioning.

Plastic Working of Steel

Plastic working of a metal such as steel is the permanent deformation accomplished by applying mechanical forces to a metal surface. The primary objective of such working is usually the production of a specific shape or size (mechanical shaping), although in some cases it may be the improvement of certain physical properties and mechanical properties of the metal (mechanical treating). Often, these two objectives can be attained simultaneously.

For the present purposes, the plastic deformation of steel can be considered to be accomplished by one of two methods: hot working and cold working. In hot working, as the name implies, the steel is heated to the proper temperature for the grade of steel and the work to be accomplished. The force requirement to deform the metal is very sensitive to the rate of application of the force; however, after deformation, the basic strength of the steel is essentially unchanged. In cold working, on the other hand, steel is generally not heated before working, and the force requirement to cause deformation is relatively insensitive to the rate of application and to temperature variations, but the basic strength of the steel is permanently increased.

The principal methods of forming steel by hot working are hammering, pressing, rolling, and extrusion; hot working by the first two of these is called forging. Other methods of hot working include rotary swaging, hot spinning, hot deep-drawing, roll forging, and die forging. Hot working of steel is generally performed as a shaping process, but can result in improving the mechanical properties of steel if properly carried out.

Cold working is generally applied to bars, wire, strip, sheet, and tubes. It results in the reduction of the cross-sectional area of the piece being worked by cold rolling, cold drawing, or cold extrusion. Cold working is employed to obtain the following effects: improved mechanical properties, better machinability, special size accuracy, bright surface, and production of thinner material than hot working can accomplish economically. See also Metal treatments.

Metallography and Heat Treatment

The outstanding advantage of steel as an engineering material is its versatility, which arises from the fact that its properties can be controlled and changed at will by heat treatment. Thus, if steel is to be formed into some intricate shape, it can be made very soft and ductile by heat treatment; if, on the other hand, it is to resist wear, it can be heat treated to a very hard, wear-resisting condition.

The physical and mechanical properties of steel depend upon the constitution of the steel, that is, the nature, distribution, and amounts of its metallographic constituents as distinct from its chemical composition.

The two constituents of steel, the amount and distribution of which control the properties, are iron and iron carbide. True enough, most plain carbon steels will also contain manganese, silicon, phosphorus, sulfur, oxygen, and traces of nitrogen, hydrogen, and other chemical elements such as aluminum and copper. These elements, however, may modify to a certain extent the major effects of the constitution in respect to iron and iron carbide, but the iron carbide is always the predominating influence. This is largely true of even medium-alloy steels, which may contain con-

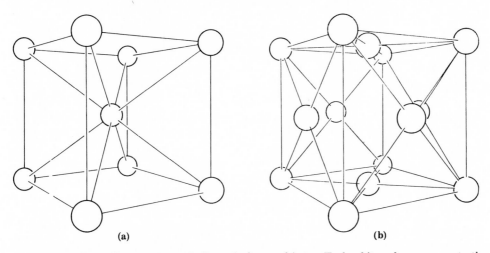

(a)   **(b)**

Fig. 25. Crystalline structure of allotropic forms of iron. Each white sphere represents the relative position of an atom in a "unit cube" of (**a**) α and δ iron, which have the body-centered-cubic form, and (**b**) γ iron, which has the face-centered-cubic form (2).

siderable percentages of such elements as nickel, chromium, molybdenum, vanadium, or titanium. The properties of such steels are still dependent primarily upon the distribution and amounts of iron and iron carbide, and the major effect of the alloying elements is to help in the control of this distribution, although the properties may be modified somewhat by solution of the alloying elements in the iron or by its combination with the iron carbide.

The metallographic name for iron in steel is ferrite. In pure iron–carbon alloys, the ferrite consists of iron with a trace of carbon in solution, but in steels it may also have considerable amounts of alloying elements such as manganese, silicon, or nickel dissolved in it. The atomic arrangement in crystals of the allotropic forms of iron is shown in Figure 25.

Cementite is the metallographic term for iron carbide in steel. This is the form in which carbon appears in steels; it belongs to the chemical species Fe_3C, and thus consists of 6.67% carbon and 93.33% iron. Little is known about its properties except that it is very hard and brittle. It is the hardest constituent of plain carbon steel

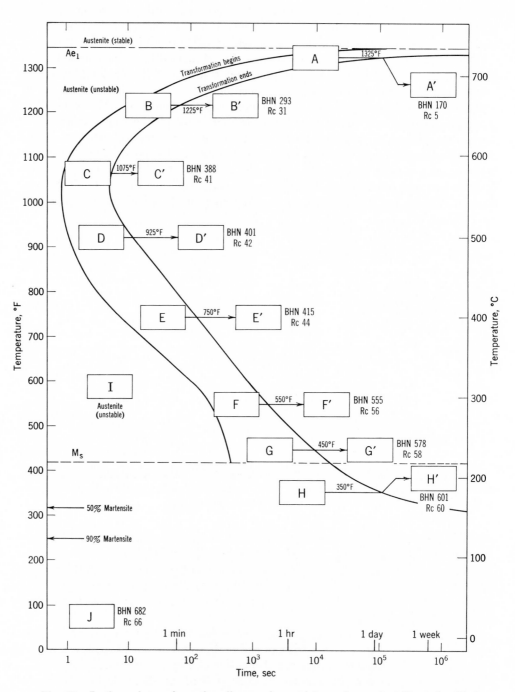

Fig. 26. Isothermal transformation diagram for a plain carbon eutectoid steel. (Carbon, 0.89%; manganese, 0.29%; austenitized at 1625°F.) The illustrations A–H (see opposite page) represent microstructures after transformation is half complete at the indicated temperature levels. The illustrations A′–H′ represent the microstructures after transformation is complete. I is the microstructure of austenite and J is that of martensite.

Fig. 26 (*continued*)

and will scratch glass and feldspar but not quartz. It has about two-thirds the induction of pure iron in a strong magnetic field.

Although austenite is not ordinarily a constituent of steel after it has been cooled, it will be described at this point since it is the important high-temperature phase of steel, the decomposition of which on cooling forms the room-temperature constituents that are being discussed. It is a homogeneous phase, consisting of a solid solution of carbon in the γ form of iron. It is formed when steel is heated to a relatively high temperature, above 1450°F. The limiting temperatures for its formation vary with composition and will be discussed in connection with the iron–carbon equilibrium diagram. The atomic structure of austenite is that of γ iron—face-centered-cubic—and the atomic spacing varies with the carbon content.

When a plain carbon steel of approximately 0.80% carbon content is cooled slowly from the temperature range at which austenite is stable, all of the ferrite and cementite precipitate together in a characteristically lamellar structure known as pearlite. It is generally similar in its characteristics to a eutectic structure but since it is formed from a solid solution rather than from a liquid phase it is known as a eutectoid structure. At carbon contents above and below 0.80%, pearlite of about 0.80% carbon is likewise formed on slow cooling, but the excess ferrite or cementite first precipitates, usually as a grain-boundary network, but occasionally also along cleavage planes of the austenite. This excess ferrite or cementite rejected by the cooling austenite is known as a proeutectoid constituent. The carbon content of a slowly cooled steel can be estimated from the relative amounts of pearlite and proeutectoid constituents in the microstructure.

Bainite is a decomposition product of austenite consisting of an aggregate of ferrite and cementite. In general, it forms at temperatures lower than those where very fine pearlite forms and higher than those at which martensite begins to form on cooling. Metallographically, its appearance is "feathery" if formed in the upper part of the temperature range, or acicular (needlelike) and resembling tempered martensite if formed in the lower part.

Martensite in steel is a metastable phase formed by the transformation of austenite below the temperature called the M_s temperature, where martensite begins to form as austenite is continuously cooled from an elevated temperature (see Fig. 26). It is an interstitial supersaturated solid solution of carbon in iron, having a body-centered tetragonal lattice. Its microstructure is acicular (needlelike).

Iron–Carbon Equilibrium Diagram

The iron–carbon equilibrium diagram (Fig. 27) furnishes a "map" showing the ranges of compositions and temperatures in which the various phases are stable. This diagram, covering the temperature range from 1112°F to the melting point of iron and carbon contents of from 0 to 5%, represents the equilibrium conditions for the entire range of steels and cast irons in both the liquid and solid states.

The portion of the iron–iron carbide diagram of interest here is that part extending from 0 to 2.01% carbon. Its application to heat treatment can be illustrated by considering the changes occurring on heating and cooling steels of selected carbon contents.

It has already been stated that iron occurs in two allotropic forms, α or δ (the latter at very high temperatures) that have a body-centered-cubic structure, and γ that has a face-centered-cubic structure (see Fig. 25). The temperatures at which these phase changes occur are known as critical temperatures and the boundaries in Figure 27 show how these temperatures are affected by composition. For pure iron, these temperatures are 1670°F for the α–γ phase change and 2534°F for the γ–δ phase change.

Changes on Heating and Cooling Pure Iron. The only changes occurring on heating or cooling pure iron are the reversible changes (1) at about 1670°F from body-centered α iron to face-centered γ iron, and (2) from the face-centered γ iron to body-centered δ iron at about 2534°F.

Changes on Heating and Cooling Hypoeutectoid Steel. Hypoeutectoid steels are those which contain less than the eutectoid percentage of carbon (0.8%). The diagram shows that the equilibrium constituents are ferrite and pearlite, the relative amounts of each depending upon the carbon content. The diagram also shows that at 1112°F the ferrite may hold in stable solution about 0.007% carbon. Up to 1340°F,

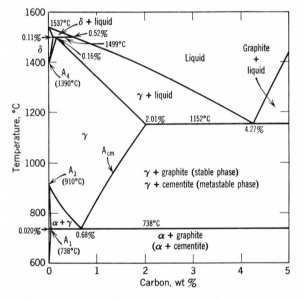

Fig. 27. The iron–carbon equilibrium diagram, for carbon contents up to 5% (2).

the solubility of carbon in the ferrite increases until at this temperature, the ferrite contains about 0.025% carbon. The first phase change on heating (if the steel contains above 0.025% carbon) occurs at 1340°F and this temperature is therefore designated as the A_1 critical temperature. On heating just above this temperature, the pearlite (ferrite and cementite) all changes to austenite. Some proeutectoid ferrite, however, remains unchanged. As temperature rises farther above A_1, the austenite dissolves more and more of the surrounding proeutectoid ferrite, becoming lower and lower in carbon content, until at the A_3 temperature the last of the proeutectoid ferrite has been absorbed into the austenite which now has the same average carbon content as the steel.

On slow cooling the reverse changes occur. The austenite first rejects ferrite (generally at grain boundaries) on cooling below A_3 and becomes progressively richer in carbon until, just above the A_1 (eutectoid) temperature, it is substantially of eutectoid composition. On cooling below A_1, this eutectoid austenite changes to pearlite so that the final product after cooling below A_1 is a mixture of ferrite and pearlite, the relative proportions of each constituent depending upon the carbon content.

Changes on Heating and Cooling Eutectoid Steels. Since no excess ferrite or cementite is present in eutectoid steel, the only change occurring on slow heating or cooling is the reversible change from pearlite to austenite at the eutectoid temperature. Thus, in the case of eutectoid steels, the A_3 and A_1 temperatures coincide and this eutectoid composition and temperature is referred to as the A_{3-1} point.

Changes on Heating and Cooling Hypereutectoid Steels. The behavior on heating and cooling hypereutectoid steels (steels containing more than 0.80% carbon) is similar to that of hypoeutectoid steels except that the excess constituent is cementite rather than ferrite, so that on heating above A_1 the austenite gradually dissolves the excess cementite until at the A_{cm} temperature all of the proeutectoid cementite has been dissolved and austenite of the same carbon content as the steel is formed. Similarly, on cooling below A_3, cementite precipitates and the carbon content of the austenite approaches the eutectoid composition. On cooling below A_1, this eutectoid austenite changes to pearlite and the room temperature constitution is, therefore, pearlite and proeutectoid cementite.

Early iron–carbon equilibrium diagrams indicated a critical temperature at about 1414°F. It has since been found that there is no true phase change at this point. However, between about 1414 and 1454°F there is a gradual magnetic change, ferrite being magnetic below the range and paramagnetic above it. This change, occurring at what formerly was called the A_2 change, is of little or no significance in regard to the heat treatment of steel.

Effect of Alloys on the Equilibrium Diagram. The iron–carbon diagram may, of course, be profoundly altered by alloying elements, and its application should be limited to plain carbon and low-alloy steels. The most important effects of the alloying elements are that (1) the number of phases which may be in equilibrium is no longer limited to two as in the iron–carbon diagram; (2) the temperature and composition range, with respect to carbon, over which austenite is stable may be increased or reduced; and (3) the eutectoid temperature and composition may be changed.

The alloying elements may be divided generally into two classes in relation to the second effect: those which enlarge the austenite field and those which reduce it. The elements which enlarge the field include manganese, nickel, cobalt, copper, carbon, and nitrogen. Because of this characteristic, these elements are referred to as austenite formers.

The commoner elements which decrease the extent of the austenite field include chromium, silicon, molybdenum, tungsten, vanadium, tin, niobium, phosphorus, aluminum, and titanium: such elements are known as ferrite formers.

Manganese and nickel lower the eutectoid temperature, while chromium, tungsten, silicon, molybdenum, and titanium generally raise it. All of these seven elements seem to lower the eutectoid carbon content.

Austenite Grain Size. A significant aspect of the behavior of steels on heating is the grain growth that occurs when the austenite, which is formed on heating above A_3 or A_{cm}, is heated higher than this temperature. The austenite, like any metal composed of a solid solution, consists of polygonal grains. As formed at a temperature just above the A_3 or A_{cm} temperature, the size of the individual grains will be very small but, as the temperature is increased above the critical temperature, the sizes of the grains will increase because of absorption of individual grains into adjacent grains. The final austenite grain size will depend, therefore, upon the temperature above the critical temperature to which the steel is heated. The grain size of the austenite has a marked influence both upon its transformation behavior during cooling, and upon the grain size of the constituents of the final microstructure. Grain growth in the austenite may be inhibited by carbides which dissolve slowly or by a suitable dispersion of nonmetallic inclusions. Hot working refines the coarse grain formed by reheating steel to the relatively high temperatures used in forging or rolling, and the grain size of hot-worked steel is determined largely by the finishing temperature; that is, the temperature at which the final stage of the hot-working process is carried out. The general effects of austenite grain size on the properties of heat-treated steel are summarized in Table 3.

Table 3. Trends in Heat-Treated Products

Property	Coarse-grain austenite	Fine-grain austenite
Quenched and tempered products		
hardenability	deeper hardening	shallower hardening
toughness	less tough	tougher
distortion	more distortion	less distortion
quench cracking	more prevalent	less prevalent
internal stress	higher	lower
Annealed or normalized products		
machinability (rough)	better	inferior
machinability (fine finish)	inferior	better

Determination of Microscopic Grain Size. The microscopic grain size of steel is customarily determined by preparing a polished plane section prepared in such a way as to delineate the grain boundaries. The grain size can be estimated by several methods that cannot be described in detail here. The results of the several methods can be expressed in such terms as (*1*) "diameter" of average grain in millimeters (reciprocal of the square root of the number of grains per mm^2), (*2*) number of grains per unit area, (*3*) number of grains per unit volume, or (*4*) a micrograin-size number obtained by comparing the microstructure of the sample with a series of standard charts.

Fine- and Coarse-Grain Steels. As was mentioned previously, austenitic-grain growth may be inhibited by undissolved carbides or by a suitable distribution of nonmetallic inclusions. Steels of this type are commonly referred to as inherently fine-grained or simply as fine-grained steels, while steels which are free from these grain-growth inhibitors are known as coarse-grained steels.

The general pattern of grain coarsening in steels of the coarse- and fine-grained types on heating above the critical temperature is as follows: The coarse-grained steel coarsens gradually and consistently as the temperature is increased, while the fine-grained steel coarsens only slightly if at all until a certain temperature known as the coarsening temperature is reached, after which abrupt coarsening occurs. Either type of steel can be heat treated so as to be either fine or coarse grained: as a matter of fact, at temperatures above its coarsening temperature, the fine-grained steel usually will exhibit a coarser grain size than the coarse-grained steel at the same temperature.

The usual method of making steels which remain fine-grained at 1700°F involves the judicious use of deoxidation with aluminum. The inhibiting agent in such steels is generally conjectured to be a submicroscopic dispersion of aluminum nitride or, perhaps at times, aluminum oxide.

Transformation of Austenite. Thus far, this article has discussed the constitution of steel on the basis of equilibrium conditions. Under such conditions, that is, with very slow cooling, it has been shown that austenite transforms to pearlite when it is cooled below the A_1 temperature. When austenite is more rapidly cooled, this transformation is depressed and does not occur just below the critical temperature but when some lower temperature is reached. The faster the cooling rate, the lower is the temperature at which transformation occurs. Furthermore, the nature of the ferrite–carbide aggregate formed when the austenite transforms varies markedly with the temperature of transformation and the properties are found to vary correspondingly. Thus, heat treatment involves a controlled supercooling of austenite, and in order to take full advantage of the wide range of structures and properties which this permits, a knowledge of the transformation behavior of austenite and the properties of the resulting aggregates is essential.

Isothermal Transformation Diagram. The transformation behavior of austenite is best studied by observing the isothermal (constant temperature) transformation at a series of temperatures below A_1. The transformation progress is ordinarily followed metallographically so that both the time-temperature relationships, and the manner in which the microstructure changes with the temperature of transformation can be established. The results of these observations customarily are presented as a plot, with temperature as the ordinate and time (on a logarithmic scale) as the abscissa. The times at which transformation begins and ends at a given temperature are plotted, and curves depicting the transformation behavior as a function of temperature are obtained by joining these points (Fig. 26). Such a diagram is referred to as an isothermal transformation (IT) diagram, as a time-temperature-transformation (TTT) diagram or, because of a similarity of the IT curves for some steels to the letter, as an S curve.

The IT diagram for a eutectoid carbon steel is shown in Figure 26. In addition to the lines depicting the beginning and end of transformation, photomicrographs showing the microstructures at the completion of transformation and also when the transformation has gone halfway to completion in the significant temperature ranges, as well as hardness values for the fully transformed structures, are shown. Thus, the diagram illustrates the characteristic subcritical austenite transformation behavior, the characteristic manner in which microstructure changes with transformation temperature, and the general relationship between these microstructural changes and hardness.

As the diagram indicates, the characteristic isothermal transformation behavior at any temperature above the temperature at which transformation to martensite begins (the M_s temperature) involves a period of time, known as the incubation period, in which no transformation occurs, followed by a period of time during which the transformation proceeds until all of the austenite has transformed. The characteristic behavior during the transformation period is a relatively slow transformation rate at the beginning of the transformation and also as the transformation approaches completion, with a much more rapid transformation rate during the period in which about 25–75% of the austenite transforms. Both the incubation period and the times required for completion of the transformation vary with the transformation temperature.

The behavior depicted in this diagram is typical of the general behavior of plain carbon steels, with the shortest incubation period occurring at a temperature of about 1000°F, and much longer times being required for transformation as the transformation temperature approaches either the A_1 critical temperature or the M_s temperature. The symbol Ae_1 in Figure 26 indicates the A_1 temperature at equilibrium. This A_1 temperature is lowered slightly during cooling and increased slightly during heating. The 1000°F temperature, at which the transformation begins in the shortest time period, is commonly referred to as the "nose" of the IT diagram. It is apparent that, if complete transformation is to occur at temperatures below this nose, the steel must be cooled to the lower temperatures rapidly enough to prevent transformation at this nose temperature. This is important because the microstructures resulting from transformation at these lower temperatures are often desired because of their superior strength and toughness.

Transformation to Pearlite. Transformation over the temperature range of about 1300–1000°F (in carbon and low-alloy steels) forms pearlitic microstructures of the characteristic lamellar type. As the transformation temperature is decreased, the lamellae become more closely spaced and the hardness increases as the lamellar spacing becomes smaller.

Transformation to Bainite. Transformation to bainite occurs over the temperature range of about 1000–450°F. The bainitic microstructures differ markedly from the pearlitic in that they are acicular (needlelike) in nature. Here again, the hardness increases as the transformation temperature decreases, though the bainite formed at the highest possible temperature is often softer than pearlite formed at a still higher temperature.

Transformation to Martensite. Transformation to martensite, which in the steel illustrated in Figure 26 begins at about 420°F, differs from transformation to pearlite or bainite in that it is not time dependent, but occurs almost instantly during cooling, and the percentage of transformation is dependent only on the temperature to which it is cooled. Thus, in this steel, transformation to martensite will start on cooling to 450°F (designated as the M_s temperature), will be 50% complete on cooling to about 300°F, and will be essentially completed at about 200°F (designated as the M_f temperature). The microstructure of martensite is likewise acicular but can be differentiated from bainite because it is generally lighter etching. It is the hardest of the transformation products of austenite, but is brittle; this brittleness can be relieved to the desired degree by tempering, as discussed later, p. 777.

Properties of Pearlite. In any steel, the pearlites are, as a class, softer than the bainites or martensites. In general, even though softer, they are less ductile than the lower-temperature bainites and for a given hardness they will be far less ductile than tempered martensite. As the transformation temperature decreases within the pearlite range, the interlamellar spacing decreases, as was described above, and these "fine" pearlites, formed near the nose of the isothermal diagram, are both harder and more ductile than the "coarse" pearlites formed at higher temperatures. Thus, although as a class pearlite tends to be soft and not exceedingly ductile, its hardness and toughness both increase markedly with decreasing transformation temperatures.

Properties of Bainite. In a given steel, bainitic microstructures generally will be found both harder and tougher than pearlite, although the hardness will be lower

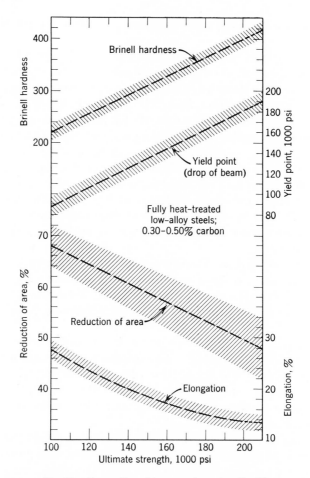

Fig. 28. Properties of tempered martensite (2).

than that of martensite. Within the class, as with pearlite, the properties generally improve as the transformation temperature decreases and "lower" bainite will compare favorably with, or exceed in toughness, tempered martensite at the same hardness. "Upper" bainite, on the other hand, may be somewhat deficient in toughness as compared with fine pearlite at the same hardness.

Properties of Martensite.   Martensite is the hardest and likewise the most brittle of the microstructures obtainable in a given steel. The hardness of martensite increases with increasing carbon content of steel, up to the eutectoid composition. The hardness of martensite, at a given carbon content, varies somewhat with the cooling rate.

Although for some applications, particularly those involving wear resistance, the high hardness of martensite is desirable in spite of the accompanying brittleness, the principal importance of this microstructure is as the starting material for tempered martensite structures, which have definitely superior properties.

Properties of Tempered Martensite.   Tempered martensitic structures are, as a class, characterized by relatively high toughness at any strength level. Their properties are illustrated in Figure 28. This diagram designates, within plus or minus 10%,

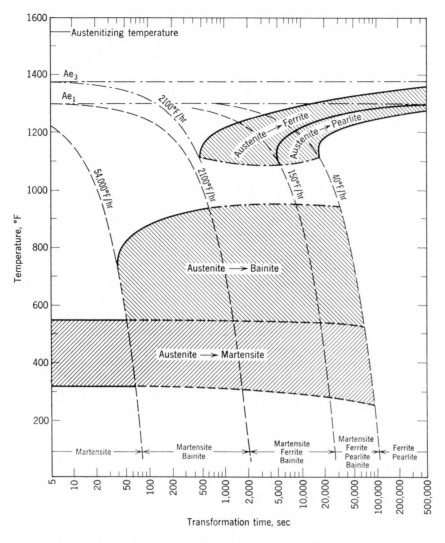

Fig. 29. Continuous-cooling transformation diagram for a 4340-type alloy steel, with super-imposed cooling curves illustrating the manner in which transformation behavior during continuous cooling governs final microstructure (2).

the usual mechanical properties of any steel with this microstructure, regardless of composition. For example, a steel consisting of tempered martensite, with an ultimate strength of 150,000 psi, might be expected to exhibit elongation of 16–20%, reduction of area of between 54 and 64%, yield point of 125,000–142,000 psi, and Brinell hardness of about 295–320. Because of its high ductility at a given hardness, this is the structure that is aimed for in heat treating for toughness by quenching and tempering.

Factors Affecting Transformation Rates. The major factors affecting transformation rates of austenite are its composition, grain size, and homogeneity. In general, increasing carbon and alloy content tend to decrease transformation rates. Increasing the grain size of the austenite tends to decrease transformation rates. All of these effects are reflected in the isothermal transformation curve for a given steel.

Transformation on Continuous Cooling. The basic information depicted by an isothermal transformation diagram tells what structure is formed at each reaction temperature if the cooling is interrupted so that the reaction goes to completion at that temperature. The information is equally useful for interpreting behaviors when the cooling proceeds directly without interruption, as in the case of the industrial heat-treating processes of annealing, normalizing, and quenching. In these processes, the time at a single temperature is generally insufficient for the reaction to go to completion; instead, the final structure consists of an association of microstructures which individually were formed at successively lower temperatures as the piece cooled. However, the tendency to form the several structures is still explained by the isothermal diagram.

The final microstructure after continuous cooling obviously depends on the times spent at the various transformation-temperature ranges through which the piece is cooled. The transformation behavior on continuous cooling thus represents an integration of these times and this integration can be carried out by a method developed by Grange and Kiefer. By this method, a continuous-cooling diagram generally similar to the isothermal transformation diagram, but depicting the transformation behavior on continuous cooling at constant rates, can be constructed (Fig. 29). This diagram lies below and to the right of the corresponding isothermal transformation diagram if plotted on the same coordinates. That is, transformation on continuous cooling will start at a lower temperature and after a longer time than the intersection of the cooling curve and the isothermal diagram would predict, and this displacement is a function of the cooling rate, being larger as the cooling rate increases.

Several cooling-rate curves have been superimposed on Figure 29. A consideration of the changes occurring during these various cooling cycles will illustrate the manner in which diagrams of this nature can be correlated with heat-treating practice and used to predict the resulting microstructure.

Considering first the relatively slow cooling rate (less than $40°F/hr$), the steel will be cooled through the regions in which transformation to ferrite and pearlite will occur and these constituents, ferrite and pearlite, will make up the final microstructure. This cooling rate corresponds to a slow cooling in the furnace such as might be used in annealing.

At a somewhat faster cooling rate ($40–150°F/hr$), such as might be obtained on normalizing a large forging, the ferrite, pearlite, bainite, and martensite fields will be traversed and the final microstructure will contain all of these constituents.

At cooling rates of $2100–54,000°F/hr$, the microstructure will be free of proeutectoid ferrite and will consist largely of bainite with a small amount of martensite present. A cooling rate of at least $54,000°F/hr$ is necessary to obtain the fully martensitic structure desired as a starting point for tempered martensite on quenching and tempering.

Thus, the final microstructure, and therefore the properties of the steel, are dependent upon the transformation behavior of the austenite and on the cooling conditions, and can be predicted if these factors are known, or can be governed by controlling either or both of these factors.

Hardenability. Hardenability refers to the depth of hardening or to the size of a piece which can be hardened under given cooling conditions, and not to the maximum hardness that can be obtained in a given steel. The maximum hardness is dependent almost entirely upon the carbon content, while the hardenability (depth of hardening) is far more dependent upon the alloy content and grain size of the austenite. Steels whose IT diagrams indicate a long time interval before the start of the transformation to pearlite are useful when larger sections are to be hardened, since if steel is to transform to bainite or martensite, it must escape any transformation to pearlite. This means that the steel must be cooled through the high-temperature transformation ranges at a rapid enough rate for transformation not to occur, even at the nose of the IT diagram. This rate which will just permit transformation to martensite without any prior transformation at a higher temperature is known as the critical cooling rate for martensite, and furnishes one method for expressing hardenability. For example, in the steel of Figure 29, the critical cooling rate for martensite is 54,000°F/hr or 15°F/sec.

Although the critical cooling rate can be used to express hardenability, it has the disadvantage that, in actual practice, cooling rates ordinarily are not constant, but vary during the cooling cycle. This is particularly true for quenching in liquids, in which case the cooling rate of the steel is always slower as its temperature approaches that of the cooling medium. It is, therefore, customary to express hardenability in terms of depth of hardening in a standardized quench. The quenching condition used in this method of expression is a hypothetical one, in which the surface of the piece is assumed to come instantly to the temperature of the quenching medium. This is known as an ideal quench, and the diameter of a round steel bar which will just quench to the desired microstructure, or corresponding hardness value, at the center in an ideal quench is known as the ideal diameter for which the symbol D_I is used. The relationships between the cooling rates of this idealized quench and those of other cooling conditions are known, so that the hardenability values in terms of ideal diameter can be used to predict the size of round or other shape which will have this same cooling rate when cooled in actual quenches whose cooling severities are known. The cooling severities (usually referred to as "severity of quench") which form the basis for these relationships are called "H values." The H value for the ideal quench is infinity and those for some commonly used cooling conditions are shown in Table 4.

Hardenability is most conveniently measured by a test in which a steel sample is subjected to a continuous range of cooling rates. The one most commonly used is the end-quench test (or Jominy test, after the inventor). In this test, a round bar, 1 in. diam and 4 in. long, is heated to the desired austenitizing temperature and quenched in a fixture by a stream of water impinging on only one end. Hardness measurements are made on flats which are ground along the length of the bar after quenching, and the results expressed as a plot of hardness versus distance from the quenched end of the

Table 4. H Values Designating Severity of Quench for Commonly Used Cooling Conditions[a]

Degree of agitation of medium	Quenching medium		
	Oil	Water	Brine
none	0.25–0.30	0.9–1.0	2
mild	0.30–0.35	1.0–1.1	2.0–2.2
moderate	0.35–0.40	1.2–1.3	
good	0.40–0.50	1.4–1.5	
strong	0.50–0.80	1.6–2.0	
violent	0.80–1.1	4.0	5.0

[a] H values are proportional to the heat-extracting capacity of the medium.

bar. The relationships between the distance from the quenched end and cooling rates in terms of ideal diameter (D_I) are known, so that hardenability evaluations in terms of D_I can be made by noting the distance from the quenched end at which the hardness corresponding to the desired microstructure occurs and using this relationship to establish the corresponding cooling rate or D_I value. This ideal-diameter value, in turn, can be used through published heat-flow tables or charts which relate the ideal-diameter value to cooling rate in quenches or cooling conditions whose H values are known, to establish the size of piece in which the desired microstructure can be obtained under the quenching conditions of the heat-treating practice to be used. The hardenability of steel is such an important attribute that it has become common practice to purchase steels to specified hardenability limits. Such steels are called H steels.

Heat-Treating Processes

Heat-treating processes usually involve heating of steel to temperatures above the A_3 point, followed by cooling at rates that will result in the desired microstructure that will give the steel the properties best suited for the purpose for which the steel is to be used. See also Metal treatments.

Heating for Austenitization. The first step in most heat treatments is to heat the steel above the temperature (A_3) at which austenite is formed. The actual austenitizing temperature should be high enough to dissolve all of the carbides so that full advantage may be taken of the hardenability effects of the alloying elements. In some cases, such as tool steels or high-carbon steels in which undissolved carbides are desired for wear resistance, it may be desirable to leave some undissolved carbides. The temperature should not be so high that pronounced grain growth occurs. The piece should be held at temperature long enough for complete solution; for low-alloy steels in a normally loaded furnace, 45 min/in. of diameter or thickness usually is adequate.

Too-rapid heating rates may set up high stresses which may result in distortion or cracking of the steel. Certain types of continuous furnaces, salt baths, and radiant-heating furnaces provide very rapid heating rates, but preheating of the steel may be necessary to avoid distortion or cracking, and sufficient time must be allowed for the steel to be heated uniformly throughout. Unless special precautions are taken, heating will cause scaling or oxidation, and may result in decarburization; the use of controlled-atmosphere furnaces and salt baths can minimize these effects.

Quenching. The primary purpose of quenching is to cool all parts of the piece being quenched rapidly enough to suppress all transformation at temperatures above the M_s temperature. The cooling rate required depends upon the size of the piece and the hardenability of the steel. The quenching media most used are water, oils, or brine. The temperature gradients set up in the piece by quenching result in high thermal and transformation stresses which may lead to cracking and distortion, and a quenching rate no faster than necessary should be employed to minimize these stresses. Agitation of the cooling medium accelerates the cooling rate and improves the uniformity of cooling. The piece should be cooled in the quench long enough for transformation to martensite to be complete throughout the piece and, in order to minimize cracking from quenching stresses, the piece should be transferred immediately to the tempering furnace, as indicated in Figure 30.

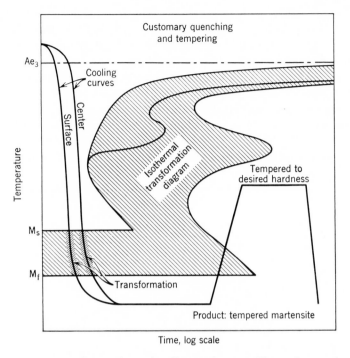

Time, log scale

Fig. 30. Schematic transformation diagram for quenching and tempering.

Tempering. The martensite formed by quenching is very hard and brittle and its formation results in high residual stresses in the steel. The purpose of tempering is to relieve these stresses and to improve the ductility, which it does at some expense of the strength or hardness of the original martensite. The operation consists of heating at temperatures below the lower critical temperature (A_1).

Measurements of the stress relaxation that occurs on tempering have indicated that, in a plain carbon steel, the level of the residual stress is significantly lowered by heating to temperatures as low as 300°F, but that temperatures of 900°F and above are required to reduce these stresses to very low values. The times and temperatures required for stress relief are thus dependent upon the elevated-temperature yield strength of the steel, since stress relief results from the localized plastic flow which occurs when the steel is heated to an elevated temperature at which the yield strength is decreased. This phenomenon may be affected markedly by composition, and particularly by alloy additions. The toughness of quenched steel, as measured by the notch impact test, first increases on tempering up to 400°F, then decreases on tempering between 400 and 600°F, and finally increases rapidly on tempering at temperatures of 800°F and above. This is a characteristic behavior and, in general, the temperature range of 450–600°F should be avoided in tempering.

In order to minimize cracking, tempering should follow quenching immediately. Allowing fully quenched pieces to stand for any appreciable period before tempering is liable to promote cracking.

The tempering of martensite results in a contraction, and if the heating is not uniform, stresses will be set up by the resulting unequal contraction which may cause distortion or even cracking. Similarly, too rapid heating may be dangerous because of the sharp temperature gradient set up between the surface and the interior of the piece. Recirculating-air furnaces can be used to obtain the uniform heating desired for tempering. Oil or salt baths are commonly used for low-temperature tempering. Lead or salt baths may be used for higher tempering temperatures.

Some steels exhibit a loss of toughness on slow cooling from temperatures of about 1000°F and above—a phenomenon known as "temper brittleness"—and a rapid cooling after tempering is generally desirable in these cases.

Martempering. A modified quenching procedure known as martempering was developed by B. F. Shepherd to minimize the high stresses set up by the transformation to martensite during the rapid cooling characteristic of ordinary quenching.

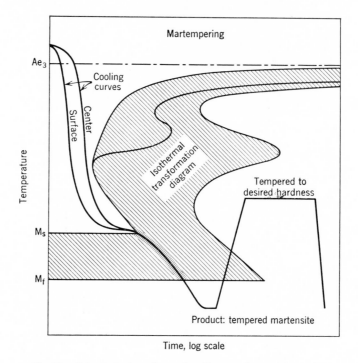

Fig. 31. Schematic transformation diagram for martempering.

This method is illustrated diagrammatically in Figure 31. In practice, it ordinarily is carried out by quenching the piece into a molten-salt bath at a temperature just above the M_s temperature. Transformation to martensite does not begin until the entire piece has attained the temperature of the salt bath and is removed to cool relatively slowly in air. Since the temperature gradient characteristic of the conventional quench is absent, the stresses set up by the transformation are much lower and a greater freedom from distortion and cracking is obtained. After martempering, the piece may be tempered to the desired strength level.

Austempering. As discussed earlier, the properties of lower bainite are generally similar in respect to strength and somewhat superior in ductility to those of tempered martensite. Austempering, which is an isothermal heat treatment that results in lower bainite, offers an alternate method of heat treatment for obtaining optimum strength and ductility.

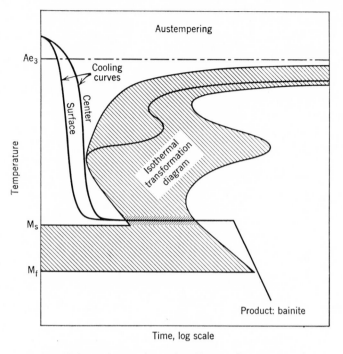

Fig. 32. Schematic transformation diagram for austempering.

The austempering treatment is illustrated diagrammatically in Figure 32. It involves quenching to the desired temperature in the lower bainite region, usually in molten salt, and holding at this temperature until transformation is complete. It is the usual practice to hold for a time twice as long as that indicated by the isothermal transformation diagram for a particular steel to ensure complete transformation of segregated areas. The piece may be quenched or air cooled to room temperature after transformation is complete and may be tempered to a lower hardness level if desired.

Normalizing. Normalizing involves reheating of steel above its upper critical temperature (A_3) and air cooling. It has two primary purposes: to refine the grain, and to obtain a carbide size and distribution which will be more favorable for carbide solution on subsequent heat treating than the as-rolled structure.

The as-rolled grain size, depending principally on the finishing temperature in the rolling operation, is subject to wide variations. The coarse grain size resulting from a high finishing temperature can be refined by normalizing to establish a uniform, relatively fine-grained microstructure.

In alloy steels, particularly if they have been slowly cooled after rolling, the carbides in the as-rolled condition tend to be rather large and massive and are difficult to dissolve in subsequent austenitization treatments. The carbide size will be subject to wide variations, depending upon the rolling and slow-cooling practice. Here again, normalizing tends to establish a more uniform and finer carbide particle size that facilitates subsequent heat treatment.

The usual practice is to normalize from 100 to 150°F above the upper critical temperature, but for some alloy steels considerably higher temperatures may be used.

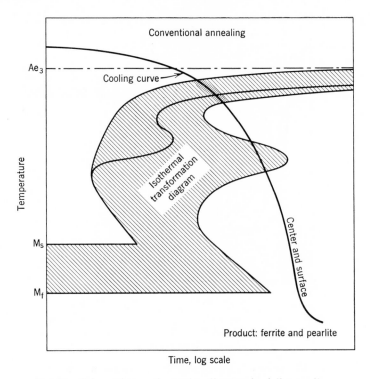

Fig. 33. Schematic transformation diagram for full annealing.

Heating may be carried out in any type of furnace that will permit uniform heating and accurate temperature control.

Annealing. The principal purposes of annealing are to relieve cooling stresses induced by hot or cold working, and to soften the steel so as to improve its machinability or formability. It may involve only a subcritical heating to relieve stresses, to recrystallize cold-worked material, or to spheroidize carbides, or it may involve heating above the upper critical temperature (A_3) with subsequent transformation to pearlite or directly to a spheroidized structure on cooling.

The most favorable microstructure for machinability in the low- or medium-carbon steels is coarse pearlite. The customary heat treatment to develop this microstructure is a full anneal, illustrated diagrammatically in Figure 33. It consists of austenitizing at a relatively high temperature so that full carbide solution is obtained, followed by slow cooling so that transformation occurs only and completely in the high-temperature end of the pearlite range. This is a simple heat treatment and is reliable for most steels. It is, however, rather time consuming since it involves slow cooling over the entire temperature range from the austenitizing temperature to a temperature well below that at which transformation is complete.

Annealing to coarse pearlite can be carried out isothermally by cooling to the proper temperature for transformation to coarse pearlite and holding at this temperature until transformation is complete. This method, called isothermal annealing, is illustrated diagrammatically in Figure 34. Isothermal annealing may save considerable time over the full-annealing process described previously, since neither the time from the austenitizing temperature to the transformation temperature, nor from

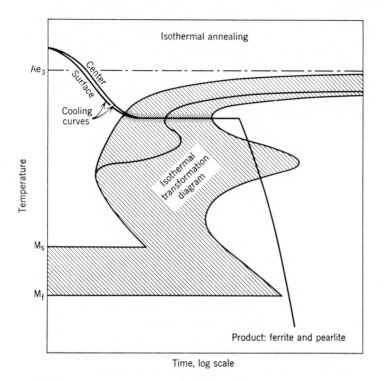

Fig. 34. Schematic transformation diagram for isothermal annealing.

the transformation temperature to room temperature, is critical and these may be speeded up as much as is desired or is practical. If extreme softness of the coarsest pearlite is not necessary, transformation may be carried out at the "nose" of the IT curve where the transformation goes to completion most rapidly and the operation is further expedited; the pearlite in this case will be much finer and the hardness higher.

Isothermal annealing can be adapted conveniently to continuous annealing, usually in specially designed furnaces, when it is commonly referred to as cycle annealing.

Spheroidize Annealing. Coarse pearlite microstructures are too hard for optimum machinability in the higher carbon steels, and such steels are customarily annealed to develop spheroidized microstructures. This may be accomplished by tempering the as-rolled, slow-cooled, or normalized materials at a temperature just below the lower critical range. Such an operation is known as subcritical annealing. Full spheroidization of the carbides may require long holding times at the subcritical temperature and the method may be slow, but it is simple and may be more convenient than annealing above the critical temperature.

It has been found, however, that the procedures described above for annealing to produce pearlite can, with some modifications, produce spheroidized microstructures. If free carbide remains after austenitizing, transformation in the temperature range where coarse pearlite ordinarily would form will proceed to spheroidized rather than pearlitic microstructures. Thus, heat treatment to form spheroidized microstructures can be carried out in a manner analogous to heat treatment to form pearlite, except for the use of lower austenitizing temperatures. Spheroidize annealing may thus involve a slow cooling similar to the full-annealing treatment to produce pearlite or it may be an isothermal treatment similar to isothermal annealing to form pearlite. An austenitizing temperature not more than 100°F above the lower critical temperature is customarily used for this supercritical annealing to produce spheroidized microstructures.

Process Annealing. Process annealing is the term used to describe the subcritical annealing of cold-worked materials. It customarily involves heating at a temperature high enough to cause recrystallization of the cold-worked material and to soften the steel. The most important example of process annealing is the box-annealing of cold-rolled low-carbon sheet steel: the sheets are enclosed in a large box which can be sealed to permit the use of a controlled atmosphere inside the box to protect the steel from oxidation during heat treatment. This annealing usually is carried out at temperatures of from about 1100 to 1300°F. The heating and holding at temperature usually takes about 24 hr, after which the charge is cooled slowly within the box, the entire process taking about 40 hr.

Carburizing. See Vol. 13, p. 304. In carburizing, a high-carbon surface layer is imparted to low-carbon steel by heating it in contact with carbonaceous materials. On quenching after carburizing, the high-carbon case becomes very hard, while the low-carbon core remains comparatively soft. The result is a very wear-resistant exterior combined with an interior possessing great toughness, particularly suitable for gears, camshafts, and so on. Carburizing is most commonly carried out by packing the steel in boxes with carbonaceous solids, sealing to exclude the atmosphere, and heating to about 1700°F for a period of time depending upon the case depth desired; this method is called pack carburizing. Carburizing may also be carried out by heating the steel in direct contact with carburizing gases, in which case the process is called gas carburizing; or, least commonly, in liquid baths of carburizing salts, in which case it is known as liquid carburizing.

Nitriding. See Vol. 13, p. 308. The nitrogen case-hardening process which is termed "nitriding" consists of subjecting machined and preferably heat-treated parts to the action of a nitrogenous medium, commonly ammonia gas, under conditions whereby surface hardness is imparted to the material without necessitating any further treatment. Wear resistance, retention of hardness at elevated temperatures, and resistance to certain types of corrosion are other properties imparted to steel by nitriding.

Classification of Steels

The applications for steel are so diverse that anything like a complete listing of uses, or a classification on the basis of application, is impossible. Because so many grades of steel are produced by more than one steelmaking process, classification by method of manufacture has no practical advantage. The most useful broad classification is based on chemical composition, under which steels can be divided into the large groups of plain carbon, alloy, and stainless steels. Within these large groups are many subdivisions, some based on chemical composition, some on physical or mechanical properties, and so on.

Table 9 shows the raw steel production by carbon, alloy, and stainless grades during recent years.

CARBON STEELS

The plain carbon steels represent by far the major percentage of steel production and have the widest diversity of application of any of the engineering materials.

Some of the important classes of mill products made of carbon steel include castings, forgings, tubular products, plates, sheet and strip, wire and wire products, structural shapes, bars, and such railway materials as rails, wheels, and axles. Carbon steels are made by all of the modern steelmaking processes and, depending upon their carbon content and the purpose for which they are to be used, may be rimmed, semikilled, or fully killed.

The American Iron and Steel Institute has published standard composition ranges for plain carbon steels. The steels in each composition range have been assigned an identifying number according to the method of numerical classification of standard steels that will be discussed later (see p. 789 and Table 5). Under this system of classification, the carbon steels are identified as belonging to one of three series: 10xx (nonresulfurized), 11xx (resulfurized), and 12xx (rephosphorized and resulfurized). The 10xx steels are made with low phosphorus and sulfur contents (phosphorus 0.04% max and sulfur 0.050% max). Sulfur in amounts as large as 0.33% max may be added to the 11xx and amounts as large as 0.35% max to the 12xx steels to improve machinability of these grades. In addition, phosphorus up to 0.12% max may be added to the 12xx steels to impart an added degree of stiffness desired in some rolled products.

In identifying a particular steel, the x's are replaced by two digits representing the av carbon content of the steel: for example, an AISI No. 1040 steel would have an av carbon content of 0.40% carbon (the tolerance for carbon content is ±0.03%, giving in this case the range of 0.37–0.44% carbon.

Factors Affecting Carbon-Steel Properties. The principal factors affecting the properties of the plain carbon steels are the carbon content and the microstructure. The general relationships between microstructure and properties and the factors governing microstructure have been discussed earlier under Metallography and heat treatment, p. 762. Most of the plain carbon steels, however, are used without heat treatment, so that the factors affecting the microstructure and thereby the properties of as-rolled or as-forged steel will be considered here.

In addition to the predominant effects of carbon content and microstructure, the properties of plain carbon steels may be modified by the effects of residual elements other than the carbon, manganese, silicon, phosphorus, and sulfur which are always present, and they may also be affected by the presence of gases, especially oxygen, nitrogen, and hydrogen, and their reaction products. These incidental elements usually are picked up from the scrap, from the deoxidizers, or from the furnace atmosphere. The gas content is largely dependent upon the melting, deoxidizing, and pouring practice, so that the final properties of plain carbon steels are, to a very considerable extent, dependent upon the steelmaking practice used in their production.

Thus, the factors governing the properties of carbon steel are primarily its carbon content and microstructure, with the microstructure being determined largely by the composition and the final rolling, forging, or heat-treating operation, and secondarily by the residual alloy, nonmetallic, and gas content of the steel which, in turn, depend upon the steelmaking practice.

Carbon Content and Properties. The average mechanical properties of as-rolled one-inch bars of carbon steels as a function of carbon content are shown in Figure 35. These values are based on statistical analyses made by several investigators and plotted by Sisco. This diagram is illustrative of the general effect of carbon content when the microstructure and grain size are held reasonably constant.

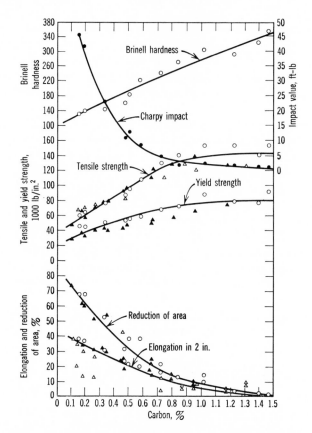

Fig. 35. Variations in average mechanical properties of as-rolled 1-in.-diam bars of plain carbon steels, as a function of carbon content. Original data points through which these average points were plotted are from work by Nead, Langenberg, Brinell (according to Wahlberg), and joint work by Roberts-Austen and Gowland (after Sisco) (2).

Microstructure and Grain Size. The carbon steels, being of relatively low hardenability, are predominantly pearlitic in the cast, rolled, or forged conditions. The constituents of the hypoeutectoid steels are, therefore, ferrite and pearlite, and of the hypereutectoid steels, cementite and pearlite. As discussed earlier, the properties of such pearlitic steels are dependent primarily upon the interlamellar spacing of the pearlite and the grain size. Both the hardness and the ductility increase as the interlamellar spacing or the pearlite-transformation temperature decreases, and the ductility increases with decreasing grain size. The austenite-transformation behavior in carbon steel is determined almost entirely by the carbon and manganese content; the effects of phosphorus and sulfur are almost negligible, and the silicon contents normally are so low that they likewise are ineffective. The carbon content ordinarily is chosen in accordance with the strength level desired and the manganese content is then selected to produce suitable microstructure and properties at that carbon level under the given cooling conditions.

Microstructure of Cast Steels. The microstructure of cast steel is usually coarse-grained, since the austenite forms at a high temperature and the pearlite is usually coarse, since the cooling through the critical range is usually quite slow, particularly

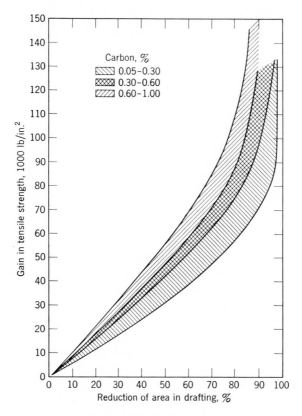

Fig. 36. Increase of tensile strength of plain carbon steel with increasing amounts of cold working (2).

if the casting is cooled in the mold. In hypoeutectoid steels, ferrite is precipitated ordinarily at the original austenite grain boundaries during cooling. In hypereutectoid steels, cementite is similarly precipitated. Such mixtures of ferrite or cementite and coarse-grained coarse pearlite have poor properties in respect to both strength and ductility, and heat treatment usually is necessary to obtain suitable microstructures and properties in cast steels.

Effects of Hot Working. Many carbon steels are used in the form of as-rolled finished sections and the microstructure and properties of these sections are determined largely by the composition, rolling practice, and cooling conditions after rolling. The rolling or hot working of these sections ordinarily is carried out in the temperature range in which the steel is austenitic, and has four major effects, as follows:

1. Considerable homogenization that tends to eliminate dendritic segregation inherited from the ingot structure occurs during the heating for rolling.

2. The dendritic structure is broken up during rolling.

3. Recrystallization takes place during rolling, so that the final austenitic grain size is determined by the temperature at which the last passes are made (the finishing temperature).

4. Dendrites and inclusions are reoriented in the rolling direction so that the final ductility in the rolling direction is markedly improved.

Thus, homogeneity and grain size of the austenite is largely determined by the rolling practice. However, the recrystallization characteristics of the austenite and, therefore, the austenite-grain size characteristic of a given finishing temperature may be affected markedly by the steelmaking practice, particularly with regard to the deoxidation practice.

Distribution of the ferrite or cementite and the nature of the pearlite is determined by the cooling rate after rolling. Since the usual practice is air cooling, the final microstructure and the properties of as-rolled sections will be dependent principally on composition and section size.

Effects of Cold Working. The manufacture of wire, sheet and strip, and tubular products often involves a cold-working operation. The effects of cold working may be eliminated by a suitable annealing operation, but some products, particularly wire, are used in the cold-worked condition.

The most pronounced effect of cold working is an increase in strength and hardness and a decrease in ductility as represented by the elongation and reduction of area. The effect of cold working on the tensile strength of plain carbon steel is shown in Figure 36.

Upon reheating cold-worked steel to the recrystallization temperature (750°F) or above, depending upon composition, amount of cold work, and other variables, the original microstructure and properties may be restored.

Heat Treatment of Carbon Steels. Although the majority of wrought (rolled or forged) carbon steels are used without a final heat treatment, heat treatment may be employed to improve the microstructure and properties for specific applications.

Annealing is practiced for applications requiring better machinability or formability than would be obtained with the as-rolled microstructure. This is usually a full anneal to form coarse pearlite, although a subcritical anneal or spheroidizing treatment is occasionally practiced. Process annealing to obtain optimum formability in cold-rolled strip and sheet and cold-worked tubing is a universal practice.

The grain size of as-rolled products is largely dependent upon finishing temperature and is difficult to control. A final normalizing treatment from a relatively low temperature may be used to establish a fine, uniform grain size for critical applications with respect to ductility and toughness.

Quenching and tempering of plain carbon steels is being increasingly practiced. Because of the relatively low hardenability of these steels, this type of treatment falls generally into two classifications. In one classification, the steel is heat treated to produce tempered martensite, but hardenability restrictions limit the practice to section sizes of not more than $3/8$ to $1/2$ in. The other classification covers the quenching and tempering of quite large sections of plain carbon steels to produce fine pearlite microstructures whose strength and ductility are much better than those of the coarse pearlitic microstructures usual in as-rolled or normalized products.

Thin sections (0.2 in. and below) of carbon steels are particularly suitable for the production of parts requiring toughness at high hardness by austempering.

Effect of Residual Elements. In addition to the carbon, manganese, phosphorus, sulfur, and silicon which are always present, carbon steels may contain small amounts of other elements. These include gases, such as hydrogen, oxygen, or nitrogen, which are introduced during the steelmaking process; nickel, copper, molybdenum, chromium, and tin, which may be present in the scrap; and aluminum, titanium, vanadium, or zirconium, which may be introduced during the deoxidation process.

The principal effect of oxygen and nitrogen in carbon steel is to cause the phenomenon called aging, which is manifested as a spontaneous increase in hardness at room temperature and is believed to be a precipitation effect.

Hydrogen has a definite embrittling effect, the mechanism of which is not completely understood. Hydrogen contents of more than about 0.005% will give rise to this effect. As discussed earlier, it is possible to reduce the content of hydrogen and other gases in steel by vacuum degassing processes.

Alloying elements such as nickel, chromium, molybdenum, and copper, which may be introduced into carbon steels with the scrap used in steelmaking, will, of course, increase the hardenability although, since the percentages are ordinarily low, this effect usually will not be large. They may, however, change the heat-treating characteristics and for applications in which ductility is important, such as low-carbon steels for deep drawing, the increased hardness from these elements may be harmful.

Tin in relatively low amounts is harmful in steels for deep drawing; in the case of most applications, however, the effect of tin in the quantities ordinarily present is negligible.

Aluminum is generally desirable as a grain refiner and tends to decrease the susceptibility of carbon steel to aging associated with strain. It has the disadvantage, however, that it tends to promote graphitization and is, therefore, undesirable in steels to be used for elevated-temperature applications. The other elements which may be introduced as deoxidizers, titanium, vanadium, or zirconium, are, unless intentionally added, ordinarily present in such small amounts as to be generally ineffective.

ALLOY STEELS

As a generic class, alloy steels may be defined as those steels which have enhanced properties owing to the presence of one or more special elements or larger proportions of elements such as silicon and manganese than are ordinarily present in carbon steel. The major classifications of steels containing alloying elements are (1) high-strength low-alloy steels; (2) AISI alloy steels; (3) alloy tool steels; (4) stainless steels; (5) heat-resisting steels; (6) electrical steels (silicon steels). Outside of these broad classes are numerous steels, some with proprietary compositions, with exceptional properties developed to meet unusually severe service requirements. The relatively small tonnage of such steels produced is no indication of their importance as engineering materials.

Functions of the Alloying Elements. In the broadest sense, alloy steels may contain up to approximately 50% of alloying elements, and the enhancement of properties may be a specific and direct function of the alloying elements, as in the instances of the increased corrosion resistance of the high-chromium steels, the enhanced electric properties of the silicon steels, the improved strength properties of the high-strength low-alloy steels, and the increased hardenability and improved tempering characteristics of the AISI alloy steels.

High-Strength Low-Alloy Steels. High-strength low-alloy steels are categorized on the basis of their mechanical properties, particularly the yield point; for example, within certain thickness limits, they have yield points ranging from 45,000–65,000 lb/in.² min, as compared with 33,000–36,000 lb/in.² for structural carbon steel. This method is in contrast to the usual method in which steels are classified as plain-carbon or structural-carbon steels, alloy steels, and stainless steels on the basis of the presence or absence of added alloying elements.

The higher mechanical properties of the high-strength low-alloy steels is obtained by the addition of several different single alloying elements and combinations of these elements (other than carbon). Thus, the different proprietary steels may have different chemical compositions but each steel must meet essentially the same minimum mechanical-property requirements. Available as sheet, strip, bar, plate, and shapes, these steels are for general structural applications and are not to be considered as special-purpose steels or as steels requiring, or adapted for, heat treatment.

To be of interest as commercial materials, high-strength low-alloy steels must have characteristics and properties that result in economies to the user when the steels are properly applied. They should be considerably stronger, and in many instances tougher, than structural carbon steel. Also, they must have sufficient ductility, formability, and weldability to be successfully fabricated by customary shop methods. In addition, improved resistance to corrosion is often required. The abrasion resistance of these steels is somewhat higher than that of structural carbon steel containing 0.15–0.20% carbon. The higher mechanical properties of the high-strength low-alloy steels permits the use of a higher unit working stress for structures built with them; this generally permits reduction in thickness of section in the structure, and this results in a decrease in weight. Alternatively, high-strength low-alloy steels may be substituted for structural carbon steel without change in section, the purpose being to produce a stronger and more durable structure with no increase in weight.

Table 5. Standard Numerical Designations of Plain Carbon and Constructional Alloy Steels (AISI–SAE Designations)

Series designation[a]	Types	Series designation[a]	Types
10xx	nonresulfurized carbon-steel grades	47xx	1.05% Ni–0.45% Cr–0.20%Mo
11xx	resulfurized carbon-steel grades	48xx	3.50% Ni–0.25% Mo
12xx	rephosphorized and resulfurized carbon-steel grades	50xx	0.28 or 0.40% Cr
13xx	1.75% Mn	51xx	0.80, 0.90, 0.95, 1.00, or 1.05% Cr
23xx	3.50% Ni	5xxxx	1.00% C–0.50, 1.00, or 1.45% Cr
25xx	5.00% Ni	61xx	0.80 or 0.95% Cr–0.10 or 0.15% V
31xx	1.25% Ni–0.65% Cr	86xx	0.55% Ni–0.50 or 0.65% Cr–0.20% Mo
33xx	3.50% Ni–1.55% Cr	87xx	0.55% Ni–0.50% Cr–0.25% Mo
40xx	0.25% Mo	92xx	0.85% Mn–2.00% Si
41xx	0.50 or 0.95% Cr–0.12 or 0.20% Mo	93xx	3.25% Ni–1.20% Cr–0.12% Mo
43xx	1.80% Ni–0.50 or 0.80% Cr–0.25% Mo	98xx	1.00% Ni–0.80% Cr–0.25% Mo
46xx	1.55 or 1.80% Ni–0.20 or 0.25% Mo		

[a] The first figure indicates the class to which the steel belongs, thus 1xxx indicates a carbon steel, 2xxx a nickel steel, and 3xxx a nickel–chromium steel. In the case of alloy steels, the second figure generally indicates the approximate percentage of the predominant alloying element. Usually, the last two or three figures (represented in the table by x's) indicate the average carbon content in "points" or hundredths of 1%. Thus, a nickel steel containing approx 3.5% nickel and 0.30% carbon would be designated as 2330.

AISI Alloy Steels. The American Iron and Steel Institute definition of alloy steels is as follows: "By common custom steel is considered to be alloy steel when the maximum of the range given for the content of alloying elements exceeds one or more of the following limits: manganese, 1.65 per cent; silicon, 0.60 per cent; copper, 0.60 per cent; or in which a definite range or a definite minimum quantity of any of the following elements is specified or required within the limits of the recognized field of constructional alloy steels: aluminum, boron, chromium up to 3.99 per cent, cobalt, columbium (niobium), molybdenum, nickel, titanium, tungsten, vanadium, zirconium, or any other alloying element added to obtain a desired alloying effect." It may be noted that steels that contain 4.00% or more of chromium are included by convention among the special types of alloy steels known as stainless steels that are discussed below.

Steels which fall within the AISI definition have been standardized and classified jointly by the American Iron and Steel Institute and the Society of Automotive Engineers, as shown in Table 5. They represent by far the largest tonnage of all alloy steels produced, and are generally known as AISI alloy steels. They are also commonly referred to as constructional alloy steels.

In the AISI steels, the effect of the alloying elements is indirect, through their influence on the microstructure of the material. The alloying elements in these steels control microstructure through their effect on hardenability, as discussed on pp. 768 and 774, and make it possible to attain desirable microstructures and corresponding desirable properties over a much wider range of sizes and sections than is possible with the carbon steels.

Alloy Tool Steels. The tool steels are discussed in the article on Tool materials, and will be mentioned only briefly here. The alloy tool steels may be classified roughly into three groups:

1. Relatively low-alloy tool steels, to which alloying elements have been added to give them higher hardenability than that of plain-carbon tool steels so that they may be hardened in heavier sections or with less drastic quenches to minimize distortion.

2. Intermediate alloy tool steels. These steels usually contain elements such as tungsten, molybdenum, or vanadium, which form hard, wear-resisting carbides.

3. High-speed tool steels. These contain large amounts of the carbide-forming elements which serve not only to furnish wear-resisting carbides but also to promote the phenomenon known as secondary hardening and thereby to increase resistance to softening at elevated temperature.

Stainless Steels. As the name implies, stainless steels are more resistant to rusting and staining than are plain carbon and lower alloy steels. This superior corrosion resistance is due to the addition of chromium to alloys of iron and carbon. Although other elements such as copper, aluminum, silicon, nickel, and molybdenum also increase the corrosion resistance of steel, they are limited in their usefulness. The steels to be considered here are confined to the iron–chromium and iron–chromium–nickel steels in which chromium is the major element for conferring corrosion resistance.

No single nation can claim credit for the development of the stainless steels: Germany, England, and the United States shared alike in the development of these materials. In 1912, Harry Brearley in England, while attempting to develop steels to resist fouling in gun barrels, reported that a composition of 12.8% chromium and 0.24% carbon was quite resistant to corrosion. Brearley suggested that this composition be used for cutlery. In fact, the present AISI Type 420 steel (12–14% chromium, 0.15% carbon) is similar to the steel suggested by Brearley.

Table 6. Standard Stainless and Heat-Resisting Steel Products

AISI type number	SAE type number	Chemical composition, %			
		Carbon	Chromium	Nickel	Other
201	30201	0.15 max	16.00–18.00	3.50–5.50	Mn 5.50–7.50 P 0.06 max N 0.25 max
202	30202	0.15 max	17.00–19.00	4.00–6.00	Mn 7.50–10.00 P 0.06 max N 0.25 max
301	30301	0.15 max	16.00–18.00	6.00–8.00	
302	30302	0.15 max	17.00–19.00	8.00–10.00	
302B	30302B	0.15 max	17.00–19.00	8.00–10.00	Si 2.00–3.00 P 0.20 max S 0.15 min
303	30303	0.15 max	17.00–19.00	8.00–10.00	Mo 0.60 max
303Se	30303Se	0.15 max	17.00–19.00	8.00–10.00	P 0.20 max S 0.06 max Se 0.15 min
303SeA		0.08 max	17.25–18.75	11.50–13.00	Se 0.15–0.35
304	30304	0.08 max	18.00–20.00	8.00–10.00	
304L		0.030 max	18.00–20.00	8.00–10.00	
305	30305	0.12 max	17.00–19.00	10.00–13.00	
307		0.07–0.15	19.50–21.50	9.00–10.50	Mo residual only
308	30308	0.08 max	19.00–21.00	10.00–12.00	
308 Mod		0.07–0.15	19.50–21.50	9.00–10.50	Mo residual only
309	30309	0.20 max	22.00–24.00	12.00–15.00	
309S	30309S	0.08 max	22.00–24.00	12.00–15.00	
309SCb		0.08 max	22.00–24.00	12.00–15.00	CbTa min, 10 times carbon Ta 0.10 max
309SCbTa		0.08 max	22.00–24.00	12.00–15.00	CbTa min, 10 times carbon
310	30310	0.25 max	24.00–26.00	19.00–22.00	
314	30314	0.25 max	23.00–26.00	19.00–22.00	
316	30316	0.08 max	16.00–18.00	10.00–14.00	Mo 2.00–3.00
316L	30316L	0.030 max	16.00–18.00	10.00–14.00	Mo 2.00–3.00
317	30317	0.08 max	18.00–20.00	11.00–15.00	Mo 3.00–4.00
318		0.10 max	16.00–18.00	10.00–14.00	Mo 2.00–3.00 CbTa min, 10 times carbon
D319		0.07 max	17.50–19.50	11.00–15.00	Mn 2.00 max Si 1.00 max Mo 2.25–3.00
321	30321	0.08 max	17.00–19.00	9.00–12.00	Ti min, 5 times carbon
330		0.25 max	14.00–16.00	33.00–36.00	
347	30347	0.08 max	17.00–19.00	9.00–13.00	CbTa min, 10 times carbon
348	30348	0.08 max	17.00–19.00	9.00–13.00	CbTa min, 10 times carbon Ta 0.10 max Co 0.20 max

Table 6 (*continued*)

AISI type number	SAE type number	Chemical composition, %			
		Carbon	Chromium	Nickel	Other
403	51403	0.15 max	11.50–13.00		
405	51405	0.08 max	11.50–14.50		Al 0.10–0.30
410	51410	0.15 max	11.50–13.50		
410Mo		0.15 max	11.50–13.50		Mo 0.40–0.60
414	51414	0.15 max	11.50–13.50	1.25–2.50	
416	51416	0.15 max	12.00–14.00		P 0.06 max S 0.15 min Mo 0.60 max
416Se	51416Se	0.15 max	12.00–14.00		P 0.06 max S 0.06 max Se 0.15 min
420	51420	over 0.15	12.00–14.00		S (no restriction)
420F	51420F	over 0.15	12.00–14.00		S (no restriction)
430	51430	0.12 max	14.00–18.00		
430F	51430F	0.12 max	14.00–18.00		P 0.06 max S 0.15 min Mo 0.60 max
430Ti		0.10 max	16.00–18.00		Ti 0.30–0.70
431	51431	0.20 max	15.00–17.00	1.25–2.50	
434A		0.05–0.10	15.00–17.00		Cu 0.75–1.10
442	51442	0.25 max	18.00–23.00		
446	51446	0.20 max	23.00–27.00		N 0.25 max
501	51501	over 0.10	4.00–6.00		Mo 0.40–0.65
502	51502	0.10 max	4.00–6.00		Mo 0.40–0.65

NOTE: SAE chemical composition (ladle) ranges may differ slightly in certain elements from AISI limits.

Manganese: All steels of AISI Type 300 series—2.00% max. All steels of AISI Type 400 and 500 series—1.00% max except Types 416, 416Se, 430F, and 430Se (1.25% max) and Type 446 (1.50% max)

Phosphorus: All steels of AISI Type 200 series—0.060% max. All steels of AISI Type 300 series—0.045% max except Types 303 and 303Se (0.20% max). All steels of AISI Type 400 and 500 series—0.040% max except Types 416, 416Se, 430F, and 430FSe (0.060% max).

Sulfur: All steels of AISI Type 200, 300, 400, and 500 series—0.30% max except Types 303, 416, and 430F (0.15% min) and Types 303Se, 416Se, and 430FSe (0.060% max).

Silicon: All steels of AISI Type 200, 300, 400, and 500 series—1.00% max except where otherwise indicated.

The development of the higher chromium–iron alloys was due to the work of F. M. Becket in the United States who, from 1903 on, was continuously attacking the problem of producing low-carbon ferrochromium from chromium ores. While investigating the effect of chromium on oxidation resistance at 2000°F, Becket noticed a marked increase as the chromium content was raised above 20%. It is significant that even now and with steels containing appreciable quantities of nickel, 20% seems to be the minimum amount of chromium necessary for oxidation resistance at 2000°F.

The austenitic iron–chromium–nickel alloys were developed in Germany during the years 1909–1912 by Benno Strauss and Edward Maurer while searching for materials for use in pyrometer tubes. Further work by Strauss and others led to the versatile 18% chromium, 8% nickel steels (popularly called 18–8) which are used so widely today. The standard AISI types of stainless steels are identified in Table 6. For the purpose of general discussion, the stainless steels may be grouped into three classes: martensitic, ferritic, and austenitic.

The martensitic stainless steels are iron–chromium alloys that are hardenable by heat treatment. They include Types 403, 410, 414, 416, 420, 431, 440A, 440B, 440C, 501, and 502 (see Table 6).

The most widely used of the martensitic grades is Type 410, containing under 0.15% carbon and 11.50–13.50% chromium. In the annealed condition, this grade may be drawn or formed. It is an air-hardening steel, and a wide range of properties may be obtained by heat treatment. In sheet or strip form, Type 410 is used extensively in the oil industry for ballast trays and liners. It is also used for furnace parts where the operating temperature is not over 1200°F and for blades and buckets in steam turbines.

Type 420, with about 0.35% carbon and resultant greater hardness, is used for cutlery. In bar form, it is used for valves, valve stems, valve seats, and shafting where resistance to corrosion and wear are needed. Type 440 may be employed for such applications as surgical instruments, especially those requiring a durable cutting edge. The necessary hardness for different applications can be obtained by selecting grade A, B, or C, which have increasingly greater carbon contents in that order.

Other martensitic grades are Types 501 and 502, the former having carbon over 0.10% and the latter having under 0.10% carbon, but both containing 4–6% chromium. These grades are also air-hardening, but do not have the corrosion resistance of the 12% chromium grades. Types 501 and 502 have wide application in the oil industry for such uses as hot-oil lines, bubble towers, valves, and plates.

The ferritic stainless steels are iron–chromium alloys that are largely ferritic and not hardenable by heat treatment (ignoring the 885°F embrittlement). They include Types 405, 430, 430F, and 446 (see Table 6).

The most common and widely used of the ferritic grades is Type 430, containing 0.12% carbon or under and 14–18% chromium. The higher chromium content of Type 430 makes its corrosion resistance superior to that of the martensitic grades and, in addition, this grade may be drawn, formed, and, with proper techniques, welded. It is widely used for automotive and architectural trim. Its resistance to nitric acid makes it useful in the manufacture and handling of this acid. Type 430 does not have high creep strength, but it is suitable for some types of service up to 1500°F and thus finds application for such parts as combustion chambers for domestic heating furnaces.

The high chromium content of Type 446 (23–27% chromium) gives this grade excellent heat-resistant characteristics although its elevated-temperature strength is only slightly better than that of carbon steel. Type 446 is used in sheet or strip form up to 2100°F. This grade does not have the good drawing characteristics of Type 430, but it may be formed. Accordingly, it is used widely for furnace parts such as muffles, burner sleeves, and annealing baskets. Its resistance to nitric and other oxidizing acids makes it suitable for much chemical-processing equipment.

The austenitic stainless steels are iron–chromium–nickel alloys not hardenable by heat treatment and predominantly austenitic as commercially heat treated. They include Types 301, 302, 302B, 303, 304, 304L, 305, 308, 309, 310, 314, 316, 316L, 317,

321, and 347. Other austenitic stainless steels include those recently developed in which all or part of the nickel of the iron–chromium–nickel type of steel is replaced by manganese and nitrogen in proper amounts, such as one proprietary steel and Types 201 and 202 (see Table 6).

The most widely used of the austenitic types of stainless steel is Type 302— popularly known as 18–8—that has excellent corrosion resistance and, because of its austenitic structure, possesses very good ductility. It may be deep drawn and may be very severely formed. It can be welded readily, with due consideration to avoiding carbide precipitation in the weld and adjacent to it by cooling after welding at a sufficiently rapid rate. Where carbide precipitation presents production problems, Types 321, 347, or 304L may be used. The applications of Type 302 are wide and varied, including kitchen equipment and utensils; dairy installations; transportation equipment; oil-, chemical-, paper-, and food-processing machinery.

The lower nickel content of Type 301 causes it to work harden more rapidly than Type 302 because of reduced austenite stability. Accordingly, while Type 301 can be drawn successfully, it does not have quite as good drawing properties as Type 302, but for the same reason, Type 301 can be cold-rolled to very high strength levels for applications where a high strength-to-weight ratio is desired.

Type 304, because of its lower carbon content, is not as prone as Type 301 to give trouble after welding due to carbide precipitation. In addition, its somewhat higher chromium content makes it slightly more resistant to general corrosion. It is used to withstand severe corrosive conditions in the paper, chemical, and other industries.

The austenitic stainless steels have good elevated-temperature strength and these grades are widely used for elevated-temperature service.

Types 321 and 347, with additions of titanium and niobium, respectively, are used in applications involving welding and where high-temperature service under corrosive conditions is required. Type 304L may be used as an alternative for Types 321 and 347 in applications involving welding and stress relieving for service below 800°F.

The addition of 2–4% molybdenum to the fundamental 18–8 composition produces Types 316 and 317, which have improved corrosion resistance. These grades are used in applications in the textile, paper, and chemical industries where strong sulfates, chlorides, and phosphates and such reducing acids as sulfuric, sulfurous, acetic, and hydrochloric acids are used in such concentrations as to make the use of a more highly corrosion-resistant alloy mandatory. Types 316 and 317 have the highest creep and rupture strengths of the commercial stainless steels.

The austenitic stainless steels most resistant to oxidation are Types 309 and 310. Because of their high chromium and nickel contents, these steels resist scaling at temperatures up to 2000 and 2100°F and, consequently, are used for furnace parts and heat exchangers. They are somewhat harder and not as ductile as the 18–8 types, but they may be drawn and formed. They can be welded readily and are finding increasing use in the manufacture of jet-propulsion motors and industrial-furnace equipment.

For applications requiring good machinability, Type 303 containing sulfur or selenium may be used.

In conclusion, with regard to the stainless steels, the chromium content seems to be the controlling variable and the effect of chromium may be enhanced by additions of molybdenum, nickel, and other elements. The mechanical properties of the stainless steels, like those of the plain carbon and lower alloy steels, are functions of the structure and composition of the material. Thus, the austenitic steels possess the best impact properties at low temperatures and the best strength at elevated temperatures, while the martensitic steels possess the highest hardness at room temperature. Thus, the stainless steels, by being available in a variety of structures, exhibit a range of mechanical properties which, combined with their excellent corrosion resistance, makes these steels highly versatile from the standpoint of design.

Steels for Elevated-Temperature Service (Heat-Resisting Steels). The term "elevated-temperature service" is an inclusive one, involving many types of operations in many industries. Some of the more conventional examples of equipment operated at high temperature are steam boilers and turbines, gas turbines, stills for cracking petroleum, tar stills, vessels for hydrogenating oils, heat-treating furnaces, and fittings for diesel and other internal-combustion engines. Numerous steels are available from which to select the proper one for each of the foregoing applications. Where unusual conditions occur, some modification of the chemical composition may be made to better adapt an existing steel grade to service conditions. In some cases, however, entirely new alloy combinations must be developed to meet service requirements. For example, the aircraft and missile industries have encountered design problems of increased complexity, requiring metals of greater strength at higher temperatures for both power plants and structures, and new steels have been and are being developed to meet these requirements.

Table 7 lists a number of steels that might be used for service at elevated temperatures, giving only the principal alloying elements for each.

Valve steels, hot-work die steels, and some alloy tool steels are used at elevated temperature, but these form special categories that will not be discussed here.

The steels to be considered here are those used in large tonnages for construction of equipment to operate under stress at elevated temperature, where creep is involved. It may be mentioned that the chemical compositions of some of these steels were given in Table 6.

The design of load-bearing structures for service at atmospheric temperature is generally based on the yield strength—or, for some applications, the tensile strength—

Table 7. Principal Alloying Elements in Some Steels That May Be Used in Elevated-Temperature Service

Ferritic steels	Austenitic steels
0.5% Mo	18% Cr–8% Ni (AISI Type 304)
0.5% Cr–0.5% Mo	18% Cr–8% Ni, with Mo (AISI Type 316)
1% Cr–0.5% Mo	18% Cr–8% Ni, with Ti (AISI Type 321)
2% Cr–0.5% Mo	18% Cr–8% Ni, with Nb (Type 347)
2.25% Cr–1% Mo	25% Cr–12% Ni (AISI Type 309)
3% Cr–0.5% Mo–1.5% Si	25% Cr–20% Ni (AISI Type 310)
5%Cr–0.5% Mo–1.5% Si	
5% Cr–0.5% Mo, with Nb added	
5% Cr–0.5% Mo, with Ti added	
9% Cr–1% Mo	
12% Cr (AISI Type 410)	
17% Cr (AISI Type 430)	
27% Cr (AISI Type 446)	

determined by ordinary room-temperature tension tests. In ordinary service at room temperature with a design stress determined in such a way, the metal behaves essentially in an elastic manner, that is, the structure undergoes an elastic deformation immediately upon load application and no further deformation occurs with time; when the load is removed the structure returns to its original dimensions.

At elevated temperature the behavior is different. A structure designed according to the principles employed for atmospheric temperature service continues to deform with time after load application, even though the design data may have been based on tension tests at the temperature of interest. This deformation with time is called "creep," since at the design stresses at which it first was recognized it occurred at a relatively slow rate. See also Vol. 13, p. 194.

In spite of the fact that plain carbon steel has lower resistance to creep than the alloy steels used for elevated-temperature applications, it is widely used in such applications up to 1000°F, where rapid oxidation commences and a chromium-bearing steel must be employed. Low-alloy steels containing small amounts of chromium and molybdenum have higher creep strengths than carbon steel and are employed where materials of higher strength are needed. Above about 1000°F, the amount of chromium required to impart oxidation resistance increases rapidly. The 2% chromium steels with added molybdenum are useful up to about 1150°F, and steels containing 10–14% chromium may be employed up to about 1300–1400°F. Above this temperature, the austenitic 18% chromium, 8% nickel stainless steels are used customarily, and their oxidation resistance is considered adequate up to about 1500°F. For service in the temperature range between 1500 and 2000°F, steels containing 25% chromium and 20% nickel, or 27% chromium, are used.

The behavior of steels at elevated temperature is quite complex, and only a few of the design considerations have been mentioned here.

Quenched and Tempered Low-Carbon Constructional Alloy Steels. A class of quenched and tempered low-carbon constructional alloy steels has been very extensively used in a wide variety of applications such as pressure vessels, earth-moving and mining equipment, and as major members of large steel structures. Their outstanding attributes and their wide usefulness warrant their consideration as a separate and important class of constructional alloy steels.

As a general class, these steels are referred to as low-carbon martensites, to differentiate them from those constructional alloy steels of higher carbon content, such as the AISI alloy steels, that develop high-carbon martensite upon quenching. They are characterized by a relatively high strength, with minimum yield strengths of 100,000 lb/in.², toughness at temperatures down to −50°F, and weldability with welded joints showing full joint efficiency when welded with low-hydrogen electrodes. They are most commonly used in the form of plates, but are also used as sheet products, bars, structural shapes, forgings, or semifinished products.

Several steel-producing companies manufacture such steels under various trade names. The composition of each company's steel is proprietary.

Maraging Steels. A group of high-nickel martensitic steels called maraging steels contain so little carbon that they are referred to as carbonfree iron–nickel martensites.

Iron–carbon martensite is hard and brittle in the as-quenched condition and becomes softer and more ductile when tempered. Carbonfree iron–nickel martensite, on the other hand, is relatively soft and ductile and becomes hard, strong, and tough when subjected to an aging treatment at 900°F.

The first iron–nickel martensitic alloys contained about 0.01% carbon, either 20 or 25% nickel, and 1.5–2.5% aluminum and titanium. Later an 18% nickel steel containing cobalt, molybdenum, and titanium was developed, and still more recently a series of 12% nickel steels containing chromium and molybdenum.

By adjustment of the content of cobalt, molybdenum, and titanium, the 18% nickel steel can attain yield strengths in the range of 200,000–300,000 lb/in.² after the aging treatment. Similarly, yield strengths of 12% nickel steel in the range of 150,000–200,000 lb/in.² can be developed by adjusting its composition.

Silicon-Steel Electrical Sheets. The silicon steels are characterized by relatively high permeability, high electrical resistance, and low hysteresis loss when used in magnetic circuits. They contain ½ to 5% silicon. First patented by Sir Robert Hadfield in England about 1900, the silicon steels have made possible the development of more powerful electrical equipment and have played an important role in the rapid growth of the electrical power industry. Reference is made here only to steels containing ½ to 5% silicon, produced in sheet form for the laminated magnetic cores of electrical equipment. Such products are referred to in the industry as electrical sheets.

Silicon-steel electrical sheets may be divided into two general classes: (*1*) grain-oriented steels, and (*2*) nonoriented steels.

The grain-oriented steels, containing about 3¼% silicon, are used in the highest-efficiency distribution and power transformers and in large turbine generators. They are processed in a special way to give them directional properties related to orientation of the crystals making up the structure of the steel in a preferred direction.

The nonoriented steels may be subdivided into three classes: (*1*) Low-silicon steels containing about ½ to 1½% silicon. These steels are used principally in the rotors and stators of motors and generators. Steels containing about 1% silicon are used also for reactors, relays, and small intermittent-duty transformers. (*2*) Intermediate-silicon steels containing about 2½–3½% silicon. These steels are used in motors and generators of average to high efficiency and in small- to medium-size intermittent-duty transformers, reactors, and motors. (*3*) High-silicon steels containing about 3¾–5% silicon. This class is used in power transformers and the highest-efficiency motors, generators, transformers, and in communications equipment.

Economics

The American steel industry is the largest in the world. In 1956, 100 years after the invention of the Bessemer process which heralded the beginning of the Age of Steel, the United States produced its three-billionth ton of steel. By 1966, another billion tons had been produced. This steel, serving in factories, on the farm, in the home, in transportation, and in other ways, has helped to make the United States the greatest industrial nation in the world with the highest living standards of any people.

The amount of steel produced each year in a country is a measure of its industrial strength. Around 1365 lb of steel are made every year for every man, woman, and child in the United States. This compares with 1320 lb per person in West Germany, 1001 lb in Canada, 973 lb in the United Kingdom, 790 lb in the Soviet Union, and 786 lb in France.

The American steel industry constantly is building new and modernized furnaces, coke ovens, rolling mills, and other facilities to make better steels and produce them more cheaply and efficiently. Such facilities require a great outlay of capital. A blast furnace with the entire equipment to operate it costs well over 25 million dollars. A single rolling mill may cost as much as 100 million dollars. From 1946 through 1967, the American steel industry spent an average of one billion dollars a year on its expansion and modernization program. Additional billions are scheduled to be spent in coming years to fill the country's growing needs for steel.

Raw Materials. The three chief raw materials used in making iron and steel are iron ore, coal, and limestone. The United States has large deposits of all three of these raw materials. See also Iron.

Major iron-ore deposits are in Minnesota, Wisconsin, and Michigan, near Lake Superior. Taken together, these deposits are the largest domestic source of iron ore. Steel companies are also importing increasing amounts of high-grade iron ore from other countries, chiefly Canada, Venezuela, Brazil, Peru, Liberia, Chile, and Mauritania.

Limestone is a very common mineral and is found in many parts of the United States.

Coal is used in the steel industry chiefly as the raw material for making the coke used as fuel in blast furnaces. Concentrations of coals suitable for making coke are found mostly in the Appalachian area, although there are isolated deposits in some central and western states.

The United States is not so fortunate with respect to the alloying elements. It must import from other nations the three most important alloying elements, nickel, chromium, and manganese, as well as cobalt, niobium, and tungsten. It is self-sufficient in boron, copper, molybdenum, titanium, and vanadium.

Employment. In recent years, more than 500,000 people on the average have been employed in the steel industry, in mills, in mines, on ships and railroads, in maintenance and repair shops, in warehouses, laboratories, power houses, and medical facilities. These people were employed in more than 4000 different occupations.

Steel was made in thirty-two of the fifty states during 1967, as shown in Table 8.

Steel-Mill Products. Table 1 listed the amounts of raw steel produced in the United States over an extended period. Table 9 shows how this production was

Table 8. Raw Steel Production in 1967 by States (1),[a] 1000 net tons

States	Production
New York	7,298
Pennsylvania	29,881
Rhode Island, Connecticut, New Jersey, Delaware, Maryland	8,132
Virginia, West Virginia, Georgia, Florida, North Carolina, South Carolina	4,268
Kentucky	2,410
Alabama, Tennessee, Mississippi	4,444
Ohio	20,378
Indiana	17,610
Illinois	10,649
Michigan	9,245
Minnesota, Missouri, Oklahoma, Texas	4,644
Arizona, Colorado, Utah, Washington, Oregon, Hawaii	4,154
California	4,100
total	127,213

[a] Production of some states is grouped with that of others in order to to avoid disclosing production by individual companies.

divided among carbon, alloy, and stainless steels from 1964 through 1967. Table 10 lists the shipments of steel products for 1964 through 1967. The difference between the total raw steel produced and the amount of steel products shipped for any year represents that part of the raw steel production that unavoidably cannot be made into finished products. Although it does not represent salable materials, the steel scrap resulting from manufacturing operations in the steel mills is not wasted, since it is returned to the steelmaking furnaces as a valuable material for making more steel. In general, an average of 32% scrap results from processing raw steel into finished products, as was mentioned earlier in the discussion of scrap for steelmaking.

Table 9. Raw Steel Production by Carbon, Alloy, and Stainless Grades, 1964–1967 (1)

Year	Total production of raw steel, 1000 net tons				Steel for castings (included in total production), 1000 net tons			
	Carbon	Alloy	Stainless	Total	Carbon	Alloy	Stain-less	Total
1967	113,190	12,572	1,451	127,213	134	59	1	184
1966	118,732	13,718	1,651	134,101	245	70	2	317
1965	116,651	13,318	1,493	131,462	198	67	2	267
1964	114,442	11,191	1,443	127,076	159	62	2	223

Markets for Steel Products. Table 11 shows how steel shipments for 1964 through 1967 were distributed according to consuming industries. The automotive and construction industries are shown to have consumed the two largest single amounts of steel during that period: the automotive industry annually consumed an average of nearly 21% of the steel industry shipments in automobiles, trucks, buses, and other products, while the consumption by the construction industry in the form of structural shapes, plates, bars, tubular products, and so on, was an average of a little over 13%. The table also shows that the container industry uses large amounts of steel in various forms for making cans and other containers. Other important consumers of steel are railroads and manufacturers of electrical equipment, home appliances, kitchen utensils, steel furniture, and other products for the home; as well as builders of agricultural machinery, oil and gas industry equipment, and machinery.

Foreign Trade

While the United States in 1967 was still the world's largest producer of steel its production has fallen from 61% of the total world output in 1945 to slightly over 23% in 1967. Production of raw steel by countries producing over 1 million tons in 1967 is given in Table 12. Between 1947 and 1966, Japan's share of world steel output increased tenfold, Italy's tripled, the U.S.S.R.'s doubled, and China produced more steel in 1966 than any country had in 1947, with the exception of the United States and the U.S.S.R.

Forty-two percent of the world's steelmaking capacity is government-owned. In the capitalist countries (excluding the United States), 28% of steelmaking capacity is government-owned.

After World War II, the United States helped to rebuild the shattered and obsolete steelmaking facilities in many countries. Still later, both the United States

Table 10. Net Shipments of Steel Products,[a] 1964–1967 (1), 1000 net tons

Steel products	1967	1966	1965	1964
ingots and steel castings	289	284	366	330
blooms, slabs, billets, sheet bars	2,479	2,135	2,696	2,572
tube rounds	26	16	16	33
skelp	2	5	111	99
wire rods	1,267	1,366	1,338	1,195
structural shapes (heavy)	5,592	6,176	6,165	5,586
steel piling	541	588	633	500
plates	7,948	9,103	9,764	8,491
rails				
standard (over 60 lb)	684	858	702	636
all other	46	43	49	39
joint bars	31	42	45	30
tie plates	145	195	138	135
track spikes	62	68	62	58
wheels (rolled and forged)	285	343	328	320
axles	181	227	199	176
bars				
hot rolled (includes light shapes)	7,961	9,126	9,344	8,401
reinforcing	3,249	3,276	3,150	3,229
cold finished	1,733	1,999	1,877	1,467
tool steel	110	121	118	102
pipe and tubing				
standard	2,712	2,734	2,513	2,264
oil country goods	1,340	1,413	1,574	1,637
line	3,095	3,110	2,777	2,634
mechanical	1,052	1,224	1,133	1,009
pressure	260	332	326	288
structural	473	420	366	305
stainless	36	see note[b]	see note[b]	see note[b]
wire				
drawn	2,507	2,798	2,842	2,518
nails and staples	334	332	321	316
barbed and twisted	102	168	107	79
woven wire fence	116	127	112	112
bale ties and baling wire	74	71	103	80
black plate	604	484	458	431
tin and terne plate, hot dipped	39	50	127	150
tin plate, electrolytic	5,948	5,294	6,074	5,501
sheets				
hot rolled	9,312	10,137	10,630	9,948
cold rolled	14,709	15,972	16,571	15,699
sheets and strip				
galvanized, hot dipped	4,219	4,545	4,491	4,052
galvanized, electrolytic	327	322	362	319
all other metallic coated	503	571	571	512
electrical	721	741	740	648
strip				
hot rolled	1,409	1,597	1,785	1,660
cold rolled	1,374	1,582	1,582	1,384
total steel products	83,897	89,995	92,666	84,945

[a] All grades, including carbon, alloy, and stainless steels.

[b] Stainless pipe and tubing not reported separately before 1967; included in other pipe and tubing classifications for prior years.

Table 11. Distribution of Net Shipments of Steel Products According to Consuming Industries,[a] 1964–1967 (1), 1000 net tons

Market classification	1967	1966	1965	1964
steel for converting and processing	2,837	3,153	3,932	2,687
forgings (not elsewhere classified)	1,208	1,323	1,250	1,062
bolts, nuts, rivets, and screws	1,128	1,320	1,234	1,229
steel service centers and distributors				
oil and gas supply houses	1,493	1,536	1,556	1,719
all other	13,370	14,864	14,813	13,845
construction, including maintenance				
oil and gas	2,509	2,514	2,308	2,038
all other	8,866	9,348	9,528	8,954
contractors' products	4,582	4,969	5,018	4,646
automotive				
vehicles, parts, etc	15,932	17,302	19,423	17,767
forgings	556	682	700	620
rail transportation				
rails, trackwork, and equipment	888	1,173	930	836
freight cars, passenger cars, and locomotives	2,337	3,159	2,875	2,633
shipbuilding and marine equipment	943	1,017	1,051	805
aircraft	102	129	94	72
oil and gas drilling	315	377	380	415
mining, quarrying, and lumbering	345	392	392	368
agricultural				
agricultural machinery	1,090	1,317	1,169	1,100
all other	319	388	314	269
machinery, industrial equipment, and tools	4,994	5,747	5,873	5,338
electrical machinery and equipment	2,808	3,021	2,985	2,654
appliances, utensils, and cutlery	2,092	2,311	2,179	2,168
other domestic and commercial equipment	2,060	2,215	2,179	2,034
ontainers, packaging, and shipping materials				
cans and closures	5,762	5,035	5,867	5,231
barrels, drums, and shipping pails	810	827	810	847
all other	683	735	654	474
ordnance and other military	1,622	686	289	214
export (reporting companies only)	1,407	1,541	2,078	2,749
nonclassified shipments	2,839	2,914	2,785	2,171
total shipments	83,897	89,995	92,666	84,945

[a] All grades, including carbon, alloy, and stainless steels.

Table 12. Production of Raw Steel by Countries, 1967,[a] 1000 net tons

Countries	Production
North America	
United States	127,213[b]
Canada	9,694
Latin America	
Argentina	1,549
Brazil	3,917
Mexico	3,340
Western Europe	
European Coal and Steel Community	
Belgium-Luxembourg	15,645
France	21,666
West Germany	40,504
Italy	17,518
Netherlands	3,752
Other Western Europe	
Austria	3,350
Spain	4,987
Sweden	5,122
Turkey	1,085
United Kingdom	26,763
Yugoslavia	2,039
Eastern Europe	
Bulgaria	1,359
Czechoslovakia	10,899
East Germany	4,645
Hungary	2,995
Poland	11,450
Rumania	4,446
U.S.S.R.	112,655
Africa	
Republic of South Africa	3,995
Far East	
India	7,400
Japan	68,521
China	14,000
North Korea	1,500
Australia	6,946

[a] Only the production of countries producing more than 1 million tons in 1967 is listed in the table. Steel production by foundries is not included in U.S. total. Total world production of raw steel in 1967 was 545,607,000 net tons, of which the communist-bloc countries (Eastern Europe, U.S.S.R., China, and North Korea) produced 163,949,000, and the capitalist countries (all others) produced 381,658,000 net tons.

[b] The United States produced 23.3% of total world production.

and the U.S.S.R., often motivated by political rivalry, financed new steel industries in developing countries where no such industry had existed before. The net result has been a world overcapacity for making steel, which has caused some foreign producers to unload their surplus production on the world market at prices at or below cost, especially on the United States market, which is the largest and least restricted by nontariff barriers. At the same time, nontariff barriers have been set up in many areas that increase the difficulty for American exports to reach those areas.

Inroads of foreign steel in the United States marketplace have been increasingly heavy. Tables 13 and 14 show how exports from the United States to foreign countries have been decreasing in recent years, while imports of steel products from foreign countries have been increasing. Table 15 lists imports of steel products by country of origin for 1967.

Table 13. Exports of Steel Products from United States, 1964–1967 (1), net tons

Products	1967	1966	1965	1964
steel-mill products				
ingots, blooms, billets, slabs, etc	303,950	339,524	677,110	886,018
wire rods	7,105	12,188	19,191	33,942
structural shapes and piling	107,120	122,058	234,340	249,789
plates	61,156	76,059	126,502	176,594
rails and accessories	48,211	45,580	52,875	58,069
bars and tool steel	107,109	106,044	170,114	175,194
pipe and tubing	234,747	265,643	239,947	285,883
wire and wire products	30,182	39,552	44,998	53,768
tin-mill products	306,128	324,962	306,341	418,215
sheets and strip	479,213	392,348	624,621	1,104,542
total steel-mill products	1,684,921	1,723,958	2,496,039	3,442,014
other steel products	286,553	302,817	341,444	293,461
total steel products	1,971,474	2,026,775	2,837,483	3,735,475

Table 14. Imports of Steel Products into United States, 1964–1967 (1), net tons

Products	1967	1966	1965	1964
steel-mill products				
ingots, blooms, slabs, billets, etc	220,290	223,853	282,620	344,765
wire rods	1,076,467	1,150,303	1,283,627	952,778
structural shapes and piling	1,063,344	946,821	928,792	638,189
plates	1,025,349	951,126	773,860	462,053
rails and accessories	36,329	26,356	23,975	13,823
bars and tool steel	1,728,349	1,718,276	1,641,832	1,174,244
pipe and tubing	1,059,949	1,057,737	929,872	789,686
wire and wire products	797,445	862,392	866,268	809,238
tin-mill products	166,237	134,404	144,989	87,608
sheets and strip	4,280,743	3,681,754	3,507,186	1,167,251
total steel-mill products	11,454,502	10,753,022	10,383,021	6,439,635
other steel products	469,849	413,107	366,460	271,470
total steel products	11,924,351	11,166,129	10,749,481	6,711,105

The economic and political reasons for the unfavorable balance of trade in steel in the United States is receiving serious study in many quarters. The problem is extremely complex, but must be solved because of the economic and strategic importance of the steel industry to the nation.

Possible Future Trends

Steelmakers constantly strive to obtain better raw materials, improve existing processes and products, and devise new processes and new products. Large expenditures are devoted to extensive research and development programs by private

Table 15. Imports of Steel-Mill Products into United States by Countries of Origin, 1967 (1)

Countries of origin	Imports, 1000 net tons	Imports, % of total
Japan	4,468	39.0
European Coal and Steel Community	4,842	42.3
West Germany	1,956	17.1
Belgium-Luxembourg	1,769	15.4
France	808	7.1
Netherlands	216	1.9
Italy	93	0.8
United Kingdom	818	7.1
Canada	630	5.5
Poland	146	1.3
Mexico	94	0.8
Sweden	85	0.7
Australia	69	0.6
Argentina	45	0.4
Yugoslavia	14	0.1
Republic of South Africa	13	0.1
Norway	8	0.1
thirty-three others	223	2.0
total	11,455	100.0

concerns, trade associations and, in some cases, national governments to achieve these ends. The scope of these programs is so extensive that only a few of the more recently publicized programs presently under development will be discussed here: these will be limited to the field of steelmaking.

Direct Steelmaking. The production of steel directly from iron ore has been an active study for many years. A successful direct process would eliminate the need for the blast furnace, the coke ovens that supply the blast furnace with fuel, agglomeration of iron ore, and the conventional steelmaking furnaces. One such process has reached the pilot-plant stage, and research is continuing to perfect it and establish it as a commercial process.

The new process involves preheating small pieces (less than $\frac{1}{4}$ in.) of iron ore and limestone to about 1700°F in a fluidized bed. The hot material passes to a melting chamber where it is heated to 3500°F by falling through a flame from high-intensity burners employing a mixture of oxygen and a fuel gas. The melted material flows into a separate reducing chamber where the molten iron oxide is reduced to iron by carbon from pulverized coal or other carbonaceous reductant. Carbon monoxide from the reaction of carbon with iron oxide is burned in the enclosed space above the bath in the reducing chamber by injecting oxygen into the space; this generates the heat required for rapid reduction to take place. Molten slag and reduced iron in the reducing chamber separate by gravity.

The process is continuous, and the metal produced consists of more than 99% iron. Alloying additions are made to the molten iron to give steel of the desired chemical composition.

This is only one of several direct steelmaking processes that are under study in several parts of the world.

Direct Reduction, Metalizing, and Prereduction. These processes have been of interest for many years. Direct-reduction processes, in general, produce either sponge iron, iron powder, or a metal resembling the product of the blast furnace (pig iron). Metalizing and prereduction involve the treatment of pelletized iron-ore concentrates to reduce their iron-oxide content largely to metallic iron while still retaining the form of pellets. The metalized or prereduced material may be used in the blast furnace to produce pig iron; however, there is growing interest in charging such material into electric-arc furnaces along with varying proportions of scrap, for conversion into steel. The electric-arc furnace is employed also to produce steel from sponge iron produced by some direct-reduction process.

Some investigators predict that the foregoing steelmaking methods, all of which circumvent the blast furnace, will grow in importance in coming years.

Spray Steelmaking. A British development, spray steelmaking consists of the treatment of molten pig iron as it runs from the blast furnace to convert it into steel without the use of conventional steelmaking furnaces.

Molten pig iron is fed from the blast furnace in a continuous stream into a reaction chamber. The molten iron passes through a ring of oxygen jets as it enters the top of the chamber. The jets atomize the falling stream of metal and oxidize the unwanted elements in the pig iron. A second and lower ring of nozzles injects powdered lime and fluxes into the atomized spray to form a slag with the oxidized impurities. Steelmaking reactions take place very rapidly because of the large surface area presented by the droplets of molten metal. The molten products of the reaction drop into a receiving ladle where the slag and metal separate, the slag is drawn off continuously. The process removes nearly all impurities from the iron. Additions can be made to the metal to adjust its composition to give the grade of steel desired.

Continuous Steelmaking. The growing application of computers for controlling individual parts of the steelmaking, rolling, and other processes has increased the probability that steelmakers will achieve the ultimate end toward which much thought and effort have been directed for many years. This end would be a continuous steelmaking plant, in which the raw materials would be fed into one end and finished steel products would emerge from the other end. Conceivably, such a plant would employ a continuous direct-reduction furnace with automatic chemical analysis and addition of alloying elements to produce molten steel of the desired composition. The steel so produced would pass continuously and successively through continuous-casting machines, continuous heating furnaces, and continuous rolling operations to make the finished products. Accurate and sensitive instruments would monitor each phase of the process, and information supplied by the instruments would enable a computer to regulate the necessary controls to keep the various phases in balance.

It is interesting to note that the processes and equipment for several of the important parts of such a plan already are available, although not completely compatible. Conceivably, future research will develop compatible new methods, or result in modifications of existing methods, that can be combined successfully into a continuous operation completely under computer control.

Bibliography

"Steel" in *ECT* 1st ed., Vol. 12, pp. 793–843, by Walter Carroll, Republic Steel Corporation.

1. *Annual Statistical Report, 1967*, American Iron and Steel Institute, New York, 1968.
2. H. E. McGannon, ed., *The Making, Shaping and Treating of Steel*, U.S. Steel Corporation, Pittsburgh, Pa., 1964.
3. *Statistisches Jahrbuch, 1966*, Wirtschaftsvereinigung Eisen- und Stahlindustrie, Düsseldorf, 1967.

4. *Statistical Highlights of the U.S. Iron and Steel Industry—Ten Years 1958–67*, American Iron and Steel Institute, New York, 1968.

General References

American Iron and Steel Institute, *Annual Statistical Report, 1967*, New York, 1968.

American Iron and Steel Institute, Steel products manuals, latest revisions, entitled: *Carbon Steel— Semifinished for Forging; Hot-Rolled and Cold-Finished Carbon-Steel Bars; Wire and Rods, Carbon Steel; Alloy Steels; Stainless and Heat-Resisting Steels.*

E. C. Bain and Harold W. Paxton, *Functions of the Alloying Elements in Steel*, 2nd ed., American Society for Metals, Novelty, Ohio, 1961.

S. L. Goodale, *Chronology of Iron and Steel*, Penton Publishing Company, Cleveland, Ohio, 1937.

C. D. King, *Seventy-Five Years of Progress in Iron and Steel*, American Institute of Mining and Metallurgical Engineers, New York, 1948.

Harold E. McGannon, ed., *The Making, Shaping and Treating of Steel*, 8th ed., United States Steel Corporation, Pittsburgh, Pa., 1964.

F. T. Sisco, *Alloys of Iron and Carbon, Properties*, Vol. II of *Alloys of Iron and Carbon*, published for the Engineering Foundation by McGraw-Hill Book Company, Inc., New York.

Society of Automotive Engineers, *SAE Handbook*, latest edition, New York.

United States Steel Corporation, *Suiting the Heat Treatment to the Job*, Pittsburgh, Pa., 1967.

HAROLD E. McGANNON
United States Steel Corporation

STERILIZATION

Sterilization is an absolute term. In its classical sense it means the complete destruction or removal of all forms of life. The number of agents capable of achieving this criterion is limited; sterilization is usually carried out by means of heat (saturated steam, dry heat, or incineration), radiation, certain chemical agents, or physical removal (such as filtration).

The term sterilization is often mistakenly used as a synonym for disinfection (especially in medicine and in the food industry). Thus in medicine, sterilization is often intended to mean the destruction of disease microorganisms only. Similarly, in the food industry it is accepted to mean the killing of only those microorganisms which cause spoilage and pathogens.

In order to clarify the meaning of sterilization, the Council on Pharmacy and Chemistry of the American Medical Association (1) has issued the following statement: "The Council on Pharmacy and Chemistry has formally gone on record as disapproving of the use of the terms sterilize, sterile, and sterilization in a bacteriologic sense other than in their correct scientific significance; that is, meaning the absence or destruction of all microorganisms. These terms are not relative and to permit their use in a relative sense not only is incorrect, but opens the way to abuse and misunderstanding."

One of the major difficulties in sterilization is to define whether or not a process has truly sterilized. Although a product should not be referred to as "practically sterile" or "commercially sterile" (since the determination of sterility is often dependent on test sampling and methodology), one may state that a product is sterile or unsterile within the limits of error inherent in the selection and application of the testing methods.

Sterilization is required in many fields, such as food processing, medicine, pharmaceutics, industrial fermentation, and space exploration. For thorough treatments of the concepts and methodology of sterilization techniques, see Lawrence and Block (2), Rubbo and Gardner (3), and Sykes (4).

The field of sterilization is a broad one. It encompasses physical, chemical, engineering, and biological principles; hence, it is an interfacial area of investigation and practical use, requiring multidisciplinary efforts. A variety of factors must be carefully considered in order to achieve repeatable sterilization. There is a tendency to compare sterilizing agents, favoring one over the other. It must be realized, however, that all sterilizing methods have their limitations. Heat may degrade, radiation may damage, chemicals may be toxic, etc. The sterilizing process chosen depends on the particular application.

"Less than Complete" Sterilization Methods

There are several techniques and processes that have been called sterilization although they are not true sterilization methods. Consequently, it is necessary to define "less than complete" sterilization methods.

Disinfection is one of these techniques and implies a process which eliminates or destroys infection. Usually this method requires a chemical agent which destroys disease organisms or other harmful germs (but generally not bacterial spores). Terms that have been used instead of disinfection in this general field are germicide (germicidal) and bactericide (bactericidal).

Antiseptics are substances which are active against bacterial sepsis, infection, putrefaction, or decay and prevent or inhibit the growth or action of microorganisms. In low concentrations antiseptics may inhibit growth; in high concentrations they may destroy microorganisms. Antiseptics are used especially on living tissue.

Sanitizers are agents which reduce microorganisms to safe levels (as determined by public-health requirements) and are commonly used to control the bacterial contamination of equipment and utensils in dairies and other food-processing plants. Sanitization implies cleaning as well as the removal of infection.

Pasteurization is the destruction of susceptible nonspore-producing organisms by mild heat or radiation treatment. The best known example of heat pasteurization is in the processing of milk. The temperature employed is either 63°C for 30 min (the Holder method) or 72°C for 20 sec (the flash method). These processes will destroy all the nonspore-forming infectious bacteria found in milk, such as *Mycobacterium tuberculosis*, *Brucellis abortus*, and various *Salmonellae*.

Radiation pasteurization is a relatively new process, and again the intention is to destroy only a portion of the microbial contamination or to render material free of a particular infectious microorganism. The objective of the elimination of a portion of the microflora is to extend the shelf life of a food.

Dynamics of Sterilization

The extent of destruction or removal of contaminating microorganisms is usually determined by measuring the number of cells surviving after various time increments of exposure to a sterilizing agent. These numbers are usually obtained by conventional plate-count techniques. Thus the definition of sterility becomes freedom from viable organisms, ie organisms capable of reproducing and growing when placed in a favorable medium. According to Schmidt (5), "The only single practical criteria of the death of microorganisms is the failure to reproduce when, as far as is known, suitable conditions for reproduction are provided. This means that any organism which fails to show evidence of growth when placed under what are considered, in the light of our present knowledge of bacterial nutrition and growth requirements, adequate growth conditions is considered as dead."

Sterilizing agents are classified as physical or chemical and may be either liquid, gaseous, or in the form of electromagnetic radiation. It is difficult, however, to make sharp distinctions between physical and chemical agents. Chemical sterilants may produce heat or osmotic pressure (physical) which contributes to the death of the organism, whereas physical sterilants may induce the formation of toxic chemicals. For example, Amaha and Sakaguchi (6) describe the death of bacterial spores treated with heat as a gradual chemical process.

The thermal death of bacteria or spores appears to be logarithmic. Chick (7) indicates that a monomolecular chemical reaction is necessary for such a first-order relationship. It is generally accepted that the interruption of cellular function by heat is due to the denaturation of critical protein in the cell. However, Oginsky and Umbreit (8) state, "We do not know, however, whether the logarithmic order of death is an expression of the monomolecular reaction of protein denaturation or of a subsequent phenomenon." Esty and Meyer (9) and Weis (10) found that the destruction curves of heat-treated *Clostridium botulinum* were essentially logarithmic. For a further discussion of the destruction rates of organisms exposed to heat, Pflug and Schmidt (11) and Ernst (12) have given comprehensive treatments.

Moist-Heat Sterilization

Moist heat may be employed in roughly three ranges: (*1*) below 100°C, (*2*) at 100°C (either in boiling water or in free-flowing steam at atmospheric pressure), (*3*) above 100°C (in saturated steam under pressure). Moist-heat (steam) sterilization above 100°C is the method of choice because of economy and convenience and is commonly used in medical and commercial applications.

KINETICS OF INACTIVATION

As pointed out previously, the order of death of heat-treated bacteria is generally considered to be logarithmic and subject to mathematical description. Many explanations have been given to explain the logarithmic order of death of bacteria. One of the most reasonable explanations, given by Rahn (13), maintains that the death of bacteria subjected to moist heat is due to the denaturation of one gene essential to reproduction. Whether or not this is an accurate explanation, it is usually considered in the evaluation of sterilizing processes. As Rahn (13) points out, "it permits to compute death rates and to draw conclusions from them which are independent of any explanation."

Thermal Death Point and Thermal Death Time. The *thermal death point* is arbitrarily defined as the lowest temperature at which a population of bacteria is killed in 10 min. This standard is used very little, however, because of the inherent variables associated with test methods and culturing. *Thermal death time* is a standard used a great deal in the canning industry; it is the shortest time necessary to kill all the bacteria in or on a menstruum at a specific temperature. Thermal-death-time (TDT) data provide a basis for the operation of canning processes and are of great practical value when measured under known conditions. Techniques for determining TDT values are now quite sophisticated, and standard procedures and equipment are in general use. These are thoroughly described and discussed by Tanner (14) and Stumbo (15). In addition, Dickerson and Read (16) have described procedures for determining the TDT with steam at subatmospheric pressure.

The logarithmic nature of the death curve is an expression of the different resistances of the individual cells of a bacterial population and suggests that progressively greater energy, time, or intensity of treatment is required to kill higher proportions of the population. If a sterilizing agent kills 90% of the organisms per x min, then the actual number killed per minute decreases with time. For example, with an initial population of 1000, 90% of 1000 (900) would be killed in x min, 90% of 100 (90) would be killed in $2x$ min, and 90% of 10 (9) would be killed in $3x$ min.

The thermal-death-time concept is fundamentally in conflict with the concept of the exponential order of death, for it specifies that all microorganisms will have been destroyed after a finite period of exposure. One suggested alternative is that the definition of thermal death time be expressed as the exposure period necessary to kill some finite fraction, perhaps 99.99%, of the organisms originally present (17).

Death-Rate Constants. Since death is a first-order exponential or logarithmic function, much use has been made of death-rate constants for comparative purposes. When the logarithm of the number of surviving organisms is plotted against the time of exposure to a sterilizing agent, a straight line is obtained. The slope of this exponential curve is described by the velocity constant K and is calculated as follows:

$$K = \frac{1}{t} \log_{10} \frac{N_0}{N_1}$$

In this equation, t = time (in minutes), N_0 = starting number of microorganisms, and N_1 = number of microorganisms surviving at time t. The reciprocal of K is the D value or decimal reduction time, which is the time in minutes required to reduce the number of organisms by 90%. D values have been used in food processing as a tool for extrapolating the thermal death point.

Temperature Coefficient. The temperature coefficient is usually expressed as Q_{10}, which is the ratio of the rate at a certain temperature to the rate at a temperature 10 Celsius degrees higher. For chemical reactions Q_{10} is usually about 2. But for steam denaturation of protein, Q_{10} for the range 50–60°C might range from 10 to 20 to 100, whereas for the same proteins in the range 120–130°C it might be 4.8, 7.7, and 23.0. Since the Q_{10} is so high, it is apparent that an increase of 2–3 degrees Celsius reduces the sterilization time by half.

FACTORS IN STEAM STERILIZATION

A complex series of factors affects the relationships observed between time and temperature in heat sterilization. One must carefully consider these factors, taking into account whether the process is to be used medically or commercially.

Microorganisms. When considering the microflora of contaminated material, the following factors should be taken into account: (1) The environment in which an organism finds itself, either immediately prior to or during a heat treatment, can influence heat resistance profoundly. (Such factors as the organic makeup of the environment, the protein content, inorganic salt content, and fat content, as well as the physical properties, influence heat resistance significantly; other factors, such as heredity, chemical nature, previous culture history, including nutrition, temperature

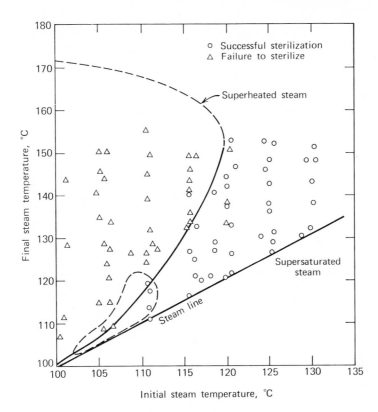

Fig. 1. The relationship between sterilizing efficiency and the amount of superheating (19).

of growth, and metabolic products, also influence heat resistance.) (*2*) Factors which operate during exposure, such as the concentration of the organisms present and the nature of the suspending medium, can influence heat resistance. (*3*) Factors which are involved in recovering microorganisms for enumeration or for sterility testing can influence the results which are obtained. Microorganisms which have survived drastic treatment of any sort are sometimes much more exacting in their nutritional requirements than untreated microorganisms. Therefore, suitable culture conditions must be present to recover sublethally treated microorganisms.

Saturated and Superheated Steam. It is well known that superheated steam is an inefficient sterilizing agent, for its effect is more like that of hot air. Some degree of superheat can be tolerated, but as superheat becomes more severe, its sterilizing efficiency is lost (18). Savage (19) has found that the division in sterilizing effect between saturated and superheated steam is sharply defined. Figure 1 describes the relationship between sterilizing efficiency and the amount of superheating.

When fabrics such as dressings, surgical gauze, etc, are sterilized, superheat may result. Superheating occurs because of the combination of heat transfer from the steam to the fabric and the hydration of the dehydrated fabric by steam (18,20–22). Excessive heat on the chamber wall will also produce superheated steam.

Effects of Air. In autoclave systems one of the important factors is air removal. If air is left in a sterilizer it can become mixed with the steam, creating a pressure which is the sum of the partial pressures of the steam and the air. As a result, if the

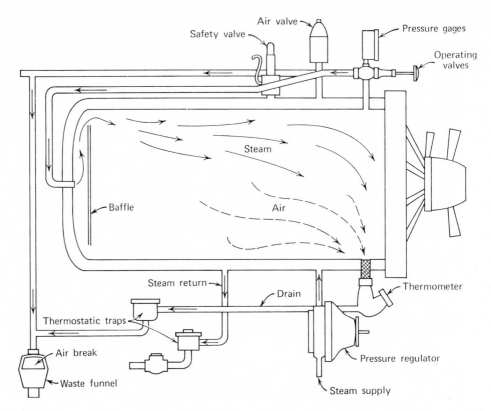

Fig. 2. Longitudinal cross section of a downward-displacement sterilizer, indicating essential parts and a steam–air flow pattern.

partial pressure of the steam is lower than when the atmosphere is all steam, the condensing temperature of the steam will be lower. In effect, the steam will be superheated, and proper sterilizing conditions may not be met. Generally, autoclaves are controlled by a pressure-regulating device. Superheat can be readily obtained if heat transfer takes place from the jacket wall to the water vapor, the temperature of the chamber rising without an increase in moisture.

If the air is not mixed with the steam, compression of the air can occur in a blind spot, thus preventing steam from entering. When this occurs sterilizing conditions will not be met in certain areas of the sterilizer. Another effect of residual air is that oxidation and consequent damage of fabrics can occur.

Air Removal. There are three general methods currently used for the removal of air. The classical method is called downward displacement. *Downward displacement* (or *gravity displacement*) takes advantage of the difference in the density of air relative to steam. As steam is admitted to the sterilizer chamber, the air is displaced downward by the steam and forced out through a drain at the bottom. Figure 2 shows a longitudinal section of a downward-displacement sterilizer typically operated by hand. Downward-displacement sterilizers that operate automatically are available from major sterilizer manufacturers. The second type of autoclave designed to remove air is the *high-vacuum sterilizer*, which has been developed since about 1960. Essentially, the air is removed prior to steam admission by a preliminary vacuum of 15 mm Hg absolute pressure. Early in the development of high-vacuum sterilizers a phenomenon known as the "small-load effect" was observed (22), in which the residual air after vacuum is readily entrained in a small pack in the sterilizer, producing an egg-shaped ball of air which is difficult to penetrate with steam. Since air entrainment is dependent upon the relative amount of air available, and since producing higher degrees of vacuum is either costly, time consuming, or both, the use of "continuous steam bleeding" (12) has been developed to circumvent this problem. This system allows a small but steady influx of steam to enter the chamber during an evacuation.

Since there are problems with both downward-displacement sterilizers and high-vacuum sterilizers (in downward-displacement systems dense and full loads are difficult to penetrate, and in high-vacuum systems there is air-entrainment in small loads), steam-pulsing systems, intermediate between the two extremes, have been developed. These systems consist of steam that pulses while a vacuum is being produced around a load of material.

Some sterilization processes have been developed in which air is purposely left in the chamber. For example, not all pharmaceutical products can be sterilized in a conventional autoclave; in the process of autoclaving, pressure is sometimes built up within the container being sterilized because of the vapor pressure of volatile components. Under these circumstances the internal pressure may be greater than the steam pressure within the chamber itself. An excessive internal pressure may result in the expansion and bursting of glass containers, collapsible tubes, plastic bags, etc. Consequently, processes have been developed in which air or some other gas is added to the autoclave at a higher pressure in order to produce sufficient total pressure to prevent bursting (23). Wilkinson and Baker have published an excellent review of steam sterilization (24).

Some highly automated sterilizers have been built, but several problems arise in using them. Since a vacuum is used to assist in removing air, there is a potential problem of air leakage during the vacuum, which can result in excessive air during the steam portion of the process. In addition, there is an increased likelihood of superheat with fabrics. Vacuums sometimes dehydrate fabrics severely, and, as mentioned above, superheat may result when fabrics are dehydrated.

Corrosion. The utility of steam sterilizers is limited by the problem of corrosion, both on the material being sterilized and in the boiler producing the steam. This is of special importance in the sterilization of surgical and dental instruments. Usually, boiler compounds are added to the boiler to prevent corrosion, and these are sometimes carried over with the steam, leaving toxic residuals on the instruments. But if boiler compounds are not added, instruments can become corroded by the steam and the residual oxygen, or occasionally by the residual carbon dioxide present. Consequently, compounds are added to the steam to prevent this problem. Holmlund (25) has reviewed this subject very well.

APPLICATIONS

Autoclaves. Autoclaving is still the method of choice for sterilization because it is relatively easy, as well as being the least expensive process. A variety of autoclave systems have been developed, as discussed previously. Practically any level of automation can be attained; in France there is even an autoclave controlled by means of programmed cards. In addition, autoclaves come in various sizes, ranging from the conventional laboratory unit used for bacteriological media, instruments, and glassware, to the large chambers or pressure cookers employed in the canning industry. Regardless of size, the operating principle is the same, steam under pressure being used to achieve the desired exposure conditions.

Figure 2 shows a modern hospital autoclave. The body of the sterilizer consists of a chamber surrounded on the sides by a steam space (steam jacket). Steam is admitted (as shown by the arrows) at the rear of the chamber, and, being lighter than air, is baffled to the upper portions of the chamber, displacing the air downward and out. The air is vented as long as the thermostatic valve in the bottom of the chamber remains open. Exposure to steam is begun after the load reaches the appropriate temperature and pressure. Table 1 lists the temperatures considered suitable for given exposure times.

Table 1. Exposure Times and Corresponding Temperatures

Temperature, °C	Exposure time, min
132	2
125	8
121	12
118	18
115	30

Different materials require different exposure times since the rate of heat transfer varies. Typical exposure times are given in Table 2.

Table 2. Exposure Times for Different Materials

Material	Exposure time, min, at 121°C
sutures, silk, cotton, nylon	15
glassware (empty, inverted)	15
syringes (unassembled) in paper covers	20
rubber gloves in muslin covers	30
instruments wrapped for storage	30
50-ml Erlenmeyer flask	12–14
2000-ml Erlenmeyer flask	30–35

Fermentation Media. In the fermentation industry, the batches of liquid that serve as media to produce antibiotics, wine, beer, etc, are sterilized in processes similar to autoclaving except that the fermentation tank acts as its own chamber. Fermenters are generally supplied with steam jackets or internal steam coils. Air can be removed by adjustment vent valves, and any desired pressure or temperature can be maintained within the tank. The many attached lines and fittings are sterilized by permitting steam to bleed through them during the processing period. Direct steam injection through a sparger (when present) is also frequently employed as an aid to coil or jacket heating.

Caution must be exercised when sterilizing plant-scale fermentation equipment (10,000–25,000 gal capacity). If sterile air is not admitted as the tank cools, a vacuum capable of destroying or seriously damaging the tank will result. Automatic vacuum breakers are therefore an essential safety device on such installations. Heat sterilization of fermentation media must often meet two incompatible standards: the total destruction of bacterial contamination and the retention of nutrient value. Several investigators have studied the heat destruction of the nutrient content of natural substances. Lankford and Lacy (26) have noted the destruction of cystine and other amino acids when they are sterilized in a medium containing glucose.

Heat sterilization, however, is not without beneficial effects for the productivity of fermentation media. In some instances compounds are produced which evidently counterbalance the destruction of some necessary components. For example, hydrolysis of such high-molecular-weight complexes as lipids, proteins, and polysaccharides may make them more available to the metabolic systems of the organism. Toda and Aiba (27) recommend that the practice of sterilizing at high temperatures for short time periods be reassessed from time to time, depending on the medium being sterilized.

Continuous Sterilization. Although batch sterilization of liquid media in a tank, as previously described, is the most common practice, continuous sterilization systems have also been widely developed. Such systems make it possible to limit overheating, to attain a better balance between sterilization and nutrient quality, and to achieve the other obvious advantages of a continuous operation. A variety of continuous sterilizers have been proposed. The usual procedure consists of heating the liquid rapidly to the specified process temperature (with or without direct injection of steam), holding it for a required period in a coil or a jacketed line (retention tube), then rapidly cooling it (generally accomplished by permitting the liquid to flash from a higher pressure to a lower one). Evaporative cooling then takes place, and where steam-injection heating has been used the previous dilution of the material may be compensated for. Some processes go even further and evacuate the system, thus cooling the fluid even more to a controlled temperature. Another way of cooling the fluid is to pass it through another heat exchanger that is cooled. An excellent discussion on the kinetics of death of bacterial spores in continuous-sterilization systems is given by Wang (28).

A continuous-processing production unit that eliminates retorting (in a pressurized chamber where steam is used to heat sealed cans of food to sterilizing temperature, as is required in the conventional canning of foods) has been developed at Trenton Foods, Trenton, Missouri (29). The process is known as Flash 18. In this method the filling operation is conducted in a room which is held at 18 psig by a pressurized air-conditioning system. The air conditioning keeps the temperature at a comfortable 75°F. Human operators can work in the room, and foods can be heated to sterilizing temperatures of 255°F without boiling taking place.

Dry-Heat Sterilization

Although considerable research has been performed on the other classical methods of sterilization, dry heat was neglected until it became necessary to find an agent for sterilizing the probes used in space exploration. The National Aeronautics and Space Administration (NASA) requires that these probes be sterilized so that they will not contaminate the planets where they are used. Contamination of planets by terrestrial microbes must be avoided because it can confuse studies of the planets' history, microbial flora, and surface environments.

Traditionally, dry heat has been used to sterilize materials which cannot be sterilized by steam, such as materials that are impermeable to steam (eg petrolatum) or materials that are damaged by steam (eg powders).

Kinetics of Inactivation.   The resistance of microorganisms to dry heat is different from their resistance to moist heat.   The temperature coefficient of dry-heat sterilization is much lower than that of moist heat.   Death does, however, appear to occur in a logarithmic manner.

Factors in Dry-Heat Sterilization.   In the past, dry-heat sterilization has been considered an oxidative process (30).   Murrell and his colleagues, however, have presented data that relate inactivation rates to water activity and temperature (31–33). The death of microorganisms subjected to dry-heat conditions appears to be closely related to their loss of moisture.   At 100–120°C, maximum spore resistance occurred at a water level in equilibrium with a water activity of 0.2–0.8 (33).   *Water activity*, a_w, is the ratio of the vapor pressure of a microbial sample to the vapor pressure of pure water at the same temperature.   The term relative humidity in gaseous systems corresponds to water activity in liquid systems.   It appears that factors that affect the rate of water loss affect the rate of spore destruction.

Inactivation due to oxidation appears to be less of a factor.   Pheil et al. (34) discuss the heat destruction of spores in various gaseous environments and report the following order of increasing resistance: carbon dioxide, oxygen, helium, and nitrogen.

Perhaps the most difficult materials to sterilize with dry heat are those which contain microorganisms encapsulated in solid materials such as crystals or plastics (35–37).   The difficulty may be due to the prevention of water loss from the microbes. Materials in this category present the greatest challenge to spacecraft sterilization.

Materials which are not sterilized by steam and must be sterilized by dry heat are oils, powders, greases, etc.   As mentioned previously, sharp surgical or dental instruments may be corroded by steam; however, they are safely sterilized by dry heat. Excessive moisture can accumulate in glassware sterilized by steam, and it, too, should be sterilized by dry heat.   The principal advantage of dry-heat sterilization is its penetrating power; given sufficient time, materials will eventually reach sterilizing conditions.   The principal disadvantages are poor heat transfer, high temperatures, long exposure periods, and degradation due to oxidation.

APPLICATIONS

The principal applications of dry-heat sterilization are in bacteriological laboratories, hospitals, and spacecraft sterilization.   Usually, the process is carried out in an oven (by gravity convection or mechanical convection).   Other methods of sterilizing by dry heat are by means of infrared radiation and by incineration (or burning).   Since infrared radiation transmits by direct rays to only the surfaces exposed to the radiation, penetration must be by conduction.   A system based on infrared radiation has been developed by Darmady, Hughes, and Tuke (38) for sterilizing syringes.   Another sterilization method, developed by Darmady et al. (39), accomplishes heating by conduction rather than by radiation and consists of a thermostatically controlled hot plate on which an aluminum block is fixed.   Syringes can be heated by placing them in holes in the block.

The most effective way of sterilizing air is by incineration (simply heating the air to high temperatures so that all organic material is oxidized).   For a discussion of this method, see Cherry, Kemp, and Parker (40).   It should be pointed out that sterilization by this means is very destructive.

Flaming, a method similar to incineration, is also commonly used for sterilizing. The item to be sterilized is held in a flame and heated until it is red hot.   Although this method is quite limited in use, it is very effective; dipping an item in alcohol, however, and then setting it aflame, is not an effective means of sterilization (41).

Chemical Sterilization

In the late fifties chemical sterilization came into greater use. This method developed because of the need to sterilize many items that cannot be exposed to heat, radiation, or other forms of sterilization. Chemical sterilization has the following advantages: (*1*) Sterilization is at low temperatures, and damage to heat- or moisture-sensitive materials is avoided. (*2*) Objects can be sterilized in their containers or packages since some of the gaseous sterilants will diffuse through plastic, paper, or fabric. (*3*) Sterilization by some gases can take place in the presence of large quantities of organic material. Chemical sterilization is generally divided into two areas, sterilization by liquids and by gases.

Ethylene Oxide (qv), CH_2—CH_2O, bp 10.8°C. The capability of ethylene oxide as a sterilant has been confirmed many times. The principal stimulus to its further development is the increasing need for a reliable method of sterilizing heat-labile materials.

Since medical progress is accompanied by a steady increase in the numbers and types of equipment and materials to be sterilized, the use of ethylene oxide will continue to be important. One wonders if the myriad of disposable medical items would have developed without the availability of heat-labile materials, materials which cannot be sterilized by dry heat or steam but which can be sterilized with ethylene oxide. The application of ethylene oxide is more complex and expensive than that of such classical processes as dry-heat or steam sterilization but is still practical.

Ethylene oxide is available undiluted as a liquid under mild pressure, or diluted with carbon dioxide or chlorofluorohydrocarbons. These other gases, which are biologically inert, are added to make a nonflammable mixture, since ethylene oxide is flammable and explosive at 3.6–100% by gaseous volume. The gas is also toxic, the inhalation toxicity being about equal to that of ammonia. With proper ventilation there is not much of a problem, but the gas should not be vented into a confined space. Ethylene oxide diffuses rapidly into and through materials. Some materials, however, take up the gas very readily, with the formation of toxic residues (42). Consequently, long aeration periods may be necessary to dilute the gas after processing. Sophisticated apparatus for sterilizing with ethylene oxide have been developed by sterilizer manufacturers, and reproducible sterility can be obtained in them. Also, some investigators have reported the use of plastic bags, desiccators, steel barrels, etc, as chambers in which sterilization can be achieved on a laboratory level. Ethylene oxide has been used in the food industry for the decontamination of spices, and in medicine for the sterilization of devices such as heart-lung machines, heart pacers, and artificial kidneys. A review of ethylene oxide sterilization has been given by Ernst and Doyle (43).

Formaldehyde (qv), CH_2O. Formaldehyde was one of the first agents to be used for sterilization. It is used in the liquid form for the preservation of animal specimens and in the gaseous form for the decontamination of open spaces, such as animal rooms. Formaldehyde is also used in solution to sterilize instruments. Although it is a gas at room temperature, the compound is unstable and condenses out in the atmosphere as paraformaldehyde, a white solid polymer. For room decontamination, formaldehyde is generally disseminated in one of the following ways: (*1*) heating paraformaldehyde (it rapidly depolymerizes to formaldehyde), (*2*) boiling 37% formalin, and (*3*) aerosolizing 37% formalin into a fine mist. In order to sterilize enclosed spaces with formaldehyde, the following criteria must be met: (*1*) The temperature must be above 70°F. (*2*) The relative humidity must be high, preferably near saturation. (*3*) 2–4 mg of formaldehyde per liter of space should be effectively disseminated.

There are two principal disadvantages in using formaldehyde. One disadvantage is that only exposed areas are sterilized, because formaldehyde condenses on readily available surfaces rather than penetrating into inaccessible areas. For this reason, it performs poorly on porous materials. A second disadvantage is that the pungent residual chemical left by formaldehyde necessitates prolonged airing before a room can be comfortably used again.

Propylene Oxide (qv), CH_3—CH_2—CH_2O. This compound is similar in properties to ethylene oxide, although it is less volatile (bp 35°C), less flammable, and less active biologically. Propylene oxide has had little application in medicine, but Rubbo and Gardner (3) describe a propylene oxide dental disinfector manufactured in Australia. Propylene oxide has been used chiefly for the decontamination of food materials, mainly spices.

Propylene oxide is only about one tenth as active as ethylene oxide, and since it has a higher boiling point it is not readily dispersed or removed. In the presence of the necessary amount of moisture, propylene oxide hydrolyzes slowly to the harmless residual propylene glycol. Ethylene oxide, however, forms toxic ethylene glycol on hydrolysis with water. Consequently, propylene oxide has replaced ethylene oxide in accordance with the 1958 Capital Food Additive Amendment to the Food, Drug, and Cosmetic Act. Since its flammability limits are 2.1 to 21.5% by vol, propylene oxide may or may not require dilution with inert gases.

Ozone (qv), O_3. This compound is frequently mentioned as a gaseous bactericidal agent and has been used to prevent the formation of mold in such places as food-storage rooms. Ozone is generated by passing air through a continuous high-voltage discharge generated between metal electrodes. Air treated in this way can contain up to 1% ozone. Ozone is incapable of any deep penetration. Thus Ingram and Haines (44) found that while 3 ppm of ozone were effective in preventing mold growth on the outside of eggs (dry, inactive organisms) 10 ppm did not delay bacterial growth on meat (moist, active organisms; organic material present). Clearly, ozone is limited in its capabilities and can be cited as a sterilizing agent only in special applications. Ozone is sometimes used in water treatment and has great potential since it leaves no toxic residual. For an excellent discussion of ozone see *Ozone Chemistry and Technology* (45), by the American Chemical Society.

Methyl Bromide (qv), CH_3Br, bp 4.6°C (see Vol. 3, p. 772). This gas has weaker bactericidal properties than ethylene oxide (being about one tenth as active) and is nonflammable. It has about the same order of activity as 10% ethylene oxide in carbon dioxide. Kolb and Schneiter (46) report that methyl bromide was bactericidal for anthrax spores. According to Munnecke et al. (47), it is also effective against fungi.

β-**Propiolactone,** CH_2CH_2CO. This compound is a colorless liquid at room temperature and boils at 163°C. It has been reported by Hoffman and Warshowsky (48) to be 4000 times as active as ethylene oxide. However, it cannot be substituted for ethylene oxide since it has very little penetrating ability. β-Propiolactone has been used very successfully by Hoffman et al. (49) and Bruch (50) as a decontaminant for rooms and buildings. Hence, it appears likely to replace formaldehyde as a gaseous sterilant. As stated previously, formaldehyde leaves a pungent residual; β-propiolactone also leaves a residual, β-hydroxypropionic acid (hydrolysis product with water).

β-Propiolactone should be used only by highly experienced operators. It is usually disseminated by means of a generator which produces aerosol droplets small enough to vaporize before they settle. The main restriction in the use of this compound is its toxicity. It has been reported to be carcinogenic by Walpole et al. (51), Roe and Glendenning (52), and Palmes et al. (53).

Peroxyacetic Acid, CH_3COOH (see Vol. 14, p. 794). This compound is used as an aerosol or a vapor in research on germfree (gnotobiotic) animals (Greenspan (54), Barrett (55), Doll (56)). Peroxyacetic acid is a strong oxidizing agent and should be used with corrosion-resistant material such as glass, plastic, or stainless steel. It is a very rapid sterilizing agent, and its decomposition product is nontoxic acetic acid.

Glutaraldehyde, $CHO—CH_2—CH_2—CH_2—CHO$. This compound has been reported to have a wide range of biocidal activity. A 2% solution buffered with 0.3% sodium bicarbonate to a pH of 7.5–8.5 is used for sterilizing plastics, rubber, thermometers, and instruments having lenses (57). Glutaraldehyde is promising in that it is both more effective and less irritating than formaldehyde solutions (3).

Other Chemicals. There are many other sterilant chemicals that have not had widespread application. Such compounds as chloropicrin (Saiki (58)), epichlorohydrin (Phillips (59)), ethyleneimine (Mayo et al. (60)), and glycidaldehyde (Dawson (61)), have been suggested as sterilizing agents.

Two chemicals which show promise because of their nontoxic residuals are diethyl pyrocarbonate, $CO(COOEt)_2$, and 2,3-epoxy-1-propanol (glycidol). Diethyl pyrocarbonate has been used to sterilize foods and beverages (62); its by-products are carbon dioxide and ethanol. Glycidol has been used to sterilize aqueous drug compositions (63); its hydrolysis product is glycerine. None of the foregoing compounds, however, appears to be as effective as ethylene oxide for sterilizing materials in depth, or β-propiolactone for sterilizing materials on their surfaces.

All the chemicals currently (1969) used for gaseous chemical sterilization appear to require an optimum relative humidity for maximum activity. For example, ethylene oxide seems to be most efficient at a relative humidity of 30–50%; propylene oxide, at 25–50%; and β-propiolactone, at over 75%. Chemical sterilizing agents are finding wider application as their capabilities become better known.

Radiation Sterilization

The use of radiation to inactivate microorganisms without exerting a deleterious effect on the item being processed offers an attractive means for sterilizing foods, disposable medical items, drugs, and some miscellaneous biochemical systems. Radiation sterilization is being used increasingly for disposable plastic items, and its use has been proposed for food, pharmaceutical products, surgical sutures, etc. Two types of radiation are used for sterilizing: (1) ionizing radiation, which consists of x rays, gamma rays, cathode rays, beta rays, and the relatively heavy particulate neutrons, protons, etc; and (2) the longer electromagnetic radiation (ultraviolet, infrared, and radio-frequency radiations). Generally, the term radiation sterilization implies the use of ionizing radiation. For reviews of the subject, see Powell and Bridges (64), Darmady et al. (65), and Silverman and Sinskey (66).

CURRENT THEORIES OF RADIATION INACTIVATION

Two theories have been proposed to explain the lethal action of ionizing radiation. The first is the target (or direct-action) theory, which proposes that the mechanism is direct ionization of DNA. The target theory of radiation sterilization is discussed in detail by Lea (67) and is supported by Hutchinson and Pollard (68).

The diffusion (or indirect-action) theory proposes that some killing of bacteria and other microorganisms occurs as a result of free-radical production in the medium, with the consequent initiation of a secondary reaction in the DNA molecules. For a discussion of this theory, see Proctor and Goldblith (69). The direct-action and indirect-action theories may be reconciled with one another by postulating that the target molecules are surrounded by a water film (see Hutchinson (70)).

RADIATION SOURCES

There are several potential sources of radiation. Two main types of radiation equipment currently available are cobalt-60 installations and electron accelerators. Because of the high cost of using this equipment, it is restricted to large-scale industrial operations and is not used in hospitals. Table 3 lists the characteristics of radiation sterilizers.

Table 3.   Some Characteristics of Radiation Sterilizers

Characteristic	Cobalt-60 source (gamma radiation)	Electron accelerator (high-energy electrons)
penetration	high (2 ft of water)	low (1 in. of water)
operation	continuous	intermittent
sterilization time	long (approx 48 hr)	short (seconds)
materials processed	small and large objects	small objects only
induced radioactivity	none	above 5 MeV
safety precautions	elaborate	less than for ^{60}Co
installations	elaborate	less elaborate than for ^{60}Co

Since the gamma radiation produced by cobalt-60 has a high penetrating ability, thick-walled concrete chambers are necessary for housing the installation. The material being sterilized may vary in size from bales of goat hair to cartons of sutures or disposable syringes and is mechanically circulated around the source so that it is irradiated to a calculated dosage of 2.5 Mrad (1 Mrad = 10^6 rad) from each side.

Electron accelerators are of two types: the Van de Graaff generator, which has an output of 1–3 MeV, and the microwave linear accelerator, whose output may vary from 3–15 MeV. The scale of this equipment is small compared to the large physical dimensions of a cobalt-60 installation. When sterilizing with an electron accelerator, a beam of electrons is directed onto a conveyor belt carrying small articles of uniform size, such as single packages of sutures or syringes.

An important consideration in choosing a radiation source is the comparative penetrating power of electrons and gamma rays. The useful range of 2-MeV electrons is about 1 cm in a material of unit density, while a reasonably energetic gamma ray will pass through more than 1 ft of water.

The International Atomic Energy Commission (71) has recommended a code of practice for the radio sterilization of medical products. This code states that the radiation dose should be dependent upon the particular item to be sterilized, the microbiological contamination found on the item, and the margin of safety required for the end use of the item. "The margin of safety is to be assessed by perusal of the data available concerning the radiation resistance of microorganisms. Since the margin of safety for a particular dose is dependent upon the initial number and species, and their resistance in the particular environment, control of the pre-sterilization load is required. This control should be exerted by quantitative and qualitative examination of the pre-sterilized bacterial contamination of articles selected from finished packaged goods before the sterilization is applied. Further, the margin of safety should be checked by exposure to the sterilization treatment of suitable test-pieces and of articles deliberately contaminated to the maximum extent within the production premises. The process must prove effective for these test-pieces or articles" (71).

FACTORS IN RADIATION STERILIZATION

The inactivation of microorganisms by radiation is a complex process involving rapid energy absorption and molecular changes followed by much slower metabolic processes and a subsequent failure to reproduce. Although our understanding of the essential effects of radiation has greatly increased, the mechanism of its reaction with microorganisms is still not clearly understood. It is known, however, that the lethal dose varies with a number of factors such as the nature of the microbial population, its culture history, and the environmental conditions during exposure.

Table 4. Resistance of Various Microorganisms to Radiation

Degree of resistance	Microorganism	Dose range, Mrad
sensitive	vegetative bacteria animal viruses (75 mμ)	0.05–0.5
moderately resistant	*Bacillus anthracis* (spores) *Clostridium* sp (spores) molds and yeasts animal viruses (20 mμ)	0.5–2.0
resistant	*Bacillus pumilus* *Micrococcus radiodurans* animal viruses (20 mμ) bacterial viruses	2.0–4.0

Inactivation of Microorganisms. The biological effect of ionizing radiation is dependent upon the quantity of energy absorbed by the irradiated material. This energy is measured in rads, one rad corresponding to the absorption of 100 erg per gram of irradiated material. Another unit frequently used is the roentgen (R), which is approximately equal to 0.83 rad.

Microorganisms exposed to irradiation do not always die immediately. In bacteria which have been subjected to a dose which prevents their multiplication, many biological functions may persist for some hours. A material is generally considered sterile when it is impossible to demonstrate the growth of microorganisms either in liquid or on solid media. Hence, the inability to multiply is the decisive criterion for inactivation.

A few microorganisms may survive irradiation and maintain their ability to multiply. However, these organisms often will take a much longer time to grow out than unirradiated organisms, and their growth requirements will often be altered. Studies of bacterial resistance to irradiation are often complicated by these circumstances.

Type of Organisms. Various degrees of resistance to radiation are seen, depending on the type of microorganism. Table 4 (3) groups a number of microorganisms according to their resistance to given doses of radiation.

There are numerous factors which can modify radiation resistance. Factors such as the presence of protective or sensitizing chemicals, the irradiation atmosphere and temperature, the water content of the cells, and the technique of recovering microorganisms after exposure, are important in radiation resistance.

PRACTICAL APPLICATIONS

One of the main industrial applications of ionizing radiation is the sterilization of hospital supplies such as sutures and plastic hypodermic syringes. Many such pharmaceuticals are heat sensitive, and ionizing radiation appears to be an ideal method for them. The developments in this area up to 1959 have been reviewed by Bellamy (72). Other investigators, such as Oliver and Tomlinson (73), Powell and Bridges (64), and Darmady et al. (65), have recommended ionizing radiation for sterilizing hospital supplies. The currently recommended dose for sterilizing hospital materials is 2.5 Mrad (71). However, not all pharmaceuticals are tolerant to radiation treatment; for example, insulin and thyroid powder are materials that are adversely affected by radiation.

Another important application of ionizing radiation is in the processing of foods. Due to an intense interest in this subject, the literature is extensive and can be found in a wide range of journals, books, official reports, and reports of national and international conferences. Consequently, it is difficult to make an accurate appraisal of the state of this field. Much of the earliest work in the radiation sterilization of food was carried out at Massachusetts Institute of Technology by Proctor and his associates. This group has reported sterilizing doses for several foods (see Table 5).

Table 5. Sterilizing Doses for Various Foods, Mrad

Food	Dose	Food	Dose
milk	0.75–1	frozen milk	1
haddock	0.9–1.5	sausage skin	1.5
minced beef	1.5	orange juice	1

One of the greatest problems in food irradiation is the retention of the wholesomeness and acceptability of some of the foods processed. The chemical changes brought about during radiation sterilization, although often quite small, may affect the palatability or the nutrient value of the food. Kung, Gaden, and King (74) have studied the effects of gamma rays on vitamins in raw whole milk and have found rapid, first-order decreases in vitamin content. At 0.5 Mrad, nearly all of the reduced ascorbic acid, 75% of the vitamin A, 60% of the tocopherols, and 40% of the carotenes in riboflavin, was destroyed. There may also be off-flavors, often characterized as having a scorched taste. Browning of meat, bleaching of fats and vegetables, and physical deterioration of some fruits, become apparent at doses of around 0.1 Mrad. Despite these obstacles a variety of products and packaging materials have been approved by the Food and Drug Administration.

Another important application of ionizing radiation is in radiation pasteurization, a process which may be used to destroy only a portion of the microbial population or to destroy pathogens that may be present in the material. Lower doses would thus be required, but refrigeration would be needed to extend the shelf life. For example, the tendency of fish, meat, eggs, fruit, etc, to spoil may be reduced by sublethal doses of irradiation. The use of low doses of irradiation to prevent the sprouting of potatoes has also been approved. Radiation pasteurization shows promise as a method of sterilization, and, as more knowledge is gained, will very likely continue to have greater practical application.

Other Radiation Systems

Ultraviolet Radiation. Nonionizing ultraviolet (uv) radiation, a component of sunlight, is responsible for a great deal of natural microbiological destruction. It is an electromagnetic radiation with low energy and poor penetrating power. Wavelengths range from about 2100 to 3280 Å, but the most effective bactericidal range is much narrower, between about 2400 and 2800 Å. Ultraviolet radiation can be produced by a low-pressure mercury-vapor arc in germicidal lamps of the hot- or cold-cathode type, although hot-cathode lamps are used most frequently. About 95% of their uv radiation is in the 2530 Å region.

Although ultraviolet radiation can act very rapidly against both spores and vegetative cells, its action is severely limited by two factors. First, because the energy of ultraviolet radiation is low, its penetration into solids is negligible and its penetration into liquids is slight. Consequently, the major applications have been in air sanitization and in the surface sterilization of food products, packaging materials, and working areas. The second disadvantage is that many proteins and similar complex molecules which normally occur in biological systems have marked absorption bands in the ultraviolet region. Serum and similar menstrua, bacteria in blood, and solutions containing significant protein concentrations, are therefore practically immune to the action of normally germicidal uv radiation. It should be realized that ultraviolet radiation is not a sterilizing agent except in special circumstances. It will substantially reduce the number of airborne microorganisms but is unlikely to eliminate them completely. Ultraviolet radiation has also been used commercially for water purification when chlorination is undesirable. The effective penetration varies with the optical density of the water; for "normal" water the intensity of radiation at a depth of 2 in. may be only 38% of that at the surface (Cortelyou et al. (75)), whereas for polluted river waters it may be as low as 30% at a depth of only 1 cm (Schmidt et al. (76)).

High-Frequency Electric Fields. There are a considerable number of reports on the effects of high-frequency electric fields on microorganisms. Most of these reports describe attempts to prove that the high frequency itself has specific lethal action apart from the lethal action produced by the heat generated in the medium during treatment. However, Sykes (4) concludes that "high-frequency voltage fields per se have no bactericidal properties and that any reported killing must be attributed entirely to internal thermal or other side effects."

Sterilization by Filtration

The term filtration refers to the physical removal of solid particles from fluids (gases or liquids). Although severely limited in application, filtration is often the only reasonable method for accomplishing a desired goal.

Absolute and Probability Filters. There are two general types of filters: absolute filters and probability filters. The *absolute filter* is a membrane or matrix with pores having diameters smaller than the least dimension of the microbial cells that are to be removed. Hence, the mechanism of retention is simply a mechanical sieving action. Absolute filters are used primarily for filtering liquids but can also be used for sterilizing small volumes of gases.

Probability filters, on the other hand, depend on random entrapment throughout the filter matrix for the removal of microorganisms. These filters are classified as depth filters, and their channels are usually of a diameter larger than that of the microorganisms which are to be retained. Consequently, sterility cannot be guaranteed, although a statistical prediction of the efficiency of removal can be made. Probability filters are used for both liquids and gases.

LIQUID FILTRATION

Filtration through bacterial-retentive filters is a common practice in the pharmaceutical industry, where it has been the primary method for sterilizing thermolabile solutions. This technique is also used for sterilizing industrial fermentation media and the liquids used on spacecrafts (when sterility is required).

Filter Types. Bacterial-retentive filters have been used for many years. A variety of special shapes and forms, with various porosities, may be obtained. They are made of such materials as porcelain, sintered glass, asbestos, diatomaceous earth, and membranes composed of biologically inert cellulosic esters or similar polymeric compounds.

Porcelain candles (maximum pore size 2.8 μ), such as Selas, have the advantage of being resistant to chemicals which do not attack silica. They may be cleaned by scrubbing, severe washing with alkaline or acidic detergents, or ignition in a laboratory furnace. Although the individual particles composing the filters are sintered together during the manufacturing process, there is some danger that particles may become loosened and go downstream with the sterile filtrate.

Sintered- or fritted-glass filters are composed of a matrix of round particles of glass joined together in the shape of a disc by means of heat. The disc is then heat-sealed into the shape of a funnel. Although sintered-glass filters carry a negative surface charge, they do not absorb solutes during filtration to the extent that other filters do; in addition, particulate or soluble material is not given off by these filters. They are washed with acidic solvents.

Asbestos-pad filters may be discarded after one use, thus eliminating the necessity for cleaning. The fibers are considered to carry a positive charge and hence to attract negatively charged bacteria. The major disadvantages of these filters are that they contaminate the filtrate with fibers and alkalinity, they retain a part of the solution being filtered, and they are not suitable for solutions affected by metals (since these will yield traces of iron).

Diatomaceous-earth filters, such as Berkefeld, are test-tube-shaped filter candles. Although they have the advantage of rapid filtration (due to their large filtering area) they are difficult to clean, absorb a considerable amount of the solution being filtered, and are not suitable for liquids affected by metals.

Membrane filters are about 150 μ thick and contain millions of uniform capillary pores per square centimeter (void volume occupying approx 80% of the total filter volume). The sterilizing grade has an average pore diameter of 0.22 μ. The membrane actually sieves out all particles of a diameter larger than the stated pore size, retaining them on the surface rather than embedding them in a matrix. Membrane filters are commonly used when examining fluids (such as drinking water, milk, and fuel) for their bacterial content and type (77,78). Membrane filters are composed of cellulosic esters or similar polymeric materials.

Mechanism. With the exception of the membrane filter, all of the filters mentioned above depend on random entrapment throughout the filter matrix for the retention of particles (and consequently are probability filters). The exact mechanism is not clear, although it appears that the charge of the bacteria and the filter media may play a significant role (whether attracting the organisms or repelling them) since some filters are positively charged, others negatively charged, and still others, neutral. Mechanical sieving may play a role as well, depending on the filter.

The mechanism of filtration with a membrane is simple mechanical screening. Because of this the major disadvantage is that the filter may become clogged.

AIR FILTRATION

The sterilization of large volumes of air is necessary for many industrial processes. The degree of efficiency required of the filter depends on the application. High efficiency (99.99–100%) is required for the aeration of deep-culture fermentation processes. A lower efficiency (90–95% reduction) is acceptable for the treatment of air in operating rooms and where aseptic procedures are required. As stated previously, most air filtration is done by probability filters.

Air filters may be composed of gauze, granular material (such as activated charcoal, sand, etc), metal wool, cotton, glass fiber, etc. The fineness of the fiber in a filter is of critical importance in determining performance. Filters constructed of fine rather than coarse fibers tend to have less spacing between fibers and thus are more efficient in entrapping particles. High-efficiency filters of large surface area are obtained by pleating the filter back and forth around fluted spaces. Absolute or high-efficiency particulate-air (HEPA) filters remove 99.97% of all particles 0.3 μ or larger and are being used increasingly in the electronics and aerospace industries for maintaining ultraclear environments.

Normally, a coarse prefilter is necessary to remove larger particles and prolong the life of the more expensive bacterial-retentive filter.

Membrane filters are used for filtering small volumes of air or gas but are not practical for filtering large volumes of air because of the higher cost; their resistance to air flow is high, and they are subject to clogging as the surface becomes covered with suspended material.

Filtration Mechanisms. The efficiency of a filter depends upon the size of the particles to be filtered, the diameter of the fibers or granules of the filter media, the packing density of the filter, the filter thickness, and the air velocity.

There are several important mechanisms which operate in fibrous or particulate filters. These include direct interception, inertial impaction, electrostatic attraction, diffusion due to Brownian movement, and gravitational sedimentation. See Dust.

In direct interception the organisms are held by contact with the surface of the filter medium. Interception takes account of those particles which are deflected with the air stream but still come close enough to the filter media to be caught. Inertial impaction refers to direct impingement on the filter medium. Microorganisms carrying a charge are attracted to the surfaces of the filter. It is important that the filter not become moist; otherwise the electric charge will be dissipated.

Diffusion is probably most important with particles of less than 0.1–0.3 μ (eg small viruses). Gravitational sedimentation is considered to be of secondary importance since the settling rate of microorganisms is extremely low. A recent trend in hospitals and in pharmaceutics is the use of the laminar-air-flow principle. This principle is based on the uniform and constant movement of a large volume of highly filtered air through a confined or enclosed space, with the purpose of carrying away and excluding airborne contamination. This concept was developed by the electronics and aerospace industries for situations where the presence of micron and submicron particles cannot be tolerated. A technology transfer has been taking place into the health field, however, and laminar flow promises to be an effective method for controlling viable particulates in hospitals. Essentially, air is passed through a bank of filters, arranged either vertically or horizontally; the opposite wall or floor is a matrix of exhaust ducts. The sterile air envelops the subject (whether it be a patient or pharmaceuticals), providing a continual aseptic environment and carrying away any contamination that is generated. Whitfield (79) and Coriell and McGarrity (80) describe the principles involved.

For a further discussion of filter sterilization, the articles by Sykes (4), Decker et al. (81), Purchas (82), Humphrey and Gaden (83), and Cherry et al. (84), are informative.

Electrostatic Filtration

Electrostatic filtration is another method of air purification, which, in theory, should sterilize, but has not been used extensively for this purpose. Essentially, air is passed through an ionizing unit where the airborne particles receive a positive charge. The charged particles are then collected or precipitated onto negatively charged plates. Electrostatic filters are somewhat expensive (but low in operating cost), less efficient than absolute filters, subject to failure in the event of an electrical stoppage, and require more servicing and cleaning than the absolute or HEPA filters.

Sterilization by a Combination of Lethal Agents

Many sterilizing agents are enhanced by the simultaneous application of another agent. There may be several reasons for using more than one agent at a time. Some obvious reasons are that (1) shorter sterilizing times are possible; (2) the object being sterilized may undergo less degradation; and (3) the process may be more economical. A brief description of sterilization processes based upon the use of more than one lethal agent follows. Thus, Koesterer (85) reports that simultaneous treatment of bacterial spores with dry heat and gamma irradiation was more effective than either agent by itself.

Kempe (86) suggests that moist heat and irradiation used together may be more effective for food preservation than either method alone. His investigation showed that a radiation dose of about one-third the usual sterilization dose reduced the amount of heat treatment required to sterilize to approximately one-fourth what it was without irradiation.

Curran and Evans (87) showed that bacterial spores may be sensitized to heat by preliminary exposure to uv radiation. Michener et al. (88) screened about 650 chemicals for their ability to reduce the heat resistance of *Clostridium* spores.

There are several instances in which the combination of steam and chemicals has been used with success. Alder et al. (89) used a combination of steam at subatmospheric pressure (low temperature) and formaldehyde to sterilize fabrics, plastics, and instruments. Similarly, McConnell and Collier (90) combined steam (at high temperatures, however) with epoxides, such as ethylene oxide, to sterilize food containers. The Allied Chemical Corporation (91) describes a process in which steam acidified with HCl or CO_2 is more effective than steam alone for sterilizing containers. Also, Shields and Wilcox (92) have been granted a patent to use a combination of HCl and steam.

Irradiation combined with chemicals has also been employed. Smolens and Stokes (93) have shown that uv irradiation followed by β-propiolactone treatment is capable of sterilizing plasma, which cannot be sterilized by either agent alone. Likewise, LoGrippo et al. (94) have reported favorably on a six-year evaluation of the treatment of human plasma with uv radiation and β-propiolactone.

Another promising combination is that of radiation, chemicals, and heat. Deasy et al. (95) have reported on the use of beta irradiation combined with heating in the presence of chlorocresol.

Another form of radiation, which has been used in combination with gaseous ethylene oxide and propylene oxide by Boucher et al., is exposure to ultrasonic vibration (sonication) (96). They found that this method gave shorter sterilization times, and concluded that sonication aided in the diffusion of the chemical agents. See Ultrasonics.

There have also been some patents covering the use of chemicals in combination with each other. Thomas (97) describes a process in which ozone was used in combination with ethylene oxide. Kaye (98) describes a process in which formic acid potentiated (enhanced) the sterilizing efficiency of epoxides such as ethylene oxide and propylene oxide. Similarly, Stonehill (99) used cationic surface-active agents to potentiate saturated dialdehydes.

Other Sterilization Methods

Some agents which reportedly act as sterilants have not yet had widespread use. Air has been reported to be sterilized by adiabatic compression such as that which occurs in reciprocating compressors (100). The mechanism is thought to involve a combination of temperature, moisture, and oil vapor. Sykes and Carter support the conclusion that adiabatic compression sterilizes (101).

Microwave radiation has been reported to inactivate microorganisms by means of an apparently nonthermal effect. Olsen et al. (102) have reviewed this subject thoroughly and conclude that effects such as molecular production of hydrogen peroxide and breakdown of the cell-wall membrane may be responsible for the lethal action of microwave radiation.

Another suggested method of sterilizing microorganisms is by means of electrohydraulic shock, which consists of discharging a high-voltage arc under the surface of a liquid medium (103–105). Treatment times of less than one minute have inactivated suspensions of bacteria, spores, and viruses (104). Gilliland and Speck (105) suggest that the mechanism of bactericidal action is nonspecific and is due to oxidation reactions mediated by free radicals. This mechanism appears to be similar to the indirect effects produced by radiation. The use of electrohydraulic shock for sterilizing is not widespread; in 1968, however, two patents were granted for the use of electrohydraulic treatment in producing antigen for immunization purposes.

Sterilization in extremely short periods of time, not longer than one tenth of a second, has been claimed for gaseous plasma (106). (A plasma is generally defined as a highly ionized body of gas composed of positively charged nuclei and negatively charged electrons.) Although extremely high temperatures are generated, little if any heat is transferred to the objects being sterilized. The mechanism of sterilization is not clearly understood. The proposed application is for sterilizing nonconductive containers (plastic, glass, ceramic, etc) for large-scale filling operations.

Sterility Testing

As stated earlier, sterility means freedom from viable organisms. In order to detect freedom from viable organisms, sterility testing is necessary. A brief description of such testing is therefore pertinent. There are two general ways for monitoring sterilization: (1) product sampling and (2) the use of sterility indicators.

Product sampling consists of taking a portion of the processed material and testing it for sterility. Testing procedures for steam, dry-heat, or ethylene oxide sterilization are outlined in the *U.S. Pharmacopeia* and the *National Formulary*. Irradiated material is tested by placing portions of the processed items in culture media. Filters may be tested by taking samples of the liquid (106) or gas (107) and determining if microorganisms or particles pass through the pores. Knudsen (108) discusses the statistical relationship between sample size and the probability of passing unsterile lots, with the conclusion that product sampling is unreliable.

Sterility indicators are often used when it becomes difficult, if not impossible, to take product samples. For example, it would be impractical to use a sterility test on an artificial kidney that has been sterilized with ethylene oxide. Sterility indicators can be chemical, physical, or biological. Chemical indicators rely on a color change after exposure to a sterilizing agent. Indicators of this type are used in steam, ethylene oxide, and radiation-sterilization processes.

Examples of physical indicators are thermocouple recorders, melting-point tubes (for steam or dry heat), pressure gages, hygrometers, particle analyzers, etc. Chemical and physical indicators are not always dependable since they do not monitor completely all the physical-chemical parameters necessary for repetitive sterilization.

Biological indicators are the most reliable means of testing for sterility. Since bacterial spores are the most resistant form of microbial life, they are the indicators of choice for determining the sterilizing efficiency of processes, devices, and chemicals. The spores of *Bacillus stearothermophilus* are commonly used for steam processes, since they are usually the most resistant to moist heat. *Bacillus subtilis* var. *niger* spores are used to monitor dry-heat and ethylene oxide processes. *Bacillus pumilus*, *Micrococcus radiodurans*, and *Streptococcus fecalis* are often used to check for sterility in radiation processes. When selecting an organism for use in monitoring the effectiveness of a sterilizing agent, it is extremely important to choose the organism most resistant to that agent. Otherwise, invalid conclusions may be drawn. A review of the proper use of sterility indicators is given by Beloian and Stuart (109).

Bibliography

"Sterilization" in *ECT* 1st ed., Vol. 12, pp. 896–916, by E. L. Gaden, Jr., and E. J. Henley, Columbia University.

1. American Medical Association, "Report of the Council on Pharmacy and Chemistry," *J. Am. Med. Assoc.* **107**, 38 (1936).
2. C. A. Lawrence and S. S. Block, eds., *Disinfection, Sterilization, and Preservation*, Lea & Febiger, Philadelphia, Pa., 1968.
3. S. D. Rubbo and J. F. Gardner, *A Review of Sterilization and Disinfection*, Lloyd-Luke (Medical Books) Ltd., London, 1965.
4. G. Sykes, *Disinfection and Sterilization*, 2nd ed., E. and F. N. Spon Ltd., London, 1965.
5. C. F. Schmidt, "Thermal Resistance of Microorganisms," in G. F. Reddish, ed., *Antiseptics, Disinfectants, Fungicides, and Sterilization*, Lea & Febiger, Philadelphia, Pa., 1954, Chap. 32.
6. M. Amaha and K. Sakaguchi, *J. Bacteriol.* **68**, 338–345 (1954).
7. H. Chick, *J. Hyg.* (*Cambridge*), **8**, 92–158 (1908).
8. E. L. Oginsky and W. W. Umbreit, *An Introduction to Bacterial Physiology*, 2nd ed., W. H. Freeman and Co., Publishers, San Francisco, 1959.
9. J. R. Esty and K. F. Meyer, *J. Infect. Diseases* **31**, 650–663 (1922).
10. H. Weis, *J. Infect. Diseases* **28**, 70–92 (1921).
11. I. J. Pflug and C. F. Schmidt, "Thermal Destruction of Microorganisms," in C. A. Lawrence and S. S. Block, eds., *Disinfection, Sterilization, and Preservation*, Lea & Febiger, Philadelphia, Pa., 1968, Chap. 6.
12. R. R. Ernst, "Sterilization by Heat," in C. A. Lawrence and S. S. Block, eds., *Disinfection, Sterilization, and Preservation*, Lea & Febiger, Philadelphia, Pa., 1968, Chap. 43.
13. O. Rahn, "Injury and Death of Bacteria by Chemical Agents," *Biodynamica*, Monograph No. 3, 1945.
14. F. W. Tanner, *The Microbiology of Foods*, Garrard Publishing Co., Champaign, Ill., 1944.
15. C. R. Stumbo, *Thermobacteriology in Food Processing*, Academic Press Inc., New York, 1965.
16. R. W. Dickerson and R. B. Read, *Appl. Microbiol.* **16**, 991–997 (1968).
17. O. Rahn, *Bacteriol. Rev.* **9**, 1 (1945).
18. C. W. Walter, *The Aseptic Treatment of Wounds*, The Macmillan Co., New York, 1948.
19. R. M. Savage, *Quart. J. Pharm. Pharmacol.* **10**, 459 (1937).
20. R. Knox, E. J. K. Penikett, and M. E. Duncan, *J. Appl. Bacteriol.* **23**, 21–27 (1960).
21. P. S. H. Henry, *J. Appl. Bacteriol.* **22**, 159–173 (1959).
22. J. H. Bowie, "The Control of Heat Sterilizers," *Symposium on Recent Developments in the Sterilization of Surgical Materials*, School of Pharmacy, University of London, England, The Pharmaceutical Press, London, 1961, pp. 109–142.
23. L. Lachman, D. Jaconia, and P. Eisman, *J. Amer. Pharm. Assoc.* **48**, 541–547 (1959).
24. G. R. Wilkinson and L. C. Baker, *Progr. Ind. Microbiol.* **5**, 231–282 (1964).
25. L. G. Holmlund, *Biotechnol. and Bioeng.* **7**, 177–198 (1965).
26. C. E. Lankford and H. Lacy, *Abstr. Papers, Bacteriol. Proc. 49th Meeting* (*Soc. Am. Bacteriologists*), May 1949.
27. K. Toda and S. Aiba, *J. Ferment. Technol.* **45**, 769–777 (1967).
28. D. I. C. Wang, *The Kinetics of Death of Bacterial Spores at Elevated Temperatures*, Ph.D. Thesis, University of Pennsylvania, 1963.
29. H. P. Milleville, *Food Processing*, pp. 76–83, March 1964.
30. J. J. Perkins, "Bacteriological and Surgical Sterilization by Heat" in G. F. Reddish, ed., *Antiseptics, Disinfectants, Fungicides, and Sterilization*, Lea & Febiger, Philadelphia, Pa., 1954, Chap. 32.
31. W. G. Murrell and W. J. Scott, *Nature* **179**, 481 (1957).
32. B. J. Marshall, W. G. Murrell, and W. J. Scott, *J. Gen. Microbiol.* **31**, 451–460 (1963).
33. W. G. Murrell and W. J. Scott, *J. Gen. Microbiol.* **43**, 411–425 (1966).
34. C. G. Pheil, I. J. Pflug, R. C. Nicholas, and J. A. L. Augustin, *Appl. Microbiol.* **15**, 120–124 (1967).
35. J. E. Doyle and R. R. Ernst, *Appl. Microbiol.* **15**, 726–730 (1967).
36. R. Angelotti, J. H. Maryanski, T. F. Butler, J. T. Peeler, and J. E. Campbell, *Appl. Microbiol* **16**, 735–745 (1968).

37. C. L. Mullican and R. K. Hoffman, *Appl. Microbiol.* **16,** 1110–1113 (1968).
38. E. M. Darmady, K. E. A. Hughes, and W. Tuke, *J. Clin. Pathol.* **10,** 291 (1957).
39. E. M. Darmady, K. E. A. Hughes, J. D. Jones, and W. Tuke, *Lancet* **2,** 769 (1958).
40. G. B. Cherry, S. D. Kemp, and A. Parker, *Prog. Ind. Microbiol.* **4,** 35–60 (1963).
41. J. E. Doyle and R. R. Ernst, *Tech. Bull. Registered Med. Technologists* **39,** 29, 30 (1969).
42. J. E. Doyle and R. R. Ernst, *Assoc. Operating Room Nurses J.* **7,** 47–51 (1968).
43. R. R. Ernst and J. E. Doyle, *Biotechnol. Bioeng.* **10,** 1–31 (1968).
44. M. Ingram and R. B. Haines, *J. Hyg.* (*Cambridge*) **47,** 146 (1949).
45. *Ozone Chemistry and Technology,* American Chemical Society, Washington, D.C., 1959.
46. R. W. Kolb and R. Schneiter, *J. Bact.* **59,** 401–411 (1949).
47. D. E. Munnecke, R. A. Ludwig, and R. E. Sampson, *Can. J. Botany* **37,** 51–58 (1959).
48. R. K. Hoffman and B. Warshowsky, *Appl. Microbiol.* **6,** 358–362 (1958).
49. R. K. Hoffman, L. M. Buchanan, and D. R. Spiner, *Appl. Microbiol.* **14,** 989–992 (1966).
50. C. W. Bruch, *Am. J. Hyg.* **73,** 1–9 (1961).
51. A. L. Walpole, D. C. Roberts, F. L. Rose, J. A. Hendry, and R. F. Homer, *Brit. J. Pharmacol.* **9,** 306–323 (1954).
52. F. J. C. Roe and D. M. Glendenning, *Brit. J. Cancer* **10,** 357–362 (1956).
53. E. D. Palmes, L. Orris, and N. Nelson, *Am. Ind. Hyg. Assoc. J.* **23,** 257–264 (1962).
54. F. P. Greenspan, M. A. Johnsen, and P. C. Trexler, *Proc. 42nd Ann. Meeting Chem. Specialties Mfrs. Assoc., Dec. 1955,* pp. 59–64.
55. J. P. Barrett, *Proc. Animal Care Panel* **9,** 127–133 (1959).
56. J. P. Doll, P. C. Trexler, L. I. Reynolds, and G. R. Bernard, *Am. Midland Naturalist* **69,** 231–239 (1963).
57. A. A. Stonehill, S. Krop, and P. M. Borick, *Am. J. Hosp. Pharm.* **20,** 458 (1963).
58. E. Saiki, *Nagoya J. Med. Sci.* **15,** 270–276; (through) *Chem. Abstr.* **48,** 2822 (1954).
59. C. R. Phillips, *Am. J. Hyg.* **50,** 280–289 (1949).
60. E. C. Mayo, J. O. Moser, and S. Kaye, *Bacteriol. Proc. 52nd Meeting* (*Soc. Am. Bactiol.*) *Boston, Mass., April 27–May 1, 1952,* p. 64.
61. F. W. Dawson, *Am. J. Hyg.* **76,** 209–215 (1962).
62. H. B. Hawley, *Paper 4* (Session 4), *Proc. Intern. Food Ind. Congr. London, 1964,* pp. 1–6.
63. U.S. Pat. 3,143,464 (Aug. 4, 1964), C. Riffkin and D. Marcus (to Olin Mathieson Chemical Corp.).
64. D. B. Powell and B. A. Bridges, *Research* **13,** 151 (1960).
65. E. M. Darmady, K. E. A. Hughes, M. M. Burt, B. M. Freeman, and D. B. Powell, *J. Clin. Pathol.* **14,** 55 (1961).
66. G. J. Silverman and T. J. Sinskey, "The Destruction of MicroOrganisms by Ionizing Irradiation," in C. A. Lawrence and S. S. Block, eds., *Disinfection, Sterilization, and Preservation,* Lea & Febiger, Philadelphia, 1968, Chap. 44.
67. O. E. Lea, *Actions of Radiations on Living Cells,* Cambridge University Press, London, 1956.
68. F. Hutchinson and E. Pollard, "Physical Principles of Radiation Action," in M. Errera and A. Forssberg, eds., *Mechanisms in Radiobiology,* Academic Press Inc., New York, 1961.
69. B. E. Proctor and S. A. Goldblith, *Food Technol.* **5,** 376 (1951).
70. F. Hutchinson, *Science* **134,** 533 (1961).
71. International Atomic Energy Commission, *Code of Practice for Radiosterilization of Medical Products,* 1967, pp. 423–431.
72. W. D. Bellamy, in W. W. Umbreit, ed., *Advances in Applied Microbiology,* Academic Press Inc., New York, 1959, pp. 49–73.
73. R. Oliver and A. H. Tomlinson, *J. Hyg.* (*Cambridge*) **58,** 465–472 (1960).
74. H. C. Kung, E. L. Gaden, Jr., and C. G. King, *J. Arg. Food Chem.* **1,** 142 (1953).
75. J. R. Cortelyou, M. A. McWhinnie, M. S. Riddiford, and T. E. Semrod, *Appl. Microbiol.* **2,** 227 (1954).
76. B. Schmidt, I. Möller, and W. Thiele, *Z. Hyg. Infektionskrankh.* **139,** 505 (1954).
77. M. Torloni and W. Borzani, *Appl. Microbiol.* **6,** 252–254 (1958).
78. H. Wolochow, *Appl. Microbiol.* **6,** 201–206 (1958).
79. W. J. Whitfield, *Bull. Parenteral Drug Assoc.* **21,** 37–45 (1967).
80. L. L. Coriell and G. J. McGarrity, *Bull. Parenteral Drug Assoc.* **21,** 46–51 (1967).
81. H. M. Decker, L. M. Buchanan, L. B. Hall, and K. Goddard, *Am. J. Public Health* **53,** 1982–1988 (1963).

82. D. B. Purchas, *Process Biochem.* **1,** 177–180 (1966).

83. A. E. Humphrey and E. L. Gaden, *J. Ind. Eng. Chem.* **47,** 924–930 (1955).

84. G. B. Cherry, S. D. Kemp, and A. Parker, *Progr. Ind. Microbiol.* **4,** 35–60 (1963).

85. M. G. Koesterer, *Develop. Ind. Microbiol.* **6,** 268–276 (1964).

86. L. L. Kempe, *Nucleonics* **18,** 108–113 (1960).

87. H. R. Curran and F. R. Evans, *J. Bacteriol.* **35,** 4–5 (1938).

88. H. D. Michener, P. A. Thompson, and J. C. Lewis, *Appl. Microbiol.* **7,** 166–172 (1959).

89. V. G. Alder, A. M. Brown, and W. A. Gillespie, *J. Clin. Pathol.* **19,** 83–89 (1966).

90. U.S. Pat. 3,042,533 (July 3, 1962), J. E. W. McConnell and C. P. Collier.

91. Brit. Pat. 1,083,700 (Sept. 20, 1967), Allied Chemical Corp.

92. U.S. Pat. 3,139,323 (June 30, 1964), J. B. Shields and D. F. Wilcox (to Foremost Dairies, Inc.).

93. J. Smolens and J. Stokes, *Proc. Soc. Exp. Biol. Med.* **86,** 538–539 (1954).

94. G. A. LoGrippo, B. R. Wolfram, and C. E. Rupo, *J. Am. Med. Assoc.* **187,** 722–726 (1963).

95. P. B. Deasy, E. Kuster, and R. F. Timoney, *Appl. Microbiol.* **16,** 810–811 (1968).

96. R. M. G. Boucher, M. A. Pisano, G. Tortora, and E. Sawicki, *Appl. Microbiol.* **15,** 1257–1261 (1967).

97. U.S. Pat. 3,117,832 (Jan. 14, 1964), A. Thomas.

98. U.S. Pat. 3,257,161 (June 21, 1966), S. Kaye.

99. U.S. Pat. 3,282,775 (Nov. 1, 1966), A. A. Stonehill (to Ethicon, Inc.).

100. W. H. Stark and G. M. Pohler, *Ind. Eng. Chem.* **42,** 1789 (1950).

101. G. Sykes and D. V. Carter, *J. Appl. Bacteriol.* **17,** 286 (1954).

102. C. M. Olsen, C. L. Drake, and S. L. Bunch, *J. Microwave Power* **1,** 45–56 (1966).

103. S. E. Gilliland and M. L. Speck, *Appl. Microbiol.* **15,** 1031–1037 (1967).

104. M. Allen and K. Soike, *Science* **156,** 524–525 (1967).

105. S. E. Gilliland and M. L. Speck, *Appl. Microbiol.* **15,** 1038–1044 (1967).

106. Brit. Pat. 1,098,693 (Jan. 10, 1968), Arthur D. Little, Inc.

107. D. M. Portner, C. R. Phillips, and R. K. Hoffman, *Appl. Microbiol.* **15,** 800–807 (1967).

108. K. R. Goddard, *Am. Soc. Heating, Refrig. Aircond. Engrs. J.* **5,** 75–82 (1963).

109. L. F. Knudsen, *J. Am. Pharm. Assoc. Sci. Ed.* **38,** 332–337 (1948).

110. A. Beloian and L. S. Stuart, "Methods of Testing for Sterility and Efficiency of Sterilizers, Sporicides, and Sterilizing Processes," in C. A. Lawrence and S. S. Block, eds., *Disinfection, Sterilization, and Preservation*, Lea & Febiger, Philadelphia, Pa., 1968, Chap. 8.

JOHN E. DOYLE
Castle Company

STEROIDS

I. Introduction

Steroids are members of a large class of organic compounds (1) which possess the perhydro-1,2-cyclopentenophenanthrene ring system (**1**), or minor variants thereof, as a common structural feature. Included are a wide variety of naturally occurring and synthetic substances, such as sterols; bile acids (see Bile constituents); adrenal-

(**1**)

cortical and sex hormones (see Hormones (Adrenal-cortical); Hormones (Sex)); various contraceptive drugs (qv); insect molting hormones (see Hormones (Survey)); cardiac-active lactones; sapogenins; and certain alkaloids (qv) and antibiotics (qv).

The term sterol (Greek *stereos*, solid) was given to the initial members of the class studied, solid alcohols obtained from the nonsaponifiable fractions of lipid extracts of animal and plant tissues. As the variety of known structural types increased, the more general term, steroid, came into usage in approx 1935. The scientific study of steroids has led to significant advances in synthetic and theoretical organic chemistry, biochemistry, and physiology. Medical advances have led to the development of a steroid pharmaceutical industry with annual worldwide sales measured in the hundreds of millions of dollars.

Nomenclature. The generally accepted rules for formal steroid nomenclature in 1969 are those approved by the International Union of Pure and Applied Chemistry in 1957 and are known as the IUPAC 1957 rules (2,3). These were revised and extended in 1967 (4). Individual compounds are named systematically as derivatives of steroidal hydrocarbons, and the more important of these are formulated and numbered below. Substituents attached to the ring system from above are designated β (solid line); those attached from below are designated α (dotted line). The rules described in references 3 and 4 are generally followed here. However, important compounds are often designated by individual trivial names.

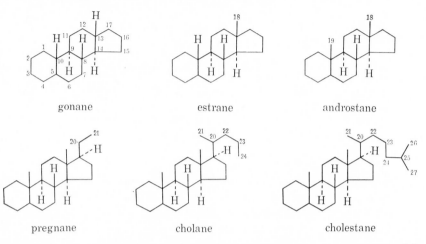

gonane   estrane   androstane

pregnane   cholane   cholestane

History. Prior to 1900 little of chemical consequence was accomplished, although a number of steroids were isolated and studied in a preliminary fashion. In 1903 A. Windaus and in 1912 H. Wieland and their collaborators inaugurated fundamental structural studies on the sterols and bile acids. Their extensive evidence (1a,1b), based primarily on stepwise oxidation sequences, taken with the dehydrogenation results of Diels (5) (formation of chrysene and Diels hydrocarbon, 3′-methyl-1,2-cyclopentenophenanthrene (**2**)) and the x-ray crystallographic studies of Bernal (6) led to the correct structure for the sterols (eg, cholesterol (**3**)) and the bile acids (eg, lithocholic acid (**4**)). This was published in 1932, independently by Roseheim and King (7) and Wieland and Dane (8). By degradation of (**3**) and (**4**) to the same tetracarboxylic acid (**5**) (9), the sterols and bile acids were shown to have identical stereochemistry at the asymmetric centers, C-8, C-9, C-10, C-13, C-14, C-17, and C-20. The exact configurations shown for (**5**) were not determined until considerably later (1a,1b).

During the final stages of the structure elucidation of cholesterol and the bile acids rapid progress was made in establishing the steroid nature of other classes of natural products by chemical correlation, as well as by dehydrogenation to the Diels hydrocarbon (**2**). The estrogenic (1929, 1930), progestational (1934), and androgenic hormones (1931–1935) were isolated and their respective structures determined shortly thereafter (1a,1b). See also Hormones (Sex).

In the period 1935–1943 investigation of the hormones of the adrenal cortex led to the isolation and characterization of some twenty-eight cortical steroids (1a,1b). See also Hormones (Adrenal-cortical). By 1960 this number had been raised to forty-seven (10), including the potent mineralocorticoid hormone, aldosterone.

In 1948 the discovery that the cortical steroid cortisone was of great value in the treatment of rheumatoid arthritis led to a great increase in volume of both academic and industrial steroid research. The impetus to develop anti-inflammatory agents

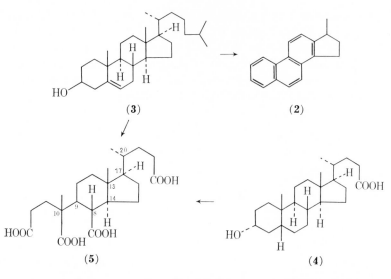

more potent than cortisone, as well as the need for more efficient processes of manufacture, led to numerous new developments in steroid chemistry, eg, partial and total synthesis, the use of photochemical and free-radical reactions, microbiological procedures for introducing oxygen at chemically inert carbon atoms, and the introduction of new physical methods for separation and structure determination.

By the early 1960s the intense interest in steroidal anti-inflammatory agents had shifted once more to the area of the sex hormones—principally to synthetic progestational agents, whose great potential as contraceptive agents had been realized. See also Contraceptive drugs.

In 1965 with the disclosure of the steroidal structure of the insect molting hormone ecdysone (see section II.5) a new field of steroid research was opened.

The demonstrated steroidal nature of many diverse and potent types of physiologically active substances would indicate that further chemically and biologically novel steroid types remain to be discovered. A very recent example concerns the potent venom of the Columbian arrow-poison frog from which the steroid alkaloid, batrachotoxin, the most active cardiotoxin known, and several closely related substances have been isolated. The structure of one of these, batrachotoxinin A, has been shown (11) to be (6).

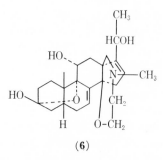

(6)

Biosynthesis. The history of steroids is intertwined with speculative and experimental approaches directed toward a correct explanation of their biogenesis. The stepwise elucidation of the mechanism of steroid biosynthesis is a triumph of modern biochemistry. It was accomplished by numerous contributions from organic and biochemists, principally K. Bloch, J. W. Cornforth, F. Lynen, and their associates, and has been reviewed recently (12,13).

While the detailed mechanism leading to the various intermediates from acetic acid to cholesterol is beyond the scope of this review, it seems instructive to sketch out its more important phases. The first step, esterification of the smallest building block, acetic acid, with coenzyme A (CoASH) is followed by successive self-condensations and reduction to the key intermediate, mevalonic acid.

Scheme 1

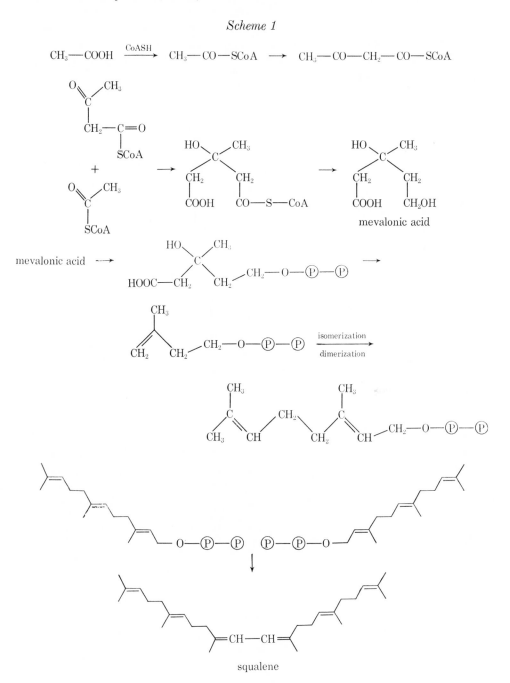

mevalonic acid

squalene

The latter is phosphorylated ($Ⓟ$ — $Ⓟ$ = pyrophosphate), then loses water and carbon dioxide, to yield isopentenylpyrophosphate (a compound that forms the first ten-carbon unit by dimerization). Further addition of a C-5 fragment produces farnesylpyrophosphate, and dimerization finally yields the important intermediate squalene, $C_{30}H_{50}$, as shown in Scheme 1.

The more remarkable requirements of enzymatic catalysis will be appreciated when one realizes that the open-chain polyolefin, squalene, has to be folded in order to yield lanosterol, a tetracyclic sterol with seven centers of asymmetry, as shown below. The earlier postulate, that the first step in this process is a selective oxidation to squalene oxide, was validated in 1966 by the exciting work of the two independent groups headed by van Tamelen (14) and Corey (15), respectively. Their work consisted in the chemical preparation of squalene oxide, followed by enzymatic, in vitro, cyclization to lanosterol. The last step must involve two hydrogen and two methyl migrations.

Returning now to the actual biogenetic process, lanosterol, through a further series of transformations involving loss of the three methyl groups at C-4 and C-14 and a shift of the double bond from Δ8 to Δ5, is converted to cholesterol:

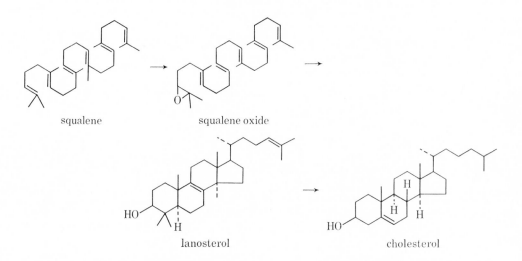

squalene squalene oxide

lanosterol cholesterol

It is of interest to mention here that polyolefin cyclizations with a degree of stereospecificity approaching that of the enzymes, were achieved by Johnson and co-workers (16) in 1968, culminating in a synthesis of d,1-dehydroprogesterone (**203**) (see section III.2).

Cholesterol is the prime source of all steroids in the human organism. Innumerable studies (see Vol. 11, pp. 79, 80) have been devoted to the direct and indirect metabolic conversions of cholesterol to the various steroidal hormones. The following simplified outline shows the major pathways leading to the most important classes of hormones:

cholesterol ⟶ progesterone ⟶ corticoids

cholic acids testosterone ⟶ estrone

II. Naturally Occurring Structural Types

In this section the structural features of the main classes of naturally occurring steroids are surveyed. These include the sterols, saponins and sapogenins, steroid alkaloids, cardiac-active lactones, and insect molting hormones (see also Vol. 11, p. 50). For a discussion of the bile acids, adrenocortical hormones, and sex hormones, see the articles Bile constituents; Hormones (Adrenal-cortical); and Hormones (Sex).

1. STEROLS

The sterols proper (17) are C_{27}–C_{29} alcohols that are distributed widely in nature. Although cholesterol is the principal sterol of the higher animals, considerably more structural diversity is found among the lower animals and throughout the plant kingdom. The hydroxyl group is invariably at position 3β in the naturally occurring sterols, and unsaturation is generally present at C-5 and quite often at C-7 and C-22. Some representative types are shown in Scheme 2.

Scheme 2

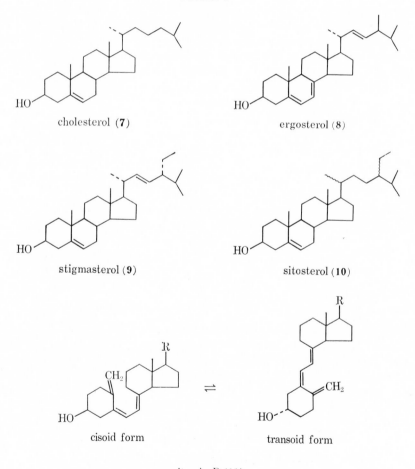

cholesterol (**7**)

ergosterol (**8**)

stigmasterol (**9**)

sitosterol (**10**)

cisoid form

transoid form

vitamin D (**11**)

ergocalciferol, vitamin D_2, R = C_9H_{17}, (**11a**)
cholecalciferol, vitamin D_3, R = C_8H_{17}, (**11b**)

Cholesterol (7) is present in all mammalian tissue either in the free state or esterified with fatty acids. The solid matter of the human brain is 17% cholesterol, and gallstones consist nearly entirely of cholesterol. As discussed under Biosynthesis (section I) all mammalian steroid hormones and bile acids are derived enzymatically from cholesterol, and this is probably true also of the structurally closely related insect molting hormones. It is likewise striking that the steroidal sapogenins and several groups of steroid alkaloids are based structurally on the cholestane framework. Besides being utilized commercially for the preparation of vitamin D$_3$ (**11b**) (see under Vitamin D below) cholesterol was the original source of hormonal steroids, which were obtained in low yields by the chromic acid oxidation of the side chain of cholesterol acetate dibromide (**18**). It was supplanted when far more efficient routes from the sapogenins and the C-22-unsaturated sterols, ergosterol (**8**) and stigmasterol (**9**), were developed. However, the recently discovered high-yield microbiological conversions of 19-oxygenated cholesterol derivatives to estrone and 19-norsteroids (see section III.1) makes cholesterol once again a significant raw material.

Ergosterol (8) is the characteristic sterol of yeast and other fungi. Its chemistry was studied intensively by Windaus and his colleagues, following their observation in 1927 that ultraviolet irradiation of ergosterol produced potent antirachitic activity (**19**). The presence of the ring-B diene system and the C-22 double bond have permitted the development of a number of routes from ergosterol (potentially available in large quantities by fermentation) to cortisone (**20**) and progesterone (**21**). Transformation of the 5,7-diene system to the 7,9-(11)-diene, followed by various oxidative procedures, led to the 11-ketone, as shown:

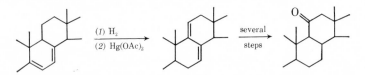

Degradation of the side chain to the pregnan-20-one structure was achieved by successive ozonizations, as indicated:

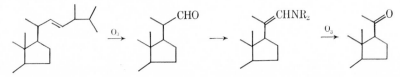

Stigmasterol (9), readily available from soybean oil, is one of the most abundant sterol raw materials. It was converted to progesterone in good yield by Oppenauer oxidation to stigmasta-4,22-dien-3-one, followed by the above ozonization sequence (**22**). A recently described variant is the quantitative cleavage of the C-22 aldehyde enamine with singlet oxygen (**23**).

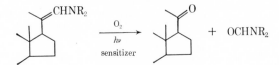

The Sitosterols (10) are the most abundant plant sterols and occur as difficultly separable mixtures, probably epimeric at C-20 and C-24. The microbiological degradation of the side chain of 19-oxygenated cholesterol intermediates leading to estrone is also applicable to the corresponding sitosterol derivatives (24).

    Vitamin D (**11**) (25), the nutritional factor required for proper bone development, is produced on irradiation of ergosterol ($\rightarrow$ vitamin D_2 (**11a**)) and 7-dehydrocholesterol ($\rightarrow$ vitamin D_3 (**11b**)). The preferred steric arrangement is the extended 6,7-*S-trans* structure. Details of the combined photochemical and thermal sequence leading from ergosterol or 7-dehydrocholesterol have been studied intensively since 1927, mainly by Windaus, Heilbronn, Velluz, Havinga, and their colleagues (26); the principal constituents are shown in Scheme 3.

Scheme 3

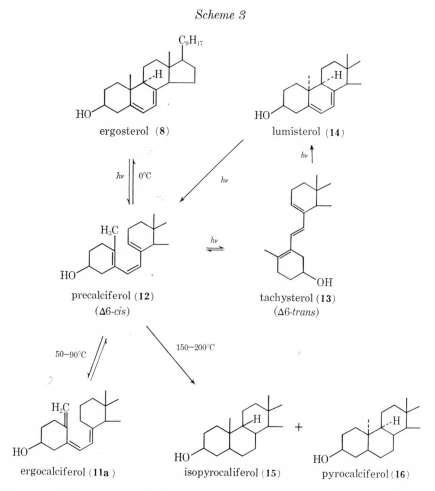

Ergosterol (**8**) on irradiation is converted reversibly to precalciferol (**12**), which on warming undergoes a reversible 1,7 sigmatropic hydrogen shift to ergocalciferol (**11a**). Precalciferol (**12**) is also in photochemical equilibrium with its Δ6-*trans* isomer tachysterol (**13**), from which the 10α-methyl-9βH-5,7-diene, lumisterol (**14**), is obtained. The latter on irradiation produces precalciferol (**12**) and not tachysterol (**13**). Precalciferol on heating to 150–200°C is converted to a mixture of the 9,10-*cis* 5,7-dienes, isopyrocalciferol (**15**), and pyrocalciferol (**16**). The striking facts that (**12**) on photolysis is interconvertible only with the 9,10-*trans* species (**8**) and (**14**), whereas thermally it is converted only to the 9,10-*cis* species (**15**) and (**16**), have been rationalized by Woodward and Hoffmann as consequences of the conservation of orbital symmetry (27). The 1,7-hydrogen transfer in (**12**)⇌(**11a**) has also been treated theoretically and is predicted to occur antarafacially (27a)—ie, through the plane of the ring system from one side of the C-19 to the opposite side of C-9.

In 1968 a metabolite of vitamin D_3, 25-hydroxycholecalciferol (**17**), was isolated from hog blood (28). The fact that this material is 40% more active than vitamin D_3 in rats suggests that (**17**) is the actual active form of the vitamin.

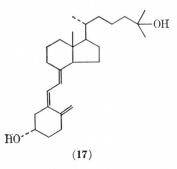

(**17**)

Methylsterols (29). Some representative methylsterols are shown in Scheme 4. *Lanosterol* (4,4,14α-trimethylcholest-8,24-dien-3β-ol) (**18**), the best known of the trimethyl sterols or tetracyclic triterpenes, is found along with other trimethylsterols and cholesterol in wool fat. It is the cyclization product of squalene and the precursor of cholesterol in the animal scheme of steroid biosynthesis (see section I). *Cycloartenol* (**19**) isolated from various plant sources, with its unique 9,10 cyclopropyl bridge common to the *Buxus* alkaloids (see section II.3), may occupy an important position in the botanical scheme of steroid biogenesis. *Euphol* (**20**) is a plant trimethylsterol which differs from lanosterol solely in configuration at C-13, C-14, and C-17, possibly reflecting a different mode of enzymatically imposed folding of squalene during the cyclization stage. *Lophenol*, 4α-methylcholest-7-en-3β-ol (**21**), has been obtained from both animal and plant sources. Its 4α-methyl substitution is common to three closely related steroidal acids produced by microorganisms and possessing unusual 9β, 13α, and 14β stereochemistry. These substances, *fusidic acid* (**22**) (30), *cephalosporin P-1* (**23**) (31), and *helvolic acid* (**24**) (32), have evoked considerable interest because of their antibiotic properties. Their structures were determined with certainty in 1966 and 1967. (For cephalosporin C and related β-lactam systems, see Penicillins.)

2. SAPONINS AND SAPOGENINS (33)

Saponins. The steroidal saponins are plant glycosides that characteristically lower the surface tension of water. This property is the basis of their utilization as foaming agents and, probably, as fish poisons. Although nontoxic orally in warm-blooded animals, they cause hemolysis on injection. Some of them, notably *digitonin*, possess the unique property of forming insoluble 1:1 complexes with 3β-hydroxy-steroids. Chemically the saponins consist of a linear arrangement of one to six hexose or pentose glycoside units joined to the sapogenin aglycone at its C-3 hydroxyl group. Present-day interest (in 1969) centers nearly entirely on the sapogenin aglycones, certain of which (diosgenin, hecogenin) are commercially useful as raw materials for steroid hormone synthesis.

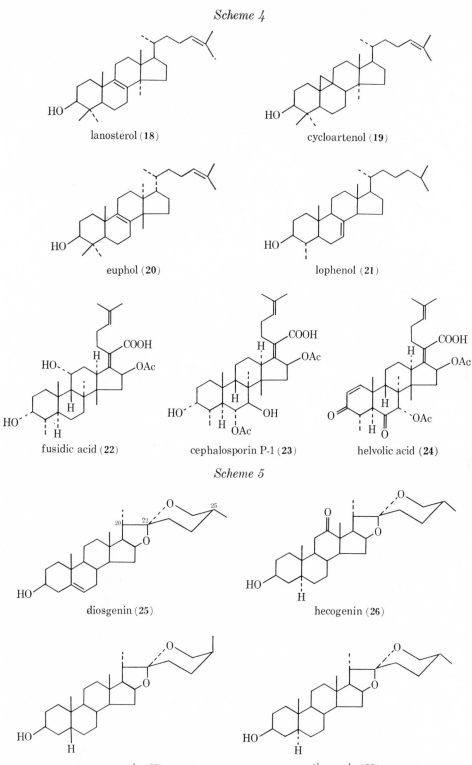

Scheme 4

lanosterol (**18**)

cycloartenol (**19**)

euphol (**20**)

lophenol (**21**)

fusidic acid (**22**)

cephalosporin P-1 (**23**)

helvolic acid (**24**)

Scheme 5

diosgenin (**25**)

hecogenin (**26**)

sarsasapogenin (**27**)

tigogenin (**28**)

Sapogenins. These C-27 cholestane derivatives are obtained from the saponins by acid or enzymatic hydrolysis and possess a unique spiroketal side chain. The spiroketal formulation was proposed by Marker in 1939 (34), and the last stereochemical structural details of a complex series of interconversions at C-20, C-22, and C-25 were settled in 1958 (35). Representative structures are shown in Scheme 5.

By 1940 Marker had developed an efficient three-step process for the cleavage of the spirostane side chain, as shown below. It led to pregn-16-en-20-ones in yields that, on commercial development, exceeded 80% (36). Application to *diosgenin* (**25**)

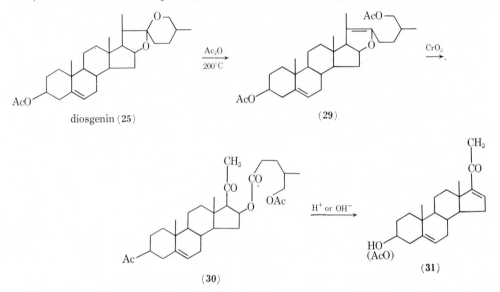

led to 3β-acetoxypregn-5,16-dien-20-one (**31**), which was readily convertible to progesterone, Reichstein's "substance S" (pregn-4-ene-17,21-diol-3,20-dione) (see also Vol. 11, pp. 85, 86); to compounds of the androstane and 19-nor series; and, by microbiological hydroxylation at C-11, to the anti-inflammatory corticoids (see also Contraceptive drugs; Hormones (Adrenal-cortical); Hormones (Sex)). These developments have dramatically reduced the price of medically important steroids, eg, progesterone, which dropped from approx $80/g in 1945 to approx $0.13/g in 1969.

Hecogenin (**26**), oxygenated at C-12 and easily available from the waste liquors of sisal fiber processing (37), is a prime raw material for synthesis of the 11-oxygenated cortical hormones and their analogs (see Vol. 11, p. 84). The conversion of hecogenin (**26**) to 11-oxotigogenin (**34**) in 55% overall yield was an important sequence in a commercial route to cortisone (38) and is shown below.

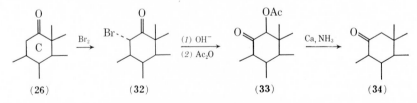

Δ9(11)-Tigogenin (**36**), obtained as indicated (39), is an important intermediate in routes to 9α-fluoro-11β-hydroxycorticoids via 3β-acetoxypregn-9(11),16-dien-20-one (**37**) (40).

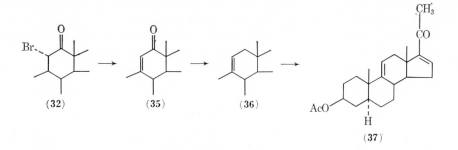

3. STEROID ALKALOIDS

The field of steroid alkaloids is currently one of the most active areas of steroid research. Despite the large number of characterized examples, steroid alkaloids may be classified structurally into four principal groups based on the parent carbon skeleton.

Pregnane Alkaloids. The alkaloids of the *Apocynaceae* and *Buxaceae* (41,41a), which comprise to date well over one hundred compounds based on the pregnane framework, exhibit remarkable structural diversity. Representative products of this type are shown in Scheme 6.

Scheme 6

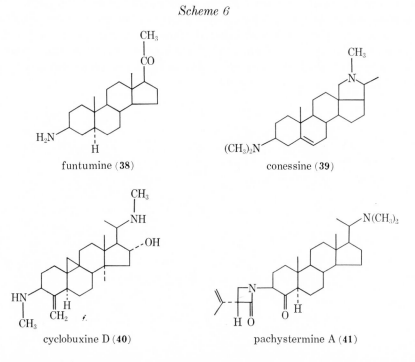

funtumine (**38**) conessine (**39**)

cyclobuxine D (**40**) pachystermine A (**41**)

Funtumine (**38**) and the corresponding 20α-hydroxy compound, funtumidine, are obtained from the leaves of *Funtumia latifolia*, an equatorial African tree, in sufficient quantity (ca 15–20 g per kilogram of leaves) to be considered as a steroid hormone raw material (42). Oxidation of the 3α-amino function of (**38**) by Ruschig's procedure (43) gave excellent yields of pregnane-3,20-dione.

Conessine (**39**) (see also Vol. 1, p. 775), the most available of the holarrhena alkaloids, has been of interest because of its functionalized C-18 moiety. It was converted into 18-oxygenated steroids (**44**) and has been the subject of several syntheses (**45**).

Cyclobuxine D (**40**) is the most abundant of a number of closely related alkaloids of *Buxus sempervirens* (boxwood). Its unusual structure was proved by conversion to (**42**). The same compound was also obtained from cycloeucalenol (**43**) of which the structure was known (**46**).

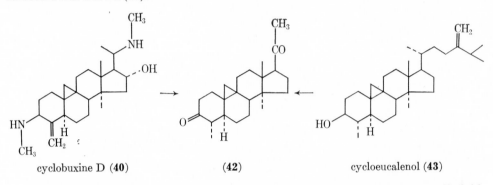

cyclobuxine D (**40**)   (**42**)   cycloeucalenol (**43**)

Pachystermine A (**41**), a major component of the twenty-seven pregnane alkaloids isolated to date from the common ground cover, *Pachysandria terminalis*, is notable for its β-lactam-part structure, a feature analogous to that of the penicillins (**47**).

Solanum Alkaloids (**48**).   This group comprises about forty steroidal alkamines found generally as glycosides and isolated from about 250 species of the families *Solanaceae* and *Liliaceae*. These are all C-27 cholestane derivatives and belong to five structural groups of which the solasodine (**44**) and the solanidine (**46**) types (see also Vol. 1, p. 775) are by far the most common.

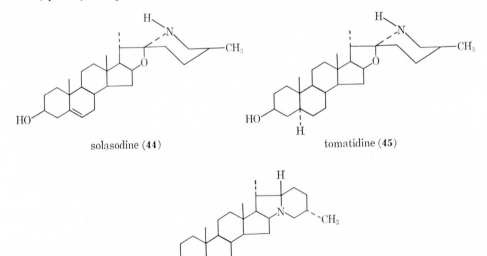

solasodine (**44**)   tomatidine (**45**)

solanidine (**46**)

Solasodine (**44**) and *tomatidine* (**45**) have been considered as alternatives to the sapogenins as source materials for hormonal steroids, and three routes to pregnane derivatives have been described. The first process, developed in 1951, was patterned after Marker's degradation of the sapogenin side chain (**36**) and gave the corresponding 3β-acetoxypregn-16-en-20-ones (**49**) in yields of about 65–70% (**49**).

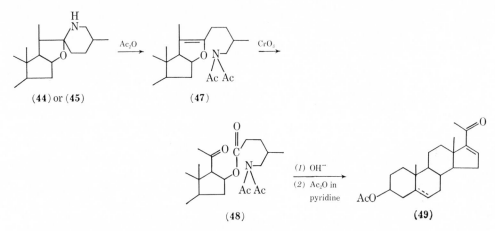

(44) or (45)   (47)

(48)   (49)

(1) OH⁻
(2) Ac₂O in pyridine

The second route (50) involved acid-catalyzed deamination of the *N*-nitroso compound (**50**), followed by oxidation to give product (**49**) in about 30% yield, as shown in Scheme 7.

Scheme 7

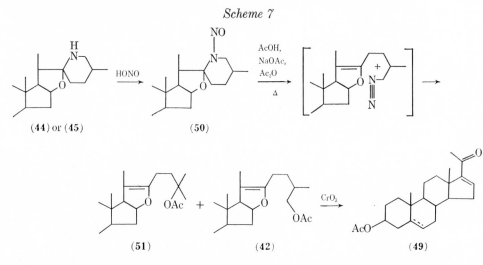

(44) or (45)   (50)

(51)   +   (42)   (49)

In the recently developed third process, photolysis of the *N*-chloro compound (**51**)

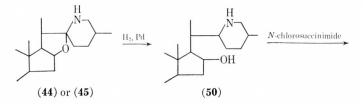

(44) or (45)   (50)

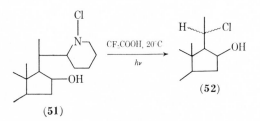

(51)   (52)

in trifluoracetic acid (Löffler-Freytag reaction) gave a mixture of the 20α- and 20β-chloro-16β-ols (**52**) in 80% yield (51).

Solanidine (**46**), the readily available main alkaloid of the potato plant, has been the subject of considerable study, but the tertiary nitrogen grouping has so far resisted cleavage to useful pregnane intermediates.

Veratrum Alkaloids (52).   The veratrum alkaloids (see also Vol. 1, pp. 775, 805) consist of two distinct C-27 series, designated the jerveratrum and the ceveratrum groups.   The former is closely related to the solanidane type, while the latter is characterized by the presence of seven to nine oxygen atoms, largely as hydroxyl groups.

Important members of the jerveratrum group are the C-nor-D-homo compounds *jervine* (**53**) and *veratramine* (**54**).   On the supposition that jervine possessed a normal steroid skeleton it was considered a possible source material for 11-oxygenated corticoid synthesis.   However, the structural studies of Fried, Wintersteiner, et al. (53) led to the correct C-nor-D-homo formulations (**53**) and (**54**) (see also reference 220).

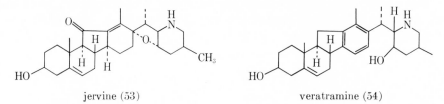

jervine (53)   veratramine (54)

The ceveratrum alkaloids occur free, eg (**55**) and (**56**), or partly esterified with a variety of aliphatic and aromatic acids.   A number of the esters possess high hypotensive activity (54,55).

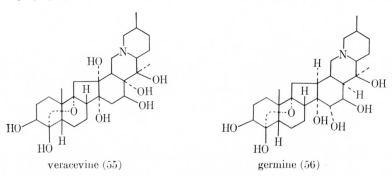

veracevine (55)   germine (56)

Salamandra Alkaloids.   The last class of steroid alkaloids consists of several highly toxic related substances isolated from the skin glands of various salamandar species.   The structures of these compounds were determined in 1967 (56).   The main alkaloid from *S. maculosa taeniata* is *samandarine* (**57**).   The unique structural feature of most members of the group is the ring-A oxazolidine moiety.   Samandarine was synthesized in 1967 from testosterone (57).

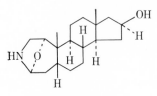

samandarine (57)

4. CARDIAC–ACTIVE LACTONES (58)

The **cardenolides** are $5\beta H,14\beta$-hydroxy-α,β-unsaturated γ-lactones widely distributed in the plant kingdom as glycosides from which the genins are obtained by acid hydrolysis. This class has been intensively studied by T. Reichstein and his associates who have isolated and determined the structure of many glycosides and the component genins and sugars. Several of the naturally occurring glycosides have been used as heart stimulants since ancient times. In small doses they tend to slow and strengthen the heart beat, but excessive doses can cause the heart to stop. *Digitoxin*, the active principle of the drug digitalis from *Digitalis purpurea* (purple foxglove), is a linear triglycoside of the hexose digitose and the cardenolide, digitoxigenin (**58**).

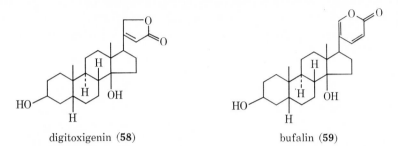

digitoxigenin (**58**)   bufalin (**59**)

The **bufodienolides** are $5\beta H,14\beta$-hydroxy-α-pyrones found in the venom of many toad species either in the free state or as conjugates with suberylarginine. They are also found as glycosides in a number of plant species. A typical genin is *bufalin* (**59**), obtained from the venom of a Chinese toad.

Currently there is active interest in the synthesis of these substances (59). Two syntheses of digitoxigenin (**58**) have been reported (60), as well as one of periplogenin, 5β-hydroxydigitoxigenin (61) and one of bufalin (**59**) (61a).

Two new types of naturally occurring steroid lactones have been described. Withifarin A (**60**), from various *Solanaceae* species, possesses tumor-growth-inhibitor activity (62). Antheridiol (**60a**), secreted by the aquatic fungus *Achlya bisexualis*, functions as a sex hormone in that organism (62a). The proposed structure was confirmed by synthesis (62b).

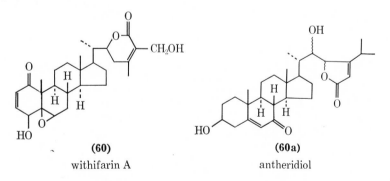

(**60**)   (**60a**)

withifarin A   antheridiol

5. INSECT MOLTING HORMONES

The postembryonic growth and development of insects is controlled by three hormonal factors, (*1*) the juvenile hormone, methyl *trans,trans,cis*-10-epoxy-7-ethyl-3,11-dimethyl-2,6-tridecadienoate (63), concerned with larval growth; (*2*) the molting or metamorphosis hormone (ecdysone and related substances), concerned with the larval–larval, larval–pupal, and pupal–adult molting processes; and (*3*) the as yet un-characterized brain hormone, which controls the production and release of the molting hormone. The present intensive interest in these substances, and in insect biochemistry in general, may lead to new and more effective methods of insect control. (See also Vol. 11, p. 50.)

Ecdysone. The silkworm molting hormone, ecdysone, was isolated in crystalline form in 1954 (25 mg from 500 kg of silkworm pupae) by Butenandt and Karlson after eleven years of research (64). Chemical studies (65) indicated the substance to be a pentahydroxy α,β-unsaturated cholestenone derivative, 22R-2β,3β,14α,-22,26-penta-hydroxy-5β-cholest-7-en-6-one, $C_{27}H_{44}O_6$ (**61**). The detailed structure and stereochem-istry was determined by x-ray crystallographic studies and published in 1965 (66).

Shortly thereafter two syntheses of ecdysone were achieved. The Schering (Ber-lin)–Hoffman LaRoche synthesis is shown in Scheme 8 (67) and that of a Syntex group is shown in Scheme 9 (68).

Scheme 8

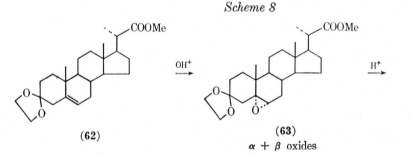

(**62**)   (**63**)
α + β oxides

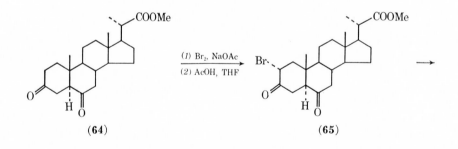

(**64**)   (**65**)

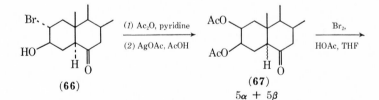

(**66**)   (**67**)
5α + 5β

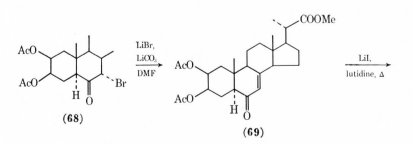

(**68**)   (**69**)

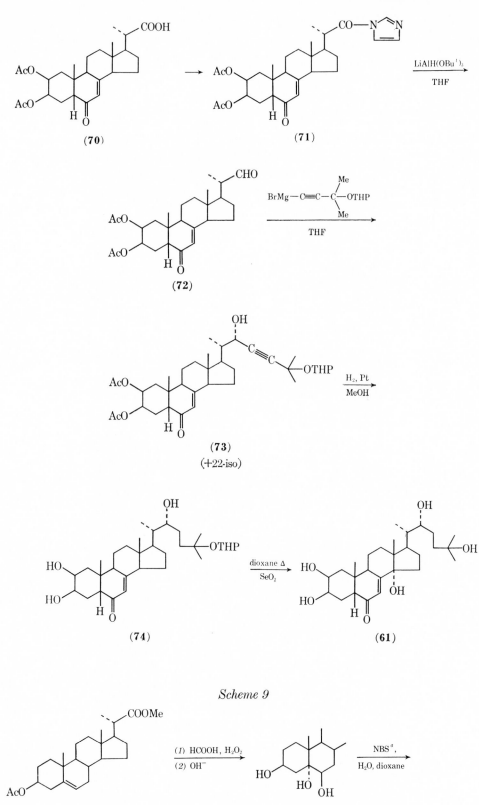

Scheme 9

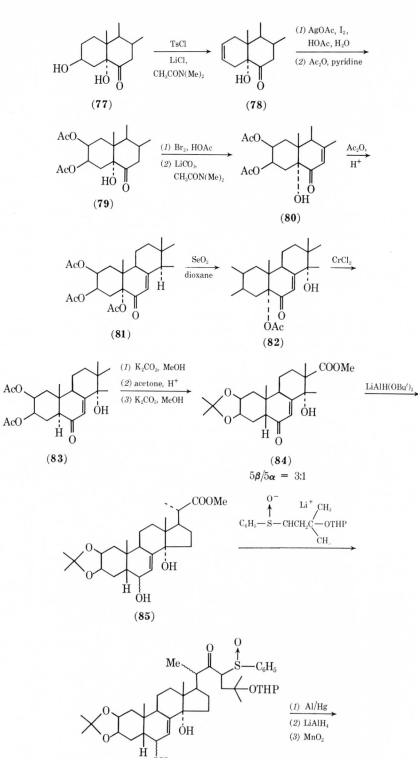

(**77**)   (**78**)

(**79**)   (**80**)

(**81**)   (**82**)

(**83**)   (**84**)

$5\beta/5\alpha = 3:1$

(**85**)

(**86**)

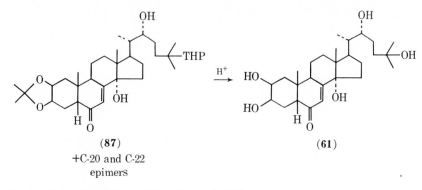

(87)
+C-20 and C-22
epimers

(61)

^a NBS, *N*-bromsuccinimide; Ts, tosyl (*p*-toluenesulfonyl).

In both cases the required A/B-*cis* stereochemistry results on equilibration of 2β,3β-oxygenated A/B-*trans* 6-ketones, because of strong 1,3-diaxial interaction between the 2β substituent and the 10β-methyl group in compounds of the A/B-*trans* series. The Schering-Roche synthesis was significantly improved and shortened by conversion of ergosterol (**8**) to the 2β,3β-diacetoxy-Δ7-6-ketone (analog of (**69**) in scheme 8), which was taken to the aldehyde (**72**) by ozonization of the side-chain double bond (69). In the Syntex synthesis generation of the side chain was made more efficient by conversion of methyl ester (**84**) to the corresponding aldehyde and condensation of the latter with the lithium salt of 3-methylbut-1-yn-3-ol tetrahydropyranyl (THP) ether (70), in a similar but independently conceived manner as that utilized in Scheme 8.

Ecdysone Derivatives. A number of substances, structurally closely related to ecdysone, with potent molting hormone activity, have been isolated from various species of insects, crustacea, and plants, especially of the genus *Podocarpae*. These include crustecdysone, also called ecdysterone (20-hydroxyecdysone (**88**)) (for isolation and structure, see reference 71; for synthesis see reference 72); ponasterone A (25-deoxy-20-hydroxyecdysone (**89**)) (for isolation and structure, see reference 73; for synthesis see reference 74); ponasterone B (**90**) (75), ponasterone C (**91**) (75), podecdysone A (20-hydroxy-24-ethylecdysone) (**92**) (76), polypodine B (5β, 20-dihydroxyecdysone) (**93**) (77), and cyasterone (**93a**) (78), as illustrated in Scheme 10.

Scheme 10

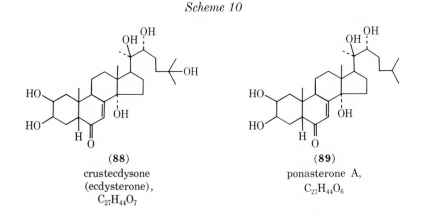

(88)
crustecdysone
(ecdysterone),
$C_{27}H_{44}O_7$

(89)
ponasterone A,
$C_{27}H_{44}O_6$

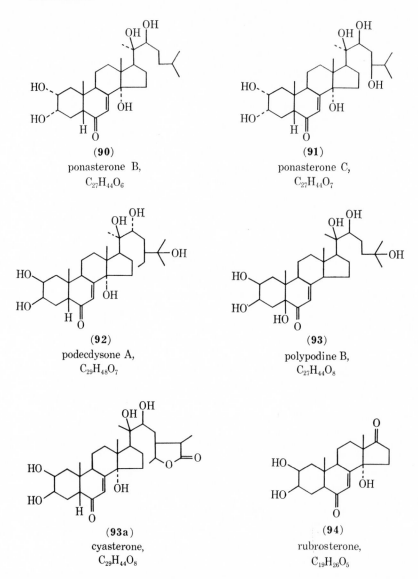

(90)
ponasterone B,
$C_{27}H_{44}O_6$

(91)
ponasterone C,
$C_{27}H_{44}O_7$

(92)
podecdysone A,
$C_{29}H_{48}O_7$

(93)
polypodine B,
$C_{27}H_{44}O_8$

(93a)
cyasterone,
$C_{29}H_{44}O_8$

(94)
rubrosterone,
$C_{19}H_{26}O_5$

Inspection of formulas (88) to (93) shows that hormonal activity is maintained despite variation in the side-chain structure, as well as in the α or β configuration of the ring-A *cis*-glycol system. Although the hormones are obtained in exceedingly small amounts on workup of insect or crustacean tissues, certain of the above compounds are present in far greater quantity in plants; eg, 9.5 g of ponasterone A from 6 kg of dried leaves of *Podocarpus nakaii* (73,75). Many species of plants are screened, and it would appear that this source might well be superior at present to chemical synthesis for the production of active materials.

The C-19 steroid rubrosterone, $2\beta,3\beta,14\alpha$-trihydroxy-5β-androst-7-en-6,17-dione (94), isolated from plant sources which contain ecdysterone and therefore a possible metabolite of the latter, has been synthesized (79). Although essentially devoid of molting hormone activity (94) and the related 20-ketopregnane analog stimulate protein synthesis in mice (80).

In concluding this section mention should be made of the remarkable observation that the water beetle, *Dytiscus marginalis*, secretes the vertebrate mineralocorticoid hormone cortexone, 21-hydroxy-pregn-4-en-3,20-dione, or 11-desoxycorticosterone (**95**) in relatively large quantities (0.4 mg per beetle-equivalent to 1000 ox adrenal glands) for use as a defensive agent (81) (see also Vol. 11, p. 87). Similar insect species have been found to secrete a variety of related C-21 pregnenones, as well as mammalian C-19 male and C-18 female hormones (81a).

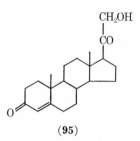

(**95**)

III. Synthesis

1. PARTIAL SYNTHESIS

The described multitude of natural products containing the steroid skeleton has always presented an opportunity and a challenge to researchers in this field: namely, to seek economically feasible conversions of abundantly available natural products into medicinally useful and therefore more valuable compounds. This preoccupation has led to spectacular progress in the past, notably in the variety of corticoid partial syntheses, which have already been reviewed in the article Hormones (Adrenal-cortical) and elsewhere (1a,1b).

The most important medical breakthrough for steroids in the 1960s was the development and broad acceptance of the oral contraceptives (see Contraceptive drugs; Hormones (Sex)). Because the predominant ovulation inhibitors are 19-nor-steroids, heavy demand was generated for this class of compounds. Some advances in the conversion of easily accessible steroids and sterols to estrone and other 19-nor-steroids are discussed below.

A-Ring Aromatization. The previously used pyrolytic aromatization (82) has been superseded by the use of less drastic procedures to accomplish the expulsion of C-19 methyl groups. Tsuda's method (83) of heating cross-conjugated androstene derivatives, eg (**96**), with zinc gives good yields in some cases, as in the preparation of 9(11)-dehydroestrone (**97**) a 75% yield, but only a 40% yield when applied to 11β-hydroxyandrosta-1,4,8-triene-3,17-dione and a 15% yield with androsta-1,4,6-triene-3,17-dione, thus limiting its applicability.

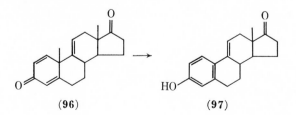

(**96**)   (**97**)

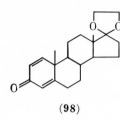
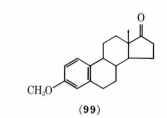

(**98**)   (**99**)

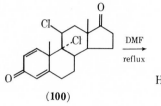
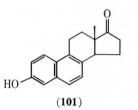
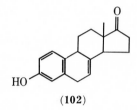

(**100**)   (**101**)   (**102**)

Scheme 11

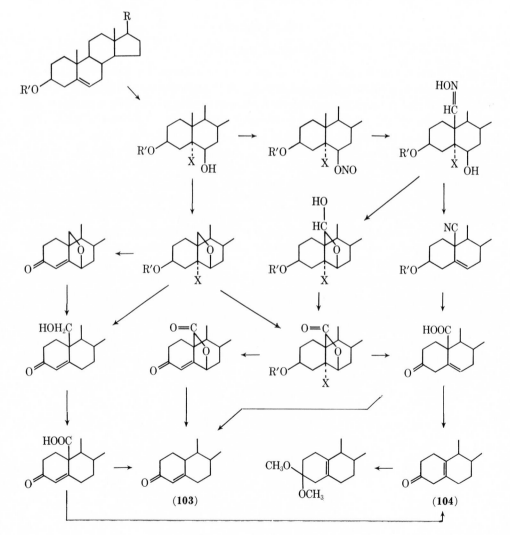

(**103**)   (**104**)

Dryden and co-workers (84) have described a reductive aromatization of dienes that appears to be much broader in scope. A yield of 75% of 3-methoxyestrone (**99**) was attained by treating the 17-ethylene ketal of androsta-1,4-dien-3,17-dione (**98**) with an excess of the radical anion derived from lithium metal and biphenyl in the presence of diphenylmethane in an appropriate solvent (see p. 852).

A method (85) for the preparation of steroids with aromatic A and B rings is illustrated by the rearrangement of 9α,11β-dichloroandrosta-1,4-diene-3,17-dione (**100**) to equilenin (**101**) (see p. 852).

A similar approach (86), starting with a 1,4,8-trien-11β-ol, also gave equilenin (**101**), which was eventually converted into equilin (**102**).

19-Norsteroids from C-19 Functionalized Intermediates. The spectacular progress achieved in the various intramolecular functionalizations of the C-19 methyl group of steroids came as a result of pioneering work on photolytic hydrogen abstraction from nonactivated carbon atoms (the Barton reaction (87)), judicious application of ether formation by treatment of alcohols with lead tetraacetate and excess iodine (the hypoiodite reaction (88)), and related work by Bowers and co-workers (89).

A summary (90) of the more important processes, leading from the less expensive androstenes to the biologically more desirable structures (**103**) and (**104**) (partially shown) is illustrated in Scheme 11. (Courtesy Verlag Chemie GmbH, Gy.)

This approach is applicable to the more complex 6-dehydro-17-acetoxy-19-nor-progesterone (**107**), starting with 17-acetoxypregnenolone (**105**) (91), as shown in Scheme 12.

Scheme 12

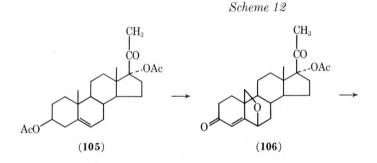

(**105**)   (**106**)

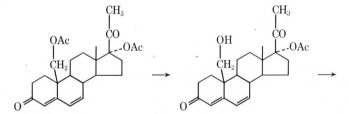

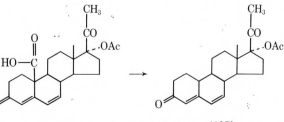

(**107**)

An approx 32% yield of (**107**) from (**106**) was achieved when the intermediates were processed without purification.

The chemical accessibility of 19-hydroxysteroids has given new impetus to a method of aromatization investigated earlier (92), the use of microorganisms. Thus, in 1965, Sih and Wang (24) described the microbiological side-chain degradation and aromatization of 3β-acetoxy-19-hydroxycholest-5-ene (**108**) to estrone (**109**) in a yield over 70%.

This combination of chemical and microbiological steps represents a long-sought economical conversion of the abundantly available cholesterol into 19-norsteroids.

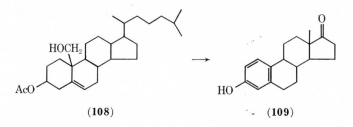

(**108**)   (**109**)

Another example of a novel microbiological degradation is the isolation of ca 65% of androst-4-ene-3,16-dione (**111**) after incubation of the readily available diosgenone (**110**) with *Fusarium solanii* (93).

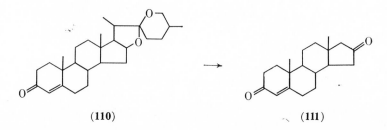

(**110**)   (**111**)

It is too early to judge the economical importance of these new microbial processes, but for those who can produce the 19-hydroxylated intermediates efficiently the final steps by the use of microorganisms do present a realistic alternative to the purely chemical routes to 19-norsteroids.

2. TOTAL SYNTHESIS (90,94,95)

Since the time of the elucidation of the structure of the steroid ring system in 1932 major consideration has been given to problems of total synthesis. This task presented not only a formidable intellectual challenge, but could also fulfill an economic need— namely, independence from natural sources, which not only might be limited, but also subject to other variables, such as seasonal, climatic, and political factors.

Aromatic Steroid Systems. At the outset, because of the stereochemical complexity of the saturated steroid structure (cholesterol has nine asymmetric centers and 256 racemates are theoretically possible), attention was focused on the stereochemically simpler substances, equilenin (**101**) (two asymmetric centers) and estrone (**109**) (four asymmetric centers). The synthesis of *d*-equilenin, the first synthesis of a naturally occurring steroid, was achieved in 1939 by Bachmann, Cole, and Wilds (96) from the known tricyclic ketone (**112**) (97) (see Scheme 13). Reduction of unsaturated acid (**117**) produced nearly equivalent amounts of racemates (**118a**) and (**118b**), the latter leading to equilenin and the former to isoequilenin.

Scheme 13

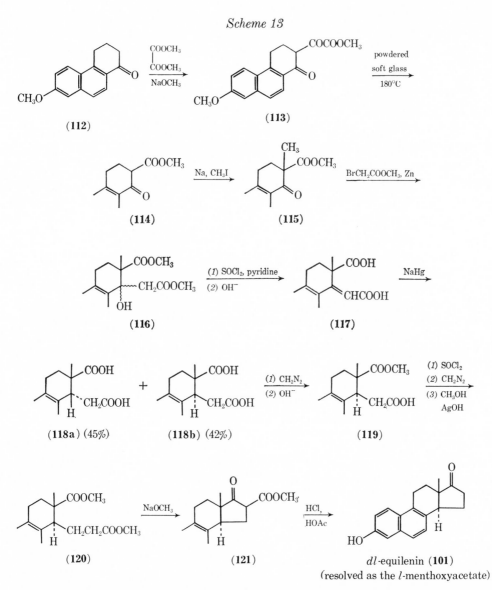

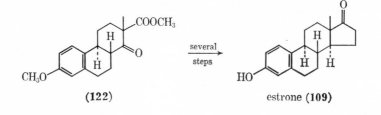

Proceeding from the same tricyclic ketone (**112**), Johnson and co-workers completed two alternative syntheses of equilenin, characterized by greater stereospecificity than the original synthesis and published in 1945 (98) and 1950 (99). The first synthesis of *d*-estrone (**109**) was accomplished by Anner and Miescher in 1948 (100), who succeeded in crystallizing three of the four racemates of the previously prepared tricyclic keto ester (**122**). One of these (isomer A), when put through the Bachmann ring-D procedure (see Scheme 13) led to *dl*-estrone (**109**) (resolved as the 1-menthoxyacetate) and *dl*-14-isoestrone.

Three additional syntheses of estrone (see also Vol. 11, p. 112) have been reported by Johnson et al. (101). As a result of the efforts of Bachmann (102), Miescher (100), and Johnson (103) all eight possible racemates of the estrone structure have been prepared. A number of relatively brief and efficient routes to estrone have been developed which are discussed below.

Saturated Steroid Systems. In 1951 two syntheses of the saturated steroid ring system were achieved by groups headed by Sir Robert Robinson (104) and R. B. Woodward (105), respectively. The *Robinson synthesis* marked the culmination of his pioneering efforts in this field which led inter al. to the key method of constructing cyclohexenone systems (Michael condensation of an enolate anion with an alkyl vinyl ketone or the equivalent Mannich base, and base-catalyzed cyclization of the resultant 1,5-diketone) (106). He also developed the use of removable blocking groups, such

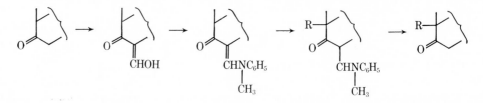

as the methylanilinomethylene group, for directing alkylation of ketones to the less favored site (107), and was responsible for an ingenious synthesis of *dl*-isoequilenin (108).

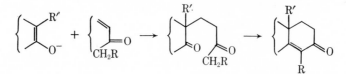

Scheme 14

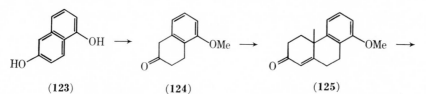

(123)   (124)   (125)

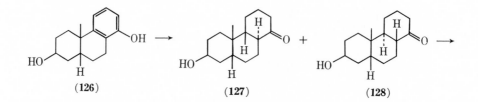

(126)   (127)   (128)

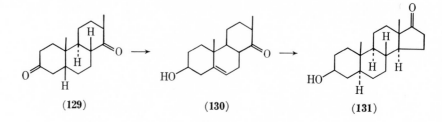

(129)   (130)   (131)

Starting from 1,6-dihydroxynaphthalene the Robinson synthesis led to the tricyclic diol (**126**), as shown in Scheme 14. Hydrogenation of the aromatic ring of (**126**) gave a mixture of the *cis, syn, trans* (**127**) and *cis, anti, trans* (**128**) ketones, in which the former predominated. Resolution of (**128**) and conversion to the tricyclic dione (**129**) (Reich diketone), derived from desoxycholic acid, proved that (**128**) in fact has the correct stereochemistry. The dione (**129**) was converted into (**130**) (Köster-Logemann ketone), derived from cholesterol. Application of the Bachmann ring-D sequence to (**130**) then led to authentic 3β-hydroxyandrostan-17-one (epiandrosterone) (**131**). Because of the numerous interrelations of steroid chemistry this was equivalent

Scheme 15

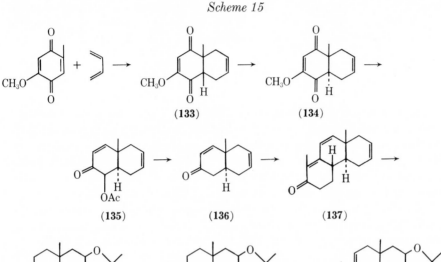

(**133**)   (**134**)

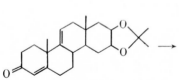

(**135**)   (**136**)   (**137**)

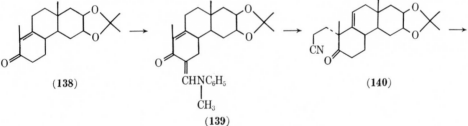

(**138**)   (**139**)   (**140**)

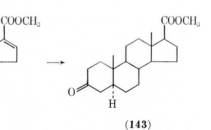

(**141**)   (**142**)   (**143**)

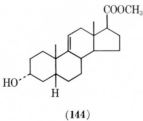

(**144**)

to the synthesis of other androstanes and pregnanes, such as testosterone, progesterone, 11-desoxycorticosterone, etc.

The Robinson synthesis, as well as most of the earlier routes to estrone and equilenin, were of the ABC → D type in which the elements of ring D were added to a tricyclic species corresponding to rings A, B, and C. The *Woodward synthesis* (see Scheme 15) involved a CD → B → A sequence and marked the first successful use of the Diels-Alder reaction in steroid synthesis. An early attempted route to the estrone structure using unsymmetrical reactants failed because the isolated adduct had the methyl "down" structure (**132**) (109).

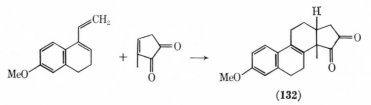

(**132**)

This type of structural ambiguity was avoided by Woodward et al. by having one of the reactants symmetrical. The synthesis led to *dl*-methyl 3-oxoetia-4,9(11),16-trienate (**142**), resolved by reduction to a 3β-ol–3α-ol mixture from which the +β-ol was obtained by precipitation with digitonin. Back oxidation gave +(**142**) (identical with a naturally derived sample) which was interrelated via (**143**) with ring C-saturated androstanes and pregnanes, and via the 9(11)-unsaturated ester (**144**), to ring C-substituted steroids, in particular to cortisone. All steps in which an asymmetric center was generated occurred stereoselectively in the desired sense except for the base-catalyzed addition of acrylonitrile to (**139**), in which the required isomer (**140**) was the minor component. However, it was shown later that by inverting the order of addition of the 1-carbon and 3-carbon units the desired stereochemistry could be made to predominate (110,110a).

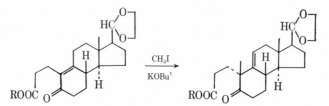

Syntheses of the C-27 sterols (eg cholestanol, cholesterol) were achieved by the Robinson and Woodward groups by the reaction of 3β-hydroxypregnan-20-one with isohexylmagnesium bromide, followed by dehydration and hydrogenation.

A comparatively simple route to *dl-epiandrosterone* (**131**) was described by Johnson et al. in 1953 (111) (see Scheme 16). 5-Methoxy-2-tetralone, on successive annelation with 1-diethylamino-3-pentanone and methyl vinyl ketone, gave the tetracyclic ketone (**146**) in which only one asymmetric center is present. The condensations followed a single pathway determined by anion stabilization via conjugation with the aromatic ring. Complete reduction of (**146**) with lithium and ethanol in liquid ammonia followed by catalytic hydrogenation led to the thermodynamically most favored *trans,anti,trans* system (**147**) in which six new asymmetric centers with the correct stereochemistry have been introduced. Conversion of (**147**) to the furfurylidene derivative (**148**) and methylation led to a mixture of (**149**) and its 13α-methyl isomeride in which the latter predominated due to the greater accessibility of the α side of C-13 in the intermediate enolate anion. The required D-ring cyclopentanone system (**131**) was generated from (**149**) by ozonization to the diacid (**150**), and Dieckmann condensation of the corresponding diester followed by hydrolysis and decarboxylation.

Scheme 16

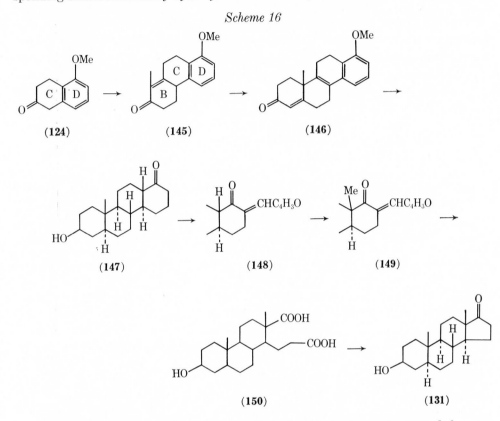

Cortisone. The great interest in cortical steroids in the early 1950s led to two total syntheses of cortisone (see also Hormones (Adrenal-cortical)). Barkley et al. at Monsanto Chemical Co. modified the Woodward synthesis into a direct synthesis (110,112) and Sarett and his colleagues at Merck and Co. developed a new route, shown in Scheme 17, characterized by greater stereospecificity in the introduction of asymmetric centers than obtained in previous steroid syntheses (113).

The synthesis followed the BC → ABC → ABCD route. The Diels-Alder adduct (**151**) of ethoxypentadiene and benzoquinone was hydrogenated, reduced with lithium aluminum hydride, and treated with acid to give the keto diol (**153**). The indicated stereochemistry of (**152**), (**153**), and the tricyclic keto diol (**154**) is determined by the *cis*-B/C-ring junction generated in the Diels-Alder reaction. Ketalization of the ring A carbonyl group, selective oxidation of the less hindered hydroxyl group, and equilibration then gave the *trans*-B/C ketol (**155**). Successive alkylation with methyl iodide and methyallyl iodide gave the β-methyl, α-methallyl compound (**156**), the 11β-hydroxyl group effectively blocking β-side reagent approach at C-13. Resolution was carried out on the glyoxylic acid (**163**) and further known transformations led to *cortisone acetate* (**166**).

Scheme 17

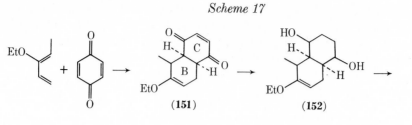

(151)　　(152)

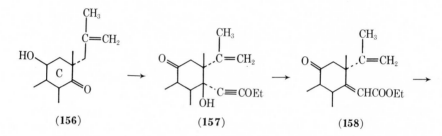

(153)　　(154)　　(155)

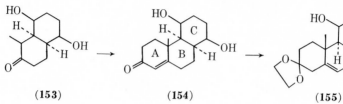

(156)　　(157)　　(158)

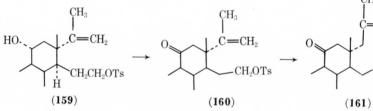

(159)　　(160)　　(161)

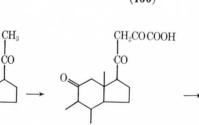

(162)　　(163)　　(164)

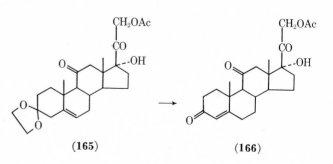

(165)　　(166)

Aldosterone (see also Hormones (Adrenal-cortical)). The tricyclic ketone (155) was also utilized in a number of routes to the mineralocorticoid hormone, aldosterone (169), by Wettstein and his associates (114). An additional total synthesis of aldosterone from the hydrochrysene ketone (146) was developed by Johnson (115). Aldosterone was subsequently also obtained by a novel three-step process from corticosterone developed by Barton et al. (116), in which the key reaction was the photolytic conversion of the 11β-nitrite (167) to aldosterone-18-oxime (168). Other radical transfer routes from 20β-hydroxy intermediates were developed by Jeger and Wettstein and their associates (117).

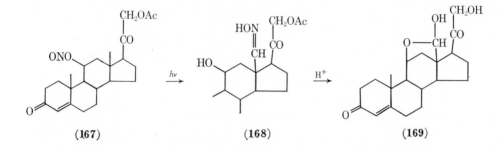

(167)   (168)   (169)

Practical Routes to 19-Nor Systems. The above total syntheses, although marked by the increasing use of ingenious selective and stereospecific reactions, never became commercially practicable. To compete with partial synthesis a total synthesis should be characterized by brevity, stereospecificity, and early generation of optical activity (chirality), either by resolution or asymmetric synthesis from symmetrical (prochiral) precursors. In the last several years, with the greatly increased demand for 19-nor-steroids as oral contraceptive agents, a number of relatively simple routes to estrane and modified gonane systems have been developed (90,95) of which two, those of Velluz et al. (118) (Scheme 18) and Torgov et al. (119) (Scheme 19), appear to have the greatest industrial potential.

Both routes utilize 2-methylcyclopentane-1,3-dione (171) as a preformed ring-D moiety. This substance, as well as its 2-alkyl analogs, is now readily available (120). The use of (171) stems from the earlier somewhat analogous use of 2-methylcyclohexane-1,3-dione in a synthesis of D-homosteroids by Miescher et al. (121).

The *Velluz process* (Scheme 18) effectively incorporates features of previous syntheses in a novel manner, particularly the use of methyl 5-oxo-6-heptenoate (170) (compare references 110 and 121) in the initial annelation reaction and the use of Grignard addition to the enol lactone (174) to complete the elements of rings A and B (compare reference 105). Compound (175) is a versatile intermediate which has been converted into A-aromatic (122), 19-nor (123), and 13-methylsteroids, eg, cortisone (124). However, the degree of stereospecificity of the methylation (175) → (180) has recently been questioned (125). 10-Methylsteroids have also been obtained from 5(10)-dehydro-19-norsteroids via carbenoid addition to the double bond (126,209).

Conventional optical resolution had originally been carried out by the Velluz group on (172) (Scheme 18) with the inevitable loss of one isomer. However, microbiological reduction of the symmetrical cyclopentandione (181)—the Michael adduct of (170) and (171)—with *Rhizopus arrhizus* led stereospecifically to the optically active ketol (182) in which both asymmetric centers possess the desired chirality (127).

Scheme 18

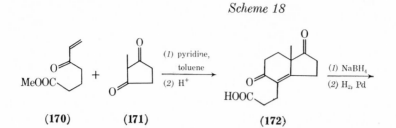

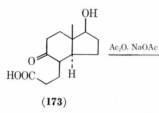

(**170**)   (**171**)   (**172**)

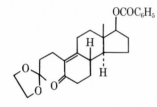

(**173**)

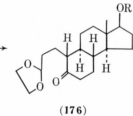

(**174**)

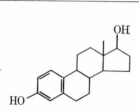

(**175**)

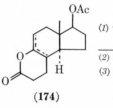

(**176**)

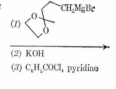

(**177**)

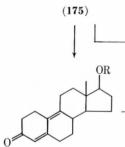

(**178**)

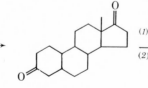

(**179**)

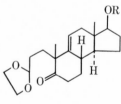

(**180**)

cortisone

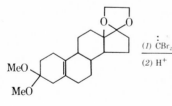

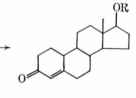

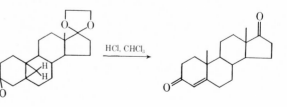

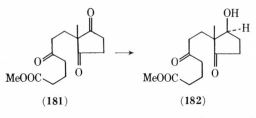

(181)   (182)

The *Torgov synthesis* (Scheme 19) leads directly to A-aromatic steroids transformable by Birch reduction (128) (see also Vol. 6, pp. 63, 65), to 19-nor-Δ4 or Δ5(10)-en-3-ones.   Originally (129) 2-methylcyclohexane-1,3-dione was utilized as the ring-D moiety and the synthesis led to D-homoestrone methyl ether.   The D ring of the latter was then contracted by oxidation of the furfurylidene derivative and cyclization of the derived diester by a procedure of Johnson (111).   Subsequently (in 1963) five research groups successfully utilized 2-methyl-cyclopentane-1,3-dione as the D-ring component (130,130a).   The intermediate estrapentaene (**186**) had previously been obtained by cyclodehydration of (**188a**) and converted to estrone by Hughes and Smith (130a,131).

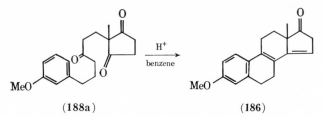

(188a)   (186)

Scheme 19

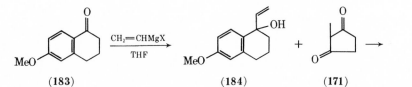

(183)   (184)   (171)

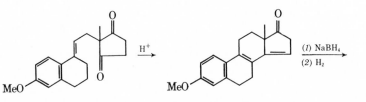

(185)   (186)

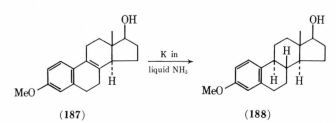

(187)   (188)

The mechanism of the key step, the condensation of vinyl carbinol (**184**) with 2-alkyl-1,3-diones, originally believed to be base-catalyzed (129,132), was shown, in fact, to be catalyzed by the acidic 1,3-dione component (133).   Mechanistic considerations led to a generally superior modification involving use of the isothiuronium salt (189) derived from (184) in the coupling reaction.

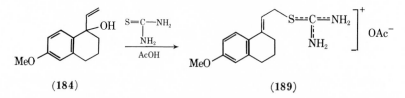

(184)   (189)

This modification has been utilized as well in syntheses of bisdehydrodoisynolic acid (134), 13-amino-19-norsteroids (135), and A-nor-1-thio-3-azasteroids (136). In accord with the acid-catalysis mechanism it was possible to combine both the condensation and ring-closure steps. Vinyl carbinol (184) and 2-methylcyclopentane-1,3-dione (171) in hot acetic acid–xylene produced the estrapentaene (186) directly (133).

The symmetrical tricyclic dione (185) has proved to be a fruitful substrate for asymmetric operations to produce optically active intermediates without isomer loss as in conventional optical resolution.

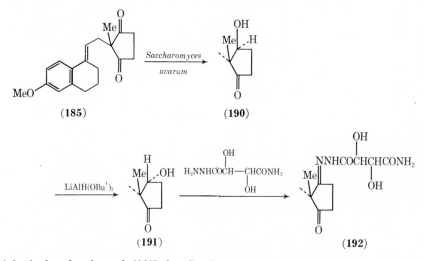

Microbiological reduction of (185) by *Saccharomyces uvarum* gave primarily an optically active ketol (190) (methyl, OH-*cis*) which led to natural estradiol (137). Chemical reduction of (185) with lithium aluminum tri-*tert*-butoxide was essentially stereospecific, occurring from the less hindered side under reagent-approach control. Resolution of the racemic ketol product (191) via the derived hemisuccinate gave the optically active ketol (191) (methyl, OH-*trans*) which led to natural 17-isoestradiol and estrone (133,138). The enantiomeric ketol could be reconverted to dione (185) by oxidation and therefore recycled. Microbiological reduction of (185) with *Bacillus thuringiensis* occurred in the same *trans* sense but produced only the useless enantiomer of ketol (191) (137). Derivatization of dione (185) with optically active tartramic hydrazide led to the optically active derivative (192) (139). Although reaction occurs at either carbonyl group the equilibrium is displaced in favor of (192) because of its greater insolubility. Further treatment of (192) gave estradiol.

By utilizing 2-substituted cyclopentane-1,3-diones it has been possible to obtain a variety of C-13-substituted analogs of various well-known C-13-methyl-19-norsteroids.

These include the 13-alkyl (140,141), 13-phenyl (142), and 13-amino (135) analogs. The 13-ethyl analog, norgestrel (**193**), is a potent progestational agent currently (1969) being produced commercially by total synthesis.

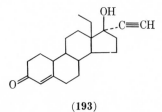

(**193**)

Recent developments in the total synthesis of steroids include a novel annelation procedure involving isoxazole intermediates developed by Stork and associates (125) which has been applied in new syntheses of *dl*-D-homotestosterone (**199**) and *dl*-progesterone (**200**), as shown in Scheme 20. Introduction of the C-10 β-methyl group by reductive alkylation ((**197**) → (**198**)) was completely stereospecific in contrast to earlier methods (110,124).

Scheme 20

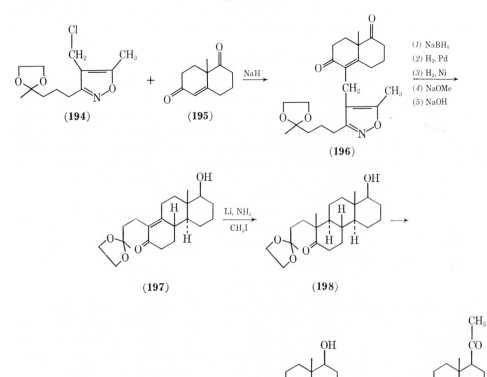

The polyene cyclization procedures of Johnson et al. have produced steroid systems stereospecifically in laboratory simulation of the biogenetic process (see under Biosynthesis, section I), including an efficient synthesis of *dl*-16-dehydroprogesterone (**203**) (143).

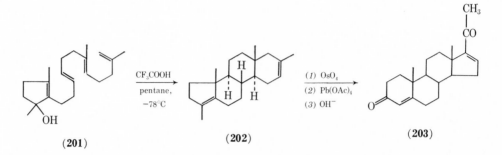

(**201**)   (**202**)   (**203**)

Space limitation prevents discussion of the total syntheses of lanosterol (Woodward, Barton, et al. (144)), the steroidal sapogenin tigogenin (**28**) (see section II.2) (Sondheimer et al. (145,146)), the cardenolide digitoxigenin (**58**), (section II.4) (Sondheimer et al.; Engel et al. (60)), and a number of steroid alkaloids (see section II.3), including conessine (**39**) (Johnson, Stork, Nagata (45)), jervine (**53**) (Masamune (147)), veratramine (**54**) (Johnson (148)), and samandarine (**57**) (57). For syntheses of the insect molting hormone ecdysone, see section II.5.

IV. Modified Steroids

The history of the anti-inflammatory drugs has shown that chemical modifications of the naturally occurring adrenocorticoids have led to new drugs with increased or advantageously modified activities (1a,1b) (see also Hormones (Adrenal-cortical)). In the 1960s attempts increased to prepare better and newer analogs not only of the corticoids but also of many other biologically active types of steroids. Since it is not possible to list all the new chemical modifications only the more significant ones are described here. Emphasis has been placed on novel structural types (differing from the more conventional modifications) which are obtained by methylation or fluorination at different points of the skeleton (see also Vol. 11, pp. 87–91, especially structures (**44**), (**51**), and (**53**), and various examples in Table 2). While biological activities are reported whenever possible, the steroids described below are classified according to their chemical structures.

1. APPENDED HETEROCYCLES

a. **Fused Ring Structures.** Steroids, having a heterocyclic ring attached to the carbocyclic nucleus, have gained importance following the discovery that androstano-[3,2-*c*]pyrazoles (149) exhibit good anabolic effects with reduced androgenicity; and the disclosure (150) that fusion of a phenyl-substituted pyrazole to that same position of certain corticoids resulted in much enhanced anti-inflammatory activities.

Clinton and co-workers (149) have found that the formylation product (**205**) of a 3-ketoandrostane (**204**) reacted easily with hydrazine to yield 17β-hydroxy-17α-methylandrostano [3,2-*c*]pyrazole (stanozolol) (see also Vol. 11, pp. 102 and 105), which has since been introduced into medical practice.

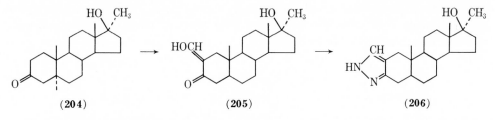

(204)   (205)   (206)

Subsequently, these authors have effected the same transformations with androstanes having double bonds in the 4 or in the 4 and 6 positions, respectively, and also
with 19-nor analogs. Regarding the reaction mechanism, it is of interest that the
formylation of A/B-*cis*-3-ketosteroids also yields predominantly the 2-hydroxymethyl-
ene derivatives (151) and, consequently, also A/B-*cis*[3,2-*c*]pyrazoles, even though
the normal enolization of A/B-*cis*-3-ketosteroids is toward C-4. Scheme 21 illustrates
these relationships and the transformations used to prove them.

Scheme 21

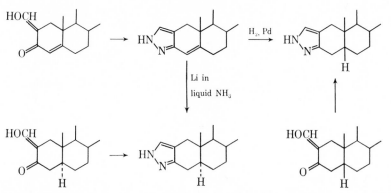

The Merck group (150) has prepared the 2′-phenyl analogs of a series of corticoids
and found that they considerably enhanced the anti-inflammatory activity of the parent steroids. They obtained the 2′-phenyl derivative (207), the most powerful anti-
inflammatory steroid ever described with an activity 2000 times that of cortisol. It is
interesting to note that moving the phenyl group to the 1′ position, as in (208), causes
a very sharp drop in activity (152).

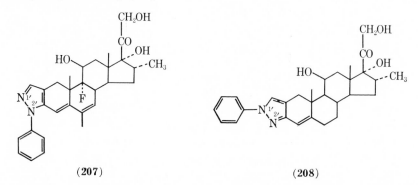

(207)   (208)

Many other interesting heterocycles appended to the A ring of steroids have been
described. While the isoxazoles (209) were similar to the pyrazoles in the androstene

series (149), they were inactive in the corticoid series (153). The Merck group also prepared compounds of partial structures (**209**)–(**213**) in the cortical series, which showed varying degrees of activity (153).

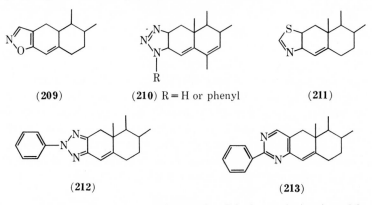

(**209**)   (**210**) R = H or phenyl   (**211**)

(**212**)   (**213**)

Fused pyrimidines were also investigated by Zderic et al. (154) and by Ruggieri and Gandolfi (155); the latter also prepared bisheterocyclic steroids, eg (**214**), shown in Scheme 22. Others (156) have fused diazaheterocycles to the A ring of estrone, as in (**215**); even polycycles have been appended to saturated A rings, as in (**216**) and (**217**). The variations have by no means been limited to the A ring of the steroid molecule, as structures (**218**)–(**221**) exemplify (see Scheme 22). For various methods of preparation and many further examples, see reference 157.

Scheme 22

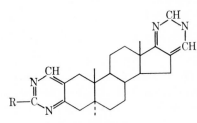

(**214**)   (**215**)

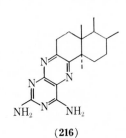

(**216**)   (**217**)

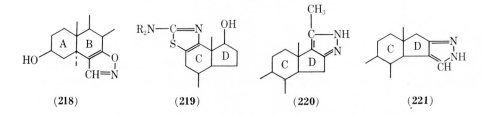

(**218**)   (**219**)   (**220**)   (**221**)

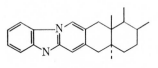

b. **Spiro Structures.** Steroids having heteroatom-containing rings that are attached by a spiro structure deserve special mention. When dihydrotestosterone is reacted with dimethylsulfonium methylide it gives the β-epoxide (**222**); upon reaction with dimethylsulfoxonium methylide (158), however, the isomeric α-oxide is obtained.

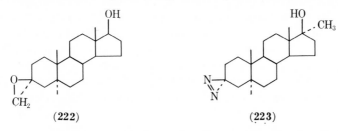

(222)   (223)

Another spiro structure attached to the C-3 position is the diaziridine (**223**) which is reported (159) to exhibit a favorable anabolic-to-androgenic ratio. Its preparation involves reaction of the corresponding C-3 ketone with ammonia and hydroxylamine-o-sulfonic acid.

Spiro derivatives attached to the C-17 position have gained considerable importance. This is due to the discovery (160) that 3-(3-keto-17β-hydroxyandrost-4-en-17α-yl)propanoic acid lactone (**226**) blocked the effect of aldosterone when given to rats. The ensuing modifications of this molecule (161) resulted in the more potent and orally active spironolactone (**227**), Aldactone (registered trademark Searle & Co.), a clinically useful aldosterone antagonist causing sodium diuresis without potassium excretion. The chemical reactions leading to this class of compounds are shown in Scheme 23.

Scheme 23

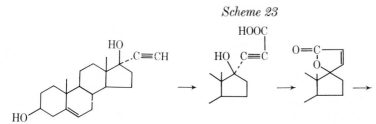

(224)

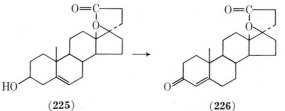

(225)   (226)

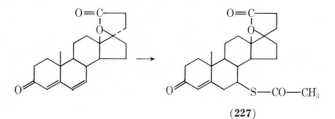

(227)

Carbonation of the Grignard derivative of (**224**) gave the desired acetylenic acid, which was partially hydrogenated, cyclized, and again hydrogenated selectively to the spironolactone (**225**). Oppenauer oxidation yielded (**226**), which was dehydrogenated with chloranil; thiolacetic acid was added selectively to obtain Aldactone (**227**).

A simplified structure (**232**), possessing about the same oral activity in rats as (**227**), was described by Arth and co-workers (162). Elaboration of the spiroxenone ring was achieved by reacting the Grignard reagent prepared from the tetrahydropyranyl (THP) ether of propargyl alcohol with dehydroepiandrosterone (**228**) and selectively hydrogenating the acetylenic triple bond of (**229**). The obtained product was oxidized by the Oppenauer method to (**230**), the THP protecting group removed, and the spiroether (**231**) formed by treatment with toluenesulfonyl chloride, as shown in Scheme 24.

Scheme 24

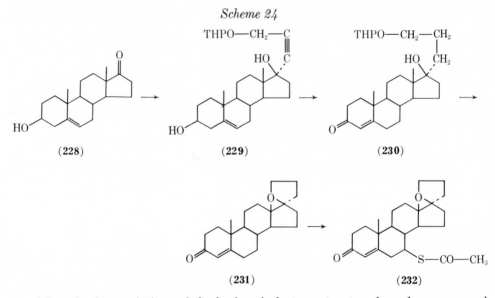

(**228**)   (**229**)   (**230**)

(**231**)   (**232**)

Many further variations of the basic spirolactone structure have been prepared, notably the 5-membered lactone (**233**) having an inverted configuration (163); the 6-membered lactone (**234**) (161); the 5-membered lactam (**235**) by two groups working independently (164,165); and other spiroethers, eg (**236**), with a 4-membered ring (166), but none of these have gained any significance (167).

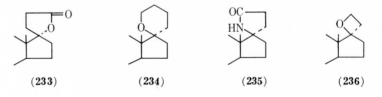

(**233**)   (**234**)   (**235**)   (**236**)

2. STEROIDS WITH A SKELETAL HETEROATOM

This class of modified steroids contains structures in which one or several carbon atoms of the steroid carbon skeleton have been replaced by heteroatoms. Although medicinal success has only been modest, compared to the huge efforts expanded in this field, research along these lines continues unabatedly. Because of chemical considerations, this class is discussed in two parts, according to methods of preparation.

a. **By Total Synthesis.**   Recent advances in the total synthesis of 19-norsteroids
(see section II.2) have been successfully adapted to the preparation of steroids with a
heteroatom in the 6 position.   Thus, in 1962 Huisman and co-workers (168) have
described the synthesis of 6-azaestrone (**241**) (see Scheme 25) from 7-methoxy-1,2,3,4-
tetrahydro-*N*-tosylquinolone (**237**) (itself prepared in four steps from methoxyaniline)
in a sequence that closely follows the general outline of the Torgov-type estrone syntheses (130) (see Scheme 19).   After sodium borohydride reduction of the C-17 ketone
(**238**), hydrogenation was stereospecific, yielding mostly the C/D-*trans* isomer (**239**),
whose structure was easily determined by correlation of NMR data with those of the
carbocyclic series.

Scheme 25

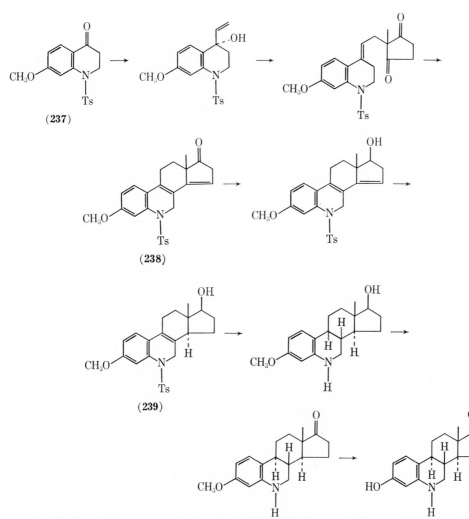

Birch reduction gave a mixture of isomers which were separated after Oppenauer
oxidation at the C-17 ketone stage.   The B/C *trans* juncture of the major isomer (**240**)

was inferred from many analogies and relevant physicochemical data. Demethylation yielded 6-azaestrone (**241**).

6-Azaequilenin (**243**), which had previously been prepared by Burckhalter and Watanabe (169), was obtained by Huisman (170) from the alcohol (**239**) by oxidative detosylation to (**242**) and two additional, conventional steps.

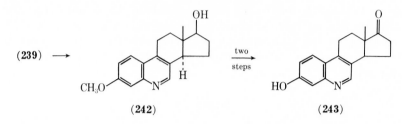

(239) ⟶

(242)   (243)

A very similar sequence was published almost simultaneously by Smith and co-workers (171). The groups of both Huisman and Smith have subsequently published (172) related total syntheses leading to 3-methoxy-6-oxaestrone (**244**) (where X = O) and 3-methoxy-6-thioestrone (**244a**) (where X = S), as well as 3-ethoxy-4-azaestrone (**245**).

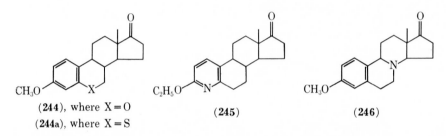

(**244**), where X = O
(**244a**), where X = S

(**245**)   (**246**)

Especially in the estrogen series, virtually every carbon atom has been replaced by nitrogen. 3-Methoxy-8-azaestrone (**246**) is typical for those compounds in which the nitrogen atom is common to two rings.

Scheme 26

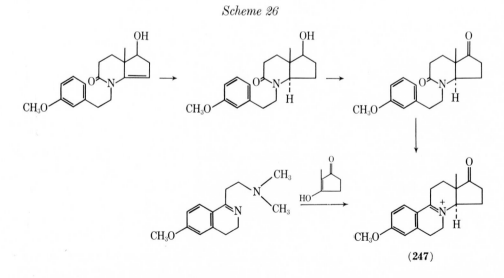

(247)

Two different approaches to 3-methoxy-8-azaestrone (**246**) are shown in Scheme 26. In the first synthesis (173) rings C and D are prepared first and cyclization of ring

B is the last step; the second approach (174) starts with the preformed AB ring system. Hydrogenation of compound (**247**) gave the desired 3-methoxy-8-azaestrone.

The latter approach has been used by Birch and Subba Rao (175) for the synthesis of 13-aza-18-norequilenin (**248**), as shown in Scheme 27.

Scheme 27

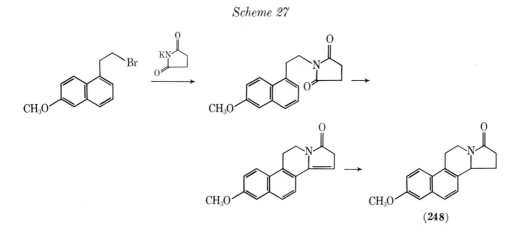

Syntheses of 8,13-diazasteroids (**249**), ie structures containing two nitrogen atoms common to three rings, have been published from two different laboratories (176).

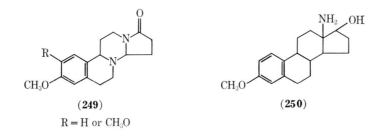

(**249**)

R = H or CH₃O

(**250**)

A structure formally considered to be a C-18 azasteroid, 13-amino-18-norestradiol-3-methyl ether (**250**), was prepared (177) in 1968 by a total synthesis similar to that of estrone.

b. **By Partial Synthesis.** The partial synthesis of compounds in which a carbon atom of the steroidal ring structure is to be replaced by a heteroatom, necessitates the following operations: (a) opening of the designated ring, (b) insertion of the heteroatom, and (c) recyclization with or without ring enlargement. In the following brief review of these steps (178), only the most typical examples are considered.

When Baeyer-Villiger-type oxidations are used, as in the case of *saturated ketones*, all three operations are accomplished in one step, eg with peracetic acid and an acid catalyst, as in the examples (179,180) shown below.

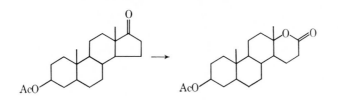

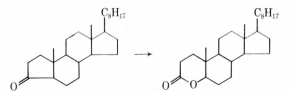

The obvious drawbacks are the rather drastic conditions, as well as the necessarily occurring ring enlargement. Somewhat similar in applicability, as well as in disadvantages, is the Beckmann rearrangement of ketoximes for the insertion of nitrogen atoms (181).

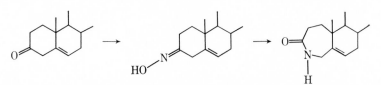

The Schmidt reaction has also been utilized (182) in a similar, but single-step process.

Unsaturated ketones, eg (**251**), can be cleaved by ozonization, followed by oxidation to the new ketoacids (**252**); the latter are versatile intermediates, allowing cyclization (183) to enol lactones (**253**) or insertion of nitrogen, using ammonia directly or via the corresponding oximes (**254**) by reductive cyclization. These reactions (184,185) yield unsaturated (**255**) and saturated (**256**), lactams, respectively, as shown in Scheme 28.

Scheme 28

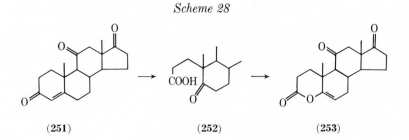

(**251**)   (**252**)   (**253**)

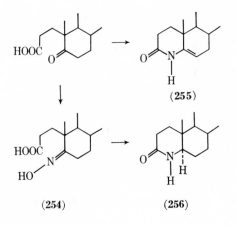

(**254**)   (**256**)

Secoacid–aldehydes are another useful class of intermediates. Prepared, eg, from enol acetates, they may undergo quite a variety of transformations, leading to a multitude of possible products. This is well illustrated in a recent paper by Baran (186), which describes the following reactions:

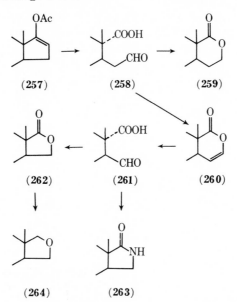

Ozonolysis of the enol acetate (**257**), followed by hydrolysis, yields the secoacid–aldehyde (**258**) which is reduced with sodium borohydride and the intermediate acid–alcohol cyclized to the saturated lactone (**259**). Alternatively (**258**) may be cyclized to the enol lactone (**260**) upon treatment with *p*-toluenesulfonic acid in refluxing toluene. The latter is again ozonized, and the resulting aldehyde–acid (**261**) utilized for lactonization to (**262**) or nitrogen insertion to (**263**). Just as the lactones can be reduced to cyclic ethers, eg (**264**), the lactams, in general, yield cyclic amines.

Secoacid–aldehydes prepared from α,β-unsaturated ketones proved to be important intermediates. They were utilized by Pappo and Jung (187) for the preparation of 17β-hydroxy-17α-methyl-2-oxaandrostan-3-one (**267**), which was found to be a useful anabolic agent with relatively low androgenicity. It was prepared from the 3-keto-androst-1-ene (**265**) by treatment with lead tetraacetate and reduction of the intermediate secoaldehyde (**266**) to the secoalcohol which was cyclized without isolation.

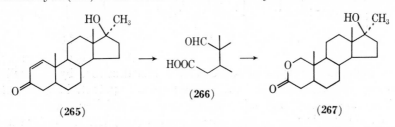

By appropriate modification of the opening of ring A between C_1 and C_2, the same authors also succeeded in preparing the 2-oxa derivatives of 17α-methyltestosterone and progesterone which retained many of the biological properties of their carboxylic progenitors.

At the same time, in an independent effort, Hirschmann and co-workers (188) had prepared 2-oxacortisol (**271**) which, however, did not gain significance as an anti-inflammatory agent. It was obtained by selective osmylation of prednisone BMD (**268**), followed by lead tetraacetate cleavage to the tricyclic ester–aldehyde (**269**) (where R = CH₃). Upon hydrolysis the sodium salt of the corresponding acid–aldehyde (**269**) (where R = Na) could be selectively reduced with sodium borohydride and cyclized to the unsaturated lactone (**270**). Removal of the protecting BMD (bis-(methylene dioxide)) group afforded 2-oxacortisol (**271**), as shown in Scheme 29.

Scheme 29

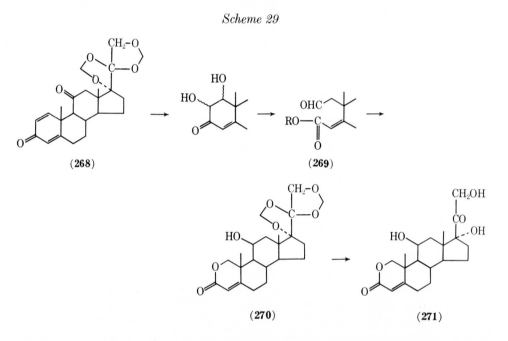

Testololactone and its Δ′ unsaturated analog have been obtained by the *micro-biological degradation of progesterone* with a variety of organisms (188a).

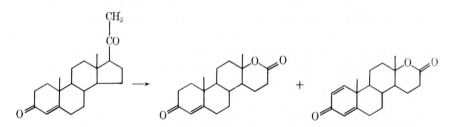

An entirely different type of azasteroid was first described by Counsell and co-workers (189), who regarded this class of compounds as potential *hypocholesterolemic agents*. They were found to inhibit endogenous cholesterol synthesis in clinical trials (190). Of the numerous aza and diazacholesterols (191) the 22,25-diaza derivative (**273**) seems to be representative, and its preparation from the readily accessible 20α-aminopregn-5-en-3β-ol-3-acetate (**272**) is shown below. The final reduction was done with lithium aluminum hydride in dioxane.

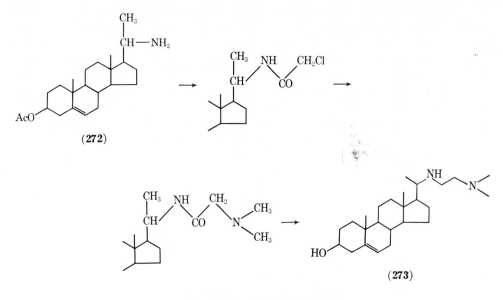

(272)

(273)

3. OTHER MODIFICATIONS

a. **Cyclopropyl Steroids.** The preparation of $3\alpha,5\alpha$-cyclosteroids (**275**) (i-steroids) by solvolysis of the appropriate cholesterol derivatives (**274**) and the subsequent transformations of i-steroids, as well as the important mechanistic implications, have been reviewed comprehensively (reference 1f, p. 1075).

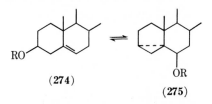

(274)

(275)

The $3\beta,5\beta$ analog (**277**) has been prepared (192) by photolysis of the diene (**276**) in ethanol. Acid treatment of (**277**) provided a good entry into the C-3-substituted A-norsteroid series (**278**).

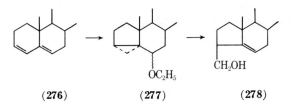

(276)

(277)

(278)

Solvolysis of the 3β-hydroxy-$\Delta5(10)$ structure (**279**) has been shown (193) to give a $3\alpha, 5\alpha$-cyclo structure (**280**) with a 10β-hydroxyl group.

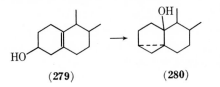

(279)

(280)

Preparations of 5α,7α-cyclosteroids (**285**) by solvolysis of, eg, cholest-4-en-7β-yl-
p-toluenesulfonate (**281**) (where R = Ts) (a pseudocholesterol) have not been successful because this homoallylic system differs in its steric environment from that of cholesterol. Once formed, however, the appropriate 5α,7α-cyclosteroid (**285**) did undergo
an acid-catalyzed rearrangement to (**281**) (where R = H). A much-improved preparation (194) of (**285**) involves hydroboration of pseudocholesterol benzoate (**281**)
(where R = Bz) to (**282**) followed by oxidation and hydrolysis to the ketoalcohol
(**283**) which gave (**284**) on treatment with 5% methanolic potassium hydroxide, and
(**285**) on reduction with lithium aluminum hydride, as shown below.

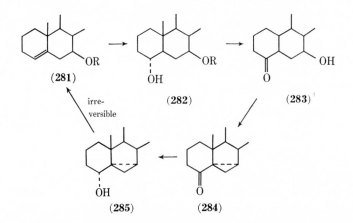

Gassman and Hymans (195) described in 1967 the preparation of the last member
of this group, a 5β,7β-cyclosteroid (**287**), again by photolysis of a diene (**286**).

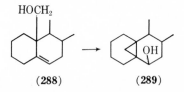

The homoallylic rearrangement of various C-19 substituted, Δ5-steroids (**288**) has
been studied by several groups (196), and it was established that the resulting products
have cyclopropyl structures, as in (**289**).

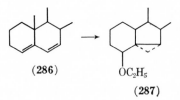

Earlier, Šorm and co-workers (197), in their investigation of aminosteroids, opened
the lactam ring of (**290**) and obtained the 13,14-cyclosteroid (**291**) (see p. 879).

A class of cyclopropylsteroids that has gained biological importance comprises the
structures in which cyclopropyl is fused to the A ring. Compounds of this type have
been investigated by Wiechert and co-workers (198).

(**290**)   (**291**)

Initially, preparation involved the selective reaction of an androsta-1,4,6-trien-3-one (**292**) with diazomethane; the pyrazoline (**293**) thus obtained was pyrolized or converted with an acidic catalyst to the desired 1α,2α-methylene compound (**294**). Later it was found that the methylene transfer reaction (199) of dimethyloxosulfonium methylide with the enone (**292**) could also be applied directly to yield (**294**).

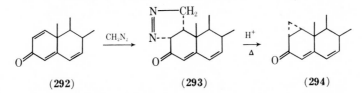

(**292**)   (**293**)   (**294**)

Biological interest has been centered on the androstene (**295**), which showed a favorable ratio of anabolic vs androgenic activity, and on the progesterone derivative Cyproterone (registered trade name, Schering A.G., Berlin) (**296**), which is a very potent antiandrogen, but which also affects libido adversely.

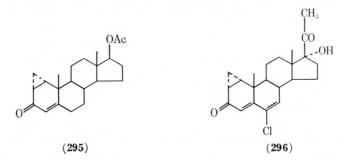

(**295**)   (**296**)

On methylene transfer, linear conjugated dienones, such as (**297**), gave the expected 6,7-methylene derivatives (**298**) and (**299**), in ratios that varied with the general structure of the steroid substrate (199).

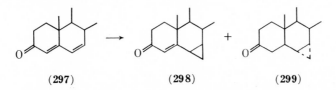

(**297**)   (**298**)   (**299**)

Further variations of cyclopropyl structure include the 1β,2β-methylenesteroids (**300**) prepared by a Simmons-Smith addition (198a), the more complex derivatives, such as a potent progestin (**301**) (198b), or the 15β,16β-methylenesteroid (**302**), for which good anabolic activity is claimed (198c).

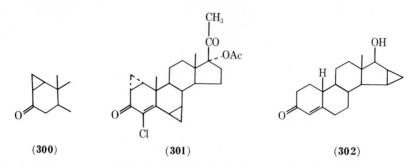

(300)   (301)   (302)

Fried and co-workers (199,199a) have performed the addition of difluoromethylene to the conjugated double bonds of enones and dienones. The required difluorocarbene is usually generated by decomposition of sodium chlorodifluoroacetate at elevated temperatures. For a detailed discussion of the stereochemistry of the adducts obtained (eg (303)–(305)) which are substituted cyclopropyl derivatives, the original publication should be consulted.

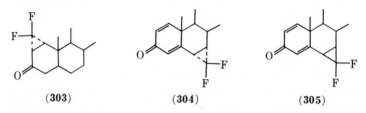

(303)   (304)   (305)

b. **Unnatural Steroids.** Steroids with unnatural configuration at the ring junctures form a broad class of compounds, loosely defined as unnatural steroids. (For a discussion of the first active steroid of unnatural configuration, Ehrenstein's 14-iso-17-iso-19-norprogesterone (19-nor-14β,17α-pregn-4-ene-3,20-dione), see Vol. 6, pp. 63 and 65). Not included are possible by-products of the total syntheses described in section III. 2.

The structures which have an inverted stereochemistry at both C-9 and C-10 are better known as "retrosteroids" and possess interesting pharmacological properties. Work in this series dates back to the irradiation of ergosterol (306), which, under photolytic conditions, yielded lumisterol$_2$ (307) with the 9β,10α structure (200). (See also section II.1.)

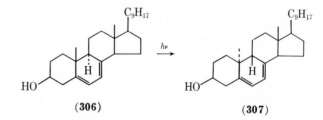

(306)   (307)

The latter served as starting material for the pioneering work of Westerhof and co-workers, who in a series of papers (201) have described their extensive investigations in this field. This work began by converting lumisterol$_2$ to a 3-keto-Δ4 structure, which they subjected to routine side-chain degradation, to obtain the retroprogesterone (308), as briefly shown in Scheme 30.

Scheme 30

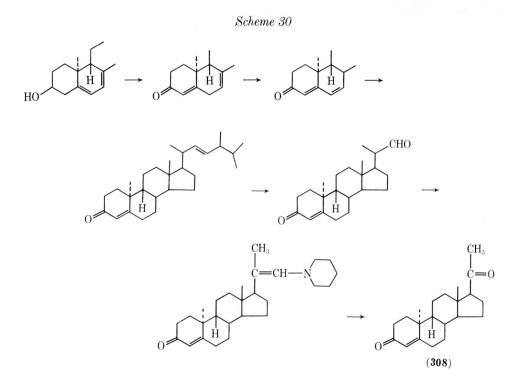

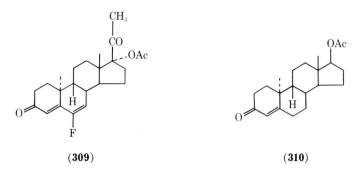

(**308**)

Hydrogesterone, the Δ6 analog of (**308**), has gained clinical acceptance as a useful progestogen and has prompted Westerhof and co-workers to repeat most of the well-known chemical transformations of the natural steroids by preparing more potent progestins, such as (**309**), and retroandrogens, such as (**310**), and, in conjunction with a Swiss group (202), to synthesize various retrocorticoids as well.

(**309**)   (**310**)

In order to overcome the limitations of the photochemically obtained starting materials, Uskokovic and co-workers (203) have described conversion of an accessible, normal steroid to a retrosteroid skeleton, shown in Scheme 31. Their work starts with the degradation of ring A of 11α-hydroxyprogesterone, via the 11-mesylate and the secoketoacid (**311**) to the tricycle (**312**). Upon reduction and partial reoxidation, ketol (**313**) was obtained; this was hydrogenated to a mixture of saturated tricycles in which the desired (**314**) predominated. A-ring annelation with methyl vinyl ketone, followed by oxidation, afforded the desired retroprogesterone (**308**). The total synthesis of the three-ring BCD intermediate (**314**) and of retroprogesterone (**308**) has also been described (204).

Scheme 31

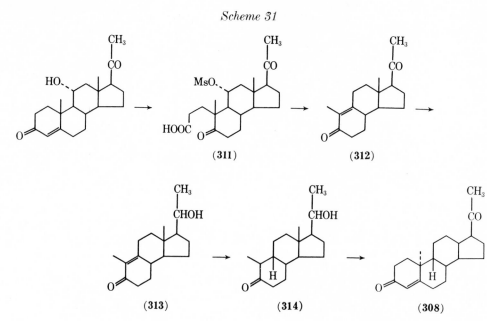

(311)   (312)

(313)   (314)   (308)

An entry into the 19-nor-retrosteroid series was provided by Smith and co-workers (205), who converted 9β-estradiol (**315**), an intermediate previously obtained via total synthesis, into 9β,10α-estr-4-en-3-one (**316**) by the following steps that closely mimic those of the natural series:

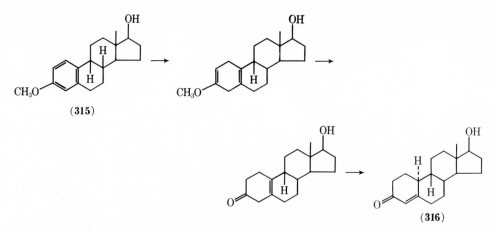

(315)

(316)

A variety of 19-norsteroids with unnatural configurations was prepared in 1968 (206) by methods similar to this sequence.

Androgens with only the configuration at C-10 inverted have been investigated by several groups. The first preparation involving a photochemical step was a lengthy one (207). Later Fishman and co-workers (208) described the chemical transformations leading from the rather difficultly accessible starting material (**317**) to 17β-hydroxy-5α,10α-androstan-3-one (**318**).

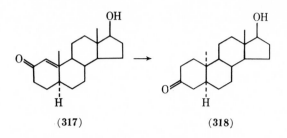

(317)   (318)

A more generally applicable method, affording 10α-testosterone (**321**), has been described by Ginsig and Cross (209). It hinges on the successful α-side methylenation of the available alcohol (**319**), by means of a controlled Simmons-Smith reaction. Base-catalyzed isomerization of the cyclopropyl ketone (**320**) (obtained after oxidation) yielded the desired (**321**).

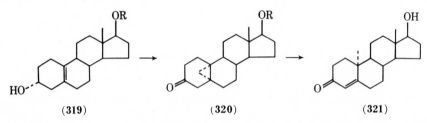

(319)   (320)   (321)

An interesting rearrangement of steroid 5,6-epoxides has been found to occur in a strongly acidic medium, yielding products with an inverted configuration, as in (**323**), at every ring juncture of the molecule (210). Although the details of the reaction mechanism need further clarification, the phenomenon, fittingly called "backbone rearrangement," and illustrated below with 5β,6β-epoxide (**322**), seems to be a general one (211). Proof of the novel structures has also been obtained (212) by the chemical synthesis of products of the type (**323**).

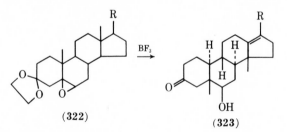

(322)   (323)

c. **Nor- and Homosteroids.** This section contains examples of various steroidlike structures prepared by ring contraction and/or expansion. Many of the compounds cited as examples have been found to possess biological activities. Also included are some recent developments in this field. An excellent treatment of the methodology and mechanism of ring contractions and expansions (1f), as well as a systematic bibliography of ring contractions (213), have been published. The synthesis (214) of A-norcortisone (**328**) is a good example of ring contraction via a benzylic acid rearrangement. The side-chain protected prednisolone (**324**) was osmylated selectively to (**325**) which on dehydration gave the diosphenol (**326**). Benzylic acid rearrangement gave (**327**) which on oxidative cleavage and dehydration, followed by removal of the BMD group, afforded the desired (**328**) devoid of significant anti-inflammatory activity.

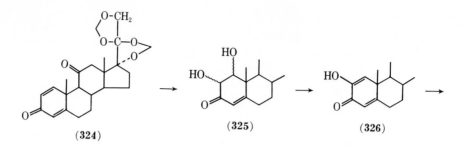

(324)   (325)   (326)

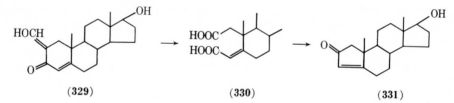

(327)   (328)

A good example of the conversion of 3-keto-Δ4-steroids into their A-nor analogs is the preparation (215) of A-nortestosterone, starting from the 2-hydroxymethylene derivative of testosterone (**329**). Selective ozonization, followed by peroxide cleavage, afforded the diacid (**330**), which after acetic anhydride treatment could be pyrolized to A-nortestosterone (**331**). The biological properties of A-nortestosterone differed from those of the parent testosterone in that the A-nor compound was only weakly androgenic and even antiandrogenic.

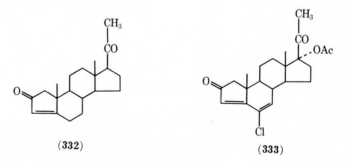

(329)   (330)   (331)

Interestingly, A-norprogesterone (**332**), prepared by the same method, proved to be nonprogestational but antiandrogenic. These unusual biological properties have stimulated further work in this field.

(332)   (333)

Thus, (**333**), whose preparation was not reported (216) until 1967, proved to be the first progestationally active compound in this series. In another development,

Jacques and Pincus (217) have described the antifertility activity of the 2,17-bis-ethynyl-A-norandrostanediol (**334**) and related structures.

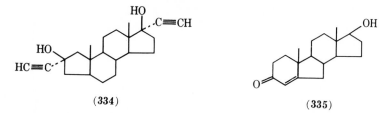

(**334**)   (**335**)

The B-nor analogs of androgens, eg (**335**), have also been investigated because of their antiandrogenic properties (218). Their preparation involves oxidative cleavage of the B ring, followed by recyclization. The B-nor-19-norsteroids (**336**) and (**337**) were prepared by total synthesis in 1968 but their biological properties have been disappointing (219).

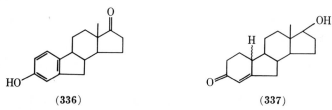

(**336**)   (**337**)

Most of the C-ring contractions of steroids are accompanied by D-ring expansion. Thus the chemically prepared C-nor-D-homosteroids mimic the structure of the naturally found alkaloids, jervine and veratramine, and their degradation products. An example is the C-nor-D-homosteroid rearrangement first described by a Merck group (220), as shown below.

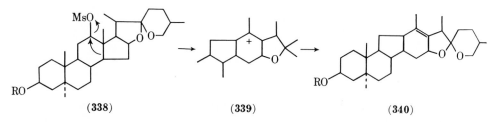

(**338**)   (**339**)   (**340**)

Solvolysis of the mesylate (**338**) with concerted movement of the C-13, C-14 bond gives the intermediate tertiary carbonium ion (**339**), which is converted into the C-nor-D-homo product (**340**) by proton loss from C-17.

Interest in C-nor-D-homosteroids has also prompted various degradative studies of the naturally occurring alkaloids having this ring system; a skeletal analog (221) of C-nor-D-homoprogesterone (**341**) and C-nor-D-homoestrone (**342**) (222) is an example of compounds prepared by suitable transformations of such degradation products.

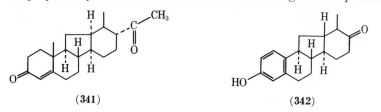

(**341**)   (**342**)

On the other hand, not only the C-nor-D-homo ring structure, but also veratramine and jervine have been prepared by ingenious total syntheses (147,148, 223).

D-Norsteroids, a class that has not attained any biological significance, have been prepared by several groups (224) according to the following general scheme, starting with a diazoketone:

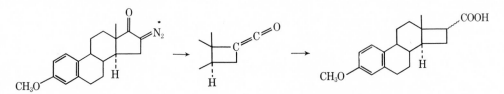

Conventional ring-expansion methods, such as reaction of ketones with diazomethane, or nitrous acid treatment of aminomethylcarbinols, have been used successfully with numerous steroid examples (1f).   More recently Birch and co-workers (225,226) have prepared A-homosteroids starting from readily available dihydroestrone derivatives, such as (**343**).

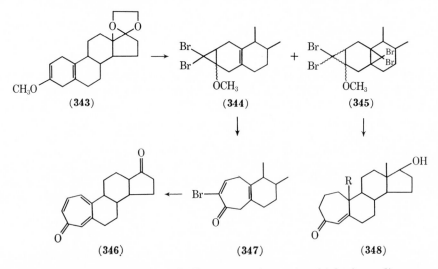

Addition of dibromocarbene to (**343**) gave a mixture in which, depending on reaction conditions, the monoadduct (**344**) or the bisadduct (**345**) predominated.   The former, upon reaction with silver salts and presumably via (**347**), gave the tropone analog (**346**) of estrone.   The bisadduct (**345**) was converted into A-homotestosterone (**348**) (where R = CH₃) in several steps.   The preparation of A-homo-19-nortestosterone (**348**) (where R = H) was accomplished in the course of another investigation (227).

Biologically active D-homo analogs, eg (**350**), of the androgenic hormones have been prepared by Demjanov rearrangement (228) of the corresponding 17-aminomethyl-17-hydroxyandrostanes (**349**) (see p. 887).

Similar treatment of the 7-cyanohydrin of androstane-3β,17β-diol-7-one diacetate (**350a**) gave a B-homoketone, eventually converted to B-homodihydrotestosterone (**350b**), which exhibited favorable anabolic/androgenic activity (228a) (see p.

D-Homoandrostane-3,17α-dione has also been obtained by total syntheses (121),

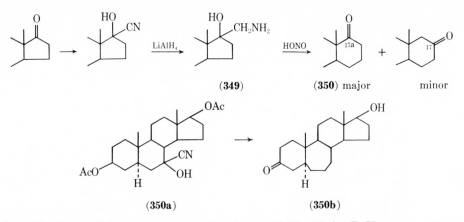

(**349**)　　　　　　(**350**) major　　　　　minor

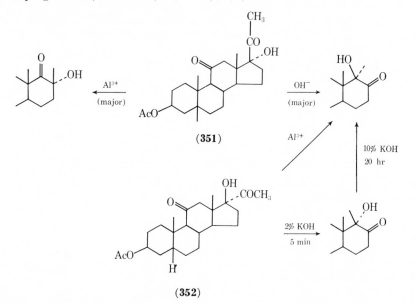

(**350a**)　　　　　　　　　　　(**350b**)

as have the 19-nor-D-homoestrogens and androgens (129, 130a). D-Homoprogesterone (229) and D-homocortisone (230) have been prepared by partial synthesis.

17-Hydroxy-20-oxopregnanes readily undergo characteristic rearrangement to D-homo systems with Lewis acid and base catalysis, as illustrated below for the 3β-acetoxy-5β-pregnane-11,20-diones (**351**) and (**352**) (1f).

(**351**)

(**352**)

The expansion of ring D with concomitant aromatization has been studied extensively by Jacques and co-workers (231). In this rearrangement 17α-ethynylcarbinols (**353**) are treated with hot formic acid to yield, via several postulated intermediates, D-homo aromatic steroids of type (**354**).

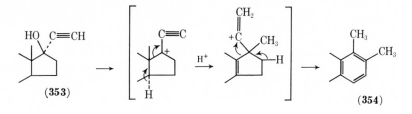

(**353**)　　　　　　　　　　　　　　　　　　　　　　(**354**)

Appendix

The use of modern physical measurements and refined methods of separation has been an important factor in the spectacular advances achieved in steroid research and technology. Conversely, development of some of these methods was stimulated by problems of steroid research, just as the steroid molecule has often served as a convenient testing ground for new physical measurements.

Nuclear magnetic resonance has become a major factor in the structure determination of steroids. Recognition of the additivity of various effects upon the chemical shift of the C-18 and C-19 methyl protons (232) has greatly contributed to the early acceptance of NMR. An authoritative book with many examples of steroids has appeared (233).

Optical rotatory dispersion (234) has played a decisive role in the recognition of stereochemical relationships and in solving conformational problems. It is properly complemented by **circular dichroism** measurements, another technique developed (235) for solving problems of steroid stereochemistry, which has, however, gained importance in other fields as well. Both methods of measurement have been very well described and exemplified by Crabbé (236).

The ever-increasing number of newly discovered and characterized natural products, many of them sterols and steroids, is witness to the wide applicability of **mass spectroscopy**. In addition, the fragmentation patterns of hundreds of known steroids have been recorded and studied. Most of the data are contained in an excellent up-to-date book by Budzikiewicz, Djerassi, and Williams (237).

None of these relatively new methods has diminished the importance of ultraviolet and infrared spectroscopy, which continue to provide useful information on structural problems.

The advantages of the newer separation techniques, such as thin-layer chromatography (238) and gas–liquid chromatography (239), were recognized early by workers in the field; these methods are widely used in research and special industrial applications.

Bibliography

"Sterols and Steroids" in *ECT* 1st ed., Vol. 12, pp. 917–947, by R. B. Turner, The Rice Institute, and L. I. Conrad, American Cholesterol Products, Inc. "Steroids" in Suppl. Vol. 1, pp. 849–888, by G. Anner and A. Wettstein, Ciba Ltd.

1. General References:
    a. L. F. Fieser and M. Fieser, *Steroids*, Reinhold Publishing Corp., New York, 1959.
        A detailed general treatise.
    b. C. W. Shoppee, *Chemistry of the Steroids*, 2nd ed., Butterworth & Co., Ltd., London, 1964.
        A detailed general treatise.
    c. W. Klyne, *The Chemistry of the Steroids*, Methuen & Co., Ltd., London, 1960.
        A nontechnical introduction.
    d. J. Jacques, H. Kagan, and G. Ourisson, *Optical Rotatory Power—Steroids*, Pergamon Press, Inc., Oxford, England, 1965.
        Data and references to 21,000 optically active steroids described up to Jan. 1, 1961, with some references to 1963.
    e. *Elsevier's Encyclopedia of Organic Chemistry*, Vol. 14 and 5 supplements, Elsevier Publishing Co., Amsterdam, 1940–1965.
        Chemistry and references to individual compounds.

f. N. L. Wendler, "Rearrangements in Steroids," in P. DeMayo, ed., *Molecular Rearrangements*, Vol. 2, Interscience Publishers, a div. of John Wiley & Sons, Inc., New York, 1964.

g. C. Djerassi, *Steroid Reactions*, Holden-Day, Inc., San Francisco, 1963.
Numerous examples of important procedures in steroid chemistry.

h. R. I. Dorfman, ed., *Methods in Hormone Research*, 5 vols., Academic Press, Inc., New York, 1962–1966.
Methods of chemical analysis and bioassay of steroids; steroid activity in animals and man.

i. N. Applezweig, *Steroid Drugs*, Vol. 1, McGraw-Hill Book Co., Inc., New York, 1962; Vol. 2, Holden-Day, Inc., San Francisco, 1964.

j. *Annual Report of the Chemical Society (London)*.

k. *Annual Reports of Medicinal Chemistry*, sponsored by the Division of Medicinal Chemistry of the American Chemical Society, Academic Press, Inc., New York.

2. International Union of Pure and Applied Chemistry, "Definitive Rules for Nomenclature of Steroids," *J. Am. Chem. Soc.* **82**, 5577 (1960); see also reference 1c, pp. 36–45.

3. Reference 1d, pp. 1a–11a.

4. IUPAC-IUB, "Revised Tentative Rules for Steroid Nomenclature," *Steroids* **13**, 277, 1961.

5. O. Diels, W. Gädke, and P. Kording, *Ann.* **459**, 1 (1927).

6. J. D. Bernal, *Chem. Ind.* **51**, 466 (1932).

7. O. Rosenheim and H. King, *Nature* **130**, 315 (1932); *Chem. Ind.* **51**, 954 (1932); **52**, 299 (1933).

8. H. Wieland and E. Dane, *Z. Physiol. Chem.* **210**, 268 (1932).

9. H. Wieland, E. Dane, and E. Scholz, *Z. Physiol. Chem.* **211**, 261 (1932). A. Windaus, *Ber.* **42**, 3770 (1909).

10. Reference 1b, pp. 247–249.

11. T. Tokuyama, J. Daly, B. Witkop, I. L. Karle, and J. Karle, *J. Am. Chem. Soc.* **90**, 1917 (1968).

12. R. B. Clayton, *Quart. Rev. (London)* **19**, 168, 201 (1965).

13. E. Stapley in P. Bernfield, ed., *Biogenesis of Natural Products*, Pergamon Press, Inc., New York, 1968.

14. E. E. van Tamelen, J. D. Willett, R. B. Clayton, and K. E. Lord, *J. Am. Chem. Soc.* **88**, 4752 (1966).

15. E. J. Corey, W. E. Russey, and P. R. Ortiz de Montellano, *J. Am. Chem. Soc.* **88**, 4750 (1966).

16. W. S. Johnson, *Accounts Chem. Res.* **1**, 1 (1968).

17. Reference 1a, pp. 341–363. Reference 1b, pp. 45–80.

18. Reference 1a, pp. 504–511.

19. A. Windaus, A. Hess, O. Rosenheim, R. Pohl, and T. A. Webster, *Chemiker Z.* **51**, 113 (1927). Reference 1a, pp. 92, 94–124.

20. Reference 1a, pp. 661–667.

21. Reference 1a, pp. 555–556.

22. M. E. Herr and F. W. Heyl, *J. Am. Chem. Soc.* **74**, 3627 (1952).

23. J. E. Huber, *Tetrahedron Letters* **1968**, 3271.

24. C. J. Sih and K. C. Wang, *J. Am Chem. Soc.* **87**, 1387 (1965). C. J. Sih, S. S. Lee, Y. Y. Tsong, K. C. Wang, and F. N. Chang, *J. Am. Chem. Soc.* **87**, 2765 (1965).

25. Reference 1a, pp. 90–168.

26. E. Havenga and J. L. M. A. Schlatmann, *Tetrahedron* **16**, 146 (1961). Reference 1a, pp. 146–150. Reference 1f, pp. 1052–1056.

27. R. B. Woodward and R. Hoffmann, *J. Am. Chem. Soc.* **87**, 395 (1965) and following communications.

27a. R. Hoffmann and R. B. Woodward, *Accounts Chem. Res.* **1**, 17 (1968).

28. J. W. Blunt, H. F. DeLuca, and H. K. Schnoes, *Chem. Commun.* **1968**, 801; *Chem. Eng. News* **46**, 21 (Aug. 5, 1968).

29. Reference 1a, pp. 364–402.

30. W. O. Godtfredsen, W. von Daehne, S. Vangedal, A. Marquet, D. Arigoni, and A. Melera, *Tetrahedron Letters* **1965**, 3505.

31. T. G. Halsall, Sir E. R. H. Jones, G. Lowe, and C. E. Newall, *Chem. Commun.* **1966**, 685.

32. S. Okuda, S. Iwasaki, M. I. Sair, Y. Machida, A. Inoue, and K. Tsuda, *Tetrahedron Letters* **1967**, 2295.

890 **STEROIDS**

33. Reference 1a, pp. 810–846; reference 1b, pp. 398–432.

34. R. E. Marker and E. Rohrmann, *J. Am. Chem. Soc.* **61,** 2072 (1939).

35. Reference 1a, pp. 818–830.

36. R. E. Marker and E. Rohrmann, *J. Am. Chem. Soc.* **61,** 3592 (1939); **62,** 518 (1940).

37. R. K. Callow, J. W. Cornforth, and P. C. Spensley, *Chem. Ind. (London)* **1951,** 699; **1952,** 426.

38. J. Elks, G. H. Phillipps, T. Walker, and L. J. Wyman, *J. Chem. Soc.* **1956,** 4330. J. H. Chapman, J. Elks, G. H. Phillipps, and L. J. Wyman, *J. Chem. Soc.* **1956,** 4344.

39. C. Djerassi, H. Martinez, and G. Rosencranz, *J. Org. Chem.* **16,** 303 (1951). R. F. Hirschmann, S. Snoddy, and N. L. Wendler, *J. Am. Chem. Soc.* **75,** 3252 (1953).

40. T. R. Carrington, S. Eardley, J. Elks, G. F. H. Green, G. I. Gregory, A. G. Long, and J. C. P. Sly, *J. Chem. Soc.* **1961,** 4560 and earlier papers.

41. R. H. F. Manske, ed., *The Alkaloids,* Academic Press, Inc., New York, 1950–1968.

41a. V. Cerný and F. Šorm, "Alkaloids of the Apocynaceae and Buxaceae," in reference 41, Vol. IX, 1967, pp. 305–426.

42. M. M. Janot, Q. Khuong-Huu, and R. Goutarel, *Compt. Rend.* **246,** 3076 (1958). R. Goutarel, *Bull. Soc. Chim. France,* **1964,** 1665.

43. G. Erhart, H. Ruschig, and W. Aumüller, *Angew. Chem.* **52,** 363 (1939).

44. R. Pappo, *J. Am. Chem. Soc.* **81,** 1010 (1959). F. Buzzetti, W. Wicki, J. Kalvoda, and O. Jeger, *Helv. Chim. Acta* **42,** 388 (1959).

45. J. A. Marshall and W. S. Johnson, *J. Am. Chem. Soc.* **84,** 1485 (1962). G. Stork, S. D. Darling, I. T. Harrison, and P. S. Wharton, *J. Am. Chem. Soc.* **84,** 2018 (1962). W. Nagata, T. Teresawa, and T. Aoki, *Tetrahedron Letters* **1963,** 865, 869.

46. K. S. Brown and S. M. Kupchan, *J. Am. Chem. Soc.* **84,** 4592 (1962); **86,** 4424 (1964).

47. T. Kikuchi and S. Uyeo, *Tetrahedron Letters* **1965,** 3473; *Chem. Pharm. Bull. (Tokyo)* **15,** 549 (1967).

48. K. Schreiber, "The Solanum Alkaloids," in reference 41, Vol. X, 1968, pp. 1–192.

49. Y. Sato, A. Katz, and E. Mosettig, *J. Am. Chem. Soc.* **73,** 880 (1951) and **74,** 538 (1952). Y. Sato, N. Ikekawa, and E. Mosettig, *J. Org. Chem.* **25,** 783 (1960) and references therein. See also R. Kuhn, I. Löw, and H. Trischmann, *Chem. Ber.* **85,** 416 (1952).

50. K. Schreiber and H. Rönsch, *Tetrahedron Letters* **1963,** 937.

51. G. Adam and K. Schreiber, *Chem. Ind. (London)* **1965,** 989; *Tetrahedron* **22,** 3581 (1966).

52. S. M. Kupchan and A. W. By, "The Veratrum Alkaloids," in reference 41, Vol. X, 1968, pp. 193–285.

53. J. Fried, O. Wintersteiner, M. Moore, B. M. Iselin, and A. Klingsberg, *J. Am Chem. Soc.* **73,** 2970 (1951).

54. D. H. R. Barton, O. Jeger, V. Prelog, and R. B. Woodward, *Experientia* **10,** 81 (1954).

55. S. M. Kupchan and C. R. Narayanan, *J. Am. Chem. Soc.* **81,** 1913 (1959).

56. G. Habermehl, "The Salamandra Alkaloids," in reference 41, Vol. IX, 1967, pp. 427–439.

57. S. Hara and K. Oka, *J. Am. Chem. Soc.* **89,** 1041 (1967).

58. Reference 1a, pp. 727–809; reference 1b, pp. 326–397.

59. F. Sondheimer, *Chemistry in Britain* **1,** 454 (1965).

60. N. Danieli, Y. Mazur, and F. Sondheimer, *J. Am. Chem. Soc.* **84,** 875 (1962); *Tetrahedron* **22,** 3189 (1966). C. R. Engel and G. Bach, *Steroids* **3,** 593 (1964).

61. R. Deghenghi, A. Phillip, and R. Gaudry, *Tetrahedron Letters* **1963,** 2045.

61a. F. Sondheimer, W. McCrae, and W. G. Salmond, *J. Am. Chem. Soc.* **91,** 1228 (1969).

62. D. Lavie, S. Greenfield, and E. Glotter, *J. Chem. Soc.* **1966** (C) 1753, and following papers. S. M. Kupchan, R. M. Doskotch, P. Bollinger, A. T. McPhail, G. A. Sim, and J. A. Saenz-Renauld, *J. Am. Chem. Soc.* **87,** 5805 (1965).

62a. C. P. Arsenault, K. Biemann, A. W. Barksdale, and T. C. McMorris, *J. Am. Chem. Soc.* **90,** 5635 (1968).

62b. A. Edwards, J. S. Mills, J. Sundeen, and J. H. Fried, *J. Am. Chem. Soc.* **91,** 1248 (1969).

63. H. Röller, K. H. Dahm, C. C. Sweeley, and B. M. Trost, *Angew. Chem.* **79,** 190 (1967). K. H. Dahm, B. M. Trost, and H. Röller, *J. Am. Chem. Soc.* **89,** 529 (1967).

64. A. Butenandt and P. Karlson, *Z. Naturforsch.* **9b,** 389 (1954). P. Karlson, *Angew. Chem.* **75,** 257 (1963).

65. P. Karlson, H. Hoffmeister, H. Hummel, P. Hocks, and G. Spiteller, *Chem. Ber.* **98,** 2394 (1965) and earlier papers.

66. R. Huber and W. Hoppe, *Chem. Ber.* **98**, 2403 (1965).

67. U. Kerb, P. Hocks, R. Wiechert, A. Furlenmeier, A. Fürst, A. Langemann, and G. Wald-
vogel, *Tetrahedron Letters* **1966**, 1387. A. Furlenmeier, A. Fürst, A. Langemann, G. Wald-
vogel, P. Hocks, U. Kerb, and R. Wiechert, *Helv. Chim. Acta.* **49**, 1591 (1966). R. Wiechert,
U. Kerb, P. Hocks, A. Furlenmeier, A. Fürst, A. Langemann, and G. Waldvogel, *Helv. Chim.
Acta* **49**, 1581 (1966). U. Kerb, G. Schulz, P. Hocks, R. Wiechert, A. Furlenmeier, A. Fürst,
A. Langemann, and G. Waldvogel, *Helv. Chim. Acta* **49**, 1601 (1966).

68. J. B. Siddall, J. P. Marshall, A. Bowers, A. D. Cross, J. A. Edwards, and J. H. Fried, *J. Am.
Chem. Soc.* **88**, 379 (1966). J. B. Siddall, A. D. Cross, and J. H. Fried, *J. Am. Chem. Soc.* **88**, 862
(1966).

69. A. Furlenmeier, A. Fürst, A. Langemann, G. Waldvogel, P. Hocks, U. Kerb, and R. Wiechert, *Experientia* **22**, 573 (1966).

70. I. T. Harrison, J. B. Siddall, and J. H. Fried, *Tetrahedron Letters* **1966**, 3457.

71. F. Hampshire and D. H. S. Horn, *Chem. Commun.* **1966**, 37. D. H. S. Horn, E. J. Middleton,
J. A. Wunderlich, and F. Hampshire, *Chem. Commun.* **1966**, 339. C. T. Takemoto, S. Ogawa,
N. Nishimoto, and H. Hoffmeister, *Z. Naturforsch.* **22b**, 681 (1967).

72. G. Hüppi and J. B. Siddall, *J. Am. Chem. Soc.* **89**, 6790 (1967). U. Kerb, R. Wiechert, A.
Furlenmeier, and A. Fürst, *Tetrahedron Letters* **1968**, 4277.

73. K. Nakanishi, M. Koreeda, S. Sasaki, M. L. Chang, and H. Y. Hsu, *Chem. Commun.* **1966**,
915. H. Moriyama and K. Nakanishi, *Tetrahedron Letters* **1968**, 111. T. Takemoto, S.
Arihara, and H. Hikino, *Tetrahedron Letters* **1968**, 4199.

74. G. Hüppi and J. B. Siddall, *Tetrahedron Letters* **1968**, 1113.

75. K. Nakanishi, M. Koreeda, M. L. Chang, and H. Y. Hsu, *Tetrahedron Letters* **1968**, 1105.

76. M. N. Galbraith, D. H. S. Horn, Q. N. Porter, and R. J. Hackney, *Chem. Commun.* **1968**, 971.

77. J. Jizba, V. Herout, and F. Šorm, *Tetrahedron Letters* **1967**, 5139.

78. T. Takemoto, Y. Hikino, K. Nomoto, and H. Hikino, *Tetrahedron Letters* **1967**, 3191.

79. T. Takemoto, Y. Hikino, H. Hikino, S. Ogawa, and N. Nishimoto, *Tetrahedron Letters* **1968**,
3052.

80. H. Hikino, Y. Hikino, and T. Takemoto, *Tetrahedron Letters* **1968**, 4253. P. Hocks, U. Kerb,
R. Wiechert, A. Furlenmeier, and A. Fürst, *Tetrahedron Letters* **1968**, 4281.

81. H. Schildknecht, R. Siewerlt, and U. Maschwitz, *Angew. Chem.* **78**, 392 (1966)

81a. *Nachr. Chem. Techn.* **16**, 311 (1968).

82. Reference 1a, p. 479.

83. K. Tsuda, E. Ohki, and S. Nozoe, *J. Org. Chem.* **26**, 2614 (1961); **28**, 789 (1963).

84. H. L. Dryden, Jr., G. M. Webber, and J. Wieczorek, *J. Am. Chem. Soc.* **86**, 742 (1964).

85. M. Heller, R. H. Lenhard, and S. Bernstein, *J. Am. Chem. Soc.* **86**, 2309 (1964).

86. E. J. Bailey, A. Gale, G. H. Phillipps, P. T. Siddons, and G. Smith, *Chem. Commun.* **1967**,
1253.

87. A. L. Nussbaum and C. H. Robinson, *Tetrahedron* **17**, 35 (1962).

88. K. Heusler and J. Kalvoda, *Angew. Chem.* **76**, 518 (1964).

89. A. Bowers, R. Vilotti, J. A. Edwards, E. Denot, and D. Halpern, *J. Am. Chem. Soc.* **84**, 3204
(1962) and subsequent papers.

90. T. B. Windholz and M. Windholz, *Angew. Chem.* **76**, 249 (1964).

91. J. Kalvoda and G. Anner, *Helv. Chim. Acta* **50**, 269 (1967).

92. H. Hagiwara, S. Noguchi, and M. Nishikawa, *Chem. Pharm. Bull. (Tokyo)* **8**, 84 (1960).

93. E. Dondo and T. Mitsugi, *J. Am. Chem. Soc.* **88**, 4737 (1966).

94. J. W. Cornforth in J. W. Cook, ed., *Progress in Organic Chemistry*, Vol. 3, Academic Press,
Inc., New York, 1955; I. V. Torgov, *Pure Appl. Chem.* **6**, 525 (1963).

95. L. Velluz, J. Volls, and G. Nominé, *Angew. Chem.* **77**, 185 (1965).

96. W. E. Bachmann, W. Cole, and A. L. Wilds, *J. Am. Chem. Soc.* **61**, 974 (1939); **62**, 824 (1940).

97. A. Butenandt and G. Schramm, *Chem. Ber.* **68**, 2083 (1935).

98. W. S. Johnson, J. W. Petersen, and C. D. Gutsche, *J. Am. Chem. Soc.* **67**, 2274 (1945); **69**,
2942 (1947).

99. W. S. Johnson and V. L. Stromberg, *J. Am. Chem. Soc.* **72**, 505 (1950).

100. G. Anner and K. Miescher, *Helv. Chim. Acta* **31**, 2173 (1948); **32**, 1957 (1949); **33**, 1379 (1950).

101. W. S. Johnson, D. K. Banerjee, W. P. Schneider, C. D. Gutsche, W. E. Shelberg, and L. J.
Chinn, *J. Am. Chem. Soc.* **74**, 2832 (1952). W. S. Johnson, R. G. Christiansen, and R. E.

Ireland, *J. Am. Chem. Soc.* **79,** 1995 (1957). W. S. Johnson, J. E. Cole, J. Walker, and P. A. Robins, *Proc. Chem. Soc.* **1958,** 114, and *J. Chem. Soc.* **1962,** 244.

102. W. E. Bachmann, S. Kushner, and A. C. Stevenson, *J. Am. Chem. Soc.* **64,** 974 (1942).

103. W. S. Johnson, I. A. David, H. C. Dehm, R. J. Highet, E. W. Warnhoff, W. D. Wood, and E. T. Jones, *J. Am. Chem. Soc.* **80,** 661 (1958).

104. H. M. E. Cardwell, J. W. Cornforth, S. R. Duff, H. Holtermann, and Sir R. Robinson, *Chem. Ind. (London)* **1951,** 389; *J. Chem. Soc.* **1953,** 361.

105. R. B. Woodward, F. Sondheimer, D. Taub, K. Heusler, and W. McLamore, *J. Am. Chem. Soc.* **73,** 2403 (1951); **74,** 4223 (1952).

106. E. DeFeu, F. J. McQuillin, and Sir R. Robinson, *J. Chem. Soc.* **1937,** 53.

107. A. J. Birch and Sir R. Robinson, *J. Chem. Soc.* **1944,** 501.

108. Sir R. Robinson, *J. Chem. Soc.* **1938,** 1390; A. Koebner and Sir R. Robinson, *J. Chem. Soc.* **1938,** 1994; A. J. Birch, R Jaeger, and Sir R. Robinson, *J. Chem. Soc.* **1945,** 582.

109. E. Dane and J. Schmitt, *Ann.* **537,** 246 (1939). G. Singh, *J. Am. Chem. Soc.* **78,** 6109 (1956).

110. L. B. Barkley, W. S. Knowles, H. Raffelson, and Q. E. Thompson, *J. Am. Chem. Soc.* **78,** 4111 (1956).

110a. G. Stork, H. J. E. Loewenthal, and P. C. Mukharji, *J. Am. Chem. Soc.* **78,** 501 (1956).

111. W. S. Johnson, B. Bannister, B. Bloom, A. D. Kemp, R. Pappo, E. R. Rogier, and J. Szmuszkovicz, *J. Am. Chem. Soc.* **75,** 2275 (1953). W. S. Johnson, J. J. Korst, R. A. Clement, and J. Dutta, *J. Am. Chem. Soc.* **82,** 614 (1960).

112. L. B. Barkley, M. W. Farrar, W. S. Knowles, H. Raffelson, and Q. E. Thompson, *J. Am. Chem. Soc.* **75,** 4110 (1953). A. J. Speziale, J. A. Stephens, and Q. E. Thompson, *J. Am. Chem. Soc.* **76,** 5011, 5014 (1954).

113. L. H. Sarett, G. E. Arth, R. M. Lukes, R. E. Beyler, G. I. Poos, W. F. Johns, and J. M. Constantin, *J. Am. Chem. Soc.* **74,** 4974 (1952); G. E. Arth, G. I. Poos, and L. H. Sarett, *J. Am. Chem. Soc.* **77,** 3834 (1955) and earlier papers.

114. J. Schmidlin, G. Anner, J. R. Billeter, and A. Wettstein, *Experientia* **11,** 365 (1955). K. Heusler, H. Ueberwasser, P. Wieland, J. R. Billeter, J. Schmidlin, G. Anner, and A. Wettstein, *Helv. Chim. Acta* **42,** 1586 (1959) and references cited therein. See also A. Lardon, O. Schindler, and T. Reichstein, *Helv. Chim Acta* **40,** 666 (1957). W. J. Van der Burg, D. A. van Dorp, O. Schindler, C. M. Siegman, and S. A. Szpilfogel, *Rec. Trav. Chim.* **77,** 171 (1958).

115. W. S. Johnson, J. C. Collins, R. Pappo, and M. B. Rubin, *J. Am. Chem. Soc.* **80,** 2585 (1958).

116. D. R. H. Barton, G. M. Beaton, G. M. Geller, and M. M. Pechet, *J. Am. Chem. Soc.* **82,** 2640, 2641 (1960); **83,** 750, 1771, 2400 (1961).

117. K. Heusler, J. Kalvoda, C. Meystre, P. Wieland, G. Anner, A. Wettstein, G. Cainelli, D. Arigoni, and O. Jeger, *Experientia* **16,** 21 (1960); *Helv. Chim. Acta* **44,** 502 (1961).

118. L. Velluz, G. Nominé, G. Amiard, V. Torelli, and J. Cérède, *Compt. Rend.* **257,** 3086 (1963).

119. S. N. Ananchenko and I. V. Torgov, *Tetrahedron Letters* **1963,** 553, and references cited therein.

120. V. J. Grenda, G. W. Lindberg, N. L. Wendler, and S. H. Pines, *J. Org. Chem.* **32,** 1236 (1967). H. Schick, G. Lehmann, and G. Hilgetag, *Angew. Chem.* **79,** 97 (1967). R. Bucourt, A. Pierdet, G. Costerousse, and E. Toromanoff, *Bull. Soc. Chim. France* **1965,** 645.

121. P. Wieland, H. Ueberwasser, G. Anner, and K. Miescher, *Helv. Chim. Acta* **36,** 376, 646, 1231 (1953).

122. L. Velluz, G. Nominé, J. Mathieu, E. Toromanoff, D. Bertin, M. Vignau, and J. Tessier, *Compt. Rend.* **250,** 1510 (1960).

123. L. Velluz, G. Nominé, J. Mathieu, E. Toromanoff, D. Bertin, J. Tessier, and A. Pierdet, *Compt. Rend.* **250,** 1084 (1960).

124. L. Velluz, G. Nominé, J. Mathieu, E. Toromanoff, D. Bertin, R. Bucourt, and J. Tessier, *Compt. Rend.* **250,** 1293 (1960).

125. G. Stork and J. E. McMurry, *J. Am. Chem. Soc.* **89,** 5464 (1967).

126. A. J. Birch, J. M. Brown, and G. S. R. Subba Rao, *J. Chem. Soc.* **1964,** 3309; P. Turnbull, K. Syhora, and J. H. Fried, *J. Am. Chem. Soc.* **88,** 4765 (1966).

127. P. Bellet, G. Nominé, and J. Mathieu, *Compt. Rend.* **263c,** 88 (1966).

128. A. J. Birch and H. Smith, *Quart. Rev. (London)* **1958,** 12, 17.

129. S. N. Ananchenko, V. Y. Limanov, V. N. Leonov, V. N. Rzheznikov, and I. V. Torgov. *Tetrahedron Letters* **1962,** 1355, and earlier papers.

130. S. N. Ananchenko and I. V. Torgov, *Tetrahedron Letters* **1963**, 1553. T. B. Windholz, J. H. Fried, and A. A. Patchett, *J. Org. Chem.* **28**, 1092 (1963). T. Miki, K. Hiraga, and T. Asako, *Proc. Chem. Soc.* **1963**, 139, and *Chem. Pharm. Bull. (Tokyo)* **13**, 1285 (1965). D. J. Crispin and J. S. Whitehurst, *Proc. Chem. Soc.* **1963**, 22.

130a. G. H. Douglas, J. M. H. Groves, D. Hartley, G. A. Hughes, B. J. McLaughlin, J. Siddall, and H. Smith, *J. Chem. Soc.* **1963**, 5072.

131. G. A. Hughes and H. Smith, *Chem. Ind. (London)* **1960**, 1022.

132. S. N. Ananchenko, T'ao-Jeng-O, and I. V. Torgov, *Izv. Akad. Nauk SSSR Otd. Khim. Nauk* **1962**, 298.

133. C. H. Kuo, D. Taub, and N. L. Wendler, *Angew. Chem.* **77**, 1142 (1965); *J. Org. Chem.* **33**, 3126 (1968).

134. W. R. J. Simpson, D. Babbe, J. A. Edwards, and J. H. Fried, *Tetrahedron Letters* **1967**, 3209.

135. D. B. R. Johnston, F. S. Waksmunski, T. B. Windholz, and A. A. Patchett, *Chimia (Aarau)* **22**, 84 (1968).

136. C. Lehmann, H. Schick, B. Lücke, and G. Hilgetag, *Chem. Ber.* **101**, 787 (1968).

137. H. Gibian, K. Kieslich, H. J. Koch, H. Kosmol, C. Rufer, E. Schröder, and R. Vössing, *Tetrahedron Letters* **1966**, 2321. H. Kosmol, K. Kieslich, R. Vössing, H. J. Koch, K. Petzold, and H. Gibian, *Ann.* **701**, 198 (1967). C. Rufer, E. Schröder, and H. Gibian, *Ann.* **701**, 206 (1967).

138. C. H. Kuo, D. Taub, and N. L. Wendler, *Chem. Ind. (London)* **1966**, 1340.

139. R. Bucourt, L. Nedelec, J. C. Gasé, and J. Weill-Raynal, *Bull. Soc. Chim. France* **1967**, 561.

140. H. Smith, G. A. Hughes, G. H. Douglas, G. R. Wendt, G. C. Buzby, R. A. Edgren, J. Fisher, T. Foell, B. Gadsby, D. Hartley, D. Herbst, A. B. A. Jansen, K. Ledig, B. J. McLaughlin, J. McMenamin, T. W. Pattison, P. C. Phillips, R. Rees, J. Siddall, J. Suida, L. L. Smith, J. Tokolics, and D. H. P. Watson, *J. Chem. Soc.* **1964**, 4472.

141. L. Velluz, G. Nominé, R. Bucourt, A. Pierdet, and P. Dufay, *Tetrahedron Letters* **1961**, 127. A. V. Zakharychev, D. R. Legidze, S. N. Ananchenko, and I. V. Torgov, *Izv. Akad. Nauk. SSSR Otd. Khim. Nauk* **1965**, 760. K. Hiraga, *Chem. Pharm. Bull. (Tokyo)* **13**, 1289 (1965). C. Rufer, H. Kosmol, E. Schröder, K. Kieslich, and H. Gibian, *Ann.* **702**, 141 (1967).

142. T. B. Windholz, R. D. Brown, and A. A. Patchett, *Steroids* **6**, 409 (1965).

143. W. S. Johnson, M. F. Semmelhock, M. U. S. Sultanbawa, and L. A. Dolak, *J. Am. Chem. Soc.* **90**, 2994 (1968).

144. R. B. Woodward, A. A. Patchett, D. H. R. Barton, D. A. J. Ives, and R. B. Kelly, *J. Am. Chem. Soc.* **76**, 2852 (1954); *J. Chem Soc.* **1957**, 1131.

145. Y. Mazur, N. Danieli, and F. Sondheimer, *J. Am. Chem. Soc.* **81**, 3161 (1959).

146. *Ibid.*, **82**, 5889 (1960).

147. T. Masamune, M. Tagasugi, A. Murai, and K. Kobayashi, *J. Am. Chem. Soc.* **89**, 4521 (1967).

148. W. S. Johnson, H. A. P. DeJongh, C. E. Coverdale, J. W. Scott, and V. Burckhardt, *J. Am. Chem. Soc.* **89**, 4523 (1967).

149. R. O. Clinton, A. J. Manson, F. W. Stonner, A. L. Beyler, G. O. Potts, and A. Arnold, *J. Am. Chem. Soc.* **81**, 1513 (1959) and subsequent papers.

150. R. Hirschmann, N. G. Steinberg, P. Buchschacher, J. H. Fried, G. J. Kent, M. Tishler, and S. L. Steelman, *J. Am. Chem. Soc.* **85**, 120 (1963) and subsequent papers.

151. R. O. Clinton, R. L. Carke, F. W. Stonner, A. J. Manson, K. F. Jennings, and D. K. Phillips, *J. Org. Chem.* **27**, 2800 (1962).

152. S. L. Steelman and R. F. Hirschman, in A. B. Eisenstein, ed., *The Adrenal Cortex*, Little, Brown & Co., Inc., New York, 1967. (An authoritative review of structure activity relationship in adrenal corticoid steroids.)

153. H. Mrozik, P. Buchschacher, J. Hannah, and J. H. Fried, *J. Med. Chem.* **7**, 584 (1964).

154. A. J. Zderic, O. Halpern, H. Carpio, A. Ruiz, D. C. Limon, L. Magagaña, H. Jimenez, A. Bowers, and H. J. Ringold, *Chem. Ind.(London)* **1960**, 1625.

155. P. deRuggieri and G. Gandolfi, in L. Martini and A. Pecile, eds., *Hormonal Steroids, Biochemistry, Pharmacology, and Therapeutics*, Vol. II, Academic Press, Inc., New York, 1965, p. 69.

156. R. B. Conrow and S. Bernstein, *Steroids* **11**, 151 (1968).

157. A. A. Achrem and U. A. Titov, *Usp. Khim.* **36**, 745 (1967). P. deRuggieri, G. Gandolfi, U. Guzzi, D. Chiaramonti, and C. Ferrari, *Farmaco (Pavia) Ed. Sci.* **20**, 280 (1965).

158. C. E. Cook, R. C. Corley, and M. E. Wall, *Tetrahedron Letters* **1965**, 891.

159. R. F. R. Church, A. S. Kende, and M. J. Weiss, *J. Am. Chem. Soc.* **87**, 2665 (1965).

160. J. A. Cella and C. M. Kagawa, *J. Am. Chem. Soc.* **79**, 4808 (1957).

161. J. A. Cella, E. A. Brown, and R. R. Burtner, *J. Org. Chem.* **24**, 743 (1959); E. A. Brown, R. D. Muir, and J. A. Cella, *J. Org. Chem.* **25**, 96 (1960).

162. G. E. Arth, H. Schwam, L. H. Sarett, and M. Glitzer, *J. Med. Chem.* **6**, 617 (1963).

163. H. J. Hess, *J. Org. Chem.* **27**, 1096 (1962).

164. A. A. Patchett, F. Hoffman, G. G. Giarusso, H. Schwam, and G. E. Arth, *J. Org. Chem.* **27**, 3822 (1962).

165. L. N. Nysted and R. R. Burtner, *J. Org. Chem.* **27**, 3175 (1962).

166. E. A. Brown, *J. Med. Pharm. Chem.* **10**, 546 (1967).

167. G. DeStevens, *Diuretics*, Academic Press, Inc., New York, 1963, p. 120. (A recent review of aldosterone antagonists.)

168. W. N. Speckamp, U. K. Pandit, and H. O. Huisman, *Rec. Trav. Chim.* **82**, 39 (1963).

169. J. H. Burckhalter and H. Watanabe, *Chem. Eng. News* **41**, 40 (1963).

170. H. O. Huisman, W. N. Speckamp, H. deKonig, and U. K. Pandit, *Tetrahedron Letters* **1964**, 1275.

171. H. Smith, G. H. Douglas, and C. R. Walk, *Experientia* **20**, 418 (1964).

172. P. Morand and J. Lyall, *Chem. Rev.* **68**, 85 (1968). H. O. Huisman, *Bull. Soc. Chim. (France)* **1968**, 13. (Two articles containing pertinent references, as well as a complete bibliography of heterocyclic steroidal estrogens.)

173. R. I. Weltzer, D. M. Lustgarten, R. J. Stanaback, and R. E. Brown, *Tetrahedron Letters* **1963**, 1581; *J. Org. Chem.* **31**, 1489 (1966).

174. R. Clarkson, *J. Chem. Soc.* **1965**, 4900.

175. A. J. Birch and G. S. R. Subba Rao, *J. Chem. Soc.* **1965**, 3007.

176. J. H. Burckhalter and H. N. Abramson, *Chem. Comm.* **1966**, 805; E. C. Taylor and K. Lenard, *Chem. Comm.* **1967**, 97.

177. D. B. R. Johnston, F. S. Waksmunski, T. B. Windholz, and A. A. Patchett, *Chimia (Aarau)* **22**, 84 (1968).

178. L. Tökés in reference 1g, p. 457. (A comprehensive review of partial synthesis.)

179. L. H. Knox, R. Vilotti, F. A. Kincl, and H. J. Ringold, *J. Org. Chem.* **26**, 501 (1961).

180. J. T. Edward and P. F. Morand, *Can. J. Chem.* **38**, 1325 (1960).

181. C. W. Shoppee, G. Kruger, and R. N. Mirrington, *J. Chem. Soc.* **1962**, 1050.

182. N. J. Doorenbos and M. T. Wu, *J. Org. Chem.* **26**, 2548 (1961).

183. E. Caspi, B. T. Khan, and W. Schmid, *J. Org. Chem.* **26**, 3894 (1961).

184. N. J. Doorenbos, C. L. Huang, C. R. Tammoria, and M. T. Wu, *J. Org. Chem.* **26**, 2546 (1961).

185. J. McKenna and A. Tulley, *J. Chem. Soc.* **1960**, 945.

186. J. S. Baran, *J. Med. Chem.* **10**, 1039 (1967).

187. R. Pappo and C. J. Jung, *Tetrahedron Letters* **1962**, 365.

188. R. F. Hirschmann, N. G. Steinberg, and R. Walker, *J. Am. Chem. Soc.* **84**, 1270 (1962).

188a. J. Fried, R. W. Thoma, and A. Klingsberg, *J. Am. Chem. Soc.* **75**, 576, 1953.

189. R. E. Counsell, P. D. Klimstra, R. E. Ranney, and D. L. Cook, *J. Med. Pharm. Chem.* **5**, 720 (1962).

190. E. P. M. Bhattathiry and M. D. Siperstein, *J. Clin. Invest.* **42**, 1613 (1963).

191. R. E. Counsell, P. D. Klimstra, L. N. Nysted, and R. E. Ranney, *J. Med. Chem.* **8**, 45 (1965). See also L. Velluz, D. Bertin, L. Nedelec, and C. Plotka, *Compt. Rend.* **255**, 436 (1962).

192. W. G. Dauben and J. A. Ross, *J. Am. Chem. Soc.* **81**, 6521 (1959). See also G. Just and V. diTullio, *Can. J. Chem.* **42**, 2153 (1964).

193. W. F. Johns, *J. Org. Chem.* **29**, 1490 (1964).

194. A. R. Davies and G. H. R. Summers, *J. Chem. Soc.* **1967** C, 909.

195. P. G. Gassman and W. E. Hymans, *Chem. Comm.* **1967**, 795.

196. J. J. Bonet, H. Wehrli, and K. Schaffner, *Helv. Chim. Acta* **45**, 2615 (1962). J. Tadanier, *J. Org. Chem.* **31**, 2124 (1966). K. Syhora, J. A. Edwards, and A. D. Cross, *J. Org. Chem.* **31**, 3411 (1966).

197. A. Kasal, V. Czerný, and F. Šorm, *Collection Czech. Chem. Commun.* **28**, 411 (1963).

198. R. Wiechert and E. Kaspar, *Chem. Ber.* **93**, 1716 (1960). H. Laurent, H. Muller, and R. Wiechert, *Chem. Ber.* **99**, 3836 (1966).

198a. R. Wiechert, O. Engelfried, U. Kerb, H. Laurent, H. Müller, and G. Schultz, *Chem. Ber.* **99**, 1188 (1966).

198b. R. Wiechert, *Angew. Chem.* **79**, 815 (1967).

198c. O. Schmidt, K. Przewowsky, G. Schultz, and R. Wiechert, *Chem. Ber.* **101**, 939 (1968).

199. N. H. Dyson, J. A. Edwards, and J. H. Fried, *Tetrahedron Letters* **1966**, 1841.

199a. C. Beard, N. H. Dyson, and J. H. Fried, *Tetrahedron Letters* **1966**, 3281; C. Beard, I. T. Harrison, L. Kirkham, and J. H. Fried, *Tetrahedron Letters,* **1966**, 3287; G. Tarzia, N. H. Dyson, I. T. Harrison, J. A. Edwards, and J. H. Fried, *Tetrahedron Letters* **1967**, 387.

200. J. Castells, E. R. H. Jones, G. D. Meakins, and R. W. J. Williams, *J. Chem. Soc.* **1959**, 1159.

201. P. Westerhof and E. H. Reerink, *Rec. Trav. Chim.* **79**, 771 (1960) and subsequent papers. J. H. Hartog and P. Westerhof, *Rec. Trav. Chim.* **84**, 918 (1965); P. Westerhof and J. H. Hartog, *Rec. Trav. Chim.* **86**, 235 (1967).

202. H. Els, G. Englert, M. Müller, and A. Fürst, *Helv. Chim. Acta* **48**, 989 (1965) and later papers.

203. M. Uskokovic, J. Iacobelli, R. Philion, and T. Williams, *J. Am. Chem. Soc.* **88**, 4538 (1966).

204. Z. G. Hajós, D. R. Parrish, and E. P. Oliveto, *Tetrahedron Letters,* **1966**, 6495. A. M. Krubiner, G. Saucy, and E. P. Oliveto, *J. Org. Chem.* **33**, 3548 (1968).

205. J. M. H. Graves, G. A. Hughes, T. Y. Jen, and H. Smith, *J. Chem. Soc.* **1964**, 5488. See also J. A. Edwards, P. Crabbé, and A. Bowers, *J. Am. Chem. Soc.* **85**, 3313 (1963).

206. P. Crabbé, A. Cruz, and J. Iriarte, *Can. J. Chem.* **46**, 349 (1968).

207. R. Wenger, H. Dutler, H. Wehrli, K. Schaffner, and O. Jeger, *Helv. Chim. Acta* **45**, 2420 (1960).

208. J. A. Settepani, M. Torigoe, and J. Fishman, *Tetrahedron Letters* **1965**, 3661.

209. R. Ginsig and A. D. Cross, *J. Am. Chem. Soc.* **87**, 4629 (1965). E. Farkas, J. M. Owen, M. Debono, R. M. Molloy, and M. M. Marsh, *Tetrahedron Letters,* **1966**, 1023.

210. J. W. Blunt, M. P. Hartshorn, and D. N. Kirk, *Chem. Comm.* **1966**, 160, and *Tetrahedron Letters* **1966**, 3195; M. P. Hartshorn and D. N. Kirk, *Tetrahedron Letters* **1966**, 3913.

211. G. Snatzke and H. W. Fehlhaber, *Ann.* **676**, 188 (1964). M. Fétizon and P. Foy, *Chem. Comm.* **1967**, 1005.

212. J. C. Jacquesy, J. Levisalles, and J. Wagnon, *Chem. Comm.* **1967**, 25.

213. B. G. McFarland, in reference 1g, p. 427.

214. R. F. Hirschmann, G. A. Bailey, R. Walker, and J. M. Chemerda, *J. Am. Chem. Soc.* **81**, 2822 (1959).

215. F. L. Weisenborn and H. E. Applegate, *J. Am. Chem. Soc.* **81**, 1960 (1959). See also T. L. Jacobs and N. Takahashi, *J. Am. Chem. Soc.* **80**, 4865 (1958).

216. P. Diassi, S. D. Levine, and R. M. Palmere, *J. Med. Chem.* **10**, 551 (1967).

217. J. Jacques and G. Pincus, in reference 155, Vol. I, Academic Press, Inc., New York, 1962, p. 3. See also S. L. Steelman and D. J. Patanelli, *Proc. 2nd Internatl. Congr. Hormonal Steroids, Milan, 1966,* p. 559; and A. Heymes, M. J. Brienne, J. Jacques, D. B. R. Johnston, and T. B. Windholz, *ibid.,* p. 232.

218. R. I. Dorfman, J. Fajkos, and J. Joska, *Steroids* **3**, 675 (1964) and the references to the synthetic work cited therein. H. L. Saunders, K. Holden, and J. F. Kerwin, *Steroids* **3**, 687 (1964).

219. H. Heidepriem, C. Rufer, H. Kosmol, E. Schröder, and K. Kieslich, *Ann.* **712**, 155 (1968).

220. R. F. Hirschmann, C. S. Snoddy, Jr., and N. L. Wendler, *J. Am. Chem. Soc.* **74**, 2693 (1952).

221. T. Masamune, K. Orito, and A. Murai, *Bull. Chem. Soc. Japan* **39**, 2503 (1966).

222. S. M. Kupchan, A. W. By, and M. S. Flon, *J. Org. Chem.* **33**, 911 (1968). See also W. F. Johns and I. Laos, *J. Org. Chem.* **30**, 4220 (1965).

223. W. S. Johnson, J. M. Cox, D. W. Graham, and H. W. Whitlock, Jr., *J. Am. Chem. Soc.* **89**, 4524 (1967). W. S. Johnson, N. Cohen, E. R. Habicht, Jr., D. P. G. Hamon, G. P. Rizzi, and D. J. Faulkner, *Tetrahedron Letters* **1968**, 2829, and references cited.

224. J. Meinwald and J.-L. Ripoll, *J. Am. Chem. Soc.* **89**, 7075 (1967). (See also the complete bibliographical references cited therein.)

225. A. J. Birch, J. M. H. Graves, and J. B. Siddall, *J. Chem. Soc.* **1963**, 4234.

226. A. J. Birch and G. S. R. Subba Rao, *Tetrahedron Letters* **1966**, Suppl. 7, 391.

227. R. Hayashi, *Chem. Pharm. Bull. (Tokyo)* **15**, 38 (1967).

228. M. W. Goldberg and R. Monnier, *Helv. Chim. Acta* **23**, 376, 840 (1940); M. W. Goldberg and E. Wydler, *Helv. Chim. Acta* **26**, 1142 (1943); M. W. Goldberg, J. Sicé, H. Robert, and P. A. Plattner, *Helv. Chim. Acta* **30**, 1441 (1947). N. L. Wendler, D. Taub, and H. L. Slates, *J. Am. Chem. Soc.* **77**, 3559 (1955).

228a. H. J. Ringold, *J. Am. Chem. Soc.* **82,** 961 (1960).

229. B. Riegel, R. M. Dodson, and B. P. Sollman, *J. Am. Chem. Soc.* **75,** 5132 (1953).

230. R. O. Clinton, H. C. Neumann, A. J. Manson, S. C. Laskowski, and R. G. Christiansen, *J. Am. Chem. Soc.* **80,** 3389, 3395 (1958).

231. M. Dvolaitzky, A. M. Giroud, and J. Jacques, *Bull. Soc. Chim.* **1963,** 62, and subsequent papers.

232. R. F. Zürcher, *Helv. Chim. Acta* **44,** 1380 (1961).

233. N. S. Bhacca and D. H. Williams, *Applications of NMR Spectroscopy in Organic Chemistry*, Holden-Day, Inc., San Francisco, 1964.

234. C. Djerassi, *Optical Rotatory Dispersion*, McGraw-Hill Book Co., New York, 1960.

235. L. Velluz and N. Legrand, *Angew. Chem.* **73,** 603 (1961).

236. P. Crabbé, *Optical Rotatory Dispersion and Circular Dichroism in Organic Chemistry*, Holden-Day, Inc., San Francisco, 1964.

237. H. Budzikiewicz, C. Djerassi, and D. H. Williams, *Mass Spectrometry of Organic Compounds*, Holden-Day, Inc., San Francisco, 1967.

238. E. Stahl, *Thin Layer Chromatography*, Academic Press, Inc., New York, 1965.

239. W. J. A. VandenHeuvel, C. C. Sweeley, and E. C. Horning, *J. Am. Chem. Soc.* **82,** 3481 (1960).

DAVID TAUB AND
THOMAS B. WINDHOLZ
Merck, Sharp & Dohme

STIBINE, SbH_3.   See Antimony compounds, Vol. 2, p. 572.

STIGMASTEROL, $C_{29}H_{47}OH$.   See Steroids.